Get Connected to
ConnectED

- **100% Online**
- **One-Stop Shop, One Personalized Password**
- **Easy Intuitive Navigation**
- **Resources, Resources, Resources**

For Students

Leave your books at school. Now you can go online and interact with your **StudentWorks Plus** digital Student Edition from any place, any time!

For Teachers

ConnectED is your one-stop online center for everything you need to teach using **Florida Math Connects, Course 2**, including: **TeacherWorks Plus** digital Teacher Edition, lesson planning and scheduling tools, pacing, and assessment.

For Parents

Get homework help, help your student prepare for testing, and review math topics.

Get Connected to the way students learn and teachers teach TODAY!

Glencoe McGraw-Hill

Florida
Math
Connects
Plus

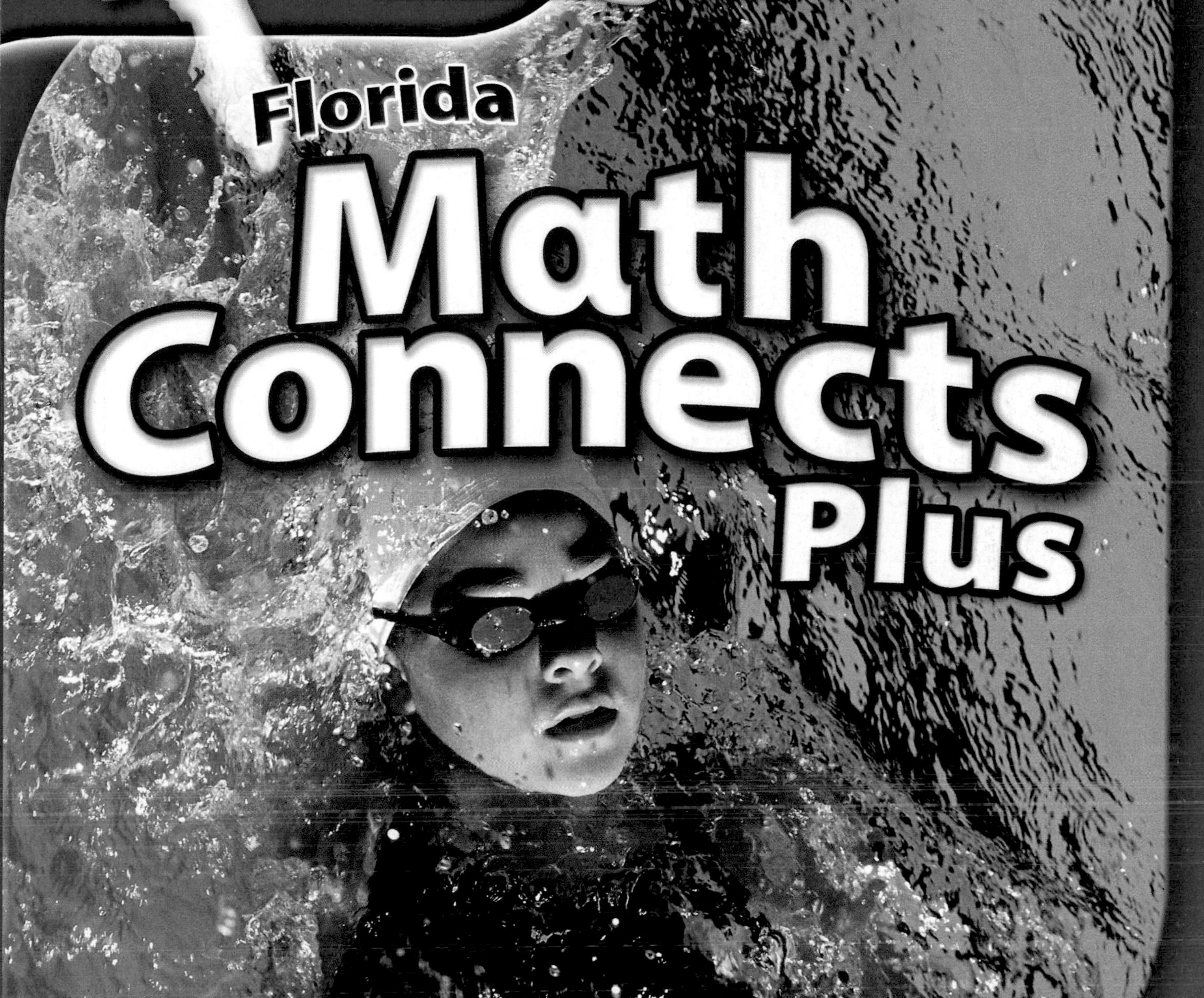

Authors

Carter • Cuevas • Day • Malloy • Kersaint • Luchin • McClain
Molix-Bailey • Price • Reynosa • Silbey • Vielhaber • Willard

McGraw Hill Glencoe

Course 2

The McGraw-Hill Companies

 Glencoe

Send all inquiries to:
Glencoe/McGraw-Hill
8787 Orion Place
Columbus, OH 43240-4027

ISBN: 978-0-07-891643-4
MHID: 0-07-891643-7   *Math Connects,* Course 2

Printed in the United States of America.

4 5 6 7 8 9 10   RJE   18 17 16 15 14 13 12 11 10

Front-Loaded for Florida Success

Master the NGSSS

NGSSS Review

Included in this section are Practice by Standards and Practice On Your Own questions.

After the Test

Authors

Our lead authors ensure that the Macmillan/McGraw-Hill and Glencoe/McGraw-Hill mathematics programs are truly vertically aligned by beginning with the end in mind—success in Algebra 1 and beyond. By "backmapping" the content from the high school programs, all of our mathematics programs are well articulated in their scope and sequence, ensuring that the content in each program provides a solid foundation for moving forward. These authors also worked closely with the entire K–12 author team to ensure vertical alignment of the instructional approach and visual design.

Lead Authors, K–12

John A. Carter, Ph.D.
Assistant Principal for Teaching and Learning
Adlai E. Stevenson High School
Lincolnshire, Illinois

Areas of Expertise: Using technology and
   manipulatives to visualize concepts;
   English-Language Learners

Gilbert J. Cuevas, Ph.D.
Professor of Mathematics Education
Texas State University–San Marcos
San Marcos, Texas

Areas of Expertise: Applying concepts
   and skills in mathematically rich contexts;
   Mathematical Representations

Roger Day, Ph.D., NBCT
Mathematics Department Chairperson
Pontiac Township High School
Pontiac, Illinois

Areas of Expertise: Understanding and
   applying probability and statistics

Carol E. Malloy, Ph.D.
Associate Professor
University of North Carolina at Chapel Hill
Chapel Hill, NC

Areas of Expertise: Representations and
   critical thinking; Student Success in Algebra 1

Get Connected Meet the authors at glencoe.com.

Authors, Courses 1–3

Gladis Kersaint, Ph.D.
Associate Professor of
 Mathematics Education,
 K–12
University of South Florida
Tampa, Florida

Kay McClain, Ed.D.
Research Professor
Arizona State University
Phoenix, Arizona

Rhonda J. Molix-Bailey
Mathematics Consultant
DeSoto, Texas

Beatrice Moore Luchin
Mathematics Consultant
Houston, Texas

Jack Price, Ed. D.
Professor Emeritus
California State
 Polytechnic University
Pomona, California

Mary Esther Reynosa
Instructional Supervisor for
 Mathematics Education
Northside Independent
 School District
San Antonio, Texas

Robyn Silbey
Math Content Coach
Montgomery County Public
 Schools
Rockville, Maryland

Kathleen Vielhaber
Mathematics Consultant
St. Louis, Missouri

Teri Willard, Ed.D.
Assistant Professor
Central Washington University
Ellensburg, Washington

Contributing Author

This program is the beneficiary of the imagination of
Dinah Zike through the contribution of the Foldables
Study Organizers.

Dinah Zike
Educational Consultant
Dinah-Might Activities, Inc.
San Antonio, Texas

Consultants

Mathematical Content

Carol Newman
Retired Mathematics Curriculum Specialist K–5
Broward County Schools
Ft. Lauderdale, Florida

Melissa D. Young
Mathematics Specialist
Differentiated Accountability Model, Region III
Orlando, Florida

Differentiated Instruction

Jennifer Taylor-Cox, Ph.D.
Educational Consultant
Innovative Instruction: Connecting Research and
    Practice in Education
Severna Park, Maryland

Gifted and Talented

Shelbi K. Cole
Research Assistant
University of Connecticut
Storrs, Connecticut

Problem Solving

Dr. Stephen Krulik
Professor Emeritus–Math Education
Temple University
Philadelphia, Pennsylvania

Reading in the Content Areas

Sue Z. Beers
President/Consultant
Tools for Learning, Inc.
Jewell, IA

Reading and Vocabulary

Douglas Fisher
Professor
San Diego State University
San Diego, CA

Reviewers

Ernestine D. Austin
Facilitating Teacher/Basic
  Skills Teacher
LORE School
Ewing, NJ

Susie Bellah
Kindergarten Teacher
Lakeland Elementary
Humble, Texas

Megan Bennett
Elementary Math
  Coordinator
Hartford Public Schools
Hartford, CT

Susan T. Blankenship
5th Grade Teacher—Math
Stanford Elementary School
Stanford, KY

Wendy Buchanan
3rd Grade Teacher
The Classical Center at Vial
Garland, TX

Anthony Dentino
Supervisor of Mathematics
Brick Township Schools
Brick, NJ

Lorrie L. Drennon
Math Teacher
Collins Middle School
Corsicana, TX

Monica Engel
Educator Second Grade
Pioneer Elementary
  School
Bolingbrook, IL

Pamela Fleming Lowe
Fourth Grade eMINTS
  Teacher
O'Neal Elementary
Poplar Bluff, MO

Brenda M. Foxx
Principal
University Park Elementary
University Park, MD

Katherine A. Frontier
Elementary Teacher
Laidlaw
Western Springs, IL

Susan J. Furphy
5th Grade Teacher
Nisley Elementary
Grand Junction, CO

Peter Gatz
Student Services
  Coordinator
Brooks Elementary
Aurora, IL

Amber Gregersen
Teacher—2nd Grade
Nisley Elementary
Grand Junction, CO

Martha J. Hickman
2nd Grade Teacher
Dr. James Craik
  Elementary School
Pomfret, MD

Carol H. Joyce
5th Grade Teacher
Nathanael Greene
  Elementary
Liberty, NC

Stella K. Kostante
Curriculum Coach
Roosevelt Elementary
Pittsburgh, PA

Lauren May, NBCT
4th Grade Teacher
May Watts Elementary
  School
Naperville, IL

Lorraine Moore
Grade 3 Math Teacher
Cowpens Elementary School
Cowpens, SC

Shannon L. Moorhead
4th Grade Teacher
Centerville Elementary
Anderson, SC

Gina M. Musselman, M.Ed
Kindergarten Teacher
Padeo Verde Elementary
Peoria, AZ

Jen Neufeld
3rd Grade Teacher
Kendall
Naperville, IL

Cathie Osiecki
K–5 Mathematics
  Coordinator
Middletown Public Schools
Middletown, CT

Phyllis L. Pacilli
Elementary Education
  Teacher
Fullerton Elementary
Addison, IL

Cindy Pearson
4th/5th Grade Teacher
John D. Spicer Elementary
Haltom City, TX

Jo J. Puree
Educator
Lackamas Elementary
Yelm, WA

Teresa M. Reynolds
Third Grade Teacher
Forrest View Elementary
Everett, WA

Sandra Signorelli Coelho
Associate Director for
  Mathematics
PIMMS at Wesleyan
  University
Middletown, CT

Florida Reviewers

Natalie Angelis
Math Department Chair
Hunter's Creek Middle
  School
Orlando, FL

Jennifer Calderon
Math Teacher
Sunrise Middle School
Ft. Lauderdale, FL

Denise B. Dorsett
Math Instructor
Walter C. Young Middle
  School
Pembroke Pines, FL

Idonia Dorta
Mathematics Consultant
Miami, FL

James N. Gibbs III
AVID Coordinator
Burns Middle School
Brandon, FL

Pamela Q. Guyton
Middle Grades
  Mathematics Teacher
Odyssey Middle School
Orlando, FL

LaChandra Hogan
Teacher/Math Dept. Chair
Apollo Middle School
Hollywood, FL

Susan K. Loucks
Mathematics Teacher
Safety Harbor Middle
  School
Safety Harbor, FL

Shannon M. Richards
Mathematics Teacher
River Oaks Middle School
Charleston, SC
(formerly from Lutz, FL)

Jennifer Schorr
Math Coach
Millennium Middle School
Tamarac, FL

Jeanette K. Scott
Mathematics Department
  Chair
McNicol Middle School
Hollywood, FL

Shioban Smith-Haye
Mathematics
Apollo Middle School
Hollywood, FL

Welcome to the
Next Generation
Sunshine State Standards

The Next Generation Sunshine State Standards...

consist of Big Ideas and Supporting Ideas. The Big Ideas tell you what you will primarily learn in your grade. The Supporting Ideas will help you connect concepts and prepare you for future mathematics.

Here are your Grade 7 Big Ideas.

☆ **BIG Idea 1** Develop an understanding of and apply proportionality, including similarity.

You will learn about Big Idea 1 in Chapters 4, 5, and 6.

☆ **BIG Idea 2** Develop an understanding of and use formulas to determine surface areas and volumes of three-dimensional shapes.

You will learn about Big Idea 2 in Chapter 8.

☆ **BIG Idea 3** Develop an understanding of operations on all rational numbers and solving linear equations.

You will learn about Big Idea 3 in Chapters 1, 2, and 3.

Here are your Grade 7 Supporting Ideas.

☆ **Supporting Idea** Geometry and Measurement

You will learn about Geometry and Measurement in Chapters 9 and 10.

☆ **Supporting Idea** Number and Operations

You will learn about Number and Operations in Chapters 1, 2, and 3.

☆ **Supporting Idea** Data Analysis

You will learn about Data Analysis in Chapter 7.

☆ **Supporting Idea** Probability

You will learn about Probability in Chapter 7.

Multi-Part Lessons

How will my book help me learn the Big Ideas and Supporting Ideas?

Chapters 1–13 of your book contain Multi-Part Lessons. Each Multi-Part Lesson:

- ensures in-depth coverage of the Big Ideas and Supporting Ideas,

- provides lots of opportunities to explore new ideas with hands-on activities, and

- allows you plenty of time to really understand new concepts.

Contents

CHAPTER 0 Start Smart

CHAPTER 1 Integers

Multi-Part Lesson
1-1 Integers and the Coordinate Plane

Multi-Part Lesson
1-2 Add and Subtract Integers

Multi-Part Lesson
1-3 Multiply and Divide Integers

The ☆**BIG Idea** 3
Develop an understanding of operations on all rational numbers and solving linear equations.

Supporting
☆**Idea**
Number and Operations

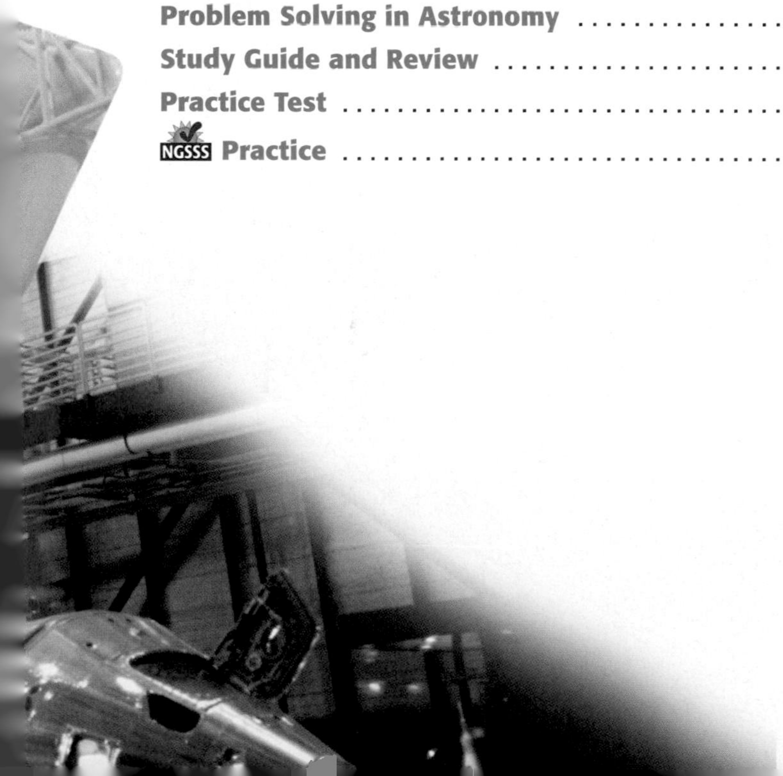

CHAPTER 2 Rational Numbers

CHAPTER 3 Linear Equations

The ☆BIG Idea 3
Develop an understanding of operations on all rational numbers and solving linear equations.

Supporting ☆Idea
Number and Operations

CHAPTER 4
Proportions and Similarity

CHAPTER
5 Linear Functions

The **★BIG Idea** 1
Develop an understanding of and apply proportionality, including similarity.

CHAPTER 6 Percents

CHAPTER
7 Data Analysis and Probability

Supporting
☆ Idea

Data Analysis
Probability

CHAPTER 9 Measurement and Proportional Reasoning

Supporting ☆ Idea
Geometry and Measurement

CHAPTER 10 Transformations

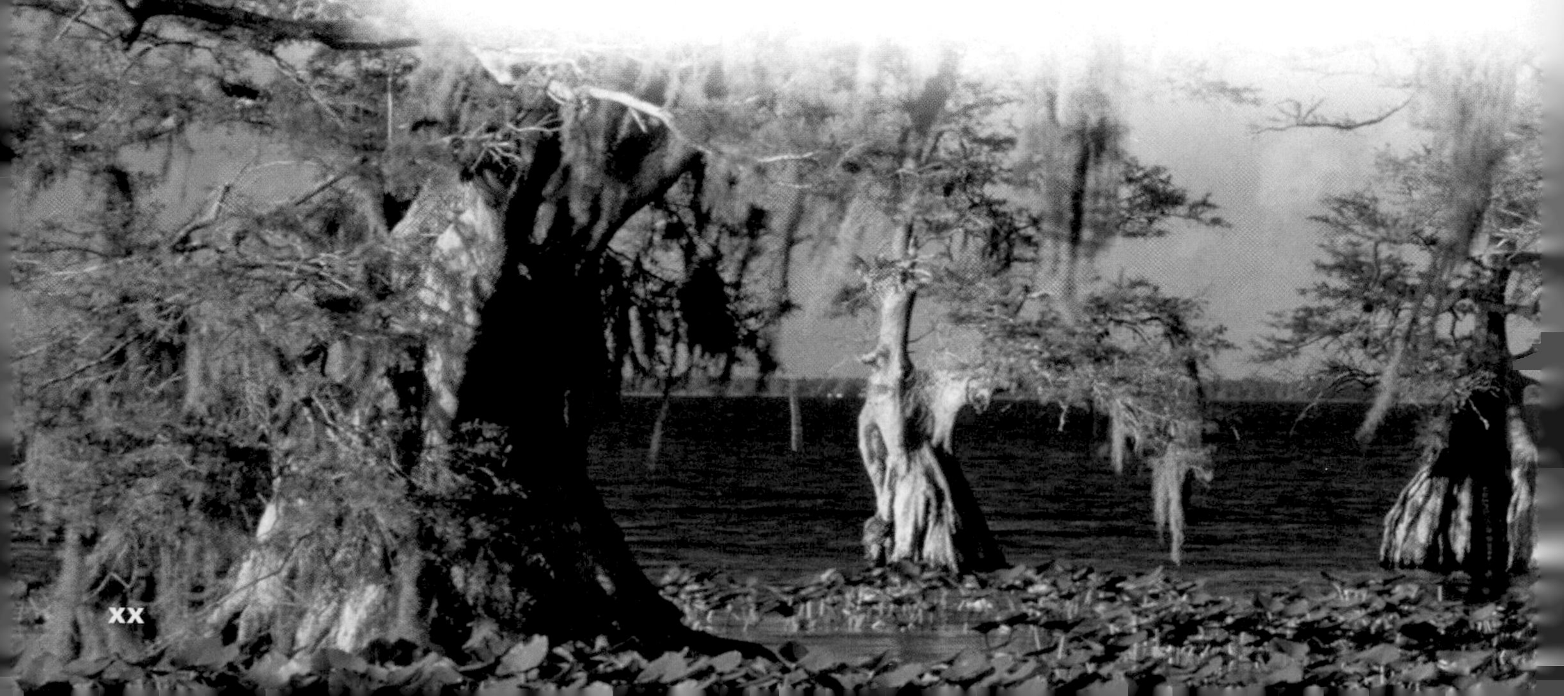

NGSSS Review

Tips for Success **FL1**

Practice

The ☆ BIG Ideas

Supporting ☆ Ideas

Optional Projects

Problem-Solving Projects

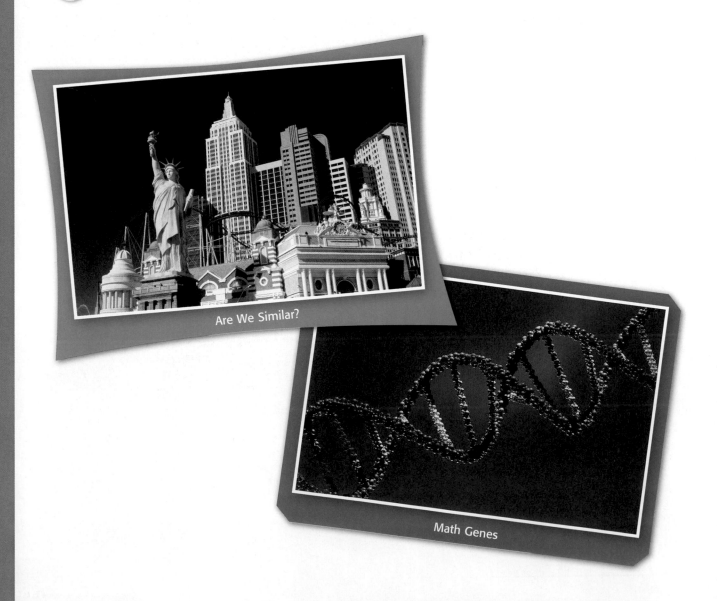

Are We Similar?

Math Genes

CHAPTER
11 Geometry and Spatial Reasoning

CHAPTER
12 Statistics

CHAPTER
13 Inequalities, Functions, and Monomials

Student Handbook

To the Student

Let's Get Started!

Your math book has many features that will help you learn the Florida Big Ideas and Supporting Ideas. Some of these features are listed below.

- The **Main Idea** and ☀ **NGSSS** standard(s) are at the beginning of each lesson.

- The **New Vocabulary** words are bolded and **highlighted in yellow**.

- **Get Connected** directs you to online resources such as homework help and self-check quizzes.

- **Get Animated** Computer animations for examples and activities are indicated by the Get Animated button.

- ● = **Step-by-Step Solutions** will coach you through selected problems.

- Your **FOLDABLES** help you to organize your notes.

You can use the activity at the right to help you find these and other special features in your book.

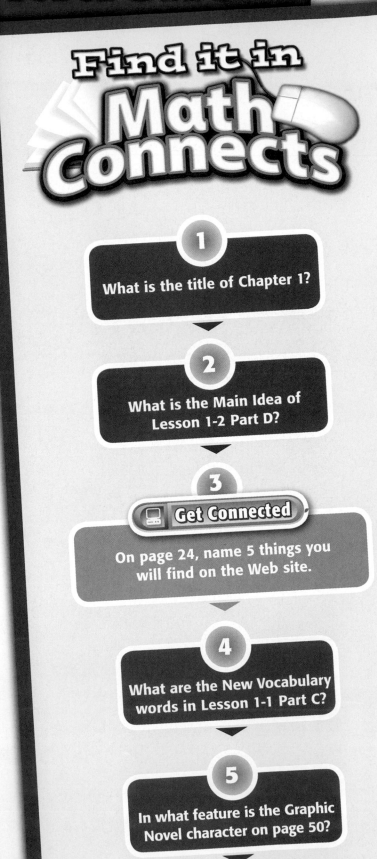

Find it in Math Connects

1 What is the title of Chapter 1?

2 What is the Main Idea of Lesson 1-2 Part D?

3 Get Connected
On page 24, name 5 things you will find on the Web site.

4 What are the New Vocabulary words in Lesson 1-1 Part C?

5 In what feature is the Graphic Novel character on page 50?

6 **Get Connected**

On page 24, what is the Web address that allows you to take a Self-Check Quiz?

7

What is the Key Concept shown in Lesson 1-3 Part C?

8

How many Examples are shown in Lesson 1-3 Part D?

9

On what page will you find the Study Guide and Review for Chapter 1?

10

Which Activity is animated in Lesson 1-2 Part B?

11

How does the Study Tip on page 57 help you?

12

How many Exercises are there in Lesson 1-1 Part B?

13 **Get Connected**

What career will you Get Connected to on pages 66–67?

14

What is the title of the Graphic Novel in Chapter 1?

FINISH

Move Forward!

Data File

The following pages contain data that you'll use throughout the book.

Incredible Hulk Coaster

Amusement Park: Universal's Islands of Adventure, Orlando, Florida

Length: 3,700 feet

Height: 110 feet

Speed: 67 miles per hour

Duration: 2 minutes, 15 seconds

Vehicles: 3

Riders per vehicle: 32

Manatee

Length: 8 to 13 feet (2.4 to 4 meters)

Weight: 440 to 1,300 pounds (200 to 600 kilograms)

Habitat: Manatees live in the shallow, marshy coastal areas and rivers of the Caribbean Sea, the Gulf of Mexico, the Amazon Basin, and West Africa.

Temperature

Record Temperatures in Florida					
Record	°F	°C	Date	Location	Elevation (feet)
High	109	42.8	June 29, 1931	Monticello	207
Low	−2	−18.9	February 13, 1899	Tallahassee	193

Florida Stadiums

Stadium	Location	Capacity
Daytona International Speedway	Daytona Beach	168,000
Ben Hill Griffin Stadium	Gainesville	88,548
Doak Campbell Stadium	Tallahassee	82,300
Municipal Stadium	Jacksonville	76,877
Dolphin Stadium	Miami Gardens	75,540
Miami Orange Bowl	Miami	72,319

The John and Mable Ringling Museum of Art

SARASOTA, FLORIDA

Regular Ticket Prices

$19 Adults

$16 Seniors

$6 Students, children 6–17, active U.S. military, Florida teachers

Free: Children under 6 and museum members

Daytona Beach

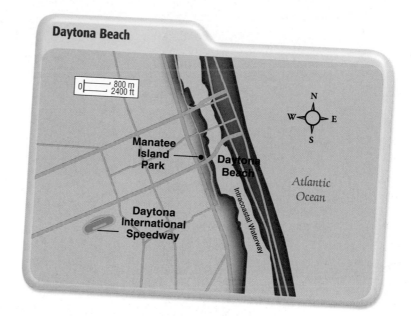

Alafia River Bike Trail

ALAFIA RIVER STATE PARK

This former phosphate mine has some of the most challenging bicycling trails in Florida. Its unique topography offers radical elevation changes during the 14 miles of trail. The average time to complete the trail is 2 hours and 1 minute at an average speed of 7.27 miles per hour.

Four Seasons Hotel & Tower

MIAMI

Height: 789 feet (240 meters)

Floors: 70

Hotel: Floors 30 through 40 house hotel residences, which range in size from 600 square feet to 2,000 square feet.

Condominiums: 184 units, which range in size from 1,697 square feet to 6,603 square feet.

Office space: 200,000 square feet

Foundation: The tower is supported by caissons six feet in diameter that run 140 feet deep, which is about 40 feet into bedrock.

Lake Okeechobee

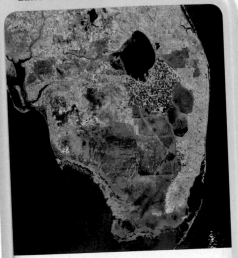

Referred to locally as Lake O or The Big Lake, Lake Okeechobee is the second-largest freshwater lake within the United States. Okeechobee covers 730 square miles (1,890 square kilometers). The lake varies in depth from 1 to 12 feet (0.2 to 4 meters). The lake has a dike that is 20 feet (6 meters) high to prevent floods. The dike has a paved pathway along the entire perimeter and is part of the Florida Trail, a 1,400-mile-long trail that is a National Scenic Trail.

Florida Fruit Drinks

Florida Fruity Frost

6 bananas
$1\frac{1}{2}$ qt orange juice
1 grated lemon rind
$\frac{3}{4}$ qt crushed pineapple
$\frac{3}{4}$ qt sugar
$\frac{1}{2}$ tbsp salt
$1\frac{1}{2}$ qt milk

Tampa's Lowry Park Zoo

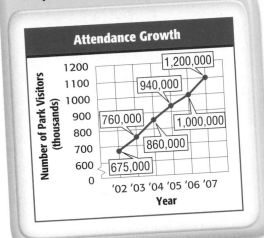

Attendance Growth

Number of Park Visitors (thousands) vs. Year ('02 '03 '04 '05 '06 '07)

675,000
760,000
860,000
940,000
1,000,000
1,200,000

Great Blue Heron

Length: $3\frac{1}{5}$–$4\frac{1}{2}$ feet (1–1.4 meters)

Wingspan: $5\frac{1}{2}$–$6\frac{3}{5}$ feet (1.7–2 meters)

Weight: $4\frac{3}{5}$–$7\frac{3}{10}$ pounds (2.1–2.5 kilograms)

Habitat: The Great Blue Heron can be found living near bodies of water throughout much of North America, including Florida. Herons nest in trees or bushes near fresh and saltwater marshes, swamps, flooded meadows, lake edges, or shorelines.

Florida Gators Men's Basketball

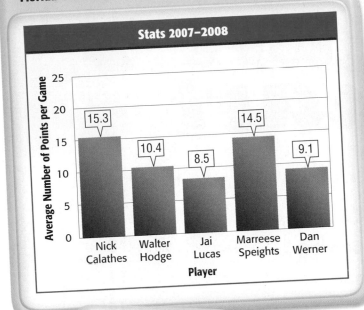

Stats 2007–2008

Average Number of Points per Game vs. Player

- Nick Calathes: 15.3
- Walter Hodge: 10.4
- Jai Lucas: 8.5
- Marreese Speights: 14.5
- Dan Werner: 9.1

Florida Seminoles Women's Soccer

Number of Goals Scored, 2007	
Mami Yamaguchi	24
Sanna Talonen	18
Amanda DaCosta	6
Kirsten van de Ven	7
Erika Sutton	5

Major Age Groups

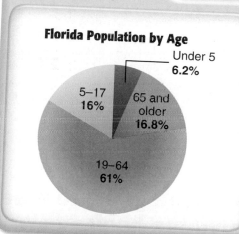

Florida Population by Age

- Under 5: **6.2%**
- 5–17: **16%**
- 65 and older: **16.8%**
- 19–64: **61%**

Downtown Tallahassee Historic Trail

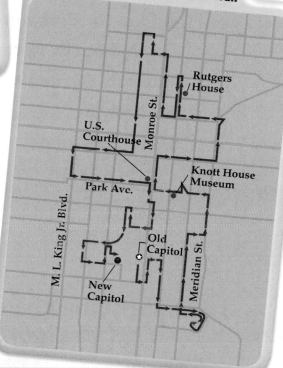

Rutgers House
Monroe St.
U.S. Courthouse
Knott House Museum
Park Ave.
M. L. King Jr. Blvd.
Old Capitol
New Capitol
Meridian St.

Florida's Old State Capitol

Built: 1845
Dome added: 1902
Last used as Capitol: 1978
Opened as a museum: 1982
Style: Classical Revival
Architect: Frank P. Milburn
Free tours: (self guided)
Mon.–Fri. 9:00 A.M.–4:30 P.M.,
Sat. 10:00 A.M.–4:30 P.M.,
Sun. and holidays
12:00 NOON to 4:30 P.M.

start smart

Let's Review

Here are some characters we are going to meet as you move through the book.

Jamar

"I look for bugs everywhere I go. Someday I want to work for the zoo in the entomology area."

Caitlyn

"I love to sing and play the drums. I like to play the drums to the beat of the music!"

Dario

"In my spare time I race go-karts. I want to be a NASCAR driver when I grow up."

Divya

"My favorite subject in school is science. I'd like to be a science teacher."

Blake

"I take tennis lessons every morning before school. I want to be a tennis pro."

Theresa

"My favorite sport is soccer. My mom and I go to see professional soccer games."

Hiroshi

"My mother is a professional cyclist. I enjoy riding with her on the weekends."

Marisol

"I love nature. When I visit the local park, I enjoy hearing the ranger give talks about plants and wildlife."

Seth

"I take golf lessons from a local professional at the country club. I want to be on the golf team in high school."

Aisha

"Math is my favorite subject. I love to play math games and solve problems to keep my skills sharp."

Raul

"Every year at my family reunion all the kids participate in karaoke. Last year I was the family champion."

Hannah

"I enjoy reading and spending time at the hospital reading to blind patients."

Let's Get Started!

We're going to review a little before you begin Chapter 1.

A Plan for Problem Solving

Ice Cream ▶
July is National Ice
Cream Month.

NGSSS

Reinforcement of MA.6.A.5.3
Estimate the results of computations with fractions, decimals, and percents and judge the reasonableness of the results.

ICE CREAM Every year, each American consumes about 23.2 quarts of ice cream. However, Americans in the north-central United States consume about 18.5 quarts more. How much ice cream is consumed every year by Americans in the north-central United States?

In mathematics, there is a *four-step problem-solving plan* you can use to help you solve any problem.

Understand
- Read the problem carefully.
- What information is given?
- What do you need to find out?

Plan
- How do the facts relate to each other?
- Select a strategy for solving the problem. There may be several that you can use.
- Estimate the answer.

Solve
- Use your plan to solve the problem.
- If your plan does not work, make a new plan.
- What is the solution?

Check
- Does your answer fit the facts given in the problem?
- Is your answer reasonable?

Use the Four-Step Plan

1 **ICE CREAM** Refer to the information on page 8. How much ice cream is consumed every year by Americans in the north-central United States?

Understand You know that each American consumes 23.2 quarts of ice cream and that Americans in the north-central United States consume 18.5 quarts more. You need to find how much ice cream is consumed in the north-central United States.

Plan To find the total amount, add 23.2 and 18.5.

Estimate $20 + 20 = 40$

Solve
$$
\begin{array}{r}
23.2 \\
+\ 18.5 \\
\hline
41.7
\end{array}
$$
    Line up the decimal points.
    Add as with whole numbers.

Check for Reasonableness $41.7 \approx 40$ ✓

So, 41.7 quarts of ice cream are consumed each year by Americans in the north-central United States.

Check Check by subtracting. Since $41.7 - 23.2 = 18.5$, the answer is correct. ✓

> **Read Math**
> The symbol ≈ means *is about equal to.*

 CHECK Your Progress

a. **SCHOOL** The Fort Couch Middle School cafeteria has a special lunch every Thursday. How much will you save by buying the special on Thursday instead of getting each item separately on any other day?

Entreé		Sides	
Chili	$1.49	Salad	$1.19
Chicken Fingers	$1.39	Fruit	$0.99
Hamburger	$1.99	Tortilla Chips	$1.29
		Thursday Special	
All Drinks	$0.99	Chili, Salad, and Drink	$3.49

b. **GEOMETRY** The courtyard at Eastmoor Middle School is shaped like a rectangle that is 18.8 feet long. The width of the courtyard is 4.8 feet less than the length. What is the total distance around the courtyard?

Use the four-step plan to solve each problem.

1. **SCIENCE** The table shows the average lengths of the bones in a human leg. How much longer is the average femur than the average tibia?

Bones in a Human Leg	
Bone	**Length (in.)**
Femur (upper leg)	19.88
Tibia (inner lower leg)	16.94
Fibula (outer lower leg)	15.94

2. **FINANCIAL LITERACY** Terry opened a savings account in December with $150 and saved $30 each month beginning in January. Calculate the value of Terry's account at the end of July.

3. **GEOMETRY** Numbers that can be represented by a triangular arrangement of dots are called *triangular numbers*. The first five triangular numbers are shown below. Describe the pattern in the first five numbers. Then list the next three triangular numbers.

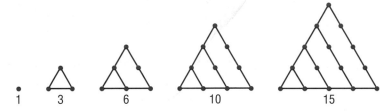

1   3   6   10   15

4. **SCHOOL** The Boosters expect 500 people at the annual awards banquet. If each table seats 8 people, how many tables are needed?

5. **PATTERNS** The sequence 1, 1, 2, 3, 5, 8, … is called the *Fibonacci sequence*. List the next three numbers in this sequence.

6. **TRAVEL** A commuter train departs from a train station and travels to the city each day. The schedule shows the first five departure and arrival times.

   a. How often does the commuter train arrive in the city?

   b. What is the latest time that passengers can depart from the train station if they need to arrive in the city no later than noon?

Commuter Train Schedule	
Departure	**Arrival**
6:30 A.M.	6:50 A.M.
7:15 A.M.	7:35 A.M.
8:00 A.M.	8:20 A.M.
8:45 A.M.	9:05 A.M.
9:30 A.M.	9:50 A.M.

Real-World Link…
The numbers in the Fibonacci sequence can be observed in a pinecone. There are usually 34 spirals of seed heads going one way and 55 going the other.

7. **MOVIES** The table shows the concession stand prices, including tax, at Mega Movies. Marlon ordered 2 medium drinks and 1 large popcorn. He gave the cashier $10. How much change should he receive?

Mega Movies Menu			
Drinks		**Popcorn**	
small	$1.99	small	$2.49
medium	$2.75	medium	$3.50
large	$3.50	large	$3.95

Estimate with Decimals

Yellowstone ▶
Yellowstone is the oldest national park. It is located in Wyoming, Montana, and Idaho.

NGSSS

☀ **Reinforcement of MA.6.A.5.3** Estimate the results of computations with fractions, decimals, and percents and judge the reasonableness of the results.

Most Visited U.S. National Parks

Great Smoky Mountains	9.192
Grand Canyon	4.402
Yosemite	3.304
Olympic	3.143
Yellowstone	2.836

Annual Visitors (millions)

PARKS The graphic shows the five most-visited national parks in the United States. About how many people visit Yellowstone and Olympic National Parks annually?

Estimation is a good way to provide quick answers when an exact answer is not necessary. It is also an excellent way to check whether your answer is reasonable.

EXAMPLE **Estimate by Rounding**

 PARKS Refer to the information above. Estimate the total number of annual visitors to Yellowstone and Olympic National Parks.

Round each number to the nearest unit for easier adding.

2.836	⟶	3	2.836 rounds to 3.
+ 3.143	⟶	+ 3	3.143 rounds to 3.
		6	

About 6 million visitors go to these two parks annually.

 CHECK Your Progress

a. PARKS Estimate how many more annual visitors go to Grand Canyon National Park than Yosemite.

b. FOOD The table shows the prices of fruit and nut mixes. Estimate the cost of 2.8 pounds of trail mix and 2.3 pounds of sweet and salty mix.

Fruit & Nut Mixes	
Type of Mix	**Price per Pound ($)**
Trail	4.38
Yogurt nut	4.62
Sweet and salty	4.69

Another way to estimate a sum is to use clustering. This strategy is used when all the numbers are close to a common value.

 EXAMPLE Estimate by Clustering

2 **PARKS** Refer to the graphic on page 11. Estimate the number of annual visitors to the Grand Canyon, Yosemite, Olympic, and Yellowstone National Parks.

There are four numbers clustered around 3 million.

$$\left.\begin{array}{l} 4.402 \\ 3.304 \\ 3.143 \\ 2.836 \end{array}\right\} \quad 4 \times 3 \text{ million} = 12 \text{ million}$$

There were about 12 million annual visitors to the Grand Canyon, Yosemite, Olympic, and Yellowstone National Parks.

 CHECK Your Progress

c. HOMEWORK The table shows the amount of time Nicholas spent on his homework each week in the last month. Estimate the total amount of time Nicholas spent on his homework.

Time Spent on Homework				
Week	1	2	3	4
Time (h)	11.24	9.47	12.36	10.38

Vocabulary Link

Everyday Use
Compatible Able to live or work together without conflict.

Math Use
Compatible Numbers that are easy to compute mentally.

Compatible numbers are numbers that are easy to compute mentally. You can use compatible numbers when estimating quotients.

 EXAMPLE Estimate with Compatible Numbers

3 Estimate $47.3 \div 7.7$.

$47.3 \div 7.7 \approx \mathbf{47.3 \div 8}$ Round 7.7 to 8.

$\approx \mathbf{48 \div 8}$ Change 47.3 to 48 because 48 and 8 are compatible numbers.

≈ 6

So, $47.3 \div 7.7$ is about 6.

 CHECK Your Progress

Estimate by rounding and using compatible numbers.

d. $25.8 \div 5.1$ **e.** $63.1 \div 6.4$ **f.** $35.7 \div 11.4$

Estimate by rounding.

1. $8.56 + 5.34$
2. $6.8 + 2.4$
3. $6.9 + 5.2$
4. $23.84 + 12.13$
5. $34.84 - 17.69$
6. $40.79 - 6.8$
7. $34.3 \quad 18.9$
8. $65.48 - 9.3$
9. 6.4×7.1
10. 21.4×3.7
11. 4.4×39.5
12. 7.9×30.3

13. **TOYS** The table shows the amount of sales of different toys in a recent year.

    a. Estimate the total amount of sales of electronics, sports, and action figures.

    b. About how much more was spent on arts and crafts than on building sets?

Toy Sales	
Kind	**Amount (billions)**
Sports	$2.9
Arts and crafts	$2.6
Action figures	$1.3
Electronics	$1.1
Building sets	$0.7

Estimate by clustering.

14. $18.4 + 22.5 + 20.7$
15. $56.9 + 63.2 + 59.3 + 61.1$
16. $42.3 + 41.5 + 39.8 + 40.4$
17. $77.8 + 75.6 + 81.2 + 79.9$

18. **HORSES** A quarter horse can run 49.5 miles per hour for a short distance. At this speed, about how far could a quarter horse run in 3.3 hours?

19. **WEATHER** The average yearly precipitation for New York City is 47.25 inches. About how much precipitation does the area receive each month?

20. **BASEBALL** The graph shows ticket prices for several major league baseball teams.

    a. About how much more would two Chicago Cubs tickets cost than two Chicago White Sox tickets?

    b. The average price for a soda and hot dog at a New York Yankees game is $6.25. About how much would a family pay for four tickets, four sodas, and four hot dogs?

Major League Baseball Ticket Prices

Estimate with compatible numbers.

21. $30.67 \div 5.4$
22. $985 \div 30.4$
23. $24.6 \div 3.1$
24. $3.2\overline{)17.3}$
25. $24.9\overline{)76.1}$
26. $4.4\overline{)43.9}$

Multiply Decimals

Koalas ▶
Koalas are often called koala bears, but that is not correct. Koalas are marsupials, not bears.

NGSSS

Reinforcement of MA.6.A.1.2 Multiply and divide fractions and decimals efficiently.

KOALAS Koalas spend about 0.75 of each day sleeping. How many hours does a koala sleep each day?

To multiply decimals, multiply as with whole numbers. The product has the same number of decimal places as the sum of the decimal places of the factors.

Real-World EXAMPLE **Multiply a Decimal by a Whole Number**

 KOALAS Refer to the information above. How long does a koala sleep each day?

There are 24 hours in each day. So, multiply 0.75 by 24.

$$
\begin{array}{r}
24 \\
\times\, 0.75 \quad \longleftarrow \text{2 decimal places} \\
\hline
120 \\
168 \\
\hline
18.00 \quad \text{Count two decimal places from the right and place the decimal point.}
\end{array}
$$

A koala sleeps 18 hours each day.

 CHECK Your Progress

a. **KOALAS** A koala eats about 1.125 pounds of eucalyptus leaves each day. How many pounds of eucalyptus leaves will a koala eat in 5 days?

Everyday Use

Annex To attach to something, as in a building that is added to another building.

Math Use

Annex To place a zero at the beginning or end of a decimal.

If there are not enough decimal places in the product, you need to annex zeros to the left.

EXAMPLES Multiply Decimals

Multiply.

2 1.3×0.9

Estimate $1 \times 1 = 1$

$$
\begin{array}{r}
1.3 \quad \longleftarrow \text{1 decimal place} \\
\times\, 0.9 \quad \longleftarrow \text{1 decimal place} \\
\hline
1.17 \quad \longleftarrow \text{2 decimal places}
\end{array}
$$

Check for Reasonableness $1.17 \approx 1$ ✓

3 0.054×1.6

$$
\begin{array}{r}
0.054 \quad \longleftarrow \text{3 decimal places} \\
\times\, 1.6 \quad \longleftarrow \text{1 decimal place} \\
\hline
324 \quad\quad \\
540 \quad\quad \\
\hline
0.0864 \quad
\end{array}
$$
Annex a zero on the left so the answer has four decimal places.

Check for Reasonableness $0.0864 \approx 0$ ✓

CHECK Your Progress

Multiply.

b. 15.8×11 **c.** 88×2.5 **d.** 33×0.03

Practice and Problem Solving

Place the decimal point in each product. Add zeros if necessary.

1. $1.32 \times 4 = 528$ **2.** $0.07 \times 1.1 = 77$ **3.** $0.4 \times 0.7 = 28$

4. $1.9 \times 0.6 = 114$ **5.** $1.4 \times 0.09 = 126$ **6.** $5.48 \times 3.6 = 19728$

7. INSECTS The graphic shows the speeds of three different insects.

    a. At this speed, how far can a bumblebee fly in 2 hours?

    b. How far can a dragonfly fly in 3.5 hours?

    c. How much farther can a hornet fly in 3 hours than a bumblebee?

How Fast Do Insects Fly?

Insect	Speed (mph)
Dragonfly	15.6
Hornet	12.8
Bumblebee	6.4

Multiply.

8. 0.6×2 **9.** 0.7×18 **10.** 8×0.3

11. 36×0.46 **12.** 380×1.25 **13.** 42×0.17

14. 0.4×16 **15.** 0.23×0.2 **16.** 12.2×12.4

17. 0.44×5.5 **18.** 0.44×55 **19.** 44×0.55

20. PETS One can of dog food costs $0.56. How much will 4 cans of dog food cost?

21. SCHOOL SUPPLIES Leonardo buys two 3-ring binders and a package of notebook paper. If he pays using a $20 bill, how much change will he receive?

School Supplies	
Item	**Cost**
3-ring binder	$3.95
Package of pens	$2.19
Notebook paper	$1.99
Ruler	$0.75

22. CELL PHONES A new brand of cell phone is 3.5 inches long. One inch is approximately equal to 2.54 centimeters. How long is the cell phone in centimeters?

23. MEASUREMENT Find the area of a rectangle that has a base of 7.5 meters and a height of 1.5 meters. (*Hint*: The formula for the area of a rectangle is $A = bh$.)

24. EARNINGS Cora earns $10.75 per hour. What are her total weekly earnings if she works 34.5 hours? Round to the nearest cent.

25. SKATING The cost of 5 youth tickets at a skating rink is $26.25. Three skaters need to rent skates for $5.50 each. What is the total cost of 5 tickets and 3 skate rentals?

26. FIELD TRIPS Each student who attends the field trip to the science museum must pay $6.00 for transportation and $5.75 for admission. There are 65 students attending the field trip. How much money is needed for transportation and admission?

27. FIND THE ERROR Raul is finding 2.6×2.2. Find his mistake and correct it.

$$
\begin{array}{r}
2.6 \\
\times\, 2.2 \\
\hline
57.2
\end{array}
$$

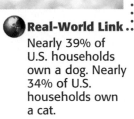

START SMART 0-4

Multiply by Powers of 10

Earth Fact ▶
It takes 8 minutes for the light from the Sun to reach us.

NGSSS

Reinforcement of MA.6.A.1.2 Multiply and divide fractions and decimals efficiently.

EARTH The planet Earth is 92 million miles from the Sun. The number 1,000,000 is a *power of 10*.

$$1,000,000 = 10 \times 10 \times 10 \times 10 \times 10 \times 10 \text{ or } 10^6$$

Study the decimals in the table. To multiply a decimal by a power of 10 that is greater than one, count the number of zeros in the power of 10. Then move the decimal point that many places *to the right*.

Decimal × Power of 10	Product
19.7×10^1 (or 10)	= 197
19.7×10^2 (or 100)	= 1,970
19.7×10^3 (or 1,000)	= 19,700
19.7×10^4 (or 10,000)	= 197,000

Real-World EXAMPLE

1 **EARTH** Refer to the information above. Write Earth's distance from the Sun in standard form.

92 million $= 92 \times 1,000,000$ The word *million* means 1,000,000.

$= 92.000000$ Move the decimal point 6 places to the right. Annex zeros as needed.

$= 92,000,000$ Remove the decimal point and add commas.

So, Earth is 92,000,000 miles from the Sun.

CHECK Your Progress

Write each number in standard form.

a. The diameter of Earth is about 8 thousand miles.

b. The diameter of Jupiter is about 89 thousand miles.

EXAMPLES **Multiply by a Power of 10 Greater than 1**

Find each product.

2 **12.562 × 100**

$$12.562 \times 100 = 12.562 \quad \text{Move the decimal point two places to the right.}$$

$$= 1{,}256.2$$

Study Tip

Check for Reasonableness The product of a number and a power of ten that is greater than one will always be *greater than* the original number.

3 **0.59 × 10⁴**

$$0.59 \times 10^4 = 0.5900 \quad \text{Move the decimal point four places to the right.}$$

$$= 5{,}900$$

CHECK Your Progress

c. 12.53×10 **d.** 4.6×10^3

To multiply a decimal by a power of 10 that is less than 1, count the number of places after the decimal point. Then move the decimal point that number of places *to the left*.

Decimal × Power of 10	Product
$19.7 \times 0.1 \left(\text{or } \frac{1}{10^1}\right)$	$= 1.97$
$19.7 \times 0.01 \left(\text{or } \frac{1}{10^2}\right)$	$= 0.197$
$19.7 \times 0.001 \left(\text{or } \frac{1}{10^3}\right)$	$= 0.0197$

EXAMPLES **Multiply by a Power of 10 Less than 1**

Find each product.

4 **10.5 × 0.01**

$$10.5 \times 0.01 = 10.5 \quad \text{Move the decimal point two places to the left.}$$

$$= 0.105$$

Study Tip

Check for Reasonableness The product of a number and a decimal between 0 and 1 is always *less than* the original number.

5 **5,284 × 0.00001**

$$5{,}2284 \times 0.00001 = 05284 \quad \text{Move the decimal point five places to the left.}$$

$$= 0.05284$$

CHECK Your Progress

e. 78.4×0.01 **f.** 13.58×0.01

Find each product.

1. 0.05×100
2. 4.527×10^2
3. $2.78 \times 1,000$
4. 5.49×10^3
5. 0.1×0.8
6. 0.925×10
7. 99.44×10^2
8. 0.01×16
9. 1.32×10^3
10. $0.56 \times 10,000$
11. 1.4×0.001
12. 11.23×10^5
13. 68.94×0.01
14. 0.8×10^4
15. 28.1×0.01
16. 9.3×10^7
17. $625,799 \times 0.0001$
18. 8.72×10^6

19. **SPORTS** The attendance at the Louisiana Superdome in a recent year was 560 thousand people. Write the number of people in standard form.

CELL PHONES The table shows the number of times per month cell phone subscribers did each activity.

Cell Phone Subscribers	
Activity	**Number**
sent text message	78 million
purchased ringtone	20 million
used personal E-mail	16.9 million
played mobile game	7.2 million

20. How many subscribers purchased a ringtone? Write the number in standard form.

21. How many more subscribers used personal E-mail than played a mobile game? Write your answer in standard form.

22. **MONEY** The shoes shown are on sale for one tenth off the original price. What is the sale price?

$59.98

23. **STAMPS** It costs $0.41 to mail each invitation for the school honors banquet. How much does it cost to send 100 invitations?

24. **SCIENCE** The diameter of the Sun is about 864,000 miles. Which planet has a diameter that is about 0.1 the diameter of the Sun?

Planet	Diameter (mi)
Venus	7,521
Earth	7,926
Saturn	74,975
Jupiter	88,732

Real-World Link
Saturn is known for its rings, but it also has 60 known moons that circle it.

25. **MUSIC** It costs $0.99 to download one song from the Internet. How much does it cost to download 10 songs?

Divide Decimals

Olympics ▶
Usain Bolt also ran the 100-meter event at the Beijing Olympics in a world-record time of 9.69 seconds.

NGSSS

Reinforcement of **MA.6.A.1.2** Multiply and divide fractions and decimals efficiently.

SPORTS Jamaican sprinter Usain Bolt holds the world record for running 200 meters in 19.3 seconds. What was his speed in meters per second?

To find Bolt's average speed, divide 200 meters by 19.3 seconds. Dividing decimals is similar to dividing whole numbers.

EXAMPLE **Divide a Decimal by a Whole Number**

① Find $25.8 \div 2$.   **Estimate** $26 \div 2 = 13$

QUICK Review

Division
Dividend → 25.8
Divisor → 2
Quotient → 12.9

$$\begin{array}{r} 12.9 \\ 2\overline{)25.8} \\ -2 \\ \hline 5 \\ -4 \\ \hline 18 \\ -18 \\ \hline 0 \end{array}$$

Place the decimal directly above the decimal point in the dividend. Divide as with whole numbers.

Check by Multiplying $12.9 \times 2 = 25.8$ ✓

 CHECK Your Progress

a. $8.7 \div 3$ **b.** $613.8 \div 66$

To divide by a decimal, multiply both the divisor and dividend by the same power of ten so that the divisor is a whole number. Then divide.

$$\text{divisor} \longrightarrow 0.5 \overline{)4.5} \longleftarrow \text{dividend}$$

EXAMPLE Divide Decimals

 Find $199.68 \div 9.6$.   **Estimate** $200 \div 10 = 20$

```
         20.8
9.6)199.68      Move each decimal point one place to the right.
  − 192
     768
    − 768
       0      Check for Reasonableness  20.8 ≈ 20 ✓
```

CHECK Your Progress

c. $9.81 \div 0.3$ **d.** $5.76 \div 3.2$

In many real-world situations, the remainder is not zero. So, the quotient is usually rounded to a certain place-value position.

Real-World EXAMPLE

 SPORTS Refer to the information on page 20. Divide 200 by 19.3 to find Usain Bolt's speed in meters per second. Round your answer to the nearest tenth.

Estimate $200 \div 20 = 10$

```
          10.36
19.3)200.000      Move each decimal point one place to the right.
   − 193
      70
     − 0
      700
    − 579
     1210
   − 1158
       62
```

QUICKReview

Rounding
Look at the digit to the right of the tenths place. Since 6 is greater than 5, 10.36 is rounded to 10.4.

Check for Reasonableness $10.4 \approx 10$ ✓

Usain Bolt's speed is about 10.4 meters per second.

CHECK Your Progress

e. FOOD Mrs. Myers bought 2.5 pounds of hamburger for $5.20. How much did she pay in dollars per pound?

Find each quotient.

1. $812 \div 0.4$
2. $0.34 \div 0.2$
3. $2.5\overline{)14.4}$
4. $2.5\overline{)90}$
5. $4.4 \div 0.8$
6. $88.8 \div 444$
7. $6.6\overline{)5.94}$
8. $0.33\overline{)2475}$
9. $20.24 \div 2.3$
10. $45 \div 0.09$
11. $36\overline{)1.8}$
12. $0.366\overline{)0.4392}$

13. **MONEY** Sachi bought four bottles of nail polish for a total of $23.96. If each bottle cost the same, how much did each cost?

4 for $23.96

14. **NUTRITION** There are 74.4 grams of sugar in 3 servings of grapes. How many grams of sugar are in a single serving of grapes?

15. **FINANCIAL LITERACY** Shiro wants to buy a pair of in-line skates that cost $140.75. So far, he has saved $56.25. He can save $6.50 each week. In how many weeks will he have enough money to purchase the in-line skates?

16. **FOOD** Refer to the table that shows the size and cost of two different packages of fruit chews.

Fruit Chews		
Box	Cost	Size of Bags
Large-sized	$4.89	13 ounces
Regular-sized	$2.59	6.5 ounces

a. Which package costs less per ounce?

b. Would it make sense to buy one large package or two regular packages? Explain your reasoning.

17. **BASEBALL** Red Sox outfielder Jason Bay had 7 hits in 17 times at bat. To find his batting average, divide the number of hits by the number of times at bat. To the nearest thousandth, what was Jason Bay's batting average?

18. **OLYMPICS** Usain Bolt ran the 100-meter event in 9.69 seconds and the 200-meter event in 19.3 seconds. Was his speed in meters per second faster in the 100-meter event or the 200-meter event? How much faster?

19. **FIND THE ERROR** Caitlyn is finding $11\overline{)61.6}$. Find her mistake and correct it.

$$\begin{array}{r} 0.56 \\ 11\overline{)61.6} \end{array}$$

1. **GEOMETRY** A *diagonal* connects two nonconsecutive vertices in a figure, as shown below. How many diagonals does a figure with 7 sides have?

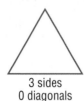

3 sides   4 sides   5 sides
0 diagonals 2 diagonals 5 diagonals

2. **WHALES** A baby blue whale gains about 200 pounds each day. About how many pounds does a baby blue whale gain per hour?

3. **LAKES** The table lists the sizes of six of the largest lakes in North Carolina. About how many times as large is High Rock Lake than Hyco Lake?

Lake	Size (acres)
Lake Mattamuskeet	40,000
Falls Lake	12,000
Hyco Lake	3,750
Lake Gaston	20,000
Lake James	6,500
High Rock Lake	15,000

4. **BIRDS** Most hummingbirds flap their wings about 50 times per second. How many times can a hummingbird flap its wings in one minute?

Estimate.

5. $1.8 + 13.9$

6. $19.5 - 6.3$

7. 4.8×3.1

8. $88.9 \div 33.7$

9. **MONEY** Mr. Booker earns $19.50 per hour. If he works 40 hours per week, about how much money does he earn in one week?

Multiply.

10. 0.9×3

11. 42×0.57

12. 0.8×0.5

13. 2.6×1.34

14. **MEASUREMENT** Emily lives 22 miles from her grandmother. One mile is approximately equal to 1.609 kilometers. How many kilometers is it from Emily's home to her grandmother's?

Find each product.

15. 0.04×100

16. 6.98×0.01

17. **ANTS** An ant can carry an item 10 times its body mass. How much can the ant shown carry?

mass = 0.003 g

18. **MUSIC** Enrique downloaded 10 songs for $9.90. What was the cost per song?

Find each quotient.

19. $9.81 \div 3$

20. $5.8 \div 4$

21. $8.24 \div 0.2$

22. $45.9 \div 4.59$

23. **FOOD** Selma bought 4.5 pounds of bananas for $3.24. How much did the bananas cost per pound?

24. **SCIENCE** It takes Pluto 247.69 Earth years to revolve once around the Sun. It takes Jupiter 11.86 Earth years to revolve once around the Sun. About how many times longer does it take Pluto than Jupiter to revolve once around the Sun?

25. **PHONES** Infinity, a long-distance phone company, charges 40¢ per call plus 4¢ per minute. Freedom, another long-distance company, charges 6¢ per minute and no connection fee. Which company charges less for a 90-minute call?

Integers

The ★BIG Idea

Add, subtract, multiply, and divide rational numbers and solve linear equations.

FOLDABLES® Study Organizer

Make this Foldable to help you organize your notes. Begin with two sheets of $8\frac{1}{2}$" by 11" paper.

1 Fold one sheet in half from top to bottom. Cut along fold from edges to margin.

2 Fold the other sheet in half from top to bottom. Cut along fold between margins.

3 Insert first sheet through second sheet and align folds.

4 Label each inside page with a lesson number and title.

1-1
Integers and the
Coordinate Plane

Review Vocabulary

numerical expression (Prior Grade) expression numerica a combination of numbers and operations

$$3 + (4 \cdot 5)$$

Key Vocabulary

	English	Español
p. 29	integer	entero
p. 29	negative integer	entero negative
p. 29	positive integer	entero positivo
p. 30	absolute value	valor absoluto
p. 33	coordinate plane	plano de coordenadas

Multilingual eGlossary glencoe.com

Get Connected glencoe.com

- Study using the **eBook**
- Explore with **Get Animated**
- Get extra help from **Personal Tutor**
- Use **virtual manipulatives** for additional help
- Take a **Self-Check Quiz**

Are You Ready for Chapter 1?

You have two options for checking prerequisite skills for this chapter.

Text Option Take the Quick Check below. Refer to the Quick Review for help.

QUICK Check	QUICK Review

Evaluate. (Prior Grade)

1. $54 \div (6 + 3)$

2. $29 + 46 - 34$

3. $7 + 50 \div 5$

4. $20 + 30 - 38$

5. $18 + 2(4 - 1)$

6. $(4 + 13 \times 2) \div 3$

7. $(30 \div 6) + (3 - 1)$

8. $5 + (91 \div 7)$

EXAMPLE 1

Evaluate $48 \div 6 + 2 \cdot 5$.

Follow the order of operations.

$48 \div 6 + 2 \cdot 5$

$= 8 + 2 \cdot 5$ Divide 48 by 6.

$= 8 + 10$ Multiply 2 by 5.

$= 18$ Add.

Use the coordinate plane to name the ordered pair for each point. (Prior Grade)

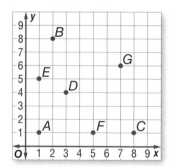

9. A

10. B

11. C

12. D

13. E

14. F

15. G

EXAMPLE 2

Use the coordinate plane to name the ordered pair for point M.

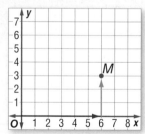

Start from the origin. Point M is located 6 units to the right and 3 units up.

So, point M corresponds to the ordered pair (6, 3).

Online Option  Take the Online Readiness Quiz at <u>glencoe.com</u>.

Writing Math

Compare and Contrast

When you compare, you notice how things are alike. When you contrast, you notice how they are different.

I know *compare* means to tell how things are alike. But what does *contrast* mean? Can you help?

The table below shows two monthly plans a cell phone company offers.

Plan A	Plan B
$34.99	$34.99
200 anytime minutes	300 anytime minutes
200 text messages	100 text messages
Free weekend minutes	Free weekend minutes

To compare and contrast the monthly plans, make a list of how they are alike and how they are different.

Alike/Compare

- The monthly cost is the same.
- They both have free weekend minutes.

Different/Contrast

- Plan B has more anytime minutes.
- Plan A has more text messages.

Practice

1. Write a few sentences that compare and contrast the figures below.

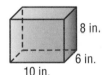

8 in.
6 in.
10 in.

8 in.
8 in.
8 in.

2. Write a few sentences that compare and contrast the numbers below.

$$30\% \qquad 0.3 \qquad \frac{3}{10}$$

3. Refer to page 29. Compare and contrast negative and positive integers.

4. Compare and contrast the units below.

inch   foot   meter

5. Compare and contrast a rectangle and a square.

NGSSS
LA.7.3.2.2 The student will draft writing by organizing information into a logical sequence and combining or deleting sentences to enhance clarity.

Explore Absolute Value

Main Idea

Use models to find the absolute value of an integer.

NGSSS

MA.7.A.3.1 Use and justify **the rules for** adding, subtracting, multiplying, dividing, and **finding the absolute value of integers.**

Get Connected
glencoe.com

SCUBA DIVING A scuba diver is diving at −130 feet. At the same time, a hiker is at the top of a cliff 130 feet *above* the surface of the water. Compare and contrast −130 feet and 130 feet.

ACTIVITY

What do you need to find? how −130 feet and 130 feet are the same and how they are different

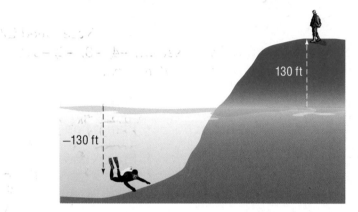

Both the hiker and the diver are the same distance from the surface of the water. The hiker is *above* and the diver is *below*.

Analyze the Results

1. Write about a real-world situation with two values that can be represented by −10 and 10. Compare and contrast them.

2. Refer to the street map at the right. Compare and contrast walking from the house to the school and walking from the house to the park.

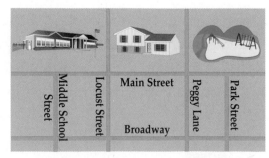

3. **Write** **MATH** Find the definition of *absolute* in a dictionary. Explain how the definition could be applied to math.

Main Idea
Read and write integers, and find the absolute value of an integer.

NGSSS
MA.7.A.3.1 Use and justify the rules for adding, subtracting, multiplying, dividing, and **finding the absolute value of integers.**

New Vocabulary
integer
negative integer
positive integer
graph
absolute value

Get Connected
glencoe.com

Integers and Absolute Value

SKATEBOARDING The bottom of a skateboarding ramp is 8 feet below street level. A value of −8 represents 8 feet *below* street level.

1. For this situation, what would a value of −10 represent?

2. The top deck of the ramp is 5 feet *above* street level. How can you represent 5 feet *above* street level?

Numbers like 5 and −8 are called integers. An **integer** is any number from the set {…, −4, −3, −2, −1, 0, 1, 2, 3, 4, …}, where … means *continues without end*.

Negative integers are integers less than zero. They are written with a − sign.

Positive integers are integers greater than zero. They are written with or without a + sign.

Zero is neither negative nor positive.

Real-World EXAMPLES

WEATHER Write an integer for each situation.

1 **an average temperature of 5 degrees below normal**

Because it represents *below* normal, the integer is −5.

2 **an average rainfall of 5 inches above normal**

Because it represents *above* normal, the integer is 5.

✓ CHECK Your Progress

Write an integer for each situation.

a. 6 degrees above normal   **b.** 2 inches below normal

Integers can be graphed on a number line. To **graph** an integer on the number line, draw a dot on the line at its location.

EXAMPLE **Graph Integers**

3 Graph the set of integers {4, −6, 0} on a number line.

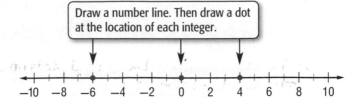

Draw a number line. Then draw a dot
at the location of each integer.

✓ **CHECK Your Progress**

Graph each set of integers on a number line.

c. {−2, 8, −7} **d.** {−4, 10, −3, 7}

On the number line below, notice that −5 and 5 are each 5 units from 0, even though they are on opposite sides of 0. Numbers that are the same distance from zero on a number line have the same **absolute value**.

Read Math

Absolute Value
|−5| *absolute value of*
  negative five

Key Concept **Absolute Value**

Words The absolute value of a number is the distance between the number and zero on a number line.

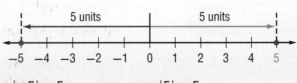

Examples |−5| = 5 |5| = 5

EXAMPLES **Evaluate Expressions**

Evaluate each expression.

4 |−4|

The graph of −4 is
4 units from 0.
So, |−4| = 4.

Study Tip

Order of Operations
The absolute value bars
are considered to be a
grouping symbol. When
evaluating |−5| − |2|,
evaluate the absolute
values before subtracting.

5 |−5| − |2|

|−5| − |2| = 5 − 2 |−5| = 5, |2| = 2
So, |−5| − |2| = 3.

✓ **CHECK Your Progress**

e. |8| **f.** 2 + |−3| **g.** |−6| − 5

✓ CHECK Your Understanding

Examples 1 and 2
(p. 29)

Write an integer for each situation.

1. a loss of 11 yards
2. 6°F below zero
3. a deposit of $16
4. 250 meters above sea level
5. **FOOTBALL** The quarterback lost 15 yards on one play. Write an integer to represent the number of yards lost.

Example 3
(p. 30)

Graph each set of integers on a number line.

6. {11, −5, −8}
7. {2, −1, −9, 1}

Examples 4 and 5
(p. 30)

Evaluate each expression.

8. $|-9|$

9. $1 + |7|$

10. $|-11| - |-6|$

Practice and Problem Solving

● = **Step-by-Step Solutions** begin on page R1.
Extra Practice is on page EP2.

Examples 1 and 2
(p. 29)

Write an integer for each situation.

11. a profit of $9
12. a bank withdrawal of $50
13. 53°C below zero
14. 7 inches more than normal
15. 2 feet below flood level
16. 160 feet above sea level
17. an elevator goes up 12 floors
18. no gains or losses on first down

19. **GOLF** In golf, scores are often written in relationship to *par*, the average score for a round at a certain course. Write an integer to represent a score that is 7 under par.

20. **PETS** Jasmine's pet guinea pig gained 8 ounces in one month. Write an integer to describe the amount of weight her pet gained.

Example 3
(p. 30)

Graph each set of integers on a number line.

21. {0, 1, −3}
22. {3, −7, 6}
23. {−5, −1, 10, −9}
24. {−2, −4, −6, −8}

Examples 4 and 5
(p. 30)

Evaluate each expression.

25. $|10|$
26. $|-12|$
27. $|-7| - 5$
28. $7 + |4|$
29. $|-9| + |-5|$
30. $|18| - |-10|$
31. $|-10| \div 2 \times |5|$
32. $12 - |-8| + 7$
33. $|27| \div 3 - |-4|$

34. **SCUBA DIVING** One diver descended 10 feet and another ascended 8 feet. Which situation has the greater absolute value? Explain.

35. **FIND THE DATA** Refer to the Data File on pages 2–5. Choose some data and write a real-world problem in which you would represent a positive and a negative integer. Explain their meanings.

H.O.T. Problems

36. **REASONING** If $|x| = 3$, what is the value of x?

37. **CHALLENGE** Two numbers A and B are graphed on a number line. Is it *always*, *sometimes*, or *never* true that $A - |B| \leq A + B$? Explain.

38. **NUMBER SENSE** Explain why -18 is less than -10. Which one has the greater absolute value? Justify your reasoning.

39. **Which One Doesn't Belong?** Identify the expression that is not equal to the other three. Explain your reasoning.

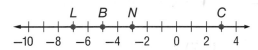

| $\|15 - \|-5\|\|$ | $\|-4\| + 6$ | $-\|7 + 3\|$ | $\|-10\|$ |

40. **Write MATH** Write a real-world situation that uses negative integers. Explain what the negative integer means in that situation.

NGSSS Practice   MA.5.A.6.3, MA.7.A.3.1

41. Which point has a coordinate with the greatest absolute value?

A number line with points labeled L, B, N, C:

```
      L   B   N           C
  ←—+—+—●—+—●—+—●—+—+—+—+—●—+—→
   -10  -8  -6  -4  -2   0   2   4
```

A. Point B

B. Point C

C. Point L

D. Point N

42. Which statement about these real-world situations is NOT true?

F. A $100 check deposited in a bank can be represented by $+100$.

G. A loss of 15 yards in a football game can be represented by -15.

H. A temperature of 20 below zero can be represented by -20.

I. A submarine diving 300 feet under water can be represented by $+300$.

43. Rachel recorded the low temperatures for one week in the table.

Day	Temperature (°F)
Sunday	2
Monday	−6
Tuesday	4
Wednesday	−8
Thursday	2
Friday	0
Saturday	−1

On which day was the low temperature the farthest from 0°F?

A. Monday   **C.** Wednesday

B. Tuesday   **D.** Friday

44. Write an integer to represent the temperature shown on the thermometer.

F. $-11°$F

G. $-10°$F

H. $10°$F

I. $11°$F

Main Idea

Graph points on a coordinate plane.

NGSSS

 **MA.7.G.4.3** Identify and plot ordered pairs in all four quadrants of the coordinate plane.

New Vocabulary

coordinate plane
quadrant
***x*-axis**
***y*-axis**
origin
ordered pair
***x*-coordinate**
***y*-coordinate**

Get Connected
glencoe.com

The Coordinate Plane

GPS A GPS, or global positioning system, is a satellite-based navigation system. A GPS map of Tallahassee, Florida, is shown.

1. Suppose Mr. Diaz starts at Carter Howell Strong Park and drives 2 blocks east. Name the street he will cross.

2. Using the words *north*, *south*, *east*, and *west*, write directions to go from Old City Cemetery to Carter Howell Strong Park.

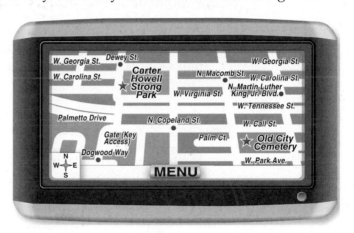

A **coordinate plane** is formed when two number lines intersect. The number lines separate the coordinate plane into four regions called quadrants.

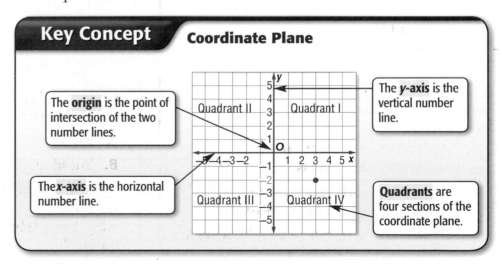

Key Concept Coordinate Plane

The **origin** is the point of intersection of the two number lines.

The **y-axis** is the vertical number line.

The **x-axis** is the horizontal number line.

Quadrants are four sections of the coordinate plane.

An **ordered pair** is a pair of numbers, such as (3, −2), used to locate a point in the coordinate plane.

The *x*-coordinate corresponds to a number on the *x*-axis.   **(3, −2)**   The *y*-coordinate corresponds to a number on the *y*-axis.

When locating an ordered pair, moving *right* or *up* on a coordinate plane is in the *positive* direction. Moving *left* or *down* is in the *negative* direction.

EXAMPLE **Naming Points Using Ordered Pairs**

1 Write the ordered pair that corresponds to point *D*. Then state the quadrant or axis on which the point is located.

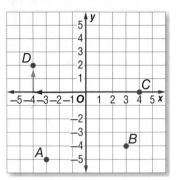

- Start at the origin.
- Move left on the *x*-axis to find the *x*-coordinate of point *D*, which is −4.
- Move up to find the *y*-coordinate, which is 2.

So, point *D* corresponds to the ordered pair (−4, 2). Point *D* is located in Quadrant II.

CHECK Your Progress

Write the ordered pair that corresponds to each point. Then state the quadrant or axis on which the point is located.

a. *A*   **b.** *B*   **c.** *C*

EXAMPLE **Graph an Ordered Pair**

2 Graph and label point *K* at (2, −5) on a coordinate plane.

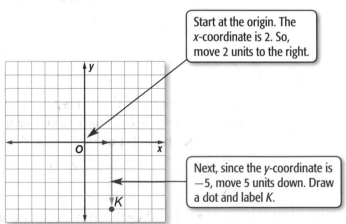

Start at the origin. The *x*-coordinate is 2. So, move 2 units to the right.

Next, since the *y*-coordinate is −5, move 5 units down. Draw a dot and label *K*.

Read Math

Scale When no numbers are shown on the *x*- or *y*-axis, you can assume that each square is 1 unit long on each side.

CHECK Your Progress

Graph and label each point on a coordinate plane.

d. *L*(−4, 2)   **e.** *M*(−5, −3)   **f.** *N*(0, 1)

3 **AQUARIUMS** A map can be divided into a coordinate plane where the *x*-coordinate represents how far to move right or left and the *y*-coordinate represents how far to move up or down. What exhibit is located at (6, 5)?

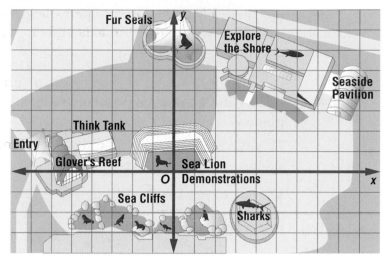

Start at the origin. Move 6 units to the right and then 5 units up. Explore the Shore is located at (6, 5).

4 **In which quadrant is the Shark Exhibit located?**

The Shark Exhibit is located in Quadrant IV.

CHECK Your Progress

g. Name the ordered pair that represents the location of the Think Tank.

h. What is located at the origin?

Real-World Link · · · · ·
The leatherback turtle is the world's largest turtle, weighing as much as 1,100 pounds. Its shell can measure over 5 feet long.

CHECK Your Understanding

Example 1
(p. 34)

Write the ordered pair corresponding to each point graphed at the right. Then state the quadrant or axis on which each point is located.

1. *P*   2. *Q*

3 *R*   4. *S*

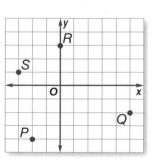

Example 2
(p. 34)

Graph and label each point on a coordinate plane.

5. $T(2, 3)$ 6. $U(-4, 6)$ 7. $V(-5, 0)$ 8. $W(1, -2)$

Examples 3 and 4
(p. 35)

9. **GEOGRAPHY** Use the map in Example 3 above.

a. What exhibit is located at $(0, -3)$?

b. In which quadrant is the Seaside Pavilion located?

● = **Step-by-Step Solutions** begin on page R1.
Extra Practice is on page EP2.

Example 1
(p. 34)

Write the ordered pair corresponding to each point graphed at the right. Then state the quadrant or axis on which each point is located.

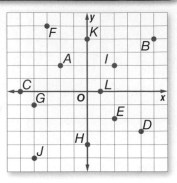

10. A	**11.** B	**12.** C
13. D	**14.** E	**15.** F
16. G	**17.** H	**18.** I
19. J	**20.** K	**21.** L

Example 2
(p. 34)

Graph and label each point on a coordinate plane.

22. $M(5, 6)$	**23.** $N(-2, 10)$	**24.** $P(7, -8)$	**25.** $Q(3, 0)$
26. $R(-1, -7)$	**27.** $S(8, 1)$	**28.** $T(-3, 7)$	**29.** $U(5, -2)$
30. $V(0, 6)$	**31.** $W(-5, -7)$	**32.** $X(-4, 0)$	**33.** $Y(0, -5)$

Example 3
(p. 35)

34. GEOGRAPHY Use the world map.

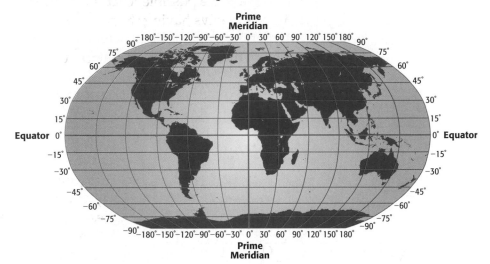

a. The world map can be divided into a coordinate plane where (x, y) represents (degrees longitude, degrees latitude). In what continent is the point (30° longitude, −15° latitude) located?

b. Which of the continents is located in Quadrant II?

c. In which continent is the point (−60° longitude, 0° latitude) located?

d. Name a continent on the map that is located in Quadrant I.

Graph and label each point on a coordinate plane.

35 $X(1.5, 3.5)$ **36.** $Y\left(3\frac{1}{4}, 2\frac{1}{2}\right)$ **37.** $Z\left(2, 1\frac{2}{3}\right)$

38. GEOMETRY Graph four points on a coordinate plane so that they form a square when connected. Identify the ordered pairs.

39. RESEARCH Use the Internet or other resources to explain why the coordinate plane is sometimes called the Cartesian plane.

40. **OPEN ENDED** Create a display that shows how to determine in what quadrant a point is located without graphing. Then provide an example that demonstrates how your graphic is used.

41. **FIND THE ERROR** Hannah is plotting the point $(-3, 4)$. Find her mistake and correct it.

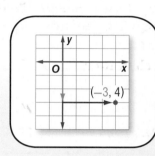

42. **CHALLENGE** Find the possible locations for any ordered pair with x- and y-coordinates always having the same sign. Explain.

43. **Write MATH** Explain why the location of point $A(1, -2)$ is different than the location of point $B(-2, 1)$.

 NGSSS Practice   MA.5.G.5.1, MA.7.G.4.3

44. Which of the following points lie within the triangle graphed at the right?

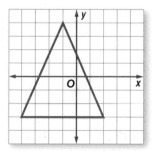

   A. $A(-4, -1)$

   B. $B(1, 3)$

   C. $C(-1, 2)$

   D. $D(2, -2)$

45. Which point on the grid **best** represents the location of the lunch room?

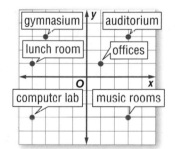

   F. $(4, -1)$

   G. $(-4, 1)$

   H. $(1, 4)$

   I. $(1, -4)$

Write an integer for each situation. (Lesson 1-1B)

46. six feet below sea level

47. 13 units to the left on a number line

48. gain of 14 pounds

49. deposit $430 into a bank account

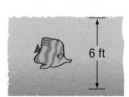

6 ft

Explore Add Integers

Main Idea

Use counters to model the addition of integers.

NGSSS

 MA.7.A.3.1 Use and justify the rules for adding, subtracting, multiplying, dividing, and finding the absolute value of **integers.** *Also addresses MA.7.A.3.2.*

New Vocabulary

zero pair

Get Connected
glencoe.com

FOOTBALL In football, forward progress is represented by a positive integer. Losing yardage is represented by a negative integer. On the first play, a team loses 5 yards and on the second play, they lose 2 yards. What is the team's total yardage on the two plays?

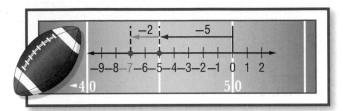

ACTIVITY

① **What do you need to find?** the total yardage on the two plays

Use counters to find the total yardage.

STEP 1 Combine a set of 5 negative counters and a set of 2 negative counters.

STEP 2 Find the total number of counters.

So, $-5 + (-2) = -7$. The football team lost 7 yards on the two plays.

The following two properties are important when modeling operations with integers.

- When one positive counter is paired with one negative counter, the result is called a **zero pair**. The value of a zero pair is 0.

- You can add or remove zero pairs from a mat because adding or removing zero does not change the value of the counters on the mat.

ACTIVITY

2 Use counters to find −4 + 2.

STEP 1 Combine 4 negative counters with 2 positive counters.

STEP 2 Remove all zero pairs.

STEP 3 Find the number of counters remaining.

So, −4 + 2 = −2.

Practice and Apply

Use counters or a drawing to find each sum.

1. 5 + 6	**2.** −3 + (−5)	**3.** −5 + (−4)
4. 7 + 3	**5.** −2 + (−5)	**6.** −8 + (−6)
7. −6 + 5	**8.** 3 + (−6)	**9.** −2 + 7
10. 8 + (−3)	**11.** −9 + 1	**12.** −4 + 10

Analyze the Results

13. Write two addition sentences where the sum is positive. In each sentence, one addend should be positive and the other negative.

14. Write two addition sentences where the sum is negative. In each sentence, one addend should be positive and the other negative.

15. Write two addition sentences where the sum is zero. Describe the numbers.

16. GAME SHOWS A contestant has −350 points after the first two rounds of questions. What is his point standing after earning 500 points in the third round?

17. MAKE A CONJECTURE What is a rule you can use to determine how to find the sum of two integers with the same sign? two integers with different signs?

PART   A   **B**   C   D

Main Idea

Add integers.

NGSSS

 MA.7.A.3.1 Use and justify the rules for adding, subtracting, multiplying, dividing, and finding the absolute value of **integers.** *Also addresses MA.7.A.3.2.*

New Vocabulary

opposites
additive inverse

 Get Connected
glencoe.com

Add Integers

SCIENCE Atoms are made of negative charges (electrons) and positive charges (protons). The helium atom shown has a total of 2 electrons and 2 protons.

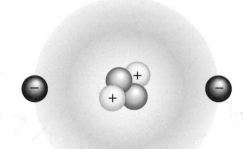

1. Represent the electrons in an atom of helium with an integer.

2. Represent the protons in an atom of helium with an integer.

3. Each proton-electron pair has a value of 0. What is the total charge of an atom of helium?

Combining protons and electrons in an atom is similar to adding integers.

EXAMPLE   **Add Integers with the Same Sign**

 Find $-3 + (-2)$.

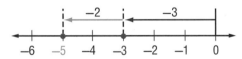

Start at 0. Move 3 units left to show -3.

From there, move 2 units left to show -2.

So, $-3 + (-2) = -5$.

 CHECK Your Progress

a. $-5 + (-7)$ b. $-10 + (-4)$

Key Concept   **Add Integers with the Same Sign**

Words   To add integers with the same sign, add their absolute values. The sum is:

• positive if both integers are positive.

• negative if both integers are negative.

Examples $7 + 4 = 11$ $-7 + (-4) = -11$

EXAMPLE **Add Integers with the Same Sign**

2 Find $-26 + (-17)$.

$-26 + (-17) = -43$ Both integers are negative, so the sum is negative.

 CHECK Your Progress

c. $-14 + (-16)$

d. $23 + 38$

Vocabulary Link

Everyday Use

Opposite something that is across from or is facing the other way, as in running the opposite way

Math Use

Opposite two numbers that are the same distance from 0 on a number line

The integers 5 and -5 are called **opposites** because they are the same distance from 0, but on opposite sides of 0. Two integers that are opposites are also called **additive inverses**.

Key Concept   **Additive Inverse Property**

Words   The sum of any number and its additive inverse is 0.

Example $5 + (-5) = 0$

When you add integers with different signs, start at zero. Move right for positive integers. Move left for negative integers.

 EXAMPLES   **Add Integers with Different Signs**

3 Find $5 + (-3)$.

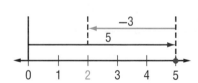

So, $5 + (-3) = 2$.

4 Find $-3 + 2$.

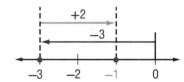

So, $-3 + 2 = -1$.

 CHECK Your Progress

e. $6 + (-7)$

f. $-15 + 19$

Key Concept   **Add Integers with Different Signs**

Words   To add integers with different signs, subtract their absolute values. The sum is:

- positive if the positive integer's absolute value is greater.
- negative if the negative integer's absolute value is greater.

Examples $9 + (-4) = 5$ $-9 + 4 = -5$

EXAMPLES **Add Integers with Different Signs**

⑤ Find 7 + (−1).

$7 + (-1) = 6$ Subtract absolute values; $7 - 1 = 6$. Since 7 has the greater absolute value, the sum is positive.

⑥ Find −8 + 3.

$-8 + 3 = -5$ Subtract absolute values; $8 - 3 = 5$. Since -8 has the greater absolute value, the sum is negative.

 Find 2 + (−15) + (−2).

$$2 + (-15) + (-2) = 2 + (-2) + (-15)$$ Commutative Property (+)

$$= [2 + (-2)] + (-15)$$ Associative Property (+)

$$= 0 + (-15)$$ Additive Inverse Property

$$= -15$$ Additive Identity Property

> **QUICK Review**
>
> **Commutative Properties**
> $a + b = b + a$
> $a \cdot b = b \cdot a$
> **Associative Properties**
> $a + (b + c) = (a + b) + c$
> $a \cdot (b \cdot c) = (a \cdot b) \cdot c$
> **Identity Properties**
> $a + 0 = a$
> $a \cdot 1 = a$

✓ CHECK Your Progress

g. $10 + (-12)$ **h.** $-13 + 18$ **i.** $(-14) + (-6) + 6$

Real-World EXAMPLE

⑧ ROLLER COASTERS The graphic shows the change in height at several points on a roller coaster. Write an addition sentence to find the height at point D in relation to point A.

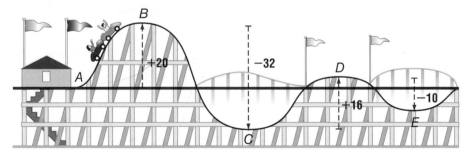

$$20 + (-32) + 16 = 20 + 16 + (-32)$$ Commutative Property (+)

$$= 36 + (-32)$$ $20 + 16 = 36$

$$= 4$$ Subtract absolute values. Since 36 has the greater absolute value, the sum is positive.

Point D is 4 feet higher than point A.

✓ CHECK Your Progress

j. WEATHER The temperature is $-3°$F. An hour later, it drops $6°$ and 2 hours later, it rises $4°$. Write an addition sentence to describe this situation. Then find the sum and explain its meaning.

✓ CHECK Your Understanding

Examples 1–7
(pp. 40–42)

Add.

1. $-6 + (-8)$
2. $4 + 5$
3. $-3 + 10$
4. $-15 + 8$
5. $7 + (-11)$
6. $14 + (-6)$
7. $-17 + 20 + (-3)$
8. $15 + 9 + (-9)$
9. $-4 + 12 + (-9)$

Example 8
(p. 42)

10. **MONEY** Sofia owes her brother $25. So, she gives her brother the $18 she earned dog-sitting for the neighbors. Write an addition expression to describe this situation. Then find the sum and explain its meaning.

Practice and Problem Solving

 = **Step-by-Step Solutions** begin on page R1.
Extra Practice is on page EP2.

Examples 1–6
(pp. 40–42)

Add.

11. $-22 + (-16)$
12. $-10 + (-15)$
13. $6 + 10$
14. $17 + 11$
15. $18 + (-5)$
16. $13 + (-19)$
17. $-19 + 24$
18. $-12 + 10$

Example 7
(p. 42)

19. $21 + (-21) + (-4)$
20. $-8 + (-4) + 12$
21. $-34 + 25 + (-25)$
22. $-16 + 16 + 22$
23. $25 + 3 + (-25)$
24. $7 + (-19) + (-7)$

Example 8
(p. 42)

Write an addition expression to describe each situation. Then find each sum and explain its meaning.

25. **SCUBA DIVING** Lena was scuba diving 14 meters below the surface of the water. She saw a nurse shark 3 meters above her.

26. **PELICANS** A pelican starts at 60 feet above sea level. It descends 60 feet to catch a fish.

27. **FINANCIAL LITERACY** Stephanie has $152 in the bank. She withdraws $20. Then she deposits $84.

28. **FOOTBALL** A quarterback is sacked for a loss of 5 yards. On the next play, his team receives a penalty and loses 15 more yards. Then the team gains 12 yards on the third play.

29. **GRAPHIC NOVEL** Refer to the graphic novel frame below to find the total profit or loss for each color of T-shirt.

We are creating T-shirts to be sold for Homecoming!

Green T-shirt:
Short sleeve shirt: $8.00
Printing: $6.00
Selling price: $15.00
White T-shirt:
Long sleeve shirt: $10.00
Printing: $7.00
Selling price: $20.00
Black T-shirt:
Short sleeve: $8.00
Printing on Front: $4.00
Printing on Back: $3.00
Selling price: $18.00

H.O.T. Problems

30. **OPEN ENDED** Give an example of an addition sentence containing at least four integers whose sum is zero.

31. **CHALLENGE** Name the property illustrated by the following.

    a. $x + (-x) = 0$ **b.** $x + (-y) = -y + x$

CHALLENGE Simplify.

32. $8 + (-8) + a$ 33. $x + (-5) + 1$ 34. $-9 + m + (-6)$ 35. $-1 + n + 7$

36. **Write MATH** Explain how you know whether a sum is positive, negative, or zero without actually adding.

NGSSS Practice   MA.7.A.3.1

37. **THINK SOLVE EXPLAIN** **SHORT RESPONSE** Write an addition sentence to represent the number line below.

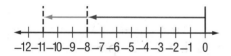

$$-12\ -11\ -10\ -9\ -8\ -7\ -6\ -5\ -4\ -3\ -2\ -1\ \ 0$$

38. At 8 A.M., the temperature was 3°F below zero. By 1 P.M., the temperature rose 14°F and by 10 P.M., dropped 12°F. What was the temperature at 10 P.M.?

    A. 5°F above zero

    B. 5°F below zero

    C. 1°F above zero

    D. 1°F below zero

39. What is the value of $-8 + 7 + (-3)$?

    F. -18

    G. -4

    H. 2

    I. 18

40. Which of the following expressions is represented by the number line?

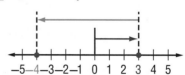

$$-5\ -4\ -3\ -2\ -1\ \ 0\ \ 1\ \ 2\ \ 3\ \ 4\ \ 5$$

    A. $-4 + 3$ **C.** $3 + (-7)$

    B. $-4 + 7$ **D.** $0 + (-7)$

Write the ordered pair corresponding to each point graphed at the right. Then state the quadrant or axis on which each point is located. (Lesson 1-1C)

41. J 42. K 43. L 44. M

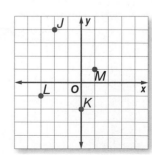

Write an integer for each situation. (Lesson 1-1B)

45. a bank deposit of $75   46. a loss of 8 pounds

47. 13° below zero   48. a gain of 4 yards

44   Chapter 1 Integers

Explore Subtract Integers

Main Idea
Use counters to model the subtraction of integers.

NGSSS
 MA.7.A.3.1 Use and justify the rules for adding, **subtracting,** multiplying, dividing, and finding the absolute value of **integers.** *Also addresses MA.7.A.3.2.*

Get Connected glencoe.com

DOLPHINS At a local aquarium, a popular attraction features dolphins. Dolphins jump through rings that are 5 meters above the surface of the water. To prepare, they start from 6 meters below the surface of the water. What is the difference between the two distances?

ACTIVITY

1 **What do you need to find?** the difference between the height of the rings and the depth at which the dolphins start

Use counters to find 5 − (−6), the difference between the two distances.

STEP 1 Place 5 positive counters on the mat. Remove 6 negative counters. However, there are 0 negative counters.

STEP 2 Add 6 zero pairs to the mat.

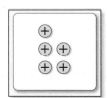

STEP 3 Now you can remove 6 negative counters. Find the remaining number of counters.

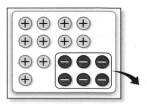

So, 5 − (−6) = 11. The difference between the two distances is 11 meters.

Use counters to find each difference.

2 −6 − (−3)

> **STEP 1** Place 6 negative counters on the mat.
>
> **STEP 2** Remove 3 negative counters.
>
> So, −6 − (−3) = −3.

3 −5 − 1

> **STEP 1** Place 5 negative counters on the mat. Remove 1 positive counter. However, there are 0 positive counters.

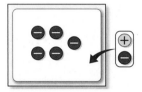

> **STEP 2** Add 1 zero pair to the set.

> **STEP 3** Now you can remove 1 positive counter. Find the remaining number of counters.
>
> So, −5 − 1 = −6.

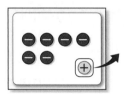

Practice and Apply

Use counters or a drawing to find each difference.

1. 7 − 6	**2.** 5 − (−3)	**3.** 6 − (−3)	**4.** 5 − 8
5. −7 − (−2)	**6.** −7 − 3	**7.** −5 − (−7)	**8.** −2 − 9

Analyze the Results

9. Write two subtraction sentences where the difference is positive. Use a combination of positive and negative integers.

10. Write two subtraction sentences where the difference is negative. Use a combination of positive and negative integers.

11. **Write MATH** Jake owes his sister $3. She decides to "take away" his debt. That is, he doesn't have to pay her back. Write a subtraction sentence for this situation. Explain why subtracting a negative integer is the same as adding.

Main Idea
Use the rules for subtracting integers.

NGSSS

MA.7.A.3.1 Use and justify the rules for adding, **subtracting**, multiplying, dividing, and finding the absolute value of **integers.** *Also addresses MA.7.A.3.2.*

Get Connected
glencoe.com

Subtract Integers

Explore You can use a number line to model a subtraction sentence.

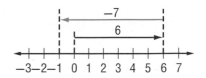

1. Write a related addition sentence for the subtraction sentence.

Use a number line to find each difference. Write an equivalent addition sentence for each.

2. $1 - 5$ 3. $-2 - 1$ 4. $-3 - 4$ 5. $0 - 5$

When you subtract 7, the result is the same as adding its opposite, -7.

opposite

$$6 - 7 = -1 \qquad 6 + (-7) = -1$$

same result

Key Concept   Subtract Integers

Words   To subtract an integer, add its opposite.

Examples $4 - 9 = 4 + (-9) = -5$ $7 - (-10) = 7 + (10) = 17$

EXAMPLES   Subtract Positive Integers

① **Find $8 - 13$.**

$8 - 13 = 8 + (-13)$ To subtract 13, add -13.

$\qquad\quad = -5$ Simplify.

② **Find $-10 - 7$.**

$-10 - 7 = -10 + (-7)$ To subtract 7, add -7.

$\qquad\qquad = -17$ Simplify.

 CHECK Your Progress

a. $6 - 12$ b. $-20 - 15$ c. $-22 - 26$

EXAMPLES **Subtract Negative Integers**

3 **Find $1 - (-2)$.**

$1 - (-2) = 1 + 2$ To subtract -2, add 2.

$\quad\quad\quad = 3$ Simplify.

4 **Find $-10 - (-7)$.**

$-10 - (-7) = -10 + 7$ To subtract -7, add 7.

$\quad\quad\quad\quad = -3$ Simplify.

 **CHECK Your Progress**

d. $4 - (-12)$ **e.** $-15 - (-5)$ **f.** $18 - (-6)$

 EXAMPLE **Evaluate an Expression**

5 **ALGEBRA** Evaluate $x - y$ if $x = -6$ and $y = -5$.

$x - y = -6 - (-5)$ Replace x with -6 and y with -5.

$\quad\quad = -6 + (5)$ To subtract -5, add 5.

$\quad\quad = -1$ Simplify.

 **CHECK Your Progress**

Evaluate each expression if $a = 5$, $b = -8$, and $c = -9$.

g. $b - 10$ **h.** $a - b$ **i.** $c - a$

Real-World EXAMPLE

Real-World Link · · · · ·
The mean surface temperature on the Moon during the day is 107°C.

6 **SPACE** The temperatures on the Moon vary from −173°C to 127°C. Find the difference between the maximum and minimum temperatures.

Subtract the lower temperature from the higher temperature.

Estimate $100 + 200 = 300$

$127 - (-173) = 127 + 173$ To subtract -173, add 173.

$\quad\quad\quad\quad = 300$ Simplify.

So, the difference between the temperatures is 300°C.

 CHECK Your Progress

j. **MONEY** Brenda had a balance of −$52 in her account. The bank charged her a fee of $10 for having a negative balance. What is her new balance?

CHECK Your Understanding

Examples 1 and 2
(p. 47)

Subtract.

1. $14 - 17$

2. $10 - 30$

3 $-4 - 8$

4. $-2 - 23$

Examples 3 and 4
(p. 48)

5. $14 - (-10)$

6. $5 - (-16)$

7. $-3 - (-1)$

8. $-11 - (-9)$

Example 5
(p. 48)

ALGEBRA Evaluate each expression if $p = 8$, $q = -14$, and $r = -6$.

9. $r - 15$

10. $q - r$

11. $p - q$

Example 6
(p. 48)

12. EARTH SCIENCE The sea surface temperatures range from $-2°C$ to $31°C$. Find the difference between the maximum and minimum temperatures.

Practice and Problem Solving

 = **Step-by-Step Solutions** begin on page R2.
Extra Practice is on page EP3.

Examples 1 and 2
(p. 47)

Subtract.

13. $0 - 10$

14. $13 - 17$

15. $-9 - 5$

16. $-8 - 9$

17. $12 - 26$

18. $31 - 48$

19. $-25 - 5$

20. $-44 - 41$

Examples 3 and 4
(p. 48)

21. $4 - (-19)$

22. $27 - (-8)$

23. $-11 - (-42)$

24. $-27 - (-19)$

25. $52 - (-52)$

26. $15 - (-14)$

27. $-27 - (-33)$

28. $-18 - (-20)$

Example 5
(p. 48)

ALGEBRA Evaluate each expression if $f = -6$, $g = 7$, and $h = 9$.

29. $g - 7$

30. $f - 6$

31. $-h - (-9)$

32. $f - g$

33. $h - f$

34. $g - h$

35. $5 - f$

36. $4 - (-g)$

Example 6
(p. 48)

37 ANALYZE TABLES Use the information below.

State	Alabama	California	Florida	Louisiana	New Mexico
Lowest Elevation (ft)	0	−282	0	−8	2,842
Highest Elevation (ft)	2,407	14,494	345	535	13,161

a. What is the difference between the highest elevation in Alabama and the lowest elevation in Louisiana?

b. Find the difference between the lowest elevation in New Mexico and the lowest elevation in California.

c. Find the difference between the highest elevation in Florida and the lowest elevation in California.

d. What is the difference between the lowest elevation in Alabama and Louisiana?

ALGEBRA Evaluate each expression if $h = -12$, $j = 4$, and $k = 15$.

38. $-j + h - k$

39. $|h - j|$

40. $k - j - h$

H.O.T. Problems

41. **OPEN ENDED** Write a subtraction sentence using integers. Then, write the equivalent addition sentence and explain how to find the sum.

42. **FIND THE ERROR** Hiroshi is finding $-15 - (-18)$. Find his mistake and correct it.

$$-15 - (-18) = -15 + (-18)$$
$$= -33$$

43. **CHALLENGE** *True* or *False*? When n is a negative integer, $n - n = 0$.

44. **Write MATH** If x and y are positive integers, is $x - y$ always positive? Explain.

NGSSS Practice   MA.7.A.3.1

45. Which sentence about integers is NOT always true?

   A. positive − positive = positive
   B. positive + positive = positive
   C. negative + negative = negative
   D. positive − negative = positive

46. Morgan drove from Los Angeles (elevation 330 feet) to Death Valley (elevation −282 feet). What is the difference in elevation between Los Angeles and Death Valley?

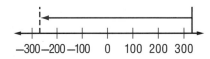

   F. 48 feet   H. 582 feet
   G. 148 feet   I. 612 feet

Spiral Review

Add. (Lesson 1-2B)

47. $10 + (-3)$ 48. $-2 + (-9)$ 49. $-7 + (-6)$ 50. $-18 + 4$

51. In which quadrant does the ordered pair $(5, -6)$ lie?
   (Lesson 1-1C)

Evaluate each expression. (Lesson 1-1B)

52. $|-12|$

53. $|-3| + |-5|$

54. $|-25| \div 5 - |-3|$

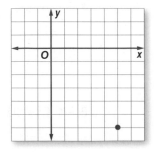

Write an integer for each situation. (Lesson 1-1B)

1. dropped 45 feet

2. a bank deposit of $100

3. gained 8 pounds

4. lost a $5 bill

5. **OCEANS** The deepest point in the world is the Mariana Trench in the Western Pacific Ocean at a depth of 35,840 feet below sea level. Write this depth as an integer. (Lesson 1-1B)

Evaluate each expression. (Lesson 1-1B)

6. $|-16|$

7. $|24|$

8. $|-9| - |3|$

9. $|-13| + |-1|$

Graph and label each point on a coordinate plane. (Lesson 1-1C)

10. $D(4, -3)$

11. $E(-1, 2)$

12. $F(0, -5)$

13. $G(-3, 0)$

14. **NGSSS PRACTICE** Which line contains the ordered pair $(-1, 4)$? (Lesson 1-1C)

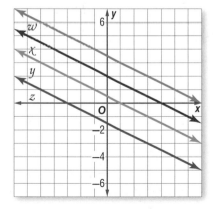

A. line w

C. line y

B. line x

D. line z

Add. (Lesson 1-2B)

15. $3 + 4 + (-3)$

16. $7 + (-11)$

17. $-5 + (-6)$

18. $8 + (-1) + 1$

19. **NGSSS PRACTICE** Kendra deposited $78 into her savings account. Two weeks later, she deposited a check for $50 into her account and withdrew $27. Which of the following expressions represents the amount of money left in her account? (Lesson 1-2B)

F. $\$78 + (-\$50) + (-\$27)$

G. $\$78 + (-\$50) + \$27$

H. $\$78 + \$50 + (-\$27)$

I. $\$78 + \$50 + \$27$

Subtract. (Lesson 1-2D)

20. $9 - 15$

21. $-3 - 10$

22. $8 - (-12)$

23. $-4 - (-13)$

24. **ANALYZE TABLES** The table shows the record low temperatures for Des Moines, Iowa. (Lesson 1-2D)

Month	Temperature (°F)
January	−24
May	30

What is the difference between the low temperature for January and the low temperature for May?

25. **CHEMISTRY** The melting point of mercury is −36°F and its boiling point is 672°F. What is the difference between these two temperatures? (Lesson 1-2D)

26. **NGSSS PRACTICE** During two plays of a football game, the Valley Tigers had a loss of 4 yards and a gain of 16 yards. Which of the following expressions represents the difference between the number of yards? (Lesson 1-2D)

A. $-4 + 16$

C. $4 + 16$

B. $-4 + (-16)$

D. $4 - 16$

1-3 Multiply and Divide Integers

PART A B C D

Problem-Solving Investigation

Main Idea Solve problems by looking for a pattern.

P.S.I. TEAM +

Look for a Pattern

LAURA: I've been practicing free throws every day after school to get ready for basketball tryouts. Now, I can make 3 free throws out of every 5 attempts.

YOUR MISSION: Look for a pattern to find the number of free throws Laura can make after 30 attempts.

Understand	Laura can make an average of 3 free throws out of every 5 attempts. You need to find the number of free throws she can make after 30 attempts.
Plan	Look for a pattern. Then extend the pattern to find the solution.
Solve	Laura can make 3 free throws out of every 5 she attempts. Extend the pattern.

	+3	+3	+3	+3	+3	
Free throws	3	6	9	12	15	18
Attempts	5	10	15	20	25	30
	+5	+5	+5	+5	+5	

She can make 18 free throws out of 30 attempts.

Check	She makes free throws a little more than half the time. Since 18 is a little more than 15, the answer is reasonable. ✓

Analyze the Strategy

1. Suppose Laura can make 4 out of 5 attempts. Find the number of free throws she can make after 30 attempts.

 NGSSS

MA.7.A.3.2 Add, subtract, multiply, and **divide integers, fractions, and termination decimals,** and perform exponential operations with rational bases and whole number exponents **including solving problems in everyday contexts.** *Also addresses MA.7.A.3.1.*

- Look for a pattern.
- Guess, check, and revise.
- Make a list.
- Choose an operation.

Use the *look for a pattern* strategy to solve Exercises 2–4.

2. **DISPLAYS** A display of cereal boxes is stacked as shown below.

If the display contains 7 rows of boxes and the top three rows are shown, how many boxes are in the display?

3. **FINANCIAL LITERACY** Peter is saving money to buy an MP3 player. After one month, he has $50. After 2 months, he has $85. After 3 months, he has $120. After 4 months, he has $155. He plans to keep saving at the same rate. How long will it take Peter to save enough money to buy an MP3 player that costs $295?

4. **INSECTS** The table shows how many times a cricket chirps at different temperatures. If this pattern continues, about how many times will a cricket chirp when the temperature is 60°F?

Outside Temperature (°F)	Chirps per Minute
70	120
75	140
80	160
85	180

Use any strategy to solve Exercises 5–10.

5. **COINS** Adelina has exactly six coins that total $0.86. What are the coins?

6. **DIVING** The table shows a diver's position after several minutes. If she keeps descending at this rate, find the diver's position after ten minutes.

Time (min)	Position (ft)
1	−15
2	−30
3	−45

7. **GEOMETRY** The pattern below is made from toothpicks. How many toothpicks would be needed for the sixth term in the pattern?

First term   Second term   Third term

8. **GOLF** Allie's golf scores for the first five holes are given in the table. What is her total score after the first five holes?

Hole	Score
1	0
2	1
3	−1
4	−2
5	3

9. **NATURE** A sunflower usually has two different spirals of seeds, one with 34 seeds and the other with 55 seeds.

The numbers 34 and 55 are part of the Fibonacci sequence: 1, 1, 2, 3, 5, 8, 13, 21, 34, 55, … . Find the pattern in the Fibonacci sequence and identify the next two terms.

10. **Write MATH** Write a problem that could be solved by looking for a pattern. Then solve.

Explore **Multiply and Divide Integers**

SCHOOL The number of students who bring their lunch to Phoenix Middle School has been decreasing at a rate of 4 students per month. What integer represents the total change after three months?

ACTIVITY

1 **What do you need to find?** the total change in the number of students who bring their lunch to school

The integer −4 represents a decrease of 4 students each month. After three months, the total change will be 3 × (−4). Use counters to model 3 groups of 4 negative counters.

STEP 1 Place 3 sets of 4 negative counters on the mat.

STEP 2 Count the number of negative counters.

The integer −12 represents the total change in the number of students who bring their lunch to school.

If the first factor is *negative*, you will need to remove counters from the mat.

ACTIVITY

2 **Use counters to find −2 × (−4).**

The expression −2 × (−4) means to *remove* 2 sets of 4 negative counters.

STEP 1 Place 2 sets of 4 zero pairs on the mat.

STEP 2 Then remove 2 sets of
4 negative counters
from the mat. There are
8 positive counters
remaining.

So, $-2 \times (-4) = 8$.

You can model division by separating algebra counters into equal-size groups.

ACTIVITY

3 **Model $-9 \div 3$ using algebra counters.**

STEP 1 Place 9 negative counters on the mat to
represent -9.

STEP 2 Separate the counters into 3 equal-size
groups. There are 3 negative counters in
each of the three groups.

So, $-9 \div 3 = -3$.

Practice and Apply

Find each product. Use models if needed.

1. $7 \times (-2)$ 2. $2 \times (-3)$ 3. $4 \times (-4)$ 4. $8 \times (-1)$

5. $-5 \times (-1)$ 6. $-2 \times (-2)$ 7. $-4 \times (-3)$ 8. $-6 \times (-2)$

Find each quotient. Use models if needed.

9. $-12 \div 4$ 10. $-18 \div 9$ 11. $-20 \div 5$ 12. $-10 \div 2$

13. $-6 \div 6$ 14. $-14 \div 7$ 15. $-16 \div 4$ 16. $-8 \div 2$

Analyze the Results

17. How are the operations -5×4 and $4 \times (-5)$ the same? How do they differ?

18. MAKE A CONJECTURE Write a rule you can use to find the sign of the product
of two integers given the sign of both factors. Justify your rule.

19. When the dividend is negative and the divisor is positive, is the quotient
positive or negative? How does this compare to a multiplication problem
when one factor is positive and one is negative?

20. MAKE A CONJECTURE Write a rule you can use to find the sign of the quotient
of two integers. Justify your rule.

1-3 Multiply and Divide Integers

Main Idea

Use the rules for multiplying integers.

NGSSS

MA.7.A.3.1 Use and justify **the rules for** adding, subtracting, **multiplying**, dividing, and finding the absolute value of **integers**. *Also addresses MA.7.A.3.2.*

Get Connected
glencoe.com

Multiply Integers

COOKING Genevieve's freezer decreases the temperature of a piece of pie by 3° every minute. What is the change in degrees after 4 minutes?

1. Write a multiplication sentence to represent the situation above.

2. How could you model the multiplication sentence above with counters?

Remember that multiplication is the same as repeated addition.

$4(-3) = (-3) + (-3) + (-3) + (-3)$ −3 is used as an addend four times.

     $= -12$

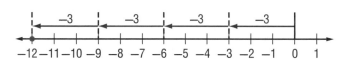

The Commutative Property of Multiplication states that you can multiply in any order. So, $4(-3) = -3(4)$.

Key Concept   Multiply Integers with Different Signs

Words   The product of two integers with different signs is negative.

Examples $6(-4) = -24$ $-5(7) = -35$

EXAMPLES **Multiply Integers with Different Signs**

1 Find $3(-5)$.

   $3(-5) = -15$ The integers have different signs. The product is negative.

2 Find $-6(8)$.

   $-6(8) = -48$ The integers have different signs. The product is negative.

 CHECK Your Progress

a. $9(-2)$ **b.** $-7(4)$

The product of two positive integers is positive. You can use a pattern to find the sign of the product of two negative integers.

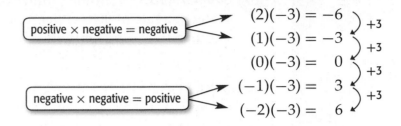

Each product is 3 more than the previous product. This pattern can also be shown on a number line.

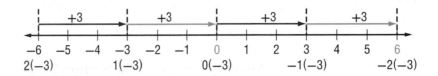

Study Tip

Multiplying by Zero
The Multiplicative Property of Zero states that when any number is multiplied by zero, the product is zero.

Key Concept   Multiply Integers with the Same Sign

Words   The product of two integers with the same sign is positive.

Examples $2(6) = 12$ $-10(-6) = 60$

EXAMPLES   **Multiply Integers with the Same Sign**

3 Find $-11(-9)$.

$-11(-9) = 99$ The integers have the same sign. The product is positive.

4 Find $(-4)^2$.

$(-4)^2 = (-4)(-4)$ There are two factors of -4.

$\qquad = 16$ The product is positive.

5 Find $-3(-4)(-2)$.

$-3(-4)(-2) = [-3(-4)](-2)$ Associative Property

$\qquad\qquad = 12(-2)$ $-3(-4) = 12$

$\qquad\qquad = -24$ $12(-2) = -24$

QUICK Review

Exponents

When expressing a number using exponents, the base is the factor and the exponent tells how many times to use the base as a factor.
$a^3 = a \cdot a \cdot a$

 CHECK Your Progress

c. $-12(-4)$ **d.** $(-5)^2$ **e.** $-7(-5)(-3)$

Real-World Link · · · ·
The MIR submersible that explored the *Titanic* shipwreck was able to descend to −20,000 feet.

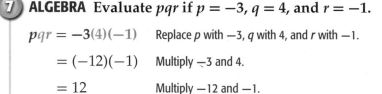

Real-World EXAMPLE

6 **SUBMERSIBLES** A submersible is diving from the surface of the water at a rate of 90 feet per minute. What is the depth of the submersible after 7 minutes?

If the submersible descends 90 feet per minute, then after 7 minutes, the vessel will be at 7(−90) or −630 feet. The submersible will descend to 630 feet below the surface.

CHECK Your Progress

f. FINANCIAL LITERACY Mr. Simon's bank automatically deducts a $4 monthly maintenance fee from his savings account. What integer represents the change in his savings account from one year of fees?

Negative numbers are often used when evaluating algebraic expressions.

EXAMPLE **Evaluate Expressions**

7 **ALGEBRA** Evaluate pqr if $p = -3$, $q = 4$, and $r = -1$.

$$pqr = -3(4)(-1) \qquad \text{Replace } p \text{ with } -3, q \text{ with 4, and } r \text{ with } -1.$$
$$= (-12)(-1) \qquad \text{Multiply } -3 \text{ and 4.}$$
$$= 12 \qquad\qquad \text{Multiply } -12 \text{ and } -1.$$

CHECK Your Progress

g. Evaluate xyz if $x = -7$, $y = -4$, and $z = 2$.

CHECK Your Understanding

Examples 1 and 2
(p. 56)

Multiply.

1. $6(-10)$ **2.** $11(-4)$ **3.** $-2(14)$ **4.** $-8(5)$

Examples 3–5
(p. 57)

Multiply.

5. $-15(-3)$ **6.** $-7(-9)$ **7.** $(-8)^2$

8. $(-3)^3$ **9.** $-1(-3)(-4)$ **10.** $2(4)(5)$

Example 6
(p. 58)

11. MONEY Tamera owns 100 shares of a certain stock. Suppose the price of the stock drops by $3 per share. Write a multiplication expression to find the change in Tamera's investment. Explain your answer.

Example 7
(p. 58)

ALGEBRA Evaluate each expression if $f = -1$, $g = 7$, and $h = -10$.

12. $5f$ **13** fgh

= **Step-by-Step Solutions** begin on page R2.
Extra Practice is on page EP3.

Practice and Problem Solving

Examples 1–3
(pp. 56–57)

Multiply.

14. 8(−12)　　**15.** 11(−20)　　**16.** −15(4)　　**17.** −7(10)

18. −7(11)　　**19.** 25(−2)　　**20.** −20(−8)　　**21.** −16(−5)

Examples 4 and 5
(p. 57)

22. $(−6)^2$　　**23.** $(−5)^3$　　**24.** $(−4)^3$　　**25.** $(−9)^2$

26. −4(−2)(−8)　　**27.** −3(−2)(1)　　**28.** −9(−1)(−5)　　**29.** −4(3)(−2)

Example 6
(p. 58)

Write a multiplication expression to represent each situation. Then find each product and explain its meaning.

30. **ECOLOGY** Wave erosion causes a certain coastline to recede at a rate of 3 centimeters each year. This occurs uninterrupted for a period of 8 years.

31 **EXERCISE** Ethan burns 650 Calories when he runs for 1 hour. Suppose he runs 5 hours in one week.

Example 7
(p. 58)

ALGEBRA Evaluate each expression if $w = 4$, $x = −8$, $y = 5$, and $z = −3$.

32. −4w　　**33.** 7wz　　**34.** −2wx　　**35.** wyx

36. **MULTIPLE REPRESENTATIONS** When a movie is rented it has a due date. If the movie is not returned on time, a late fee is assessed. Kaitlyn is charged $5 each day for a movie that is 4 days late.

　　a. **WORDS** Explain why $4 \times (−5) = −20$ describes the situation.

　　b. **ALGEBRA** Write an expression to represent the fee when the movie is x days late.

　　c. **WORDS** Kaitlyn resolved the problem of the late movie and didn't have to pay the late fees. Explain why $(−4) \times (−5) = 20$ represents this situation. Why is the product a positive integer?

ALGEBRA Evaluate each expression if $a = −6$, $b = −4$, $c = 3$, and $d = 9$.

37. $−3a^2$　　**38.** $−cd^2$　　**39.** $−2a + b$　　**40.** $b^2 − 4ac$

41. **GRAPHIC NOVEL** Refer to the graphic novel frame below. How many T-shirts would Hannah and Dario need to sell to make up the loss in profit?

H.O.T. Problems

42. OPEN ENDED Write a multiplication sentence with a product of -18.

43. NUMBER SENSE Explain how to evaluate each expression as simply as possible.

    a. $(-9)(-6)(15)(-7 + 7)$ **b.** $(-15)(-26) + (-15)(25)$

44. CHALLENGE Evaluate $(-1)^{50}$. Explain your reasoning.

45. Write MATH Explain when the product of three integers is positive.

NGSSS Practice   **MA.7.A.3.1**

46. The temperature drops 2 degrees per hour for 3 hours. Which expression does NOT describe the change in temperature?

    A. $-2(3)$

    B. $-2 + (-2) + (-2)$

    C. $-2 - 2 - 2$

    D. $2(3)$

47. GRIDDED RESPONSE Which number is the seventh number in the sequence shown?

Position	1	2	3	4	5	6	7
Number	1	-2	4	-8	16	?	?

 **Spiral Review**

48. ANT FARMS The table below shows the number of ants in an ant farm on different days. The number of ants doubles every ten days. (Lesson 1-3A)

Day	51	61	71
Number of Ants	320	640	1,280

    a. How many ants were in the farm on Day 1?

    b. How many ants will be in the farm on Day 91?

49. VIDEO GAMES Nieves and her three friends are playing a video game. The table shows their scores at the end of the first round. (Lesson 1-2D)

    a. What is the difference between the highest and lowest scores?

    b. By how many points is Nieves losing to Polly?

Player	Score
Nieves	-189
Polly	-142
Saul	230
Harry	-48

ALGEBRA Evaluate each expression if $x = -4$, $y = 6$, and $z = 1$. (Lesson 1-2B)

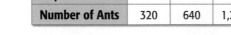

50. $x + (-2)$ **51.** $-1 + z$ **52.** $-15 + y$ **53.** $x + y$

Main Idea
Use the rules for dividing integers.

NGSSS

MA.7.A.3.1 Use and justify **the rules for** adding, subtracting, multiplying, **dividing**, and finding the absolute value of **integers**. *Also addresses MA.7.A.3.2.*

Get Connected
glencoe.com

Divide Integers

Explore You can find the product of $5 \times (-3)$ on a number line. Start at zero and then move -3 units five times.

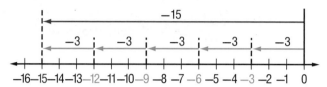

1. What is the product of $5 \times (-3)$?

2. What division sentence is also shown on the line?

3. Draw a number line to find the product of $4 \times (-2)$. Then find the related division sentence.

Division of numbers is related to multiplication. When finding the quotient of two integers, you can use a related multiplication sentence.

The factor in the multiplication sentence …

$2(6) = 12 \longrightarrow 12 \div 2 = 6$

$4(5) = 20 \longrightarrow 20 \div 4 = 5$

… is the quotient in the division sentence.

Since multiplication and division sentences are related, you can use them to find the quotient of integers with different signs.

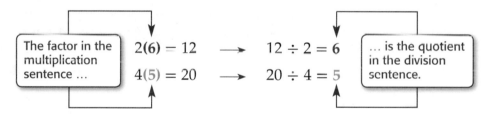

different signs

$2(-6) = -12 \longrightarrow -12 \div 2 = -6$

$-2(-6) = 12 \longrightarrow 12 \div (-2) = -6$

negative quotient

Key Concept   **Divide Integers with Different Signs**

Words   The quotient of two integers with different signs is negative.

Examples $33 \div (-11) = -3$ $-64 \div 8 = -8$

EXAMPLES **Divide Integers with Different Signs**

1 **Find 80 ÷ (−10).**   The integers have different signs.

$80 \div (-10) = -8$ The quotient is negative.

2 **Find $\dfrac{-55}{11}$.**   The integers have different signs.

$\dfrac{-55}{11} = -5$ The quotient is negative.

CHECK Your Progress

a. $20 \div (-4)$ **b.** $\dfrac{-81}{9}$ **c.** $-45 \div 9$

Study Tip

Dividing Integers
Division of integers with same or different signs follows the same rules as the ones for multiplication.

You can also use multiplication and division sentences to find the quotient of integers with the same sign.

| same signs | $4(5) = 20$ | → | $20 \div 4 = 5$ | positive quotient |
| | $-4(5) = -20$ | → | $-20 \div (-4) = 5$ | |

Key Concept **Divide Integers with the Same Sign**

Words   The quotient of two integers with the same sign is positive.

Examples $15 \div 5 = 3$ $-64 \div (-8) = 8$

EXAMPLES **Divide Integers with the Same Sign**

3 **Find −14 ÷ (−7).**   The integers have the same sign.

$-14 \div (-7) = 2$ The quotient is positive.

4 **ALGEBRA** Evaluate $-16 \div x$ if $x = -4$.

$-16 \div x = -16 \div (-4)$ Replace x with −4.

$= 4$ Divide. The quotient is positive.

CHECK Your Progress

d. $-24 \div (-4)$ **e.** $-9 \div (-3)$ **f.** $\dfrac{-28}{-7}$

g. ALGEBRA Evaluate $a \div b$ if $a = -9$ and $b = -3$.

Real-World EXAMPLE

5 **ANIMALS** One year, the estimated Australian koala population was 1,000,000. After 10 years, there were about 100,000 koalas. Find the average change in the koala population per year.

$$\frac{N - P}{10} = \frac{100,000 - 1,000,000}{10}$$ N is the new population, 100,000. P is the previous population, 1,000,000.

$$= \frac{-900,000}{10} \text{ or } -90,000 \quad \text{Divide.}$$

The koala population has changed by $-90,000$ per year.

✓ CHECK Your Progress

h. WEATHER The average temperature in January for North Pole, Alaska, is $-24.4°C$. Use the expression $\frac{9C + 160}{5}$ to find this temperature in degrees Fahrenheit. Round to the nearest degree.

Key Concept — Operations with Integers

Operation	Rule
Add	**Same Signs:** Add absolute values. The sum has the same sign as the integers.
	Different Signs: Subtract absolute values. The sum has the sign of the integer with the greater absolute value.
Subtract	To subtract an integer, add its opposite.
Multiply and Divide	**Same Signs:** The product or quotient is positive. **Different Signs:** The product or quotient is negative.

✓ CHECK Your Understanding

Examples 1–3
(p. 62)

Divide.

1. $32 \div (-8)$ **2.** $-16 \div 2$ **3.** $\frac{42}{-7}$

4. $-30 \div (-5)$ **5.** $55 \div 11$ **6.** $\frac{-16}{-4}$

Example 4
(p. 62)

ALGEBRA Evaluate each expression if $x = 8$ and $y = -5$.

7 $15 \div y$ **8.** $xy \div (-10)$

Example 5
(p. 63)

9. TEMPERATURE The lowest recorded temperature in Wisconsin is $-55°F$ on February 4, 1996. Use the expression $\frac{5(F - 32)}{9}$ to find this temperature in degrees Celsius. Round to the nearest tenth.

Practice and Problem Solving

● = **Step-by-Step Solutions** begin on page R2.
Extra Practice is on page EP4.

Example 1
(p. 62)

Divide.

10. $50 \div (-5)$ **11.** $56 \div (-8)$ **12.** $-18 \div 9$ **13.** $-36 \div 4$

Examples 2 and 3
(p. 62)

14. $-15 \div (-3)$ **15.** $-100 \div (-10)$ **16.** $\dfrac{22}{-2}$ **17.** $\dfrac{84}{-12}$

18. $\dfrac{-26}{13}$ **19.** $\dfrac{-27}{3}$ **20.** $\dfrac{-21}{-7}$ **21.** $\dfrac{-54}{-6}$

22. Divide -200 by -100.   **23.** Find the quotient of -65 and -13.

Example 4
(p. 62)

ALGEBRA Evaluate each expression if $r = 12$, $s = -4$, and $t = -6$.

24. $-12 \div r$ **25.** $72 \div t$ **26.** $r \div s$ **27.** $rs \div 16$

28. $\dfrac{t - r}{3}$ **29.** $\dfrac{8 - r}{-2}$ **30.** $\dfrac{s + t}{5}$ **31.** $\dfrac{t + 9}{-3}$

Example 5
(p. 63)

32. FINANCIAL LITERACY Last year, Mr. Engle's total income was $52,000, while his total expenses were $53,800. Use the expression $\dfrac{I - E}{12}$, where I represents total income and E represents total expenses, to find the average difference between his income and expenses each month.

33. SCIENCE The boiling point of water is affected by changes in elevation. Use the expression $\dfrac{-2A}{1,000}$, where A represents the altitude in feet, to find the number of degrees Fahrenheit at which the boiling point of water changes at an altitude of 5,000 feet.

ALGEBRA Evaluate each expression if $d = -9$, $f = 36$, and $g = -6$.

34. $\dfrac{-f}{d}$ **35.** $\dfrac{12 - (-f)}{-8}$ **36.** $\dfrac{f^2}{d^2}$ **37.** $g^2 \div f$

38. PLANETS The temperature on Mars ranges widely from $-207°$F at the winter pole to almost $80°$F on the dayside during the summer. Use the expression $\dfrac{-207 + 80}{2}$ to find the average of the temperature extremes on Mars.

39 **ANALYZE GRAPHS** The *mean* of a set of data is the sum of the data divided by the number of items in the data set. The graph shows the approximate depths at which certain fish are found in the Caribbean. What is the mean depth of the fish shown?

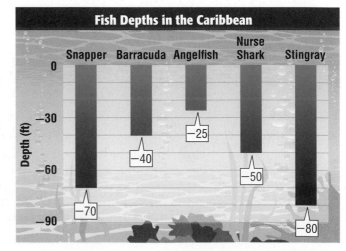

40. OPEN ENDED Write a division sentence with a quotient of -12.

41. Which One Doesn't Belong? Identify the expression that does not belong with the other three. Explain your reasoning.

| $-66 \div 11$ | $-32 \div (-4)$ | $16 \div (-4)$ | $-48 \div 4$ |

42. CHALLENGE Find values for x, y, and z so that all of the following statements are true.

- $y > x$, $z < y$, and $x < 0$
- $z \div 2$ and $z \div 3$ are integers
- $x \div z = -z$
- $x \div y = z$

43. Write MATH Evaluate $-2 \cdot (2^2 + 2) \div 2^2$. Justify each step in the process.

NGSSS Practice   MA.5.A.1.1, MA.7.A.3.1

44. THINK SOLVE EXPLAIN **SHORT RESPONSE** The table shows the points that each student lost on the first math test. Each question on the test was worth an equal number of points.

Student	Points
Christopher	-24
Nythia	-16
Raul	-4

If Christopher answered 6 questions incorrectly, how many questions did Nythia answer incorrectly? Explain.

45. On December 24, 1924, the temperature in Fairfield, Montana, fell from $63°F$ at noon to $-21°F$ at midnight. What was the average temperature change per hour?

- **A.** $-3.5°F$
- **B.** $-7°F$
- **C.** $-42°F$
- **D.** $-84°F$

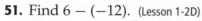
Spiral Review

Multiply. (Lesson 1-3C)

46. $14(-2)$ **47.** $-20(-3)$ **48.** $-5(7)$ **49.** $(-9)^2$

50. DISPLAYS A display of cereal boxes has one box in the top row, two boxes in the second row, three boxes in the third row, and so on, as shown. How many rows of boxes will there be in a display of 45 boxes? (Lesson 1-3A)

51. Find $6 - (-12)$. (Lesson 1-2D)

52. Name the quadrant in which the point $(-4, -3)$ could be found on the coordinate plane. (Lesson 1-1C)

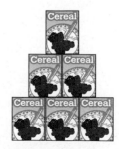

Space Storms

Predicting

Did you know that *space weather*, or the conditions on the Sun and in space, can directly affect communication systems and power grids here on Earth? If you enjoy learning about the mysteries of space, then you should consider a career involving space weather. A space weather forecaster uses spacecraft, telescopes, radar, and supercomputers to monitor the sun, solar winds, and the space environment in order to forecast the weather in space.

Choose a Major
Are you interested in a career as a space weather forecaster? Take some of the following courses in high school.

- Calculus
- Introduction To Astronomy
- Chemistry
- Physics
- Earth/Space Science

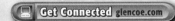

Get Connected glencoe.com

NGSSS

MA.7.A.3.1 Use and justify rules for adding, subtracting, multiplying, dividing, and finding the absolute value of integers.

Real-World Math

Use the information in the table to solve each problem.

1. Graph the average temperatures for Earth, Jupiter, Mars, Mercury, Neptune, and Saturn on a number line. Label the points.

2. The temperatures on Mercury range from −279°F to 800°F. What is the difference between the highest and lowest temperatures?

3. The dwarf planet Pluto has an average temperature of −375°F. How much greater is the average temperature on Saturn than the average temperature on Pluto?

4. How much greater is the average temperature on Earth than the average temperature on Jupiter?

5. One of Neptune's moons, Triton, has a surface temperature that is 61°F less than Neptune's average temperature. What is Triton's surface temperature?

6. The temperature on Mars can reach a low of −187°C. Find the value of the expression $\dfrac{9(-187) + 160}{5}$ to determine this temperature in degrees Fahrenheit.

Average Temperature of Planets	
Planet	**Average Temperature (°F)**
Earth	59
Jupiter	−166
Mars	−85
Mercury	333
Neptune	−330
Saturn	−220
Uranus	−320
Venus	867

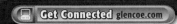

• STUDY *TO GO*
• Vocabulary Review
• Multilingual eGlossary

FOLDABLES® Study Organizer

Be sure the following Key Concepts are noted in your Foldable.

1-1
Integers and the Coordinate Plane

Key Concepts

Absolute Value (Lesson 1-1)
• The absolute value of a number is the distance the number is from zero on a number line.

Integer Operations (Lessons 1-2 and 1-3)
• To add integers with the same sign, add their absolute value. The sum is positive if both integers are positive and negative if both integers are negative.

$$-2 + (-3) = -5$$

• To add integers with different signs, subtract their absolute values. The sum has the sign of the integer with the larger absolute value.

$$-7 + 1 = -6 \qquad -3 + 5 = 2$$

• To subtract an integer, add its opposite.

$$-2 - 3 = -2 + (-3) \text{ or } -5$$

• The product or quotient of two integers with different signs is negative.

$$6(-2) = -12 \qquad -10 \div 2 = -5$$

• The product or quotient of two integers with the same sign is positive.

$$-4(-5) = 20 \qquad -12 \div (-4) = 3$$

Key Vocabulary

absolute value (p. 30)
additive inverse (p. 41)
coordinate plane (p. 33)
graph (p. 29)
integer (p. 29)
negative integer (p. 29)
opposites (p. 41)
ordered pair (p. 33)
origin (p. 33)
positive integer (p. 29)
quadrant (p. 33)
x-axis (p. 33)
x-coordinate (p. 33)
y-axis (p. 33)
y-coordinate (p. 33)

Vocabulary Check

State whether each sentence is *true* or *false*. If *false*, replace the underlined word or number to make a true sentence.

1. Integers less than zero are <u>positive</u> integers.

2. The <u>origin</u> is the point where the *x*-axis and *y*-axis intersect.

3. The <u>absolute value</u> of 7 is −7.

4. The sum of two negative integers is <u>positive</u>.

5. The <u>*x*-coordinate</u> of the ordered pair (2, −3) is −3.

6. Two integers that are opposites are also called <u>additive inverses</u>.

7. The product of a positive and a negative integer is <u>negative</u>.

8. The *x*-axis and the *y*-axis separate the plane into four <u>coordinates</u>.

9. The quotient of two negative integers is <u>negative</u>.

Multi-Part Lesson Review

1-1 Integers and the Coordinate Plane

Integers and Absolute Value (pp. 29–32)

Write an integer for each situation.

10. a loss of $150

11. 350 feet above sea level

12. a loss of 8 yards

13. **JUICE** Mavis drank 48 milliliters of apple juice before replacing the carton in the refrigerator. Write an integer that shows the change in the volume of juice in the carton.

Evaluate each expression.

14. $|100|$

15. $|-32|$

16. $|-16| + |9|$

17. $|7 + 12| + |-14|$

18. **PLANETS** The average temperature of Saturn is 218°F below zero. What is the absolute value of the integer that represents this temperature?

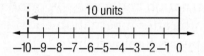 MA.7.A.3.1

EXAMPLE 1 Write an integer for an altitude of 8 feet.

Since this situation represents an elevation *above* the ground, 8 represents the situation.

EXAMPLE 2 Write an integer for a loss of 5 pounds.

This situation represents a decrease in weight, so −5 represents this situation.

EXAMPLE 3 Evaluate $|-10|$.

On the number line, the graph of −10 is 10 units from 0.

```
              10 units
        ←─────────────────
    ┼─┼─┼─┼─┼─┼─┼─┼─┼─┼─┼
   −10−9−8−7−6−5−4−3−2−1 0
```

So, $|-10| = 10$.

The Coordinate Plane (pp. 33–37)

Graph and label each point on a coordinate plane.

19. $F(1, -4)$ **20.** $G(-4, 2)$

21. $H(-2, -3)$ **22.** $I(4, 0)$

23. **ROUTES** Starting at the school, Pilar walked 1 block east and 3 blocks south. From there, she walked 5 blocks west and 4 blocks north to the park. If the school represents the origin, what is the ordered pair for the park?

MA.7.G.4.3

EXAMPLE 4 Graph and label the point $S(3, -1)$.

Draw a coordinate plane. Move 3 units to the right. Then move 1 unit down. Draw a dot and label it $S(3, -1)$.

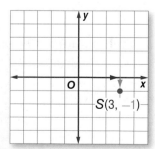

1-2 Add and Subtract Integers

Add Integers (pp. 40–44)

MA.7.A.3.1,
MA.7.A.3.2

Add.

24. $-6 + 8$

25. $-4 + (-9)$

26. $7 + (-12)$

27. $-18 + 18$

28. $-2 + 9$

29. $-10 + (-5)$

30. $6 + (-9)$

31. $17 + -17$

32. HIKING Alicia hiked 75 feet up a mountain. She then hiked 22 feet higher. Then, she descended 8 feet, and finally climbed up another 34 feet. What is the final change in Alicia's elevation?

33. HIBERNATION A black bear can weigh as much as 900 pounds when it starts hibernating. It loses 350 pounds during hibernation and gains 50 pounds two months after hibernation ends. What is the bear's final weight?

EXAMPLE 5 Find $-4 + 3$.

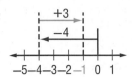

So, $-4 + 3 = -1$.

EXAMPLE 6 **POPULATION** The population of Ankeny grew by 2,394. Then it decreased 1,459. Then it decreased 3,490 more. What is the net change in population?

The changes in population can be represented by the addition sentence $2,394 + (-1,459) + (-3,490)$.

$2,394 + (-1,459) + (-3,490) = -2,555$

So, the net change in population is $-2,555$.

Subtract Integers (pp. 47–50)

MA.7.A.3.1,
MA.7.A.3.2

Subtract.

34. $-5 - 8$

35. $3 - 6$

36. $5 - (-2)$

37. $-4 - (-8)$

38. $-3 - 7$

39. $12 - 17$

40. $4 - (-7)$

41. $-10 - (-9)$

42. GOLF Owen shot 2 under par while his friend Nathan shot 3 over par. By how many shots was Owen's score better than Nathan's?

43. VOLCANOES The summit of an oceanic volcano once had an elevation of $-3,780$ feet. The summit now has an elevation of -800 feet. What was the change in elevation?

EXAMPLE 7 Find $-3 - 9$.

$-3 - 9 = -3 + (-9)$ To subtract 9, add -9.

      $= -12$ Simplify.

EXAMPLE 8 **STOCKS** On Wednesday, a company's stock closed at $13.54. On Thursday, it closed at $12.28. What was the change in the closing price?

To find the change in closing price, subtract $13.54 from $12.28.

$12.28 - \$13.54 = -\$1.26$

The change in closing price is $-\$1.26$.

1-3 Multiply and Divide Integers

MA.7.A.3.1, MA.7.A.3.2

PSI: Look for a Pattern (pp. 52–53)

Solve. Look for a pattern.

44. HEALTH The average person blinks 12 times per minute. At this rate, how many times does the average person blink in 12 hours?

45. SALARY Koko gets a job that pays $31,000 per year. She is promised a $2,200 raise after each year. At this rate, what will her salary be after 7 years?

46. DOGS A kennel determined that they need 144 feet of fencing to board 2 dogs, 216 feet to board 3 dogs, and 288 feet to board 4 dogs. If this pattern continues, how many feet of fencing is needed to board 8 dogs?

EXAMPLE 9 **THEATER** A theater has 18 seats in the first row, 24 seats in the second row, 30 seats in the third row, and so on. If this pattern continues, how many seats are in the sixth row?

Begin with 18 seats and add 6 seats for each additional row.

So, there are 48 seats in the sixth row.

Row	Number of Seats
1	18
2	24
3	30
4	36
5	42
6	48

MA.7.A.3.1, MA.7.A.3.2

Multiply Integers (pp. 56–60)

Multiply.

47. $-4(3)$ **48.** $8(-6)$

49. $-5(-7)$ **50.** $-2(40)$

ALGEBRA Evaluate each expression if $a = -4$, $b = -7$, and $c = 5$.

51. ab **52.** $-3c$

53. bc **54.** abc

EXAMPLE 10 Find $-4(3)$.

$-4(3) = -12$ The integers have different signs. The product is negative.

EXAMPLE 11 Evaluate xyz if $x = -6$, $y = 11$, and $z = -10$.

$xyz = (-6)(11)(-10)$

$= (-66)(-10)$ Multiply -6 and 11.

$= 660$ Multiply -66 and -10.

MA.7.A.3.1, MA.7.A.3.2

Divide Integers (pp. 61–65)

Divide.

55. $-45 \div (-9)$ **56.** $36 \div (-12)$

57. $-12 \div 6$ **58.** $-81 \div (-9)$

EXAMPLE 12 Find $-72 \div (-9)$.

$-72 \div (-9) = 8$ The integers have the same sign. The quotient is positive.

1. **WEATHER** Adam is recording the change in the outside air temperature for a science project. At 8:00 A.M., the high temperature was 42°F. By noon, the outside temperature had fallen 11°F. By mid-afternoon, the outside air temperature had fallen another 12°F and by evening, it had fallen an additional 5°F. Write an integer that describes the final change in temperature.

Evaluate each expression.

2. $|-3|$

3. $|-18| - |6|$

4. **STOCKS** A certain stock dropped 9 points one day and gained 13 points the following day. What was the net change in the stock's worth?

5. **FREEZING POINTS** The table shows the freezing points of various chemicals.

Chemical	Freezing Point (°F)
Carbon dioxide (dry ice)	−109
Water	32
Hydrogen	−435

  a. What is the difference between the freezing point of dry ice and the freezing point of hydrogen?

  b. What is the difference between the freezing points of water and dry ice?

6. **DEBT** Amanda owes her brother $24. If she plans to pay him back an equal amount from her piggy bank each day for six days, describe the change in the amount of money in her piggy bank each day.

Write the ordered pair for each point graphed. Then name the quadrant in which each point is located.

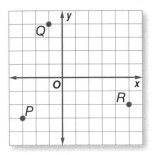

7. P 8. Q 9. R

10. **NGSSS** **PRACTICE** Kendrick created a 6-week schedule for practicing the piano. If the pattern continues, how many hours will he practice during the sixth week?

The table shows the number of hours he practiced in the first three weeks.

Week	1	2	3
Hours	4	7	10

  A. 15 hours   C. 19 hours

  B. 18 hours   D. 22 hours

Add, subtract, multiply, or divide.

11. $12 + (-9)$ 12. $-3 - 4$

13. $-7 - (-20)$ 14. $-7(-3)$

15. $5(-11)$ 16. $-36 \div (-9)$

17. $-15 + (-7)$ 18. $8 + (-6) + (-4)$

19. $-9 - 7$ 20. $-13 + 7$

21. **THINK SOLVE EXPLAIN** **EXTENDED RESPONSE** Rectangle $ABCD$ has vertices $A(-4, -2)$, $B(-4, 5)$, and $C(6, 5)$.

  Part A Graph points A, B, and C on a coordinate plane.

  Part B Find the coordinates of point D.

  Part C Explain how you found the coordinates for point D.

Gridded Response: Integers

To fill in a grid for a gridded-response question, first write your answer in the boxes at the top of the answer grid. Then fill in a bubble under each box to match your answer.

NGSSS PRACTICE EXAMPLE

Firefly squid are typically found 365 meters below the ocean's surface, or at a depth of −365 meters. Some are found at a depth 183 meters higher than this. At what depth can the shallower firefly squid be found?

$-365 + 183 = -182$

The shallower squid are at a depth of −182 meters. So, the answer is −182. Fill in −182.

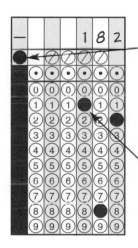

or

Write the (−) in the answer box, then fill in the ⊖ bubble.

Write 1, 8, and 2 in separate answer boxes. Fill in the 1 bubble under the 1, the 8 bubble under the 8, and the 2 bubble under the 2.

Work on It

The lowest point in Egypt is the Qattara Depression, which has an elevation of −133 meters. The highest point is Mount Catherine, which has an elevation of 2,629 meters. What is the difference in meters between the highest and lowest points? Fill in your answer on an answer grid.

Test Hint

The bubbles must be filled in completely and accurately for you to receive credit for your answer.

Read each question. Then fill in the correct answer on the answer document provided by your teacher or on a sheet of paper.

1. The table shows the daily low temperatures for Cleveland, Ohio, over five days.

Day	Temperature
1	15°F
2	−2°F
3	8°F
4	−6°F
5	5°F

Which expression can be used to find the average daily low temperature during the five days?

A. $(15 + 2 + 8 + 6 + 5) \div 5$

B. $15 + 2 + 8 + 6 + 5 \div 5$

C. $[15 + (-2) + 8 + (-6) + 5] \div 5$

D. $15 + (-2) + 8 + (-6) + 5 \div 5$

2. Three vertices of a parallelogram are given as coordinates $(-5, 3)$, $(-2, 7)$, and $(1, -3)$ in the graph. Which coordinates best represent the location of the fourth vertex of the parallelogram?

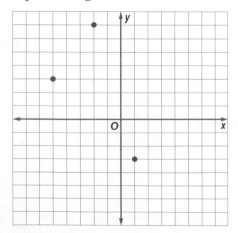

F. $(1, 4)$ **H.** $(1, -4)$

G. $(4, 1)$ **I.** $(-1, 4)$

3. **GRIDDED RESPONSE** The lowest point in Japan is Hachiro-gata (elevation −4 m), and the highest point is Mount Fuji (elevation 3,776 m). What is the difference in elevation, in meters, between Mount Fuji and Hachiro-gata?

4. **GRIDDED RESPONSE** A submarine is cruising 8 meters below the surface. The captain orders a dive of another 17 meters. What is the new cruising depth of the submarine in meters?

5. In which quadrant is point P located?

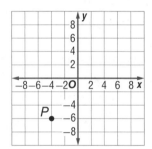

A. Quadrant I   **C.** Quadrant III

B. Quadrant II   **D.** Quadrant IV

6. Which integer added to −9 gives a sum of 3?

F. 12   **H.** 3

G. 6   **I.** −12

7. By the end of the third quarter of a football game, Ricky had gained 112 yards and had lost 12 yards. If Ricky lost an additional 8 yards and gained 22 yards in the fourth quarter, which equation could be used to represent his total yardage for the game?

A. $112 + 12 + 8 + 22 = 154$

B. $112 + (-12) + (-8) + 22 = 114$

C. $112 + 12 + (-8) + (-22) = 94$

D. $(-112) + (-12) + 8 + 22 = -94$

8. **GRIDDED RESPONSE** Bobby is diving 50 feet below sea level at the beach. His sister is at the swimming pool deck, which is 15 feet above sea level. What is the difference, in feet, between the pool deck and Bobby's position?

9. **SHORT RESPONSE** Larry borrowed $12,000 from his grandfather to buy a car. He bought a used car, so, he returned $4,411 to his grandfather. Write and solve an equation using integers that shows the total amount that Larry owes his grandfather.

10. Pablo and three of his friends are playing paintball. The table shows their scores at the end of one round.

Player	Score
Pablo	−189
Winston	−124
Nevin	130
Marsella	48

By how many points is Winston beating Pablo?

F. 65

G. 135

H. 178

I. 313

11. Each of the first 4 pit stops a racecar driver makes loses ten seconds off the leader. The pit crew makes adjustments, and at each of the next two pit stops he gains 7 seconds on the leader. How much time is the driver off the leader?

A. 40 seconds

B. 14 seconds

C. −26 seconds

D. −54 seconds

12. **SHORT RESPONSE** A rectangle and a square are graphed on a coordinate plane. Name an ordered pair that is inside the rectangle but outside the square.

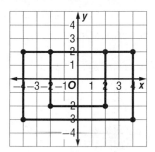

13. **EXTENDED RESPONSE** The use of the computer to download music has decreased the sales of music CDs. Use the following table to answer the questions.

Year	Estimated Number of New Music CD Releases
2000	36,000
2001	32,000
2002	34,000
2003	8,000
2004	14,000
2005	10,000
2006	12,000

Part A During which year was there the greatest decrease in CD releases from the previous year? What was the decrease?

Part B Write and evaluate an expression that shows the change in CD releases from 2004 to 2005.

NEED EXTRA HELP?													
If You Missed Question...	1	2	3	4	5	6	7	8	9	10	11	12	13
Go to Lesson...	1-3D	1-1C	1-2D	1-2D	1-1C	1-2B	1-2B	1-2D	1-2B	1-2D	1-3C	1-1C	1-2D
For help with NGSSS...	A.3.1	G.4.3	A.3.1	A.3.1	G.4.3	A.3.1	A.3.1	A.3.1	A.3.1	A.3.1	A.3.1	G.4.3	A.3.1

Rational Numbers

The ★BIG Idea

Develop an understanding of operations on all rational numbers and solving linear equations.

FOLDABLES®
Study Organizer

Make this Foldable to help you organize your notes. Begin with two sheets of $8\frac{1}{2}$" by 11" paper.

1 Stack two sheets of paper $\frac{3}{4}$ inch apart.

Rational Numbers

2 Roll up bottom edges so that all tabs are the same size.

3 Crease and staple along the fold.

4 Write the chapter title on the front. Label each tab with a lesson number and title.

2-1 Rational Numbers
2-2 Add and Subtract Fractions
2-3 Multiply and Divide Fractions

Review Vocabulary

simplest form (Prior Grade) **forma reducida**
a fraction is in simplest form when the GCF of the numerator and the denominator is 1

$$\frac{4}{12} = \frac{4 \div 4}{12 \div 4} = \frac{1}{3}$$

Key Vocabulary

	English	Español
p. 85	rational number	número racional
p. 91	like fractions	fracciones semejantes
p. 98	unlike fractions	fracciones con distinto denominador
p. 126	exponent	exponente

Multilingual eGlossary glencoe.com

 **Get Connected**
glencoe.com

- Study using the **eBook**
- Explore with **Get Animated**
- Get extra help from **Personal Tutor**
- Use **virtual manipulatives** for additional help
- Take a **Self-Check Quiz**

When Will I Use This?

Caitlyn, Theresa, and Aisha in
GET ORGANIZED

Thanks for coming over to help organize my closet!

Sure.

No problem. I live to organize.

I bought a really great new closet organizer! I can't wait to install it!

Uh oh.

I'm not sure this will fit in your closet. It seems a bit big.

CLOSET ORGANIZERS

It says that the size of each storage cube is $18\frac{3}{4}''$ and there are three of them.

I'll measure the space, then we can figure it out.

I measured the closet rod, and it is $12\frac{7}{8}''$. I wrote it all down.

$$18\frac{3}{4} + 18\frac{3}{4} + 18\frac{3}{4} + 12\frac{7}{8}$$

YIKES!! Fractions! How are we going to add them up??

We are doomed!!

Theresa, just breathe! We can figure it out!

Your Turn!
You will solve this problem in Chapter 2.

Are You Ready for Chapter 2?

You have two options for checking prerequisite skills for this chapter.

Text Option Take the Quick Check below. Refer to the Quick Review for help.

QUICK Check

State which decimal is greater. (Prior Grade)

1. 0.6, 0.61

2. 1.25, 1.52

3. 0.33, 0.13

4. 1.08, 10.8

5. LUNCH Kirsten spent $4.21 on lunch while Almanzo spent $4.12. Who spent the greater amount?

Graph on a number line.

6. $2\frac{1}{4}$

7. $5\frac{1}{2}$

8. $\frac{4}{5}$

9. $1\frac{1}{3}$

10. MEASUREMENT Jenna is baking a cake that requires $2\frac{3}{4}$ cups of flour and $1\frac{1}{2}$ cups of sugar. Graph the amounts of flour and sugar on a number line.

Write in simplest form. (Prior Grade)

11. $\frac{16}{20}$

12. $\frac{15}{25}$

13. $\frac{10}{10}$

14. $\frac{13}{14}$

15. SPORTS A survey reported that 15 out of every 50 teens like to ski. Write a fraction in simplest form of the results.

QUICK Review

EXAMPLE 1

State which decimal is greater, 7.4 or 7.04.

7.4

7.04

↑

7.4 is greater.

Line up the decimal points and compare place value. The 4 in the tenths place is greater than the 0 in the tenths place.

EXAMPLE 2

Graph $3\frac{2}{3}$ on a number line.

Find the two whole numbers that $3\frac{2}{3}$ lies between.

$3 < 3\frac{2}{3} < 4$

Since the denominator is 3, divide each space into 3 sections.

Place a dot at $3\frac{2}{3}$.

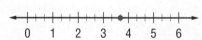

EXAMPLE 3

Write $\frac{45}{100}$ in simplest form.

Find the prime factorization of 45 and 100.

$45 = 3 \times 3 \times 5$

$100 = 2 \times 2 \times 5 \times 5$

The GCF is 5.

$\frac{45}{100} = \frac{45 \div 5}{100 \div 5} = \frac{9}{20}$

Online Option  Get Connected Take the Online Readiness Quiz at **glencoe.com**.

2-1 Rational Numbers

PART A B C

Explore The Number Line

Main Idea

Graph rational numbers on the number line.

NGSSS

 Preparation for MA.7.A.5.1 Express rational numbers as terminating or repeating decimals.

Get Connected
glencoe.com

You have already graphed integers and positive fractions on a number line. In this Activity, you will graph negative fractions.

ACTIVITY

Use models to graph $-\frac{3}{4}$ on a number line.

STEP 1 Draw a number line with arrows on each end. Place a fraction strip divided in fourths above the number line. Mark a 0 on the right side and a -1 on the left side.

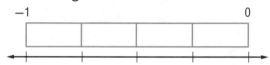

STEP 2 Starting from the right, shade three fourths. Label the number line with $-\frac{1}{4}$, $-\frac{2}{4}$, and $-\frac{3}{4}$.

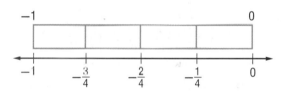

STEP 3 Draw a dot on the number line above the $-\frac{3}{4}$ mark.

Practice and Apply

Graph each fraction on a number line. Use a fraction strip.

1. $-\frac{3}{8}$
2. $-\frac{1}{3}$
3. $-1\frac{2}{5}$
4. $-2\frac{5}{6}$

Graph each pair of numbers on a number line. Then write which number is less.

5. $-\frac{7}{8}, -\frac{3}{8}$
6. $-\frac{5}{8}, -1\frac{1}{8}$
7. $-\frac{13}{8}, -\frac{3}{8}$
8. $-1\frac{7}{8}, -1\frac{5}{8}$

9. **Write MATH** How does graphing $-\frac{3}{4}$ differ from graphing $\frac{3}{4}$?

Main Idea

Write fractions as terminating or repeating decimals and write decimals as fractions.

NGSSS

 MA.7.A.5.1 Express rational numbers as terminating or repeating decimals.

New Vocabulary

terminating decimal
repeating decimal
bar notation

Get Connected
glencoe.com

Terminating and Repeating Decimals

NASCAR The table shows the winning speeds for a 10-year period at the Daytona 500.

1. What fraction of the speeds are between 130 and 145 miles per hour?

2. Express this fraction using words and then as a decimal.

3. What fraction of the speeds are between 145 and 165 miles per hour? Express this fraction using words and then as a decimal.

Daytona 500		
Year	Winner	Speed (mph)
1999	J. Gordon	148.295
2000	D. Jarrett	155.669
2001	M. Waltrip	161.783
2002	W. Burton	142.971
2003	M. Waltrip	133.870
2004	D. Earnhardt Jr.	156.345
2005	J. Gordon	135.173
2006	J. Johnson	142.667
2007	K. Harvick	149.335
2008	R. Newman	152.672

Our decimal system is based on powers of 10 like 10, 100, and 1,000. If the denominator of a fraction is a power of 10, you can use place value to write the fraction as a decimal.

Words	Fraction	Decimal
seven tenths	$\dfrac{7}{10}$	0.7

If the denominator of a fraction is a *factor* of 10, 100, 1,000, or any greater power of ten, you can use mental math and place value.

EXAMPLES   **Use Mental Math**

Write each fraction or mixed number as a decimal.

① $\dfrac{7}{20}$

Think $\dfrac{7}{20} = \dfrac{35}{100}$ $\times 5$ ... $\times 5$

So, $\dfrac{7}{20} = 0.35$.

② $5\dfrac{3}{4}$

$5\dfrac{3}{4} = 5 + \dfrac{3}{4}$ Think of it as a sum.

$= 5 + 0.75$ You know that $\dfrac{3}{4} = 0.75$.

$= 5.75$ Add mentally.

So, $5\dfrac{3}{4} = 5.75$.

CHECK Your Progress

a. $\dfrac{3}{10}$ **b.** $\dfrac{3}{25}$ **c.** $-6\dfrac{1}{2}$

Any fraction can be written as a decimal by dividing its numerator by its denominator. Division ends when the remainder is zero.

EXAMPLES Use Division

3 Write $\frac{3}{8}$ as a decimal.

$$
\begin{array}{r}
0.375 \\
8\overline{)3.000} \\
-\,24 \\
\hline
60 \\
-\,56 \\
\hline
40 \\
-\,40 \\
\hline
0
\end{array}
$$

Divide 3 by 8.

Division ends when the remainder is 0.

So, $\frac{3}{8} = 0.375$.

4 Write $-\frac{1}{40}$ as a decimal.

$$
\begin{array}{r}
0.025 \\
40\overline{)1.000} \\
-\,80 \\
\hline
200 \\
-\,200 \\
\hline
0
\end{array}
$$

Divide 1 by 40.

So, $-\frac{1}{40} = -0.025$.

 CHECK Your Progress

Write each fraction or mixed number as a decimal.

d. $-\frac{7}{8}$ **e.** $2\frac{1}{8}$ **f.** $7\frac{9}{20}$

In Examples 1–4, the decimals 0.35, 5.75, 0.375, and 0.025 are called terminating decimals. A **terminating decimal** is a decimal whose digits end. **Repeating decimals** have a pattern in their digits that repeats forever. Consider $\frac{1}{3}$.

$$
\begin{array}{r}
0.333\ldots \\
3\overline{)1.000} \\
-\,9 \\
\hline
10 \\
-\,9 \\
\hline
10 \\
-\,9 \\
\hline
1
\end{array}
$$

The number 3 repeats. The repetition of 3 is represented by three dots.

You can use **bar notation** to indicate that a number pattern repeats indefinitely. A bar is written over only the digits that repeat.

$0.33333\ldots = 0.\overline{3}$ $0.121212\ldots = 0.\overline{12}$ $11.3858585\ldots = 11.3\overline{85}$

Vocabulary Link

Everyday Use

Terminate coming to an end, as in terminate a game

Math Use

Terminate a decimal whose digits end

EXAMPLE **Write Fractions as Repeating Decimals**

5 Write $\frac{7}{9}$ as a decimal.

$$
\begin{array}{r}
0.777\ldots \\
9\overline{)7.000} \\
-63 \\
\hline
70 \\
-63 \\
\hline
70 \\
-63 \\
\hline
7
\end{array}
$$

Divide 7 by 9.

> Notice that the remainder will never be zero. That is, the division never ends.

So, $\frac{7}{9} = 0.777\ldots$ or $0.\overline{7}$.

 **CHECK Your Progress**

Write each fraction or mixed number as a decimal. Use bar notation if the decimal is a repeating decimal.

g. $\frac{2}{3}$ **h.** $-\frac{3}{11}$ **i.** $8\frac{1}{3}$

Every terminating decimal can be written as a fraction with a denominator of 10, 100, 1,000, or a greater power of ten. Use the place value of the final digit as the denominator.

numerator

$$0.25 = \frac{25}{100}$$

hundredths place

Real-World EXAMPLE

6 **FISH** Use the table to find what fraction of the fish in an aquarium are goldfish. Write in simplest form.

$0.15 = \frac{15}{100}$ The final digit, 5, is in the hundredths place.

$\quad\;\; = \frac{3}{20}$ Simplify.

So, $\frac{3}{20}$ of the fish are goldfish.

Fish	Amount
Guppy	0.25
Angelfish	0.4
Goldfish	0.15
Molly	0.2

 CHECK Your Progress

Determine the fraction of the aquarium made up by each fish. Write the answer in simplest form.

j. molly   **k.** guppy   **l.** angelfish

Real-World Link ·····
The recommended water temperature for goldfish is 65–72°F.

CHECK Your Understanding

Examples 1–5
(pp. 80–82)

Write each fraction or mixed number as a decimal. Use bar notation if the decimal is a repeating decimal.

1. $\dfrac{2}{5}$

2. $-\dfrac{9}{10}$

3. $7\dfrac{1}{2}$

4. $-4\dfrac{3}{20}$

5 $\dfrac{1}{8}$

6. $-3\dfrac{5}{8}$

7. $\dfrac{5}{9}$

8. $1\dfrac{5}{6}$

Example 6
(p. 82)

Write each decimal as a fraction or mixed number in simplest form.

9. -0.22

10. 0.1

11. 4.6

12. HOCKEY During a hockey game, an ice resurfacer travels 0.75 mile during each ice resurfacing. What fraction represents this distance?

Practice and Problem Solving

 = **Step-by-Step Solutions** begin on page R3.
Extra Practice is on page EP4.

Examples 1–5
(pp. 80–82)

Write each fraction or mixed number as a decimal. Use bar notation if the decimal is a repeating decimal.

13. $\dfrac{4}{5}$

14. $\dfrac{1}{2}$

15. $-4\dfrac{4}{25}$

16. $-7\dfrac{1}{20}$

17. $\dfrac{5}{16}$

18. $\dfrac{3}{16}$

19. $-\dfrac{33}{50}$

20. $-\dfrac{17}{40}$

21. $5\dfrac{7}{8}$

22. $9\dfrac{3}{8}$

23. $-\dfrac{4}{9}$

24. $-\dfrac{8}{9}$

25. $-\dfrac{1}{6}$

26. $-\dfrac{8}{11}$

27. $5\dfrac{1}{3}$

28. $2\dfrac{6}{11}$

Example 6
(p. 82)

Write each decimal as a fraction or mixed number in simplest form.

29. -0.2

30. -0.9

31. 0.55

32. 0.34

33. 5.96

34. 2.66

35 INSECTS A praying mantis can be 30.5 centimeters long. What mixed number represents this length?

36. GROCERIES Suppose you buy a 1.25-pound package of ham for $4.99. What fraction of a pound did you buy?

37. FIND THE DATA Refer to the Data File on pages 2–5 of your book. Choose some data and write a real-world problem in which you would write a percent as a decimal.

Write each of the following as an improper fraction.

38. -13

39. $7\dfrac{1}{3}$

40. -1.028

41. -3.2

42. MUSIC Nicolás practiced playing the cello for 2 hours and 18 minutes. Write the time Nicolás spent practicing as a decimal.

43. OPEN ENDED Write a fraction that is equivalent to a terminating decimal between 0.5 and 0.75.

44. CHALLENGE Fractions in simplest form that have denominators of 2, 4, 8, 16, and 32 produce terminating decimals. Fractions with denominators of 6, 12, 18, and 24 produce repeating decimals. What causes the difference? Explain.

45. 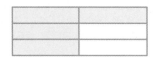 **MATH** The value of pi (π) is 3.1415926.... The mathematician Archimedes believed that π was between $3\frac{1}{7}$ and $3\frac{10}{71}$. Was Archimedes correct? Explain your reasoning.

NGSSS Practice   MA.6.A.5.1, MA.7.A.5.1

46. Tanya drew a model for the fraction $\frac{4}{6}$.

Which decimal is equal to $\frac{4}{6}$?

A. 0.666   **C.** 0.667

B. $0.\overline{6}$ **D.** $0.66\overline{7}$

47. Based on the information given in the table, what fraction represents $0.\overline{8}$?

F. $\frac{4}{5}$

G. $\frac{80}{99}$

H. $\frac{5}{6}$

I. $\frac{8}{9}$

Decimal	Fraction
$0.\overline{3}$	$\frac{3}{9}$
$0.\overline{4}$	$\frac{4}{9}$
$0.\overline{5}$	$\frac{5}{9}$
$0.\overline{6}$	$\frac{6}{9}$

 Spiral Review

Divide. (Lesson 1-3D)

48. $-42 \div 6$ **49.** $36 \div (-3)$ **50.** $-45 \div (-3)$

51. FINANCIAL LITERACY Jordan withdraws $14 each week from his savings account for 7 weeks. Write a multiplication expression to represent this situation. Then find the product and explain its meaning. (Lesson 1-3C)

Find each sum. (Lesson 1-2B)

52. $-8 + (-3)$ **53.** $-10 + 9$ **54.** $12 + (-20)$ **55.** $-15 + 15$

56. DIVING Valentina jumped into 10 feet of water and touched the bottom of the pool before she surfaced. Write an integer to describe where Valentina was in relation to the surface of the water when she was at the bottom of the pool. (Lesson 1-1B)

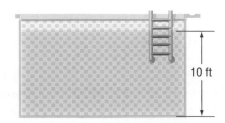

10 ft

Main Idea
Compare and order fractions and decimals.

NGSSS
 MA.7.A.5.1 Express rational numbers as terminating or repeating **decimals.**

New Vocabulary
rational numbers
common denominator
least common denominator (LCD)

Get Connected
glencoe.com

Compare and Order Rational Numbers

SOFTBALL The batting average of a softball player is found by comparing the number of hits to the number of times at bat. Felisa had 50 hits in 175 at bats, and Harmony had 42 hits in 160 at bats.

1. Write the two batting averages as fractions.

2. Which girl had the better batting average? Explain.

3. Describe two methods you could use to compare the batting averages.

A **rational number** is a number that can be expressed as a fraction. Fractions, terminating and repeating decimals, percents, and integers are all rational numbers. The points corresponding to rational numbers begin to "fill in" the number line.

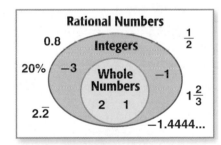

EXAMPLE **Compare Rational Numbers**

1 **Replace the ● with <, >, or = to make** $-1\frac{5}{6}$ ● $-1\frac{1}{6}$ **a true sentence.**

Graph each rational number on a number line. Mark off equal-size increments of $\frac{1}{6}$ between -2 and -1.

$$-2 \quad -1\frac{5}{6} \quad -1\frac{4}{6} \quad -1\frac{3}{6} \quad -1\frac{2}{6} \quad -1\frac{1}{6} \quad -1$$

The number line shows that $-1\frac{5}{6} < -1\frac{1}{6}$.

CHECK Your Progress

a. Replace the ● with <, >, or = to make $-5\frac{5}{9}$ ● $-5\frac{1}{9}$ a true sentence.

A **common denominator** is a common multiple of the denominators of two or more fractions. The **least common denominator** or **LCD** is the LCM of the denominators. You can use the LCD to compare fractions.

QUICK Review

LCD
To find the least common denominator for $\frac{7}{12}$ and $\frac{8}{18}$, find the LCM of 12 and 18.
$12 = 2 \times 2 \times 3$
$18 = 2 \times 3 \times 3$
$LCM = 2 \times 2 \times 3 \times 3$
$\qquad = 36$

 EXAMPLE   **Compare Rational Numbers**

② Replace the ● with <, >, or = to make $\frac{7}{12}$ ● $\frac{8}{18}$ a true sentence.

The LCD of the denominators 2 and 3 is 6.

$$\frac{7}{12} = \frac{7 \times 3}{12 \times 3} \qquad\qquad \frac{8}{18} = \frac{8 \times 2}{18 \times 2}$$

$$\quad = \frac{21}{36} \qquad\qquad\qquad \quad = \frac{16}{36}$$

Since $\frac{21}{36} > \frac{16}{36}$, $\frac{7}{12} > \frac{8}{18}$.

CHECK Your Progress

Replace each ● with <, >, or = to make a true sentence.

b. $\frac{5}{6}$ ● $\frac{7}{9}$ **c.** $\frac{1}{5}$ ● $\frac{7}{50}$ **d.** $-\frac{9}{16}$ ● $-\frac{7}{10}$

You can also compare fractions by writing each fraction as a decimal and then comparing the decimals.

Real-World EXAMPLE

 Real-World Link · · · ·
The first roller shoe was introduced in 2001.

③ **ROLLER SHOES** In Mr. Huang's math class, 6 out of 32 students own roller shoes. In Mrs. Trevino's math class, 5 out of 29 students own roller shoes. In which class does a greater fraction of students own roller shoes?

Since the denominators are large, write $\frac{6}{32}$ and $\frac{5}{29}$ as decimals and then compare.

$6 \div 32 = 0.1875 \qquad 5 \div 29 \approx 0.1724$ Divide.

Since $0.1875 > 0.1724$, $\frac{6}{32} > \frac{5}{29}$.

A greater fraction of students in Mr. Huang's class own roller shoes.

CHECK Your Progress

e. **BOWLING** Twelve out of 32 students in second period class like to bowl. In fifth period class, 12 out of 29 students like to bowl. In which class does a greater fraction of the students like to bowl?

Not all numbers are rational numbers. The Greek letter π (pi) represents the nonterminating and nonrepeating number whose first few digits are 3.1415927… . This number is an *irrational* number.

EXAMPLE Order Rational Numbers

④ **List the numbers 3.44, π, 3.14, and $3.\overline{4}$ in order from least to greatest.**

Line up the decimal points and compare using place value.

3.140	Annex a zero.	3.440	Annex a zero.
3.1415926…	$\pi \approx 3.1415926…$	3.444…	$3.\overline{4} = 3.444…$
Since $0 < 1$, $3.14 < \pi$.		Since $0 < 4$, $3.44 < 3.\overline{4}$.	

So, the order of the numbers from least to greatest is 3.14, π, 3.44, and $3.\overline{4}$.

Check Graph each number on a number line.

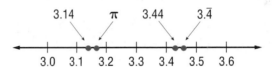

The number line confirms the order of the numbers is correct.

CHECK Your Progress

f. RAIN The amount of rain on four consecutive days was 0.3 inch, $\frac{3}{5}$ inch, 0.75 inch, and $\frac{2}{3}$ inch. List the amounts from least to greatest.

These fraction-decimal equivalents are used frequently. It will be useful to memorize them.

Key Concept Fraction-Decimal Equivalents

$\frac{1}{4} = 0.25$	$\frac{1}{5} = 0.2$	$\frac{1}{8} = 0.125$	$\frac{1}{10} = 0.1$
$\frac{1}{2} = 0.5$	$\frac{2}{5} = 0.4$	$\frac{3}{8} = 0.375$	$\frac{3}{10} = 0.3$
$\frac{3}{4} = 0.75$	$\frac{3}{5} = 0.6$	$\frac{1}{3} = 0.\overline{3}$	$\frac{7}{10} = 0.7$
$1 = 1.00$	$\frac{4}{5} = 0.8$	$\frac{2}{3} = 0.\overline{6}$	$\frac{9}{10} = 0.9$

Lesson 2-1 Rational Numbers **87**

Examples 1 and 2
(pp. 85–86)

Replace each ● with <, >, or = to make a true sentence. Use a number line if necessary.

1. $-\frac{4}{9}$ ● $-\frac{7}{9}$ **2.** $-1\frac{3}{4}$ ● $-1\frac{6}{8}$ **3.** $\frac{3}{8}$ ● $\frac{6}{15}$ **4.** $2\frac{4}{5}$ ● $2\frac{7}{8}$

Example 3
(p. 86)

5. SOCCER The table shows the average saves for two soccer goalies. Who has the better average, Elliot or Shanna? Explain.

Name	Average
Elliot	3 saves out of 4
Shanna	7 saves out of 11

6. SCHOOL On her first quiz in social studies, Meg answered 23 out of 25 questions correctly. On her second quiz, she answered 27 out of 30 questions correctly. On which quiz did Meg have the better score?

Example 4
(p. 87)

7. INSECTS The lengths of four insects are 0.02 inch, $\frac{1}{8}$ inch, 0.1 inch, and $\frac{2}{3}$ inch. List the lengths in inches from least to greatest.

Practice and Problem Solving

● = **Step-by-Step Solutions** begin on page R3.
Extra Practice is on page EP4.

Examples 1 and 2
(pp. 85–86)

Replace each ● with <, >, or = to make a true sentence. Use a number line if necessary.

8. $-\frac{3}{5}$ ● $-\frac{4}{5}$ **9.** $-\frac{5}{7}$ ● $-\frac{2}{7}$ **10.** $-7\frac{5}{8}$ ● $-7\frac{1}{8}$ **11.** $-3\frac{2}{3}$ ● $-3\frac{4}{6}$

12. $\frac{7}{10}$ ● $\frac{2}{3}$ **13** $\frac{4}{7}$ ● $\frac{5}{8}$ **14.** $\frac{2}{3}$ ● $\frac{10}{15}$ **15.** $-\frac{17}{24}$ ● $-\frac{11}{12}$

16. $2\frac{3}{4}$ ● $2\frac{2}{3}$ **17.** $6\frac{2}{3}$ ● $6\frac{1}{2}$ **18.** $5\frac{5}{7}$ ● $5\frac{11}{14}$ **19.** $3\frac{11}{16}$ ● $3\frac{7}{8}$

Example 3
(p. 86)

20. MONEY The table shows how much copper is in each type of coin. Which coin contains the greatest amount of copper?

Coin	Amount of Copper
Dime	$\frac{12}{16}$
Nickel	$\frac{3}{4}$
Penny	$\frac{1}{400}$
Quarter	$\frac{23}{25}$

21. BASKETBALL Gracia and Jim were shooting free throws. Gracia made 4 out of 15 free throws. Jim *missed* 6 out of 16 free throws. Who made the free throw a greater fraction of the time?

Example 4
(p. 87)

Order each set of numbers from least to greatest.

22. $0.23, 0.19, \frac{1}{5}$ **23.** $\frac{8}{10}, 0.81, 0.805$ **24.** $-0.615, -\frac{5}{8}, -0.62$

25. $-1.4, -1\frac{1}{25}, -1.25$ **26.** $7.49, 7\frac{49}{50}, 7.5$ **27.** $3\frac{4}{7}, 3\frac{3}{5}, 3.47$

Replace each ● with <, >, or = to make a true sentence. Use a number line if necessary.

28. 0.4 ● 112 out of 250   **29.** 3 out of 5 ● 0.59

30. 0.82 ● 5 out of 6   **31.** 9 out of 20 ● 0.45

MEASUREMENT Replace each ● with <, >, or = to make a true sentence.

32. $\frac{5}{8}$ yard ● $\frac{1}{16}$ yard   **33.** 0.25 pound ● $\frac{2}{9}$ pound

34. $2\frac{5}{6}$ hours ● 2.8 hours   **35** $1\frac{7}{12}$ gallons ● $1\frac{5}{8}$ gallons

MEASUREMENT Order each of the following from least to greatest.

36. 4.4 miles, $4\frac{3}{8}$ miles, $4\frac{5}{12}$ miles   **37.** 6.5 cups, $6\frac{1}{3}$ cups, 6 cups

38. 1.2 laps, 2 laps, $\frac{1}{2}$ lap   **39.** $\frac{1}{5}$ gram, 5 grams, 1.5 grams

40. ANIMALS Use the table that shows the lengths of small mammals.

Animal	Length (ft)
Eastern Chipmunk	$\frac{1}{3}$
Kitti's Hog-Nosed Bat	$0.8\overline{3}$
European Mole	$\frac{5}{12}$
Masked Shrew	$\frac{1}{6}$
Spiny Pocket Mouse	0.25

  a. Which animal is the smallest mammal?

  b. Which animal is smaller than the European Mole but larger than the Spiny Pocket Mouse?

  c. Order the animals from greatest to least size.

41. GRAPHIC NOVEL Refer to the graphic novel frame below for Exercises a–b.

Refer to page 77 to learn about our project.

We can do this! All we need to do is find a common denominator for all of the measurements before we add.

  a. Rewrite the organizer dimensions so they all have a common denominator.

  b. If the closet organizer has a total width of $69\frac{1}{8}$ inches and the closet is $69\frac{3}{4}$ inches wide, will the organizer fit?

42. Which One Doesn't Belong? Identify the ratio that does not have the same value as the other three. Explain your reasoning.

| 12 out of 15 | 0.08 | 80% | $\frac{4}{5}$ |

43. CHALLENGE Explain how you know which number, $1\frac{15}{16}$, $\frac{17}{8}$, or $\frac{63}{32}$, is nearest to 2.

44. Write MATH Write a word problem about a real-world situation in which you would compare rational numbers. Then solve the problem.

NGSSS Practice   MA.6.A.5.2, MA.7.A.5.1

45. Which point shows the location of $\frac{7}{2}$ on the number line?

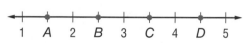

    1   A   2   B   3   C   4   D   5

  A. point A

  B. point B

  C. point C

  D. point D

46. Which list of numbers is ordered from least to greatest?

  F. $\frac{1}{4}$, $4\frac{1}{4}$, 0.4, 0.04

  G. 0.04, 0.4, $4\frac{1}{4}$, $\frac{1}{4}$

  H. 0.04, $\frac{1}{4}$, 0.4, $4\frac{1}{4}$

  I. 0.4, $\frac{1}{4}$, 0.04, $4\frac{1}{4}$

47. Which of the following fractions is closest to 0?

  A. $-\frac{3}{4}$ **C.** $\frac{7}{12}$

  B. $-\frac{2}{3}$ **D.** $\frac{5}{8}$

Spiral Review

Write each decimal as a fraction or mixed number in simplest form. (Lesson 2-1B)

48. 0.6   **49.** 0.15   **50.** 2.8

51. ALGEBRA Evaluate $xy \div (-4)$ if $x = 12$ and $y = -2$. (Lesson 1-3D)

Multiply. (Lesson 1-3C)

52. $14(-5)$ **53.** $(-3)(-3)(-3)$ **54.** $-10(2)(-8)$

55. HIKING Two people are hiking in the Grand Canyon. One is 987 feet below the rim and the other is 1,200 feet below the rim. Find the vertical distance between them. (Lesson 1-2D)

56. Evaluate $|5| + |-10|$. (Lesson 1-1B)

Main Idea
Add and subtract fractions with like denominators.

NGSSS

MA.7.A.3.2 Add, subtract, multiply, and divide integers, **fractions**, and terminating decimals, and perform exponential operations with rational bases and whole number exponents **including solving problems in everyday contexts.**

New Vocabulary
like fractions

Get Connected
glencoe.com

Add and Subtract Like Fractions

SHOES Sean surveyed ten classmates to find which type of tennis shoe they like to wear.

1. What fraction liked cross trainers? high tops?

2. What fraction likes either cross trainers or high tops?

Fractions that have the same denominators are called **like fractions**.

Tennis Shoes

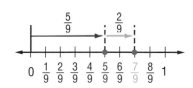

Shoe Type	Number
Cross Trainer	5
Running	3
High Top	2

Key Concept — Add and Subtract Like Fractions

Words To add or subtract like fractions, add or subtract the numerators and write the result over the denominator.

Examples

Numbers

$$\frac{5}{10} + \frac{2}{10} = \frac{5+2}{10} \text{ or } \frac{7}{10}$$

$$\frac{11}{12} - \frac{4}{12} = \frac{11-4}{12} \text{ or } \frac{7}{12}$$

Algebra

$$\frac{a}{c} + \frac{b}{c} = \frac{a+b}{c}, \text{ where } c \neq 0$$

$$\frac{a}{c} - \frac{b}{c} = \frac{a-b}{c}, \text{ where } c \neq 0$$

EXAMPLES Add Like Fractions

Add. Write in simplest form.

1 $\dfrac{5}{9} + \dfrac{2}{9}$

$\dfrac{5}{9} + \dfrac{2}{9} = \dfrac{5+2}{9}$ Add the numerators.

$= \dfrac{7}{9}$ Simplify.

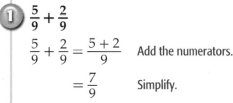

2 $-\dfrac{3}{5} + \left(-\dfrac{1}{5}\right)$

$-\dfrac{3}{5} + \left(-\dfrac{1}{5}\right) = -\dfrac{3}{5} + -\dfrac{1}{5}$

$= \dfrac{-3 + (-1)}{5}$ Add the numerators.

$= \dfrac{-4}{5} \text{ or } -\dfrac{4}{5}$ Use the rules for adding integers.

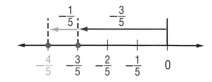

CHECK Your Progress

a. $\dfrac{1}{3} + \dfrac{2}{3}$ **b.** $-\dfrac{3}{7} + \dfrac{1}{7}$ **c.** $-\dfrac{2}{5} + \left(-\dfrac{2}{5}\right)$

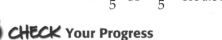

Subtract. Write in simplest form.

3 $\dfrac{9}{10} - \dfrac{1}{10}$

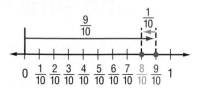

$\dfrac{9}{10} - \dfrac{1}{10} = \dfrac{9-1}{10}$ Subtract the numerators.

$\qquad\qquad = \dfrac{8}{10}$ or $\dfrac{4}{5}$ Simplify.

QUICK Review

Subtracting Integers
To subtract an integer, add its opposite.
$-9 - (-4) = -9 + 4$
$\qquad\qquad = -5$

4 $-\dfrac{5}{8} - \dfrac{3}{8}$

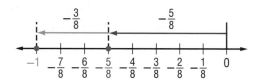

$-\dfrac{5}{8} - \dfrac{3}{8} = -\dfrac{5}{8} + \left(-\dfrac{3}{8}\right)$ To subtract $\dfrac{3}{8}$, add $-\dfrac{3}{8}$.

$\qquad\qquad = \dfrac{-5 + (-3)}{8}$ Add the numerators.

$\qquad\qquad = -\dfrac{8}{8}$ or -1 Simplify.

5 Find $\dfrac{5}{8} - \dfrac{7}{8}$. Write in simplest form.

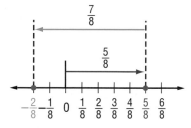

$\dfrac{5}{8} - \dfrac{7}{8} = \dfrac{5-7}{8}$ Subtract the numerators.

$\qquad\qquad = -\dfrac{2}{8}$ or $-\dfrac{1}{4}$ Simplify.

Check $-\dfrac{2}{8} + \dfrac{7}{8} = \dfrac{5}{8}$ ✓

 CHECK Your Progress

d. $-\dfrac{5}{9} - \dfrac{2}{9}$

e. $-\dfrac{11}{12} - \left(-\dfrac{5}{12}\right)$

f. $-\dfrac{3}{4} - \dfrac{1}{4}$

g. $\dfrac{5}{9} - \dfrac{2}{9}$

h. $\dfrac{11}{12} - \dfrac{5}{12}$

i. $\dfrac{7}{10} - \dfrac{3}{10}$

Real-World EXAMPLE

6 POPULATION About $\frac{6}{100}$ of the population of the United States lives in Florida. Another $\frac{4}{100}$ lives in Ohio. How much more of the U.S. population lives in Florida than in Ohio?

$$\frac{6}{100} - \frac{4}{100} = \frac{6-4}{100} \qquad \text{Subtract the numerators.}$$

$$= \frac{2}{100} \text{ or } \frac{1}{50} \qquad \text{Simplify.}$$

About $\frac{1}{50}$ more of the U.S. population lives in Florida than in Ohio.

Check 6 hundredths minus 4 hundredths equals 2 hundredths. ✓

✓ CHECK Your Progress

j. JUICE Two-fifths quart of pineapple juice was added to a bowl containing $\frac{3}{5}$ quart of orange juice. How many total quarts of pineapple juice and orange juice are in the bowl?

 ## CHECK Your Understanding

Examples 1–5
(pp. 91–92)

Add or subtract. Write in simplest form.

1. $\frac{3}{5} + \frac{1}{5}$

2. $\frac{2}{7} + \frac{1}{7}$

3 $-\frac{3}{4} + \left(-\frac{3}{4}\right)$

4. $\frac{3}{8} - \frac{1}{8}$

5. $-\frac{4}{5} - \left(-\frac{1}{5}\right)$

6. $\frac{2}{7} - \frac{6}{7}$

Example 6
(p. 93)

7. STATES Of the 50 states in the United States, 14 have an Atlantic Ocean coastline and 5 have a Pacific Ocean coastline. What fraction of U.S. states have either an Atlantic Ocean or Pacific Ocean coastline?

8. LUNCH The table shows the lunch count for three seventh-grade classes. Write the fraction in simplest form that represents how much more of the seventh-grade class is buying lunch rather than packing it.

Lunch Count		
Class	**Buying**	**Packing**
Mrs. Savage	15	10
Mr. LeGault	19	8
Miss Cappizella	12	12

Practice and Problem Solving

● = **Step-by-Step Solutions** begin on page R3.
Extra Practice is on page EP5.

Examples 1–5
(pp. 91–92)

Add or subtract. Write in simplest form.

9. $\frac{4}{5} + \frac{3}{5}$

10. $\frac{5}{7} + \frac{6}{7}$

11. $\frac{3}{8} + \left(-\frac{7}{8}\right)$

12. $-\frac{1}{9} + \left(-\frac{5}{9}\right)$

13. $-\frac{5}{6} + \left(-\frac{5}{6}\right)$

14. $-\frac{15}{16} + \left(-\frac{7}{16}\right)$

15. $\frac{9}{10} - \frac{3}{10}$

16. $\frac{5}{8} - \frac{3}{8}$

17. $\frac{5}{14} - \left(-\frac{1}{14}\right)$

18. $-\frac{5}{9} - \frac{2}{9}$

19. $\frac{7}{12} - \frac{2}{12}$

20. $\frac{15}{18} - \frac{13}{18}$

Example 6
(p. 93)

21. **GRADES** In Mr. Navarro's first period class, $\frac{17}{28}$ of the students got an A on their math test. In his second period class, $\frac{11}{28}$ of the students got an A. What fraction more of the students got an A in Mr. Navarro's first period class than in his second period class? Write in simplest form.

22. **COOKING** A recipe for Michigan blueberry pancakes calls for $\frac{3}{4}$ cup flour, $\frac{1}{4}$ cup milk, and $\frac{1}{4}$ cup blueberries. How much more flour is needed than milk? Write in simplest form.

23. **INSTANT MESSENGER** The table shows the Instant Messenger abbreviations students at Hillside Middle School use the most.

a. What fraction of these students uses LOL or CUL8R when using Instant Messenger?

b. What fraction of these students uses L8R or BRB when using Instant Messenger?

Instant Messenger Abbreviations	
L8R (Later)	$\frac{48}{100}$
LOL (Laughing out loud)	$\frac{26}{100}$
BRB (Be right back)	$\frac{19}{100}$
CUL8R (See you later)	$\frac{7}{100}$

Use the order of operations to add or subtract. Write in simplest form.

24. $\frac{4}{5} + \frac{1}{5} + \frac{3}{5}$

25. $\frac{7}{8} + \left(-\frac{5}{8}\right) - \frac{1}{8}$

26. $\frac{13}{14} - \frac{5}{14} + \frac{6}{14}$

27. $\frac{2}{3} + \frac{2}{3} + \frac{2}{3}$

28. $\frac{4}{15} + \left(-\frac{9}{15}\right) + \frac{1}{15}$

29. $\frac{5}{7} - \frac{3}{7} + \frac{6}{7}$

30. **VOLCANOES** The graph shows the location of volcanic eruptions. What fraction represents the volcanic eruptions for both North and South America? How much larger is the section for Asia and South Pacific than for Europe? Write in simplest form.

31. **MEASUREMENT** How much longer than $\frac{5}{16}$ inch is $\frac{13}{16}$ inch?

32. **MEASUREMENT** What is the total of $1\frac{3}{4}$ cups and $\frac{3}{4}$ cup?

Worldwide Volcano Eruptions, 2006

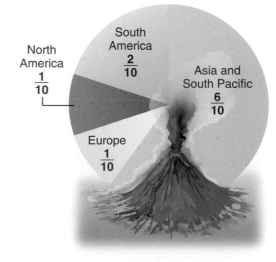

North America $\frac{1}{10}$

South America $\frac{2}{10}$

Asia and South Pacific $\frac{6}{10}$

Europe $\frac{1}{10}$

33. **OPEN ENDED** Select two like fractions with a difference of $\frac{1}{3}$ and with denominators that are *not* 3. Justify your selection.

34. **CHALLENGE** Simplify the following expression.

$$\frac{14}{15} + \frac{13}{15} - \frac{12}{15} + \frac{11}{15} - \frac{10}{15} + \cdots - \frac{4}{15} + \frac{3}{15} - \frac{2}{15} + \frac{1}{15}$$

35. **Write MATH** Write a simple rule for adding and subtracting like fractions.

NGSSS Practice   MA.7.A.3.2

36. A group of friends bought two large pizzas and ate only part of each pizza. The pictures show how much of the pizzas were left.

First Pizza   Second Pizza

How many pizzas did they eat?

A. $\frac{3}{8}$ B. $\frac{5}{8}$ C. $1\frac{1}{4}$ D. $1\frac{3}{8}$

37. At a school carnival, homemade pies were cut into 8 equal-sized pieces. Eric sold 13 pieces, Elena sold 7 pieces, and Tanya sold 10 pieces. Which expression can be used to find the total number of pies sold by Eric, Elena, and Tanya?

F. $13 + 7 + 10$

G. $8(13 + 7 + 10)$

H. $\frac{13}{8} \times \frac{7}{8} \times \frac{10}{8}$

I. $\frac{13}{8} + \frac{7}{8} + \frac{10}{8}$

Replace each ⬤ with <, >, or = to make a true sentence. (Lesson 2-1C)

38. $2\frac{7}{8}$ ⬤ 2.75

39. $\frac{-1}{3}$ ⬤ $\frac{-7}{3}$

40. $\frac{5}{7}$ ⬤ $\frac{4}{5}$

41. $3\frac{6}{11}$ ⬤ $3\frac{9}{14}$

Write each decimal as a fraction. (Lesson 2-1B)

42. 0.56

43. 0.375

44. 0.07

45. 0.019

ALGEBRA Find each sum or difference if $a = -3$ and $b = 2$. (Lessons 1-2B and 1-2D)

46. $a + b$

47. $a - b$

48. $b - a$

49. **WEATHER** Kody is recording the change in the outside air temperature for a science project. At 8:00 A.M., the high temperature was 42°F. Write an integer that describes the final change in temperature. (Lesson 1-2B)

Time	Change in Temperature
Noon	−11°F
3:00 P.M.	−12°F
6:00 P.M.	−5°F

50. **AIR CONDITIONING** Jacob turned on the air conditioning and the temperature decreased 8 degrees. Write an integer to represent the change in temperature. (Lesson 1-1B)

Explore Unlike Fractions With Models

Main Idea

Use models to add and subtract fractions with unlike denominators.

NGSSS

MA.7.A.3.2 Add, subtract, multiply, and divide integers, **fractions**, and terminating decimals, and perform exponential operations with rational bases and whole number exponents **including solving problems in everyday contexts.**

Get Connected
glencoe.com

TELEVISION Half of Brandon's class likes reality TV best, and $\frac{1}{5}$ of the class likes sports TV best. What fraction of the class likes either reality or sports TV?

ACTIVITY

1 What do you need to find? what fraction of the class likes reality or sports television

STEP 1 Model each fraction with fraction tiles.

$\frac{1}{2}$ | **½** |

$\frac{1}{5}$ | **⅕** |

STEP 2 To add, line up the end of the shaded part of the first tile with the beginning of the second tile.

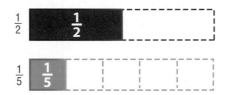

STEP 3 Test different fraction tiles below the model, lining up each with the beginning of the first tile. Do the marks line up? If not, try another tile.

Once the correct tile is found, shade the sections between the beginning of the tile to the point where they line up.

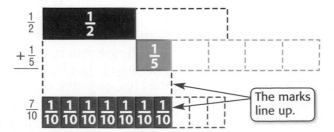

The marks line up.

$\frac{1}{2} + \frac{1}{5} = \frac{7}{10}$

So, $\frac{7}{10}$ of the class prefer reality or sports TV.

2 Use fraction strips to find $\frac{7}{8} - \frac{3}{4}$.

STEP 1 Model each fraction.

STEP 2 To subtract, line up the ends of the shaded parts of each strip.

STEP 3 Test different fraction strips below the model, checking to see if the marks line up. Then shade the sections between the beginning of the strip and the point where they line up.

The marks line up.

So, $\frac{7}{8} - \frac{3}{4} = \frac{1}{8}$.

Practice and Apply

Use fraction strips to add or subtract.

1. $\frac{1}{10} + \frac{2}{5}$
2. $\frac{1}{6} + \frac{1}{2}$
3. $\frac{1}{2} + \frac{3}{4}$
4. $\frac{3}{8} - \frac{1}{4}$
5. $\frac{8}{9} - \frac{1}{3}$
6. $\frac{2}{3} - \frac{1}{4}$

Analyze the Results

Use the models from Activities 1 and 2 to complete the following.

7. $\frac{1}{2} + \frac{1}{5} = \frac{\blacksquare}{10} + \frac{\blacksquare}{10}$
8. $\frac{7}{8} - \frac{3}{4} = \frac{\blacksquare}{8} - \frac{\blacksquare}{8}$

9. **MAKE A CONJECTURE** What is the relationship between the number of separations on the answer fraction strip and the denominators of the fractions added or subtracted?

10. **Write MATH** Two thirds of the baseball team at Park Street Middle School lives within walking distance of the practice field. Another $\frac{1}{6}$ of the team lives close enough to ride their bike. What fraction of the team lives close enough to the practice field to walk or ride their bike there? Explain your reasoning.

Main Idea

Add and subtract fractions with unlike denominators.

NGSSS

MA.7.A.3.2 Add, subtract, multiply, and divide integers, **fractions**, and terminating decimals, and perform exponential operations with rational bases and whole number exponents **including solving problems in everyday contexts.**

New Vocabulary

unlike fractions

Get Connected
glencoe.com

Add and Subtract Unlike Fractions

MEASUREMENT The table shows the fractions of one hour for different minutes.

1. Write each fraction in simplest form.

2. What fraction of one hour is equal to the sum of 15 minutes and 20 minutes? Write in simplest form.

3. Explain why $\frac{1}{6}$ hour $+ \frac{1}{3}$ hour $= \frac{1}{2}$ hour.

4. Explain why $\frac{1}{12}$ hour $+ \frac{1}{2}$ hour $= \frac{7}{12}$ hour.

Number of Minutes	Fraction of One Hour
1	$\frac{1}{60}$
5	$\frac{5}{60}$
10	$\frac{10}{60}$
15	$\frac{15}{60}$
20	$\frac{20}{60}$
30	$\frac{30}{60}$

Before you can add two **unlike fractions**, or fractions with different denominators, one or both of the fractions must be renamed so that they have a common denominator.

Key Concept · Add or Subtract Unlike Fractions

To add or subtract fractions with different denominators,

- Rename the fractions using the least common denominator (LCD).
- Add or subtract as with like fractions.
- If necessary, simplify the sum or difference.

EXAMPLE   Add Unlike Fractions

1. Find $\frac{1}{2} + \frac{1}{4}$.

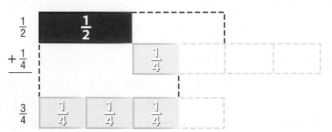

Method 1   Use a model.

Method 2 Use the LCD.

The least common denominator of $\frac{1}{2}$ and $\frac{1}{4}$ is 4.

$$\frac{1}{2} + \frac{1}{4} = \frac{1 \times 2}{2 \times 2} + \frac{1 \times 1}{4 \times 1} \quad \text{Rename using the LCD, 4.}$$

$$= \frac{2}{4} + \frac{1}{4} \quad \text{Add the fractions.}$$

$$= \frac{3}{4} \quad \text{Simplify.}$$

Using either method, $\frac{1}{2} + \frac{1}{4} = \frac{3}{4}$.

 CHOOSE Your Method

Add. Write in simplest form.

a. $\frac{1}{6} + \frac{2}{3}$ **b.** $\frac{9}{10} + \left(-\frac{1}{2}\right)$ **c.** $\frac{1}{4} + \frac{3}{8}$

EXAMPLE **Subtract Unlike Fractions**

2 Find $\frac{2}{3} - \frac{1}{2}$.

Method 1 Use a model.

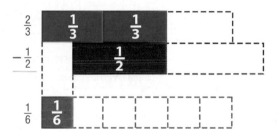

Method 2 Use the LCD.

The least common denominator of $\frac{2}{3}$ and $\frac{1}{2}$ is 6.

$$\frac{2}{3} - \frac{1}{2} = \frac{2 \times 2}{3 \times 2} - \frac{1 \times 3}{2 \times 3} \quad \text{Rename using the LCD, 6.}$$

$$= \frac{4}{6} - \frac{3}{6} \quad \text{Subtract the fractions.}$$

$$= \frac{1}{6} \quad \text{Simplify.}$$

Study Tip

Check for Reasonableness
Estimate the difference in Example 2.

$\frac{2}{3} - \frac{1}{2} \approx \frac{1}{2} - \frac{1}{2}$ or 0.

Compare $\frac{1}{6}$ to the estimate.

$\frac{1}{6} \approx 0$. So, the answer is reasonable.

Check by adding $\frac{1}{6} + \frac{1}{2} = \frac{1}{6} + \frac{3}{6} = \frac{4}{6}$ or $\frac{2}{3}$ ✓

Using either method, $\frac{2}{3} - \frac{1}{2} = \frac{1}{6}$.

 CHOOSE Your Method

Subtract. Write in simplest form.

d. $\frac{5}{8} - \frac{1}{4}$ **e.** $\frac{3}{4} - \frac{1}{3}$ **f.** $\frac{1}{2} - \left(-\frac{2}{5}\right)$

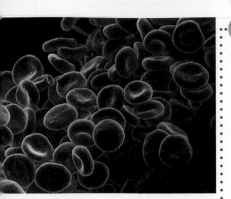

 Real-World EXAMPLE

3 HEALTH Use the table to find the fraction of the population that has type A or type B blood.

Find $\frac{21}{50} + \frac{1}{10}$.

Blood Type Frequencies				
ABO Type	O	A	B	AB
Fraction	$\frac{11}{25}$	$\frac{21}{50}$	$\frac{1}{10}$	$\frac{1}{25}$

The least common denominator of $\frac{21}{50}$ and $\frac{1}{10}$ is 50.

$$\frac{21}{50} + \frac{1}{10} = \frac{21 \times 1}{50 \times 1} + \frac{1 \times 5}{10 \times 5}$$ Rename using the LCD, 50.

$$= \frac{21}{50} + \frac{5}{50}$$ Add the fractions.

$$= \frac{26}{50} \text{ or } \frac{13}{25}$$ Simplify.

So, $\frac{13}{25}$ of the population has type A or type B blood.

Real-World Link · · · · ·
Two to three drops of blood contain about one billion red blood cells.

CHECK Your Progress

g. SURVEY The graphic shows the results of an online survey of over 36,000 youth. How much greater was the part of youth that said their favorite way to be "artsy" was by drawing than by acting? Write in simplest form.

What is your favorite way to be artsy?

Drawing $\frac{8}{25}$

Acting $\frac{7}{50}$

Making music $\frac{7}{50}$

Taking pictures $\frac{11}{100}$

Writing $\frac{3}{50}$

CHECK Your Understanding

Examples 1 and 2
(pp. 98–99)

Add or subtract. Write in simplest form.

1. $\frac{4}{9} + \frac{1}{3}$
2. $-\frac{5}{6} + \left(-\frac{4}{9}\right)$
3. $\frac{3}{8} - \left(-\frac{1}{4}\right)$
4. $\frac{4}{5} - \frac{3}{10}$

5 $\frac{1}{6} + \frac{3}{8}$
6. $\frac{2}{3} + \frac{5}{6}$
7. $\frac{7}{12} - \frac{5}{6}$
8. $\frac{3}{4} - \frac{1}{3}$

Example 3
(p. 100)

Choose an operation to solve each problem. Explain your reasoning. Then solve the problem. Write in simplest form.

9. **MEASUREMENT** Cassandra cuts $\frac{5}{16}$ inch off the top of a photo and $\frac{3}{8}$ inch off the bottom. How much shorter is the total height of the photo now?

10. **CHORES** A bucket was $\frac{7}{8}$ full with soapy water. After washing the car, the bucket was only $\frac{1}{4}$ full. What part of the water was used?

Practice and Problem Solving

= **Step-by-Step Solutions** begin on page R3.
Extra Practice is on page EP5.

Examples 1 and 2
(pp. 98–99)

Add or subtract. Write in simplest form.

11. $\frac{3}{5} + \frac{1}{10}$

12. $\frac{5}{8} + \frac{1}{4}$

13. $\frac{5}{6} - \left(-\frac{2}{3}\right)$

14. $\left(-\frac{7}{10}\right) - \frac{2}{5}$

15. $\frac{1}{15} + \left(-\frac{3}{5}\right)$

16. $\frac{7}{12} + \frac{7}{10}$

17. $\frac{5}{8} + \frac{11}{12}$

18. $\frac{7}{9} + \frac{5}{6}$

19. $\frac{7}{9} - \frac{1}{3}$

20. $\frac{4}{5} - \frac{1}{6}$

21. $-\frac{4}{9} - \frac{2}{15}$

22. $\frac{3}{10} - \left(-\frac{1}{4}\right)$

Example 3
(p. 100)

Choose an operation to solve each problem. Explain your reasoning. Then solve the problem. Write in simplest form.

23. **MEASUREMENT** Ebony is building a shelf to hold the two boxes shown. What is the least width she should make the shelf?

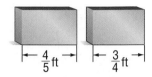
$\leftarrow \frac{4}{5}$ ft $\rightarrow$ $\leftarrow \frac{3}{4}$ ft $\rightarrow$

24. **MEASUREMENT** Mrs. Escalante was riding a bicycle on a bike path. After riding $\frac{2}{3}$ of a mile, she discovered that she still needed to travel $\frac{3}{4}$ of a mile to reach the end of the path. How long is the bike path?

25. **MEASUREMENT** Makayla bought $\frac{1}{4}$ pound of ham and $\frac{5}{8}$ pound of turkey. How much more turkey did she buy?

26. **ANIMALS** The three-toed sloth can travel $\frac{3}{20}$ mile per hour while a giant tortoise can travel $\frac{17}{100}$ mile per hour. How much faster, in miles per hour, is the giant tortoise?

Simplify.

27. $\frac{1}{7} + \frac{1}{2} + \frac{5}{28}$

28. $\frac{1}{4} + \frac{5}{6} + \frac{7}{12}$

29. $\frac{1}{6} + \left(\frac{2}{3} - \frac{1}{4}\right)$

30. $\frac{5}{6} - \left(\frac{1}{2} + \frac{1}{3}\right)$

31. $1 + \frac{1}{4}$

32. $1 - \frac{5}{8}$

33. $2 + \frac{2}{3}$

34. $3 - \frac{1}{6}$

35. **MONEY** Chellise saves $\frac{1}{5}$ of her allowance and spends $\frac{2}{3}$ of her allowance at the mall. What fraction of her allowance remains?

36. **ANALYZE TABLES** Pepita and Francisco each spend an equal amount of time on homework. The table shows the fraction of time they spend on each subject. Determine the missing fraction for each student.

Homework	Fraction of Time	
	Pepita	Francisco
Math	■	$\frac{1}{2}$
English	$\frac{2}{3}$	■
Science	$\frac{1}{6}$	$\frac{3}{8}$

ALGEBRA Evaluate each expression in simplest form if $a = \frac{3}{4}$ and $b = \frac{5}{6}$.

37. $\frac{1}{2} + a$

38. $b - \frac{7}{10}$

39. $b - a$

40. $a + b$

41 **BOOK REPORTS** Four students were scheduled to give book reports in a 1-hour class period. After the first report, $\frac{2}{3}$ hour remained. If the next two students' reports took $\frac{1}{6}$ hour and $\frac{1}{4}$ hour, respectively, what fraction of the hour remained for the final student's report? Justify your answer.

42. **CELL PHONES** One hundred sixty cell phone owners were surveyed. What fraction of owners prefers using their cell phone for text messaging or taking pictures?

How Do You Use a Cell Phone?

43. **MEASUREMENT** LaTasha and Colin are jogging on a track. LaTasha jogs $\frac{1}{4}$ of a mile and then stops. Colin jogs $\frac{5}{8}$ of a mile, stops, and then turns around and jogs $\frac{1}{2}$ of a mile. Who is farther ahead on the track? How much farther? Explain.

H.O.T. Problems

44. **CHALLENGE** Fractions whose numerators are 1, such as $\frac{1}{2}$ or $\frac{1}{3}$, are called *unit fractions*. Describe a method you can use to add two unit fractions mentally. Explain your reasoning and use your method to find $\frac{1}{99} + \frac{1}{100}$.

45. **OPEN ENDED** Provide a counterexample to the following statement.

The sum of three fractions with odd numerators is never $\frac{1}{2}$.

46. **FIND THE ERROR** Theresa is finding $\frac{1}{4} + \frac{3}{5}$. Find her mistake and correct it.

$$\frac{1}{4} + \frac{3}{5} = \frac{1+3}{4+5}$$

47. **Write MATH** To make a cake, Felicia needs 1 cup of flour, but she only has a $\frac{2}{3}$-cup measure and a $\frac{3}{4}$-cup measure. Which method will bring her closest to having the amount of flour she needs? Explain.

   a. Fill the $\frac{2}{3}$-cup measure twice.   **c.** Fill the $\frac{2}{3}$-cup measure once.

   b. Fill the $\frac{3}{4}$-cup measure twice.   **d.** Fill the $\frac{3}{4}$-cup measure once.

48. The table gives the number of hours Orlando spent at football practice for one week.

Day	Time (h)
Monday	$\frac{1}{2}$
Tuesday	2
Wednesday	$\frac{1}{3}$
Thursday	$\frac{5}{6}$
Friday	$\frac{1}{2}$
Saturday	$\frac{3}{4}$

How many more hours did he practice on Thursday than on Saturday?

A. $\frac{2}{3}$ h

B. $\frac{1}{3}$ h

C. $\frac{1}{4}$ h

D. $\frac{1}{12}$ h

49. Which of the following is the prime factored form of the lowest common denominator of $\frac{7}{12} + \frac{11}{18}$?

F. 2×3

G. 2×3^2

H. $2^2 \times 3^2$

I. $2^3 \times 3$

50. Brett has $\frac{5}{6}$ of his weekly allowance left to spend. He has budgeted $\frac{1}{8}$ of his allowance to save for a new video game. How much of his weekly allowance will he have left after putting the savings away?

A. $\frac{4}{7}$

B. $\frac{3}{8}$

C. $\frac{7}{12}$

D. $\frac{17}{24}$

Add or subtract. Write in simplest form. (Lesson 2-2A)

51. $\frac{7}{10} + \frac{1}{10}$ **52.** $\frac{3}{8} - \frac{1}{8}$ **53.** $\frac{5}{18} + \frac{7}{18}$ **54.** $\frac{11}{20} - \frac{3}{20}$

55. FOOTBALL The Iowa Hawkeyes recorded the yardage shown in the table over 6 plays. Order the yardages from least to greatest. (Lesson 2-1C)

Play	1	2	3	4	5	6
Yardage	9	−2	5	0	12	−7

ALGEBRA Find each sum if $a = 7$ and $b = -5$. (Lessons 1-2B, 1-3C)

56. $a + b$ **57.** $a - b$ **58.** $b - a$

59. $a \cdot b$ **60.** $a \cdot a$ **61.** $b \cdot b$

62. $|ab|$ **63.** $|a| + b$ **64.** $a + |b|$

65. Tia looked at the outside temperature before she went to bed and saw that it was 0°F. When she got up the next morning, it had dropped 4°. Write an integer to represent the change in temperature. (Lesson 1-1B)

Main Idea

Add and subtract mixed numbers.

NGSSS

 MA.7.A.3.2 Add, subtract, multiply, and divide integers, **fractions**, and terminating decimals, and perform exponential operations with rational bases and whole number exponents **including solving problems in everyday contexts.**

Get Connected
glencoe.com

Add and Subtract Mixed Numbers

BABIES The birth weights of several babies in the hospital nursery are shown.

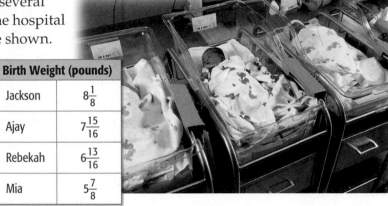

Birth Weight (pounds)	
Jackson	$8\frac{1}{8}$
Ajay	$7\frac{15}{16}$
Rebekah	$6\frac{13}{16}$
Mia	$5\frac{7}{8}$

1. Write an expression to find how much more Ajay weighs than Mia.

2. Rename the fractions using the LCD.

3. Find the difference of the fractional parts of the mixed numbers.

4. Find the difference of the whole numbers.

5. **MAKE A CONJECTURE** Explain how to find $7\frac{15}{16} - 5\frac{7}{8}$. Then use your conjecture to find the difference.

To add or subtract mixed numbers, first add or subtract the fractions. If necessary, rename them using the LCD. Then add or subtract the whole numbers and simplify if necessary.

EXAMPLES Add and Subtract Mixed Numbers

① Find $7\frac{4}{9} + 10\frac{2}{9}$. Write in simplest form.

Estimate $7 + 10 = 17$

$$\begin{array}{r} 7\frac{4}{9} \\ + 10\frac{2}{9} \\ \hline 17\frac{6}{9} \text{ or } 17\frac{2}{3} \end{array}$$ Add the whole numbers and fractions separately.

Simplify.

Check for Reasonableness $17\frac{2}{3} \approx 17$ ✓

CHECK Your Progress

a. $6\frac{1}{8} + 2\frac{5}{8}$ **b.** $5\frac{1}{5} + 2\frac{3}{10}$ **c.** $1\frac{5}{9} + 4\frac{1}{6}$

2 Find $8\frac{5}{6} - 2\frac{1}{3}$. Write in simplest form.

Estimate $9 - 2 = 7$

$$8\frac{5}{6} \rightarrow 8\frac{5}{6}$$

$$-2\frac{1}{3} \rightarrow -2\frac{2}{6} \qquad \text{Rename the fraction using the LCD. Then subtract.}$$

$$\overline{\qquad\qquad \quad 6\frac{3}{6} \text{ or } 6\frac{1}{2}} \quad \text{Simplify.}$$

Check for Reasonableness $6\frac{1}{2} \approx 7$ ✓

 CHECK Your Progress

Subtract. Write in simplest form.

d. $5\frac{4}{5} - 1\frac{3}{10}$ **e.** $13\frac{7}{8} - 9\frac{3}{4}$ **f.** $8\frac{2}{3} - 2\frac{1}{2}$

g. $7\frac{3}{4} - 4\frac{1}{3}$ **h.** $11\frac{5}{6} - 3\frac{1}{8}$ **i.** $9\frac{4}{7} - 5\frac{1}{2}$

Study Tip

Fractions Greater Than One An improper fraction has a numerator that is greater than or equal to the denominator. Examples of improper fractions are $\frac{5}{4}$ and $2\frac{6}{5}$.

Sometimes when you subtract mixed numbers, the fraction in the first mixed number is less than the fraction in the second mixed number. In this case, rename the first fraction as a fraction greater than or equal to one in order to subtract.

EXAMPLES **Rename Mixed Numbers to Subtract**

3 Find $2\frac{1}{3} - 1\frac{2}{3}$.

Estimate $2 - 1\frac{1}{2} = \frac{1}{2}$

Since $\frac{1}{3}$ is less than $\frac{2}{3}$, rename $2\frac{1}{3}$ before subtracting.

$$2\frac{1}{3} \qquad = \qquad 1\frac{3}{3} + \frac{1}{3} \text{ or } 1\frac{4}{3}$$

Change 1 to $\frac{3}{3}$.

$$2\frac{1}{3} \rightarrow 1\frac{4}{3} \quad \text{Rename } 2\frac{1}{3} \text{ as } 1\frac{4}{3}.$$

$$-1\frac{2}{3} \rightarrow -1\frac{2}{3} \quad \text{Subtract the whole numbers and then the fractions.}$$

$$\overline{\qquad\qquad \quad \frac{2}{3}}$$

Check for Reasonableness $\frac{2}{3} \approx \frac{1}{2}$ ✓

Find $8 - 3\frac{3}{4}$.   **Estimate** $8 - 4 = 4$

Using the denominator of the fraction in the subtrahend, $8 = 8\frac{0}{4}$.

Since $\frac{0}{4}$ is less than $\frac{3}{4}$, rename 8 before subtracting.

$$8 \longrightarrow 7\frac{4}{4} \qquad \text{Rename 8 as } 7 + \frac{4}{4} \text{ or } 7\frac{4}{4}.$$

$$\frac{-3\frac{3}{4}}{} \longrightarrow \frac{-3\frac{3}{4}}{4\frac{1}{4}} \qquad \begin{array}{l} \text{Subtract.} \\[1em] \text{Check for Reasonableness } 4\frac{1}{4} \approx 4 \ \checkmark \end{array}$$

CHECK Your Progress

j. $11\frac{2}{5} - 2\frac{3}{5}$ **k.** $5\frac{3}{8} - 4\frac{11}{12}$ **l.** $7 - 1\frac{1}{2}$

Real-World EXAMPLE

 MEASUREMENT An urban planner is designing a skateboard park. What will be the length of the park and the parking lot combined?

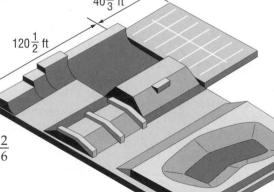

$40\frac{1}{3}$ ft

$120\frac{1}{2}$ ft

$$120\frac{1}{2} + 40\frac{1}{3} = 120\frac{3}{6} + 40\frac{2}{6}$$

$$= 160 + \frac{5}{6}$$

$$= 160\frac{5}{6}$$

The total length is $160\frac{5}{6}$ feet.

CHECK Your Progress

m. MEASUREMENT Jermaine walked $1\frac{5}{8}$ miles on Saturday and $2\frac{1}{2}$ miles on Sunday. How many more miles did he walk on Sunday?

 CHECK Your Understanding

Examples 1–4
(pp. 104–106)

Add or subtract. Write in simplest form.

1. $1\frac{5}{7} + 8\frac{1}{7}$ **2.** $8\frac{1}{2} + 3\frac{4}{5}$ **3.** $7\frac{5}{6} - 3\frac{1}{6}$ **4.** $9\frac{4}{5} - 2\frac{3}{4}$

5 $3\frac{1}{4} - 1\frac{3}{4}$ **6.** $5\frac{2}{3} - 2\frac{3}{5}$ **7.** $11 - 6\frac{3}{8}$ **8.** $16 - 5\frac{5}{6}$

Example 5
(p. 106)

9. CARS A hybrid car's gas tank can hold $11\frac{9}{10}$ gallons of gasoline. It contains $8\frac{3}{4}$ gallons of gasoline. How much more gasoline is needed to fill the tank?

Practice and Problem Solving

 = **Step-by-Step Solutions** begin on page R4.
Extra Practice is on page EP5.

Examples 1–4
(pp. 104–106)

Add or subtract. Write in simplest form.

10. $2\frac{1}{9} + 7\frac{4}{9}$ **11.** $3\frac{2}{7} + 4\frac{3}{7}$ **12.** $10\frac{4}{5} - 2\frac{1}{5}$ **13.** $8\frac{6}{7} - 6\frac{5}{7}$

14. $9\frac{4}{5} - 2\frac{3}{10}$ **15.** $11\frac{3}{4} - 4\frac{1}{3}$ **16.** $8\frac{5}{12} + 11\frac{1}{4}$ **17.** $8\frac{3}{8} + 10\frac{1}{3}$

18. $9\frac{1}{5} - 2\frac{3}{5}$ **19.** $6\frac{1}{4} - 2\frac{3}{4}$ **20.** $6\frac{3}{5} - 1\frac{2}{3}$ **21.** $4\frac{3}{10} - 1\frac{3}{4}$

22. $14\frac{1}{6} - 7\frac{1}{3}$ **23.** $12\frac{1}{2} - 6\frac{5}{8}$ **24.** $8 - 3\frac{2}{3}$ **25.** $13 - 5\frac{5}{6}$

Example 5
(p. 106)

Choose an operation to solve each problem. Explain your reasoning. Then solve the problem. Write your answer in simplest form.

26. HIKING If Sara and Maggie hiked both of the trails listed in the table, how far did they hike altogether?

Trail	Length (mi)
Woodland Park	$3\frac{2}{3}$
Mill Creek Way	$2\frac{5}{6}$

27. JEWELRY Margarite made the jewelry shown. If the necklace is $10\frac{5}{8}$ inches longer than the bracelet, how long is the necklace that Margarite made?

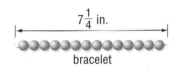

28. GARDENS The length of Kasey's garden is $4\frac{5}{8}$ feet. Find the width of Kasey's garden if it is $2\frac{7}{8}$ feet shorter than the length.

29. HAIRSTYLES Before Alameda got her haircut, the length of her hair was $9\frac{3}{4}$ inches. After her haircut, the length was $6\frac{1}{2}$ inches. How many inches did she have cut?

Add or subtract. Write in simplest form.

30. $10 - 3\frac{5}{11}$ **31.** $24 - 8\frac{3}{4}$ **32.** $6\frac{1}{6} + 1\frac{2}{3} + 5\frac{5}{9}$ **33.** $3\frac{1}{4} + 2\frac{5}{6} - 4\frac{1}{3}$

34. TIME Karen wakes up at 6:00 A.M. It takes her $1\frac{1}{4}$ hours to shower, get dressed, and comb her hair. It takes her $\frac{1}{2}$ hour to eat breakfast, brush her teeth, and make her bed. At what time will she be ready for school?

MEASUREMENT Find the perimeter of each figure. Write in simplest form.

35

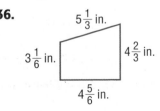

$2\frac{3}{8}$ yd $2\frac{3}{8}$ yd

$2\frac{3}{8}$ yd

36.

$5\frac{1}{3}$ in.

$3\frac{1}{6}$ in. $4\frac{2}{3}$ in.

$4\frac{5}{6}$ in.

37. **OPEN ENDED** A board with length $3\frac{7}{8}$ feet needs to be cut from a $5\frac{1}{2}$-foot existing board. Write and solve a subtraction problem to find the amount of wood that would be left after the cut is made.

38. **CHALLENGE** A string is cut in half. One of the halves is thrown away. One fifth of the remaining half is cut away and the piece left is 8 feet long. How long was the string initially? Justify your answer.

39. **Write MATH** The fence of a rectangular garden is constructed from 12 feet of fencing wire. Suppose that one side of the garden is $2\frac{5}{12}$ feet long. Explain how to find the length of the other side.

NGSSS Practice   MA.7.A.3.2

40. The distance from home plate to the pitcher's mound is 60 feet 6 inches and from home plate to second base is 127 feet $3\frac{3}{8}$ inches. Find the distance from the pitcher's mound to second base.

   A. 68 ft $3\frac{1}{4}$ in.

   B. 67 ft $8\frac{3}{4}$ in.

   C. 67 ft $2\frac{5}{8}$ in.

   D. 66 ft $9\frac{3}{8}$ in.

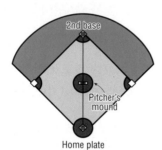

41. A recipe for party mix calls for $4\frac{3}{4}$ cups of cereal. The amount of peanuts needed is $1\frac{2}{3}$ cups less than the amount of cereal needed. How many cups of peanuts and cereal are needed?

   F. $3\frac{1}{12}$ cups

   G. $6\frac{1}{2}$ cups

   H. $7\frac{5}{6}$ cups

   I. $8\frac{1}{2}$ cups

Spiral Review

42. **SCHOOL** Kai did $\frac{1}{5}$ of her homework in class and $\frac{1}{3}$ more on the bus. What fraction of homework does she still need to do? (Lesson 2-2C)

Add or subtract. Write in simplest form. (Lesson 2-2A)

43. $\frac{7}{10} + \frac{2}{10}$

44. $\frac{5}{8} - \frac{3}{8}$

45. $\frac{7}{18} + \frac{11}{18}$

46. $\frac{13}{20} - \frac{3}{20}$

47. In which quadrant does the ordered pair $(5, -6)$ lie? (Lesson 1-1C)

48. **EARTH SCIENCE** The highest and lowest points in California are shown in the table. What is the difference in elevations? (Lesson 1-2D)

Location	Elevation
Mount Whitney	14,494 ft above sea level
Death Valley	282 ft below sea level

Write each fraction or mixed number as a decimal. Use bar notation if the decimal is a repeating decimal. (Lesson 2-1B)

1. $\dfrac{7}{8}$ **2.** $-\dfrac{2}{9}$ **3.** $3\dfrac{13}{20}$

Write each decimal as a fraction in simplest form. (Lesson 2-1B)

4. 0.6   **5.** 0.48   **6.** −7.02

7. ANIMALS The maximum height of an Asian elephant is 9.8 feet. What mixed number represents this height? (Lesson 2-1B)

Replace each ● with <, >, or = to make a true sentence. (Lesson 2-1C)

8. $-\dfrac{3}{5}$ ● $-\dfrac{5}{9}$ **9.** $4\dfrac{7}{12}$ ● $4\dfrac{6}{8}$ **10.** $\dfrac{13}{20}$ ● 0.65

11. WATER The table at the right shows the fraction of each state that is water. Order the states from least to greatest fraction of water. (Lesson 2-1C)

What Part is Water?	
State	**Fraction**
Alaska	$\dfrac{3}{41}$
Michigan	$\dfrac{40}{97}$
Wisconsin	$\dfrac{1}{6}$

Add or subtract. Write in simplest form.
(Lesson 2-2A)

12. $-\dfrac{11}{15} - \dfrac{1}{15}$ **13.** $\dfrac{4}{14} - \dfrac{3}{14}$

14. $-\dfrac{1}{9} + \dfrac{2}{9}$ **15.** $\dfrac{5}{8} + \dfrac{3}{8}$

16. SCIENCE $\dfrac{39}{50}$ of Earth's atmosphere is made up of nitrogen while only $\dfrac{21}{100}$ is made up of oxygen. What fraction of Earth's atmosphere is either nitrogen or oxygen? (Lesson 2-2C)

Add or subtract. Write in simplest form.
(Lesson 2-2D)

17. $8\dfrac{3}{4} - 2\dfrac{5}{12}$ **18.** $5\dfrac{1}{6} - 1\dfrac{1}{3}$

19. $2\dfrac{5}{9} + 1\dfrac{2}{3}$ **20.** $2\dfrac{3}{5} + 6\dfrac{13}{15}$

21. NGSSS PRACTICE The table shows the weight of a newborn infant for its first year. (Lesson 2-2D)

Month	Weight (lb)
0	$7\dfrac{1}{4}$
3	$12\dfrac{1}{2}$
6	$16\dfrac{5}{8}$
9	$19\dfrac{4}{5}$
12	$23\dfrac{3}{20}$

During which three-month period was the infant's weight gain the greatest?

A. 0–3 months   **C.** 6–9 months

B. 3–6 months   **D.** 9–12 months

22. MEASUREMENT How much does a $50\dfrac{1}{4}$-pound suitcase weigh after $3\dfrac{7}{8}$ pounds are removed in simplest form? (Lesson 2-2D)

23. NGSSS PRACTICE The table gives the average annual snowfall for several U.S. cities. (Lesson 2-2D)

City	Average Snowfall (in.)
Anchorage, AK	$70\dfrac{4}{5}$
Mount Washington, NH	$259\dfrac{9}{10}$
Buffalo, NY	$93\dfrac{3}{5}$
Birmingham, AL	$1\dfrac{1}{2}$

On average, how many more inches of snow does Mount Washington, New Hampshire, receive than Anchorage, Alaska?

F. $330\dfrac{7}{10}$ in.   **H.** $166\dfrac{3}{10}$ in.

G. $189\dfrac{1}{10}$ in.   **I.** $92\dfrac{1}{10}$ in.

Explore Multiply Fractions with Models

Main Idea

Use area models to multiply fractions and mixed numbers.

NGSSS

 MA.7.A.3.2 Add, subtract, **multiply**, and divide integers, **fractions**, and terminating decimals, and perform exponential operations with rational bases and whole number exponents including solving problems in everyday contexts.

Get Connected
glencoe.com

Just as the product 3×4 is the number of square units in a rectangle, the product of two fractions can be shown using area models.

ACTIVITY

① Find $\frac{3}{4} \times \frac{2}{3}$ using a geoboard.

The first factor is 3 *fourths* and the second factor is 2 *thirds*.

STEP 1 Use one geoband to show fourths and another to show thirds on the geoboard.

STEP 2 Use geobands to form a rectangle. Place one geoband on the peg to show 3 fourths and another on the peg to show 2 thirds.

STEP 3 Connect the geobands to show a small rectangle.

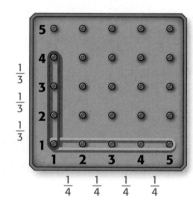 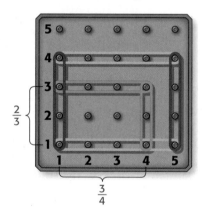

The area of the small rectangle is 6 square units. The area of the large rectangle is 12 square units. So, $\frac{3}{4} \times \frac{2}{3} = \frac{6}{12}$ or $\frac{1}{2}$.

ACTIVITY

② Find $2 \times \frac{1}{4}$ using an area model.

STEP 1 Draw two squares side by side. Shade a rectangle that is 2 units long and $\frac{1}{4}$ unit wide.

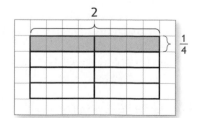

STEP 2 Rearrange the shaded parts into a unit square.

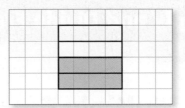

Since $\frac{2}{4}$ or $\frac{1}{2}$ of the unit square is shaded, $2 \times \frac{1}{4} = \frac{1}{2}$.

ACTIVITY

3 Find $1\frac{2}{3} \times \frac{1}{2}$ using a model.

STEP 1 Draw two squares side by side. Shade a rectangle that is $1\frac{2}{3}$ units long and $\frac{1}{2}$ unit wide.

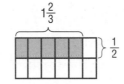

STEP 2 Rearrange the shaded parts into a unit square.

Since $\frac{5}{6}$ of the unit square is shaded, $1\frac{2}{3} \times \frac{1}{2} = \frac{5}{6}$.

Practice and Apply

Write a multiplication sentence for the product shown in each model.

1.

2.

Find each product using a geoboard or an area model.

3. $\frac{1}{4} \times \frac{1}{3}$ **4.** $\frac{1}{2} \times \frac{1}{2}$ **5.** $\frac{3}{4} \times \frac{1}{2}$ **6.** $\frac{2}{3} \times \frac{1}{4}$

7. $3 \times \frac{2}{3}$ **8.** $2 \times \frac{2}{5}$ **9.** $1\frac{1}{4} \times \frac{1}{5}$ **10.** $2\frac{1}{2} \times \frac{3}{4}$

Analyze the Results

11. MAKE A CONJECTURE Refer to Activities 1–3. How are the numerators and denominators of the factors related to each product?

12. Write MATH Write a rule you can use to multiply two fractions.

Main Idea

Multiply fractions and mixed numbers.

NGSSS

 MA.7.A.3.2 Add, subtract, **multiply**, and divide integers, **fractions**, and terminating decimals, and perform exponential operations with rational bases and whole number exponents **including solving problems in everyday contexts.**

Get Connected
glencoe.com

Multiply Fractions

LUNCH Two thirds of the students at the lunch table ordered a hamburger for lunch. One half of those students ordered cheese on their hamburgers.

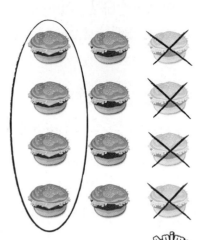

1. What fraction of the students at the lunch table ordered a cheeseburger?

2. How are the numerators and denominators of $\frac{2}{3}$ and $\frac{1}{2}$ related to the fraction in Exercise 1?

Key Concept — Multiply Fractions

Words To multiply fractions, multiply the numerators and multiply the denominators.

Examples

Numbers	**Algebra**
$\frac{1}{2} \times \frac{2}{3} = \frac{1 \times 2}{2 \times 3}$ or $\frac{2}{6}$	$\frac{a}{b} \cdot \frac{c}{d} = \frac{a \cdot c}{b \cdot d}$ or $\frac{ac}{bd}$, where $b, d \neq 0$

EXAMPLES — Multiply Fractions

Multiply. Write in simplest form.

① $\frac{1}{2} \times \frac{1}{3}$

$\frac{1}{2} \times \frac{1}{3} = \frac{1 \times 1}{2 \times 3}$ ← Multiply the numerators.
    ← Multiply the denominators.

$= \frac{1}{6}$ Simplify.

② $2 \times \left(-\frac{3}{4}\right)$

$2 \times \left(-\frac{3}{4}\right) = \frac{2}{1} \times \left(\frac{-3}{4}\right)$ Write 2 as $\frac{2}{1}$ and $-\frac{3}{4}$ as $\frac{-3}{4}$.

$= \frac{2 \times (-3)}{1 \times 4}$ ← Multiply the numerators.
    ← Multiply the denominators.

$= \frac{-6}{4}$ or $-1\frac{1}{2}$ Simplify.

CHECK Your Progress

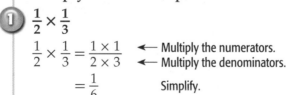

a. $\frac{3}{5} \times \frac{1}{2}$ b. $\frac{1}{3} \times \frac{3}{4}$ c. $\frac{2}{3} \times (-4)$

If the numerator and denominator of either fraction have common factors, you can simplify before multiplying.

QUICK Review

GCF
the greatest of the common factors of two or more numbers; *Example:* The GCF of 8 and 2 is 2.

EXAMPLE ## Simplify Before Multiplying

3 Find $\frac{2}{7} \times \frac{3}{8}$. Write in simplest form.

$$\frac{2}{7} \times \frac{3}{8} = \frac{\overset{1}{\cancel{2}}}{7} \times \frac{3}{\underset{4}{\cancel{8}}}$$ Divide 2 and 8 by their GCF, 2.

$$= \frac{1 \times 3}{7 \times 4} \text{ or } \frac{3}{28}$$ Multiply.

✓ **CHECK Your Progress**

Multiply. Write in simplest form.

d. $-\frac{1}{3} \times \left(-\frac{3}{7}\right)$ **e.** $\frac{4}{9} \times \frac{1}{8}$ **f.** $\frac{5}{6} \times \frac{3}{5}$

EXAMPLE ## Multiply Mixed Numbers

4 Find $\frac{1}{2} \times 4\frac{2}{5}$. Write in simplest form. **Estimate** $\frac{1}{2} \times 4 = 2$

Study Tip

Simplifying If you forget to simplify before multiplying, you can always simplify the final answer. However, it is usually easier to simplify before multiplying.

Method 1   Rename the mixed number.

$$\frac{1}{2} \times 4\frac{2}{5} = \frac{1}{\underset{1}{\cancel{2}}} \times \frac{\overset{11}{\cancel{22}}}{5}$$ Rename $4\frac{2}{5}$ as an improper fraction, $\frac{22}{5}$.
Divide 2 and 22 by their GCF, 2.

$$= \frac{1 \times 11}{1 \times 5}$$ Multiply.

$$= \frac{11}{5} \text{ or } 2\frac{1}{5}$$ Simplify.

Method 2   Use mental math.

The mixed number $4\frac{2}{5}$ is equal to $4 + \frac{2}{5}$.

So, $\frac{1}{2} \times 4\frac{2}{5} = \frac{1}{2}\left(4 + \frac{2}{5}\right)$. Use the Distributive Property to multiply, then add mentally.

$$\frac{1}{2}\left(4 + \frac{2}{5}\right) = 2 + \frac{1}{5}$$ **Think** Half of 4 is 2 and half of 2 fifths is 1 fifth.

$$= 2\frac{1}{5}$$ Rewrite the sum as a mixed number.

So, $\frac{1}{2} \times 4\frac{2}{5} = 2\frac{1}{5}$. **Check for Reasonableness** $2\frac{1}{5} \approx 2$ ✓

✓ **CHOOSE Your Method**

Multiply. Write in simplest form.

g. $\frac{1}{4} \times 8\frac{4}{9}$ **h.** $5\frac{1}{3} \times 3$ **i.** $-1\frac{7}{8} \times \left(-2\frac{2}{5}\right)$

5 **SLEEP** Humans sleep about $\frac{1}{3}$ of each day. If each year is equal to $365\frac{1}{4}$ days, determine the number of days in a year the average human sleeps.

Words	Humans sleep about $\frac{1}{3}$ of $365\frac{1}{4}$ days.
Variable	Let d represent the number of days a human sleeps.
Equation	$d = \frac{1}{3} \cdot 365\frac{1}{4}$

$d = \frac{1}{3} \cdot 365\frac{1}{4}$ Write the equation.

$d = \frac{1}{3} \cdot \frac{1{,}461}{4}$ Rename the mixed number as an improper fraction.

$d = \frac{1}{\underset{1}{\cancel{3}}} \cdot \frac{\overset{487}{\cancel{1{,}461}}}{4}$ Divide 3 and 1,461 by their GCF, 3.

$d = \frac{487}{4}$ or $121\frac{3}{4}$ Multiply. Then rename as a mixed number.

The average human sleeps $121\frac{3}{4}$ days each year.

6 **ANIMALS** The house cat has an average lifespan that is $\frac{4}{5}$ of a lion's. If a lion's average lifespan is 15 years, find the average lifespan of a house cat.

Words	The lifespan of a house cat is $\frac{4}{5}$ that of the lion.
Variable	Let c represent the lifespan of a house cat.
Equation	$c = \frac{4}{5} \cdot 15$

$c = \frac{4}{5} \cdot 15$ Write the equation.

$c = \frac{4}{5} \cdot \frac{15}{1}$ Write the whole number 15 as an improper fraction.

$c = \frac{4}{\underset{1}{\cancel{5}}} \cdot \frac{\overset{3}{\cancel{15}}}{1}$ Divide 5 and 15 by their GCF, 5.

$c = \frac{12}{1}$ or 12   Multiply, then simplify.

The average lifespan of a house cat is 12 years.

Real-World Link ····

The average group of lions, called a pride, consists of about 15 lions with about $\frac{2}{3}$ of the pride being female.

CHECK Your Progress

j. COOKING Lloyd wishes to make $\frac{1}{2}$ of a recipe. If the original recipe calls for $3\frac{3}{4}$ cups of flour, how many cups should he use?

CHECK Your Understanding

Examples 1–4
(pp. 112–113)

Multiply. Write in simplest form.

1. $\frac{2}{3} \times \frac{1}{3}$

2. $-2 \times \frac{2}{5}$

3. $\frac{1}{6} \times 4$

4. $-\frac{1}{4} \times \left(-\frac{8}{9}\right)$

5. $2\frac{1}{4} \times \frac{2}{3}$

6. $-1\frac{5}{6} \times \left(-3\frac{3}{5}\right)$

Examples 5 and 6
(p. 114)

7. **WEIGHT** The weight of an object on Mars is about $\frac{2}{5}$ its weight on Earth. How much would an 80-pound dog weigh on Mars?

Practice and Problem Solving

● = **Step-by-Step Solutions** begin on page R4.
Extra Practice is on page EP6.

Examples 1–4
(pp. 112–113)

Multiply. Write in simplest form.

8. $\frac{3}{4} \times \frac{1}{8}$

9. $\frac{2}{5} \times \frac{2}{3}$

10. $-9 \times \frac{1}{2}$

11. $\frac{4}{5} \times (-6)$

12. $-\frac{1}{5} \times \left(-\frac{5}{6}\right)$

13. $-\frac{4}{9} \times \left(-\frac{1}{4}\right)$

14. $\frac{2}{3} \times \frac{1}{4}$

15. $\frac{1}{12} \times \frac{3}{5}$

16. $\frac{4}{7} \times \frac{7}{8}$

17 $\frac{2}{5} \times \frac{15}{16}$

18. $\left(-1\frac{1}{2}\right) \times \frac{2}{3}$

19. $3\frac{1}{3} \times -\frac{1}{5}$

Examples 5 and 6
(p. 114)

20. **DVDs** Each DVD storage case is about $\frac{1}{5}$ inch thick. What will be the height in simplest form of 12 cases sold together?

21. **PIZZA** Mark left $\frac{3}{8}$ of a pizza in the refrigerator. On Friday, he ate $\frac{1}{2}$ of what was left of the pizza. What fraction of the entire pizza did he eat on Friday?

22. **MEASUREMENT** The width of a vegetable garden is $\frac{1}{3}$ times its length. If the length of the garden is $7\frac{3}{4}$ feet, what is the width in simplest form?

23. **RECIPES** A recipe to make one batch of blueberry muffins calls for $4\frac{2}{3}$ cups of flour. How many cups of flour are needed to make 3 batches of blueberry muffins in simplest form?

Multiply. Write in simplest form.

24. $4\frac{2}{3} \times \frac{4}{7}$

25. $\frac{5}{8} \times 2\frac{1}{2}$

26. $-14 \times 1\frac{1}{7}$

27. $3\frac{3}{4} \times 8$

28. $9 \times 4\frac{2}{3}$

29. $4 \times 7\frac{5}{6}$

30. $-3\frac{1}{4} \times \left(-2\frac{2}{3}\right)$

31. $5\frac{1}{3} \times 3\frac{3}{4}$

32. **MEASUREMENT** The width of the fish tank is $\frac{2}{5}$ of its length. What is the width of the fish tank in simplest form?

33. **BICYCLING** Philip rode his bicycle at $9\frac{2}{5}$ miles per hour. If he rode for $\frac{3}{4}$ of an hour, how many miles in simplest form did he cover?

30 in.

Evaluate each verbal expression.

34. one half of five eighths

35. four sevenths of two thirds

36. nine tenths of one fourth

37. one third of eleven sixteenths

38. GRAPHIC NOVEL Refer to the graphic novel frame below for Exercises a–b.

a. If the height of the closet is 96 inches and Aisha would like to have 4 rows of cube organizers, what is the most the height of each cube organizer can be?

b. Aisha would like to stack 3 shoe boxes on top of each other at the bottom of the closet. If the height of each shoe box is $4\frac{1}{2}$ inches, what is the total height of the 3 boxes?

MEASUREMENT For Exercises 39–42, use measurement conversions.

39. Find $\frac{1}{2}$ of $\frac{1}{4}$ of a gallon.

40. What is $\frac{1}{60}$ of $\frac{1}{24}$ of a day?

41. Find $\frac{1}{100}$ of $\frac{1}{1,000}$ of a kilometer.

42. What is $\frac{1}{12}$ of $\frac{1}{3}$ of a yard?

ALGEBRA Evaluate each expression if $a = 4$, $b = 2\frac{1}{2}$, and $c = 5\frac{3}{4}$.

43. $a \times b + c$

44. $b \times c - a$

45. $2bc$

46. TELEVISION One evening, $\frac{2}{3}$ of the students in Rick's class watched television. Of those students, $\frac{3}{8}$ watched a reality show. Of the students that watched the show, $\frac{1}{4}$ of them recorded the show. What fraction of the students in Rick's class watched and recorded a reality TV show?

47 FOOD Alano wants to make one and a half batches of the pasta salad recipe shown at the right. How much of each ingredient will Alano need? Explain how you solved the problem.

Pasta Salad Recipe	
Ingredient	**Amount**
Broccoli	$1\frac{1}{4}$ c
Cooked pasta	$3\frac{3}{4}$ c
Salad dressing	$\frac{2}{3}$ c
Cheese	$1\frac{1}{3}$ c

48. FIND THE DATA Refer to the Data File on pages 2–5. Choose some data and write a real-world problem in which you would multiply fractions.

49. CHALLENGE Two positive improper fractions are multiplied. Is the product *sometimes, always,* or *never* less than 1? Explain your reasoning.

50. OPEN ENDED Write a real-world problem that involves finding the product of $\frac{3}{4}$ and $\frac{1}{8}$.

51. Write MATH Explain the difference in the processes of addition and multiplication of fractions.

NGSSS Practice   **MA.6.A.1.2, MA.7.A.3.2**

52. Of the dolls in Marjorie's doll collection, $\frac{1}{5}$ have red hair. Of these, $\frac{3}{4}$ have green eyes. What fraction of Marjorie's doll collection has both red hair and green eyes?

  A. $\frac{2}{9}$

  B. $\frac{3}{20}$

  C. $\frac{4}{9}$

  D. $\frac{19}{20}$

53. Which description gives the relationship between a term and n, its position in the sequence?

Position	1	2	3	4	5	n
Value of Term	$\frac{1}{4}$	$\frac{1}{2}$	$\frac{3}{4}$	1	$1\frac{1}{4}$	

  F. Subtract 4 from n.

  G. Add $\frac{1}{4}$ to n.

  H. Multiply n by $\frac{1}{4}$.

  I. Divide n by $\frac{1}{4}$.

 **Spiral Review**

54. MEASUREMENT How much longer is a $2\frac{1}{2}$-inch-long piece of string than a $\frac{2}{5}$-inch-long piece of string? (Lesson 2-2C)

Add or subtract. Write in simplest form. (Lesson 2-2A)

55. $\frac{3}{7} + \frac{1}{7}$ **56.** $\frac{5}{8} + \left(-\frac{7}{8}\right)$ **57.** $\frac{5}{6} + \frac{1}{6}$ **58.** $\frac{7}{10} - \frac{3}{10}$

Replace each ⬤ with <, >, or = to make a true sentence. (Lesson 2-1C)

59. $\frac{5}{12}$ ⬤ $\frac{2}{5}$ **60.** $\frac{3}{16}$ ⬤ $\frac{1}{8}$ **61.** $3\frac{7}{6}$ ⬤ $3\frac{6}{5}$

62. EARTH SCIENCE The table describes the deepest land depressions in the world in feet below sea level. Order the integers from greatest depth to least depth. (Lesson 1-1B)

Depth (ft)			
−220	−436	−511	−282
−383	−505	−235	−230

Problem-Solving Investigation

Main Idea Solve problems by drawing a diagram.

P.S.I. TEAM +

Draw a Diagram

CACEY: I drop a ball from a height of 12 feet. It hits the ground and bounces up half as high as it fell. This is true for each successive bounce.

YOUR MISSION: Draw a diagram to find the height the ball reaches after the fourth bounce.

Understand	You know the ball is dropped from a height of 12 feet. It bounces up half as high.
Plan	Draw a diagram to show the height of the ball after each bounce.
Solve	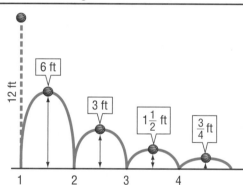
	The ball reaches a height of $\frac{3}{4}$ foot after the fourth bounce.
Check	Start at 12 feet. Multiply by $\frac{1}{2}$ for each bounce: $12 \cdot \frac{1}{2} \cdot \frac{1}{2} \cdot \frac{1}{2} \cdot \frac{1}{2} = \frac{12}{16}$ or $\frac{3}{4}$. ✓

Analyze the Strategy

1. Determine what height a ball would reach after the fourth bounce if it is dropped from 12 feet and bounces up $\frac{2}{3}$ as high.

NGSSS

MA.7.A.3.2 Add, subtract, multiply, and divide integers, **fractions,** and terminating decimals, and perform exponential operations with rational bases and whole number exponents **including solving problems in everyday contexts.**

- Draw a diagram.
- Look for a pattern.
- Choose an operation.

Use the *draw a diagram* strategy to solve Exercises 2–4.

2. **TRAVEL** Mr. Garcia has driven 60 miles, which is $\frac{2}{3}$ of the way to his sister's house. How much farther does he have to drive to get to his sister's house?

```
|------ 60 miles -----|
|   30   |   30   |        |
```

3. **DISTANCE** Alejandro and Pedro are riding their bikes to school. After 1 mile, they are $\frac{4}{5}$ of the way there. How much farther do they have to go?

4. **VOLUME** A swimming pool is being filled with water. After 25 minutes, $\frac{1}{6}$ of the swimming pool is filled. How much longer will it take to completely fill the pool, assuming the water rate is constant?

Use any strategy to solve Exercises 5–11.

5. **BASEBALL** Of Lee's baseball cards, $\frac{1}{5}$ show California players. Of these, $\frac{3}{8}$ show San Diego Padres players. Is the fraction of Lee's collection that shows Padres players $\frac{23}{40}$, $\frac{4}{13}$, or $\frac{3}{40}$?

6. **FRACTIONS** Marta ate a quarter of a whole pie. Edwin ate $\frac{1}{4}$ of what was left. Cristina then ate $\frac{1}{3}$ of what was left. What fraction of the pie remains?

7. **GAMES** Eight members of a chess club are having a tournament. In the first round, every player will play a chess game against every other player. How many games will be in the first round of the tournament?

8. **MEASUREMENT** Kiaya is adding a 2-inch border to the length and width of a photograph as shown.

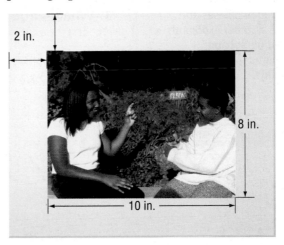

2 in.

8 in.

10 in.

Find the area of the border to be added to the original photograph.

9. **RACES** Anna, Isabela, Mary, and Rachana ran a race. Anna is just ahead of Rachana. Rachana is two places behind Isabela. Isabela is a few seconds behind the leader, Mary. Place the girls in order from first to last.

10. **SEATS** The number of seats in the first row of a concert hall is 6. The second row has 9 seats, the third row has 12 seats, and the fourth row has 15 seats. How many seats will be in the eighth row?

11. **Write MATH** Write a real-world problem that could be solved by drawing a diagram. Exchange your problem with a classmate and solve.

Main Idea

Divide fractions and mixed numbers.

NGSSS

MA.7.A.3.2 Add, subtract, multiply, and **divide** integers, **fractions**, and terminating decimals, and perform exponential operations with rational bases and whole number exponents **including solving problems in everyday contexts.**

Get Connected
glencoe.com

Divide Fractions

Explore Cut two paper plates into four equal pieces each to show $2 \div \frac{1}{4}$.

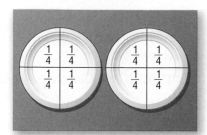

1. How many $\frac{1}{4}$s are in 2 plates?

2. How would you model $3 \div \frac{1}{2}$?

3. What is true about $3 \div \frac{1}{2}$ and 3×2?

Dividing 2 by $\frac{1}{4}$ is the same as multiplying 2 by the reciprocal of $\frac{1}{4}$, which is 4.

$$\text{reciprocals}$$
$$2 \div \frac{1}{4} = 8 \qquad 2 \cdot 4 = 8$$
$$\text{same result}$$

Is this pattern true for any division expression?

Consider $\frac{7}{8} \div \frac{3}{4}$, which can be rewritten as $\dfrac{\frac{7}{8}}{\frac{3}{4}}$.

$$\frac{\frac{7}{8}}{\frac{3}{4}} = \frac{\frac{7}{8} \times \frac{4}{3}}{\frac{3}{4} \times \frac{4}{3}} \qquad \text{Multiply the numerator and denominator by the reciprocal of } \frac{3}{4}, \text{ which is } \frac{4}{3}.$$

$$= \frac{\frac{7}{8} \times \frac{4}{3}}{1} \qquad \frac{3}{4} \times \frac{4}{3} = 1$$

$$= \frac{7}{8} \times \frac{4}{3}$$

So, $\frac{7}{8} \div \frac{3}{4} = \frac{7}{8} \times \frac{4}{3}$.

Key Concept — Divide by Fractions

Words To divide by a fraction, multiply by its multiplicative inverse, or reciprocal.

Examples **Numbers** **Algebra**

$$\frac{7}{8} \div \frac{3}{4} = \frac{7}{8} \cdot \frac{4}{3} \qquad \frac{a}{b} \div \frac{c}{d} = \frac{a}{b} \cdot \frac{d}{c}, \text{ where } b, c, d \neq 0$$

EXAMPLE Divide by Fractions

1 Find $\frac{3}{4} \div \left(-\frac{1}{2}\right)$. Write in simplest form.

Estimate $1 \div \left(-\frac{1}{2}\right) = \blacksquare$

Think How many groups of $\frac{1}{2}$ are in 1? $1 \div \frac{1}{2} = 2$, so $1 \div \left(-\frac{1}{2}\right) = -2$.

$\frac{3}{4} \div \left(-\frac{1}{2}\right) = \frac{3}{4} \cdot \left(-\frac{2}{1}\right)$ Multiply by the reciprocal of $-\frac{1}{2}$, which is $-\frac{2}{1}$.

$= \frac{3}{\overset{2}{4}} \cdot \left(-\frac{\overset{1}{2}}{1}\right)$ Divide 4 and 2 by their GCF, 2.

$= -\frac{3}{2}$ or $-1\frac{1}{2}$ Multiply.

Check for Reasonableness $-1\frac{1}{2} \approx -2$ ✓

CHECK Your Progress

Divide. Write in simplest form.

a. $\frac{3}{4} \div \frac{1}{4}$ **b.** $-\frac{4}{5} \div \frac{8}{9}$ **c.** $-\frac{5}{6} \div \left(-\frac{2}{3}\right)$

To divide by a mixed number, first rename the mixed number as a fraction greater than one. Then multiply the first fraction by the reciprocal, or multiplicative inverse, of the second fraction.

EXAMPLE Divide by Mixed Numbers

2 Find $\frac{2}{3} \div 3\frac{1}{3}$. Write in simplest form.

Estimate $\frac{1}{2} \div 3 = \frac{1}{2} \cdot \frac{1}{3}$ or $\frac{1}{6}$

$\frac{2}{3} \div 3\frac{1}{3} = \frac{2}{3} \div \frac{10}{3}$ Rename $3\frac{1}{3}$ a fraction greater than one.

$= \frac{2}{3} \cdot \frac{3}{10}$ Multiply by the reciprocal of $\frac{10}{3}$, which is $\frac{3}{10}$.

$= \frac{\overset{1}{2}}{\underset{1}{3}} \cdot \frac{\overset{1}{3}}{\underset{5}{10}}$ Divide out common factors.

$= \frac{1}{5}$ Multiply.

Check for Reasonableness $\frac{1}{5}$ is close to $\frac{1}{6}$. ✓

CHECK Your Progress

Divide. Write in simplest form.

d. $5 \div 1\frac{1}{3}$ **e.** $-\frac{3}{4} \div 1\frac{1}{2}$ **f.** $2\frac{1}{3} \div 5$

g. NUTS In planning for a party, $5\frac{1}{4}$ pounds of cashews will be divided into $\frac{3}{4}$-pound bags. How many such bags can be made?

Real-World EXAMPLE

3 **WOODWORKING** Students in a woodworking class are making butterfly houses. The side pieces of the house need to be $8\frac{1}{4}$ inches long. How many side pieces can be cut from a board measuring $49\frac{1}{2}$ inches long?

To find how many side pieces can be cut, divide $49\frac{1}{2}$ by $8\frac{1}{4}$.

Estimate Use compatible numbers. $48 \div 8 = 6$

$$49\frac{1}{2} \div 8\frac{1}{4} = \frac{99}{2} \div \frac{33}{4} \quad \text{Rename the mixed numbers as fractions greater than one.}$$

$$= \frac{99}{2} \cdot \frac{4}{33} \quad \text{Multiply by the reciprocal of } \frac{33}{4}, \text{ which is } \frac{4}{33}.$$

$$= \frac{\overset{3}{\cancel{99}}}{\underset{1}{\cancel{2}}} \cdot \frac{\overset{2}{\cancel{4}}}{\underset{1}{\cancel{33}}} \quad \text{Divide out common factors.}$$

$$= \frac{6}{1} \text{ or } 6 \quad \text{Multiply.}$$

So, 6 side pieces can be cut.

Check for Reasonableness Compare to the estimate. $6 = 6$ ✓

 CHECK Your Progress

h. **FOOD** Suppose a small box of cereal contains $12\frac{2}{3}$ cups of cereal. How many $1\frac{1}{3}$-cup servings are in the box? Write in simplest form.

i. **MEASUREMENT** The area of a rectangular bedroom is $146\frac{7}{8}$ square feet. If the width of the bedroom is $11\frac{3}{4}$ feet, find the length in simplest form.

✓ CHECK Your Understanding

Examples 1 and 2
(p. 121)

Divide. Write in simplest form.

1. $\frac{1}{8} \div \frac{1}{3}$ **2.** $-\frac{3}{5} \div \left(-\frac{1}{4}\right)$ **3.** $-3 \div \left(-\frac{6}{7}\right)$ **4.** $\frac{3}{4} \div 6$

5. $\frac{1}{2} \div 7\frac{1}{2}$ **6.** $\frac{4}{7} \div \left(-1\frac{2}{7}\right)$ **7.** $5\frac{3}{5} \div 4\frac{2}{3}$ **8.** $6\frac{1}{2} \div 3\frac{5}{7}$

Example 3
(p. 122)

9. **FOOD** Deandre has 7 apples and each apple is divided evenly into eighths. How many apple slices does Deandre have?

10. **WALKING** On Saturday, Lindsay walked $3\frac{1}{2}$ miles in $1\frac{2}{5}$ hours. What was her walking pace in miles per hour? Write in simplest form.

Practice and Problem Solving

● = **Step-by-Step Solutions** begin on page R5.
Extra Practice is on page EP6.

Examples 1 and 2
(p. 121)

Divide. Write in simplest form.

11. $\frac{3}{8} \div \frac{6}{7}$

12. $\frac{5}{9} \div \frac{5}{6}$

13. $-\frac{2}{3} \div \left(-\frac{1}{2}\right)$

14. $-\frac{7}{8} \div \frac{3}{4}$

Example 3
(p. 122)

15. $6 \div \left(-\frac{1}{2}\right)$

16. $-\frac{4}{9} \div (-2)$

17. $2\frac{2}{3} \div 4$

18. $5 \div \frac{1}{3}$

19. **FOOD** Mason has 8 cups of popcorn kernels to divide into $\frac{2}{3}$-cup portions. How many portions will there be?

20. **MOVIES** Cheryl is organizing her movie collection. If each movie case is $\frac{3}{4}$ inch wide, how many movies can fit on a shelf 5 feet wide?

Divide. Write in simplest form.

21. $\frac{2}{3} \div 2\frac{1}{2}$

22. $\frac{8}{9} \div 5\frac{1}{3}$

23. $-4\frac{1}{2} \div 6\frac{3}{4}$

24. $-5\frac{2}{7} \div \left(-2\frac{1}{7}\right)$

25 $3\frac{4}{5} \div 1\frac{1}{3}$

26. $9\frac{1}{2} \div 2\frac{5}{6}$

27. $-5\frac{1}{5} \div \frac{2}{3}$

28. $-6\frac{7}{8} \div \left(-\frac{3}{4}\right)$

29. **ICE CREAM** Vinh bought $4\frac{1}{2}$ gallons of ice cream to serve at his birthday party. If a pint is $\frac{1}{8}$ of a gallon, how many pint-sized servings can be made?

30. **BEVERAGES** William has $8\frac{1}{4}$ cups of fruit juice. If he divides the juice into $\frac{3}{4}$-cup servings, how many servings will he have?

31. **BIRDS** Use the table that gives information about several types of birds of prey. Write your answers in simplest form.

a. How many times as heavy is the Golden Eagle as the Red-Tailed Hawk?

b. How many times as heavy is the Golden Eagle as the Northern Bald Eagle?

Bird	Maximun Weight (lb)
Golden Eagle	$13\frac{9}{10}$
Northern Bald Eagle	$9\frac{9}{10}$
Red-Tailed Hawk	$3\frac{1}{2}$

Real-World Link
Red-tailed hawks are large, stocky birds. Females are larger than males and can weigh up to $3\frac{1}{2}$ pounds.

Draw a model of each verbal expression and then evaluate the expression. Explain how the model shows the division process.

32. one half divided by two fifths

33. five eighths divided by one fourth

34. one and three eighths divided by one half

35. two and one sixth divided by two thirds

36. **PIZZA** A concession stand sells three types of pizza. The diagram shows how much pizza of each type was left when the concession stand closed. If the pizza is sold in slices that are $\frac{1}{8}$ of a whole pizza, how many more slices can be sold?

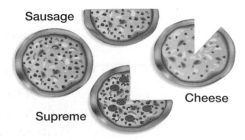

Sausage

Cheese

Supreme

ALGEBRA Evaluate each expression if $g = -\frac{1}{6}$, $h = \frac{1}{2}$, and $j = 3\frac{2}{3}$. Write in simplest form.

37. $j \div h$ **38.** $g \div j$ **39.** $3g \div h$ **40.** $h \div \left(\frac{1}{2}j\right)$

41 **SHOPPING** A supermarket sells pretzels in $\frac{3}{4}$-ounce snack-sized bags or $12\frac{1}{2}$-ounce regular-sized bags. How many times larger is the regular-sized bag than the snack-sized bag in simplest form?

42. MEASUREMENT A recipe calls for $2\frac{2}{3}$ cups of brown sugar and $\frac{2}{3}$ cup of confectioner's sugar. How many times greater is the number of cups of brown sugar in the recipe than of confectioner's sugar in simplest form?

43. SCHOOL The table shows the number of hours students spend studying each week during the school year. Write your answers in simplest form.

a. How many times greater was the number of students who spent over 10 hours each week studying than those who spent only 1–2 hours each week studying?

b. How many times greater was the number of students who spent 3 or more hours each week studying than those who spent less than 3 hours each week studying?

Weekly Study Hours	
Hours	**Fraction of Students**
None	$\frac{1}{50}$
1–2	$\frac{2}{25}$
3–5	$\frac{11}{50}$
6–7	$\frac{17}{100}$
8–10	$\frac{1}{5}$
Over 10	$\frac{19}{100}$
Not sure	$\frac{3}{25}$

44. SCHOOL SUPPLIES Tara bought a dozen folders. She took $\frac{1}{3}$ of the dozen and then divided the remaining folders equally among her four friends. What fraction of the dozen did each of her four friends receive and how many folders was this per person?

45. WEATHER A meteorologist has issued a thunderstorm warning. So far, the storm has traveled 35 miles in $\frac{1}{2}$ hour. If it is currently 5:00 P.M. and the storm is 105 miles away from you, at what time will the storm reach you? Explain how you solved the problem.

46. **MULTIPLE REPRESENTATIONS** Jorge recorded the distance that five of his friends live from his house on the chart that is shown.

a. NUMBERS Thuy lives about how many times farther away than Jamal?

b. ALGEBRA Write and solve an equation to find the mean number of miles that Jorge's friends live from his house. Write your answer in simplest form.

c. BAR DIAGRAM Draw a bar diagram that can be used to find how many more miles Lon travels than Lucia to get to Jorge's house.

Student	Miles
Lucia	$5\frac{1}{2}$
Lon	$8\frac{2}{3}$
Sam	$12\frac{5}{6}$
Jamal	$2\frac{7}{9}$
Thuy	$17\frac{13}{18}$

QUICK Review

Mean
To find the mean of a data set, find the sum of the data and then divide by the number of terms in the data set.

47. CHALLENGE If $\frac{5}{6}$ is divided by a certain fraction $\frac{a}{b}$, the result is $\frac{1}{4}$. What is the fraction $\frac{a}{b}$?

48. FIND THE ERROR Blake is finding $\frac{4}{5} \div \frac{6}{7}$. Find his mistake and correct it.

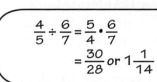

$$\frac{4}{5} \div \frac{6}{7} = \frac{5}{4} \cdot \frac{6}{7}$$
$$= \frac{30}{28} \text{ or } 1\frac{1}{14}$$

49. **Write MATH** If you divide a proper fraction by another proper fraction, is it possible to get a mixed number as an answer? Explain your reasoning.

NGSSS Practice   MA.7.A.3.2

50. Which expression represents the **least** value?

A. $298 + \frac{1}{2}$

B. $298 - \frac{1}{2}$

C. $298 \times \frac{1}{2}$

D. $298 \div \frac{1}{2}$

51. How many small boxes of peanuts shown can be filled from the large box of peanuts?

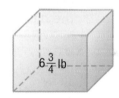

$6\frac{3}{4}$ lb $1\frac{1}{8}$ lb

F. 4   H. 6

G. 5   I. 7

Spiral Review

52. ROCK CLIMBING A rock climber stops to rest at a ledge 150 feet above the ground. If this represents 75% of the total climb, how high above the ground is the top of the rock? (Lesson 2-3C)

53. Find $\frac{1}{10} \times \frac{5}{8}$. Write in simplest form. (Lesson 2-3B)

Write an integer for each situation. (Lesson 1-1B)

54. 9°C below zero

55. a gain of 20 feet

Replace each ● with <, >, or = to make a true sentence. (Lesson 1-1B)

56. $-8 \bullet -3$ **57.** $26 \bullet -30$ **58.** $14 \bullet |-15|$ **59.** $-40 \bullet |40|$

60. Find the absolute value of -101. (Lesson 1-1B)

Main Idea
Use powers and exponents.

NGSSS

MA.7.A.3.2 Add, subtract, multiply, and divide integers, fractions, and terminating decimals, and **perform exponential operations with rational bases and whole number exponents including solving problems in everyday contexts.**

New Vocabulary
factors
exponent
base
powers
squared
cubed
standard form
exponential form

Get Connected
glencoe.com

Powers and Exponents

 **TEXT MESSAGING** Suppose you text one of your friends. That friend then texts two friends after one minute. The pattern continues.

1. How many text messages will be sent at 4 minutes?

2. What is the relationship between the number of 2s and the number of minutes?

Minutes	Number of Text Messages	
0	1	= 1
1	1 × 2	= 2
2	2 × 2	= 4
3	2 × 2 × 2	= 8

Two or more numbers that are multiplied together to form a product are called **factors**. When the same factor is used, you may use an exponent to simplify the notation. The **exponent** tells how many times the base is used as a factor. The common factor is called the **base**.

$$16 = \mathbf{2 \cdot 2 \cdot 2 \cdot 2} = \mathbf{2}^4 \leftarrow \text{exponent}$$
$$\uparrow$$
$$\text{base}$$

Numbers expressed using exponents are called **powers**.

Powers	Words
5^2	five to the second power or five **squared**
4^3	four to the third power or four **cubed**
2^4	two to the fourth power

EXAMPLES Write Powers as Products

Write each power as a product of the same factor.

 1 7^5

$$7^5 = 7 \cdot 7 \cdot 7 \cdot 7 \cdot 7$$

 2 $\left(\frac{1}{3}\right)^2$

$$\left(\frac{1}{3}\right)^2 = \frac{1}{3} \cdot \frac{1}{3}$$

 CHECK Your Progress

a. 6^4 **b.** 1^3 **c.** $\left(\frac{2}{9}\right)^5$

You can evaluate, or find the value of, powers by multiplying the factors. Numbers written without exponents are in **standard form**.

V🖉cabulary Link

Everyday Use

Evaluate to find what something is worth

Math Use

Evaluate find the value of

EXAMPLES **Write Powers in Standard Form**

Evaluate each expression.

 2^5

$$2^5 = 2 \cdot 2 \cdot 2 \cdot 2 \cdot 2$$
$$= 32$$

④ $\left(-\dfrac{1}{4}\right)^3$

$$\left(-\dfrac{1}{4}\right)^3 = -\dfrac{1}{4} \cdot -\dfrac{1}{4} \cdot -\dfrac{1}{4}$$
$$= -\dfrac{1}{64}$$

✓ **CHECK Your Progress**

d. 10^2 **e.** 7^3 **f.** $\left(\dfrac{1}{5}\right)^4$

Numbers written with exponents are in **exponential form**.

EXAMPLE **Write Numbers in Exponential Form**

⑤ Write $3 \cdot 3 \cdot 3 \cdot 3$ in exponential form.

3 is the base. It is used as a factor 4 times. So, the exponent is 4.

$$3 \cdot 3 \cdot 3 \cdot 3 = 3^4$$

✓ **CHECK Your Progress**

Write each product in exponential form.

g. $\dfrac{2}{3} \cdot \dfrac{2}{3} \cdot \dfrac{2}{3}$ **h.** $12 \cdot 12 \cdot 12 \cdot 12 \cdot 12 \cdot 12$

✓ CHECK Your Understanding

Examples 1 and 2 (p. 126)

Write each power as a product of the same factor.

1. 9^3 **2.** 8^5 $\left(\dfrac{2}{3}\right)^4$

Examples 3 and 4 (p. 127)

Evaluate each expression.

4. 2^4 **5.** 10^3 **6.** $\left(-\dfrac{1}{7}\right)^2$

7. POPULATION There are approximately 5^{10} people living in North Carolina. About how many people is this?

Example 5 (p. 127)

Write each product in exponential form.

8. $\dfrac{2}{5} \cdot \dfrac{2}{5} \cdot \dfrac{2}{5} \cdot \dfrac{2}{5} \cdot \dfrac{2}{5} \cdot \dfrac{2}{5}$ **9.** $1 \cdot 1 \cdot 1 \cdot 1$ **10.** $4 \cdot 4 \cdot 4 \cdot 4 \cdot 4$

● = **Step-by-Step Solutions** begin on page R5.
Extra Practice is on page EP7.

Examples 1 and 2
(p. 126)

Write each power as a product of the same factor.

11. 1^5

12. $\left(\frac{3}{4}\right)^2$

13. $\left(\frac{3}{8}\right)^8$

14. 8^6

15. 9^4

16. 10^4

Examples 3 and 4
(p. 127)

Evaluate each expression.

17. 2^6

18. 4^3

19. $\left(-\frac{1}{7}\right)^4$

20. 4^6

21. 1^{10}

22. $\left(\frac{1}{10}\right)^1$

23. BIKING In a recent year, the number of 12- to 17-year-olds that went off-road biking was 10^6. Write this number in standard form.

24. TRAINS The Maglev train in China is the fastest passenger train in the world. Its average speed is 3^5 miles per hour. Write this speed in standard form.

Example 5
(p. 127)

Write each product in exponential form.

25. $3 \cdot 3$

26. $\frac{2}{7} \cdot \frac{2}{7} \cdot \frac{2}{7} \cdot \frac{2}{7}$

27. $1 \cdot 1 \cdot 1 \cdot 1 \cdot 1 \cdot 1 \cdot 1 \cdot 1$

28. $\frac{1}{6} \cdot \frac{1}{6} \cdot \frac{1}{6} \cdot \frac{1}{6} \cdot \frac{1}{6}$

Write each power as a product of the same factor.

29. *four to the fifth power*

30. *nine squared*

Evaluate each expression.

31. *six to the fourth power*

32. *6 cubed*

33 **GEOMETRY** Refer to the puzzle cube at the right.

  a. Suppose the puzzle cube is made entirely of unit cubes. Find the number of unit cubes in the puzzle. Write using exponents.

  b. Why do you think the expression 3^3 is sometimes read as *3 cubed*?

34. NUMBERS Write $5 \cdot 5 \cdot 5 \cdot 5 \cdot 4 \cdot 4 \cdot 4$ in exponential form.

35. COMPUTERS A gigabyte is a measure of computer data storage capacity. One gigabyte stores 2^{30} bytes of data. Use a calculator to find the number in standard form that represents two gigabytes.

Order the following powers from least to greatest.

36. $6^5, 1^{14}, 4^{10}, 17^3$

37. $2^8, 15^2, 6^3, 3^5$

38. $5^3, 4^6, 2^{11}, 7^2$

39. OPEN ENDED Select a number between 1,000 and 2,000 that can be expressed as a power.

H.O.T. Problems

40. CHALLENGE Write two different powers that have the same value.

41. Which One Doesn't Belong? Identify the number that does not belong with the other three. Explain your reasoning.

| 121 | 361 | 576 | 1,000 |

42.  **MATH** Analyze the number pattern shown at the right. Then write a convincing argument as to the value of 2^0. Based on your argument, what do you think will be the value of 2^{-1}?

$$2^4 = 16$$
$$2^3 = 8$$
$$2^2 = 4$$
$$2^1 = 2$$
$$2^0 = ?$$

NGSSS Practice   MA.7.A.3.2

43. Which model represents 6^3?

A.
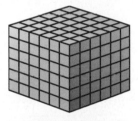

B.

C.

12
6

D.

44. Find $\frac{5}{6} \div \frac{4}{7}$. Write in simplest form. (Lesson 2-3D)

45. FAMILY At Nelia's family reunion, $\frac{4}{5}$ of the people are 18 years of age or older. Half of the remaining people are under 12 years old. If 20 children are under 12 years old, how many people are at the reunion? Use the *draw a diagram* strategy. (Lesson 2-3C)

46. COOKING Lauren had $4\frac{2}{3}$ cups of chopped walnuts. She used $1\frac{1}{4}$ cups in a recipe. How many cups of chopped walnuts are left? (Lesson 2-2C)

Problem Solving in Fashion Design

A flair for *Fashion*

Do you enjoy reading fashion magazines, keeping up with the latest trends, and creating your own unique sense of style? You might want to consider a career in fashion design. Fashion designers create new designs for clothing, accessories, and shoes. In addition to being creative and knowledgeable about current fashion trends, fashion designers need to be able to take accurate measurements and calculate fit by adding, subtracting, and dividing measurements.

Choose a Major
Are you interested in a career as a fashion designer? Take some of the following courses in high school.

- Algebra
- Art
- Digital Design
- Geometry

 Get Connected glencoe.com

NGSSS

MA.7.A.3.2 Add, subtract, multiply, and divide integers, **fractions,** and terminating decimals...
including solving problems in everyday contexts.

Amount of Fabric Needed (yards)

Dress Style	Size 8	Size 10	Size 12	Size 14
A	$3\frac{3}{8}$	$3\frac{1}{2}$	$3\frac{3}{4}$	$3\frac{7}{8}$
B	$3\frac{1}{4}$	$3\frac{1}{2}$	$3\frac{7}{8}$	4

Real-World Math

Use the information in the table to solve each problem. Write in simplest form.

1. For size 8, does Dress Style A or B require more fabric? Explain.

2. How many yards of fabric are needed to make Style A in sizes 8 and 14?

3. Estimate how many yards of fabric are needed to make Style B in each of the sizes shown. Then find the actual amount of fabric.

4. For Style B, how much more fabric is required for size 14 than for size 12?

5. A designer has half the amount of fabric needed to make Style A in size 10. How much fabric does she have?

6. A bolt has $12\frac{1}{8}$ yards of fabric left on it. How many dresses in Style B size 12 could be made? How much fabric is left over?

🖥 **Get Connected** glencoe.com

• STUDY **TO GO**
• Vocabulary Review
• Multilingual eGlossary

FOLDABLES® Study Organizer

Be sure the following Key Concepts are noted in your Foldable.

Key Concepts

Terminating and Repeating Decimals
(Lesson 2-1)

• A terminating decimal is a decimal whose digits end. Repeating decimals have a pattern in their digits that repeats forever.

Adding and Subtracting Fractions
(Lesson 2-2)

• To add or subtract fractions, rename the fractions using the LCD. Then add or subtract the numerators and write the result over the denominator.

Multiplying and Dividing Fractions
(Lesson 2-3)

• To multiply fractions, multiply the numerators and multiply the denominators.

• To divide by a fraction, multiply by its multiplicative inverse, or reciprocal.

Exponent (Lesson 2-3)

• An exponent tells how many times the base is used as a factor.

$$2 \times 2 \times 2 = 2^3 \quad \overset{\leftarrow \text{ exponent}}{\underset{\leftarrow \text{ base}}{}}$$

Key Vocabulary

bar notation (p. 81)

base (p. 126)

common denominator (p. 86)

cubed (p. 126)

exponent (p. 126)

exponential form (p. 127)

factors (p. 126)

least common denominator (LCD) (p. 86)

like fractions (p. 91)

powers (p. 126)

rational numbers (p. 85)

repeating decimal (p. 81)

squared (p. 126)

standard form (p. 127)

terminating decimal (p. 81)

unlike fractions (p. 98)

Vocabulary Check

Choose the correct term or number to complete each sentence.

1. 1.875 is an example of a (terminating, repeating) decimal.

2. A common denominator for the fractions $\frac{2}{3}$ and $\frac{1}{4}$ is (7, 12).

3. To add like fractions, add the (numerators, denominators).

4. When dividing by a fraction, multiply by its (value, reciprocal).

5. Fractions with different denominators are called (like, unlike) fractions.

6. The mixed number $2\frac{4}{7}$ can be renamed as $\left(2\frac{7}{7}, 1\frac{11}{7}\right)$.

7. When multiplying fractions, multiply the numerators and (multiply, keep) the denominators.

Multi-Part Lesson Review

2-1 Rational Numbers

Terminating and Repeating Decimals (pp. 80–84)

 MA.7.A.5.1

Write each fraction or mixed number as a decimal. Use bar notation if the decimal is a repeating decimal.

8. $\frac{3}{4}$ 9. $\frac{7}{8}$ 10. $\frac{5}{9}$

Write each decimal as a fraction in simplest form.

11. 0.7   12. 0.44   13. 0.05

14. **RUNNING** Jeremy ran a mile in 5 minutes and 8 seconds. Write this time in minutes as a decimal.

EXAMPLE 1 Write $\frac{2}{3}$ as a decimal.

$$\begin{array}{r} 0.666... \\ 3\overline{)2.000} \\ -18 \\ \hline 20 \\ -18 \\ \hline 20 \\ -18 \\ \hline 2 \end{array}$$

Since the pattern continues to repeat, a bar is placed over the 6 to indicate it repeats infinitely. So, $\frac{2}{3} = 0.\overline{6}$.

Compare and Order Rational Numbers (pp. 85–90)

 MA.7.A.5.1

Replace each ● with <, >, or = to make a true sentence.

15. $\frac{3}{8}$ ● $\frac{2}{3}$ 16. -0.45 ● $-\frac{9}{20}$

17. $\frac{8}{9}$ ● 85%   18. $-3\frac{3}{4}$ ● $-3\frac{5}{8}$

19. **SCHOOL** Michael received a $\frac{26}{30}$ on his English quiz and an 81% on his biology test. In which class did he receive the higher score?

EXAMPLE 2 Replace each ● with <, >, or = to make $\frac{3}{5}$ ● $\frac{5}{8}$ a true sentence.

Find equivalent fractions. The LCD is 40.

$\frac{3}{5} = \frac{3 \times 8}{5 \times 8} = \frac{24}{40}$ $\frac{5}{8} = \frac{5 \times 5}{8 \times 5} = \frac{25}{40}$

Since $\frac{24}{40} < \frac{25}{40}$, then $\frac{3}{5} < \frac{5}{8}$.

2-2 Add and Subtract Fractions

Add and Subtract Like Fractions (pp. 91–95)

 MA.7.A.3.2

Add or subtract. Write in simplest form.

20. $-\frac{5}{8} + \frac{1}{8}$ 21. $\frac{7}{12} + \frac{1}{12}$

22. $\frac{7}{10} + \frac{3}{10}$ 23. $\frac{6}{7} - \frac{2}{7}$

24. $\frac{11}{12} - \frac{7}{12}$ 25. $\frac{7}{9} - \left(-\frac{4}{9}\right)$

26. **MEASUREMENT** How much longer is $\frac{17}{20}$ hour than $\frac{13}{20}$ hour? Write in simplest form.

EXAMPLE 3 Find $\frac{3}{8} + \left(-\frac{1}{8}\right)$. **Estimate** $\frac{1}{2} + 0 = \frac{1}{2}$

$\frac{3}{8} + \left(-\frac{1}{8}\right) = \frac{3 + -1}{8}$ Add the numerators.

$= \frac{2}{8}$ or $\frac{1}{4}$ Simplify.

EXAMPLE 4 Find $\frac{7}{12} - \frac{5}{12}$. **Estimate** $\frac{1}{2} - \frac{1}{2} = 0$

$\frac{7}{12} - \frac{5}{12} = \frac{7 - 5}{12}$ Subtract the numerators.

$= \frac{2}{12}$ or $\frac{1}{6}$ Simplify.

2-2 Add and Subtract Fractions (continued)

Add and Subtract Unlike Fractions (pp. 98–103)

 MA.7.A.3.2

Add or subtract. Write in simplest form.

27. $\frac{1}{2} + \frac{2}{3}$ **28.** $\frac{5}{8} + \frac{1}{4}$

29. $\frac{7}{9} - \frac{1}{12}$ **30.** $\frac{9}{10} - \frac{1}{4}$

31. $\frac{7}{9} - \frac{1}{6}$ **32.** $\frac{4}{5} + \frac{2}{10}$

33. RUNNING Teresa ran $\frac{5}{6}$ mile while Yolanda ran $\frac{1}{4}$ mile. By what fraction did Teresa run more than Yolanda?

EXAMPLE 5 Find $\frac{3}{8} + \frac{2}{3}$. Estimate $\frac{1}{2} + \frac{1}{2} = 1$

The LCD of $\frac{3}{8}$ and $\frac{2}{3}$ is 24.

$$
\begin{array}{ccccc}
\frac{3}{8} & \rightarrow & \frac{3 \times 3}{8 \times 3} & \rightarrow & \frac{9}{24} \\
+\frac{2}{3} & \rightarrow & \frac{2 \times 8}{3 \times 8} & \rightarrow & +\frac{16}{24} \\
& & & & \overline{\frac{25}{24} \text{ or } 1\frac{1}{24}}
\end{array}
$$

Add and Subtract Mixed Numbers (pp. 104–108)

 MA.7.A.3.2

Add or subtract. Write in simplest form.

34. $-3\frac{2}{15} + 6\frac{9}{15}$ **35.** $4\frac{1}{3} - 2\frac{2}{3}$

36. $8\frac{2}{7} + 1\frac{6}{7}$ **37.** $7\frac{11}{12} - 4\frac{3}{12}$

38. $7\frac{3}{5} - 5\frac{1}{3}$ **39.** $5\frac{3}{4} - \left(-1\frac{1}{6}\right)$

40. BABYSITTING Lucas watched his little sister for $2\frac{1}{2}$ hours on Friday, $3\frac{2}{3}$ hours on Saturday, and $1\frac{3}{4}$ hours on Sunday. For how many hours did Lucas watch his little sister in simplest form?

EXAMPLE 6 Find $5\frac{2}{3} + 3\frac{1}{2}$.

$$5\frac{2}{3} + 3\frac{1}{2} = 5\frac{4}{6} + 3\frac{3}{6} \quad \text{Rename the fractions.}$$

$$= 8\frac{7}{6} \quad \begin{array}{l}\text{Add the whole numbers and add}\\ \text{the fractions.}\end{array}$$

$$= 9\frac{1}{6} \quad 8\frac{7}{6} = 8 + 1\frac{1}{6} \text{ or } 9\frac{1}{6}$$

EXAMPLE 7 Find $4\frac{1}{5} - 2\frac{3}{5}$.

$$4\frac{1}{5} - 2\frac{3}{5} = 3\frac{6}{5} - 2\frac{3}{5} \quad \text{Rename } 4\frac{1}{5} \text{ as } 3\frac{6}{5}.$$

$$= 1\frac{3}{5} \quad \begin{array}{l}\text{Subtract the whole numbers and}\\ \text{subtract the fractions.}\end{array}$$

2-3 Multiply and Divide Fractions

Multiply Fractions (pp. 112–117)

 MA.7.A.3.2

Multiply. Write in simplest form.

41. $\frac{3}{5} \times \frac{10}{21}$ **42.** $4 \times \left(-\frac{13}{20}\right)$

43. $2\frac{1}{3} \times \frac{3}{4}$ **44.** $4\frac{1}{2} \times 2\frac{1}{12}$

45. FOOD An average slice of American cheese is about $\frac{1}{8}$-inch thick. What is the height of a package containing 20 slices in simplest form?

EXAMPLE 8 Find $3\frac{1}{2} \times 2\frac{3}{4}$.

$$3\frac{1}{2} \times 2\frac{3}{4} = \frac{7}{2} \times \frac{11}{4} \quad \text{Rename } 3\frac{1}{2} \text{ and } 2\frac{3}{4}.$$

$$= \frac{7 \times 11}{2 \times 4} \quad \begin{array}{l}\text{Multiply the numerators and}\\ \text{multiply the denominators.}\end{array}$$

$$= \frac{77}{8} \text{ or } 9\frac{5}{8} \quad \text{Simplify.}$$

Multiply and Divide Fractions (continued)

PSI: Draw a Diagram (pp. 118–119)

 MA.7.A.3.2

Solve each problem by drawing a diagram.

46. PAINTING Marian is painting a fence that is 72 feet long. She has already painted $\frac{5}{8}$ of the fence. How many feet of fence does she have left to paint?

47. COOKIES A cookie jar contains three types of cookies: oatmeal, chocolate chip, and sugar. Sixty percent are chocolate chip. Half of the remaining cookies are oatmeal. If there are 9 oatmeal cookies, how many cookies are in the jar?

EXAMPLE 9 Ramiro has filled $\frac{1}{3}$ or 50 gallons of his fish tank. Find the total capacity of the fish tank.

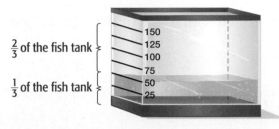

If $\frac{1}{3}$ of the fish tank is 50 gallons, then $\frac{2}{3}$ of the fish tank is 100 gallons. So, the missing two thirds must be 100 gallons. The total capacity of the fish tank is $50 + 100$, or 150 gallons.

Divide Fractions (pp. 120–125)

 MA.7.A.3.2

Divide. Write in simplest form.

48. $\frac{3}{5} \div \frac{6}{7}$ **49.** $4 \div \frac{2}{3}$

50. $2\frac{3}{4} \div \frac{5}{6}$ **51.** $-\frac{2}{5} \div 3$

52. $4\frac{3}{10} \div 2\frac{1}{5}$ **53.** $-\frac{2}{7} \div \frac{8}{21}$

54. MEASUREMENT How many $\frac{1}{8}$-inch lengths are in $6\frac{3}{4}$ inches?

EXAMPLE 10 Find $2\frac{4}{5} \div \frac{7}{10}$.

$2\frac{4}{5} \div \frac{7}{10} = \frac{14}{5} \div \frac{7}{10}$ Rename $2\frac{4}{5}$.

$= \frac{\overset{2}{\cancel{14}}}{\underset{1}{\cancel{5}}} \cdot \frac{\overset{2}{\cancel{10}}}{\underset{1}{\cancel{7}}}$ Multiply by the reciprocal of $\frac{7}{10}$.

$= \frac{4}{1}$ or 4   Simplify.

Powers and Exponents (pp. 126–129)

 MA.7.A.3.2

Write each power as a product of the same factor.

55. 3^4 **56.** 9^6

57. 5^1 **58.** 7^5

59. Write *5 to the fourth power* as a product of the same factor.

EXAMPLE 11 Write 2^3 as a product of the same factor.

The base is 2. The exponent 3 means that 2 is used as a factor 3 times.

$2^3 = 2 \cdot 2 \cdot 2$

Write each fraction or mixed number as a decimal. Use bar notation if the decimal is a repeating decimal.

1. $\frac{7}{9}$ **2.** $4\frac{5}{8}$ **3.** $\frac{91}{100}$

Write each decimal as a fraction in simplest form.

4. 0.84   **5.** 0.006   **6.** 0.42

Replace each ● with <, >, or = to make a true sentence.

7. $-\frac{2}{3}$ ● $\frac{4}{7}$ **8.** $3\frac{5}{8}$ ● $3\frac{3}{5}$ **9.** $\frac{11}{20}$ ● 0.55

Add, subtract, multiply, or divide. Write in simplest form.

10. $-\frac{4}{15} + \frac{8}{15}$ **11.** $\frac{7}{10} - \frac{1}{6}$

12. $\frac{5}{8} + \frac{2}{5}$ **13.** $6 + \frac{8}{21}$

14. $-4\frac{5}{12} - 2\frac{1}{12}$ **15.** $6\frac{7}{9} + 3\frac{5}{12}$

16. $8\frac{4}{7} - 1\frac{5}{14}$ **17.** $4\frac{5}{6} - \left(-1\frac{2}{3}\right)$

18. ✪ **NGSSS** **PRACTICE** Use the diagram to find the total distance Joe drove.

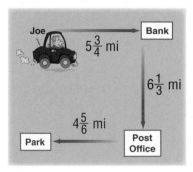

A. $15\frac{9}{13}$ miles   **C.** $\frac{11}{12}$ mile

B. $\frac{7}{12}$ mile   **D.** $16\frac{11}{12}$ miles

19. **SPORTS** Tyler's football practice lasted $2\frac{1}{2}$ hours. If $\frac{1}{4}$ of the time was spent catching passes, how much time was spent catching passes?

20. **FINANCIAL LITERACY** For his birthday, Keith received a check from his grandmother. Of this amount, the table shows how he spent or saved the money. Two weeks later, he withdrew $\frac{2}{3}$ of the amount he had deposited into his savings account. What fraction of the original check did he withdraw from his savings account?

Fraction of Check	How Spent or Saved
$\frac{2}{5}$	Spent on baseball cards
$\frac{1}{4}$	Spent on a CD
$\frac{7}{20}$	Deposited into savings account

21. **MEASUREMENT** An ounce is $\frac{1}{16}$ of a pound. How many ounces are in $8\frac{3}{4}$ pounds?

Write each power as a product of the same factor. Evaluate the expression.

22. 3^5 **23.** 15^4

24. **MEASUREMENT** Gregory wants to stain a 15-foot by 15-foot deck. One can of stain covers 200 square feet of surface. Is one can of stain enough to cover the entire deck? Explain your reasoning.

25. 📝 **THINK SOLVE EXPLAIN** **EXTENDED RESPONSE** For a measurement experiment in class, students measured the distance around their heads. The chart shows the results for part of the class.

Student	Distance Around Head (in.)
Max	17.5
Juan	$17\frac{3}{8}$
Hue	$16\frac{7}{8}$
Kobe	17.25
Martha	16.8

Part A Which student had the greatest head size?

Part B Which student had the least head size?

Part C Arrange the head sizes in order from least to greatest.

Gridded Response: Gridding Mixed Numbers

A mixed number cannot be written in the answer grid of a gridded-response question. Write the answer as an improper fraction and then fill in the grid.

NGSSS PRACTICE EXAMPLE

The tail of a salamander is $\frac{2}{3}$ of its total length. The salamander is 7 inches long. How many inches long is its tail?

$\frac{2}{3} \times 7 = \frac{2}{3} \times \frac{7}{1}$ Rename 7 as an improper fraction.

$\qquad = \frac{14}{3}$ or $4\frac{2}{3}$ Multiply.

The tail of the salamander is $\frac{14}{3}$ or $4\frac{2}{3}$ inches long. Since $4\frac{2}{3}$ cannot be written in the answer grid, fill in $\frac{14}{3}$.

Correct   **NOT Correct**

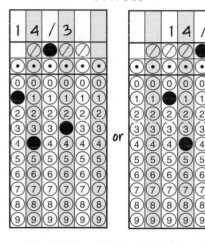

or

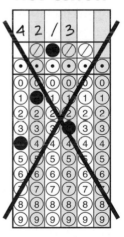

 ## Work on It

Juliette played the same song twice on her MP3 player. It took $9\frac{1}{2}$ minutes. How many minutes long is the song? Fill in your answer on a grid like the one shown above.

Test Hint

Don't forget to include the fraction bar in the answer box.

Read each question. Then fill in the correct answer on the answer sheet provided by your teacher or on a sheet of paper.

1. **SHORT RESPONSE** Mrs. Brown needs to make two different desserts for a party. The first recipe requires $2\frac{1}{4}$ cups of flour and the second recipe requires $\frac{3}{4}$ cup less than the first. Write an equation that can be used to find the number of cups of flour needed for the second recipe.

2. The fraction $\frac{5}{6}$ is found between which pair of fractions on a number line?

   A. $\frac{1}{4}$ and $\frac{5}{8}$

   B. $\frac{1}{3}$ and $\frac{4}{9}$

   C. $\frac{11}{12}$ and $\frac{31}{36}$

   D. $\frac{7}{12}$ and $\frac{17}{18}$

3. At 7 A.M., the temperature was 15°F below zero. By 2 P.M. the temperature rose 32°F and by 5 P.M. it dropped 10°F. What was the temperature at 5 P.M.?

   F. 10°F   **H.** 7°F

   G. 9°F   **I.** 11°F

4. **GRIDDED RESPONSE** A diver is swimming 11 meters below the surface. The diver sees a shark 19 meters below him. How many meters from the surface is the shark?

5. **GRIDDED RESPONSE** Name the x-coordinate for point P on the graph.

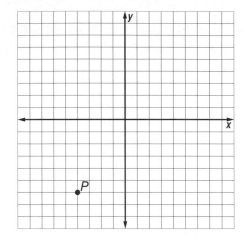

6. The table shows the distance Kelly swam over a four-day period. What was the total distance, in miles, that Kelly swam?

Kelly's Swimming	
Day	**Distance (mi)**
Monday	1.5
Tuesday	$2\frac{3}{4}$
Wednesday	2.3
Thursday	$3\frac{1}{2}$

   A. 10.5 miles   **C.** $10\frac{1}{20}$ miles

   B. $10\frac{1}{4}$ miles   **D.** 9 miles

7. Which of the following gives the correct meaning of the expression $\frac{5}{8} \div \frac{1}{3}$?

   F. $\frac{5}{8} \div \frac{1}{3} = \frac{8}{5} \times \frac{3}{1}$

   G. $\frac{5}{8} \div \frac{1}{3} = \frac{5+1}{8+3}$

   H. $\frac{5}{8} \div \frac{1}{3} = \frac{5}{8} \times \frac{3}{1}$

   I. $\frac{5}{8} \div \frac{1}{3} = \frac{5}{8} \times \frac{1}{3}$

8. Mrs. Blackwell has part of a pie left.

If the whole pie serves 12 people, what is the most reasonable estimate of the number of slices of pie Mrs. Blackwell has left?

A. 10 slices **C.** 7 slices

B. 9 slices **D.** 6 slices

9. **GRIDDED RESPONSE** Nate had 25 action figures. He gave away 10 to his brother. He then got 3 new action figures as a gift. How many action figures does Nate have now?

10. Which expression represents the least value?

F. $678 \div \frac{1}{3}$ **H.** $678 \times \frac{1}{3}$

G. $678 + \frac{1}{3}$ **I.** $678 - \frac{1}{3}$

11. **GRIDDED RESPONSE** Jacob had $25 for back-to-school shopping. He bought a shirt for $15 and then returned a shirt he bought a week ago and got $20 in return. How much money in dollars does Jacob have now?

12. **GRIDDED RESPONSE** Evan runs $2\frac{3}{8}$ miles each week. He runs $\frac{3}{4}$ mile on Mondays and $\frac{3}{4}$ mile on Tuesdays. If the only other day he runs each week is Thursday, how far does he run on Thursday?

13. **THINK SOLVE EXPLAIN** **SHORT RESPONSE** A recipe for a batch of cookies calls for 2.5 cups of flour for 24 cookies. Manuel wants to make 36 cookies. How many cups of flour will he need?

14. **THINK SOLVE EXPLAIN** **EXTENDED RESPONSE** A box of laundry detergent contains 35 cups. It takes $1\frac{1}{4}$ cups per load of laundry.

Part A Write an equation to represent how many loads ℓ you can wash with one box.

Part B How many loads can you wash with one box?

Part C How many loads can you wash with 3 boxes?

NEED EXTRA HELP?														
If You Missed Question...	1	2	3	4	5	6	7	8	9	10	11	12	13	14
Go to Lesson...	2-2A	2-1A	1-2B	1-2D	1-1C	2-2C	2-3D	2-3B	1-2D	2-3B	1-2D	2-2C	2-3B	2-3D
For help with NGSSS...	A.3.2	A.5.1	A.3.1	A.3.1	G.4.3	A.3.2	A.3.2	A.3.2	A.3.1	A.3.2	A.3.1	A.3.2	A.3.2	A.3.2

Linear Equations

The ☆BIG Idea

Solve linear equations.

FOLDABLES®
Study Organizer

Make this Foldable to help you organize your notes. Begin with a sheet of 11" by 17" paper.

1 Fold the short sides toward the middle.

2 Fold the top to the bottom.

3 Open. Cut along the second fold to make four tabs.

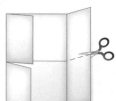

4 Label each of the tabs as shown.

Addition and Subtraction Equations / Multiplication and Division Equations / Multi-step Equations / Equations with Rational Coefficients

Review Vocabulary

solution (Prior Grade) **solución** a value for the variable that makes an equation true

The solution of 12 = **x** + 7 is **5**.

Key Vocabulary

	English	Español
p. 150	equivalent equation	ecuaciones equivalentes
p. 157	coefficient	coeficiente
p. 159	formula	formula
p. 172	two-step equation	ecuación de dos pasos

Multilingual eGlossary glencoe.com

Get Connected
glencoe.com

- Study using the **eBook**
- Explore with **Get Animated**
- Get extra help from **Personal Tutor**
- Use **virtual manipulatives** for additional help
- Take a **Self-Check Quiz**

When Will I Use This?

Seth, Marisol, and Jamar in Movie Night

Hey guys! Help me pick out some movies for movie night at school.

How much money can we spend?

Don't forget the popcorn.

Student council gave us $100. They want us to pick out as many movies as we can and...

Don't forget the popcorn.

Yes, popcorn. Don't worry Seth, I won't forget the popcorn.

The DVDs are $19 each. I hope we can get a few different movies. What do you think? A comedy? A thriller? A drama?

...and popcorn?

Yes, Seth, and popcorn! Jamar, how much will we need for popcorn?

I think we'll need $39 for popcorn.

Mmm... popcorn.

Hey! I have a great idea! Let's just skip the movie and have a popcorn party. We can use the $100 and have all kinds of different popcorn! And while we're at it, let's order a pizza!

Seth, I'm beginning to get the idea that you haven't eaten dinner yet.

You got it.

Right. Thinking with your stomach. Let's pick out some movies now.

We have $100, and popcorn is $39, and DVDs cost $19 each. I wonder how many DVDs we can get.

Your Turn!
You will solve this problem in Chapter 3.

Are You Ready for Chapter 3?

You have two options for checking prerequisite skills for this chapter.

Text Option Take the Quick Check below. Refer to the Quick Review for help.

QUICK Check

Write the phrase as an algebraic expression. (Prior Grade)

1. 3 more runs than the Pirates scored
2. a number increased by eight
3. ten dollars more than Grace has

Identify the solution of each equation from the list given. (Prior Grade)

4. $8 + w = 17$; 7, 8, 9
5. $d - 12 = 5$; 16, 17, 18
6. $6 = 3y$; 2, 3, 4
7. $7 \div c = 7$; 0, 1, 2
8. $a + 8 = 23$; 13, 14, 15
9. $25 + d = 54$; 28, 29, 30
10. $10 = 45 - n$; 35, 36, 37

Solve each equation mentally. (Prior Grade)

11. $p + 3 = 9$
12. $5 + y = 20$
13. $40 = 25 + m$
14. $14 - n = 10$
15. $47 = x - 3$
16. $18 = 25 - h$

17. **AGE** The equation $13 + a = 51$ describes the sum of the ages of Elizabeth and her mother. If a is Elizabeth's mother's age, how old is Elizabeth's mother?

QUICK Review

EXAMPLE 1

Write the phrase as an algebraic expression.

Words: five dollars more than Jennifer earned

Variable: Let d represent the number of dollars Jennifer earned.

Expression: $d + 5$

EXAMPLE 2

Is 3, 4, or 5 the solution of the equation $x + 8 = 12$?

Value of x	$x + 8 = 12$	Are both sides equal?
3	$3 + 8 = 12$ $11 \neq 12$	no
4	$4 + 8 = 12$ $12 = 12$	yes ✓
5	$5 + 8 = 12$ $13 \neq 12$	no

The solution is 4 since replacing x with 4 results in a true sentence.

EXAMPLE 3

Solve $18 = 3h$ mentally.

$18 = 3h$ What number times 3 is 18?

$18 = 3 \cdot 6$ You know that $3 \cdot 6$ is 18.

$h = 6$

The solution is 6.

Online Option  Take the Online Readiness Quiz at **glencoe.com**.

Reading Math

Identify Key Information

> Have you ever tried to solve a long word problem and didn't know where to start? Start by reading the problem carefully.

STEP 1 Look for key words.

> During a recent Super Bowl, an estimated 12.4 million pounds of potato chips were consumed. This was 3.1 million pounds more than the number of pounds of tortilla chips consumed. How many pounds of tortilla chips were consumed?

> The word *this* refers to the number of pounds of potato chips.

> The potato chips were 3.1 million pounds *more than* the tortilla chips.

STEP 2 Write the important information in one sentence.

> The number of pounds of potato chips was 3.1 million pounds more than the number of pounds of tortilla chips.

STEP 3 Replace any phrases with numbers that you know.

> 12.4 million was 3.1 million more than the number of pounds of tortilla chips.

Practice

Write the important information in one sentence. Replace any phrases with numbers that you know. Do not solve the problem.

1. **BASEBALL** Last year, Scott attended 13 Minnesota Twins baseball games. This year, he attended 24. How many more games did he attend this year?

2. **HOT AIR BALLOONS** Miyoki paid $140 for a four-hour hot air balloon ride. The cost of each hour was the same. Find the cost per hour of the ride.

NGSSS
LA.7.3.2.2 The student will draft writing by organizing information into a logical sequence and combining or deleting sentences to enhance clarity.

3-1   Addition and Subtraction Equations

Problem-Solving Investigation

Main Idea Solve problems using the *work backward* strategy.

P.S.I. TEAM +

Work Backward

MIGUEL: Yesterday, I earned extra money by doing yard work for my neighbor. Then I spent $5.50 at the convenience store and four times that amount at the bookstore. Now I have $7.75 left.

YOUR MISSION: Work backward to find how much money Miguel had before he went to the convenience store and the bookstore.

Understand	You know he has $7.75 left. You need to find the amount he started with.
Plan	Start with the end result and work backward.
Solve	He has $7.75 left.
	Undo the four times $5.50 spent at the bookstore. Since $5.50 × 4 is $22, add $7.75 and $22.
	Undo the $5.50 spent at the convenience store. Add $5.50 and $29.75.
	So, Miguel had $35.25 to start with.
Check	Assume Miguel started with $35.25. He spent $5.50 and $22. He had $35 — $5.50 — $22 or $7.75 left. So, $35.25 is correct. ✓

$$\begin{array}{r} \$7.75 \\ + \$22.00 \\ \hline \$29.75 \\ + \ \$5.50 \\ \hline \$35.25 \end{array}$$

Analyze the Strategy

1. Explain when you would use the *work backward* strategy to solve a problem.

2. Describe how to solve a problem by working backward.

3. **Write MATH** Write a problem that could be solved by working backward. Then write the steps you would take to find the solution to your problem.

 NGSSS

MA.7.A.5.2 Solve non-routine problems by working backwards.

- Work backward.
- Look for a pattern.
- Draw a diagram.
- Choose an operation.

Use the *work backward* strategy to solve Exercises 4–7.

4. **MONEY** Marisa spent $8 on a movie ticket. Then she spent $5 on popcorn and one half of what was left on a drink. She has $2 left. How much did she have initially?

5. **NUMBER THEORY** A number is multiplied by −3. Then 6 is subtracted from the product. After adding −7, the result is −25. What is the number?

6. **TIME** Timothy's morning schedule is shown. At what time does Timothy wake up if he arrives at school at 9:00 A.M.?

Timothy's Schedule	
Activity	**Time**
Wake up	▪
Get ready for school — 45 min	▪
Walk to school — 25 min	9:00 A.M.

7. **LOGIC** A small box contains 4 tennis balls. Six of these boxes are inside a medium box. Eight medium boxes are inside each large box, and 100 large boxes are shipped in a large truck. How many tennis balls are on the truck?

Use any strategy to solve Exercises 8–15.

8. **GEOGRAPHY** The land area of North Dakota is 68,976 square miles. This is about 7 times the land area of Vermont. Estimate the land area of Vermont.

9. **AGE** Brie is two years older than her sister Kiana. Kiana is 4 years older than their brother Jeron, who is 8 years younger than their brother Percy. Percy is 16 years old. How old is Brie?

10. **ELEVATION** New Orleans, Lousiana, has an elevation of −8 feet related to sea level. Death Valley, California, is 274 feet lower than New Orleans. What is the elevation of Death Valley?

11. **GEOMETRY** Draw the sixth figure in the pattern shown.

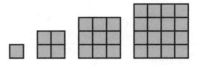

12. **WATERFALLS** Angel Falls in Venezuela is 3,212 feet high. It is 87 feet higher than 2.5 times the height of the Empire State Building. Find the height of the Empire State Building.

13. **AIRCRAFT** An aircraft carrier travels about 6 inches per gallon of fuel. Raquel's car travels about 28 miles per gallon of fuel. There are 5,280 feet in one mile. How many more inches per gallon does Raquel's car get than an aircraft carrier?

14. **SCHOOL SUPPLIES** Alexandra wishes to buy 5 pens, 1 ruler, and 7 folders.

Item	Cost
Pens	$2.09
Ruler	$0.99
Folder	$1.19

If there is no tax, is $20 enough to pay for Alexandra's school supplies? Explain your reasoning.

15. **MONEY** Antonio has saved $27 in cash to spend at the arcade. If he has 10 bills, how many of each kind of bill does he have?

Explore

Main Idea

Write and solve addition and subtraction equations using bar diagrams.

NGSSS

MA.7.A.3.3 Formulate and use different strategies to solve one-step and two-step **linear equations,** including equations with rational coefficients.

Get Connected
glencoe.com

Solve Addition and Subtraction Equations with Bar Diagrams

CELL PHONES In 2008, 15 of the 50 states had a law banning the use of handheld cell phones while driving a school bus. How many states did *not* have this law?

ACTIVITY

1 **What do you need to find?** how many states did not have a cell phone law for school bus drivers

You can represent this situation with an equation.

STEP 1 Draw a bar diagram that represents the total number of states and how many have passed a law.

50 states	
states with a law	states that do not have a law
15	?

STEP 2 Write an equation from the bar diagram. Let x represent the states that do not have a cell phone law for school bus drivers.

$$15 + x = 50$$

STEP 3 Use the *work backward* strategy to solve the equation. Since $15 + x = 50$, $x = 50 - 15$. So, $x = 35$.

Check $15 + 35 = 50$ ✓

In 2008, there were 35 states that did *not* have a law banning the use of cell phones by bus drivers.

Analyze the Results

1. Suppose by 2011, nine more states adopt similar laws. How would the equation change?

2. How would the diagram change if the U.S. Virgin Islands and Puerto Rico were counted with the United States?

2 BASEBALL CARDS Jack had some baseball cards. He sold 7 of them. Then he had 29 left. Write and solve a subtraction equation to find the number he had at the beginning.

STEP 1 Draw a bar diagram representing the sentence. Let n represent the number.

sold	number left

n baseball cards

7 — 29

STEP 2 Write a subtraction equation from the bar diagram.

$$n - 7 = 29$$

STEP 3 Solve the equation by working backward. Since $n - 7 = 29$, then $n = 29 + 7$. So, $n = 36$.

Check $36 - 7 = 29$ ✓

If 7 less than a number is 29, the number is 36.

Practice and Apply

BAR | DIAGRAM Draw a bar diagram and write an equation for each situation. Then solve the equation.

3. The sum of a number and four is equal to 18.

4. Two more than the number of frogs is 4.

5. A number of students increased by 10 is 28.

6. A number decreased by 15 is 22.

7. **BABYSITTING** Katie earned $15 babysitting this week. Last week she earned $46. How much more did she earn last week than this week?

8. **AGES** The median age of people living in Arizona is 1 year older than the median age of people living in the United States. If the median age in Arizona is 34, what is the median age of people living in the United States?

9. **Write MATH** Write a real-world problem that can be represented by the bar diagram below.

money spent for DVD	money left

n

$19 — $8

Explore

Solve Equations Using Algebra Tiles

Main Idea

Solve one-step equations using models.

NGSSS

MA.7.A.3.3 Formulate and use different strategies to solve one-step and two-step **linear equations,** including equations with rational coefficients.

Get Connected
glencoe.com

On the balance at the right, the paper bag contains a certain number of orange blocks. (Assume that the paper bag weighs nothing.) Without looking in the bag, how can you determine the number of blocks it contains?

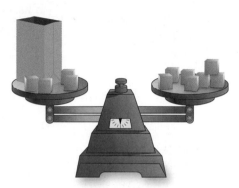

One way is to remove 4 blocks from each side of the balance. So, the bag contains 3 blocks.

In algebra, an *equation* is like a balance. The weights on each side of the balance are equal. The expressions on each side of an equation are equal. You can use algebra tiles to model and solve equations.

ACTIVITY

1 **Solve $x + 4 = 7$ using algebra tiles.**

> **STEP 1**   Model the equation.
>
> $$x + 4 \qquad = \qquad 7$$

> **STEP 2**   Remove the same number of 1-tiles from each side of the mat so that the variable is by itself on one side.
>
> $$x + 4 - 4 \qquad = \qquad 7 - 4$$

> **STEP 3**   The number of 1-tiles remaining on the right side of the mat represents the value of x.
>
> $$x \qquad = \qquad 3$$

Therefore, $x = 3$.

Check Since $3 + 4 = 7$, the solution is correct. ✔

A *zero pair* is a number paired with its opposite, like 2 and −2. You can add or subtract a zero pair from either side of an equation without changing its value, because the value of a zero pair is zero.

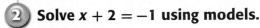

(2) Solve $x + 2 = -1$ using models.

STEP 1   Model the equation.

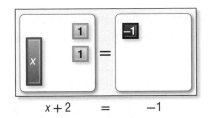

$$x + 2 \quad = \quad -1$$

STEP 2   Add 2 negative tiles to the left side of the mat and add 2 negative tiles to the right side of the mat to form zero pairs on the left.

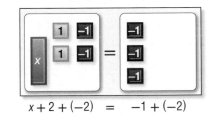

$$x + 2 + (-2) \quad = \quad -1 + (-2)$$

STEP 3   Remove all of the zero pairs from the left side. There are 3 negative tiles on the right side of the mat.

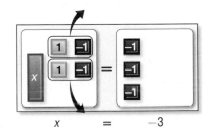

$$x \quad = \quad -3$$

Therefore, $x = -3$.

Check Since $-3 + 2 = -1$, the solution is correct. ✓

Practice and Apply

Solve each equation using algebra tiles.

1. $x + 4 = 4$ **2.** $5 = x + 4$ **3.** $4 = 1 + x$ **4.** $2 = 2 + x$

5. $-2 = x + 1$ **6.** $x - 3 = -2$ **7.** $x - 1 = -3$ **8.** $4 = x - 2$

9. Explain how the *work backward* strategy is used to solve equations.

10. How is solving an equation similar to keeping a scale in balance?

11. MAKE A CONJECTURE Write a rule that you can use to solve an equation like $x + 3 = 2$ without using models or a drawing.

12. Write MATH Write a real-world problem that can be solved using algebra tiles.

Main Idea

Solve addition and subtraction equations.

NGSSS

MA.7.A.3.3 Formulate and use different strategies to solve one-step and two-step linear equations, including equations with rational coefficients. *Also addresses MA.7.A.3.2.*

New Vocabulary

equation
equivalent equation

Get Connected
glencoe.com

Solve One-Step Addition and Subtraction Equations

VIDEO GAMES Max had some video games, and then he bought two more games. Now he has six games.

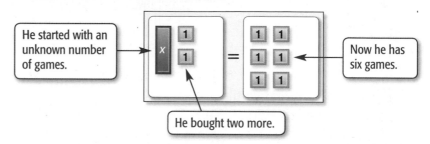

He started with an unknown number of games.

Now he has six games.

He bought two more.

1. What does x represent in the figure?

2. What addition equation is shown in the figure?

3. How many games did Max have in the beginning?

An **equation** is a sentence stating that two quantities are equal. You can solve the equation $x + 2 = 6$ by subtracting 2 from each side of the equation.

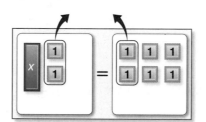

$$\begin{array}{rcl} x + 2 &=& 6 \\ -2 &=& -2 \\ \hline x &=& 4 \end{array}$$

The equations $x + 2 = 6$ and $x = 4$ are **equivalent equations** because they have the same solution, 4.

Key Concept — Subtraction Property of Equality

Words If you subtract the same number from each side of an equation, the two sides remain equal.

Symbols If $a = b$, then $a - c = b - c$.

Examples

Numbers	Algebra
$\begin{array}{rcl} 6 &=& 6 \\ -2 &=& -2 \\ \hline 4 &=& 4 \end{array}$	$\begin{array}{rcl} x + 2 &=& 6 \\ -2 &=& -2 \\ \hline x &=& 4 \end{array}$

EXAMPLE **Solve Addition Equations**

① Solve $x + 6 = 4$. Check your solution.

$$x + 6 = 4 \qquad \text{Write the equation.}$$
$$\underline{-6 = -6} \qquad \text{Subtraction Property of Equality}$$
$$x - -2 \qquad \text{Simplify.}$$

Check $\quad x + 6 = 4 \qquad$ Write the original equation.

$$-2 + 6 \stackrel{?}{=} 4 \qquad \text{Replace } x \text{ with } -2.$$

$$4 = 4 \checkmark \qquad \text{The sentence is true.}$$

The solution is -2.

 Study Tip

Solutions Notice that your new equation, $x = -2$, has the same solution as the original equation, $x + 6 = 4$.

Real-World Link · · · ·
The deeper the descent of a dive, the quicker the diver consumes air. Most divers can spend 45 minutes to an hour at 40 feet below the surface.

✓ CHECK Your Progress

Solve each equation. Check your solution.

a. $y + 6 = 9$ **b.** $x + 3 = 1$ **c.** $-3 = a + 4$

Real-World EXAMPLE *Get Animated*

② **MARINE BIOLOGY** Clown fish and angelfish are popular tropical fish. An angelfish can grow to be 12 inches long. If an angelfish is 8.5 inches longer than a clown fish, how long is a clown fish?

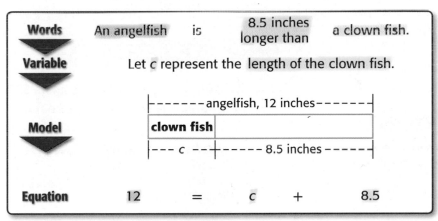

| **Words** | An angelfish | is | 8.5 inches longer than | a clown fish. |

Variable   Let c represent the length of the clown fish.

Model

```
|-------angelfish, 12 inches-------|
| clown fish |                     |
|--- c ---+----- 8.5 inches -----|
```

Equation   12   = c +   8.5

$$12 = c + 8.5 \qquad \text{Write the equation.}$$
$$\underline{-8.5 = -8.5} \qquad \text{Subtraction Property of Equality}$$
$$3.5 = c \qquad \text{Simplify.}$$

A clown fish is 3.5 inches long.

✓ CHECK Your Progress

d. **WEATHER** The highest recorded temperature in Warsaw, Missouri, is 118°F. This is 158° greater than the lowest recorded temperature. Write and solve an equation to find the lowest recorded temperature.

Words   If you add the same number to each side of an equation, the two sides remain equal.

Symbols   If $a = b$, then $a + c = b + c$.

Examples

Numbers	Algebra
$\begin{aligned} 5 &= 5 \\ +3 &= +3 \\ \hline 8 &= 8 \end{aligned}$	$\begin{aligned} x - 2 &= 4 \\ +2 &= +2 \\ \hline x &= 6 \end{aligned}$

 EXAMPLE   **Solve a Subtraction Equation**

3   Solve $x - 2 = 1$. Check your solution.

$$\begin{aligned} x - 2 &= 1 && \text{Write the equation.} \\ +2 &= +2 && \text{Addition Property of Equality} \\ \hline x &= 3 && \text{Simplify.} \end{aligned}$$

The solution is 3.   **Check** $3 - 2 = 1$ ✓

 CHECK Your Progress

Solve each equation. Check your solution.

e. $y - 3 = 4$ **f.** $r - 4 = -2$ **g.** $q - 8 = -9$

Real-World EXAMPLE

4   **SHOPPING** A pair of shoes costs $25. This is $14 less than the cost of a pair of jeans. Find the cost of the jeans.

Words	Shoes	are	$14 less than	jeans.
Variable		Let j represent the cost of jeans.		
Equation	25	=	j −	14

$$\begin{aligned} 25 &= j - 14 && \text{Write the equation.} \\ +14 &= +14 && \text{Addition Property of Equality} \\ \hline 39 &= j && \text{Simplify.} \end{aligned}$$

The jeans cost $39.

 CHECK Your Progress

h. ANIMALS The average lifespan of a tiger is 17 years. This is 3 years less than the average lifespan of a lion. Write and solve an equation to find the average lifespan of a lion.

Example 1
(p. 151)

Solve each equation. Check your solution.

1. $n + 6 = 8$ **2.** $7 = y + 2$

3. $m + 5 = 3$ **4.** $-2 = a + 6$

Example 2
(p. 151)

5. BAR | DIAGRAM Orville and Wilbur Wright made the first airplane flights in 1903. Wilbur's flight was 364 feet. This was 120 feet longer than Orville's flight. Draw a bar diagram to represent the flights. Then write and solve an equation to find the length of Orville's flight.

Example 3
(p. 152)

Solve each equation. Check your solution.

6. $x - 5 = 6$ **7.** $-1 = c - 6$

Example 4
(p. 152)

8. PRESIDENTS John F. Kennedy was the youngest president to be inaugurated. He was 43 years old. This was 26 years younger than the oldest president to be inaugurated—Ronald Reagan. Write and solve an equation to find how old Reagan was when he was inaugurated.

Practice and Problem Solving

 = **Step-by-Step Solutions** begin on page R6.
Extra Practice is on page EP7.

Examples 1 and 3
(pp. 151–152)

Solve each equation. Check your solution.

9. $a + 3 = 10$ **10.** $y + 5 = 11$ **11.** $9 = r + 2$

12. $14 = s + 7$ **13.** $x + 8 = 5$ **14.** $y + 15 = 11$

15 $r + 6 = -3$ **16.** $k + 3 = -9$ **17.** $s - 8 = 9$

18. $w - 7 = 11$ **19.** $-1 = q - 8$ **20.** $-2 = p - 13$

Examples 2 and 4
(pp. 151–152)

BAR | DIAGRAM Write an equation. Use a bar diagram if needed. Then solve the equation.

21. MUSIC Last week Tiffany practiced her bassoon a total of 7 hours. This was 2 hours more than she practiced the previous week. How many hours did Tiffany practice the previous week?

22. CIVICS In the 2008 presidential election, Ohio had 20 electoral votes. This is 14 votes less than Texas had. How many electoral votes did Texas have in 2008?

23. AGES Zack is 15 years old. This is 3 years younger than his brother Louis. How old is Louis?

24. BASKETBALL The Miami Heat scored 79 points in a recent game. This was 13 points less than the Chicago Bulls scored. How many points did the Chicago Bulls score?

Solve each equation. Check your solution.

25. $a - 3.5 = 14.9$ **26.** $x - 2.8 = 9.5$ **27.** $r - 8.5 = -2.1$

28. $z - 9.4 = -3.6$ **29.** $n + 1.4 = 0.72$ **30.** $b + 2.25 = 1$

31. $m + \dfrac{5}{6} = \dfrac{11}{12}$ **32.** $y + \dfrac{1}{2} = \dfrac{3}{4}$ **33.** $s - \dfrac{1}{9} = \dfrac{5}{18}$

34. $-\dfrac{1}{3} = r - \dfrac{3}{4}$ **35.** $-\dfrac{5}{6} + c = -\dfrac{11}{12}$ **36.** $-\dfrac{33}{34} = t - \dfrac{13}{17}$

For Exercises 37–42, write an equation. Then solve the equation.

37. MONEY Suppose you have d dollars. After you pay your sister the $5 you owe her, you have $18 left. How much money did you have?

38. FINANCIAL LITERACY Suppose you have saved $38. How much more do you need to save to buy a small television that costs $65?

39. GEOMETRY The sum of the measures of the angles of a triangle is 180°. Find the missing measure.

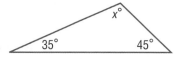

40. VOLCANOES Alaska, Hawaii, and Washington have active volcanoes. Alaska has 43, Hawaii has 5, and Washington has v. If they have 52 active volcanoes in all, how many volcanoes does Washington have?

41 GOLF The table shows Cristie Kerr's scores for four rounds of the 2008 U.S. Women's Open. Her total score was even with par. What was her score for the third round?

Round	Score
First	−1
Second	−3
Third	s
Fourth	+2

42. BUSINESS At the end of the day, the closing price of XYZ Stock was $62.87 per share. This was $0.62 less than the opening price. Find the opening price.

43. MULTIPLE REPRESENTATIONS The table shows information about the tallest wooden roller coasters.

Tallest Wooden Roller Coasters	Height (feet)	Drop (feet)	Speed (mph)
Son of Beast	218	214	s
El Toro	181	176	70
The Rattler	180	d	65
Voyage	173	154	67
Colossos	h	159	75

a. **ALGEBRA** The difference in speeds of Son of Beast and The Rattler is 13 miles per hour. If Son of Beast has the greater speed, write and solve a subtraction equation to find its speed.

b. **BAR | DIAGRAM** The Rattler has a drop that is 52 feet less than El Toro. Draw a bar diagram and write an equation to find the height of The Rattler.

c. **ALGEBRA** Let h represent the height of the Colossos roller coaster. Explain why $h + 10 = 180$ and $h + 48 = 218$ are equivalent equations. Then explain the meaning of the solution.

44. **FIND THE ERROR** Aisha is finding $b + 5 = -8$. Find her mistake and correct it.

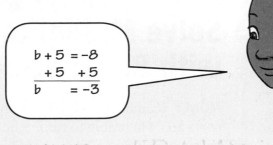

$$b + 5 = -8$$
$$\underline{+5 \quad +5}$$
$$b \quad = -3$$

45. **CHALLENGE** Suppose $x + y = 11$ and the value of x increases by 2. If their sum remains the same, what must happen to the value of y?

46. **Write MATH** Write a problem about a real-world situation that can be represented by the equation $p - 25 = 50$.

 NGSSS Practice   MA.6.A.3.1, MA.7.A.3.3

47. The Oriental Pearl Tower in China is 1,535 feet tall. It is 280 feet shorter than the Canadian National Tower in Canada. Which equation can be used to find the height of the Canadian National Tower?

   A. $1{,}535 + h = 280$
   B. $h = 1{,}535 - 280$
   C. $1{,}535 = h - 280$
   D. $280 - h = 1{,}535$

48. Which of the following statements is true concerning the equation $x + 3 = 7$?

   F. To find the value of x, add 3 to each side.
   G. To find the value of x, add 7 to each side.
   H. To find the value of x, find the sum of 3 and 7.
   I. To find the value of x, subtract 3 from each side.

49. **CREDIT CARDS** Alicia paid off $119 of her credit card balance and made an additional $62.75 in purchases. If she now owes $90.45, what was her starting balance? (Lesson 3-1A)

50. **LIGHT** The speed of light is about 67^3 kilometers per second. How many kilometers per second is this? (Lesson 2-3E)

Write each fraction or mixed number as a decimal. Use bar notation if the decimal is a repeating decimal. (Lesson 2-1B)

51. $\dfrac{5}{9}$

52. $\dfrac{5}{6}$

53. $\dfrac{4}{11}$

Explore

Solve Multiplication Equations with Bar Diagrams

Main Idea

Write and solve one-step multiplication equations using bar diagrams.

NGSSS

 MA.7.A.3.3 Formulate and use different strategies to solve one-step and two-step **linear equations,** including equations with rational coefficients.

Get Connected
glencoe.com

MONEY Kumar is saving his money to buy a new DVD player that costs $63. He is able to tutor 9 hours in a week. How much should he charge per hour to have enough money by the end of the week?

ACTIVITY

What do you need to find? how much he should charge per hour

STEP 1 Draw a bar diagram that represents the money he needs to earn and the number of hours he is available to tutor that week.

			$63					
hour 1	hour 2	hour 3	hour 4	hour 5	hour 6	hour 7	hour 8	hour 9
?	?	?	?	?	?	?	?	?

STEP 2 Write an equation from the bar diagram. Let x represent the amount he should charge each hour.

$$9x = 63$$

STEP 3 Use the *work backward* strategy to solve the equation. Since $9x = 63$, $x = 63 \div 9$. So, $x = 7$.

Check $9 \times 7 = 63$ ✓

Kumar should charge $7 an hour.

Practice and Apply

BAR DIAGRAM Draw a bar diagram and write an equation for each situation. Then solve the equation.

1. **DANCE CLASS** Keyani spent $70 for 4 hours of dance classes. How much did she spend per hour of dance class?

2. **TEXT MESSAGING** The screen on Lin's cell phone allows for 8 lines of text per message. The maximum number of characters for each message is 160. How many characters can each line hold?

Main Idea
Solve one-step multiplication and division equations.

NGSSS
MA.7.A.3.3 Formulate and use different strategies to solve one-step and two-step linear equations, including equations with rational coefficients.

New Vocabulary
coefficient
formula

Get Connected
glencoe.com

Solve One-Step Multiplication and Division Equations

Explore Suppose three friends order an appetizer of nachos that costs $6. They agree to split the cost equally. The figure below illustrates the multiplication equation $3x = 6$, where x represents the amount each friend pays.

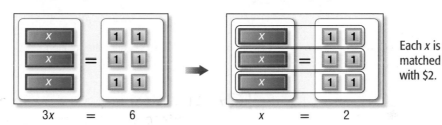

Each x is matched with $2.

The solution of $3x = 6$ is 2.

So, each friend pays $2.

Solve each equation using models or a drawing.

1. $3x = 12$
2. $2x = -8$
3. $8 = 2x$
4. $3x = -9$

5. What operation did you use to find each solution?

6. How can you use the 8 being multiplied by x to solve $8x = 40$?

The expression $3x$ means 3 *times the value of* x. The numerical factor of a multiplication expression like $3x$ is called a **coefficient**. So, 3 is the coefficient of $3x$.

> ### Key Concept · Division Property of Equality
>
> **Words** If you divide each side of an equation by the same nonzero number, the two sides remain equal.
>
> **Symbols** If $a = b$ and $c \neq 0$, then $\dfrac{a}{c} = \dfrac{b}{c}$.
>
> **Examples**
> | Numbers | Algebra |
> |---|---|
> | $8 = 8$ | $2x = -6$ |
> | $\dfrac{8}{2} = \dfrac{8}{2}$ | $\dfrac{2x}{2} = \dfrac{-6}{2}$ |
> | $4 = 4$ | $x = -3$ |

EXAMPLES **Solve Multiplication Equations**

1 Solve $20 = 4x$. Check your solution.

$20 = 4x$ Write the equation.

$\dfrac{20}{4} = \dfrac{4x}{4}$ Division Property of Equality

$5 = x$ $20 \div 4 = 5$

The solution is 5. Check the solution.

2 Solve $-8y = 24$. Check your solution.

$-8y = 24$ Write the equation.

$\dfrac{-8y}{-8} = \dfrac{24}{-8}$ Division Property of Equality

$y = -3$ $24 \div (-8) = -3$

The solution is -3. Check the solution.

 CHECK Your Progress

Solve each equation. Check your solution.

a. $30 = 6x$ **b.** $-6a = 36$ **c.** $-9d = -72$

Real-World EXAMPLE

3 **TEXT MESSAGING** Lelah sent 574 text messages last week. On average, how many messages did she send each day?

Words	Total	is equal to	number of days	times	number of messages.
Variable	Let m represent the number of messages Lelah sent.				
Equation	574	$=$	7	$\cdot$	m

$574 = 7m$ Write the equation.

$\dfrac{574}{7} = \dfrac{7m}{7}$ Division Property of Equality

$82 = m$ $574 \div 7 = 82$

Lelah sent 82 messages on average each day.

Real-World Link · · · · ·
Over 60% of teenagers' text messages are sent from their homes—even when a landline is available.

 CHECK Your Progress

d. **TRAVEL** Mrs. Acosta's car can travel an average of 24 miles on each gallon of gasoline. Write and solve an equation to find how many gallons of gasoline she will need for a trip of 348 miles.

Key Concept — Multiplication Property of Equality

Words If you multiply each side of an equation by the same number, the two sides remain equal.

Examples

	Numbers	Algebra
	$3 = 3$	$\dfrac{x}{4} = 7$
	$3(-6) = 3(-6)$	$\dfrac{x}{4}(4) = 7(4)$
	$-18 = -18$	$x = 28$

EXAMPLE Solve Division Equations

4 Solve $\dfrac{a}{-4} = -9$.

$\dfrac{a}{-4} = -9$ Write the equation.

$\dfrac{a}{-4}(-4) = -9(-4)$ Multiplication Property of Equality

$a = 36$ $-9 \cdot (-4) = 36$

 CHECK Your Progress

e. $\dfrac{y}{-3} = -8$ **f.** $\dfrac{m}{5} = -7$ **g.** $30 = \dfrac{b}{-6}$

Vocabulary Link

Everyday Use

Formula A plan or method for doing something.

Math Use

Formula An equation that shows the relationship among certain quantities.

A **formula** is an equation that shows the relationship among certain quantities. One of the most common formulas is the equation $d = rt$, which gives the relationship among distance d, rate r, and time t. The formula can also be written as $r = \dfrac{d}{t}$ or $t = \dfrac{d}{r}$.

Real-World EXAMPLE

5 **DISTANCE** The distance d Tina travels in her car while driving 60 miles per hour for 3 hours is given by the equation $\dfrac{d}{3} = 60$. How far did she travel?

$\dfrac{d}{3} = 60$ Write the equation.

$\dfrac{d}{3}(3) = 60(3)$ Multiplication Property of Equality

$d = 180$ $60 \cdot 3 = 180$

Tina traveled 180 miles.

 CHECK Your Progress

h. **ANIMALS** A Fitch ferret has a mass of about 2 kilograms. To find its weight in pounds p, you can use the equation $\dfrac{p}{2} = 2.2$. How many pounds does a Fitch ferret weigh?

Examples 1, 2, and 4
(pp. 158–159)

Solve each equation. Check your solution.

1. $6c = 18$ **2.** $15 = 3z$ **3.** $-8x = 24$

4. $-9r = -36$ **5.** $\dfrac{p}{9} = 9$ **6.** $\dfrac{a}{12} = -3$

Example 3
(p. 158)

7. WORK Antonia earns $6 per hour helping her grandmother. Write and solve an equation to find how many hours she needs to work to earn $48.

Example 5
(p. 159)

8. SHARKS A shark can swim at an average speed of 25 miles per hour. At this rate, how far can a shark swim in 2.4 hours? Use $r = \dfrac{d}{t}$.

Practice and Problem Solving

● = **Step-by-Step Solutions** begin on page R6.
Extra Practice is on page EP8.

Examples 1 and 2
(p. 158)

Solve each equation. Check your solution.

9. $7a = 49$ **10.** $9e = 27$ **11.** $2x = -6$

12. $-4j = 36$ **13.** $-12y = 60$ **14.** $-4s = -16$

Example 4
(p. 159)

15 $\dfrac{m}{10} = 7$ **16.** $\dfrac{u}{6} = 9$ **17.** $\dfrac{h}{-3} = 12$

18. $-30 = \dfrac{q}{-5}$ **19.** $-8 = \dfrac{c}{-10}$ **20.** $\dfrac{r}{20} = -2$

BAR | DIAGRAM **Write an equation. Use a bar diagram if needed. Then solve the equation.**

Example 3
(p. 158)

21. MONEY Brandy wants to buy a digital camera that costs $300. If she saves $15 each week, in how many weeks will she have enough money for the camera?

22. COMPUTERS The width of a computer monitor is 1.25 times as long as its height. Find the height of the computer monitor at the right.

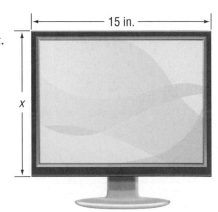

Example 5
(p. 159)

23 SPEED A race car can travel at a rate of 205 miles per hour. At this rate, how far would it travel in 3 hours? Use $r = \dfrac{d}{t}$.

24. INSECTS A dragonfly, the fastest insect, can fly a distance of 50 feet at a speed of 25 feet per second. Find the time in seconds. Use $d = rt$.

25. HURRICANES A certain hurricane travels 20.88 kilometers per hour. The distance from Cuba to Key West is 145 kilometers. Write and solve a multiplication equation to find how long it would take the hurricane to travel from Cuba to Key West.

26. **OPEN ENDED** Describe a real-world situation in which you would use a division equation to solve a problem. Then write your equation.

27. **FIND THE ERROR** Raul is solving $-6x - 72$. Find his mistake and correct it.

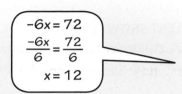

$$-6x = 72$$
$$\frac{-6x}{6} = \frac{72}{6}$$
$$x = 12$$

28. **CHALLENGE** Solve $3|x| = 12$. Explain your reasoning.

Write MATH Write a real-world problem that could be represented by each equation.

29. $2x = 16$

30. $3x = 75$

31. $4x = -8$

 **NGSSS Practice**   MA.6.A.3.1, MA.6.G.4.3, MA.5.G.5.4, MA.7.A.3.3

32. A football player can run 20 yards in 3.4 seconds. Which equation could be used to find y, the number of yards the football player can run in a second?

   A. $20y = 3.4$

   B. $3.4 - y = 20$

   C. $3.4y = 20$

   D. $20 + y = 3.4$

33. **SHORT RESPONSE** Use the formula $A = bh$ to find the base in inches of a rhombus with a height of 7 inches and an area of 56 square inches.

ALGEBRA Solve each equation. Check your solution. (Lesson 3-1D)

34. $y + 8 = -2$

35. $x - 7 = -2$

36. $20 = z + 23$

37. **NUMBERS** A number is halved. Then 5 is added and 2 is multiplied by the sum. Finally, 3 is added to the product. If the final sum is 25, what was the beginning number? Use the *work backward* strategy.
(Lesson 3-1A)

Explore

Main Idea

Write and solve equations with rational coefficients using bar diagrams.

NGSSS

MA.7.A.3.3 Formulate and use different strategies to solve one-step and two-step **linear equations**, including equations with rational coefficients.

Get Connected
glencoe.com

Solve Equations with Rational Coefficients

TALENT SHOW Two thirds of Chen's homeroom class plan to participate in the school talent show. If 16 students from the class plan to participate, how many students are in the homeroom class?

ACTIVITY

What do you need to find? how many students are in Chen's homeroom class

You can represent this situation with an equation.

STEP 1 Draw a bar diagram that represents the total number of students in the class and how many plan to participate.

|----number of students in class----|
| | | |
|--------16--------|

STEP 2 Write an equation from the bar diagram. Let c represent the total number of students in the class.

$$\frac{2}{3}c = 16$$

STEP 3 Find the number of students represented by the sections of the bar.

|--number of students in class, c--|
| 8 | 8 | 8 |
|------- 16 ------|

Since each section represents 8 students, there are 8×3 or 24 students in the class. **Check** $\frac{2}{3} \times 24 = 16$ ✓

Practice and Apply

1. Suppose $\frac{3}{4}$ of the class planned to participate. How would the diagram and equation be different?

2. **BAR DIAGRAM** Eliana is spending $\frac{3}{5}$ of her monthly allowance money on a costume for the talent show. She plans to spend $24. Draw a bar diagram to represent the situation. Then write and solve an equation to find the amount of Eliana's monthly allowance.

Main Idea
Solve equations with rational coefficients.

NGSSS

MA.7.A.3.3 Formulate and use different strategies to solve one-step and two-step **linear equations, including equations with rational coefficients.** *Also addresses MA.7.A.3.2.*

New Vocabulary
multiplicative inverse
reciprocal

Get Connected
glencoe.com

Solve Equations with Rational Coefficients

HOMEWORK Shawnda spends $\frac{1}{2}$ hour doing homework after school. Then she spends another $\frac{1}{2}$ hour doing homework before bed. In all, she spends $2 \cdot \frac{1}{2}$ or 1 hour doing homework.

1. Copy and complete the table below.

$\frac{3}{2} \times \frac{2}{3} = \blacksquare$	$\frac{1}{5} \times \blacksquare = 1$	$\frac{5}{6} \times \frac{6}{5} = \blacksquare$	$\frac{7}{8} \times \frac{8}{7} = \blacksquare$
$\blacksquare \times \frac{5}{7} = 1$	$\frac{2}{6} \times \frac{6}{2} = \blacksquare$	$\frac{7}{1} \times \blacksquare = 1$	$\blacksquare \times 8 = 1$

2. What is true about the products in Exercise 1?

Two numbers with a product of 1 are called **multiplicative inverses**, or **reciprocals**.

Key Concept — Inverse Property of Multiplication

Words   The product of a number and its multiplicative inverse is 1.

Examples

Numbers	**Algebra**
$\frac{3}{4} \times \frac{4}{3} = 1$	$\frac{a}{b} \cdot \frac{b}{a} = 1$, for $a, b \neq 0$

EXAMPLES — Find Multiplicative Inverses

1 Find the multiplicative inverse of $\frac{2}{5}$.

Since $\frac{2}{5} \cdot \frac{5}{2} = 1$, the multiplicative inverse of $\frac{2}{5}$ is $\frac{5}{2}$, or $2\frac{1}{2}$.

2 Find the multiplicative inverse of $2\frac{1}{3}$.

$2\frac{1}{3} = \frac{7}{3}$ Rename the mixed number as an improper fraction.

Since $\frac{7}{3} \cdot \frac{3}{7} = 1$, the multiplicative inverse of $2\frac{1}{3}$ is $\frac{3}{7}$.

CHECK Your Progress

Find the muliplicative inverse of each number.

a. $\frac{5}{6}$ **b.** $1\frac{1}{2}$ **c.** 8 **d.** $\frac{4}{3}$

Sometimes the coefficient of a term in a multiplication equation is a rational number. If the coefficient is a decimal, divide each side by the coefficient. If the coefficient is a fraction, multiply each side by the reciprocal of the coefficient.

Decimal	Fraction
$0.75x = 3.75$	$\frac{2}{3}x = 4$
$\frac{0.75x}{0.75} = \frac{3.75}{0.75}$	$\frac{3}{2} \cdot \frac{2}{3}x = \frac{3}{2} \cdot 4$
$x = 5$	$x = 6$

Division

$$0.75\overline{)3.75} \\ \underline{-3.75} \\ 0$$
5.

EXAMPLE **Decimal Coefficients**

3 Solve $16 = 0.25n$. Check your solution.

$16 = 0.25n$	Write the equation.
$\frac{16}{0.25} = \frac{0.25n}{0.25}$	Division Property of Equality
$64 = n$	Simplify.

Check $\quad 16 = 0.25n$ $\qquad$ Write the original equation.

$\qquad\qquad 16 \stackrel{?}{=} 0.25 \cdot 64$ $\quad$ Replace n with 64.

$\qquad\qquad 16 = 16 \checkmark$ $\qquad$ This sentence is true.

The solution is 64.

CHECK Your Progress

Solve each equation. Check your solution.

e. $6.4 = 0.8m$ $\qquad$ **f.** $-2.8p = 4.2$ $\qquad$ **g.** $-4.7k = -10.81$

Real-World Link · · · · · ·

Each year, over 1.5 billion gallons of ice cream are produced in the United States.

Real-World EXAMPLE

4 **ICE CREAM** Jaya's softball coach agreed to buy ice cream cones for all of the team members. Ice cream cones are $0.80 each. How many ice cream cones can the coach buy with $10?

Each cone costs $0.80. Let n represent the number of team members. Write and solve an equation.

$0.80n = 10$	Write the equation.
$\frac{0.8n}{0.80} = \frac{10}{0.80}$	Division Property of Equality
$n = 12.5$	Simplify.

Since the number of ice cream cones must be a whole number, there is enough money for 12 ice cream cones.

164 **Chapter 3** Linear Equations

EXAMPLE   **Solve a Multiplication Equation**

5 Solve $\frac{3}{4}x = \frac{12}{20}$. Check your solution.

$$\frac{3}{4}x = \frac{12}{20}$$ Write the equation.

$$\left(\frac{4}{3}\right) \cdot \frac{3}{4}x = \left(\frac{4}{3}\right) \cdot \frac{12}{20}$$ Multiply each side by the reciprocal of $\frac{3}{4}$, $\frac{4}{3}$.

$$\overset{1}{\underset{1}{\frac{4}{3}}} \cdot \overset{1}{\underset{1}{\frac{3}{4}}}x = \overset{1}{\underset{1}{\frac{4}{3}}} \cdot \overset{4}{\underset{5}{\frac{12}{20}}}$$ Divide by common factors.

$$x = \frac{4}{5}$$ Simplify.

Check $\frac{3}{4}x = \frac{12}{20}$ Write the original equation.

$$\frac{3}{4}\left(\frac{4}{5}\right) \overset{?}{=} \frac{12}{20}$$ Replace x with $\frac{4}{5}$.

$$\frac{12}{20} = \frac{12}{20} \checkmark$$ This sentence is true.

Study Tip

Fractions as Coefficients
The expression $\frac{3}{4}x$ can be read as $\frac{3}{4}$ of x, $\frac{3}{4}$ multiplied by x, $3x$ divided by 4, or $\frac{x}{4}$ multiplied by 3.

CHECK Your Progress

h. $\frac{1}{2}x = 8$

i. $-\frac{3}{4}x = 9$

j. $-\frac{7}{8}x = -\frac{21}{64}$

Real-World EXAMPLE Get Animated

6 **SCHOOL PLAY** Valerie needs $\frac{2}{3}$ yard of fabric to make each hat for the school play. Write and solve an equation to find how many hats can she make with 6 yards of fabric.

Each hat needs $\frac{2}{3}$ yard of fabric. So, $\frac{2}{3}$ of some number n is 6. Draw a bar diagram.

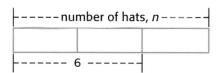

Write and solve a multiplication equation.

$$\frac{2}{3}n = 6$$ Write the equation.

$$\left(\frac{3}{2}\right) \cdot \frac{2}{3}n = \left(\frac{3}{2}\right) \cdot 6$$ Multiply each side by $\frac{3}{2}$.

$$n = 9$$ Simplify.

Valerie can make 9 hats.

CHECK Your Progress

k. **TRAIL MIX** Wilson has 9 pounds of trail mix. How many $\frac{3}{4}$-pound bags of trail mix can he make?

Lesson 3-2 Multiplication and Division Equations   **165**

Examples 1 and 2
(p. 163)

Find the multiplicative inverse of each number.

1. $\frac{8}{5}$ **2.** $\frac{2}{9}$ **3.** $5\frac{4}{5}$ **4.** 9

Solve each equation. Check your solution.

Examples 3 and 5
(pp. 164–165)

5. $1.6k = 3.2$ **6.** $3.9 = 1.3y$ **7.** $-2.5b = 20.5$

8. $-\frac{1}{2} = -\frac{5}{18}h$ **9.** $\frac{3}{8}a = \frac{12}{40}$ **10.** $-6 = \frac{4}{7}x$

Examples 4 and 6
(pp. 164–165)

11. FRUIT Three fourths of the fruit in a refrigerator are apples. There are 24 apples in the refrigerator. Write and solve an equation to find how many pieces of fruit are in the refrigerator.

12. FINANCIAL LITERACY Dillon deposited $\frac{3}{4}$ of his paycheck into the bank. The deposit slip shows how much he deposited. Write and solve an equation to find the amount of his paycheck.

Great Savings Bank

Dillon Gates
Name

Amount Deposited: **$46.50**

Practice and Problem Solving

 = **Step-by-Step Solutions** begin on page R6.
Extra Practice is on page EP8.

Examples 1 and 2
(p. 163)

Find the multiplicative inverse of each number.

13. $\frac{5}{6}$ **14.** $\frac{11}{2}$ **15.** $\frac{1}{6}$ **16.** $\frac{1}{10}$

17. 3   **18.** 14   **19.** $5\frac{1}{8}$ **20.** $6\frac{2}{3}$

Examples 3 and 5
(pp. 164–165)

Solve each equation. Check your solution.

21. $1.2x = 6$ **22.** $2.8 = 0.4d$ **23.** $-2.4b = 14.4$

24. $-5w = -24.5$ **25.** $3.6h = -10.8$ **26.** $2.8m = 12.88$

27. $\frac{2}{5}t = \frac{12}{25}$ **28.** $\frac{24}{16} = \frac{3}{4}a$ **㉙** $\frac{7}{8}k = \frac{5}{6}$

30. $\frac{2}{3} = \frac{8}{3}b$ **31.** $-\frac{1}{2}g = -3\frac{1}{3}$ **32.** $\frac{3}{5}c = -6\frac{1}{4}$

Examples 4 and 6
(pp. 164–165)

33. LIFE SCIENCE The average growth per month of human hair is 0.5 inch. Write and solve an equation to find how long it takes hair to grow 3 inches.

34. SEWING Jocelyn has nine yards of fabric to make table napkins for a senior citizens' center. She needs $\frac{3}{8}$ yard for each napkin. Write and solve an equation to find the number of napkins that she can make with this amount of fabric.

For Exercises 35–38, write an equation. Then solve.

35. CAVES The self-guided Mammoth Cave Discovery Tour includes an elevation change of 140 feet. This is $\frac{7}{15}$ of the elevation change on the Wild Cave Tour. What is the elevation change on the Wild Cave Tour?

36. MUSEUMS Twenty-four students brought their permission slips to attend the class field trip to the local art museum. If this represented $\frac{4}{5}$ of the class, how many students are in the class?

37 MEASUREMENT If one serving of cooked rice is $\frac{3}{4}$ cup, how many servings will $16\frac{1}{2}$ cups of rice yield?

38. HIKING After Alana hiked $2\frac{5}{8}$ miles along a hiking trail, she realized that she was only $\frac{3}{4}$ of the way to the end of the trail. How long is the trail?

39. GRAPHIC NOVEL Refer to the graphic novel frame below. Write and solve an equation to find how many movies they have time to show.

H.O.T. Problems

40. REASONING Complete the statement: If $8 = \frac{m}{4}$, then $m - 12 = \blacksquare$. Explain.

41. Which One Doesn't Belong? Identify the pair of numbers that does not belong with the other three. Explain.

| $\frac{9}{6}, \frac{6}{9}$ | $4, \frac{1}{4}$ | $\frac{3}{5}, 5$ | $\frac{2}{7}, \frac{7}{2}$ |

42. CHALLENGE The formula for the area of a trapezoid is $A = \frac{1}{2}h(b_1 + b_2)$, where b_1 and b_2 are both bases and h is the height. Find the value of h in terms of A, b_1, and b_2. Justify your answer.

43. Write MATH Explain the Multiplication Property of Equality. Then give an example of an equation in which you would use this property.

44. Audrey drove 200 miles in 3.5 hours. Which equation can you use to find the rate r at which Audrey was traveling?

   A. $200 = 3.5r$

   B. $200 \cdot 3.5 = r$

   C. $\frac{r}{3.5} = 200$

   D. $200r = 3.5$

45. A high-speed train travels 100 miles in $\frac{2}{3}$ hour. Which speed represents the rate of the train?

   F. 50 mph

   G. 75 mph

   H. 100 mph

   I. 150 mph

46. The table shows the results of a survey.

Music Preference	
Type	**Fraction of Students**
Pop	$\frac{5}{8}$
Jazz	$\frac{1}{8}$
Rap	$\frac{1}{4}$

If there are 420 students surveyed, which equation can be used to find the number of students s who prefer rap?

   A. $\frac{1}{4}s = 420$ **C.** $s + \frac{1}{4} = 420$

   B. $s = \frac{1}{4} \cdot 420$ **D.** $420 + s = \frac{1}{4}$

47. THINK SOLVE EXPLAIN **SHORT RESPONSE** Nithia earns $6.25 per hour at work. She wants to earn $100 for a class camping trip. Use the formula below to find h, the number of hours she will have to work to earn the money.

$$6.25h = 100$$

ALGEBRA Solve each equation. Check your solution. (Lessons 3-2B, 3-1D)

48. $4f = 28$ **49.** $-3y = -15$ **50.** $\frac{p}{14} = 3$ **51.** $\frac{x}{30} = 15$

52. $7 = x + 8$ **53.** $k - 3 = -14$ **54.** $c - 14 = 27$ **55.** $-11 = n + 2$

56. BAKING Carlota is making brownies for a bake sale. She is tripling the recipe at the right. How much cocoa powder will she need for three batches of brownies? (Lesson 2-3B)

57. CRAFTS Kyle bought $\frac{5}{6}$ yard of fabric to make a craft item. He used $\frac{3}{4}$ yard in making the item. How much fabric was left over? (Lesson 2-2C)

Brownies (makes 1 batch)
2 cups white sugar
1 cup butter
$\frac{1}{2}$ cup cocoa powder
1 teaspoon vanilla extract
4 eggs
$1\frac{1}{2}$ cups all-purpose flour
$\frac{1}{2}$ teaspoon baking powder
$\frac{1}{2}$ teaspoon salt

58. CAVERNS Adriana is 52 feet underground touring the Lewis and Clark Caverns. She climbs up a ladder 15 feet. What is her new location? (Lesson 1-2B)

1. **GIFT** Tom and Angela shared the cost of a gift for Jael. Angela contributed two dollars more than twice the amount that Tom contributed, who spent $6.00 on the gift. Use the *work backward* strategy to determine how much Angela spent on the gift. (Lesson 3-1A)

Solve each equation. Check your solution.
(Lesson 3-1D)

2. $21 + m = 33$

3. $a - 5 = -12$

4. $p + 1.7 = -9.8$

5. $56 = k - (-33)$

6. **GEOMETRY** The sum of the measures of the angles of a triangle is 180°. Write and solve an equation to find the missing measure m.
(Lesson 3-1D)

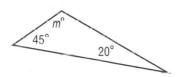

7. **NGSSS PRACTICE** Trevor's test score was 5 points lower than Ursalina's test score. If Ursalina scored 85 on the test, which equation would give Trevor's score d when solved? (Lesson 3-1D)

A. $85 = d + 5$

B. $d - 5 = 85$

C. $80 = d + 5$

D. $d - 5 = 80$

8. **PETS** Cameron has 11 adult Fantail goldfish. This is 7 fewer Fantail goldfish than his friend Julia has. Write and solve a subtraction equation to determine the number of Fantail goldfish g that Julia has. (Lesson 3-1D)

9. **MEASUREMENT** The Grand Canyon has a maximum depth of almost 5,280 feet. An average four-story apartment building has a height of 66 feet. Write and solve a multiplication equation to determine the number of apartment buildings b, stacked on top of each other, that would fill the depth of the Grand Canyon. (Lesson 3-2B)

Solve each equation. Check your solution.
(Lesson 3-2B)

10. $5f = -75$

11. $\frac{w}{3} = 16$

12. $63 = 7y$

13. $-28 = -2d$

14. $\frac{g}{12} = 6$

15. $15 = \frac{b}{15}$

16. **NGSSS PRACTICE** Michelann drove 44 miles per hour and covered a distance of 154 miles. Which equation accurately describes this situation if h represents the number of hours Michelann drove? (Lesson 3-2B)

F. $154 = 44 + h$

G. $44h = 154$

H. $154 = 44 \div h$

I. $h - 44 = 154$

17. **LAWN SERVICE** Trey estimates he will earn $470 next summer cutting lawns in his neighborhood. This amount is 2.5 times the amount a he earned this summer. Write and solve a multiplication equation to find how much Trey earned this summer. (Lesson 3-2B)

Solve each equation. Check your solution.
(Lesson 3-2D)

18. $-1.3x = 3.9$

19. $3.7k = -4.44$

20. $2.56 = 1.6c$

21. $\frac{3}{4}z = 12$

22. $\frac{2}{5}n = 8$

23. $\frac{7}{8} = \frac{1}{4}p$

Explore

Main Idea

Write and solve two-step equations using bar diagrams.

NGSSS

MA.7.A.3.3 **Formulate and use different strategies to solve** one-step and **two-step linear equations,** including equations with rational coefficients.

Get Connected
glencoe.com

Solve Two-Step Equations with Bar Diagrams

SPORTS Two identical basketballs and five identical tennis balls weigh a total of 52 ounces. Each tennis ball weighs 2 ounces. What is the weight of a basketball?

ACTIVITY

(1) **What do you need to find?** the weight of a basketball

> **STEP 1** Draw a bar diagram that represents the two basketballs and five tennis balls. Label the parts.

basketball	basketball	tennis	tennis	tennis	tennis	tennis
?	?	2 oz	2 oz	2 oz	2 oz	2 oz

52 oz

> **STEP 2** Write an equation from the bar diagram. Let x represent the weight of a basketball.
>
> $$2x \quad + \quad 10 \quad = \quad 52$$

> **STEP 3** Use the *work backward* strategy to find the weight of the basketballs. Since $2x + 10 = 52$, $2x = 52 - 10$ or 42, and $42 \div 2 = 21$.
>
> **Check** $2 \cdot 21 + 10 = 52$ ✓

The weight of one basketball is 21 ounces.

Analyze the Results

1. Suppose there were 10 identical tennis balls and 3 identical soccer balls that had a total weight of 53 ounces. You want to find the weight of one soccer ball. How would the above equation change?

2. **BAR DIAGRAM** Ryan is saving money to buy a skateboard that costs $85. He has already saved $40 and plans to save the same amount each week for three weeks. Draw a bar diagram and write an equation to find how much he should save each week. Then solve the equation.

2 **COMPUTERS** Adriana bought a computer and three pieces of software that cost the same amount. She spent a total of $1,220, with $995 of it for the computer. Write and solve an equation to find the cost of one piece of software.

What do you need to find? the cost of one piece of software

STEP 1 Draw a bar diagram to represent the situation.

⊢------------------------------ $1,220 ------------------------------⊣

computer	software	software	software

⊢------------- $995 -------------⊣--- ? --⊢-- ? --⊢-- ? --⊣

STEP 2 Write an equation from the bar diagram. Let x represent the cost of one piece of software.

$$3x \quad + \quad 995 \quad = \quad 1,220$$

STEP 3 Use the *work backward* strategy to find the cost of one piece of software. Since $3x + 995 = 1,220$, $3x = 225$ and $x = 225 \div 3$ or 75.

Each piece of software costs $75. **Check** $3 \cdot 75 + 995 = 1,220$ ✓

Analyze the Results

3. How much more does the computer cost than the three pieces of software?
4. How would the equation change if she purchased the computer and three pieces of software during a sale in which she received one piece of software free with the purchase of two?

Practice and Apply

BAR | DIAGRAM Draw a bar diagram and write an equation for each situation. Then solve the equation.

5. **GROCERY** Lindsey is buying a pound of cheese and 2 pounds of lunch meat at the deli counter. The cheese is $3.99 per pound and her total cost at the deli counter is $14.97. What is the cost per pound of the lunch meat?

6. **MAIL** It costs $0.42 to mail a letter. Jacob needs to mail a letter and 3 packages having equal size and weight. The post office charges a total of $4.92. What is the cost of mailing each package?

7. **Write MATH** Write a real-world problem that could be solved by the bar diagram.

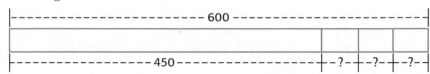

Main Idea

Solve two-step equations.

NGSSS

MA.7.A.3.3 **Formulate and use different strategies to solve** one-step and **two-step linear equations, including equations with rational coefficients.** *Also addresses MA.7.A.3.2.*

New Vocabulary

two-step equation

Get Connected
glencoe.com

Solve Two-Step Equations

 Explore

A florist charges $2 for each balloon in an arrangement and a $3 delivery fee. You have $9 to spend. The model illustrates the equation $2x + 3 = 9$, where x represents the number of balloons.

To solve $2x + 3 = 9$, remove three 1-tiles from each side of the mat. Then divide the remaining tiles into two equal groups. The solution of $2x + 3 = 9$ is 3.

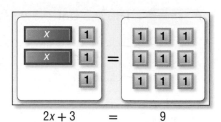

$2x + 3 \;=\; 9$

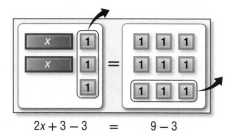

$2x + 3 - 3 \;=\; 9 - 3$

Solve each equation by using algebra tiles or a drawing.

1. $2x + 1 = 5$

2. $3x + 2 = 8$

3. $2 = 5x + 2$

$x \;=\; 3$

A **two-step equation** has two different operations. To solve a two-step equation, undo the operations in reverse order of the order of operations.

EXAMPLE Solve a Two-Step Equation

① Solve $2x + 3 = 9$. Check your solution.

$$
\begin{array}{lll}
2x + 3 = & 9 & \text{Write the equation.} \\
\underline{\;-3 = -3\;} & & \text{Undo the addition first by subtracting 3 from each side.} \\
2x \;\;= & 6 & \\
\dfrac{2x}{2} \;= & \dfrac{6}{2} & \text{Next, undo the multiplication by dividing each side by 2.} \\
x \;\;= & 3 & \text{Simplify.}
\end{array}
$$

Check Since $2(3) + 3 = 9$, the solution is 3. ✔

 CHECK Your Progress

Solve each equation. Check your solution.

  a. $2x + 4 = 10$ **b.** $3x + 5 = 14$ **c.** $5 = 2 + 3x$

EXAMPLES Solve Two-Step Equations

2 Solve $3x + 2 = 23$. **Check your solution.**

$3x + 2 = 23$	Write the equation.
$\underline{ - 2 = -2}$	Undo the addition first by subtracting 2 from each side.
$3x = 21$	
$\dfrac{3x}{3} = \dfrac{21}{3}$	Division Property of Equality
$x = 7$	Simplify.

Check	$3x + 2 = 23$	Write the original equation.
	$3(7) + 2 \stackrel{?}{=} 23$	Replace x with 7.
	$23 = 23 \checkmark$	The sentence is true.

The solution is 7.

3 Solve $-2y - 7 = 3$. **Check your solution.**

$-2y - 7 = 3$	Write the equation.
$\underline{ + 7 = +7}$	Undo the subtraction first by adding 7 to each side.
$-2y = 10$	
$\dfrac{-2y}{-2} = \dfrac{10}{-2}$	Division Property of Equality
$y = -5$	Simplify.

The solution is -5. Check the solution.

4 Solve $4 + \dfrac{1}{5}r = -1$. **Check your solution.**

$4 + \dfrac{1}{5}r = -1$	Write the equation.
$\underline{-4 \phantom{+\frac{1}{5}r} = -4}$	Undo the addition first by subtracting 4 from each side.
$\dfrac{1}{5}r = -5$	
$5 \cdot \dfrac{1}{5}r = 5 \cdot (-5)$	Multiplication Property of Equality
$r = -25$	Simplify.

The solution is -25. Check the solution.

✓ CHECK Your Progress

d. $4x + 5 = 13$ **e.** $-5s + 8 = -2$ **f.** $-2 + \dfrac{2}{3}w = 10$

Key Concept — Solving Two-Step Equations

Step 1 Undo the addition or subtraction first.

Step 2 Then undo the multiplication or division.

5 **MOVIES** Toya wants to have her birthday party at the movies. It costs $27 for pizza and $8.50 per friend for the movie tickets. How many friends can Toya have at her party if she has $78 to spend?

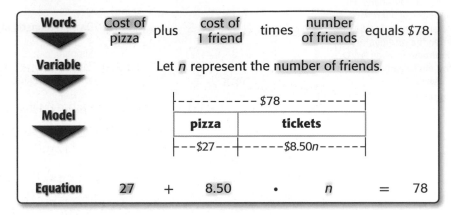

| Words | Cost of pizza | plus | cost of 1 friend | times | number of friends | equals $78. |

Variable Let n represent the number of friends.

Model

```
|-------------- $78 --------------|
| pizza      |      tickets       |
|---$27---|------$8.50n------|
```

| Equation | 27 | + | 8.50 | · | n | = | 78 |

Real-World Link · · · ·

Most teenagers see more than 7 movies a year.

$$27 + 8.50n = 78 \qquad \text{Write the equation.}$$
$$\underline{-27 \qquad\qquad = -27} \qquad \text{Subtract 27 from each side.}$$
$$8.50n = 51$$
$$\frac{8.50n}{8.50} = \frac{51}{8.50} \qquad \text{Division Property of Equality}$$
$$n = 6 \qquad 51 \div 8.50 = 6$$

Check
$$27 + 8.50n = 78 \qquad \text{Write the original equation.}$$
$$27 + 8.50(6) \stackrel{?}{=} 78 \qquad \text{Replace } n \text{ with 6.}$$
$$27 + 51 \stackrel{?}{=} 78 \qquad \text{Simplify.}$$
$$78 = 78 \ \checkmark \qquad \text{The sentence is true.}$$

Toya can have 6 friends at her party.

 CHECK Your Progress

g. FITNESS A fitness club is having a special offer where you pay $22 to join plus a $16 monthly fee. You have $150 to spend. Write and solve an equation to find how many months you can use the fitness club.

CHECK Your Understanding

Examples 1–4
(pp. 172–173)

Solve each equation. Check your solution.

1. $3x + 1 = 7$ 　　　　　 **2.** $4h - 6 = 22$ 　　　　　 **3** $-6r + 1 = -17$

4. $-3y - 5 = 10$ 　　　　 **5.** $13 = 1 + 4s$ 　　　　 **6.** $-7 = 1 + \frac{2}{3}n$

Example 5
(p. 174)

7. MONEY Syreeta wants to buy some CDs, each costing $14, and a DVD that costs $23. She has $65 to spend. Write and solve an equation to find how many CDs she can buy.

Practice and Problem Solving

● = **Step-by-Step Solutions** begin on page R6.
Extra Practice is on page EP8.

Examples 1–4
(pp. 172–173)

Solve each equation. Check your solution.

8. $3x + 1 = 10$ **9.** $5x + 4 = 19$ **10.** $2t + 7 = -1$

11. $6m + 1 = -23$ **12.** $-4w - 4 = 8$ **13.** $-7y + 3 = -25$

14. $-8s + 1 = 33$ **15.** $-2x + 5 = -13$ **16.** $-3 + 8n = -5$

17. $5 + 4d = 37$ **18.** $14 + \frac{2}{3}p = 8$ **19.** $25 + \frac{11}{12}y = 47$

Example 5
(p. 174)

| BAR | DIAGRAM | Write an equation. Use a bar diagram if needed. Then solve the equation.

20. BICYCLES Cristiano is saving money to buy a new bike that costs $189. He has saved $99 so far. He plans on saving $10 each week. In how many weeks will Cristiano have enough money to buy a new bike?

21. PETTING ZOOS It costs $10 to enter a petting zoo. Each cup of food to feed the animals is $2. If you have $14, how many cups of food can you buy?

Solve each equation. Check your solution.

22. $2r - 3.1 = 1.7$ **23.** $4t + 3.5 = 12.5$ **24.** $10 = b(2 \div 3)$

25. $5w + 9.2 = 19.7$ **26.** $16 = 0.5r - 8$ **27.** $n + 9 \div 3 = 14$

28. GRAPHIC NOVEL Refer to the graphic novel frame below. Jamar figured that they need to spend $39 for popcorn. Write and solve an equation to find how many movies they can purchase.

Help us figure how many movies we can buy. Refer to p. 141 for details.

I think we'll need $39 for popcorn

Mmmm... popcorn.

29 TEMPERATURE Temperature is usually measured on the Fahrenheit scale (°F) or the Celsius scale (°C). Use the formula $F = 1.8C + 32$ to convert from one scale to the other.

a. Convert the temperature for Alaska's record low in July to Celsius. Round to the nearest degree.

b. Hawaii's record low temperature is $-11°C$. Find the difference in degrees Fahrenheit between Hawaii's record low temperature and the record low temperature for Alaska in January.

Alaska Record Low Temperatures (°F) by Month	
January	−80
April	−50
July	16
October	−48

H.O.T. Problems

30. **CHALLENGE** Refer to Exercise 29. Is there a temperature in the table at which the number of degrees Celsius is the same as the number of degrees Fahrenheit? If so, find it. If not, explain why not.

31. **CHALLENGE** Suppose your school is selling magazine subscriptions. Each subscription costs $20. The company pays the school half of the total sales in dollars. The school must also pay a one-time fee of $18. What is the fewest number of subscriptions that can be sold to earn a profit of $200?

32. **Write MATH** Write a real-world problem that would be represented by the equation $2x + 5 = 15$.

NGSSS Practice   MA.6.A.1.3, MA.6.A.3.2, MA.7.A.3.3

33. A rental car company charges $30 a day plus $0.05 a mile. This is represented by the equation below, where m is the number of miles and c is the total cost of the rental.

$$c = 30 + 0.05m$$

If the Boggs family paid $49.75 for their car rental, how many miles did they travel?

A. 95 miles   C. 295 miles

B. 195 miles   D. 395 miles

34. **GRIDDED RESPONSE** The Rodriguez family went on a vacation. They started with $1,875. They spent $140 each day and have $895 left for the rest of their trip. Use the equation below to find d, the number of days they have been on their vacation so far.

$$1,875 - 140d = 895$$

How many days have they vacationed?

ALGEBRA Solve each equation. Check your solution. (Lesson 3-2D)

35. $\frac{1}{2}f = \frac{3}{4}$ 36. $-\frac{3}{4}y = \frac{-15}{16}$ 37. $\frac{3}{5}p = 12$ 38. $\frac{11}{12} = \frac{11}{13}n$

Find the multiplicative inverse of each number. (Lesson 3-2D)

39. $\frac{6}{7}$ 40. $\frac{4}{13}$ 41. 8   42. $5\frac{1}{4}$

43. **WEATHER** The table shows how much rain fell in Albuquerque and Denver. Which city had the greater fraction of inches of rain per day? Explain. (Lesson 2-1C)

44. Find $|7 + -12|$. (Lesson 1-1B)

City	Amount of Rain (in.)	Number of Days
Albuquerque, NM	9	60
Denver, CO	15	90

Main Idea

Use algebra tiles to solve equations with variables on each side of the equation.

NGSSS

MA.7.A.3.3 **Formulate and use different strategies to solve** one-step and two-step **linear equations,** including equations with rational coefficients.

Get Connected
glencoe.com

Equations with Variables on Each Side

Some equations have variables on each side of the equal sign.

ACTIVITY

Solve $x + 5 = 2x + 2$ using algebra tiles.

STEP 1   Model the equation.

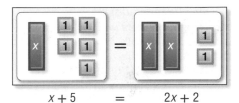

$$x + 5 \quad = \quad 2x + 2$$

STEP 2   Remove one x-tile from each side of the mat. All of the x-tiles are on one side of the mat.

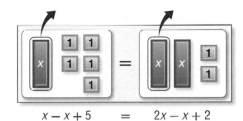

$$x - x + 5 \quad = \quad 2x - x + 2$$

STEP 3   Now you can remove two 1-tiles from each side. There are 3 tiles on the left side of the mat.

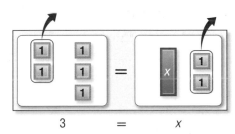

$$3 \quad = \quad x$$

The solution is 3.

Analyze the Results

Use algebra tiles to model and solve each equation.

1. $3x - 2 = 2x + 1$ 2. $2x + 6 = 4x - 2$

3. $x + 1 = 3x - 3$ 4. $2x - 9 = 5x + 3$

5. Does it matter whether you remove x-tiles or 1-tiles first? Explain.

6. What property of equality allows you to remove an x-tile from each side of the mat?

Main Idea

Use the properties of equality to simplify and solve equations with variables on each side.

NGSSS

MA.7.A.3.3 Formulate and use different strategies to solve one-step and two-step **linear equations, including equations with rational coefficients. MA.7.A.3.4 Use the properties of equality to represent an equation in a different way and to show that two equations are equivalent in a given context.** *Also addresses MA.7.A.3.2.*

Get Connected
glencoe.com

Solve Equations with Variables on Each Side

FOOD Julian takes two orders at the fast food restaurant where he works. One order is for two hamburgers and three orders of fries. The other order is for three hamburgers and one order of fries. The two orders cost the same.

1. If an order of fries costs $2, write expressions for each order.

2. How could you show the expressions are equal?

You can use the properties of equality to solve equations with variables on each side. The new equation is equivalent to the original equation.

EXAMPLE **Writing Equivalent Equations**

 Express $2x + 6 = 3x + 2$ as an equivalent equation.

Method 1 Subtract a Variable

$$
\begin{array}{ll}
2x + 6 = \quad 3x + 2 & \text{Write the equation.} \\
\underline{-2x \qquad = -2x} & \text{Subtract } 2x \text{ from each side of the equation.} \\
6 = \quad x + 2 & \text{Simplify.}
\end{array}
$$

Method 2 Subtract a Number

$$
\begin{array}{ll}
2x + 6 = 3x + 2 & \text{Write the equation.} \\
\underline{\quad -2 = \quad -2} & \text{Subtract 2 from each side of the equation.} \\
2x + 4 = 3x & \text{Simplify.}
\end{array}
$$

So, $2x + 6 = 3x + 2$ is equivalent to $6 = x + 2$ and $2x + 4 = 3x$.

 CHECK Your Progress

Express each equation as another equivalent equation using properties of equality. Justify your answer.

a. $2x + 4 = x + 6$ **b.** $3x - 4 = x - 6$

To solve equations with variables on each side, use the Properties of Equality to write an equivalent equation with the variable on one side. Then solve the equation.

 EXAMPLE **Equations with Variables on Each Side**

2 Solve $5x = x + 16$.

$5x = x + 16$	Write the equation.
$5x - x = x - x + 16$	Subtraction Property of Equality
$4x = 16$	Simplify.
$\dfrac{4x}{4} = \dfrac{16}{4}$	Division Property of Equality
$x = 4$	Simplify. Check your solution.

CHECK Your Progress

Solve each equation. Check your solution.

c. $7x = 5x + 6$ **d.** $3x - 2 = x + 10$

Real-World Link · · · · ·

The Jacksonville Suns, a minor league baseball team for the Los Angeles Dodgers, hold the season attendance record at 420,495 fans.

Real-World EXAMPLE

 TICKETS If you pay a one-time fee of \$20, you can purchase reserve tickets for your local minor league baseball team for only \$4 a game. Regular tickets sell at the stadium for \$6. Write and solve an equation to find how many reserve tickets you would need to buy to equal the cost of regular tickets. Let x represent the number of tickets purchased.

$20 + 4x = 6x$	Write the equation.
$20 + 4x - 4x = 6x - 4x$	Subtraction Property of Equality
$20 = 2x$	Simplify.
$\dfrac{20}{2} = \dfrac{2x}{2}$	Division Property of Equality
$10 = x$	Simplify.

Check $20 + 4(10) = 60, 6(10) = 60.$ ✔

So, ten reserve tickets would have to be purchased to equal the cost of the regular tickets.

CHECK Your Progress

e. BASKETBALL Bill averages 10 points a game and has 110 points for the season. Aaron averages 12 points a game and has 96 points for the season. Write and solve an equation to find how many games it will take until they tie in points scored if they continue at the same rate.

Example 1
(p. 178)

Express each equation as another equivalent equation. Justify your answer.

1. $4x + 8 = 2x + 40$ **2.** $9x - 2 = 34 + 3x$ **3.** $6x - 7 = 43 + x$

Example 2
(p. 179)

Solve each equation. Check your solution.

4. $\frac{x}{3} - 15 = 12 + x$ **5.** $\frac{1}{4}x - 8 = 5$ **6.** $11 + 4x = 7 + 5x$

7 $3 - x = 4 - 3x$ **8.** $-7 + x = -8 - x$ **9.** $-x + 4 = -9.8 + x$

Example 3
(p. 179)

10. RENTAL CARS Use the table to write and solve an equation to find the number of miles a rental car must be driven in one day for each company to cost the same.

	Per Day Charge	Per Mile Charge
Rentals R Us	$25	$0.45
EZ Rental	$40	$0.25

Practice and Problem Solving

● = **Step-by-Step Solutions** begin on page R7.
Extra Practice is on page EP9.

Example 1
(p. 178)

Express each equation as another equivalent equation. Justify your answer.

11. $6x + 14 = 20 + 4x$ **12.** $15x + 6 = 71 + 10x$ **13.** $6x - 3 = 33 + 3x$

14. $16 - 2x = 2x + 4$ **15.** $4x - 15 = 5 + 2x$ **16.** $4x - 13 = 11 - 2x$

Example 2
(p. 179)

Solve each equation. Check your solution.

17. $\frac{x}{3} + 3 = 4 + \frac{x}{6}$ **18.** $5x - 12 = 3x - 2$ **19.** $\frac{x}{4} - 8 = 16 - \frac{3}{4}x$

20. $9 - 4x = 2x + 6$ **21.** $18.6 - 2x = 3x - 2.4$ **22.** $7.5 + x = 4.5 + 4x$

23. $-7 + x = \frac{x}{10} - 16$ **24.** $-73 + 3x = 15 + 11x$ **25.** $-1 - 5x = 15x - 6$

26. $3x - 11 = 34 + 2x$ **27.** $-20 - 2x = 2x + 4$ **28.** $143 + 2x = -10x - 1$

Example 3
(p. 179)

29 SHOPPING Manny bought car wash supplies for $48 and 3 buckets for his car wash team. Jin did not buy any car wash supplies but bought 7 buckets. All the buckets cost the same amount, and they both spent the same amount of money. Write and solve an equation to find the cost of one bucket.

30. BABYSITTING Catie charges an initial amount of $5 for babysitting and then $3 per hour. Jolisa does not charge an initial amount but charges $4 per hour. Write and solve an equation to find how many hours each girl will have to work to earn the same amount.

31. ALGEBRA Explain how the two given equations are equivalent.

$$-2b - 11 = -7b + 14$$

$$-25 = -5b$$

32. OPEN ENDED Write a real-world problem that could be solved by using the equation $4x + 8 = 2x + 32$. Then solve the equation.

33. CHALLENGE If $4x + 2 = y$ and $3x - 1 = y$, find the value of y.

34. Write MATH Explain in words how to solve the equation $2 - 4x = 6x - 8$.

NGSSS Practice   MA.6.A.3.2, MA.7.A.3.3

35. Rena spent $18 including tax on ribbon she bought at a craft store. The price of the ribbon, including tax, was $3 for two spools. In the equation $18 = r(3 \div 2)$, r represents the number of spools of ribbon Rena bought. How many spools of ribbon did Rena buy?

   A. 6   C. 18

   B. 12   D. 36

36. THINK SOLVE EXPLAIN SHORT RESPONSE Gary bought a box of 230 tennis balls for $110. He made a profit of $97 after selling all the balls. Each ball was sold at the same price. Use the equation below to find b, the selling price of one ball.

$$230b - 110 = 97$$

37. THINK SOLVE EXPLAIN EXTENDED RESPONSE Damian and Sergio bought the baseball cards shown in the table. Sergio also bought gum that cost $0.99. All of the cards cost the same and the boys spent the same amount of money.

Boy	Number of Cards	Packs of Gum
Sergio	12	1
Damian	15	0

Part A Write an equation to represent the situation.

Part B Solve the equation from Part **A**.

Part C How many cards could Sergio buy if he would have bought 2 packs of gum but spent the same amount of money?

Spiral Review

Solve each equation. Check your solution. (Lesson 3-3B)

38. $6 + 2x = 16$ **39.** $5 + 3n = -4$ **40.** $-3 = 4k + 9$ **41.** $9 = 5y + 12$

42. BOOKS Of the books on a shelf, $\frac{2}{3}$ are mysteries. Write and solve an equation to find how many books are on the shelf when there are 10 mystery books. (Lesson 3-2D)

43. FAMILIES The table gives details about families of students at Park Street Intermediate School. Which category has the most students?

(Lesson 2-1C)

Number of Siblings	Fraction of Students
0–1	$\frac{2}{5}$
2–3	$\frac{7}{12}$
4 or more	$\frac{1}{60}$

Evaluate each expression. (Lesson 1-1B)

44. $|17|$ **45.** $|-253|$

VET TECHS
DON'T MONKEY AROUND

If you love being around animals, enjoy working with your hands, and are good at analyzing problems, a challenging career in veterinary medicine might be a perfect fit for you. Veterinary technicians help veterinarians by helping to diagnose and treat medical conditions. They may work in private clinics, animal hospitals, zoos, aquariums, or wildlife rehabilitation centers.

Choose a Major
Are you interested in a career as a veterinary technician? Take some of the following courses in high school.

- Algebra
- Animal Science and Services
- Biology
- Chemistry
- Veterinary Assisting

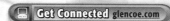
Get Connected glencoe.com

GOLDEN LION TAMARIN MONKEYS

Measure	Minimum	Maximum
Body length	7.9 in.	ℓ
Tail length	t	15.7 in.
Weight	12.7 oz	28 oz

EMPEROR TAMARIN MONKEYS

Measure	Minimum	Maximum
Body length	9.2 in.	b
Tail length	14 in.	16.6 in.
Weight	10.7 oz	w

NGSSS

MA.7.A.3.3 Formulate and use different strategies to solve one-step and two-step linear equations, including equations with rational coefficients.

Real-World Math

For each problem, use the information in the tables to write an equation. Then solve the equation.

1. The minimum tail length of an emperor tamarin is 1.6 inches greater than that of a golden lion tamarin. What is the minimum tail length of a golden lion tamarin?

2. The minimum body length of a golden lion tamarin is 5.3 inches less than the maximum body length. What is the maximum body length?

3. Tamarins live an average of 15 years. This is 13 years less than the years that one tamarin in captivity lived. How long did the tamarin in captivity live?

4. The maximum weight of a golden lion tamarin is about 1.97 times the maximum weight of an emperor tamarin. What is the maximum weight of an emperor tamarin? Round to the nearest tenth.

5. For an emperor tamarin, the maximum total length, including the body and tail, is 27 inches. What is the maximum body length of an emperor tamarin?

📱 **Get Connected** glencoe.com

• STUDY**TO GO**
• Vocabulary Review
• Multilingual eGlossary

FOLDABLES®
Study Organizer

Be sure the following Key Concepts are noted in your Foldable.

Key Concepts

Addition and Subtraction Equations
(Lesson 3-1)
• If you add or subtract the same number from each side of an equation, the two sides remain equal.

Multiplication and Division Equations
(Lesson 3-2)
• If you multiply each side of an equation by the same number, the two sides remain equal.

• If you divide each side of an equation by the same nonzero number, the two sides remain equal.

Multi-Step Equations (Lesson 3-3)
• To solve an equation with variables on each side like $3x + 3 = x + 5$:

Step 1 Combine variable terms by adding or subtracting one of the variable terms to each side.

Step 2 Combine constant terms by adding or subtracting one of the constant terms to each side.

Step 3 Undo the multiplication or division.

$$2x = 2 \text{ so } x = 1$$

Key Vocabulary

coefficient (p. 157)

equation (p. 150)

equivalent equation (p. 150)

formula (p. 159)

multiplicative inverse (p. 163)

reciprocal (p. 163)

two-step equation (p. 172)

Vocabulary Check

State whether each sentence is *true* or *false*. If *false*, replace the underlined word or number to make a true sentence.

1. The expression $\frac{1}{3}y$ means <u>one third of y</u>.

2. Another term for multiplicative inverse is <u>reciprocal</u>.

3. The formula <u>$d = rt$</u> gives the distance d traveled at a rate of r for t units of time.

4. The algebraic expression representing the words *six less than m* is <u>$6 - m$</u>.

5. Use the <u>*work backward*</u> strategy when you are given a final result and asked to find an earlier amount.

6. The word *each* sometimes suggests the operation of <u>division</u>.

7. In solving the equation $4x + 3 = 15$, first <u>divide each side by 4</u>.

8. The solution of the equation $p + 4.4 = 11.6$ is <u>7.2</u>.

9. The process of solving a <u>two-step equation</u> uses the *work backward* strategy.

10. The coefficient in the term $15x$ is <u>x</u>.

11. The reciprocal of $\frac{2}{3}$ is <u>$-\frac{2}{3}$</u>.

12. The word *per* sometimes suggests the operation of <u>subtraction</u>.

Multi-Part Lesson Review

 **3-1** **Addition and Subtraction Equations**

 MA.7.A.3.3

PSI: Work Backward (pp. 144–145)

13. BASEBALL Last baseball season, Nelson had four less than twice the number of hits Marcus had. Nelson had 48 hits. How many hits did Marcus have last season?

14. BANKING Trina had $320 in her savings account after a withdrawal of $75 and a deposit of $120. How much did she have in her account originally?

EXAMPLE 1 A number is divided by 2. Then 4 is added to the quotient. After subtracting 3, the result is 18. What is the number?

Start with the final value and work backward with each resulting value until you arrive at the starting value.

$18 + 3 = 21$ Undo subtracting 3.

$21 - 4 = 17$ Undo adding 4.

$17 \cdot 2 = 34$ Undo dividing by 2.

Solve One-Step Addition and Subtraction Equations (pp. 150–155)

 MA.7.A.3.3

Solve each equation. Check your solution.

15. $x + 5 = 8$ **16.** $r + 8 = 2$

17. $p + 9 = -4$ **18.** $s - 8 = 15$

19. $n - 1 = -3$ **20.** $w - 9 = 28$

21. $b + \dfrac{1}{2} = \dfrac{3}{4}$ **22.** $t - \dfrac{5}{7} = \dfrac{20}{21}$

23. COOKIES Hector baked some chocolate chip cookies for himself and his sister. His sister ate 6 of these cookies. If there were 18 cookies left, write and solve an equation to find how many cookies c Hector baked.

24. ANIMALS A giraffe is 3.5 meters taller than a camel. If a giraffe is 5.5 meters tall, how tall is a camel?

EXAMPLE 2 Solve $x + 6 = 4$.

$$
\begin{array}{rl}
x + 6 = & 4 \\
\underline{-6 = -6} & \text{Subtraction Property of Equality} \\
x = & -2
\end{array}
$$

EXAMPLE 3 Solve $y - 3 = -2$.

$$
\begin{array}{rl}
y - 3 = & -2 \\
\underline{+3 = +3} & \text{Addition Property of Equality} \\
y = & 1
\end{array}
$$

EXAMPLE 4

AMUSEMENT PARKS Admission to a popular amusement park is $8.75 more than the previous year's admission price. If this year's admission price is $20, write and solve an equation to find the previous year's admission.

$$
\begin{array}{rl}
A + 8.75 = & 20 \quad \text{Write the equation.} \\
\underline{-8.75 = -8.75} & \text{Subtraction Property of Equality} \\
A = & 11.25
\end{array}
$$

So, the previous year's admission was $11.25.

3-2 **Multiplication and Division Equations**

Solve One-Step Multiplication and Division Equations (pp. 157–161)

Solve each equation. Check your solution.

25. $7c = 28$ **26.** $-8w = 72$

27. $10y = -90$ **28.** $-12r = -36$

29. $\dfrac{a}{3} = 4$ **30.** $\dfrac{x}{9} = 6$

31. $\dfrac{y}{13} = 3$ **32.** $-\dfrac{f}{7} = 7$

33. MONEY Matt borrowed $98 from his father. He plans to repay his father at $14 per week. Write and solve an equation to find the number of weeks w required to pay back his father.

34. SKYSCRAPERS The Willis Tower in Chicago is divided into 110 stories. Each story is about 13 feet high. Write and solve a division equation to find the total height of the tower.

EXAMPLE 5   **Solve $-4b = 32$.**

$-4b = 32$

$\dfrac{-4b}{-4} = \dfrac{32}{-4}$ Division Property of Equality

$b = -8$

EXAMPLE 6   **Solve $\dfrac{b}{7} = -6$.**

$\dfrac{b}{7} = -6$

$\dfrac{b}{7} \cdot 7 = -6 \cdot 7$ Multiplication Property of Equality

$b = -42$

Solve Equations with Rational Coefficients (pp. 163–168)

Solve each equation. Check your solution.

35. $-3.4 = 1.7d$ **36.** $0.5x = 0.75$

37. $0.42y = 1.26$ **38.** $1.5t = 30$

39. $\dfrac{4}{5}r = 1$ **40.** $-2 = \dfrac{2}{5}m$

41. $-\dfrac{3}{4}p = 12$ **42.** $-\dfrac{3}{10}z = -6$

43. BLIMP A blimp travels 300 miles in 7.5 hours. Assuming the blimp travels at a constant speed, write and solve an equation to find the speed of the blimp. Use the formula $d = rt$.

44. GIFT BASKETS Shelli uses $2\dfrac{1}{4}$ feet of ribbon on each gift basket that she sells. Write and solve an equation to find the number of baskets she can make if she has 144 feet of ribbon.

EXAMPLE 7   **Solve $2.5r = 30$.**

$2.5r = 30$

$\dfrac{2.5r}{2.5} = \dfrac{30}{2.5}$ Division Property of Equality

$r = 12$

EXAMPLE 8   **Solve $-4 = \dfrac{2}{3}s$.**

$-4 = \dfrac{2}{3}s$

$\left(\dfrac{3}{2}\right)-4 = \left(\dfrac{3}{2}\right)\dfrac{2}{3}s$ Multiplication Property of Equality

$-6 = s$

Multi-Step Equations

 MA.7.A.3.3

Solve Two-Step Equations (pp. 172–176)

Solve each equation. Check your solution.

45. $3y - 12 = 6$ **46.** $6x - 4 = 20$

47. $2x + 5 = 3$ **48.** $\frac{3}{5}m + 6 = -4$

49. $10c - 8 = 90$ **50.** $\frac{1}{3}r - 20 = -5$

51. DVDs Blake had 6 times the amount of DVDs that Daniel had. Blake just bought 5 more. Write and solve an equation to find how many DVDs Daniel had if Blake now has 155.

52. COFFEE A coffee shop sells an insulated refill cup for $9. Each time the shop fills the cup, it costs $1.50. Write and solve an equation to find how many refills can be purchased if $24 is spent on the mug and refills.

EXAMPLE 9   Solve $3p - 4 = 8$.

$$3p - 4 = 8$$
$$\underline{+ 4 = + 4} \quad \text{Addition Property of Equality}$$
$$3p = 12$$
$$\frac{3p}{3} = \frac{12}{3} \quad \text{Division Property of Equality}$$
$$p = 4$$

Solve Equations with Variables on Each Side (pp. 178–181)

 MA.7.A.3.3, MA.7.A.3.4

Solve each equation. Check your solution.

53. $-7h - 4 = h + 4$

54. $m + 1 = 2m + 7$

55. $5x - 12 = 3x + 6$

56. $12b = 7b + 5$

57. $3.21 - 7y = 10y - 1.89$

58. $\frac{x}{4} + 5 = 4 + \frac{x}{2}$

59. VIDEOS A video store has two membership plans. Under plan A, a yearly membership costs $30 plus $1.50 for each rental. Under plan B, the yearly membership costs $12 plus $3 for each rental. What number of rentals results in the same yearly cost?

EXAMPLE 10   Solve $5x + 4 = 3x - 2$.

$$5x + 4 = 3x - 2$$
$$5x - 3x + 4 = 3x - 3x - 2 \quad \begin{array}{l}\text{Subtraction Property} \\ \text{of Equality}\end{array}$$
$$2x + 4 = -2 \quad \text{Simplify.}$$
$$2x + 4 - 4 = -2 - 4 \quad \begin{array}{l}\text{Subtraction Property} \\ \text{of Equality}\end{array}$$
$$2x = -6 \quad \text{Simplify.}$$
$$\frac{2x}{2} = \frac{-6}{2} \quad \begin{array}{l}\text{Division Property} \\ \text{of Equality}\end{array}$$
$$x = -3 \quad \text{Simplify.}$$

Solve each equation. Check your solution.

1. $x + 5 = -8$

2. $y - 11 = 15$

3. $12 = z + 14$

4. $13 = t - 13$

5. $s + 1.5 = 2.7$

6. $\frac{1}{3} + r = \frac{5}{6}$

7. **FLOWERS** The number of tulips in Paula's garden is 8 less than the number of marigolds. If there are 16 tulips, write and solve an equation to determine the number of marigolds m.

8. **PIZZA** Chris and Heladio shared a pizza. Chris ate two more than twice as many pieces as Heladio, who ate 3 pieces. If there were 3 pieces left, how many pieces were there initially? Use the *work backward* strategy.

Solve each equation. Check your solution.

9. $9z = -81$

10. $-6k = -72$

11. $4 = 8n$

12. $120 = \frac{a}{2}$

13. $27 = \frac{b}{3}$

14. $3.3 = \frac{c}{3}$

15. **PHONE** Susie's phone service is $0.15 per minute of use. Write and solve an equation to find how long she can talk for $5.00.

I-Call Wireless
15¢ per minute

16. **NGSSS PRACTICE** Which of the following equations does NOT have a solution of 3?

A. $3x = 9$

B. $\frac{x}{5} = 15$

C. $21 = 7x$

D. $\frac{1}{3}x = 1$

Solve each equation. Check your solution.

17. $-0.5m = -10$

18. $-14.2 = -7.1t$

19. $\frac{2}{3}w = \frac{1}{6}$

20. $6 = -\frac{3}{4}x$

21. $-\frac{1}{9}t = 7$

22. $5\frac{3}{4} = \frac{1}{8}y$

23. **ROLLER COASTERS** The track length of a popular roller coaster is 5,106 feet. The roller coaster has an average speed of about 2,000 feet per minute. At that speed, how long will it take to travel its length of 5,106 feet? Round to the nearest tenth. Use the formula $d = rt$.

Solve each equation. Check your solution.

24. $-6k + 4 = -38$

25. $3z - 7 = 17$

26. $2g - 9 = -5$

27. $n - 11 = 4 + 4n$

28. **MONEY** Keiko had $17 in savings. She receives an $11 weekly allowance. Write and solve an equation to find how many weeks it will take her to save $72.

29. $12x = 2x + 40$

30. $4x + 9 = 7x$

31. $4k + 24 = 6k - 10$

32. $2f - 6 = 7f + 24$

33. **THINK SOLVE EXPLAIN** **EXTENDED RESPONSE** A taxicab company charges $2 plus $1.25 for each mile of a trip.

Part A Write the expression for a trip of m miles.

Part B Write an equation to find the number of miles if the trip is $12.

Part C How many miles was the trip?

Part D Another taxicab company advertises $1.50 plus $1.60 per mile. If a taxicab ride is 2 miles long, is this company less expensive than the first company? Explain.

CHAPTER 3

Preparing for Standardized Tests

Multiple Choice: Using the Answer Choices

Sometimes you can find the correct answer more quickly by substituting each answer choice into the problem.

NGSSS PRACTICE EXAMPLE

Renata earns \$7.50 per hour babysitting. She spent \$16 of the total amount that she earned this week on a new CD and had \$29 left over. Use the equation below to find *h*, the number of hours she babysat this week.

$$7.5h - 16 = 29$$

A. 1.7 hours

B. 3.9 hours

C. 6 hours

D. 13 hours

Substitute each answer choice into the equation until you find the correct solution.

$7.5(1.7) - 16 = 29$ ← Substitute 1.7 for *h*.
$12.75 - 16 = 29$
$-3.25 \neq 29$ ✗

$7.5(3.9) - 16 = 29$ ← Substitute 3.9 for *h*.
$29.25 - 16 = 29$
$13.25 \neq 29$ ✗

$7.5(6) - 16 = 29$ ← Substitute 6 for *h*.
$45 - 16 = 29$
$29 = 29$ ✓

Since this is a true sentence, 6 is the solution of the equation.
So, the correct answer is C.

Work on It

The Berk family camped for 6 nights and paid a total of \$89. Their total cost, which includes an admission fee of \$5 and the cost per night *d*, can be represented by $6d + 5 = 89$. What was the cost per night?

F. \$14.00

G. \$14.83

H. \$15.67

I. \$16.60

Test Hint

Once you find the solution, you do not need to substitute the remaining answer choices into the equation.

Read each question. Then fill in the correct answer on the answer sheet provided by your teacher or on a sheet of paper.

1. A sports store sells two different field hockey kits shown in the table.

Hockey Kits	
Beginner	**Basic**
hockey stick ball shin guards	hockey stick ball

The beginner's field hockey kit costs $150. It is $15 more than three times the cost of the basic kit. What is the cost of the basic kit?

A. $35.00   C. $45.00

B. $40.00   D. $50.00

2. Which line contains the ordered pair $(-2, 4)$?

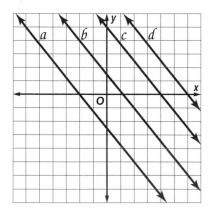

F. line a H. line b

G. line c I. line d

3. Which integer added to 12 gives a sum of -14?

A. -18 C. -24

B. -20 D. -26

4. ▤▤ **GRIDDED RESPONSE** Mrs. McDowell is making a big batch of cookies for her son's birthday. The price of the chocolate chips is 2 bags for $4.00. Use the table to determine the number of bags of chocolate chips r that Mrs. McDowell bought if she spent $12.

r	$c = r(4 \div 2)$	c
1	$c = 1(4 \div 2)$	$2
2	$c = 2(4 \div 2)$	$4
3	$c = 3(4 \div 2)$	$6

5. ▤▤ **GRIDDED RESPONSE** Aida bought a costume box containing 50 costumes for $300. She sold all of the costumes and made a $250 profit. She sold all of the costumes for the same price. Use the equation $50c - 300 = 250$, where c is the selling price of each costume. What was the selling price of one costume in dollars?

6. Which of the following problems can be solved using the equation $x - 9 = 15$?

F. Allison is 9 years younger than her sister Pam. Allison is 15 years old. What is x, Pam's age?

G. David's portion of the bill is $9 more than Jaleel's portion of the bill. If Jaleel pays $9, find x, the amount in dollars that David pays.

H. The sum of two numbers is 15. If one of the numbers is 9, what is x, the other number?

I. Calvin owns 15 CDs. If he gave 9 of them to a friend, what is x, the number of CDs he has left?

7. What value of x makes this equation true?

$$4x + 7 = 43$$

A. 12

B. 10

C. 9

D. 8

8. Which of the following coordinates lies within the triangle graphed below?

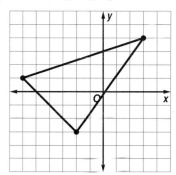

F. $(3, 4)$

G. $(2, 0)$

H. $(-3, 6)$

I. $(-1, -1)$

9. **THINK SOLVE EXPLAIN** **SHORT RESPONSE** Rico, Carolina, and Gloria have pizza that they are going to be sharing with other people. Rico gave away $\frac{1}{3}$ of his cheese pizza to Carolina and she gave him $\frac{3}{7}$ of her pepperoni. Rico then gave Gloria $\frac{1}{7}$ of his cheese pizza. How much pizza, pepperoni and cheese, does Rico have now?

10. For a warm up, Samuel runs 200 yards less than half the maximum distance he can run. This is represented by the equation $r = \frac{1}{2} x - 200$, where x represents the maximum distance he can run and r represents the distance run during his warm up. If Samuel ran 1,600 yards during his warm up, what is the maximum distance he can run?

A. 3,600 yards

B. 2,400 yards

C. 1,800 yards

D. 1,600 yards

11. Find $20 \div (-4)$.

F. -5

G. -7

H. 5

I. 4

12. **GRIDDED RESPONSE** Ines is in a hot air balloon 89 feet above the ground. A bird is flying 15 feet above the hot air balloon. How high off the ground is the bird in feet?

13. **THINK SOLVE EXPLAIN** **EXTENDED RESPONSE** A first-time bungee jumper is about to make his first jump. When the bungee jumper jumps, he will fall 5 feet every 0.5 second.

Part A Let s be the total number of seconds in a jump and h be the height of the jump. Write an equation that can be used to find s.

Part B Use your equation to calculate the total seconds for a 150-foot jump. Show your work.

NEED EXTRA HELP?													
If You Missed Question...	1	2	3	4	5	6	7	8	9	10	11	12	13
Go to Lesson...	3-3B	1-1C	1-2B	3-2B	3-3B	3-1D	3-3B	1-1C	2-2C	3-3B	1-3D	1-2B	3-3B
For help with NGSSS...	A.3.3	G.4.3	A.3.1	A.3.3	A.3.3	A.3.3	A.3.3	G.4.3	A.3.2	A.3.3	A.3.1	A.3.1	A.3.3

Proportions and Similarity

The
⭐ BIG Idea Understand and apply proportionality, including similarity.

FOLDABLES®
Study Organizer

Make this Foldable to help you organize your notes. Begin with a sheet of notebook paper.

❶ Fold lengthwise to the holes.

❷ Make equal cuts to form 6 tabs.

❸ Label the major topics as shown.

Rates

Proportional and Nonportional Relationships

Solve Proportions

Scale Dreawigs

Similar Figures

Perimeter and Area of Similar Figures

Review Vocabulary

ratio (Prior Grade) **razón** a comparison of two numbers by division; the ratio of 2 to 3 can be written as 2 out of 3, 2 to 3, 2 : 3, or $\frac{2}{3}$

the ratio of **squares** to **triangles** is **2 : 3**

Key Vocabulary

	English	Español
p. 196	rate	tasa
p. 206	proportion	proporción
p. 215	scale factor	factor de escala
p. 223	similar figures	figures semejantes

🖥 **Multilingual eGlossary** glencoe.com

Get Connected
glencoe.com

- Study using the **eBook**
- Explore with **Get Animated**
- Get extra help from **Personal Tutor**
- Use **virtual manipulatives** for additional help
- Take a **Self-Check Quiz**

When Will I Use This?

Raul, Caitlyn, and Jamar in
Campfire Song

Wow! Kayaking sure is fun! Camp is turning out to be a blast!

If Caitlyn hadn't rescued me, I'd be going in circles for hours! It took me forever to get it straight!

Now I'm so hungry I could eat a kayak!

Well, you can do that if you want to, Jamar! As for me, I need to get back to the cabin and get my camera before dinner.

Gotcha!

After that, Raul and I need to get to the campfire early to practice our song.

Song?

Yes! We have been preparing a song for the campfire tonight!

Oh yeah! That's tonight! So... um, where is the campfire exactly?

I don't know. I thought you knew!

Jamar? Do you know where it is, or how far away it is?

And Jamar saves the day! I brought a map! We can figure out how far it is from here.

CABIN   LAKE

ROPES COURSE

1 SQUARE = 75 YARDS

MESS HALL

PICNIC AREA   CAMPFIRE

Awesome! Jamar, you are the greatest!

Maybe you can use your greatness to get us to dinner quickly! I'm getting hungry!

Your Turn!
You will solve this problem in Chapter 4.

Are You Ready for Chapter 4?

You have two options for checking prerequisite skills for this chapter.

Text Option Take the Quick Check below. Refer to the Quick Review for help.

QUICK Check

FIELD TRIPS **Write each ratio as a fraction in simplest form.** (Prior Grade)

1. adults : students
2. students : buses
3. buses : people
4. adults : people
5. students : people

Seventh-Grade Field Trip	
Students	180
Adults	24
Buses	4

Determine whether the ratios are equivalent. Explain. (Prior Grade)

6. 20 nails for every 5 shingles, 12 nails for every 3 shingles
7. 2 cups of flour to 8 cups of sugar, 8 cups of flour to 14 cups of sugar
8. 12 out of 20 doctors agree, 6 out of 10 doctors agree
9. 2 DVDs to 7 CDs, 10 DVDs to 15 CDs
10. 27 students to 6 microscopes, 18 students to 5 microscopes

QUICK Review

EXAMPLE 1

SOCCER Write the ratio of wins to losses as a fraction in simplest form.

Madison Mavericks Team Statistics	
Wins	10
Losses	12
Ties	8

$$\text{wins} \rightarrow \frac{10}{12} = \frac{5}{6} \leftarrow \text{losses}$$

The ratio of wins to losses is $\frac{5}{6}$.

EXAMPLE 2

Determine whether the ratios 250 miles in 4 hours and 500 miles in 8 hours are equivalent.

Method 1

Compare the ratios written in simplest form.

$$250 \text{ miles} : 4 \text{ hours} = \frac{250}{4} \text{ or } \frac{125}{2}$$

$$500 \text{ miles} : 8 \text{ hours} = \frac{500}{8} \text{ or } \frac{125}{2}$$

The ratios simplify to the same fraction.

Method 2

Look for a common multiplier relating the two ratios.

$$\frac{250}{4} = \frac{500}{8}$$

×2, ×2

The numerator and denominator of the ratios are related by the same multiplier, 2.

The ratios are equivalent.

Online Option  Take the Online Readiness Quiz at **glencoe.com**.

Explore   Unit Rates

Main Idea
Model proportions using bar diagrams.

NGSSS
 MA.7.A.1.6 Apply proportionality to measurement in multiple contexts, including scale drawings and constant speed.

Get Connected
glencoe.com

MONEY When Jeremy gets his allowance, he agrees to save part of it. His savings and expenses are in the ratio 7 : 5. If his daily allowance is $3, how much does he save each day?

ACTIVITY

What do you need to find? how much money Jeremy saves each day

STEP 1   The ratio of savings to expenses is 7 to 5.

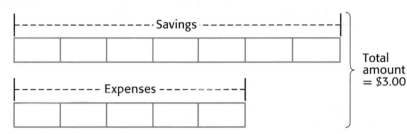

STEP 2   Let x represent each part of a bar. Write an equation.

$$7x + 5x = 3$$ Write the equation.

$$12x = 3$$ There are 12 parts in all.

$$\frac{12x}{12} = \frac{3}{12}$$ Division Property of Equality

$$x = \frac{1}{4} \text{ or } 0.25$$ Simplify.

STEP 3   Each part of the bar represents $0.25. Jeremy's savings are represented by 7 parts. 7 × $0.25 or $1.75.

So, Jeremy saves $1.75 each day.

Analyze the Results

Use a bar diagram to solve.

1. The ratio of the number of boys to the number of girls on the swim team is 7 : 6. If there are 39 athletes on the swim team, how many more boys than girls are there?

2. In a dog kennel, the number of long-haired dogs and the number of short-haired dogs are in the ratio of 5 : 3. If there are 20 long-haired dogs, how many dogs are there altogether?

Main Idea

Determine unit rates.

NGSSS

 MA.7.A.1.6 Apply proportionality to measurement in multiple contexts, including scale drawings and **constant speed.**

New Vocabulary

rate
unit rate

Get Connected
glencoe.com

Rates

Explore Choose a partner and take each other's pulse for 2 minutes.

1. Count the number of beats for each of you.

2. Write the ratio *beats* to *minutes* as a fraction.

A ratio that compares two quantities with different kinds of units is called a **rate**.

$$\dfrac{160 \text{ beats}}{2 \text{ minutes}}$$ ← The units *beats* and *minutes* are different.

When a rate is simplified so that it has a denominator of 1 unit, it is called a **unit rate**.

$$\dfrac{80 \text{ beats}}{1 \text{ minute}}$$ ← The denominator is 1 unit.

The table below shows some common unit rates.

Rate	Unit Rate	Abbreviation	Name
$\dfrac{\text{number of miles}}{1 \text{ hour}}$	miles per hour	mi/h or mph	average speed
$\dfrac{\text{number of miles}}{1 \text{ gallon}}$	miles per gallon	mi/gal or mpg	gas mileage
$\dfrac{\text{number of dollars}}{1 \text{ pound}}$	price per pound	dollars/lb	unit price

Real-World EXAMPLE   Find a Unit Rate

1 **BIKING** Adrienne biked 24 miles in 4 hours. If she biked at a constant speed, how many miles did she ride in one hour?

$24 \text{ miles in 4 hours} = \dfrac{24 \text{ mi}}{4 \text{ h}}$ Write the rate as a fraction.

$= \dfrac{24 \text{ mi} \div 4}{4 \text{ h} \div 4}$ Divide the numerator and the denominator by 4.

$= \dfrac{6 \text{ mi}}{1 \text{ h}}$ Simplify.

Adrienne biked 6 miles in one hour.

CHECK Your Progress

Find each unit rate. Round to the nearest hundredth if necessary.

a. $300 for 6 hours   **b.** 220 miles on 8 gallons

Find a Unit Rate

 JUICE Find the unit price if it costs $2 for eight juice boxes. Round to the nearest cent if necessary.

$$\$2 \text{ for eight boxes} = \frac{\$2}{8 \text{ boxes}} \qquad \text{Write the rate as a fraction.}$$

$$= \frac{\$2 \div 8}{8 \text{ boxes} \div 8} \qquad \text{Divide the numerator and the denominator by 8.}$$

$$= \frac{\$0.25}{1 \text{ box}} \qquad \text{Simplify.}$$

The unit price is $0.25 per juice box.

CHECK Your Progress

c. ESTIMATION Find the unit price if a 4-pack of mixed fruit sells for $2.12.

Compare Using Unit Rates

 DOG FOOD The prices of 3 different bags of dog food are given in the table. Which size bag has the lowest price per pound?

Dog Food Prices	
Bag Size (lb)	**Price ($)**
40	49.00
20	23.44
8	9.88

- 40-pound bag
  $49.00 ÷ 40 pounds = $1.225 per pound

- 20 pound bag
  $23.44 ÷ 20 pounds = $1.172 per pound

- 8-pound bag
  $9.88 ÷ 8 pounds = $1.235 per pound

At $1.172 per pound, the 20-pound bag sells for the lowest price per pound.

CHECK Your Progress

d. FOOD Tito wants to buy some peanut butter to donate to the local food pantry. If Tito wants to save as much money as possible, which brand should he buy?

Peanut Butter Sales	
Brand	**Sale Price**
Nutty	12 ounces for $2.19
Grandma's	18 ounces for $2.79
Bee's	28 ounces for $4.69
Save-A-Lot	40 ounces for $6.60

4 FACE PAINTING Lexi painted 3 faces in 12 minutes at the Crafts Fair. At this rate, how many faces can she paint in 40 minutes?

Real-World Link · · · · ·
Face paint can be made from 1 teaspoon cornstarch and $\frac{1}{2}$ teaspoon each of water and cold cream.

Method 1   Draw a Bar Diagram

| ⊢──────────── 12 min ────────────⊣ |
| time to paint one face | time to paint one face | time to paint one face |
| ⊢─── 4 min ───⊣─── 4 min ───⊣─── 4 min ───⊣ |

It takes 4 minutes to paint one face. In 40 minutes, Lexi can paint 40 ÷ 4 or 10 faces.

Method 2   Find a Unit Rate

Find the unit rate. Then multiply this unit rate by 40 to find the number of faces she can paint in 40 minutes.

3 faces in 12 minutes $= \dfrac{3 \text{ faces} \div 12}{12 \text{ min} \div 12} = \dfrac{0.25 \text{ faces}}{1 \text{ min}}$ Find the unit rate.

$\dfrac{0.25 \text{ faces}}{1 \text{ min}} \cdot 40 \text{ min} = 10 \text{ faces}$ Divide out the common units.

Using either method, Lexi can paint 10 faces in 40 minutes.

 CHOOSE Your Method

e. SCHOOL SUPPLIES Kimbel bought 4 notebooks for $6.32. At this same unit price, how much would he pay for 5 notebooks?

CHECK Your Understanding

Examples 1 and 2
(pp. 196–197)

Find each unit rate. Round to the nearest hundredth if necessary.

1. 90 miles on 15 gallons

2. 1,680 kilobytes in 4 minutes

3. 5 pounds for $2.49

4. 152 feet in 16 seconds

Example 3
(p. 197)

5. CDs Four stores offer customers bulk CD rates. Which store offers the best buy?

Bulk CD Offers	
Store	**Offer**
CD Express	4 CDs for $60
Music Place	6 CDs for $75
CD Rack	5 CDs for $70
Music Shop	3 CDs for $40

Example 4
(p. 198)

6. TRAVEL After 3.5 hours, Pasha had traveled 217 miles. If she travels at a constant speed, how far will she have traveled after 4 hours?

= **Step-by-Step Solutions** begin on page R7.
Extra Practice is on page EP9.

Examples 1 and 2
(pp. 196–197)

Find each unit rate. Round to the nearest hundredth if necessary.

7. 360 miles in 6 hours

8. 6,840 customers in 45 days

9. 150 people for 5 classes

10. 815 Calories in 4 servings

11 45.5 meters in 13 seconds

12. $7.40 for 5 pounds

13. $1.12 for 8.2 ounces

14. 144 miles on 4.5 gallons

15. ESTIMATION Estimate the unit rate if 12 pairs of socks sell for $5.79.

16. ESTIMATION Estimate the unit rate if a 26-mile marathon was completed in 5 hours.

Example 3
(p. 197)

17. SPORTS The results of a swim meet are shown. Who swam the fastest? Explain your reasoning.

Name	Event	Time (s)
Tawni	50-m Freestyle	40.8
Pepita	100-m Butterfly	60.2
Susana	200-m Medley	112.4

18. MONEY A grocery store sells three different packages of bottled water. Which package costs the least per bottle? Explain your reasoning.

6-pack for $3.79

9-pack for $4.50

12-pack for $6.89

Example 4
(p. 198)

19. NUTRITION Use the table at the right.

a. Which soft drink has about twice the amount of sodium per ounce than the other two? Explain.

b. Which soft drink has the least amount of sugar per ounce? Explain.

Soft Drink Nutritional Information			
Soft Drink	Serving Size (oz)	Sodium (mg)	Sugar (g)
A	12	40	22
B	8	24	15
C	7	42	30

20. WORD PROCESSING Ben can type 153 words in 3 minutes. At this rate, how many words can he type in 10 minutes?

21. FABRIC Kenji buys 3 yards of fabric for $7.47. Later he realizes that he needs 2 more yards. How much will he pay for the extra fabric?

22. ESTIMATION A player scores 87 points in 6 games. At this rate, about how many points would she score in the next 4 games?

23. JOBS Dalila earns $108.75 for working 15 hours as a holiday helper wrapping gifts. If she works 18 hours the next week, how much money will she earn?

24. POPULATION Florida has approximately 18.1 million people living in 65,795 square miles. What is the *population density* or number of people per square mile in Florida?

Estimate the unit price for each item. Justify your answers.

25.

$2.49

26.

$1.89

27.

$1.13

28. RECIPES A recipe that makes 10 mini-loaves of banana bread calls for $1\frac{1}{4}$ cups flour. How much flour is needed to make 2 dozen mini-loaves using this recipe?

29 SPORTS Use the information at the left.

a. The Boston Marathon is 26.2 miles long. What was the average speed of the record winner of the wheelchair division? Round to the nearest hundredth.

b. At this rate, about how long would it take this competitor to complete a 30-mile race?

30. MONEY Suppose that 1 euro is worth $1.25. In Europe, a book costs 19 euro. In Los Angeles, the same book costs $22.50. In which location is the book less expensive?

Real-World Link · · · ·
The record for the Boston Marathon's wheelchair division is 1 hour, 18 minutes, and 27 seconds.

31. ANIMALS Use the graph that shows the average number of heartbeats for an active adult brown bear and a hibernating brown bear.

a. What does the point (2, 120) represent on the graph?

b. What does the point (1.5, 18) represent on the graph?

c. What does the ratio of the y-coordinate to the x-coordinate for each pair of points on the graph represent?

d. Use the graph to find the bear's average heart rate when it is active and when it is hibernating.

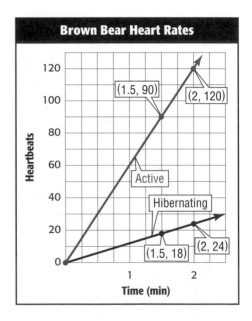

e. When is the bear's heart rate greater, when it is active or when it is hibernating? How can you tell this from the graph?

32. TIRES At Tire Depot, a pair of new tires sells for $216. The manager's special advertises the same tires selling at a rate of $380 for 4 tires. How much do you save per tire if you purchase the manager's special?

33. FIND THE DATA Refer to the Data File on pages 2–5. Choose some data and write a real-world problem in which you would compare unit rates or ratios.

34. FIND THE ERROR Seth is trying to find the unit price for a package of blank compact discs on sale at 10 for $5.49. Find his mistake and correct it.

$10 ÷ \$5.49$
$\$1.82 \text{ each}$

CHALLENGE Determine whether each statement is *sometimes*, *always*, or *never* true. Give an example or a counterexample.

35. A ratio is a rate.   **36.** A rate is a ratio.

37. **Write** MATH Describe, using an example, how a *rate* is a measure of one quantity per unit of another quantity.

 NGSSS Practice   MA.6.A.1.2, MA.7.A.1.6

38. Mrs. Ross needs to buy dish soap. There are four differently sized containers.

Dish Soap Prices	
Brand	**Price**
Lots of Suds	$0.98 for 8 ounces
Bright Wash	$1.29 for 12 ounces
Spotless Soap	$3.14 for 30 ounces
Lemon Bright	$3.45 for 32 ounces

Which brand costs the least per ounce?

A. Lots of Suds   **C.** Spotless Soap

B. Bright Wash   **D.** Lemon Bright

39. The table shows the total distance traveled by a car driving at a constant rate of speed.

Time (h)	Distance (mi)
2	130
3.5	227.5
4	260
7	455

How far will the car have traveled after 10 hours?

F. 520 miles   **H.** 650 miles

G. 585 miles   **I.** 715 miles

 **Spiral Review**

40. VIDEOS Serena can use a mail-based video rental plan that is $20 per month and pay $1.99 per movie or she can join a frequent renter's plan at the local video store for $10 per month and pay $2.99 per video. How many movies would she have to borrow using the mail-based plan before it would save her money compared to renting at the local store? (Lesson 3-3D)

Solve each equation. Check your solution. (Lesson 3-3B)

41. $5d + 12 = 2$ **42.** $13 - f = 7$ **43.** $10 = 2g + 3$ **44.** $6 = 3 - 3h$

45. Evaluate $|5| + |-10|$. (Lesson 1-1B)

Main Idea
Identify proportional and nonproportional relationships.

NGSSS

MA.7.A.1.1 Distinguish between situations that are proportional or not proportional and use proportions to solve problems.

New Vocabulary
proportional
nonproportional

Get Connected
glencoe.com

Proportional and Nonproportional Relationships

PIZZA Ms. Cochran is planning a year-end pizza party for her students. Ace Pizza offers free delivery and charges $8 for each medium pizza.

1. Copy and complete the table to determine the cost for different numbers of pizzas ordered.

Cost ($)	8			
Pizzas Ordered	1	2	3	4

2. For each number of pizzas, write the relationship of the cost and number of pizzas as a ratio in simplest form. What do you notice?

Two quantities are **proportional** if they have a constant ratio. For relationships in which this ratio is not constant, the two quantities are **nonproportional**.

$$\frac{\text{cost of order}}{\text{pizzas ordered}} = \frac{8}{1} = \frac{16}{2} = \frac{24}{3} = \frac{32}{4} \text{ or } \$8 \text{ per pizza}$$

The cost of an order is *proportional* to the number of pizzas ordered.

EXAMPLES Identify Proportional Relationships

1. **PIZZA** Uptown Pizzeria sells medium pizzas for $7 each but charges a $3 delivery fee per order. Is the cost of an order proportional to the number of pizzas ordered?

Cost ($)	10	17	24	31
Pizzas Ordered	1	2	3	4

For each number of pizzas, write the relationship of the cost and number of pizzas as a ratio in simplest form.

$\dfrac{\text{cost of order}}{\text{pizzas ordered}} \longrightarrow \dfrac{10}{1} \text{ or } 10 \qquad \dfrac{17}{2} \text{ or } 8.5 \qquad \dfrac{24}{3} \text{ or } 8 \qquad \dfrac{31}{4} \text{ or } 7.75$

Since the ratios of the two quantities are not the same, the cost of an order is *not* proportional to the number of pizzas ordered.

2 **BEVERAGES** You can use the recipe shown to make a healthier version of a popular beverage. Is the amount of mix used proportional to the amount of sugar used?

Fruit Punch
$\frac{1}{2}$ cup sugar
1 envelope of mix
2 quarts of water

Find the amount of mix and sugar needed for different numbers of batches and make a table to show these mix and sugar measures.

Cups of Sugar	$\frac{1}{2}$	1	$1\frac{1}{2}$	2
Envelopes of Mix	1	2	3	4
Quarts of Water	2	4	6	8

For each number of cups of sugar, write the relationship of the cups and number of envelopes of mix as a ratio in simplest form.

$$\frac{\text{cups of sugar}}{\text{envelopes of mix}} \longrightarrow \frac{\frac{1}{2}}{1}, \frac{1}{2}, \frac{1\frac{1}{2}}{3}, \frac{2}{4}$$

All of the ratios between the two quantities can be simplified to 0.5. The amount of mix used is proportional to the amount of sugar used.

 CHECK Your Progress

a. BEVERAGES In Example 2, is the amount of sugar used proportional to the amount of water used?

b. MONEY At the beginning of the year, Isabel had $120 in the bank. Each week, she deposits another $20. Is her account balance proportional to the number of weeks of deposits?

 **CHECK Your Understanding**

Examples 1 and 2
(pp. 202–203)

For Exercises 1–4, explain your reasoning.

1 **ELEPHANTS** An adult elephant drinks about 225 liters of water each day. Is the number of days that an elephant's water supply lasts proportional to the number of liters of water the elephant drinks?

2. PACKAGES A package shipping company charges $5.25 to deliver a package. In addition, they charge $0.45 for each pound over one pound. Is the cost to ship a package proportional to the weight of the package?

3. SCHOOL At a certain middle school, every homeroom teacher is assigned 28 students. There are 3 teachers who do not have a homeroom. Is the number of students at this school proportional to the number of teachers?

4. JOBS Andrew earns $18 per hour for mowing lawns. Is the amount of money he earns proportional to the number of hours he spends mowing?

Practice and Problem Solving

= **Step-by-Step Solutions** begin on page R7.
Extra Practice is on page EP9.

Examples 1 and 2
(pp. 202–203)

For Exercises 5–12, explain your reasoning.

5. RECREATION The Vista Marina rents boats for $25 per hour. In addition to the rental fee, there is a $12 charge for fuel. Is the number of hours you can rent the boat proportional to the total cost?

6. ELEVATORS An elevator *ascends*, or goes up, at a rate of 750 feet per minute. Is the height to which the elevator ascends proportional to the number of minutes it takes to get there?

7. PLANTS Kudzu is a vine that grows an average of 7.5 feet every 5 days. Is the length of the vine as measured on the last day proportional to the number of days of growth?

8. TEMPERATURE To convert a temperature in degrees Celsius to degrees Fahrenheit, multiply the Celsius temperature by $\frac{9}{5}$ and then add 32°. Is a temperature in degrees Celsius proportional to its equivalent temperature in degrees Fahrenheit?

9. ADVERTISING On Saturday, Querida gave away 416 coupons for a free appetizer at a local restaurant. The next day, she gave away about 52 coupons an hour.

   a. Is the number of coupons Querida gave away on Sunday proportional to the number of hours she worked that day?

   b. Is the total number of coupons Querida gave away on Saturday and Sunday proportional to the number of hours she worked on Sunday?

10. TAXES MegaMart collects a sales tax equal to $\frac{1}{16}$ of the retail price of each purchase and sends this money to the state government.

   a. Is the amount of tax collected proportional to the cost of an item before tax is added?

   b. Is the amount of tax collected proportional to the cost of an item after tax has been added?

11 MEASUREMENT Determine whether the measures for the figure shown are proportional.

   a. the length of a side and the perimeter

   b. the length of a side and the area

12. POSTAGE The table shows the price to mail a first-class letter for various weights.

Cost ($)	0.42	0.59	0.76	1.34	
Weight (oz)	1	2	3	4	5

   a. Is the cost to mail a letter proportional to its weight? Explain your reasoning.

   b. Can you determine the cost of a letter that weighs 5 ounces? Explain.

Real-World Link · · ·
Ascending at a speed of 1,000 feet per minute, the five outside elevators of the Westin St. Francis are the fastest glass elevators in San Francisco.

13. **FIND THE ERROR** Blake ran laps around the gym. His times are shown in the table. Blake is trying to decide whether the number of laps is proportional to the time. Find his mistake and correct it.

Time (min)	1	2	3	4
Laps	4	6	8	10

It is proportional because the number of laps always increases by 2.

14. **Write MATH** Write in your own words the difference between a proportional and nonproportional relationship. Give an example of each.

NGSSS Practice   MA.6.A.2.1, MA.7.A.1.1

15. Mr. Martinez is comparing the price of oranges from several different markets. Which market's pricing guide is based on a constant unit price?

A.
Number of Oranges	5	10	15	20
Total Cost ($)	3.50	6.00	8.50	11.00

C.
Number of Oranges	5	10	15	20
Total Cost ($)	3.00	6.00	9.00	12.00

B.
Number of Oranges	5	10	15	20
Total Cost ($)	3.50	6.50	9.50	12.50

D.
Number of Oranges	5	10	15	20
Total Cost ($)	3.00	5.00	7.00	9.00

16. **GRIDDED RESPONSE** The middle school is planning a family movie night where popcorn will be served. The constant relationship between the number of people n and p, the number of cups of popcorn, is shown in the table. How many people can be served with 519 cups of popcorn?

n	30	60	120	?
p	90	180	360	519

Spiral Review

17. **GROCERIES** Three pounds of pears cost $3.57. At this rate, how much would 10 pounds cost? (Lesson 4-1B)

PEARS
$3.57
3 POUNDS

Solve each equation. Check your solution. (Lesson 3-3B)

18. $4y + 19 = 7$

19. $10x + 2 = 32$

20. $48 - 8j = 16$

Main Idea

Use proportions to solve problems.

NGSSS

MA.7.A.1.1 Distinguish between situations that are proportional or not proportional and **use proportions to solve problems.**

New Vocabulary

equivalent ratios
proportion
cross products

Get Connected
glencoe.com

Solve Proportions

SHOPPING A local department store advertised a sale as shown at the right.

1. Write a ratio in simplest form that compares the cost to the number of bottles of nail polish.

2. Suppose Kate and some friends wanted to buy 6 bottles of polish. Write a ratio comparing the cost to the number of bottles of polish.

3. Is the cost proportional to the number of bottles of polish purchased? Explain.

On Sale 2 for $5

The ratios of the cost to the number of bottles of polish for two or six bottles are both equal to $\frac{5}{2}$. **Equivalent ratios** have the same value.

$$\frac{\$5}{2 \text{ bottles of polish}} = \frac{\$15}{6 \text{ bottles of polish}}$$

Key Concept — Proportion

Words — A **proportion** is an equation stating that two ratios or rates are equivalent.

Symbols

Numbers	Algebra
$\frac{6}{8} = \frac{3}{4}$	$\frac{a}{b} = \frac{c}{d}, b \neq 0, d \neq 0$

Consider the following proportion.

$$\frac{a}{b} = \frac{c}{d}$$

$$\frac{a}{\cancel{b}} \cdot \cancel{b}d = \frac{c}{\cancel{d}} \cdot b\cancel{d}$$ Multiply each side by bd and divide out common factors.

$$ad = bc$$ Simplify.

The products ad and bc are called the **cross products** of this proportion. The cross products of any proportion are equal.

$$\frac{6}{8} = \frac{3}{4} \longrightarrow 8 \cdot 3 = 24$$
$$\longrightarrow 6 \cdot 4 = 24$$

EXAMPLE **Write and Solve a Proportion**

1 **TEMPERATURE** After 2 hours, the air temperature had risen 7°F. Write and solve a proportion to find the amount of time it will take at this rate for the temperature to rise an additional 13°F.

Write a proportion. Let t represent the time in hours.

$$\text{temperature} \rightarrow \quad \frac{7}{2} = \frac{13}{t} \quad \leftarrow \text{temperature} \\ \text{time} \rightarrow \qquad\qquad\quad \leftarrow \text{time}$$

$7 \cdot t = 2 \cdot 13$ Find the cross products.

$7t = 26$ Multiply.

$\dfrac{7t}{7} = \dfrac{26}{7}$ Divide each side by 7.

$t \approx 3.7$ Simplify.

It will take about 3.7 hours to rise an additional 13°F.

 CHECK Your Progress

Solve each proportion.

a. $\dfrac{x}{4} = \dfrac{9}{10}$ **b.** $\dfrac{2}{34} = \dfrac{5}{y}$ **c.** $\dfrac{7}{3} = \dfrac{n}{2.1}$

Real-World EXAMPLE **Make Predictions**

2 **BLOOD** During a blood drive, the ratio of Type O donors to non-Type O donors was 37 : 43. About how many Type O donors would you expect in a group of 300 donors?

Write the ratio for the given information.

$$\text{Type O donors} \rightarrow \quad \frac{37}{37 + 43} \text{ or } \frac{37}{80} \\ \text{total donors} \rightarrow$$

Write a proportion. Let t represent the number of Type O donors.

$$\text{Type O donors} \rightarrow \quad \frac{37}{80} = \frac{t}{300} \quad \leftarrow \text{Type O donors} \\ \text{total donors} \rightarrow \qquad\qquad\qquad \leftarrow \text{total donors}$$

$37 \cdot 300 = 80t$ Find the cross products.

$11{,}100 = 80t$ Multiply.

$\dfrac{11{,}100}{80} = \dfrac{80t}{80}$ Divide each side by 80.

$t = 138.75$ Simplify.

There would be about 139 Type O donors.

 CHECK Your Progress

d. **RECYCLING** Recycling 2,000 pounds of paper saves about 17 trees. Write and solve a proportion to determine how many trees you would save by recycling 5,000 pounds of paper.

 Real-World Link · · · ·

There are four different blood types: A, B, AB, and O. People with Type O blood are considered *universal donors.* Their blood can be transfused into people with any blood type.

You can also use the unit rate to write an equation expressing the relationship between two proportional quantities.

 EXAMPLE **Write and Use an Equation**

③ **GASOLINE** Jaycee bought 8 gallons of gasoline for $31.12. Write an equation relating the cost to the number of gallons of gasoline. How much would Jaycee pay for 11 gallons at this same rate?

Find the unit rate between cost and gallons.

$$\frac{\text{cost in dollars}}{\text{gasoline in gallons}} = \frac{31.12}{8} \text{ or \$3.89 per gallon}$$

Words	The cost is $3.89 times the number of gallons.
Variable	Let *c* represent the cost. Let *g* represent the number of gallons.
Equation	$c = 3.89 \cdot g$

Find the cost for 11 gallons sold at the same rate.

$c = 3.89g$ Write the equation.

$c = 3.89(11)$ Replace *g* with the number of gallons.

$c = 42.79$ Multiply.

The cost for 11 gallons is $42.79.

Study Tip

Checking Your Equation
You can check to see if the equation you wrote is accurate by testing the two known quantities.

$c = 3.89g$

$31.12 = 3.89(8)$

$31.12 = 31.12$

 CHECK Your Progress

e. **TYPING** Olivia typed 2 pages in 15 minutes. Write an equation relating the number of minutes *m* to the number of pages *p* typed. If she continues typing at this rate, how many minutes will it take her to type 10 pages? to type 25 pages?

 **CHECK Your Understanding**

Example 1
(p. 207)

Solve each proportion.

① $\frac{1.5}{6} = \frac{10}{p}$

2. $\frac{3.2}{9} = \frac{n}{36}$

3. $\frac{41}{x} = \frac{5}{2}$

For Exercises 4 and 5, assume all situations are proportional.

Example 2
(p. 207)

4. **TEETH** For every 7 people who say they floss daily, there are 18 people who say they do not. Write and solve a proportion to determine how many people out of 65 you would expect to say they floss daily.

Example 3
(p. 208)

5. **TUTORING** Trina earns $28.50 tutoring for 3 hours. Write an equation relating her earnings *m* to the number of hours *h* she tutors. How much would Trina earn tutoring for 2 hours? for 4.5 hours?

Practice and Problem Solving

 = **Step-by-Step Solutions** begin on page R8.
Extra Practice is on page EP10.

Example 1
(p. 207)

Solve each proportion.

6. $\dfrac{k}{7} = \dfrac{32}{56}$ **7.** $\dfrac{x}{13} = \dfrac{18}{39}$ **8.** $\dfrac{44}{p} = \dfrac{11}{5}$ **9.** $\dfrac{2}{w} = \dfrac{0.4}{0.7}$

10. $\dfrac{6}{25} = \dfrac{d}{30}$ **11.** $\dfrac{2.5}{6} = \dfrac{h}{9}$ **12.** $\dfrac{3.5}{8} = \dfrac{a}{3.2}$ **13.** $\dfrac{48}{9} = \dfrac{72}{n}$

Example 2
(p. 207)

Assume the situations are proportional. Write and solve a proportion. Round to the nearest tenth.

14. COOKING Evarado paid $1.12 for a dozen eggs. Determine the cost of 3 eggs.

15. TRAVEL A certain vehicle can travel 483 miles on 14 gallons of gasoline. Determine how many gallons of gasoline this vehicle will need to travel 600 miles.

16. ILLNESS For every person who actually has the flu, there are 6 people who have flu-like symptoms resulting from a cold. If a doctor sees 40 patients, determine how many of these you would expect to have a cold.

17. LIFE SCIENCE For every left-handed person, there are about 4 right-handed people. If there are 30 students in a class, predict the number of students who are right-handed.

18. TRAVEL A speed limit of 100 kilometers per hour (kph) is approximately equal to 62 miles per hour (mph). Predict the following measures. Round your answers to the nearest whole number.

  a. a speed limit in mph for a speed limit of 75 kph

  b. a speed limit in kph for a speed limit of 20 mph

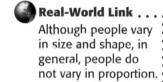

16.2 in.

64 in.

Real-World Link . . . .
Although people vary
in size and shape, in
general, people do
not vary in proportion.

Example 3
(p. 208)

19. MEASUREMENT The width of a woman's shoulders is proportional to her height. A woman who is 64 inches tall has a shoulder width of 16.2 inches. Find the height of a woman who has a shoulder width of 18.5 inches.

20. COOKING A recipe calls for $1\frac{1}{2}$ tablespoons of cinnamon for every 3 tablespoons of sugar. If you want to increase the recipe and use 6 tablespoons of sugar, how many tablespoons of cinnamon would you need? Explain your reasoning.

21. PLANETS Use the table to write a proportion relating the weights on two planets. Then find the missing weight. Round to the nearest tenth.

  a. Earth: 90 pounds; Venus: ■ pounds

  b. Mercury: 55 pounds; Earth: ■ pounds

  c. Jupiter: 350 pounds; Uranus: ■ pounds

  d. Venus: 115 pounds; Mercury: ■ pounds

Weights on Different Planets Earth Weight = 120 pounds	
Mercury	45.6 pounds
Venus	109.2 pounds
Uranus	96 pounds
Jupiter	304.8 pounds

22. FIND THE DATA Refer to the Data File on pages 2–5. Choose some data and write a real-world problem that could be solved by using a proportion.

23. REASONING A powdered drink mix calls for a ratio of powder to water of 1 : 8. If there are 32 cups of powder, how many total cups of water are needed? Explain your reasoning.

CHALLENGE Solve each equation.

24. $\dfrac{2}{3} = \dfrac{18}{x + 5}$

25. $\dfrac{x - 4}{10} = \dfrac{7}{5}$

26. $\dfrac{4.5}{17 - x} = \dfrac{3}{8}$

27. **Write MATH** Explain why it might be easier to write an equation to represent a proportional relationship rather than using a proportion.

NGSSS Practice   MA.6.A.2.2, MA.7.A.1.1

28. Barrington paid $24 for 3 previously viewed DVDs at Play-It-Again Movies. Which equation can he use to find the cost c of purchasing 12 previously viewed DVDs from the same store?

A. $c = 12 \cdot 24$

C. $c = 12 \cdot 8$

B. $c = 24 \cdot 4$

D. $c = 72 \cdot 36$

29. An amusement park line is moving about 4 feet every 15 minutes. At this rate, approximately how long will it take for a person at the back of the 50-foot line to reach the front of the line?

F. 1 hour

H. 5 hours

G. 3 hours

I. 13 hours

30. THINK SOLVE EXPLAIN **EXTENDED RESPONSE** Crystal's mother kept a record of her height at different ages. She recorded the information in a table.

Age (y)	Height (in.)
0 (birth)	19
1	25
2	30
5	42
10	55
12	60

Part A Write a ratio for each age and the corresponding height.

Part B Is the relationship between Crystal's age and her height proportional? Explain.

31. BABYSITTING Brenna charges $15, $30, $45, and $60 for babysitting 1, 2, 3, and 4 hours, respectively. Is the relationship between the number of hours and the amount charged proportional? If so, find the unit rate. If not, explain why not. (Lesson 4-1C)

Find each unit rate. Round to the nearest hundredth if necessary. (Lesson 4-1B)

32. 50 miles on 2.5 gallons

33. 2,500 kilobytes in 5 minutes

34. 5 peppers for $6.45

35. 64.8 meters in 9 seconds

Extend

Main Idea

Use proportions to estimate populations.

NGSSS

 MA.7.A.1.1 Distinguish between situations that are proportional or not proportional and **use proportions to solve problems.**

Get Connected
glencoe.com

Wildlife Sampling

Naturalists can estimate the population in a wildlife preserve by using the capture-recapture technique. You will model this technique using dried beans in a bowl to represent bears in a forest.

ACTIVITY

STEP 1 Fill a small bowl with dried beans. Scoop out some of the beans. These represent the original *captured* bears. Count and record the number of beans. Mark each bean with an × on both sides. Then return these beans to the bowl and mix well.

STEP 2 Scoop another cup of beans from the bowl and count them. This is the *sample* for Trial A. Count the beans with the ×'s. These are the *recaptured* bears. Record both numbers in a table.

Trial	Sample	Recaptured	P
A			
B			
⋮			
Total			

STEP 3 Use the proportion below to estimate the total number of beans in the bowl. This represents the total population *P*. Record the value of *P* in the table.

$$\frac{\text{captured}}{\text{total population } (P)} = \frac{\text{recaptured}}{\text{sample}}$$

STEP 4 Return all of the beans to the bowl.

STEP 5 Repeat Steps 2–4 nine times.

Analyze the Results

1. **ESTIMATION** Find the average of the estimates in column *P*. Is this a good estimate of the number of beans in the bowl? Explain your reasoning.

2. Count the actual number of beans in the bowl. How does this number compare to your estimate?

PART   A   B   C

Problem-Solving Investigation

Main Idea Solve problems by drawing a diagram.

P.S.I. TEAM +

Draw a Diagram

GRACE: I am using two different shades of blue in my painting class. One shade has a blue paint to water ratio of 3:4 and the other shade has a blue paint to water ratio of 2:3. I want to make a total of 18 ounces of mixture. How many ounces of water will I need?

YOUR MISSION: Draw a diagram to determine how many ounces of water Grace will need.

Understand	You know that she needs two mixtures of blue paint and water, one in the ratio of 3 : 4 and the other in the ratio of 2 : 3. She wants 18 ounces of mixture.
Plan	Draw a diagram to represent the two mixtures.
Solve	Start with a bar diagram representing the mixtures. 3 : 4 ratio of blue paint to water 2 : 3 ratio of blue paint to water 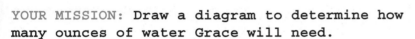 There is a total of 12 parts. Each part represents 18 ÷ 12 or 1.5 ounces. So, she will need 7 · 1.5 or 10.5 ounces of water.
Check	For each shade of paint, there is more water than blue paint. So, more than half of the total should be water. The answer is reasonable. ✓

Analyze the Strategy

1. How can drawing a diagram be useful when solving a real-world problem?

 NGSSS

MA.7.A.1.6 Apply proportionality to measurement in multiple contexts, including scale drawings and constant speed.

Mixed Problem Solving

Extra Practice is on page EP9.

- Draw a diagram.
- Look for a pattern.
- Work backward.
- Choose an operation.

Use the *draw a diagram* strategy to solve Exercises 2–5.

2. A string is cut into 3 pieces in the ratio of 1 : 2 : 4. If the longest piece is 16 in. longer than the medium piece, find the length of the original string.

Piece 1 ☐

Piece 2 ☐☐   16 in.

Piece 3 ☐☐☐☐

3. **TILES** A kitchen is 10 feet long and 8 feet wide. If kitchen floor tiles are $2\frac{1}{2}$ inches by 3 inches, how many tiles are needed for the kitchen?

4. **TRAVEL** There are four seats in Clarence's car: two in the front and two in the back. If Benny, Carlita, and Juanita are all in the car with Clarence, how many ways can they be seated in the car if Clarence is driving?

5. **GARDENING** Mr. Sanchez has a flower bed with a length of 10 meters and a width of 5 meters. If he can only change the width of the flower bed, describe what he can do to increase the perimeter by 12 meters.

Use any strategy to solve Exercises 6–13.

6. **SPORTS** Every 12 times at bat, Shim hits the ball an average of 3 times. About how many times will he hit the ball after 20 times at bat? 40? 84?

Times at Bat	Number of Hits
12	3
20	?
40	?
84	?

7. **NUMBERS** A number is halved. Then three is subtracted from the quotient, and 5 is multiplied by the difference. Finally, 1 is added to the product. If the ending number is 26, what was the beginning number?

8. **PRIZES** By reaching into a bag that has letters A, B, and C, George will select three letters without replacing them. How many possible combinations are there of how the letters could be drawn?

9. **HEALTH** The human body is about $\frac{7}{10}$ water. About how much would a person weigh if they had 70 pounds of water weight?

10. **FINANCIAL LITERACY** The ratio of Julio's money to Marcus's money was 7 : 10. After Julio bought 4 books at $4.50 each, the ratio of Julio's money to Marcus's money was 1 : 4. Use a bar diagram to find how much money Julio and Marcus have left.

11. **GEOMETRY** What is the next figure in the pattern below?

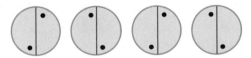

12. **BASKETBALL** Last basketball season, Simon had four less than twice the number of free throws Amit had. Simon had 48 free throws. How many free throws did Amit have last season?

13. **Write MATH** Write a problem that can be solved by drawing a diagram. Then solve the problem.

4-2 Scale Drawings and Models

Main Idea

Solve problems involving scale drawings.

NGSSS

 MA.7.A.1.6 Apply proportionality to measurement in multiple contexts, including scale drawings and constant speed. *Also addresses MA.7.A.1.1.*

New Vocabulary

scale drawing
scale model
scale
scale factor

Get Connected
glencoe.com

Scale Drawings

Explore

- Measure the length of each item in a room, such as a gymnasium.

- Record each length to the nearest $\frac{1}{2}$ foot.

1. Let 1 unit on the grid paper represent 2 feet. So, 4 units = 8 feet. Convert all your measurements to units.

2. On grid paper, make a drawing of your room like the one shown.

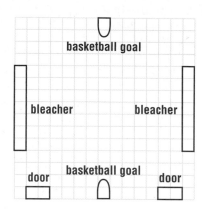

Scale drawings and **scale models** are used to represent objects that are too large or too small to be drawn or built at actual size. The **scale** gives the ratio that compares the measurements of the drawing or model to the measurements of the real object. The measurements on a drawing or model are proportional to the measurements on the actual object.

EXAMPLE   **Use a Map Scale**

1. **MAPS** What is the actual distance between Hagerstown and Annapolis?

    Step 1   Use a centimeter ruler to find the map distance between the two cities. The map distance is about 4 centimeters.

    Step 2   Write and solve a proportion using the scale. Let d represent the actual distance between the cities.

$$
\begin{array}{ccc}
 & \textbf{Scale} & \textbf{Length} \\
\text{map} \longrightarrow & \dfrac{1 \text{ centimeter}}{24 \text{ miles}} = & \dfrac{4 \text{ centimeters}}{d \text{ miles}} \longleftarrow \text{map} \\
\text{actual} \longrightarrow & & \phantom{\dfrac{4 \text{ centimeters}}{d \text{ miles}}} \longleftarrow \text{actual}
\end{array}
$$

$$1 \times d = 24 \times 4 \qquad \text{Cross products}$$

$$d = 96 \qquad \text{Simplify.}$$

The distance between the cities is about 96 miles.

 **CHECK Your Progress**

a. MAPS On the map of Arkansas shown, find the actual distance between Clarksville and Little Rock. Use a ruler to measure.

Study Tip

Scale A map scale can be written in different ways, including the following:

1 cm = 20 mi

1 cm : 20 mi

$\dfrac{1 \text{ cm}}{20 \text{ mi}}$

EXAMPLE Use a Scale Model

② **PHONES** A graphic artist is creating an advertisement for a new cell phone. If she uses a scale of 5 inches = 1 inch, what is the length of the cell phone on the advertisement?

4 in.

Write a proportion using the scale. Let a represent the length of the advertisement cell phone.

	Scale		Length	
advertisement →	$\dfrac{5 \text{ inches}}{1 \text{ inch}}$	=	$\dfrac{a \text{ inches}}{4 \text{ inches}}$	← advertisement
actual →				← actual

$5 \cdot 4 = 1 \cdot a$ Cross products

$20 = a$ Multiply.

The length of the cell phone on the advertisement is 20 inches long.

Study Tip

Scale The scale is the ratio of the drawing/model measure to the actual measure. It is not always the ratio of a smaller measure to a larger measure.

 CHECK Your Progress

b. SCOOTERS A scooter is $3\dfrac{1}{2}$ feet long. Find the length of a scale model of the scooter if the scale is 1 inch = $\dfrac{3}{4}$ feet.

A scale written as a ratio without units in simplest form is called the **scale factor**.

scale $\dfrac{\frac{1}{4} \text{ inch}}{2 \text{ feet}} = \dfrac{\frac{1}{4} \text{ inch}}{24 \text{ inches}}$ Convert 2 feet to inches.

$= \dfrac{4}{4} \cdot \dfrac{\frac{1}{4} \text{ inch}}{24 \text{ inches}}$ Multiply by $\dfrac{4}{4}$ to eliminate the fraction in the numerator. Divide out the common units.

$= \dfrac{1}{96}$ scale factor

EXAMPLE Find a Scale Factor

3 **SAILBOATS** Find the scale factor of a model sailboat if the scale is
1 inch = 6 feet.

$$\frac{1 \text{ inch}}{6 \text{ feet}} = \frac{1 \text{ inch}}{72 \text{ inches}} \qquad \text{Convert 6 feet to inches.}$$

$$= \frac{1}{72} \qquad \text{Divide out the common units.}$$

The scale factor is $\frac{1}{72}$.

CHECK Your Progress

c. **CARS** What is the scale factor of a model car if the scale is
1 inch = 2 feet?

Real-World EXAMPLE Construct a Scale Model

4 **FERRIS WHEELS** Penny made a model
of a Ferris wheel that is 60 feet tall.
The model is 15 inches tall. Penny
also makes a model of the sky needle
ride that is 100 feet tall using the
same scale. How tall is the model?

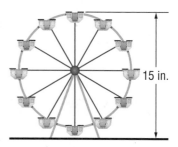

15 in.

model → $\dfrac{15 \text{ in.}}{60 \text{ ft}} = \dfrac{1 \text{ in.}}{4 \text{ ft}}$ ← actual Divide the numerator and denominator by 15 so the
numerator equals 1.

The scale is 1 inch = 4 feet. Using this scale, find the height of the
sky needle ride.

model → $\dfrac{1 \text{ in.}}{4 \text{ ft}} = \dfrac{x \text{ in.}}{100 \text{ ft}}$ ← actual

$1 \cdot 100 = 4 \cdot x$ Find the cross products.

$100 = 4x$ Multiply.

$25 = x$ Divide by 4.

The height of the sky needle model is 25 inches.

CHECK Your Progress

d. **SOLAR SYSTEM** Leah is constructing a scale model of the solar
system for science class. She knows the diameter of the sun is
1,391,900 kilometers, but would like to make it 10 inches. If
Mercury's orbit radius is 57,950,000 kilometers, how many feet
away from the sun will Mercury be in the model?

Example 1
(p. 214)

GEOGRAPHY Find the actual distance between each pair of cities in New Mexico. Use a ruler to measure.

1. Carlsbad and Artesia
2. Hobbs and Eunice
3. Artesia and Eunice
4. Lovington and Carlsbad

Example 2
(p. 215)

5. **BRIDGES** An engineer makes a model of a bridge using a scale of 1 inch = 3 yards.

50 yards

4 yards

a. What is the length of the model?

b. What is the height of the model?

Example 3
(p. 216)

Find the scale factor of each scale drawing or model.

6.

1 inch = 4 feet

7.

1 centimeter = 15 millimeters

8. **CITY PLANNING** In the aerial view of a city block at the right, the length of Main Street is 2 inches. If Main Street's actual length is 2 miles, find the scale factor of the drawing.

Main Street

Example 4
(p. 216)

9. **DECORATING** Julianne is constructing a scale model of her family room to decide how to redecorate it. The room is 14 feet long by 18 feet wide. If she wants the model to be 8 inches long, how wide will it be?

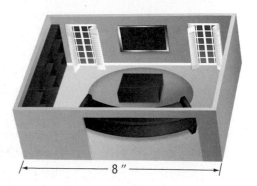

8 "

Practice and Problem Solving

= **Step-by-Step Solutions** begin on page R9.
Extra Practice is on page EP10.

Example 1
(p. 214)

GEOGRAPHY Find the actual distance between each pair of locations in South Carolina. Use a ruler to measure.

10. Columbia and Charleston

11. Hollywood and Sumter

12. Congaree Swamp and Charleston

13. Sumter and Columbia

Examples 2 and 3
(p. 215–216)

Find the length of each model. Then find the scale factor.

14.
87 ft

2 in. = 15 ft

15
36 m

0.5 cm = 1.5 m

16.
120 yd

End Zone   End Zone

1 in. = 20 yd

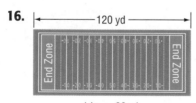

17.
$5\frac{7}{8}$ in.

1 in. = 0.5 in.

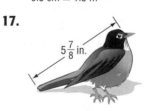

Example 4
(p. 216)

18. A model of an apartment is shown where $\frac{1}{4}$ inch represents 3 feet in the actual apartment.

a. What is the actual length of the living room?

b. Find the actual dimensions of the master bedroom.

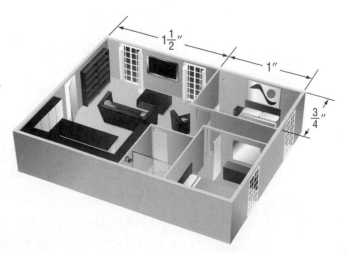

$1\frac{1}{2}''$

$1''$

$\frac{3}{4}''$

19. TREES A model of a tree is made using a scale of 1 inch : 25 feet. What is the height of the actual tree if the height of the model is $4\frac{3}{8}$ inches?

20. GEOGRAPHY A map of Bakersfield, California, has a scale of 1 inch to 5 miles. If the city is $5\frac{1}{5}$ inches across on the map, what is the actual distance across the actual city? Use estimation to check your answer.

21. ⟳ **MULTIPLE REPRESENTATIONS** Refer to the information at the left.

   a. NUMBERS Find the scale factor between the actual height of Thomas Jefferson and the statue.

   b. TABLE Make a table showing the height of the statue for every foot in height of Thomas Jefferson.

   c. ALGEBRA Write an expression to represent the height of the statue if Thomas Jefferson is x feet in height.

   d. NUMBERS Find the actual height of Thomas Jefferson if the height of the statue is 19 feet.

22. BUILDINGS If you are making a model of your bedroom, which would be an appropriate scale: 1 inch = 2 feet, or 1 inch = 12 feet? Explain.

23 **GRAPHIC NOVEL** Refer to the graphic novel frame below for Exercises a and b.

Real-World Link · · · ·
The statue of Thomas Jefferson inside the Jefferson Memorial in Washington, D.C., was made using a scale of 1 foot : 3 feet.

   a. How many units on the map will the kids go from the lake to the cabin?

   b. What is the actual distance?

H.O.T. Problems

24. OPEN ENDED On grid paper, create a scale drawing of a room in your home. Include the scale that you used.

25. REASONING Compare and contrast the terms *scale* and *scale factor*. Include an example in your comparison.

26. ✏ **Write MATH** Explain how you could use a map to estimate the actual distance between Miami, Florida, and Atlanta, Georgia.

27. A scale drawing of a doctor's office is shown.

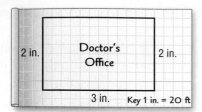

2 in.   Doctor's Office   2 in.

3 in.   Key 1 in. = 20 ft

What are the actual dimensions of the doctor's office?

A. 24 feet × 48 feet

B. 30 feet × 52 feet

C. 40 feet × 60 feet

D. 37.5 feet × 65 feet

28. ✎ **GRIDDED RESPONSE** Ernesto drew a map of his school. He used a scale of 1 inch : 50 feet. What distance in inches on Ernesto's map should represent the 625 feet between the cafeteria and the science lab?

29. A certain map has a scale of $\frac{1}{4}$ inch = 30 miles. How many miles are represented by 4 inches on this map?

F. 480 miles

G. 120 miles

H. 30 miles

I. 16 miles

GREEN MOUNTAINS NATIONAL PARK

Miles
0   30   60   90
$\frac{1}{4}$ in. = 30 mi

30. A landscape designer created the scale drawing below showing the bench that will be in the garden area.

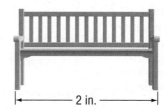

|←——— 2 in. ———→|

Which of these was the scale used for the drawing if the actual width of the bench is 6 feet?

A. $\frac{1}{4}$ inch = 1 foot

B. 3 inches = 1 foot

C. $\frac{2}{3}$ inch = 1 foot

D. 1 inch = 3 feet

Solve each proportion. (Lesson 4-1D)

31. $\frac{5}{7} = \frac{a}{35}$

32. $\frac{12}{p} = \frac{36}{45}$

33. $\frac{3}{9} = \frac{21}{k}$

34. TUTORING Michael tutors elementary school students in math for 1.5 hours each week. Is the total number of hours that he spends tutoring proportional to the number of weeks he tutors during the year? Explain your reasoning. (Lesson 4-1C)

35. FINANCIAL LITERACY Which is a better buy: 1 pound 4 ounces of cheese for $4.99 or 2 pounds 6 ounces for $9.75? Explain your reasoning. (Lesson 4-1B)

CHEESE
1 pound 4 oz. $4.99
2 pounds 6 oz. $9.75

36. Find $|-7 - (-5)|$. (Lesson 1-2D)

Main Idea

Use a spreadsheet to calculate measurements for scale drawings.

NGSSS

MA.7.A.1.6 Apply proportionality to measurement in multiple contexts, including scale drawings and constant speed.

glencoe.com

Spreadsheet Lab:
Scale Drawings

A computer spreadsheet is a useful tool for calculating measures for scale drawings. You can change the scale factors and the dimensions, and the spreadsheet will automatically calculate the new values. Suppose you want to make a scale drawing of your school.

ACTIVITY

STEP 1 Measure the rooms for your scale drawing.

STEP 2 Set up a spreadsheet like the one shown below. In this spreadsheet, the actual measures are in feet and the scale drawing measures are in inches.

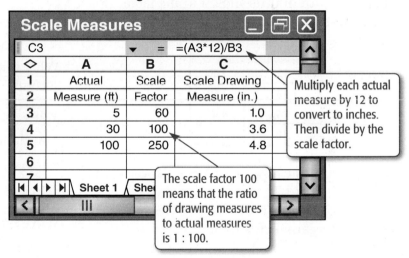

Analyze the Results

1. The length of one side of the school building is 100 feet. If you use a scale factor of 1 : 250, what is the length on your scale drawing?

2. The length of a classroom is 30 feet. What is the scale factor if the length of the classroom on a scale drawing is 3.6 inches?

3. **MAKE A SCALE DRAWING** Choose three rooms in your home and use a spreadsheet to make scale drawings. First, choose an appropriate scale and calculate the scale factor. Include a sketch of the furniture drawn to scale in each room.

Express each rate as a unit rate. (Lesson 4-1B)

1. 750 yards in 25 minutes

2. $420 for 15 tickets

3. 42 laps in 6 races

4. **NGSSS PRACTICE** In her last race, Bergen swam 1,500 meters in 30 minutes. On average, how many meters did she swim per minute? (Lesson 4-1B)

   A. 25   C. 40

   B. 30   D. 50

5. Which amount of nuts shown in the table has the best unit price? (Lesson 4-1B)

Weight (oz)	Cost ($)
12	2.50
18	3.69
24	4.95
30	6.25

6. **ICE CREAM** In one 8-hour day, Bella's Ice Cream Shop sold 72 cones of vanilla ice cream. In one hour, they sold 9 cones of vanilla ice cream. Is the total number of cones sold in one hour proportional to the number of cones sold during the day? (Lesson 4-1C)

7. **DISHES** Alan washed 60 plates in 30 minutes. It took him 3 minutes to wash 6 plates. Is the number of plates washed in 3 minutes proportional to the total number of plates he washed in 30 minutes? (Lesson 4-1C)

Solve each proportion. (Lesson 4-1D)

8. $\dfrac{33}{r} = \dfrac{11}{2}$

9. $\dfrac{x}{36} = \dfrac{15}{24}$

10. $\dfrac{5}{9} = \dfrac{4.5}{a}$

11. **NGSSS PRACTICE** A bread recipe uses 4 cups of flour and $2\frac{1}{2}$ cups of water. If a baker puts 24 cups of flour into the mixer, how many cups of water will he need? (Lesson 4-1D)

   F. 15   G. 12   H. 8   I. 6

12. The diagram shows a rectangular patio. The length and width of another patio is 4 times the length and width of the first.

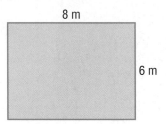

8 m

6 m

   What is the perimeter, in meters, of the second patio? (Lesson 4-2A)

13. **MAPS** Washington, D.C., and Baltimore, Maryland, are $2\frac{7}{8}$ inches apart on a map. If the scale is $\frac{1}{2}$ inch : 6 miles, what is the actual distance between the cities? (Lesson 4-2B)

14. **SCALE DRAWING** Each square has a side length of $\frac{1}{4}$ inch. (Lesson 4-2B)

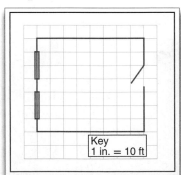

Key
1 in. = 10 ft

   a. What is the actual length of each window?

   b. What are the actual dimensions of the office space?

Main Idea
Solve problems involving similar figures.

NGSSS

MA.7.A.1.3 Solve problems involving similar figures. *Also addresses MA.7.A.1.1, MA.7.A.1.6.*

New Vocabulary
similar figures
corresponding sides
corresponding angles
indirect measurement

Get Connected
glencoe.com

Similar Figures

Explore Each pair of figures below have the same shape but different sizes. Copy each pair onto centimeter dot paper. Measure each side using a centimeter ruler.

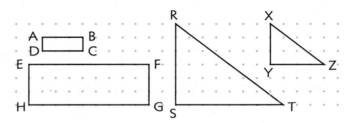

1. $\overline{AB}$ is in the same relative position as $\overline{EF}$. Name all such pairs of sides in each pair of figures.

   The notation $\overline{AB}$ means the segment with endpoints at A and B.

2. Write each ratio in simplest form.

   The notation AB means the *measure* of segment AB.

   a. $\dfrac{AB}{EF}, \dfrac{BC}{FG}, \dfrac{DC}{HG}, \dfrac{AD}{EH}$ b. $\dfrac{RS}{XY}, \dfrac{ST}{YZ}, \dfrac{RT}{XZ}$

3. What do you notice about the ratios of these sides?

4. Name all pairs of angles in the same relative position. Cut out the figures. Compare the angles by matching them up. What do you notice about the measure of these angles?

5. **MAKE A CONJECTURE** Write a sentence about the sides and angles that are in the same position.

Figures that have the same shape but not necessarily the same size are **similar figures**. Triangle *RST is similar to* triangle *XYZ*.

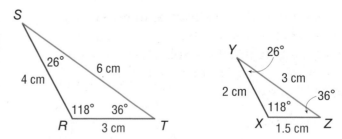

Corresponding sides — $\overline{ST}$ and $\overline{YZ}$, $\overline{SR}$ and $\overline{YX}$, and $\overline{RT}$ and $\overline{XZ}$ — are sides that are in the same relative position.

Corresponding angles — $\angle S$ and $\angle Y$, $\angle R$ and $\angle X$, and $\angle T$ and $\angle Z$ — are angles that are in the same relative position.

Key Concept — Similar Figures

Words Two figures are similar if
- the corresponding sides are proportional, and
- the corresponding angles are congruent.

Models

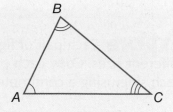

Read Math

Geometry Symbols

~ is similar to; has the same shape

≅ is congruent to; has the same size and shape

Symbols $\triangle ABC \sim \triangle DEF$

corresponding sides: $\dfrac{AB}{DE} = \dfrac{BC}{EF} = \dfrac{AC}{DF}$

corresponding angles: $\angle A \cong \angle D$; $\angle B \cong \angle E$; $\angle C \cong \angle F$

EXAMPLE Identify Similar Figures

1 Which trapezoid below is similar to trapezoid *DEFG*?

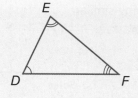

 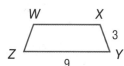 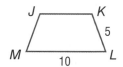

Find the ratios of the corresponding sides to see if they are the same.

Trapezoid PQRS

$\dfrac{EF}{QR} = \dfrac{4}{6}$ or $\dfrac{2}{3}$

$\dfrac{FG}{RS} = \dfrac{12}{14}$ or $\dfrac{6}{7}$

Not similar

Trapezoid WXYZ

$\dfrac{EF}{XY} = \dfrac{4}{3}$

$\dfrac{FG}{YZ} = \dfrac{12}{9}$ or $\dfrac{4}{3}$

Similar

Trapezoid JKLM

$\dfrac{EF}{KL} = \dfrac{4}{5}$

$\dfrac{FG}{LM} = \dfrac{12}{10}$ or $\dfrac{6}{5}$

Not similar

So, trapezoid *WXYZ* is similar to trapezoid *DEFG*.

CHECK Your Progress

a. Which triangle below is similar to triangle *DEF*?

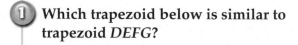

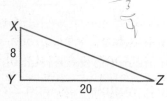 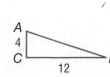 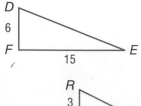

Find Missing Measures

2 **If $\triangle RST \sim \triangle XYZ$, find the length of $\overline{XY}$.**

Since the two triangles are similar, the ratios of their corresponding sides are equal. Write and solve a proportion to find XY.

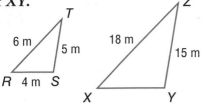

$\dfrac{RT}{XZ} = \dfrac{RS}{XY}$ Write a proportion.

$\dfrac{6}{18} = \dfrac{4}{n}$ Let n represent the length of $\overline{XY}$. Then substitute.

$6n = 18(4)$ Find the cross products.

$6n = 72$ Simplify.

$n = 12$ Divide each side by 6.   The length of $\overline{XY}$ is 12 meters.

CHECK Your Progress

b. If $\triangle ABC \sim \triangle EFD$, find the length of $\overline{AC}$.

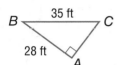

Read Math

Similarity Corresponding angles are written in the same order.

$\triangle RST \sim \triangle XYZ$

Indirect measurement uses similar figures to find the length, width, or height of objects that are too difficult to measure directly.

Real-World EXAMPLE

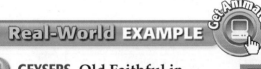

3 **GEYSERS** Old Faithful in Yellowstone National Park shoots water 60 feet into the air and casts a shadow of 42 feet. What is the height of a nearby tree that casts a shadow 63 feet long? Assume the triangles are similar.

$\dfrac{x}{60} = \dfrac{63}{42}$ Write a proportion.

$42x = 60(63)$ Find the cross products.

$42x = 3{,}780$ Simplify.

$x = 90$ Divide each side by 42.

The tree is 90 feet tall.

CHECK Your Progress

c. **PHOTOGRAPHY** Destiny wants to resize a 4-inch-wide by 5-inch-long photograph so that it will fit in a space that is 2 inches wide. What is the new length?

Example 1
(p. 224)

1. Which rectangle below is similar to rectangle *ABCD*?

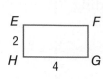

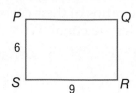

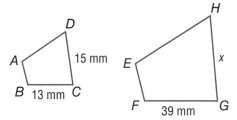

Example 2
(p. 225)

ALGEBRA Find the value of *x* in each pair of similar figures.

2.

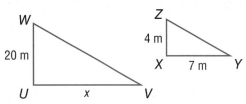

3.

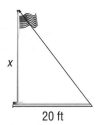

Example 3
(p. 225)

4. SHADOWS A flagpole casts a 20-foot shadow. At the same time, Humberto, who is 6 feet tall, casts a 5-foot shadow. What is the height of the flagpole? Assume the triangles are similar.

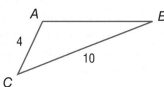

Practice and Problem Solving

● = **Step-by-Step Solutions** begin on page R9.
Extra Practice is on page EP11.

Example 1
(p. 224)

⑤ Which triangle below is similar to triangle *FGH*?

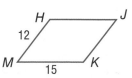

6. Which parallelogram below is similar to parallelogram *HJKM*? Assume corresponding angles are congruent.

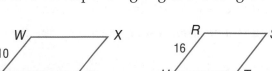

Example 2
(p. 225)

ALGEBRA Find the value of *x* in each pair of similar figures.

7.

8.

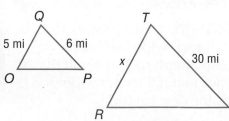

Example 3
(p. 225)

In Exercises 9 and 10, the triangles are similar. Write a proportion and solve the problem.

9. BASKETBALL What is the height of the basketball hoop?

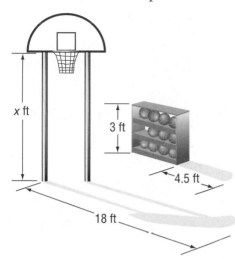

10. TREES How tall is the tree?

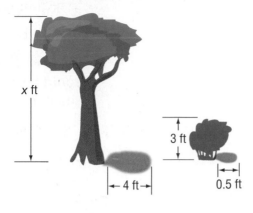

11 **GRAPHIC NOVEL** Refer to the graphic novel frame below for Exercises a and b.

a. If the red line represents the path they took, what is the total distance that the kids walked since they left the lake?

b. What will be their total distance by the time they return to the cabin?

12. FURNITURE A child's desk is made so that it is a replica of a full-size adult desk. Suppose the top of the full-size desk measures 54 inches long by 36 inches wide. If the top of the child's desk is 24 inches wide and is similar to the full-size desk, what is the length?

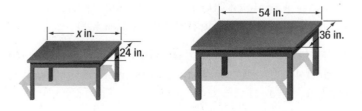

H.O.T. Problems

13. CHALLENGE Determine whether each statement is *true* or *false*. Explain.

a. Any two squares are similar.

b. Any two rectangles are similar.

14. Write MATH Write a problem about a real-world situation that could be solved using proportions and the concept of similarity. Then solve the problem.

NGSSS Practice MA.7.A.1.3

15. Which rectangle is similar to the rectangle shown?

2 in.
1 in.

A.

3 ft
3 ft

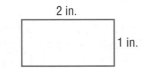

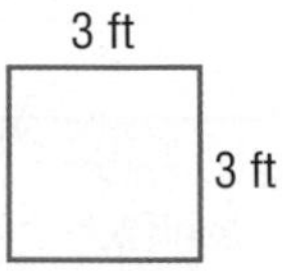

B.

16 yd
8 yd

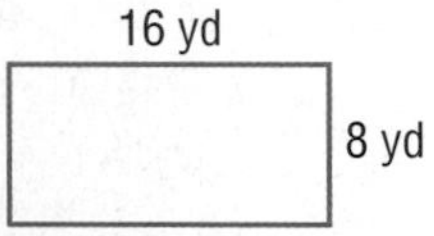

C.

28 yd
8 yd

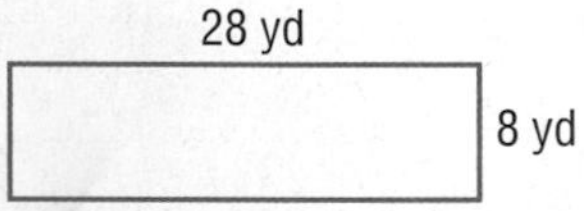

D.

12 m
4 m

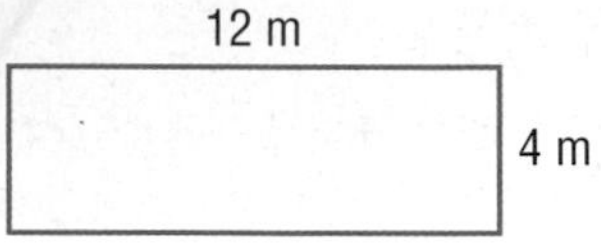

16. THINK SOLVE EXPLAIN **SHORT RESPONSE** Triangles *ABC* and *DEF* shown below represent 2 puzzle pieces. Triangle *ABC* is similar to triangle *DEF*.

D
8 cm
A
2 cm
C 5 cm B
E
x
F

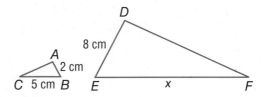

What is the length of $\overline{EF}$?

17. Horatio is 6 feet tall and casts a shadow 3 feet long. What is the height of a nearby tower if it casts a shadow 25 feet long at the same time?

h
25 ft
6 ft
3 ft
Not to scale

F. 25 feet

G. 45 feet

H. 50 feet

I. 75 feet

Spiral Review

18. COMPUTERS Designers are creating a larger model of the computer memory board. They use a scale of 20 inches = 1 inch. If the actual board is $5\frac{1}{4}$ inches long, what is the length of the model? (Lesson 4-2B)

19. RECIPES Camila is making soup. She has added $\frac{2}{3}$ of the ingredients. If she has added 4 ingredients, how many more does she have to add to be finished? (Lesson 4-2A)

Main Idea
Find the relationship between perimeters and areas of similar figures.

NGSSS

MA.7.A.1.3 Solve problems involving similar figures.
MA.7.G.4.1 Determine how changes in dimensions affect the perimeter, area, and volume of common geometric figures and apply these relationships to solve problems. *Also addresses MA.7.A.1.6.*

Get Connected
glencoe.com

Perimeter and Area of Similar Figures

Explore Suppose you double each dimension of the rectangle at the right. The new rectangle is similar to the original rectangle with a scale factor of 2.

4 in.
5 in.

1. What is the perimeter of the original rectangle?
2. What is the perimeter of the new rectangle?
3. How is the perimeter of the new rectangle related to the perimeter of the original rectangle and the scale factor?

In similar figures, the perimeters are related by the scale factor. What about area? Consider the rectangles from the Explore activity.

Original Rectangle
$A = bh$
$A = 4 \cdot 5$

New Rectangle
$A = bh$
$A = (2 \cdot 4)(2 \cdot 5)$
$= (2 \cdot 2)(4 \cdot 5)$
$= 2^2(4 \cdot 5)$

> The scale factor, 2, is used as a factor twice.

The area of the new rectangle is equal to the area of the original rectangle times the *square* of the scale factor.

Key Concept — Perimeter and Area of Similar Figures

Perimeter		Models
Words	If figure *B* is similar to figure *A* by a scale factor, then the perimeter of *B* is equal to the perimeter of *A* times the scale factor.	*a*
Symbols	$\dfrac{\text{perimeter of}}{\text{figure } B} = \dfrac{\text{perimeter of}}{\text{figure } A} \cdot \text{scale factor}$	**Figure A**
Area		*b*
Words	If figure *B* is similar to figure *A* by a scale factor, then the area of *B* is equal to the area of *A* times the square of the scale factor.	
Symbols	$\dfrac{\text{area of}}{\text{figure } B} = \dfrac{\text{area of}}{\text{figure } A} \cdot (\text{scale factor})^2$	**Figure B**

EXAMPLE **Determine Perimeter**

1 Two rectangles are similar. One has a length of 6 inches and a perimeter of 24 inches. The other has a length of 7 inches. What is the perimeter of this rectangle?

The scale factor is $\frac{7}{6}$. The perimeter of the original is 24 inches.

$x = 24\left(\frac{7}{6}\right)$ Multiply by the scale factor.

$x = \frac{\overset{4}{24}}{1}\left(\frac{7}{\underset{1}{6}}\right)$ Divide out common factors.

$x = 28$ Simplify.

So, the perimeter of the new rectangle is 28 inches.

✅ **CHECK Your Progress**

a. Triangle *LMN* is similar to triangle *PQR*. If the perimeter of △*LMN* is 64 meters, what is the perimeter of △*PQR*?

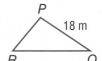

 Real-World EXAMPLE **Determine Area**

2 **CONSTRUCTION** The Eddingtons have a 5-foot by 8-foot porch on the front of their house. They are building a similar porch on the back with double the dimensions. Find the area of the back porch.

The scale factor is 2.

The area of the front porch is (5)(8) or 40 square feet.

$x = 40(2)^2$ Multiply by the square of the scale factor.

$x = 40(4)$ or 160   Evaluate the power.

The back porch will have an area of 160 square feet.

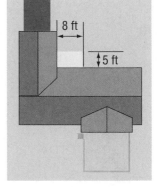

QUICK Review

Squaring Fractions
$\left(\frac{1}{20}\right)^2 = \frac{1}{20} \cdot \frac{1}{20}$
$= \frac{1}{400}$

✅ **CHECK Your Progress**

b. **MURALS** Malia is painting a mural on her bedroom wall. The image she is reproducing is $\frac{1}{20}$ of her wall and has an area of 36 square inches. Find the area of the mural.

Example 1
(p. 230)

For each pair of similar figures, find the perimeter of the second figure.

 1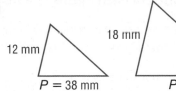

12 mm

18 mm

P = 38 mm   P = ?

2.   P = 21 ft

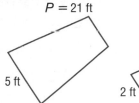

P = ?

5 ft

2 ft

Example 2
(p. 230)

3. DIGITAL PHOTOGRAPHY Julie is enlarging a digital photograph on her computer. The original photograph is 520 pixels by 780 pixels. If she enlarges it 1.5 times, what will be the area, in pixels, of the new image?

Practice and Problem Solving

● = **Step-by-Step Solutions** begin on page R9.
Extra Practice is on page EP11.

Example 1
(p. 230)

For each pair of similar figures, find the perimeter of the second figure.

4.

P = 18 ft   P = ?

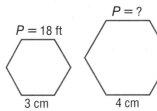

3 cm   4 cm

5.

8.4 in.   6.3 in.

P = 19.4 in.   P = ?

6. INVITATIONS For your birthday party, you make a map to your house on a 3-inch-wide by 5-inch-long index card. What will be the perimeter of your map if you use a copier to enlarge it so it is 8 inches long?

Example 2
(p. 230)

7. MODEL TRAINS Craig is making a model version of his neighborhood that uses model trains. The ratio of the model train to the actual train is 1 : 64. His neighborhood covers an area of 200,704 square feet. What will the area of the model neighborhood be?

8. ADVERTISING A company wants to reduce the size of its logo by one fourth to use on business cards. If the area of the original logo is 4 square inches, what is the area of the logo that will be used on the business cards?

9 GOLF Theo is constructing a miniature putting green in his backyard. He wants it to be similar to a putting green at the local golf course, but one third the size. The area of the putting green at the golf course is 1,134 square feet. What will the area of the putting green Theo constructs be?

10. LOGOS Mr. James is enlarging a logo for printing on the back of a T-shirt. He wants to enlarge a logo that is 3 inches by 5 inches so that the dimensions are 3 times larger than the original. How many times as large as the original logo will the area of the printing be?

11. **OPEN ENDED** Draw and label two similar figures with a scale factor of $\frac{5}{6}$. Find the perimeter and area of each figure.

12. **CHALLENGE** Two circles have circumferences of π and 3π. What is the ratio of the area of the circles? the diameters? the radii?

13. **Write MATH** A company wants to reduce the dimensions of its logo from 6 inches by 4 inches to 3 inches by 2 inches to use on business cards. Robert thinks that the new logo is $\frac{1}{4}$ the size of the original logo. Denise thinks that is $\frac{1}{2}$ of the original size. Explain their thinking.

NGSSS Practice   MA.7.A.1.3, MA.7.G.4.1

14. Two rectangular pieces of wood are similar. The ratio of the perimeters of the two pieces is 2 : 3. If the area of the smaller piece is 12 square inches, what is the area of the larger piece?

   A. 8 in^2

   B. 18 in^2

   C. 27 in^2

   D. 36 in^2

15. **THINK SOLVE EXPLAIN** **SHORT RESPONSE** A smaller copy of the 3-foot by 5-foot school flag at Brook Park Middle School is being made to appear on the front of the students' homework agenda books. The dimensions of the copy are to be $\frac{1}{6}$ of the school flag.

How many times larger is the area of the flag than the area of the copy?

Find the value of x in each pair of similar figures. (Lesson 4-3A)

16.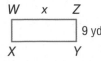

17.

18. **GEOGRAPHY** Omaha, Nebraska, and Sioux City, Iowa, are 90 miles apart. If the distance on the map is $1\frac{1}{2}$ inches, find the scale of the map. (Lesson 4-2B)

Extend

The Golden Rectangle

Main Idea

Find the value of the golden ratio.

NGSSS

MA.7.A.1.3 Solve problems involving similar figures.

Get Connected
glencoe.com

ACTIVITY

STEP 1 Cut out a rectangle that measures 34 units by 21 units. Find the ratio of the length to the width. Express it as a decimal to the nearest hundredth. Record your data in a table.

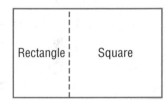

length	34	21			
width	21	13			
ratio					
decimal					

STEP 2 Cut this rectangle into two parts. One part is the largest possible square, and the other part is a rectangle. Record the rectangle's length and width. Write the ratio of length to width. Express it as a decimal to the nearest hundredth and record in the table.

Rectangle | Square

STEP 3 Repeat the procedure described in Step 2 until the remaining rectangle measures 3 units by 5 units.

Analyze the Results

1. Describe the pattern in the ratios you recorded.

2. **MAKE A CONJECTURE** If the rectangles you cut out are described as *golden rectangles*, what is the value of the *golden ratio*?

3. Write a definition for a golden rectangle. Use the word *ratio* in your definition. Then describe the shape of a golden rectangle.

4. Determine whether all golden rectangles are similar. Explain.

5. **RESEARCH** There are many examples of the golden rectangle in architecture. One is shown at the right. Use the Internet or another resource to find three places where the golden rectangle is used in architecture.

Problem Solving in Design Engineering

A Thrilling Ride!

If you have a passion for amusement parks, a great imagination, and enjoy building things, you might want to consider a career in roller coaster design. Roller coaster designers combine creativity, engineering, mathematics, and physics to develop rides that are both exciting and safe. In order to analyze data and make precise calculations, a roller coaster designer must have a solid background in high school math and science.

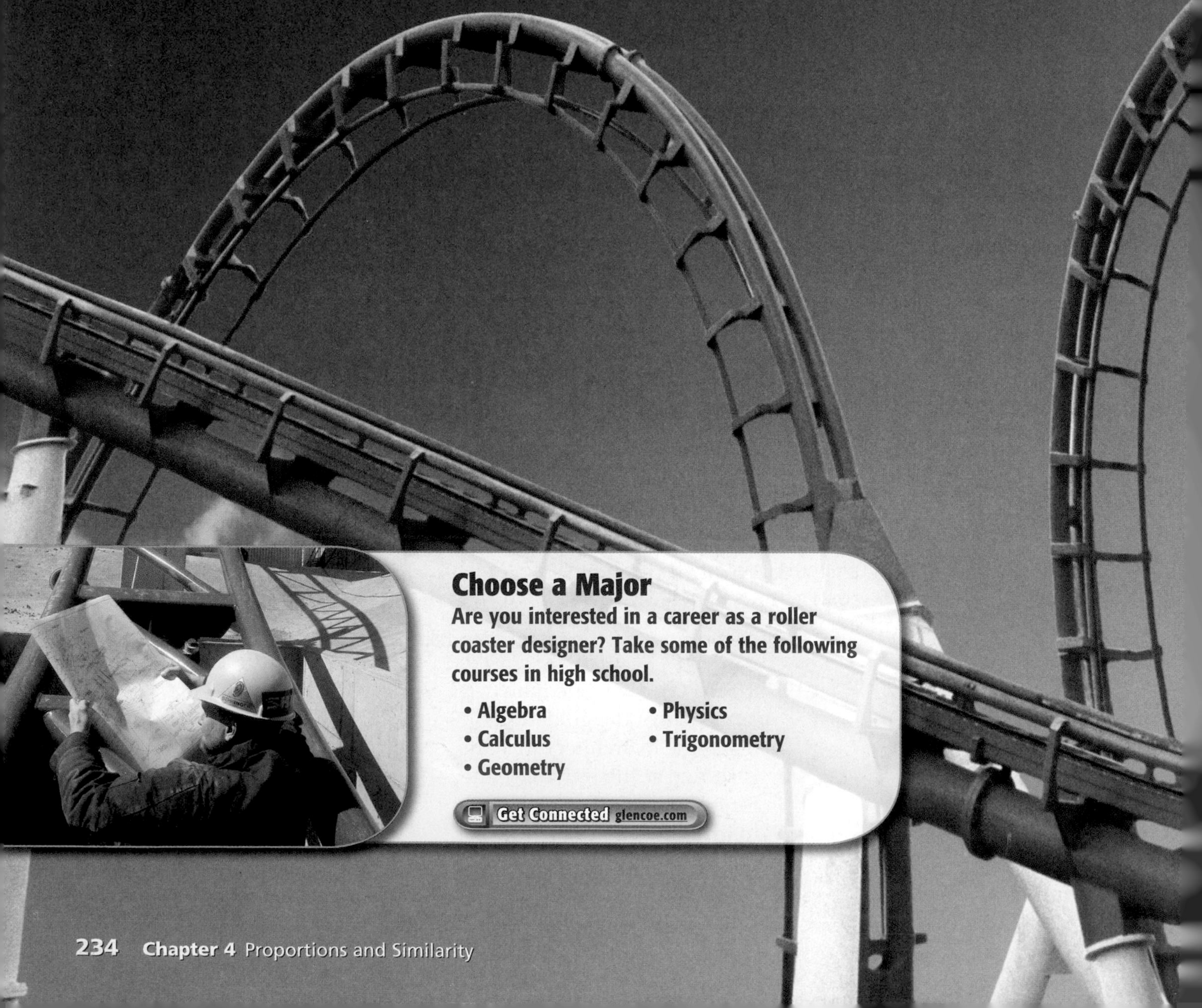

Choose a Major

Are you interested in a career as a roller coaster designer? Take some of the following courses in high school.

- Algebra
- Calculus
- Geometry
- Physics
- Trigonometry

Get Connected glencoe.com

☀ **NGSSS**

MA.7.A.1.6 Apply proportionality to measurement in multiple contexts, including **scale drawings** and constant speed.

Real-World Math

Use the information in the table to solve each problem.

1. In a scale drawing of SheiKra, a designer uses a scale of 1 inch = 16 feet. What is the height of the roller coaster in the drawing?

2. On a model of Montu, the height of the loop is 13 inches. What is the scale?

3. In a scale drawing of Montu, the height of the roller coaster is 10 inches. What is the scale factor?

4. SheiKra has a hill that goes through a tunnel. On a model of the roller coaster, the hill is 23 inches tall and the scale is 1 inch = 6 feet. What is the actual height of the tunnel hill?

5. An engineer is building a model of SheiKra. She wants the model to be about 32 inches high. Choose an appropriate scale for the model. Then use it to find the loop height of the model.

Busch Gardens Africa
Tampa, Florida

Roller Coaster	Coaster Height (ft)	Loop Height (ft)
SheiKra	200	145
Montu	150	104

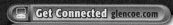
FOLDABLES
Study Organizer

Be sure the following Key Concepts are noted in your Foldable.

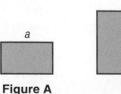

Key Concepts

Rates (Lesson 4-1)
• A rate is a comparison of two quantities with different types of units.
• When a rate is simplified so it has a denominator of 1 unit, it is a unit rate.

Proportions (Lesson 4-1)
• If two related quantities are proportional, then they have a constant ratio.
• The cross products of a proportion are equal.

Similar Figures (Lesson 4-3)
• If figure *B* is similar to figure *A* by a scale factor, then

$$\frac{\text{perimeter of figure } B}{\text{}} = \frac{\text{perimeter of figure } A}{\text{}} \cdot \text{scale factor}$$

$$\frac{\text{area of figure } B}{\text{}} = \frac{\text{area of figure } A}{\text{}} \cdot (\text{scale factor})^2$$

Figure A   Figure B

Key Vocabulary

corresponding angles (p. 223)

corresponding sides (p. 223)

cross products (p. 206)

equivalent ratios (p. 206)

indirect measurement (p. 225)

nonproportional (p. 202)

proportion (p. 206)

proportional (p. 202)

rate (p. 196)

scale (p. 214)

scale drawing (p. 214)

scale factor (p. 215)

scale model (p. 214)

similar figures (p. 223)

unit rate (p. 196)

Vocabulary Check

Choose the term from the list above that best matches each phrase.

1. two quantities that have a constant rate or ratio

2. a scale written as a ratio in simplest form without units of measurement

3. an equation that shows that two ratios or rates are equivalent

4. a ratio of two measurements with different units

5. a rate that is simplified so that it has a denominator of 1

6. two ratios that have the same value

7. the ratio of the distance on a map to the actual distance

8. figures with the same shape

9. a relationship in which the ratio is not constant

Multi-Part Lesson Review

4-1 Proportions

Rates (pp. 196–201)

MA.7.A.1.6

Find each unit rate.

10. $23.75 for 5 pounds

11. 810 miles in 9 days

12. SHAMPOO Which bottle of shampoo shown at the right costs the least per ounce?

Bottle	Price
8 oz	$1.99
12 oz	$2.59
16 oz	$3.19

EXAMPLE 1 Find the unit price of a 16-ounce box of pasta that is on sale for 96 cents.

$$16\text{-oz box for 96 cents} = \frac{96 \text{ cents} \div 16}{16 \text{ ounces} \div 16}$$

$$= \frac{6 \text{ cents}}{1 \text{ ounce}}$$

The unit price is 6 cents per ounce.

Proportional and Nonproportional Relationships (pp. 202–205)

MA.7.A.1.1

13. INTERNET An Internet company charges $30 a month. There is also a $30 installation fee. Is the number of months you can have Internet proportional to the total cost?

14. WORK On Friday, Jade washed 10 vehicles in 4 hours. The next day she washed 15 vehicles in 6 hours. Is the number of vehicles she washed proportional to the time it took her to wash them?

EXAMPLE 2 Is the amount of money earned proportional to the number of haircuts?

Earnings ($)	28	56	84	112
Haircuts	1	2	3	4

$\dfrac{\text{earnings}}{\text{haircuts}} \longrightarrow \dfrac{28}{1}, \dfrac{56}{2}, \dfrac{84}{3}, \dfrac{112}{4}$

Since these ratios are all equal to 28, the amount of money earned is proportional to the number of haircuts.

Solve Proportions (pp. 206–210)

MA.7.A.1.1

Solve each proportion.

15. $\dfrac{3}{r} = \dfrac{6}{8}$

16. $\dfrac{30}{0.5} = \dfrac{y}{0.25}$

17. $\dfrac{7}{4} = \dfrac{n}{2}$

18. $\dfrac{k}{5} = \dfrac{72}{8}$

19. $\dfrac{2}{t} = \dfrac{8}{50}$

20. $\dfrac{12}{8} = \dfrac{a}{6}$

21. SPEED A squirrel can run 1 mile in 5 minutes. How far can it travel in 16 minutes?

22. WEIGHT If 3 televisions weigh 240.6 pounds, how much do 9 of the same televisions weigh?

EXAMPLE 3 Solve $\dfrac{9}{x} = \dfrac{4}{18}$.

$\dfrac{9}{x} = \dfrac{4}{18}$ Write the proportion.

$9 \cdot 18 = x \cdot 4$ Find the cross products.

$162 = 4x$ Multiply.

$\dfrac{162}{4} = \dfrac{4x}{4}$ Divide each side by 4.

$40.5 = x$ Simplify.

4-2 Scale Drawings and Models

PSI: Draw a Diagram (pp. 212–213)

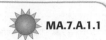

MA.7.A.1.1

Solve each problem by drawing a diagram.

23. WATER A 500-gallon hot tub is being filled with water. Eighty gallons of water are in the hot tub after 4 minutes. At this rate, how long will it take to fill the hot tub?

24. GEOMETRY Find the number of diagonals in an octagon.

EXAMPLE 4 Alvin has filled $\frac{1}{3}$ or 50 gallons of his fish tank. Find the total capacity of the fish tank.

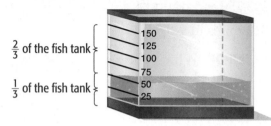

$\frac{2}{3}$ of the fish tank

$\frac{1}{3}$ of the fish tank

If $\frac{1}{3}$ of the fish tank is 50 gallons, then $\frac{2}{3}$ is 100 gallons. So, the total capacity of the fish tank is $50 + 100$, or 150 gallons.

Scale Drawings (pp. 214–220)

MA.7.A.1.6

The scale on a map is 3 centimeters = 7 kilometers. Find the actual distance for each map distance.

25. 9 cm   **26.** 21 cm

27. ARCHITECTS On an architect's blueprint, the dimensions of a room are 5 inches by 8 inches. If the actual dimensions of the room are 10 feet by 16 feet, what is the scale of the blueprint?

28. MODELS A Boeing 747 jet is 70.5 meters long and has a wingspan of 60 meters. A model of the 747 has a wingspan of 80 centimeters. What is the length of the model?

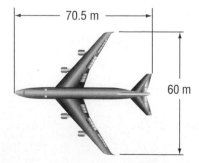

70.5 m

60 m

EXAMPLE 5 On a map, the distance between two cities is 10.9 centimeters. If the scale is 1 centimeter = 250 kilometers, what is the actual distance?

$$\begin{array}{cc} \text{Scale} & \text{Distance} \\ \text{map} \longrightarrow \dfrac{1 \text{ cm}}{250 \text{ km}} = \dfrac{10.9 \text{ cm}}{n \text{ km}} & \begin{array}{l}\longleftarrow \text{ map} \\ \longleftarrow \text{ actual}\end{array} \end{array}$$

$$1 \cdot n = 250 \cdot 10.9$$
$$n = 2{,}725$$

The actual distance is 2,725 kilometers.

EXAMPLE 6 The scale on a model of a bullfrog is 2 centimeters = 25 millimeters. Find the actual length of the bullfrog if the model length is 11 centimeters.

$$\dfrac{2 \text{ cm}}{25 \text{ mm}} = \dfrac{11 \text{ cm}}{x \text{ mm}} \quad \begin{array}{l}\longleftarrow \text{ model length} \\ \longleftarrow \text{ actual length}\end{array}$$

$2 \cdot x = 25 \cdot 11$ Find the cross products

$2x = 275$ Multiply.

$x = 137.5$ Divide each side by 2.

The actual length is 137.5 millimeters.

4-3 Similarity and Proportional Reasoning

Similar Figures (pp. 223–228)

MA.7.A.1.3

29. Which quadrilateral is similar to quadrilateral *ABCD*?

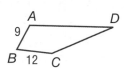

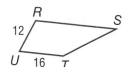

Find the value of *x* in each pair of similar figures.

30.

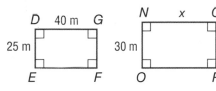

31.

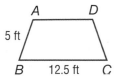 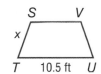

EXAMPLE 7 Find the value of *x* in the pair of similar figures.

  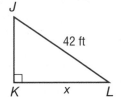

$$\frac{24\ ft}{42\ ft} = \frac{21\ ft}{x} \qquad \text{Write a proportion.}$$

$24 \cdot x = 42 \cdot 21 \qquad$ Find the cross products.

$24x = 882 \qquad$ Multiply.

$x = 36.75 \qquad$ Divide by 24.

The length of $\overline{KL}$ is 36.75 feet.

Perimeter and Area of Similar Figures (pp. 229–232)

MA.7.A.1.3, MA.7.G.4.1

32. DOLLHOUSES Franklin is building a dollhouse modeled after his house for his niece. He would like the scale factor to be $\frac{1}{12}$. If the perimeter of his house is 1,800 inches, what will be the perimeter of the dollhouse?

33. Two similar triangles have a scale factor of $\frac{1}{5}$. Find the area of the larger triangle if the area of the smaller triangle is 6 square yards.

EXAMPLE 8 Cynthia is creating a poster of a photograph she took. The photograph is 5 inches by 7 inches. What will be the area of the poster if the poster has dimensions four times the photograph?

The scale factor relating the poster and the photograph is 4.

$$\begin{array}{ccc} \text{area of} & = & \text{area of} \quad \cdot \quad (4)^2 \\ \text{poster} & & \text{photo} \end{array}$$

$$= \quad (5 \cdot 7) \quad \cdot \quad (4)^2$$

$$= \quad 560$$

The area of the poster is 560 in².

Find each unit rate. Round to the nearest hundredth if necessary.

1. 24 greeting cards for $4.80

2. 330 miles on 15 gallons of gas

3. 112 feet in 2.8 seconds

4. **NGSSS PRACTICE** At Flynn's Apple Orchard, 16 acres of land produced 368 bushels of apples. Which rate represents the number of bushels per acre?

   A. 16 : 1   C. 23 : 2

   B. 23 : 1   D. 46 : 1

5. **MEASUREMENT** Nick rides his bike 20 miles every two days. Is the distance Nick rides proportional to the number of days?

Solve each proportion.

6. $\dfrac{3}{a} = \dfrac{9}{12}$ 7. $\dfrac{5}{3} = \dfrac{20}{y}$

8. $\dfrac{2}{3} = \dfrac{x}{42}$ 9. $\dfrac{t}{21} = \dfrac{15}{14}$

10. **FOOD** Of the 30 students in a life skills class, 19 like to cook main dishes, 15 like to bake desserts, and 7 like to do both. How many students like to cook main dishes but not bake desserts? Use the *draw a diagram* strategy.

Each pair of polygons is similar. Write a proportion to find each missing measure. Then solve.

11.

12.
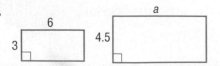

13. **NGSSS PRACTICE** On a map, 1 inch = 7.5 miles. How many miles does 2.5 inches represent?

   F. $\dfrac{1}{3}$ H. 10

   G. 3   I. 18.75

14. **BLUEPRINTS** Use the following scale drawing of a room.

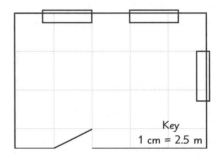

Key
1 cm = 2.5 m

   a. Use a centimeter ruler to find the length of the wall with two windows.

   b. How wide would a 1.4-meter-wide dresser appear on this drawing?

15. **THINK SOLVE EXPLAIN** **EXTENDED RESPONSE** Layla is training for a marathon. Each week she runs about 40 miles. Her coach gave her a map of the route he would like her to run.

1 inch = 0.5 miles

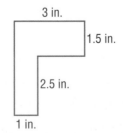

   Part A How many inches is the route on the map?

   Part B How many miles will Layla run in one loop of the route?

   Part C How many times per week will she need to complete the loop to run at least 40 miles?

Multiple Choice: Unreasonable Answer Choices

Sometimes answer choices are not reasonable for the information given in a problem. These choices can be eliminated.

NGSSS PRACTICE EXAMPLE

A scenic trail circles Lake Okeechobee in Florida. Hikers traveled on the trail from Port Mayaca to Pahokee. This distance on a map is about 1 inch. Based on the scale below, how far did the hikers travel in miles?

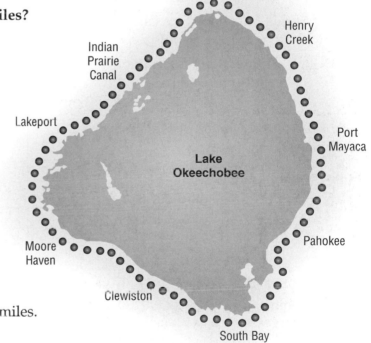

Scale
$\frac{1}{2}$ in. $= 6\frac{1}{4}$ mi

A. $2\frac{1}{2}$ miles   **C.** $6\frac{1}{4}$ miles

B. $3\frac{1}{8}$ miles   **D.** $12\frac{1}{2}$ miles

Since the distance on the map is greater than $\frac{1}{2}$ inch, the actual distance must be greater than 5 miles. So, choices A and B can be automatically eliminated.

Since 1 inch is twice as long as $\frac{1}{2}$ inch, the actual distance will be twice as long as $6\frac{1}{4}$ miles.

The correct answer is D.

Work on It

On a model of a roller coaster, the first hill is 15 inches high. The actual height of the first hill is 240 feet. If the second hill on the roller coaster is 180 feet high, how tall is the second hill on the model?

F. $11\frac{1}{4}$ inches   **H.** 16 inches

G. 12 inches   **I.** 20 inches

Test Hint

If your answer is not one of the choices given, then reread the question carefully to check that you understand what is being asked.

Read each question. Then fill in the correct answer on the answer sheet provided by your teacher or on a sheet of paper.

1. Francesca typed 496 words in 8 minutes. Which of the following is a correct understanding of this rate?

   A. At this rate, it takes 62 minutes for Francesca to type one word.

   B. At this rate, Francesca can type 62 words in 8 minutes.

   C. At this rate, Francesca can type 62 words in one minute.

   D. At this rate, Francesca can type 8 words in one minute.

2. The table shows the prices of three boxes of cereal. Which box of cereal has the **highest** unit price?

Cereal Box Size (ounces)	Price ($)
48	5.45
32	3.95
20	3.10

   F. the 20-ounce box

   G. the 32-ounce box

   H. the 48-ounce box

   I. All three boxes have the same unit price.

3. **GRIDDED RESPONSE** A bakery sells 6 bagels for $2.99 and 4 muffins for $3.29. What is the total cost in dollars of 4 dozen bagels and 16 muffins, not including tax?

4. **SHORT RESPONSE** A teacher plans to buy 5 pencils for each student in her class. Pencils come in packages of 18 and cost $1.99 per package. What other information is needed to find the cost of the pencils?

5. During a 3-hour period, 2,292 people rode the roller coaster at an amusement park. Which proportion can be used to find x, the number of people who rode the coaster during a 12-hour period if the rate is the same?

   A. $\dfrac{3}{2,292} = \dfrac{x}{12}$

   C. $\dfrac{3}{x} = \dfrac{12}{2,292}$

   B. $\dfrac{3}{2,292} = \dfrac{12}{x}$

   D. $\dfrac{x}{3} = \dfrac{12}{2,292}$

6. An architect created the scale drawing below showing a wall of a child's playhouse.

   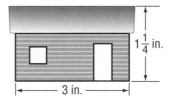

   Which of these was the scale used for the drawing if the actual height of the wall is $7\frac{1}{2}$ feet?

   F. 1 in. = 1 ft

   H. 2 in. = 12 ft

   G. $\frac{1}{2}$ in. = 1 ft

   I. $\frac{1}{4}$ in. = 1 ft

7. **SHORT RESPONSE** You can drive your car 21.7 miles with one gallon of gasoline. At that rate, how many miles can you drive with 13.2 gallons of gasoline?

8. At 8 A.M., the temperature was 13°F below zero. By 1 P.M., the temperature rose 22°F and by 6 P.M. dropped 14°F. What was the temperature at 6 P.M.?

   A. 5°F above zero

   B. 5°F below zero

   C. 21°F above zero

   D. 21°F below zero

9. Trapezoid *ABCD* is similar to trapezoid *WXYZ*. What is the length of $\overline{XY}$?

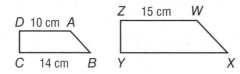

F. 20 cm   **H.** 24 cm

G. 21 cm   **I.** 27 cm

10. **GRIDDED RESPONSE** Find $15 \div (-5)$.

11. The bridge structure is supported by the triangular braces as shown.

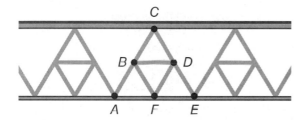

Triangles *ACE* and *ABF* are similar triangles. The scale factor from $\triangle ACE$ to $\triangle ABF$ is 0.5. If $CE = 10$ feet, what is the length of *BF*?

A. 2.5 ft   **C.** 6 ft

B. 5 ft   **D.** 12 ft

12. **THINK SOLVE EXPLAIN** **SHORT RESPONSE** Thom has a scale model of his car. The scale is 1 : 12. If the actual car has 16-inch wheels, what size are the wheels on the scale model?

16 in.

13. A recipe calls for $2\frac{1}{3}$ packages of pudding. How many batches can be made if 20 packages of pudding are available?

F. 8 batches

G. 9 batches

H. 10 batches

I. 11 batches

14. Which line contains the ordered pair $(-1, 2)$?

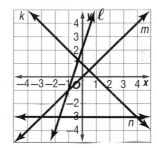

A. line *k*

B. line ℓ

C. line *m*

D. line *n*

15. **THINK SOLVE EXPLAIN** **EXTENDED RESPONSE** Heath and Jerome are brothers. At the beginning of the school year Heath wore a size 3 shoe and Jerome wore a size 5. At the end of the school year Heath wore a size 4 and Jerome wore a size 6.

Part A Jerome says they grew the same amount. Explain how he is right.

Part B Heath thinks that he grew more. Explain how he is also correct.

NEED EXTRA HELP?

If You Missed Question...	1	2	3	4	5	6	7	8	9	10	11	12	13	14	15
Go to Lesson...	4-1B	4-1B	4-1D	4-1D	4-1D	4-2B	4-1D	1-2B	4-3A	1-3D	4-3A	4-2B	2-3D	1-1C	4-1C
For help with NGSSS...	A.1.6	A.1.6	A.1.1	A.1.1	A.1.1	A.1.6	A.1.1	A.3.1	A.1.3	A.3.1	A.1.3	A.1.6	A.3.2	G.4.3	A.1.1

Linear Functions

The ☆BIG Idea

Apply proportions to the slope of a linear function.

FOLDABLES®
Study Organizer

Make this Foldable to help you organize your notes. Begin with a sheet of $8\frac{1}{2}$" by 11" construction paper and some 3×5 cards.

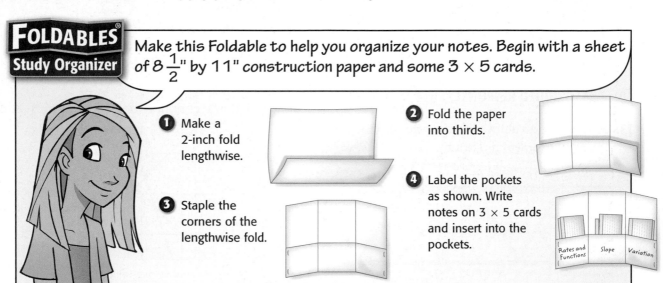

① Make a 2-inch fold lengthwise.

② Fold the paper into thirds.

③ Staple the corners of the lengthwise fold.

④ Label the pockets as shown. Write notes on 3×5 cards and insert into the pockets.

Rates and Functions | Slope | Variation

Review Vocabulary

expression (Prior Grade) **expresión** a combination of numbers, variables, and at least one operation

$$2x + 5$$

equation (p. 150) **equación** a mathematical sentence that contains an equal sign, =

$$2x + 5 = 13$$

Key Vocabulary

	English	Español
p. 248	function	función
p. 254	linear function	función lineal
p. 260	rate of change	tasa de cambio
p. 264	slope	pendiente

Multilingual eGlossary glencoe.com

Get Connected
glencoe.com

- Study using the **eBook**
- Explore with **Get Animated**
- Get extra help from **Personal Tutor**
- Use **virtual manipulatives** for additional help
- Take a **Self-Check Quiz**

When Will I Use This?

Get Animated

Seth and Hannah in **The Go-Kart Race**

Ok, here we go, finishing up lap 12...

...and he should be coming around right about...

WHOOSH!!!

...now.

click!

Hi, Hannah! How am I doing?

Lookin' good! Your times are getting faster!

Today's race is going to be 20 laps, but I need to go and take care of some things...

...like food!

That's ok. We can estimate the rest of the times based on your times so far.

The race is 20 laps, which is 5 miles. Assuming your speed is constant...

Lap	4	8	12	16	20
Distance	1 mile	2 miles	3 miles	4 miles	5 miles
Time	57.1s	114.2s	171.3s		

...we can calculate your time! You're not listening, are you?

Huh? Oh, sorry. Just thinking about hamburgers.

Your Turn!
You will solve this problem in Chapter 5.

Are You Ready for Chapter 5?

You have two options for checking prerequisite skills for this chapter.

Text Option Take the Quick Check below. Refer to the Quick Review for help.

QUICK Check

Evaluate each expression if $a = 4$, $b = 10$, and $c = 8$. (Prior Grade)

1. $a + b + c$

2. $bc - ac$

3. $b + ac$

4. $4c + 3b$

5. $2b - (a + c)$

6. $2c - b + a$

Evaluate each expression if $x = 2$, $y = 5$, and $z = -1$.

7. $x + 12$

8. $z + (-5)$

9. $4y + 8$

10. $10 + 3z$

11. $(2 + y)9$

12. $6(x - 4)$

13. $3xy$

14. $2z + y$

QUICK Review

EXAMPLE 1

Evaluate $3rt - s$ if $r = 3$, $s = -4$, and $t = 4$.

$3rt - s$	Write the expression.
$= 3(3)(4) - (-4)$	Substitute.
$= 36 - (-4)$	Multiply.
$= 36 + 4$	To subtract -4, add 4.
$= 40$	Add.

Use the coordinate grid to name the point for each ordered pair. (Lesson 1-1C)

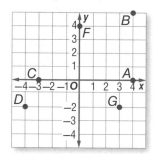

15. $(-3, 0)$

16. $(3, -2)$

17. $(-4, -2)$

18. $(0, 4)$

19. $(4, 5)$

20. $(4, 0)$

EXAMPLE 2

Graph and label the point $P(-3, 4)$.

Start at the origin. The first number in the ordered pair is the distance to the left or right on the x-axis. Since the number is -3, move three units to the *left*.

The second number in the ordered pair is the distance up or down on the y-axis. Since the number is 4, move *up* four units.

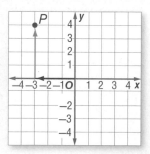

Online Option  Take the Online Readiness Quiz at **glencoe.com**.

Explore Input and Output of Functions

Main Idea

Find the input and output for a given function.

NGSSS

Preparation for MA.7.A.1.4 Graph proportional relationships and identify the unit rate as the slope of the related linear function.

 Get Connected
glencoe.com

In a *function*, there is a relationship between two quantities or sets of numbers. A function takes a number called the *input*, performs one or more operations on it, and produces a result called the *output*.

EXAMPLE

STEP 1 To make a *function machine*, draw three squares in the middle of a 3" by 5" index card.

STEP 2 Cut out the square on the left and the square on the right. Label the left "window" **INPUT** and the right "window" **OUTPUT**.

STEP 3 Write a rule such as "× 2 + 3" in the center square.

STEP 4 On another index card, list the integers from −5 to 1 in a column close to the left edge.

STEP 5 Place the function machine over the number column so that −5 is in the left window.

STEP 6 Apply the rule to the input number. The output is −5 × 2 + 3, or −7. Write −7 in the right window.

STEP 7 Slide the function machine down so that the input is −4. Find the output and write the number in the right window. Continue the process for the remaining inputs.

Analyze the Results

1. Suppose x represents the input and y represents the output. Write an algebraic equation that represents what the function machine does.

2. Make another function machine using a different rule.

Main Idea
Make function tables and write equations.

NGSSS
MA.7.A.1.4 Graph proportional relationships and **identify** the unit rate as the slope of **the related linear function.**

New Vocabulary
function
function rule
function table
domain
range

Get Connected
glencoe.com

Equations and Functions

MAGAZINES Suppose you can buy magazines for $4 each.

1. Copy and complete the table to find the cost of 2, 3, and 4 magazines.

2. Describe the pattern in the table between the cost and the number of magazines.

Number	Multiply by 4	Cost ($)
1	4 × 1	4
2		
3		
4		

A relationship that assigns exactly one *output* value for each *input* value is called a **function**. In a function, you start with an input number, perform one or more operations on it, and get an output number. The operation performed on the input is given by the **function rule**.

You can organize the input numbers, output numbers, and the function rule in a **function table**. The set of input values is called the **domain**, and the set of output values is called the **range**.

EXAMPLE **Make a Function Table**

1. **MONEY** Javier saves $20 each month. Make a function table to show his savings after 1, 2, 3, and 4 months. Then identify the domain and range.

   The domain is {1, 2, 3, 4}, and the range is {20, 40, 60, 80}.

Input	Function Rule	Output
Number of Months	Multiply by 20	Total Savings ($)
1	20 × 1	20
2	20 × 2	40
3	20 × 3	60
4	20 × 4	80

 CHECK Your Progress

a. A student movie ticket costs $3. Make a function table that shows the total cost for 1, 2, 3, and 4 tickets. Then identify the domain and range.

Study Tip

Input and Output
When *x* and *y* are used in an equation, *x* usually represents the input, and *y* usually represents the output.

Functions are often written as equations with two variables—one to represent the input and one to represent the output. Here's an equation for the situation in Example 1.

Function rule: multiply by 20

$$20x = y$$

Input: number of months

Output: total savings

Real-World EXAMPLES

2 **ANIMALS** An armadillo sleeps 19 hours each day. Write an equation using two variables to show the relationship between the number of hours *h* an armadillo sleeps in *d* days.

Input	Function Rule	Output
Number of Days (*d*)	Multiply by 19	Number of Hours Slept (*h*)
1	1 × 19	19
2	2 × 19	38
3	3 × 19	57
d	*d* × 19	19*d*

Real-World Link · · · ·
Armadillos have the ability to remain underwater for as long as six minutes. Because of the density of its armor, an armadillo will sink in water unless it inflates its stomach with air, which often doubles its size.

Words	Number of hours slept	equals	number of days	times	19 hours each day.

Variable
Let *d* represent the number of days.
Let *h* represent the number of hours.

Equation
$$h = 19d$$

3 **How many hours does an armadillo sleep in 4 days?**

$h = 19d$ Write the equation.

$h = 19(4)$ Replace *d* with 4.

$h = 76$ Multiply.

An armadillo sleeps 76 hours in 4 days.

CHECK Your Progress

BOTANIST A botanist discovers that a certain species of bamboo grows 4 inches each hour.

b. Write an equation using two variables to show the relationship between the growth *g* in inches of this bamboo plant in *h* hours.

c. Use your equation to explain how to find the growth in inches of this species of bamboo after 6 hours.

Example 1
(p. 248)

Copy and complete each function table. Then identify the domain and range.

1. $y = 3x$

x	3x	y
1	3 • 1	3
2	3 • 2	
3	3 • 3	
4		

2. $y = 4x$

x	4x	y
0	4 • 0	
1	4 • 1	
2		
3		

3. **MUSIC** Jonas downloads 8 songs each month onto his digital music player. Make a function table that shows the total number of songs downloaded after 1, 2, 3, and 4 months. Then identify the domain and range.

Examples 2 and 3
(p. 249)

4. **SPORTS** The top speed reached by a race car is 231 miles per hour.

    a. Write an equation using two variables to show the relationship between the number of miles m that a race car can travel in h hours.

    b. Use your equation to explain how to find the distance in miles the race car will travel in 3 hours.

Practice and Problem Solving

● = **Step-by-Step Solutions** begin on page R10.
Extra Practice is on page EP11.

Example 1
(p. 248)

Copy and complete each function table. Then identify the domain and range.

5. $y = 2x$

x	2x	y
0	2 • 0	0
1	2 • 1	
2		
3		

6. $y = 6x$

x	6x	y
1		
2		
3		
4		

7 $y = 9x$

x	9x	y
1		
2		
3		
4		

Make a function table for each situation. Then identify the domain and range.

8. **PIZZA** A pizza shop sells 25 pizzas each hour. At the same rate, find the number of pizzas sold after 1, 2, 3, and 4 hours.

9. **TYPING** Suppose you can type 60 words per minute. What is the total number of words typed after 5, 10, 15, and 20 minutes?

Examples 2 and 3
(p. 249)

10. **CELL PHONES** A cell phone provider charges a customer $40 for each month of service.

    a. Write an equation using two variables to show the relationship between the total amount charged c after m months of cell phone service.

    b. Use your equation to explain how to find the total cost for 6 months of cell phone service.

11. INSECTS A cricket will chirp 35 times per minute when the outside temperature is 72°F.

a. Write an equation using two variables to show the relationship between the total number of times a cricket will chirp t after m minutes at this temperature.

b. Use your equation to explain how to find the number of times a cricket will have chirped after 15 minutes at this temperature.

Real-World Link
Crickets are among the 800,000 different types of insects in the world.

Copy and complete each function table. Then identify the domain and range.

12. $y = 0.5x$

x	0.5x	y
1		
2		
3		
4		

13. $y = 1.3x$

x	1.3x	y
1		
2		
3		
4		

14. $y = -0.2x$

x	-0.2x	y
0		
1		
2		
3		

15. $y = \frac{2}{3}x$

x	$\frac{2}{3}x$	y
2		
3		
4		
5		

16. MEASUREMENT The formula for the area of a rectangle with length 6 units and width w is $A = 6w$.

a. Make a function table that shows the area in square units of a rectangle with a width of 2, 3, 4, and 5 units.

b. Study the pattern in your table. Explain how the area of a rectangle with a length of 6 units changes when the width is increased by 1 unit.

17 SCIENCE The table shows the approximate velocity of certain planets as they orbit the Sun.

a. Write an equation to show the relationship between the total number of miles m Jupiter travels in s seconds as it orbits the Sun.

b. What equation can be used to show the total number of miles m Earth travels in s seconds?

c. Use your equation to explain how to find the number of miles Jupiter and Earth each travel in 1 minute.

Orbital Velocity Around Sun	
Planet	Velocity (mi/s)
Mercury	30
Earth	19
Jupiter	8
Saturn	6
Neptune	5

18. RUNNING The average marathon running speed is 5.5 miles per hour. Find the number of miles run after 1, 2, 3, and 4 hours at this rate.

19. FIND THE ERROR Divya is finding the range for the function $y = 3x$ given the domain {2, 4, 6, 8}. Find her mistake and correct it.

> If $y = 3x$ and I have the inputs of 2, 4, 6, and 8, then the outputs should be 5, 7, 9, and 11.

20. **MATH** Explain the relationship among an *input*, an *output*, and a *function rule*.

 NGSSS Practice   **MA.7.A.1.4**

21. The table shows the number of hand painted T-shirts Mi-Ling can make after a given number of days.

Number of Days (x)	Total Number of T-Shirts (y)
1	6
2	12
3	18
4	24

Which function rule represents the data?

A. $y = 4x$ **C.** $y = 6x$

B. $y = 5x$ **D.** $y = 12x$

22. Rosa needs to have 50 posters printed to advertise a community book fair. The printing company charges $3 to print each poster. Which table represents this situation?

F.

Posters	Cost ($)
3	3
6	6
9	9
p	p

H.

Posters	Cost ($)
1	3
2	6
3	9
p	$3 + p$

G.

Posters	Cost ($)
1	3
2	6
3	9
p	$3p$

I.

Posters	Cost ($)
3	1
6	2
9	3
p	$p \div 3$

 **Spiral Review**

23. ALGEBRA The quadrilaterals are similar. Find the value of x. (Lesson 4-3A)

24. MODELS On a scale model of a building, 3 inches = 12 feet. If the model is 8 inches tall, how tall is the actual building? (Lesson 4-2B)

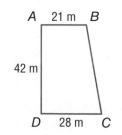

Main Idea
Graph data to demonstrate relationships.

NGSSS
 MA.7.A.1.4 Graph proportional relationships and identify the unit rate as the slope of the related linear function.

New Vocabulary
linear function

Get Connected
glencoe.com

Functions and Graphs

MONEY The Westerville Marching Band is going on a year-end trip to an amusement park. Each band member must pay an admission price of $15. In the table, this is represented by 15*m*.

1. Copy and complete the function table for the total cost of admission.

2. Graph the ordered pairs (number of members, total cost).

3. Describe how the points appear on the graph.

Total Cost of Admission		
Number of Members	15*m*	Total Cost ($)
1	15(1)	15
2	15(2)	30
3	15(3)	
4		
5		
6		

The total cost is a *function* of the number of band members. In general, the output *y* is a function of the input *x*.

The graph of the function consists of the points in the coordinate plane that correspond to *all* the ordered pairs of the form (input, output) or (*x*, *y*).

Real-World EXAMPLE

① **TEMPERATURE** The table shows temperatures in Celsius and the corresponding temperatures in Fahrenheit. Make a graph of the data to show the relationship between Celsius and Fahrenheit.

The ordered pairs (5, 41), (10, 50), (15, 59), (20, 68), (25, 77), and (30, 86) represent this function. Graph the ordered pairs.

Celsius (input)	Fahrenheit (output)
5	41
10	50
15	59
20	68
25	77
30	86

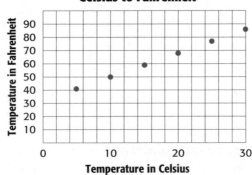

Celsius to Fahrenheit

CHECK Your Progress

a. MUSIC The table shows the money remaining on a $75 gift certificate after a certain number of CDs are bought. Make a graph to show how the number of CDs bought and the remaining balance are related.

$75 Music Gift Certificate	
Number of CDs	**Balance ($)**
1	63
2	51
3	39
4	27
5	15

Vocabulary Link

Everyday Use

Function The purpose for which something is designed or exists, or its role.

Math Use

Function A relationship that assigns one output value for each input value.

The solution of an equation with two variables consists of two numbers, one for each variable, that make the equation true. The solution is usually written as an ordered pair (x, y).

EXAMPLE **Graph Solutions of Linear Equations**

 Graph $y = 2x + 1$.

Select any four values for the input x. We chose 2, 1, 0, and -1. Substitute these values for x to find the output y.

x	$2x + 1$	y	(x, y)
2	$2(2) + 1$	5	$(2, 5)$
1	$2(1) + 1$	3	$(1, 3)$
0	$2(0) + 1$	1	$(0, 1)$
-1	$2(-1) + 1$	-1	$(-1, -1)$

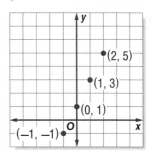

The four inputs correspond to the solutions $(2, 5)$, $(1, 3)$, $(0, 1)$, and $(-1, -1)$. Graph these ordered pairs to graph $y = 2x + 1$.

 CHECK Your Progress

Graph each equation.

b. $y = x - 3$ **c.** $y = -3x$ **d.** $y = -3x + 2$

Study Tip

Graphing Equations
Only two points are needed to graph the line. However, you can graph more points to check accuracy.

Notice that all four points in the graph lie on the same line. Draw a line through the points to graph *all* solutions of the equation $y = 2x + 1$. The point $(3, 7)$ is also on this line.

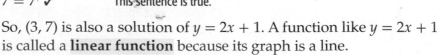

$y = 2x + 1$ Write the equation.

$7 \overset{?}{=} 2(3) + 1$ Replace x with 3 and y with 7.

$7 = 7$ ✓ This sentence is true.

So, $(3, 7)$ is also a solution of $y = 2x + 1$. A function like $y = 2x + 1$ is called a **linear function** because its graph is a line.

3 **SWIMMING** Michael Phelps swims the 400-meter individual medley at an average speed of 100 meters per minute. The equation $d = 100t$ describes the distance d that he can swim in t minutes at this speed. Represent the function by a graph.

Step 1 Select any four values for t. Select only positive numbers because t represents time. Make a function table.

t	$100t$	d	(t, d)
1	100(1)	100	(1, 100)
2	100(2)	200	(2, 200)
3	100(3)	300	(3, 300)
4	100(4)	400	(4, 400)

Step 2 Graph the ordered pairs and draw a line through the points.

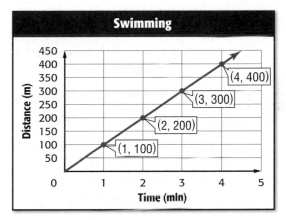

CHECK Your Progress

e. JOBS Sandi makes $6 an hour babysitting. The equation $m = 6h$ describes how much money m she earns babysitting for h hours. Represent this function by a graph.

Key Concept — Representing Functions

Words There are 12 inches in one foot.

Table

Feet	Inches
1	12
2	24
3	36
4	48

Graph

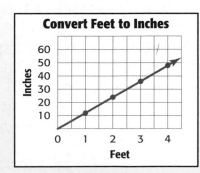

Equation $n = 12f$, where f represents the number of feet and n represents the number of inches.

Example 1
(p. 253)

Graph the function represented by each table.

1.

Total Cost of Baseballs	
Baseball	Total Cost ($)
1	4
2	8
3	12
4	16

2.

Savings Account	
Week	Amount ($)
0	300
1	350
2	400
3	450

Example 2
(p. 254)

Graph each equation.

3 $y = x - 1$

4. $y = -1x$

5. $y = -2x + 3$

Example 3
(p. 255)

6. MEASUREMENT The perimeter of a square is 4 times greater than the length of any of its sides. The equation $p = 4s$ describes the perimeter p of a square with sides s units long. Represent this function by a graph.

Practice and Problem Solving

● = **Step-by-Step Solutions** begin on page R10.
Extra Practice is on page EP12.

Example 1
(p. 253)

Graph the function represented by each table.

7.

Total Phone Bill	
Time (min)	Total ($)
0	10.00
1	10.08
2	10.16
3	10.24

8.

Calories in Fruit Cups	
Servings	Total Calories
1	70
3	210
5	350
7	490

Example 2
(p. 254)

Graph each equation.

9. $y = x + 1$

10. $y = x + 3$

11. $y = x$

12. $y = -2x$

13. $y = 2x + 3$

14. $y = 3x - 1$

Example 3
(p. 255)

Represent each function by a graph.

15. CARS A car averages 36 miles per gallon of gasoline. The function $m = 36g$ represents the miles m driven using g gallons of gasoline.

16. FITNESS A health club charges $35 a month for membership fees. The equation $c = 35m$ describes the total charge c for m months of membership.

Graph each equation.

17. $y = 0.25x$

18. $y = x + 0.5$

19 $y = 0.5x - 1$

20. SHOPPING You buy a DVD for $14 and CDs for $9 each. The equation $t = 14 + 9c$ represents the total amount t that you spend if you buy 1 DVD and c CDs. Represent this function by a graph.

H.O.T. Problems

21. **OPEN ENDED** Draw the graph of a linear function. Name three ordered pairs that satisfy the function.

22. **CHALLENGE** In the table, Darrell has recorded the temperature inside his greenhouse at certain times of the day. The greenhouse that he purchased was advertised to maintain temperatures between 65°F and 85°F.

Time	Temperature (°F)
1:00 A.M.	66
3:00 A.M.	71
6:00 A.M.	78.5
8:00 A.M.	83.5

   a. What is the rate of increase as a unit rate?

   b. Create a new chart that shows the temperatures recorded hourly from 1:00 A.M. to 8:00 A.M. using the given data in the table.

   c. Create a graph of the time and temperatures from midnight to 9:00 A.M. Is the relationship linear? Explain.

NGSSS Practice   MA.7.A.1.4

23. The graph shows the relationship between the number of hours Serefina spent jogging and the total number of miles she jogged. Which table best represents the data in the graph?

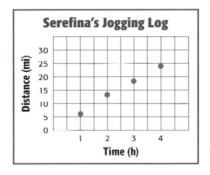

A.

Time (h)	Distance (mi)
6	4
12	3
18	2
24	1

B.

Time (h)	Distance (mi)
2	6
3	12
4	18
5	24

C.

Time (h)	Distance (mi)
1	6
2	14
3	18
4	24

D.

Time (h)	Distance (mi)
4	6
3	6
2	6
1	6

24. **HOBBIES** Sophia knits 6 rows of a blanket each hour. Write an equation using two variables to represent the total number of rows *r* completed by Sophia after time *t*. How many rows will Sophia complete after 4 hours? (Lesson 5-1B)

25. Find the value of *x* in the pair of similar figures. (Lesson 4-3A)

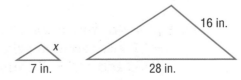

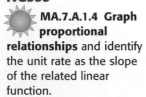

Graphing Technology:
Graphing Relationships

Main Idea

Use technology to graph relationships involving conversions of measurement.

NGSSS

 MA.7.A.1.4 Graph proportional relationships and identify the unit rate as the slope of the related linear function.

Get Connected
glencoe.com

ACTIVITY

MEASUREMENT Use the table at the right to write a function that relates the number of yards x to the number of feet y. Then graph your function.

Yards (x)	Feet (y)
1	3
2	6
3	9
4	12

STEP 1 By examining the table, you can see that the number of feet is 3 times the number of yards. Write a function.

The number of feet   is   3 times   the number of yards.
$$y \quad = \quad 3 \quad\quad x$$

STEP 2 Press $\boxed{Y=}$ and enter the function $y = 3x$ into Y1.

STEP 3 Graph the function by pressing $\boxed{\text{Graph}}$.

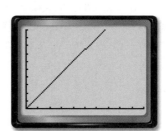

Analyze the Results

1. Test the function above using one of the values from the table and the CALC feature on your calculator. Press $\boxed{\text{2nd}}$ [CALC] 1 and then enter an x-value of 3. What y-value is displayed? What do each of these values represent and how are they represented on the graph?

2. Use your graph to convert 7 yards into feet. Explain your method.

3. **MAKE A CONJECTURE** Write a function that could be used to convert feet into yards. What is an appropriate window for a graph of this function? Graph and test your function.

4. Use your function from Exercise 3 to convert 16 feet into yards.

5. Write a function that could be used to convert 36 ounces to pounds. Indicate an appropriate window, then use a graph of the function to convert 36 ounces to pounds. (*Hint*: 1 pound = 16 ounces)

Explore Rate of Change

Main Idea

Understand slope as it relates to rate of change.

NGSSS

MA.7.A.1.4 Graph proportional relationships and identify the unit rate as the slope of the related linear function.

Get Connected
glencoe.com

PET CARE The Happy Hound is a doggie daycare where people can drop off their dogs while they are at work. Farah takes her dog to the Happy Hound several days a week. The table shows their prices. Use a graph to determine how the number of hours is related to the cost.

Pet Care 🐾	
Number of Hours	Cost ($)
1	3.00
2	6.00
3	9.00
4	12.00
5	15.00
6	18.00

ACTIVITY

What do you need to find? the relationship between number of hours and cost for pet care at Happy Hound

The cost is a function of the number of hours. So, the cost is the output y, and the number of hours is the input, x. Create a graph of the data.

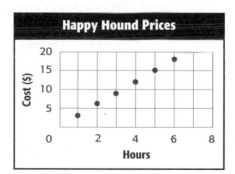

Analyze the Results

1. Is the graph linear? Explain.

2. What is the cost per hour, or unit rate, charged by the Happy Hound?

3. Examine any two consecutive ordered pairs from the table. How do the values change?

4. Is this relationship true for any two consecutive values in the table?

5. Use the graph to examine any two consecutive points. By how much does y change? By how much does x change?

6. How does this change relate to the unit rate?

5-2 Slope

Main Idea

Identify constant rate of change using tables and graphs.

NGSSS

MA.7.A.1.4 Graph proportional relationships and **identify the unit rate as the slope of the related linear function.**

New Vocabulary

rate of change
constant rate of change

Get Connected
glencoe.com

Constant Rate of Change

HEIGHTS The table shows Horacio's height at ages 9 and 12.

Age (yr)	9	12
Height (in.)	53	59

1. What is the change in Horacio's height from ages 9 to 12?

2. Over what number of years did this change take place?

3. Write a rate that compares the change in Horacio's height to the change in age. Express your answer as a unit rate and explain its meaning.

A **rate of change** is a rate that describes how one quantity changes in relation to another. A rate of change is usually expressed as a unit rate. A **constant rate of change** is the rate of change in a linear relationship.

EXAMPLE **Use a Table**

1. **FUNDRAISING** The table shows the amount of money a booster club makes washing cars for a fundraiser. Use the information to find the constant rate of change in dollars per car.

Cars Washed	
Number	**Money ($)**
5	40
10	80
15	120
20	160

+5 (...) +40
+5 (...) +40
+5 (...) +40

Find the unit rate to determine the constant rate of change.

$$\frac{\text{change in money}}{\text{change in cars}} = \frac{40 \text{ dollars}}{5 \text{ cars}}$$ The money earned increases by $40 for every 5 cars.

$$= \frac{8 \text{ dollars}}{1 \text{ car}}$$ Write as a unit rate.

So, the number of dollars earned increases by $8 for every car washed.

CHECK Your Progress

a. **PLANES** The table shows the number of miles a plane traveled while in flight. Use the information to find the constant rate of change in miles per minute.

Time (min)	30	60	90	120
Distance (mi)	290	580	870	1,160

Use a Graph

2 **DRIVING** The graph represents the distance traveled while driving on a highway. Use the graph to find the constant rate of change in miles per hour.

To find the rate of change, pick any two points on the line, such as (1, 60) and (2, 120).

$$\frac{\text{change in miles}}{\text{change in hours}} = \frac{(120 - 60) \text{ miles}}{(2 - 1) \text{ hours}}$$

$$= \frac{60 \text{ miles}}{1 \text{ hour}}$$

The distance increases by 60 miles in 1 hour. So, the rate of traveling on a highway is 60 miles per hour.

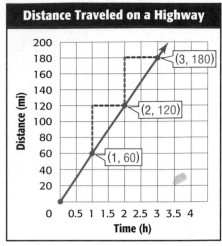

Distance Traveled on a Highway

CHECK Your Progress

b. **DRIVING** Use the graph to find the constant rate of change in miles per hour while driving in the city.

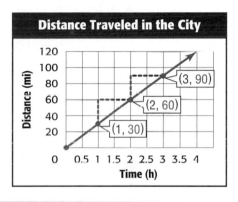

Distance Traveled in the City

Notice that the graph in Example 2 about driving on a highway represents a rate of change of 60 mph. The graph in Check Your Progress about driving in the city is not as steep. It represents a rate of change of 30 mph.

CHECK Your Understanding

Example 1
(p. 260)

1. Use the information in the table to find the constant rate of change in degrees per hour.

Temperature (°F)	54	57	60	63
Time	6 A.M.	8 A.M.	10 A.M.	12 A.M.

Example 2
(p. 261)

2. **DISTANCE** The graph shows Benito's distance from the starting line. Use the graph to find the constant rate of change.

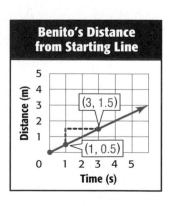

Benito's Distance from Starting Line

Practice and Problem Solving

● = **Step-by-Step Solutions** begin on page R12.
Extra Practice is on page EP12.

Example 1
(p. 260)

Find the constant rate of change for each table.

3.

Time (s)	Distance (m)
0	6
1	12
2	18
3	24

4.

Time (h)	Wage ($)
0	0
1	9
2	18
3	27

5. The number of minutes included in different cell phone plans and the costs are shown in the table.

Cost ($)	38	50	62	74	86
Minutes	1,000	1,500	2,000	2,500	3,000

What is the approximate constant rate of change in cost per minute?

Example 2
(p. 261)

Find the constant rate of change for each graph.

6.

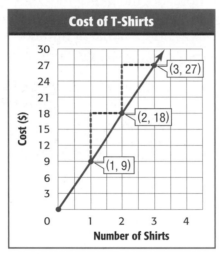

Cost of T-Shirts

(3, 27)
(2, 18)
(1, 9)

7

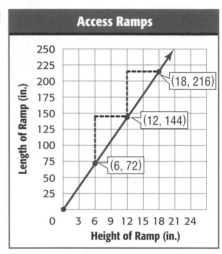

Access Ramps

(18, 216)
(12, 144)
(6, 72)

8. WATER At 1:00 P.M., the water level in a pool is 13 inches. At 2:30 P.M., the water level is 28 inches. What is the constant rate of change?

9 **GRAPHIC NOVEL** Refer to the lap times and page 245 for Exercises a and b.

Let's calculate Seth's times.

Lap Times

lap	time
4	57.1 s
8	114.2 s
12	171.3 s
16	
20	

a. How long does it take Seth to complete 1 mile if 20 laps equal 5 miles? Write the constant rate of change in miles per second.

b. Graph the distance and time on a coordinate plane with the distance on the *y*-axis and the time on the *x*-axis.

H.O.T. Problems

10. **OPEN ENDED** Make a table where the constant rate of change is 6 inches for every foot.

11. **Write MATH** Write a problem to represent a constant rate of change of $15 per item.

12. Use the information in the table to find the constant rate of change.

Number of Apples	Number of Seeds
3	30
7	70
11	110

A. $\frac{10}{1}$

B. $\frac{1}{10}$

C. $\frac{40}{4}$

D. $\frac{4}{40}$

13. **GRIDDED RESPONSE** Reggie started a running program to prepare for track season. Every day for 60 days he ran a half hour in the morning and a half hour in the evening. He averaged 6.5 miles per hour. At this rate, what is the total number of miles Reggie ran over the 60-day period?

 **Spiral Review** ....

14. **ALGEBRA** Graph $y = 3x$. (Lesson 5-1C)

Copy and complete each function table. Identify the domain and range.
(Lesson 5-1B)

15.

x	x − 4	y
4		
5		
6		
7		

16.

x	9x	y
0		
1		
2		
3		

17.

x	5x + 1	y
1		
2		
3		
4		

18. **GROCERIES** Find the unit price if Anju spent $2 for six oranges. Round to the nearest cent if necessary. (Lesson 4-1B)

19. **MONEY** Grant and his brother put their money together to buy a present for their mom. They had a total of $18 and Grant contributed $10. Write and solve an equation to represent how much his brother contributed. (Lesson 3-1D)

20. **SANDWICHES** Lawanda is making subs. She puts $1\frac{1}{2}$ slices of cheese on each sub. If she has 12 slices of cheese, how many subs can she make? (Lesson 2-3D)

Main Idea

Identify slope using tables and graphs.

NGSSS

MA.7.A.1.4 Graph proportional relationships and identify the unit rate as the slope of the related linear function.

New Vocabulary

slope

Get Connected
glencoe.com

Slope

BOOKS Hero Comics is a company that publishes comic books. They typically recycle the original copies after the binding process. The table below shows the total number of pounds of paper that has been recycled each day during the month.

Day of Month	Total Recycled (lbs)
3	36
5	60
6	72
7	84
12	144
15	180

1. Is the relationship linear? Explain.

2. Create a graph of the function. Use two points from the graph to find the constant rate of change.

In a linear relation, the vertical change (change in y-value) per unit of horizontal change (change in x-value) is always the same. This ratio is called the **slope** of the function. The constant rate of change, or unit rate of a function, is the same as the slope of the related linear function. The slope tells how steep the line is.

Key Concept   Slope

Slope is the rate of change between any two points on a line.

$$\text{slope} = \frac{\text{change in } y}{\text{change in } x} \quad \longleftarrow \text{ vertical change} \\ \longleftarrow \text{ horizontal change}$$

$$= \frac{2}{1} \text{ or } 2$$

The vertical change is sometimes called "rise" while the horizontal change is called "run." You can say that slope $= \dfrac{\text{rise}}{\text{run}}$.

Vocabulary Link

Everyday Use

Slope inclination or slant

Math Use

Slope the ratio of vertical change per unit of horizontal change; the steepness of a line

Real-World EXAMPLE **Find Slope**

① PHYSICAL SCIENCE The table below shows the relationship between the number of seconds y it takes to hear thunder after a lightning strike and the miles x you are from the lightning.

Miles (x)	0	1	2	3	4	5
Seconds (y)	0	5	10	15	20	25

Graph the data and find the slope. Explain what the slope represents.

$$\text{slope} = \frac{\text{change in } y}{\text{change in } x} \qquad \text{Definition of slope}$$

$$= \frac{25 - 15}{5 - 3} \qquad \text{Use (3, 15) and (5, 25).}$$

$$= \frac{10}{2} \quad \longleftarrow \text{seconds} \atop \longleftarrow \text{miles}$$

$$= \frac{5}{1} \qquad \text{Simplify.}$$

So, for every 5 seconds between a lightning flash and the sound of thunder, there is 1 mile between you and the lightning strike.

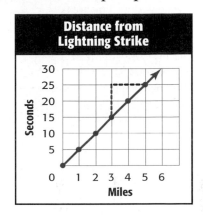

Distance from Lightning Strike

✓ CHECK Your Progress

a. WATER Graph the data about water loss in an aquarium. Then find the slope of the line. Explain what the slope represents.

Week	Water Loss (cm)
1	1.5
2	3
3	4.5
4	6

EXAMPLE **Interpret Slope**

② BANKING Renaldo opened a savings account with the $300 he earned mowing yards over the summer. Each week he withdraws $20 for expenses. Draw a graph of the account balance versus time. Find the numerical value of the slope and interpret it in words.

The slope of the line is the rate at which the account balance falls, or $-\dfrac{\$20}{1 \text{ week}}$.

This is a negative slope and therefore a negative rate of change.

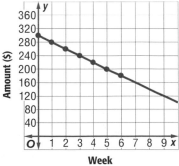

Renaldo's Savings Account

✓ CHECK Your Progress

b. Jessica buys a $10 pre-paid card for her cell phone. She pays a rate of $0.05 per text. Draw a graph of the card balance versus the number of text messages. Find the numerical value of the slope and interpret it in words.

Example 1
(p. 265)

1 **SNACKS** The table below shows the number of small packs of fruit snacks y per box x. Graph the data. Then find the slope of the line. Explain what the slope represents.

Boxes (x)	3	5	7	9
Packs (y)	24	40	56	72

Example 2
(p. 265)

2. **TEMPERATURE** At 2:00 P.M., the temperature is 81°F. At 3:00 P.M., the temperature is 78°F. Draw a graph of temperature versus time if the temperature continues to decrease at this rate from 2:00 P.M. to 6:00 P.M. Find the value of the slope and interpret it in words.

Practice and Problem Solving

● = **Step-by-Step Solutions** begin on page R12.
Extra Practice is on page EP12.

Example 1
(p. 265)

3. **CYCLING** The table shows the distance y Adriano traveled in x minutes while competing in the cycling portion of a triathlon. Graph the data. Then find the slope of the line. Explain what the slope represents.

Time (min)	45	90	135	180
Distance (km)	5	10	15	20

4. **MARKERS** The table below shows the number of markers per box. Graph the data. Then find the slope of the line. Explain what the slope represents.

Boxes	1	2	3	4
Markers	8	16	24	32

Example 2
(p. 265)

5. **MEASUREMENT** There are 3 feet for every 1 yard. Draw a graph of feet versus yards. Find the numerical value of the slope and interpret it in words.

6. **SWIMMING** Joshua swims 25 meters in 1 minute. Draw a graph of meters swam versus time. Find the value of the slope and interpret it in words.

7 **SPEED** The graph shows the average speed of two cars on the highway.

a. What does (2, 120) represent?

b. What does (1.5, 67.5) represent?

c. What does the ratio of the y-coordinate to the x-coordinate for each pair of points on the graph represent?

d. What does the slope of each line represent?

e. Which car is traveling faster? How can you tell from the graph?

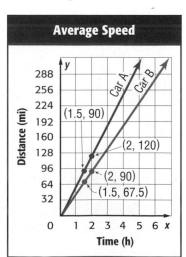

8. CHALLENGE Flavio is saving money at a rate of $30 per month. Edgardo is saving money at a rate of $35 per month. They both started saving at the same time. If you were to create a table of values and graph each function, what would be the slope of each graph?

9. FIND THE ERROR Marisol is finding the slope of the line containing the points (3, 7) and (5, 10). Find her mistake and correct it.

The slope between the two points (3, 7) and (5, 10) is found like this:

$$\text{slope} = \frac{\text{rise}}{\text{run}} = \frac{5 - 3}{10 - 7} = \frac{2}{3}$$

10. Write MATH Describe the relationship between the rate of change and the slope. How do you find each?

NGSSS Practice MA.7.A.1.4

11. SHORT RESPONSE Find the slope of the line below that shows the distance Jairo traveled while jogging.

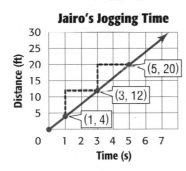

Jairo's Jogging Time

(5, 20)
(3, 12)
(1, 4)

Distance (ft) / Time (s)

12. Line *RS* represents a bike ramp.

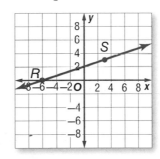

What is the slope of the ramp?

A. $-\frac{3}{1}$ C. $\frac{1}{3}$

B. $-\frac{1}{3}$ D. $\frac{3}{1}$

13. WAGES Use the information in the table to find the constant rate of change in dollars per hour. (Lesson 5-2B)

Wage ($)	0	9	18	27
Time (h)	0	1	2	3

14. Graph $y = 4x$. (Lesson 5-1C)

Extend

Graphing Technology: Compare Graphs

You can use a graphing calculator to compare and contrast relationships of graphs.

ACTIVITY

Compare and contrast the graphs of $y = 5x$ and $y = 7x$.

STEP 1   Press $\boxed{Y=}$ and enter the function $y = 5x$ into Y1. Then enter $y = 7x$ into Y2.

STEP 2   Adjust your viewing window. Press $\boxed{\text{WINDOW}}$ and change the values to allow you to compare the different graphs.

STEP 3   Finally, graph the functions by pressing $\boxed{\text{Graph}}$. Compare and contrast the graphs.

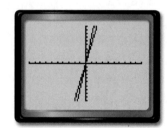

Analyze the Results

1. What happens to the graph of $y = 5x$ and $y = 7x$ as the coefficient changes in each function? Explain your reasoning.

2. Graph $y = 2x$ and $y = 2x + 1$. What happens to the graph of $y = 2x$ when you add 1 to the function? What would you expect to happen if you add 2? subtract 1?

3. What similarities do you notice among all of the functions? differences?

4. Graph $y = 3x$ and $y = -3x$. Compare and contrast the two graphs.

5. **MAKE A CONJECTURE** Explain in two or more sentences how positive and negative coefficients affect the graphs of the functions.

1. **TRAVEL** Beth drove at an average rate of 65 miles per hour for several hours. Make a function table that shows her distance traveled after 2, 3, 4, and 5 hours. Then identify the domain and range. (Lesson 5-1B)

2. **MONEY** Anthony earns extra money after school doing yard work for his neighbors. He charges $12 for each lawn he mows. (Lesson 5-1B)

   a. Write an equation to show the relationship between the number of lawns mowed m and number of dollars earned d.

   b. Find the number of dollars earned if he mows 14 lawns.

Graph each equation. (Lesson 5-1C)

3. $y = x + 1$

4. $y = 2x$

5. $y = 2x - 3$

6. $y = -x + 1$

7. **MOVIES** A student ticket to the movies costs $6. The equation $c = 6t$ describes the total cost c for t tickets. Make a function table that shows the total cost for 1, 2, 3, and 4 tickets and then graph the equation. (Lesson 5-1C)

8. Use the graph to find the constant rate of change in cost per magazine. (Lesson 5-2B)

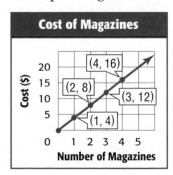

9. **NGSSS PRACTICE** The graph shows the relationship between time and water level of a pool. Which represents the rate of change? (Lesson 5-2B)

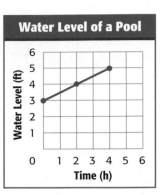

   A. increases 2 feet every 1 hour

   B. increases 1 foot every 2 hours

   C. increases 1 foot every 1 hour

   D. increases 2 feet every 2 hours

10. **MAPS** The table shows the key for a map. Graph the data. Then find the slope of the line. (Lesson 5-2C)

Distance on Map (cm)	1	2	3	4
Actual Distance (km)	20	40	60	80

11. **NGSSS PRACTICE** Line AB represents a ramp for loading a truck. What is the slope of the ramp? (Lesson 5-2C)

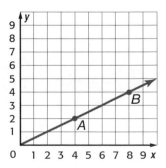

   F. $\dfrac{2}{1}$

   G. $\dfrac{1}{2}$

   H. $-\dfrac{2}{1}$

   I. $-\dfrac{1}{2}$

5-3   Variation

Problem-Solving Investigation

Main Idea Solve problems by using a graph.

P.S.I. TEAM +

Use a Graph

RICK: The table shows the study times and test scores of 13 students in Mrs. Collins's English class.

YOUR MISSION: Use a graph to predict the test score of a student who studied for 80 minutes.

Study Time and Test Scores											
Study Time (min)	120	30	60	95	70	55	90	45	75	60	10
Test Score (%)	98	75	80	93	82	78	95	74	87	83	65

Understand	You know the number of minutes studied. You need to predict the test score.	
Plan	Organize the data in a graph so you can easily see any trends.	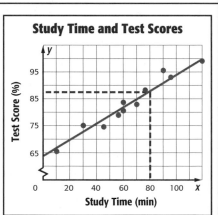
Solve	As the study times progress, the test scores increase. Draw a line that is close to as many of the points as possible. You can predict that the test score of a student who studied for 80 minutes is about 88%.	
Check	The estimate is close to the line, so the prediction is reasonable.	

Analyze the Strategy

1. Explain why analyzing a graph is a useful way to quickly make conclusions about a data set.

2. **Write** MATH Write a real-world problem in which using a graph would be a useful way to check a solution.

 NGSSS

MA.7.A.1.4 **Graph proportional relationships** and identify the unit rate as the slope of the related function.

- Use a graph.
- Guess, check, and revise.
- Look for a pattern.
- Choose an operation.

Use a graph to solve Exercises 3 and 4.

3. The table shows the relationship between Celsius and Fahrenheit temperatures.

Temperature	
Celsius	**Fahrenheit**
0	32
10	50
20	68
30	86
40	104

a. Make a graph of the data.

b. Suppose the temperature is 25° Celsius. Estimate the temperature in Fahrenheit.

4. OLYMPICS The graph shows the winning Olympic times for the women's 4 × 100-meter freestyle relay in swimming. Predict the winning time in 2012.

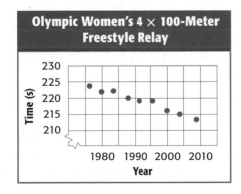

Use any strategy to solve Exercises 5–11.

5. ALGEBRA What are the next two numbers in the pattern 8, 18, 38, 78, ... ?

6. FARMING A farmer sells a bushel of corn for $3. Suppose the farmer wants to earn $165 from bushels of corn sales on Saturday. How many bushels does he need to sell to make his goal?

7. EXERCISE Flora walked 8 minutes on Sunday and, each day, plans to walk twice as long as she did the previous day. On what day will she walk over 1 hour?

8. OIL SPILLS The graph shows the number of oil spills each year.

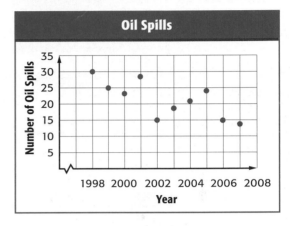

a. What does the graph indicate happened from 2002 to 2004?

b. What is the overall trend in the data?

c. Is the relationship linear?

d. Explain the difference between a linear relationship and a trend.

9. HELICOPTERS A helicopter has a maximum freight capacity of 2,400 pounds. How many crates, each weighing about 75 pounds, can the helicopter hold?

10. SKATING Moses and some of his friends are going to the movies. Suppose they each buy nachos and a beverage. They spend $36. How many friends are going to the movies with Moses?

Movie Costs	
Item	**Price**
Ticket	$6.00
Beverage	$2.25
Nachos	$3.75

11. NUMBER THEORY A whole number is squared and the result is 324. Find the number.

Proportional and Nonproportional Relationships

Main Idea

Compare and contrast proportional and nonproportional linear functions.

NGSSS

MA.7.A.1.5 **Distinguish direct variation from other relationships,** including inverse variation.

Get Connected
glencoe.com

In this activity, you will use models to explore two different functions.

ACTIVITY

STEP 1 Using centimeter cubes, arrange the cubes in towers as shown in the diagrams below.

Pattern	A				B			
Figures								
Figure Number	0	1	2	3	0	1	2	3

STEP 2 Let x represent the figure number and y represent the number of centimeter cubes in each tower. Copy and complete the table below for each pattern. Then graph the data on separate coordinate planes.

x	Process	y
0		
1		
2		
3		
4		
x		

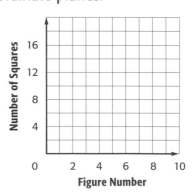

Analyze the Results

1. Compare and contrast the models, processes, and graphs of Patterns A and B.

2. Which pattern represents a proportional relationship? Which represents a nonproportional relationship? How can you tell this from the data shown in the table? from the graph?

Main Idea

Use direct variation to solve problems.

NGSSS

MA.7.A.1.5 Distinguish direct variation from other relationships, including inverse variation.

New Vocabulary

direct variation
constant of variation

 Get Connected
glencoe.com

Direct Variation

SPEED A car travels 130 miles in 2 hours, 195 miles in 3 hours, and 260 miles in 4 hours, as shown.

1. What is the constant rate of change, or slope, of the line?

2. Is the distance traveled always proportional to the driving time? What is the constant ratio?

3. Compare the constant rate of change to the constant ratio.

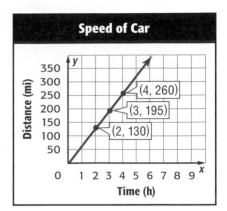

When two variable quantities have a constant ratio, their relationship is called a **direct variation**. The constant ratio is called the **constant of variation**.

Real-World EXAMPLE   Find a Constant Ratio

1 **POOLS** The height of the water as a pool is being filled is shown in the graph. Determine the rate in inches per minute.

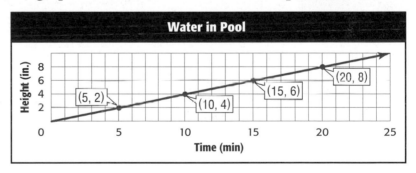

Since the graph of the data forms a line, the rate of change is constant. Use the graph to find the constant ratio.

$\dfrac{height}{time}$ ⟶ $\dfrac{2}{5}$ or $\dfrac{0.4}{1}$ $\dfrac{4}{10}$ or $\dfrac{0.4}{1}$ $\dfrac{6}{15}$ or $\dfrac{0.4}{1}$ $\dfrac{8}{20}$ or $\dfrac{0.4}{1}$

The pool fills at a rate of 0.4 inch every minute.

CHECK Your Progress

a. **SCUBA DIVING** Two minutes after a diver enters the water, he has descended 52 feet. After 5 minutes, he has descended 130 feet. At what rate is the scuba diver descending?

In a direct variation equation, the constant rate of change, or slope, is assigned a special variable, k.

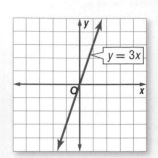
As you learned in Lesson 4-1C, not all situations with a constant rate of change are proportional relationships. Likewise, not all linear functions are direct variations.

EXAMPLE **Determine Direct Variation**

2 **PIZZA** Pizzas cost $8 each plus a $3 delivery charge. Make a table and graph to show the cost of 1, 2, 3, and 4 pizzas. Is there a constant rate? a direct variation?

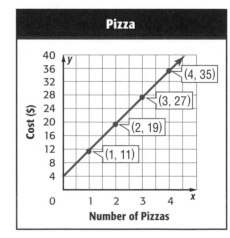

Pizza

Number of Pizzas	1	2	3	4
Cost ($)	$11	$19	$27	$35

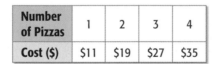

$\dfrac{\text{number of pizzas}}{\text{cost}} \longrightarrow \dfrac{11}{1}, \dfrac{19}{2}$ or 9.5, $\dfrac{27}{3}$ or 9, $\dfrac{35}{4}$ or 8.75

Because there is no constant rate, there is no direct variation.

Real-World Link · · · ·
The average American consumes 23 pounds of pizza every year.

CHECK Your Progress

b. FOOD COSTS Two pounds of cheese cost $8.40. Make a table and graph to show the cost of 1, 2, 3, and 4 pounds of cheese. Is there a constant rate? a direct variation?

EXAMPLES **Identify Direct Variation**

Determine whether each linear function is a direct variation. If so, state the constant of variation.

3

Time, x	1	2	3	4
Wages, y	12	24	36	48

Compare the ratios to check for a common ratio.

$\frac{\text{wages}}{\text{time}}$ → $\frac{12}{1}$ $\frac{24}{2}$ or $\frac{12}{1}$ $\frac{36}{3}$ or $\frac{12}{1}$ $\frac{48}{4}$ or $\frac{12}{1}$

Since the ratios are the same, the function is a direct variation. The constant of variation is $\frac{12}{1}$.

4

Time (h), x		2	3	4	5
Temperature Change (°), y		4	5	7	11

$\frac{\text{temperature}}{\text{time}}$ → $\frac{4}{2}$ or $\frac{2}{1}$ $\frac{5}{3}$ or $\frac{1.67}{1}$ $\frac{7}{4}$ or $\frac{1.75}{1}$ $\frac{11}{5}$ or $\frac{2.2}{1}$

The ratios are not the same, so the function is not a direct variation.

CHECK Your Progress

C.

Year, x	5	10	15	20
Height, y	12.5	25	37.5	50

Study Tip

Direct Variation When a relationship varies directly, the graph of the function will always go through the origin.

Concept Summary **Linear Functions**

	Table	Graph	Equation

Direct Variation Functions

x	y	$\frac{y}{x}$
−2	−6	3
−1	−3	3
1	3	3
2	6	3

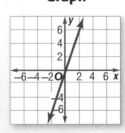

$y = 3x$

Not Direct Variation Functions

x	y	$\frac{y}{x}$
−2	−7	$\frac{-7}{2}$
−1	−4	4
1	2	2
2	5	$\frac{5}{2}$

$y = 3x - 1$

Example 1
(p. 273)

1. BAKING The number of cakes baked varies directly with the number of hours the caterers work. What is the ratio of cakes baked to hours worked?

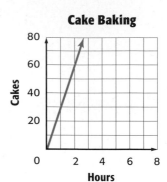

Cake Baking

Example 2
(p. 274)

2. TRANSPORTATION An airplane travels 780 miles in 4 hours. Make a table and graph to show the mileage for 2, 8, and 12 hours. Is there a direct variation?

Examples 3 and 4
(p. 275)

3. Determine whether the linear function is a direct variation. If so, state the constant of variation.

Hours, x	3	5	7	9
Miles, y	108	180	252	324

Practice and Problem Solving

● = **Step-by-Step Solutions** begin on page R13.
Extra Practice is on page EP13.

Example 1
(p. 273)

4. GARDENING Veronica is mulching her front yard. The total weight of mulch varies directly with the number of bags of mulch. What is the rate of change?

5 DOG WALKING The money Shelley earns varies directly with the number of dogs she walks. How much does Shelley earn for each dog she walks?

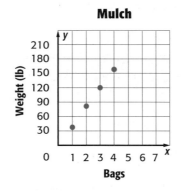

Mulch

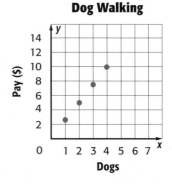

Dog Walking

Examples 2–4
(pp. 274–275)

Determine whether each linear function is a direct variation. If so, state the constant of variation.

6.

Pictures, x	3	4	5	6
Profit, y	24	32	40	48

7.

Minutes, x	185	235	275	325
Cost, y	60	115	140	180

8.

Age, x	11	13	15	19
Grade, y	5	7	9	11

9.

Price, x	20	25	30	35
Tax, y	4	5	6	7

10. PRESSURE At a 33-foot depth underwater, the pressure is 29.55 pounds per square inch (psi). At a depth of 66 feet, the pressure reaches 44.4 psi. At what rate is the pressure increasing?

11. BOOKS One month, the Allen family had a total of $3.20 in fines for 4 books. The next month, they had 7 books overdue for $5.60. What was the overdue charge per book?

12. CARPET Logan used 160 carpet squares to cover 480 square feet and 210 carpet squares to cover an additional 630 square feet. How many carpet squares would he need to cover 900 square feet?

13. MONEY The George family of 3 eats dinner for $81 at an upscale restaurant. How much will it cost the Georges for a dinner party of 15 people at the restaurant?

ALGEBRA If y varies directly with x, write an equation for the direct variation. Then find each value.

14. If $y = -14$ when $x = 8$, find y when $x = -12$.

15. Find y when $x = 15$ if $y = 6$ when $x = 30$.

16. If $y = -6$ when $x = -24$, what is the value of x when $y = -7$?

17. Find x when $y = 14$, if $y = 7$ when $x = 8$.

18. Find y when $x = 9$, if $y = 16.4$ when $x = 8.2$.

19 MEASUREMENT The number of yards in a measure varies directly with the number of feet. Using the graph at the right, find the measure of an object in yards if it is 78 feet long.

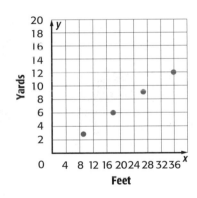

20. BAKING A cake recipe requires $3\frac{1}{4}$ cups of flour for 13 servings and $4\frac{1}{2}$ cups of flour for 18 servings. How much flour is required to make a cake that serves 28?

21. MULTIPLE REPRESENTATIONS Robert is in charge of the community swimming pool. Each spring he drains it in order to clean it. He then must refill the pool, which holds 120,000 gallons of water. Robert fills the pool at a rate of 10 gallons each minute.

a. WORDS What is the rate at which Robert will fill the pool? Is it constant?

b. GRAPHS Create a graph of the relationship.

c. ALGEBRA Write an equation for the direct variation.

22. GEOMETRY The length of the rectangle to the right varies directly with its width. What is the perimeter of a rectangle that is similar to the one shown and 14 inches long?

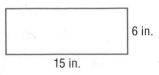

6 in.

15 in.

23. **OPEN ENDED** Identify two additional values for x and y in a direct variation relationship where $y = 11$ when $x = 18$.

24. **CHALLENGE** Find y when $x = 14$ if y varies directly as the square of x, and $y = 72$ when $x = 6$.

25. **Write MATH** Write a real-world problem involving a direct variation. Then solve your problem.

NGSSS Practice   **MA.7.A.1.5**

26. Students in a science class recorded lengths of a stretched spring, as shown in the table below.

Length of Stretched Spring	
Distance Stretched, x (centimeters)	Mass, y (grams)
0	0
2	14
5	35
9	63
12	84
15	105

Which equation best represents the relationship between the distance stretched x and the mass y of an object on the spring?

A. $y = -7x$ C. $y = -\dfrac{x}{7}$

B. $y = 7x$ D. $y = \dfrac{x}{7}$

27. Anjuli read 22 pages during a 30-minute study hall. At this rate, how many pages would she read in 45 minutes?

F. 30

G. 33

H. 45

I. 48

28. To make lemonade, Andy adds 8 tablespoons of sugar for every 12 ounces of water. If he uses 32 ounces of water, which proportion can he use to find the number of tablespoons of sugar x he should add to make the lemonade?

A. $\dfrac{8}{12} = \dfrac{32}{x}$ C. $\dfrac{8}{12} = \dfrac{x}{32}$

B. $\dfrac{8}{x} = \dfrac{32}{12}$ D. $\dfrac{x}{12} = \dfrac{8}{32}$

Spiral Review

29. **PHONE CALLS** Use the graph showing the number of people in a family and the number of weekly calls. Predict the number of weekly phone calls for a family of 10. (Lesson 5-3A)

30. Use the information in the table to find the constant rate of change in dollars per hour. (Lesson 5-2B)

Pay ($)	0	9	18	27
Time (h)	0	1	2	3

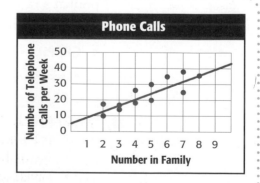

Explore Inverse Variation

Main Idea

Graph inverse variations.

NGSSS

 MA.7.A.1.5 Distinguish direct variation from other relationships, including inverse variation.

Get Connected
glencoe.com

Jackie rides her bike at an average rate of 4 miles per hour. This situation can be represented by the direct variation equation $d = 4t$, where d is the distance in miles and t is the time in hours. The rate is a constant.

Let's vary the situation a little. Suppose Jackie wants to bike 12 miles each day. Some days she rides faster than others. This situation can be represented by the equation $12 = rt$, where r is the rate.

ACTIVITY

STEP 1 Copy and complete the table for the equation $12 = rt$.

t (hours)	12	8	6	■	■	■	■
r (miles per hour)	1	1.5	2	2.5	3	3.5	4

STEP 2 Copy and complete the graph of the ordered pairs from Step 1. Connect the line with a smooth curve. The first three points are done for you.

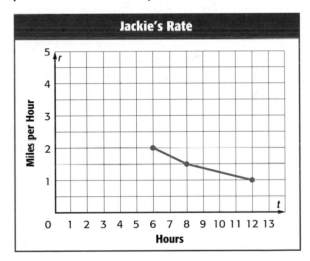

Analyze the Results

1. Is the time proportional to the rate? Explain why or why not.

2. When the product of two variables is a constant, the relationship is an *inverse variation*. Which situation is an inverse variation: Jackie biking at 4 miles per hour or biking 12 miles at varying rates? Identify the constants in each situation.

Main Idea

Use inverse variation to solve problems.

NGSSS

 MA.7.A.1.5 **Distinguish direct variation from other relationships, including inverse variation.**

New Vocabulary

inverse variation

Get Connected
glencoe.com

Inverse Variation

Explore Refer to the rectangles below.

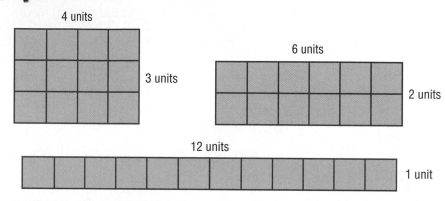

1. What is the constant in each rectangle?
2. What happens to the width as the length increases?
3. What happens to the length as the width increases?

The example above shows an inverse variation. In an **inverse variation**, the product of x and y is a constant. We say that y is inversely proportional to x.

Key Concept Inverse Variation

Words
An inverse variation is a relationship where the product of x and y is a constant k.

Symbols
$xy = k$ or $y = \dfrac{k}{x}$, where $k \neq 0$

Example
$xy = 3$ or $y = \dfrac{3}{x}$

Model

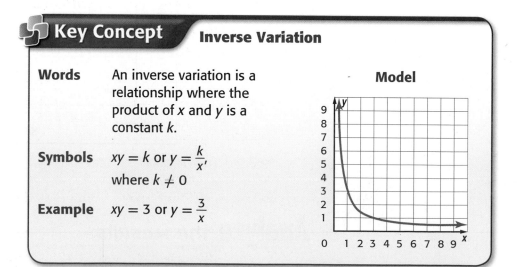

As x increases, the value of y decreases, but not at a constant rate. So, the graph of an inverse variation is not a straight line as in direct variation.

1 MUSIC The table shows the relationship between the frequency and wavelength of a musical tone. Determine if the relationship is an inverse variation. Justify your response.

Graph the data in the table.

Frequency (vibrations per second)	220	440	660	880
Wavelength (feet)	4	2	$1\frac{1}{3}$	1

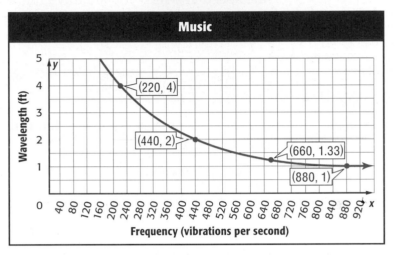

Music

The graph shows that this is an inverse variation. The x- and y-coordinates each have a product of 880.

2 CONSTRUCTION The number of carpenters needed to frame a house varies inversely as the number of days needed to complete the project. Suppose 5 carpenters can frame a certain house in 16 days. How many days will it take 8 carpenters to frame the house? Assume that they all work at the same rate.

Solve the problem by using inverse variation. Let x be the number of carpenters. Let y be the number of days.

Step 1 Find the value of k.

$xy = k$ Inverse variation

$(5)(16) = k$ Replace x with 5 and y with 16.

$80 = k$ Simplify to determine k.

Step 2 Find the number of days.

$y = \dfrac{k}{x}$ Definition of inverse variation

$y = \dfrac{80}{8}$ Replace k with 80 and x with 8.

$y = 10$ Simplify.

A crew of 8 carpenters can frame the house in 10 days.

CHECK Your Progress

a. CANDLES The table shows the relationship between the volume of wax in a candle and the time the candle burns. Graph the data in the table and determine if the relationship is an inverse variation.

Time (h)	1	2	4	8
Volume (in³)	128	64	32	16

Real-World Link · · · · ·

An average of 966,000 new homes were sold each year from 2004 through 2008 in the United States.

Example 1
(p. 281)

1 **MUSIC** The table shows the relationship between the length of a piano string and the frequency of its vibrations. Graph the data in the table and determine if the relationship is an inverse variation.

Length (in.)	48	36	24	12
Frequency (cycles/s)	360	480	720	1440

Example 2
(p. 281)

2. **TRAVEL** The time it takes to travel a certain distance varies inversely with the speed at which you are traveling. Suppose it takes 3 hours to drive from one city to another at a rate of 65 miles per hour. How long will the return trip take traveling at 55 miles per hour?

Practice and Problem Solving

● = **Step-by-Step Solutions** begin on page R13.
Extra Practice is on page EP14.

Example 1
(p. 281)

Graph the data in each table and determine if the relationship is an inverse variation.

3.

Length (m)	2.4	3	6	10
Width (m)	15	12	6	3.6

4.

Gift Card Balance ($)	50.00	42.50	27.50	5.00
Number of Movies	0	1	3	6

Example 2
(p. 281)

5. **BRICKS** The number of bricklayers needed to build a brick wall varies inversely as the number of hours needed. Four bricklayers can build a brick wall in 30 hours. How long would it take 5 bricklayers to build a wall?

6. **RUNNING** In the formula $d = rt$, the time t varies inversely with the rate r. A student running at 5 miles per hour runs one lap around the school campus in 8 minutes. If a second student takes 10 minutes to run one lap around the school campus, how fast is she running?

7 **GRAPHIC NOVEL** Refer to the graphic novel frame below. Seth applies his brakes and begins slowing. After 2 seconds the car travels 88 feet. After 4 seconds the car travels another 44 feet. It takes several more seconds for the car to come to a complete stop. Is this an example of direct or inverse variation? Explain.

Slowing down after racing is mathematical too.

H.O.T. Problems

8. **CHALLENGE** When does a graph representing an inverse variation cross the x-axis? Explain.

9. **OPEN ENDED** Identify three sets of values of x and y for the inverse variation $xy = 24$.

10. **Write MATH** Write a few sentences that compare and contrast inverse variation and direct variation.

NGSSS **Practice**   MA.7.A.1.5

11. Several people share twenty-five pieces of candy. If the situation is an inverse variation, which equation represents the situation?

   A. $xy = 125$
   B. $y = \dfrac{25}{x}$
   C. $y = 125x$
   D. $25x = y$

12. Determine k if y varies inversely as x and $y = 4.2$ when $x = -1.3$.

   F. -3.27
   G. -5.46
   H. -0.31
   I. -2.95

13. Identify the graph of $xy = k$ if $x = -2$ when $y = -4$.

   A.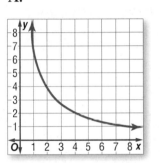
   C.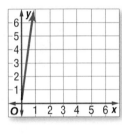
   B.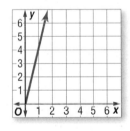
   D.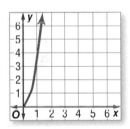

Spiral Review

14. **TRAVEL** A train traveled 203 miles in $1\frac{1}{2}$ hours. At this rate, how far will the train travel after 5 hours? Assuming that the distance traveled varies directly with the time traveled, write and solve an equation to represent the situation. (Lesson 5-3C)

15. **SKATING** Use the graph at the right to compare the number of people who skate in California to the number of people who skate in Texas. (Lesson 5-3A)

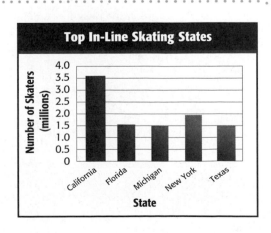

Problem Solving in Engineering

START OFF ON THE RIGHT FOOT

Did you know that more than 700 pounds of force are exerted on a 140-pound long-jumper during the landing? **Biomechanical engineers** understand how forces travel through the shoe to an athlete's foot and how the shoes can help reduce the impact of those forces on the legs. If you are curious about how engineering can be applied to the human body, a career in biomechanical engineering might be a great fit for you.

Choose a Major
Are you interested in a career as a biomechanical engineer? Take some of the following courses in high school.

- Biology
- Calculus
- Physics
- Trigonometry

Get Connected glencoe.com

NGSSS

MA.7.A.1.4 Graph proportional relationships and identify the unit rate as the slope of the related linear function.

Real-World Math

Use the information in the graph to solve each problem.

1. Find the constant rate of change for the data shown in the graph. Interpret its meaning.

2. Is there a proportional relationship between the weight of an athlete and the forces that are generated from running? Explain your reasoning.

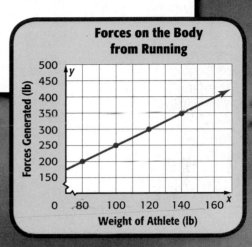

Forces on the Body from Running

🖥 **Get Connected** glencoe.com

• STUDY *TO GO*
• Vocabulary Review
• Multilingual eGlossary

FOLDABLES®
Study Organizer

Be sure the following Key Concepts are noted in your Foldable.

Key Concepts

Rates and Functions (Lesson 5-1)
• A function is a relationship that assigns exactly one *output* value for each *input* value.

Slope (Lesson 5-2)
• A constant rate of change is a rate that describes how one quantity changes in relation to another.
• The slope of a graph is the constant rate of change.

Variation (Lesson 5-3)
• Direct variation
  $\frac{y}{x}$ is a constant.

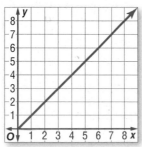

• Inverse variation xy is a constant.

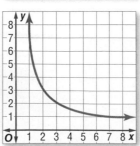

Key Vocabulary

constant of variation (p. 273)

constant rate of change (p. 260)

direct variation (p. 273)

domain (p. 248)

function (p. 248)

function rule (p. 248)

function table (p. 248)

inverse variation (p. 280)

linear function (p. 254)

range (p. 248)

rate of change (p. 260)

slope (p. 264)

Vocabulary Check

Choose the term from the list above that best matches each phrase.

1. the rate of change between any two points on a line

2. the set of input values for a function

3. a relationship when corresponding x and y values have a constant product

4. the constant ratio

5. a relation in which each element of the input is paired with exactly one element of the output according to a specified rule

6. the set of output values for a function

7. a table used to organize the input numbers, output numbers, and the function rule

8. two variable quantities have a constant ratio

9. the rate of change in a linear relationship

10. the operation performed on the input of a function

11. rate that describes how one quantity changes in relation to another

12. graph of a straight line

Multi-Part Lesson Review

5-1 Rates and Functions

Equations and Functions (pp. 248–252)

MA.7.A.1.4

Copy and complete each function table. Then identify the domain and range.

13. $y = 2x$

x	2x	y
1	2×1	2
2	2×2	
3	2×3	
4		

14. $y = 11x$

x	11x	y
0	11×0	0
1	11×1	
2		
3		

EXAMPLE 1 **GASOLINE** Curtis can drive his car 28 miles for every gallon of gasoline. Make a function table to show how many miles he can drive on 1, 2, 3, and 4 gallons. Then identify the domain and range.

Input	Function Rule	Output
Gallons of Gasoline	Multiply by 28	Total Miles
1	28×1	28
2	28×2	56
3	28×3	84
4	28×4	112

The domain is {1, 2, 3, 4} and the range is {28, 56, 84, 112}.

Functions and Graphs (pp. 253–257)

MA.7.A.1.4

Graph the function represented by the table.

15.

Texting	
Time (min)	Total Words
0	0
1	20
2	40
3	60

Graph each equation.

16. $y = 4x - 2$ **17.** $y = x + 6$

18. RUNNING Damon runs the 100-meter dash at an average speed of 8 meters per second. The equation $d = 8t$ describes the distance d that Damon can run in t seconds at this speed. Represent the function by a graph.

EXAMPLE 2 Graph $y = 3x + 2$.

Select any four values for the input x. We chose 0, 1, 2, and 3. Substitute these values for x to find the output y.

x	3x + 2	(x, y)
0	$3(0) + 2$	(0, 2)
1	$3(1) + 2$	(1, 5)
2	$3(2) + 2$	(2, 8)
3	$3(3) + 2$	(3, 11)

Graph the ordered pairs.

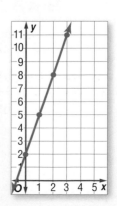

5-2 Slope

Constant Rate of Change (pp. 260–263)

Find the constant rate of change for each table.

19.

Time (min)	Laps Swam
0	0
1	2
2	4
3	6

20.

Package	Cookies
5	60
10	120
15	180
20	240

 MA.7.A.1.4

EXAMPLE 3 **WORK** The table shows the amount of money Hallie made doing yard work. Find the constant rate of change in dollars per hour.

Work	
Hours	**Money ($)**
2	12
4	24
6	36
8	48

+2 between hours, +12 between money amounts

Find the unit rate.

$$\frac{\text{change in money}}{\text{change in hours}} = \frac{12 \text{ dollars}}{2 \text{ hours}}$$

$$= \frac{6 \text{ dollars}}{1 \text{ hour}} .$$

So, the number of dollars earned increases by $6 for every hour worked.

Slope (pp. 264–267)

21. CONCRETE The table shows the amount y of concrete that a construction company can pour per x minutes. Graph the data. Then find the slope of the line. Explain what the slope means.

Time (min)	15	30	45	60
Yards	3	6	9	12

22. RAIN Yesterday 2 inches of rain fell in 1 hour. It kept raining at the same rate for several hours. Draw a graph of inches of rain versus time. Find the value of the slope and interpret it in words.

 MA.7.A.1.4

EXAMPLE 4 **READING** The graph shows the relationship between the minutes spent reading x and the average amount of words read y. Find the slope of the line. Explain what the slope represents.

$$\text{slope} = \frac{\text{rise}}{\text{run}}$$

$$= \frac{65}{1}$$

So, for every minute of reading, there are 65 words read.

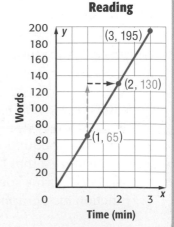

PSI: Use a Graph (pp. 270–271)

MA.7.A.1.5

STATUES For Exercises 23 and 24, use the graph that shows the heights of four freestanding statues in the world.

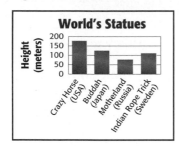

World's Statues

23. Which statue is the tallest?

24. Compare the heights of the Motherland statue and the Crazy Horse statue.

EXAMPLE 5 In the graph below, which place was favored by most students?

Favorite Vacation Places

The beach was favored by 12 students, which was the greatest number.

Direct Variation (pp. 273–278)

MA.7.A.1.5

Determine whether the linear function is a direct variation. If so, state the constant of variation.

25.

Tickets Available	80	60	40	20
Tickets Sold	40	30	20	10

26.

Distance (mi)	1,000	2,000	3,000	4,000
Time (h)	2	4	6	8

EXAMPLE 6 Determine whether the linear function is a direct variation. If so, state the constant of variation.

Number of Iron Weights	1	2	3	4	5
Total Weight (lb)	5	10	15	20	25

Since the ratio $\dfrac{\text{total weight}}{\text{number of weights}}$ are all $\dfrac{5}{1}$, the function is a direct variation.

Inverse Variation (pp. 280–283)

MA.7.A.1.5

27. **DRIVING** The time it takes to complete a driving course varies inversely with the speed at which you drive. A driver can run the course in 2 hours at an average rate of 55 miles per hour. How long will it take to drive the same course at 50 miles per hour?

EXAMPLE 7 **READING** The time it takes to read a book varies inversely with the speed at which you are reading. Suppose it took 6 days to read a book at a rate of 35 pages per day. How long will it take to read the same book at 40 pages per day?

$$xy = k \qquad\qquad y = \frac{k}{x}$$

$$(6) \cdot (35) = k \qquad\qquad y = \frac{210}{40}$$

$$210 = k \qquad\qquad y = 5\frac{1}{4} \text{ days}$$

1. Complete the function table for $y = 4x$ and identify the domain and range.

x	4x	y
5		
6		
7		
8		

2. **NAME TAGS** Charmaine can make 32 name tags per hour. Make a function table that shows the number of name tags she can make in 3, 4, 5, and 6 hours.

Graph each equation.

3. $y = x + 5$

4. $y = 3x + 2$

5. $y = -2x + 3$

6. **FINANCIAL LITERACY** Clara earns $9 per hour mowing lawns. Make a function table and graph that show her total earnings for 2, 4, 6, and 8 hours.

7. **NGSSS PRACTICE** During a bike-a-thon, Shalonda cycled at a constant rate. The table shows the distance she covered in half-hour intervals.

Time (h)	Distance (mi)
$\frac{1}{2}$	6
1	12
$1\frac{1}{2}$	18
2	24

Which of the following equations represents the distance d Shalonda covered after h hours?

A. $d = 6 + h$ C. $d = 12 + h$

B. $d = 6h$ D. $d = 12h$

8. Find the rate of change in degrees per hour.

Time (h)	0	1	2
Temperature (°C)	50	52	54

9. **MONEY** The table shows the amount of money José saved over a period of time. Graph the data. Then find the slope of the line. Explain what the slope represents.

Amount ($)	30	60	90
Weeks	1	2	3

10. **TECHNOLOGY** The time it takes to burn information onto a CD varies directly with the amount of information. If 2.5 megabytes of information take 10 seconds to burn, how long does it take to burn 10 megabytes of information?

11. **RACING** In the formula $d = rt$, the time t varies inversely with the rate r. A race car traveling 125 miles per hour completed one lap around a race track in 1.2 minutes. How fast was the car traveling if it completed the next lap in 0.8 minute?

12. **EXTENDED RESPONSE** The function $m = 6h$ represents how much money Martha makes for every hour she works.

Part A What is her hourly rate, or her unit rate, of pay?

Part B Create an input/output table of her earnings from 5 to 10 hours.

Part C Graph the function.

Part D How is the rate of change related to the graph?

Gridded Response: Decimals

When a gridded-response answer is a decimal, write the decimal point in an answer box at the top of the grid. Then fill in the decimal point bubble.

 NGSSS **PRACTICE EXAMPLE**

The graph represents a cyclist's speed in miles per hour. What is the slope of the line?

$$\text{slope} = \frac{57 - 28.5}{4 - 2} \qquad \longleftarrow \qquad \frac{\text{change in } y}{\text{change in } x}$$

$$= \frac{28.5}{2} \text{ or } 14.25 \qquad \text{The slope is } 14.25.$$

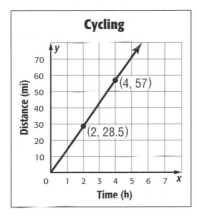

Cycling

Correct

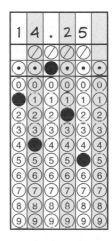

NOT Correct

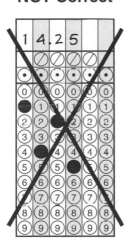

 ## Work on It

The table below shows the costs of dog treats.

Number of Treats	3	6	9
Cost ($)	2.64	5.28	7.92

What is the slope of the line that represents the cost per treat? Fill in your answer on a grid like the one shown above.

Test Hint

A decimal like 0.75 could be correctly gridded as 0.75 or as .75.

Read each question. Then fill in the correct answer on the answer document provided by your teacher or on a sheet of paper.

1. Lisa's monthly charge for phone calls c can be found using the following equation.

$$c = 15 + 1.5h$$

In the equation, h represents the number of hours of usage during a month. What is the total charge for a month in which Lisa made 10 hours of phone calls?

A. $25.00

B. $27.50

C. $30.00

D. $32.00

2. The graph of the line $y = 2x + 2$ is shown below. Which table of ordered pairs contains only points on this line?

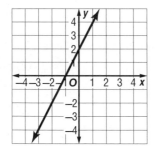

F.

x	−2	1	2
y	2	4	6

G.

x	−2	1	2
y	−2	4	6

H.

x	−2	1	2
y	−2	−4	−6

I.

x	−2	1	2
y	−2	−4	6

3. Which statement is true about the slope of line LN?

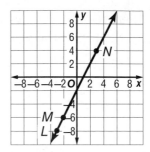

A. The slope is negative.

B. The slope between point L and point M is greater than the slope between point M and point N.

C. The slope is the same between any two points.

D. The slope between point N and M is greater than the slope between point M and L.

4. ✎ **GRIDDED RESPONSE** John is training for a marathon and has 50 days to train. He plans to run for 3 hours a day at an average speed of 4.5 miles per hour. What is the total number of miles he will run over the next 50 days?

5. ✎ **GRIDDED RESPONSE** Elia is in an airplane on her way to the Caribbean. She is currently at 7,000 feet. She looks down 150 feet and sees a cloud. How high in feet is the cloud off of the ground?

6. THINK SOLVE EXPLAIN **SHORT RESPONSE** A dinner is served at an athletic booster fundraiser. The constant relationship between the number of people served at dinner n and the number of ounces of beef used b is shown in the table below. How many people were served if 760 ounces of beef were used?

n	5	20	150	?
b	20	80	600	760

7. Line *AB* represents a walking ramp.

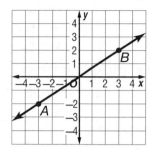

What is the slope of the ramp?

F. 1

G. $\frac{3}{4}$

H. $\frac{2}{3}$

I. $\frac{1}{3}$

8. Which expression represents the least value?

A. $430 \div \frac{1}{4}$

B. $430 + \frac{1}{4}$

C. $430 \times \frac{1}{4}$

D. $430 - \frac{1}{4}$

9. Garrett plotted points to show the locations of out-of-bounds markers for a gym class game. Which point on the grid best represents marker *L*?

F. $(-4, -6)$

G. $(-6, -4)$

H. $(4, -6)$

I. $(6, -4)$

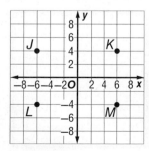

10. A family went on a vacation and used 5.4 gallons of gasoline to travel 150 miles. How many total gallons of gasoline will they need to travel 200 more miles?

A. 12.6 gallons

B. 13.1 gallons

C. 14.3 gallons

D. 16.2 gallons

11. ✎ **GRIDDED RESPONSE** Heidi went to a parade and came back with 250 pieces of candy. Heidi then gave 150 pieces of candy to her brothers who could not go to the parade. Heidi's friend then gave her 25 pieces of candy. How many pieces of candy does Heidi now have?

12. THINK SOLVE EXPLAIN **SHORT RESPONSE** Mrs. Smith has two pies for her fall feast. She has one apple pie and one pumpkin pie. After everyone got dessert, $\frac{2}{3}$ of the apple pie was eaten and $\frac{4}{5}$ of the pumpkin pie was eaten. How much total pie does Mrs. Smith have left?

13. THINK SOLVE EXPLAIN **EXTENDED RESPONSE** Use the graph below to answer the following questions.

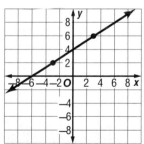

Part A What is the slope of the line?

Part B Describe the line.

NEED EXTRA HELP?

If You Missed Question...	1	2	3	4	5	6	7	8	9	10	11	12	13
Go to Lesson...	5-1B	5-1C	5-2C	5-2B	1-2B	5-1B	5-2C	2-3B	1-1C	4-1D	1-2B	2-2C	5-2C
For help with NGSSS...	A.1.4	A.1.4	A.1.4	A.1.4	A.3.1	A.1.4	A.1.4	A.3.2	G.4.3	A.1.1	A.3.1	A.3.2	A.1.4

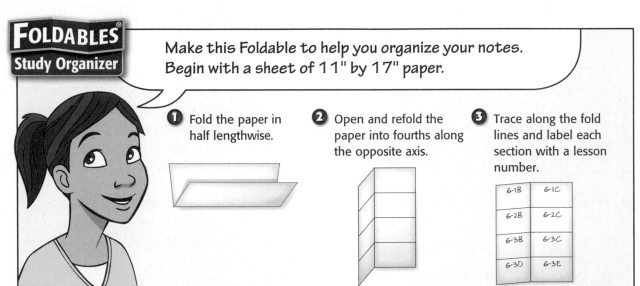

Percents

The ⭐ BIG Idea

Understand and use proportionality, including percents.

FOLDABLES® Study Organizer

Make this Foldable to help you organize your notes. Begin with a sheet of 11" by 17" paper.

1 Fold the paper in half lengthwise.

2 Open and refold the paper into fourths along the opposite axis.

3 Trace along the fold lines and label each section with a lesson number.

6-1B	6-1C
6-2B	6-2C
6-3B	6-3C
6-3D	6-3E

Review Vocabulary

percent (Prior Grade) *por ciento* a ratio that compares a number to 100

18 out of 100 is 18%

Key Vocabulary

	English	Español
p. 312	percent proportion	proporción porcentual
p. 317	percent equation	ecuación porcentual
p. 326	percent of change	porcentaje de cambio
p. 339	simple interest	interés simple

Multilingual eGlossary glencoe.com

Get Connected glencoe.com

- Study using the **eBook**
- Explore with **Get Animated**
- Get extra help from **Personal Tutor**
- Use **virtual manipulatives** for additional help
- Take a **Self-Check Quiz**

Marisol, Blake, and Hiroshi in
Amusement Park Prices

Hey guys, sorry I'm late. What'd I miss?

Hi Marisol, we're planning the class trip.

I can't wait!

Hiroshi and I have narrowed it down to three choices: *Pirate Bay*, *Funtopia*, or *Zoomland*.

Oh, those are GREAT choices. Have you gotten any group discounts?

Discounts? Um... no.

Well, let's take a look...

There. Got it!

1. Pirate Bay $35.95
   20% discount
2. Funtopia $29.75
   15% discount
3. Zoomland $38.49
   25% discount

I'll just write this on the board so we can figure out the total cost for each park.

Now it's obvious which one is the cheapest.

OBVIOUS?

Oh good grief! What would you guys do without me? Sit down, I'll explain.

Your Turn!
You will solve this problem in Chapter 6.

Are You Ready for Chapter 6?

You have two options for checking prerequisite skills for this chapter.

Text Option Take the Quick Check below. Refer to the Quick Review for help.

QUICK Check

Multiply. (Prior Grade)

1. $300 \times 0.02 \times 8$ 2. $85 \times 0.25 \times 3$
3. $560 \times 0.6 \times 4.5$ 4. $154 \times 0.12 \times 5$

5. **MONEY** If Nicole saves $0.05 every day, how much money will she have in 3 years? (Prior Grade)

Write each percent as a decimal.
(Prior Grade)

6. 40%   7. 17%   8. 110%
9. 157%   10. 3.25%   11. 8.5%

12. **FOOD** Approximately 92% of a watermelon is water. What decimal represents this amount?

13. **TAX** The sales tax in Jackson County, Florida, is 7.5%. Write this percent as a decimal.

Write each decimal as a percent.
(Prior Grade)

14. 0.7   15. 0.08   16. 0.95
17. 5.8   18. 0.675   19. 0.725

20. **SPORTS** A tennis player won 0.805 of the matches she played. What percent of the matches did she lose?

QUICK Review

EXAMPLE 1

Evaluate $240 \times 0.03 \times 5$.

$240 \times 0.03 \times 5$
$= 7.2 \times 5$ Multiply 240 by 0.03.
$= 36$ Simplify.

EXAMPLE 2

Write 9.8% as a decimal.

$9.8\% = 0.098$ Move the decimal point two places to the left and remove the percent symbol.

EXAMPLE 3

Write 0.35 as a percent.

$0.35 = 35\%$ Move the decimal point two places to the right and add the percent symbol.

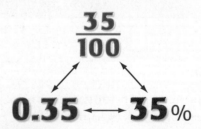

EXAMPLE 4

Write 0.2 as a percent.
$0.20 = 20\%$ Move the decimal point two places to the right and add the percent symbol.

Online Option 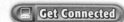 **Get Connected** Take the Online Readiness Quiz at **glencoe.com**.

Studying Math

Draw a Picture

Drawing a picture can help you better understand numbers in a word problem. For example, a *number map* can show how numbers are related to each other. Start by placing a number in the center of the map.

Have you heard the expression *a picture is worth a thousand words?*

Below is a number map that shows various meanings of the decimal 0.5. Notice that you can add both mathematical meanings and everyday meanings to the number map.

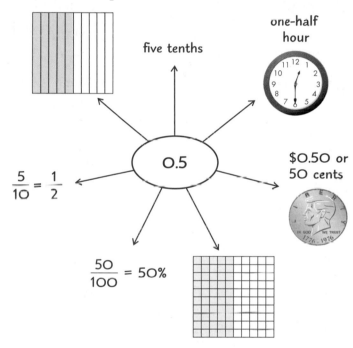

five tenths

one-half hour

$\dfrac{5}{10} = \dfrac{1}{2}$

0.5

$0.50 or 50 cents

$\dfrac{50}{100} = 50\%$

Practice

Make a number map for each number. (*Hint*: For whole numbers, think of factors, prime numbers, divisibility, place value, and so on.)

1. 0.75
2. 0.1
3. 0.01
4. 1.25
5. 2.5
6. 25
7. 45
8. 60
9. 100

10. Refer to Exercise 1. Explain how each mathematical or everyday meaning on the number map relates to the decimal 0.75.

NGSSS
LA.7.1.6.5 The student will relate new vocabulary to familiar words.

6-1 Percents

Explore Percent Diagrams

Main Idea
Use percent diagrams to solve problems.

NGSSS

MA.7.A.1.2 Solve percent problems, including problems involving discounts, simple interest, taxes, tips and percents of increase or decrease.

 Get Connected
glencoe.com

MUSIC There are 500 seventh-grade students at Heritage Middle School. Sixty percent of them play a musical instrument. How many seventh-grade students play a musical instrument?

ACTIVITY

What do you need to find? how many seventh-grade students play a musical instrument

STEP 1 Make a bar diagram that represents 100%. Make another bar of equal length to represent 500 students.

percent		100%

students		500

STEP 2 Divide each bar into ten equal parts.

percent	10%	10%	10%	10%	10%	10%	10%	10%	10%	10%	100%

students	50	50	50	50	50	50	50	50	50	50	500

STEP 3 Shade 60% on the percent bar and an equal amount on the student bar.

|---------- 60% ----------|

percent	10%	10%	10%	10%	10%	10%	10%	10%	10%	10%	100%

students	50	50	50	50	50	50	50	50	50	50	500

|----------300----------|

Since 60% corresponds to the number 300, there are 300 seventh-grade students who play a musical instrument.

Analyze the Results

1. How many seventh-grade students do *not* play a musical instrument?

2. Suppose there had been 750 seventh-grade students.

   a. What would you do differently in Step 2?

   b. What is 60% of 750?

Practice and Apply

3. **SCHOOL SPORTS** The seventh-grade class at Fort Couch Middle School had a goal of selling 300 tickets to the annual student-teacher basketball game. The eighth-grade class had a goal of selling 400 tickets.

   a. By the end of the first week, the eighth-grade students sold 30% of their goal. Draw a bar diagram to represent this situation.

   b. How many tickets had the eighth grade sold?

   c. The seventh grade sold 40% of their goal. How many tickets do the students still need to sell? Use a bar diagram to justify your solution.

4. **ALLOWANCES** The graph shows the results of a survey asking 500 teens about their allowances.

   a. Draw a bar diagram to represent how many of the teens received between $10 and $20 as a weekly allowance. (*Hint*: Since $75\% = \frac{3}{4}$, divide the bar diagram into fourths.)

   b. How many teens did *not* receive between $10 and $20? Justify your solution.

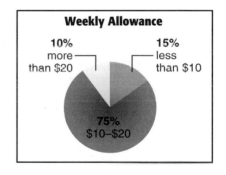

Weekly Allowance

10% more than $20

15% less than $10

75% $10–$20

5. **SOCIAL STUDIES** Reggie has memorized 60% of the 50 state capitals for a social studies test.

   a. Draw a bar diagram to represent how many state capitals Reggie has memorized.

   b. How many more capitals does he need to memorize before the test?

Write MATH

For Exercises 6 and 7, write a real-world problem for each percent diagram. Then solve your problem.

6.

10%	10%	10%	10%	10%	10%	10%	10%	10%	10%	100%

25	25	25	25	25	25	25	25	25	25	250

7.

25%	25%	25%	25%	100%

15	15	15	15	60

6-1 Percents

Main Idea

Find the percent of a number.

NGSSS

 MA.7.A.1.2 Solve percent problems, including problems involving discounts, simple interest, taxes, tips and percents of increase or decrease. *Also addresses MA.7.A.3.2, MA.7.A.5.1.*

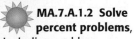 **Get Connected**
glencoe.com

Percent of a Number

PETS Some students are collecting money for a local pet shelter. The model shows that they have raised 60% of their $2,000 goal or $1,200.

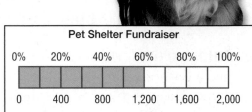

Pet Shelter Fundraiser

| 0% | 20% | 40% | 60% | 80% | 100% |

| 0 | 400 | 800 | 1,200 | 1,600 | 2,000 |

1. Sketch the model and label using decimals instead of percents.

2. Sketch the model using fractions instead of percents.

3. Use these models to write two multiplication sentences that are equivalent to 60% of 2,000 = 1,200.

To find the percent of a number such as 60% of 2,000, you can use one of the following methods.

- Write the percent as a fraction and then multiply, or

- Write the percent as a decimal and then multiply.

 EXAMPLE   **Find the Percent of a Number**

① Find 5% of 300.

> **Method 1**   **Write the percent as a fraction.**
>
> $5\% = \dfrac{5}{100}$ or $\dfrac{1}{20}$
>
> $\dfrac{1}{20}$ of 300 = $\dfrac{1}{20} \times 300$ or 15

> **Method 2**   **Write the percent as a decimal.**
>
> $5\% = \dfrac{5}{100}$ or 0.05
>
> 0.05 of 300 = 0.05 × 300 or 15

So, 5% of 300 is 15.

 CHOOSE Your Method

Find the percent of each number.

a. 40% of 70   **b.** 15% of 100   **c.** 55% of 160

EXAMPLE Use Percents Greater Than 100%

Study Tip

Check for Reasonableness 120% is a little more than 100%. So, the answer should be a little more than 100% of 75 or a little more than 75.

2 Find 120% of 75.

Method 1   Write the percent as a fraction.

$120\% = \dfrac{120}{100}$ or $\dfrac{6}{5}$

$\dfrac{6}{5}$ of $75 = \dfrac{6}{5} \times 75$

$\qquad\qquad = \dfrac{6}{5} \times \dfrac{75}{1}$ or 90

Method 2   Write the percent as a decimal.

$120\% = \dfrac{120}{100}$ or 1.2

1.2 of $75 = 1.2 \times 75$ or 90

So, 120% of 75 is 90.   Use a model to check the answer.

 CHOOSE Your Method

Find each number.

d. 150% of 20

e. 160% of 35

Real-World EXAMPLE

3 **SURVEYS** Refer to the graph. If 275 students took the survey, how many can be expected to have 3 televisions each in their houses?

To find 23% of 275, write the percent as a decimal. Then multiply.

23% of $275 = 23\% \times 275$

$\qquad\qquad\quad = 0.23 \times 275$

$\qquad\qquad\quad = 63.25$

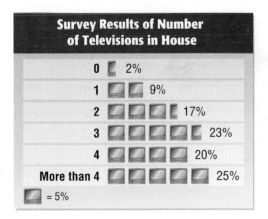

Survey Results of Number of Televisions in House

0	2%
1	9%
2	17%
3	23%
4	20%
More than 4	25%

= 5%

QUICK Review

Multiply Decimals

```
    275   ← 0 decimal places
  × 0.23  ← 2 decimal places
    825
 + 5500
  63.25   ← 2 decimal places
```

So, about 63 students can be expected to have 3 televisions each in their houses.

 CHECK Your Progress

f. **SURVEYS** Refer to the graph above. Suppose 455 students took the survey. How many can be expected to have more than 4 televisions each in their houses?

CHECK Your Understanding

Examples 1 and 2
(pp. 300–301)

Find each number. Round to the nearest tenth if necessary.

1. 8% of 50

2. 95% of 40

3. 42% of 263

4. 110% of 70

5. 115% of 20

6. 130% of 78

Example 3
(p. 301)

7. TAXES Mackenzie wants to buy a new backpack that costs $50. If the tax rate is 6.5%, how much tax will she pay when she buys the backpack?

Practice and Problem Solving

= **Step-by-Step Solutions** begin on page R14.
Extra Practice is on page EP14.

Examples 1 and 2
(pp. 300–301)

Find each number. Round to the nearest tenth if necessary.

8. 65% of 186

9. 45% of $432

10. 23% of $640

11. 54% of 85

12. 12% of $230

13. 98% of 15

14. 130% of 20

 175% of 10

16. 150% of 128

17. 250% of 25

18. 108% of $50

19. 116% of $250

20. 32% of 4

21. 5.4% of 65

22. 23.5% of 128

23. 75.2% of 130

24. 67.5% of 76

25. 18.5% of 500

Example 3
(p. 301)

26. BASEBALL Tomás got on base 60% of the times he was up to bat. If he was up to bat 5 times, how many times did he get on base?

27. TELEVISION In a recent year, 17.7% of households watched the finals of a popular reality series. There are 110.2 million households in the United States. How many households watched the finals?

Find each number. Round to the nearest hundredth if necessary.

28. $\frac{4}{5}$% of 500

29. $5\frac{1}{2}$% of 60

30. $20\frac{1}{4}$% of 3

31. 1,000% of 99

32. 100% of 79

33. 520% of 100

34. 0.15% of 250

35. 0.3% of 80

36. 0.28% of 50

37. COMMISSION In addition to her salary, Ms. Lopez earns a 3% *commission*, or fee paid based on a percent of her sales, on every vacation package that she sells. One day, she sold the three vacation packages shown. What was her total commission?

Package #1	$2,375
Package #2	$3,950
Package #3	$1,725

38. INTERNET A family pays $19 each month for Internet access. Next month, the cost will increase by 5%. After this increase, what will be the cost for the Internet access?

39. BUSINESS A store sells a certain brand of lawn mower for $275. Next year, the cost of the lawn mower will increase by 8%. What will be the cost of the lawn mower next year?

40. RADIO The graph below shows the results of a poll of 2,632 listeners. Round answers to the nearest whole number.

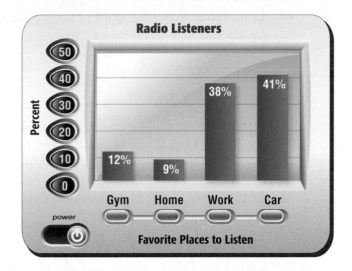

Radio Listeners

Favorite Places to Listen

a. How many people listen to the radio during work?

b. How many people like to listen to the radio while they are at the gym?

c. Determine how many more people listen to the radio in the car than at home.

Use mental math to estimate each percent.

41. 53% of 60   **42.** 24% of 48   **43.** 75% of 19

44. FRUIT Two hundred fifty people were surveyed about their favorite fruit.

Favorite Fruit	
Berries	44%
Peaches	32%
Cherries	24%

a. Of those surveyed, how many people prefer peaches?

b. Which type of fruit did more than 100 people prefer?

c. Of those surveyed, how many people did *not* prefer cherries? Explain how you arrived at the answer.

45 SCHOOL Suppose there are 20 questions on a multiple-choice test. If 25% of the answers are choice B, how many of the answers are *not* choice B?

46. GRAPHIC NOVEL Refer to the graphic novel frame below. Find the dollar amount of the group discount each student would receive at each park.

Marisol, Blake, and I want to get the best deal for our class.

1. Pirate Bay $35.95 20% discount
2. Funtopia $29.75 15% discount
3. Zoomland $38.49 25% discount

First, let's figure out what each student would be able to save on their ticket at each park.

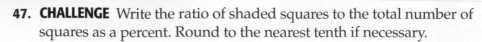

47. CHALLENGE Write the ratio of shaded squares to the total number of squares as a percent. Round to the nearest tenth if necessary.

a.   b.   c.   d.

48. CHALLENGE Suppose you add 10% of a number to the number, and then you subtract 10% of the total. Is the result *greater than*, *less than*, or *equal to* the original number? Explain your reasoning.

49. REASONING When is it easiest to find the percent of a number using a fraction? using a decimal?

50. Write MATH Give two examples of real-world situations in which you would find the percent of a number.

NGSSS Practice   MA.7.A.1.2

51. Marcos earned $300 mowing lawns this month. He plans to spend 18% repairing his lawn equipment, put 20% in his savings account, and use 35% for summer camp fees. He can spend the rest. How much of the $300 will Marcos have left to spend?

 A. $27.00   C. $81.00

 B. $55.00   D. $100.00

52. **GRIDDED RESPONSE** Tanner has 200 baseball cards. Of those, 42% are in mint condition. How many of the cards are in mint condition?

53. Suppose that y varies inversely as x and $y = 10$ when $x = 72$. Find x when $y = 24$. (Lesson 5-3E)

54. There are 16 ounces in 1 pound. How many ounces are in 2.8 pounds? (Lesson 5-3C)

55. JOGGING The table shows the number of miles Tonya jogged each week for the past several weeks. Find the total number of miles she jogged. (Lesson 2-2D)

56. BUSINESS A company reported a net loss of $2,000,000 during the first half of the year. In the second half of the year it reported a profit of $5,000,000. Write an addition problem to find the net profit or loss for the entire year. (Lesson 1-2B)

Week	Miles
1	$7\frac{1}{6}$
2	$8\frac{3}{4}$
3	10
4	$12\frac{1}{4}$
5	$6\frac{2}{3}$

Main Idea

Estimate percents by using fractions and decimals.

NGSSS

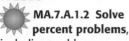

MA.7.A.1.2 Solve percent problems, including problems involving discounts, simple interest, taxes, tips and percents of increase or decrease. *Also addresses MA.7.A.3.2.*

Get Connected
glencoe.com

Percent and Estimation

MUSIC Refer to the graph below.

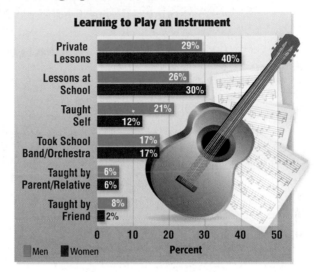

Learning to Play an Instrument

	Men	Women
Private Lessons	29%	40%
Lessons at School	26%	30%
Taught Self	21%	12%
Took School Band/Orchestra	17%	17%
Taught by Parent/Relative	6%	6%
Taught by Friend	8%	2%

0   10   20   30   40   50   **Percent**

1. What fraction of women took lessons at school? If 200 women were surveyed, how many of them took lessons at school?

2. Use a fraction to estimate the number of men who took lessons at school. Assume 200 men were surveyed.

Sometimes an exact answer is not needed when using percents. One way to estimate the percent of a number is to use a fraction.

QUICK Review

Multiplying Fractions

Remember to divide out common factors.

$$\frac{3}{5} \times 520 = \frac{3}{\cancel{5}} \times \frac{\cancel{520}^{104}}{1}$$

$$= \frac{3}{1} \times \frac{104}{1}$$

$$= 312$$

Real-World EXAMPLE

1 **SPORTS** In a recent year, quarterback Carson Palmer completed 62% of his passes. He threw 520 passes. About how many did he complete?

62% of $520 \approx 60\%$ of 520 $62\% \approx 60\%$

$\approx \frac{3}{5} \cdot 520$ $60\% = \frac{6}{10}$ or $\frac{3}{5}$

≈ 312 Multiply.

So, Carson Palmer completed about 312 out of 520 passes.

 CHECK Your Progress

a. REPTILES Box turtles have been known to live for 120 years. American alligators have been known to live 42% as long as box turtles. About how long can an American alligator live?

Another method for estimating the percent of a number is first to find 10% of the number and then multiply. For example, 70% = 7 · 10%. So, 70% equals 7 times 10% of the number.

Real-World EXAMPLE

2) **MONEY** Marita and four of her friends ordered a pizza that cost $14.72. She is responsible for 20% of the bill. About how much money will she need to pay?

Method 1   Use a fraction to estimate.

20% is $\frac{2}{10}$ or $\frac{1}{5}$.

20% of $14.72 ≈ $\frac{1}{5}$ · $15.00   20% = $\frac{1}{5}$ and round $14.72 to $15.00.

≈ $3.00   Multiply.

Method 2   Use 10% of a number to estimate.

Step 1   Find 10% of $15.00.

10% of $15.00 = 0.1 · $15.00   To multiply by 10%, move the
                    = $1.50   decimal point one place to the left.

Step 2   Multiply.

20% of $15.00 is 2 times 10% of $15.00.

2 · $1.50 = $3.00

So, Marita should pay about $3.00.

CHOOSE Your Method

b. MONEY Dante plans to put 80% of his paycheck into a savings account. His paycheck this week was $295. About how much money will he put into his savings account?

You can also estimate percents of numbers when the percent is greater than 100 or less than 1.

Study Tip

Check for Reasonableness When estimating the percent of a number and the percent is greater than 100, the estimate will always be greater than the number.

EXAMPLES   Percents Greater Than 100 or Less Than 1

3) Estimate 122% of 50.

122% is about 120%.

120% of 50 = (100% of 50) + (20% of 50)   120% = 100% + 20%

= (1 · 50) + $\left(\frac{1}{5} · 50\right)$ 100% = 1 and 20% = $\frac{1}{5}$

= 50 + 10 or 60   Simplify.

So, 122% of 50 is about 60.

④ Estimate $\frac{1}{4}$% of 589.

$\frac{1}{4}$% is one fourth of 1%. 589 is about 600.

1% of 600 = 0.01 · 600   Write 1% as 0.01.

$\qquad\qquad$ = 6 $\qquad$ To multiply by 1%, move the decimal point two places to the left.

One fourth of 6 is $\frac{1}{4}$ · 6 or 1.5. So, $\frac{1}{4}$% of 589 is about 1.5.

 CHECK Your Progress

Estimate.

c. 174% of 200 $\qquad$ **d.** 298% of 45 $\qquad$ **e.** 0.25% of 789

Real-World Link · · · · ·
The American Camp Association (ACA) reports that 10 million children attend camp annually.

Real-World EXAMPLE

⑤ **CELL PHONES** In a recent year, there were about 200 million people in the U.S. with cell phones. Of those, about 0.5% used their phone as an MP3 player. Estimate the number of people who used their phone as an MP3 player.

0.5% is half of 1%.

1% of 200 million = 0.01 · 200,000,000

$\qquad\qquad\qquad$ = 2,000,000

So, 0.5% of 200,000,000 is about $\frac{1}{2}$ of 2,000,000 or 1,000,000.

About 1,000,000 people used their phone as an MP3 player.

 CHECK Your Progress

f. ATTENDANCE Last year, 639 students attended a summer camp. Of those who attended this year, 0.9% also attended last year. About how many students attended the camp two years in a row?

 **CHECK Your Understanding**

Examples 1–4
(pp. 305–307)

Estimate.

1. 52% of 10 $\qquad$ **2.** 7% of 20 $\qquad$ **3.** 38% of 62

4. 79% of 489 $\qquad$ **5.** 151% of 70 $\qquad$ **6.** $\frac{1}{2}$% of 82

7. BIRTHDAYS Of the 78 teenagers at a youth camp, 63% have birthdays in the spring. About how many have birthdays in the spring?

Example 5
(p. 307)

8. GEOGRAPHY About 0.8% of the land in Maine is federally owned. If Maine is 19,847,680 acres, about how many acres are federally owned?

Practice and Problem Solving

= **Step-by-Step Solutions** begin on page R14.
Extra Practice is on page EP14.

Examples 1 and 3
(pp. 305–306)

Estimate.

9. 47% of 70   **10.** 39% of 120   **11** 21% of 90

12. 76% of 180   **13.** 57% of 29   **14.** 92% of 104

15. 24% of 48   **16.** 28% of 121   **17.** 88% of 207

18. 62% of 152   **19.** 65% of 152   **20.** 72% of 238

Example 2
(p. 306)

21. MONEY Carlie spent $42 at the hair salon. Her mother loaned her the money. Carlie will pay her mother 15% each week until she has repaid the loan. About how much will Carlie pay each week?

22. HEALTH You use 43 muscles to frown. When you smile, you use 32% of these same muscles. About how many muscles do you use when you smile?

Examples 3–5
(pp. 306–307)

Estimate.

23. 132% of 54   **24.** 224% of 320   **25.** $\frac{1}{2}$% of 412

26. $\frac{3}{4}$% of 168   **27.** 0.4% of 510   **28.** 0.9% of 74

29. GEOGRAPHY The United States has 12,383 miles of coastline. If 0.8% of the coastline is located in Georgia, about how many miles of coastline are in Georgia?

30. BIRDS During migration, 450,000 sandhill cranes stop to rest in Nebraska. About 0.6% of these cranes also stop to rest in Oregon. About how many sandhill cranes stop in Oregon during migration?

Estimate.

31. 67% of 8.7   **32.** 54% of 76.8   **33.** 32% of 89.9

34. 10.5% of 238   **35.** 22.2% of 114   **36.** 98.5% of 45

37 **ANALYZE GRAPHS** Use the graph shown.

   a. About how many hours does Avery spend doing her homework each day?

   b. About how many more hours does Avery spend sleeping than doing the activities in the "other" category? Justify your answer.

   c. What is the approximate number of minutes Avery spends each day on extracurricular activities?

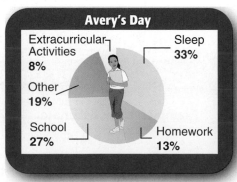

Avery's Day

Extracurricular Activities 8%
Sleep 33%
Other 19%
School 27%
Homework 13%

38. ANIMALS The average white rhinoceros gives birth to a single calf that weighs about 3.8% as much as its mother. If the mother rhinoceros weighs 3.75 tons, about how many pounds does its calf weigh?

39. FOOTBALL The table shows the number of passes attempted and the percent completed by the top five quarterbacks in the NFL for the 2007 season.

NFL Quarterbacks, 2007		
Player	**Passes Attempted**	**Percent Completed**
T. Brady	578	69
P. Manning	515	65
B. Roethlisberger	404	65
T. Romo	520	64
D. Garrard	325	64

  a. You can estimate the number of passes that Tom Brady completed by rounding 578 to 600 and 69% to 70%. Draw a bar diagram to represent this situation.

  b. Estimate the number of passes that Tom Brady completed.

  c. Is your estimate greater or less than the actual number of passes he completed? Explain.

  d. Without calculating, determine whether Ben Roethlisberger or Peyton Manning completed more passes. Justify your reasoning.

40. CLEANING A cleaning solution is made up of 0.9% chlorine bleach.

  a. About how many ounces of bleach are in 189 ounces of cleaning solution?

  b. About how many ounces of bleach would be found in 412 ounces of cleaning solution?

H.O.T. Problems

41 OPEN ENDED Write a real-world problem in which the answer can be found by estimating 12% of 50.

42. CHALLENGE Explain how you could find $\frac{3}{8}$% of $800.

43. FIND THE ERROR Jamar is estimating 1.5% of 210. Find his mistake and correct it.

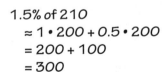

1.5% of 210
  ≈ 1 • 200 + 0.5 • 200
  = 200 + 100
  = 300

44. NUMBER SENSE Is an estimate for the percent of a number *always*, *sometimes*, or *never* greater than the actual percent of the number? Give an example or a counterexample to support your answer.

45. Write MATH Estimate 22% of 136 using two different methods. Justify the steps used in each method.

46. The graph shows the results of a survey of 510 students.

Pet Preferences

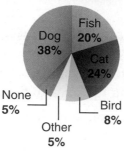

Which is the best estimate for the percent of students who prefer cats?

A. 75

B. 125

C. 225

D. 450

47. Mallory is buying bedroom furniture for $1,789.43. The dresser is 39.7% of the total cost. Which is the best estimate for the cost of the dresser?

F. $540   **H.** $720

G. $630   **I.** $810

48. Abey asked 50 students to vote for the school issue that was most important to them. The results are shown below.

Issue	Votes
Library use	11%
Time to change classes	12%
Use of electronics	17%
Lunch room rules	20%
Dress code	40%

About how many students chose "Time to change classes" as the most important issue?

A. 3   **C.** 9

B. 5   **D.** 12

Find each number. Round to the nearest tenth if necessary. (Lesson 6-1B)

49. 6% of 15

50. 72% of 90

51. 120% of 60

52. 35% of 55

53. Suppose that y varies inversely as x and $x = -16$ when $y = 4$. Find x when $y = 8$. (Lesson 5-3E)

54. ANIMALS An elephant herd can move 50 miles a day. At this rate, about how many miles can an elephant herd move each hour? (Lesson 4-1B)

Solve. Round to the nearest tenth if necessary. (Lesson 3-2B)

55. $40 = 0.8x$

56. $10r = 61$

57. $0.07t = 25$

58. $56 = 0.32n$

59. WALKING Cai walks $\frac{3}{4}$ mile to school and Lauren walks $\frac{2}{3}$ mile to school. How much farther does Cai walk than Lauren? (Lesson 2-2C)

6-2 Proportions and Equations

Explore Find Percents

Main Idea
Solve problems involving percents.

NGSSS

MA.7.A.1.2 Solve percent problems, including problems involving discounts, simple interest, taxes, tips and percents of increase or decrease.

Get Connected
glencoe.com

TICKETS The eighth grade had 300 tickets to sell to the school play and the seventh grade had 250 tickets to sell. One hour before the show, the eighth grade had sold 225 tickets and the seventh grade had sold 200 tickets. Which grade sold the greater percent of tickets?

ACTIVITY

What do you need to find? which grade sold the greater percent of tickets

STEP 1 Make a bar diagram for each grade to show 100%. Divide each bar into 10 equal parts to show 10%.

STEP 2 Find the value of each part.

8th grade: 300 ÷ 10 = 30   7th grade: 250 ÷ 10 = 25

STEP 3 Shade each bar to represent the number of tickets sold.

Eighth grade: 225 ÷ 30 = 7.5   Shade 7.5 parts.
Seventh grade: 200 ÷ 25 = 8   Shade 8 parts.

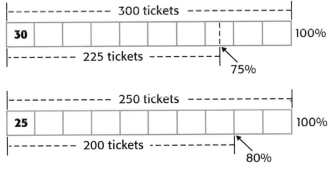

Since 80% > 75%, the seventh grade sold the greater percent.

Analyze the Results

1. Why is the percent for the seventh-grade sales greater even though they sold fewer tickets?

2. **SCHOOL** Vanlue Middle School has 600 students and Memorial Middle School has 450 students. Vanlue has 270 girls and Memorial has 243 girls. Draw a bar diagram to determine which school has the greater percent of girls. Explain.

Main Idea

Solve problems using the percent proportion.

NGSSS

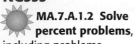 **MA.7.A.1.2 Solve percent problems**, including problems involving discounts, simple interest, taxes, tips and percents of increase or decrease. *Also addresses MA.7.A.1.1.*

New Vocabulary

percent proportion

Get Connected
glencoe.com

The Percent Proportion

MONSTER TRUCKS The tires on a monster truck weigh approximately 3,600 pounds. The entire truck weighs about 11,000 pounds.

1. Write the ratio of tire weight to total weight as a fraction.

2. Use a calculator to write the fraction as a decimal to the nearest hundredth.

3. What percent of the monster truck's weight is the tires?

In a **percent proportion**, one ratio or fraction compares part of a quantity to the whole quantity. The other ratio is the equivalent percent written as a fraction with a denominator of 100.

$$\textbf{4} \text{ out of } \textbf{5} \text{ is } \textbf{80}\%.$$

$$\begin{array}{l} \text{part} \longrightarrow \\ \text{whole} \longrightarrow \end{array} \frac{4}{5} = \frac{80}{100} \left. \rule{0pt}{2.2em}\right\} \text{percent}$$

| 10% | 10% | 10% | 10% | 10% | 10% | 10% | 10% | 10% | 10% | 100% |

| | | | | | 5 |

Key Concept	Types of Percent Problems	
Type	**Example**	**Proportion**
Find the Percent	What percent of 5 is 4?	$\dfrac{4}{5} = \dfrac{n}{100}$
Find the Part	What number is 80% of 5?	$\dfrac{p}{5} = \dfrac{80}{100}$
Find the Whole	4 is 80% of what number?	$\dfrac{4}{w} = \dfrac{80}{100}$

Find the Percent

1. **What percent of $15 is $9?**

Words	What percent of $15 is $9?
Variable	Let $n\%$ represent the percent.
Proportion	$\dfrac{\text{part}}{\text{whole}} \longrightarrow \dfrac{9}{15} = \dfrac{n}{100} \Big\}$ percent

$\dfrac{9}{15} = \dfrac{n}{100}$ Write the proportion.

$9 \cdot 100 = 15 \cdot n$ Find the cross products.

$900 = 15n$ Simplify.

$\dfrac{900}{15} = \dfrac{15n}{15}$ Divide each side by 15.

$60 = n$

So, $9 is 60% of 15.

 CHECK Your Progress

    a. What percent of 25 is 20?   **b.** $12.75 is what percent of $50?

The Percent Proportion
The whole usually comes
after the word of.

EXAMPLE **Find the Part**

2. **What number is 40% of 120?**

Words	What number is 40% of 120?
Variable	Let p represent the part.
Proportion	$\dfrac{\text{part}}{\text{whole}} \longrightarrow \dfrac{p}{120} = \dfrac{40}{100} \Big\}$ percent

$\dfrac{p}{120} = \dfrac{40}{100}$ Write the proportion.

$p \cdot 100 = 120 \cdot 40$ Find the cross products.

$100p = 4,800$ Simplify.

$\dfrac{100p}{100} = \dfrac{4,800}{100}$ Divide each side by 100.

$p = 48$

So, 48 is 40% of 120.

 CHECK Your Progress

    c. What number is 5% of 60?   **d.** 12% of 85 is what number?

Find the Whole

3 18 is 25% of what number?

Words	18 is 25% of what number?
Variable	Let w represent the whole.
Proportion	$\dfrac{\text{part} \longrightarrow}{\text{whole} \longrightarrow} \quad \dfrac{18}{w} = \dfrac{25}{100} \Big\} \text{percent}$

$\dfrac{18}{w} = \dfrac{25}{100}$ Write the proportion.

$18 \cdot 100 = w \cdot 25$ Find the cross products.

$1{,}800 = 25w$ Simplify.

$\dfrac{1{,}800}{25} = \dfrac{25w}{25}$ Divide each side by 25.

$72 = w$

So, 18 is 25% of 72.

✔️ **CHECK Your Progress**

e. 40% of what number is 26?   **f.** 80 is 75% of what number?

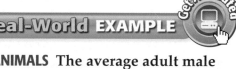 **Real-World EXAMPLE**

 4 **ANIMALS** The average adult male Western Lowland gorilla eats about 33.5 pounds of fruit each day. How much food does the average adult male gorilla eat each day?

You know that 33.5 pounds is the part. You need to find the whole.

$\dfrac{33.5}{w} = \dfrac{67}{100}$ Write the proportion.

$33.5 \cdot 100 = w \cdot 67$ Find the cross products.

$3{,}350 = 67w$ Simplify.

$\dfrac{3{,}350}{67} = \dfrac{67w}{67}$ Divide each side by 67.

$50 = w$

The average adult male gorilla eats 50 pounds of food each day.

Western Lowland Gorilla's Diet	
Food	**Percent**
Fruit	67%
Seeds, leaves, stems, and pith	17%
Insects/ insect larvae	16%

 Real-World Link · · · ·

Male Western Lowland gorillas weigh about 350–400 pounds. Females weigh about 160–200 pounds.

✔️ **CHECK Your Progress**

g. **ZOO** If 200 of the 550 reptiles in a zoo are on display, what percent of the reptiles are on display? Round to the nearest whole number.

Examples 1–3
(pp. 312–314)

Find each number. Round to the nearest tenth if necessary.

1. What percent of 50 is 18?
2. What percent of $90 is $9?
3. What number is 2% of 35?
4. What number is 25% of 180?
5 9 is 12% of which number?
6. 62 is 90.5% of what number?

Example 4
(p. 314)

7. MEASUREMENT If a box of Brand A cereal contains 10 cups of cereal, how many more cups of cereal are in a box of Brand B cereal?

Brand A Brand B 30% More Cereal

Practice and Problem Solving

● = **Step-by-Step Solutions** begin on page R15.
Extra Practice is on page EP15.

Examples 1–3
(pp. 312–314)

Find each number. Round to the nearest tenth if necessary.

8. What percent of 60 is 15?
9. $3 is what percent of $40?
10. What number is 15% of 60?
11. 12% of 72 is what number?
12. 9 is 45% of what number?
13. 75 is 20% of what number?

Example 4
(p. 314)

14. SCHOOL Roman has 2 red pencils in his backpack. If this is 25% of the total number of pencils, how many pencils are in his backpack?

15. BASKETBALL Eileen and Michelle scored 48% of their team's points. If their team had a total of 50 points, how many points did they score?

16. SHOES A pair of sneakers is on sale as shown. This is 75% of the original price. What was the original price of the shoes?

17. BOOKS Of the 60 books on a bookshelf, 24 are nonfiction. What percent of the books are nonfiction?

Sale Price $51

Find each number. Round to the nearest hundredth if necessary.

18. What percent of 25 is 30?
19. What number is 8.2% of 50?
20. 40 is 50% of what number?
21. 12.5% of what number is 24?
22. What number is 0.5% of 8?
23 What percent of 300 is 0.6?

24. ASTRONOMY Use the table shown.

a. Mercury's radius is what percent of Jupiter's radius?

b. If the radius of Mars is about 13.7% of Neptune's radius, what is the radius of Neptune?

c. Earth's radius is about 261.4% of Mercury's radius. What is the radius of Earth?

Planet	Radius (km)
Mercury	2,440
Mars	3,397
Jupiter	71,492

25. REASONING Seventy percent of the 100 students in a middle school cafeteria bought their lunch. Some of these students leave the cafeteria to attend an assembly. Now only 60% of the remaining students bought their lunch. How many students are remaining in the cafeteria? Explain your reasoning.

26. CHALLENGE Without calculating, arrange the following from greatest to least value. Justify your reasoning.

20% of 100, 20% of 500, 5% of 100

27. **Write MATH** Create a problem involving a percent that can be solved by using the proportion $\frac{3}{b} = \frac{15}{100}$.

NGSSS Practice   **MA.6.A.5.1, MA.7.A.1.2**

28. Of the 273 students in a school, 95 volunteered to work the book sale. About what percent of the students volunteered?

A. 35%

B. 65%

C. 70%

D. 75%

29. One hundred ninety-two students were surveyed about their favorite kind of TV programs. The results are shown in the table. Which kind of program did 25% of the students report as their favorite?

Favorite TV Programs	
Kind	**Number**
Music	48
Reality	44
Comedy	41
Sports	36
Drama	23

F. Music   **H.** Comedy

G. Reality   **I.** Sports

 **Spiral Review**

30. FOOD Out of 823 students, 47.2% chose pizza as their favorite food. What is a reasonable estimate for the number of students who chose pizza as their favorite food? Explain. (Lesson 6-1C)

Find each number. Round to the nearest tenth if necessary. (Lesson 6-1B)

31. What is 25% of 120?   **32.** Find 45% of 70.

33. FLOWERS Use the information in the table to write each ratio as a fraction in simplest form. (Lesson 4-1D)

a. lilies : roses

b. snapdragons : lilies

c. roses : flowers

Flower Arrangement	
Lilies	4
Roses	18
Snapdragons	6

Main Idea
Solve problems by using the percent equation.

NGSSS
 MA.7.A.1.2 Solve percent problems, including problems involving discounts, simple interest, taxes, tips and percents of increase or decrease. *Also addresses MA.7.A.3.2, MA.7.A.3.3, MA.7.A.5.1.*

New Vocabulary
percent equation

Get Connected
glencoe.com

The Percent Equation

ARTHROPODS Suppose there are 854,000 different species of spiders, insects, crustaceans, millipedes, and centipedes on Earth. The graph shows that 88% of the total number of species of arthropods are insects.

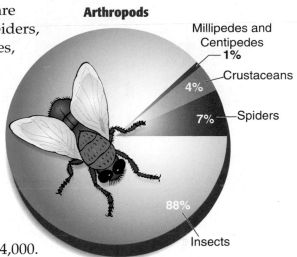

Arthropods

Millipedes and Centipedes — 1%

Crustaceans 4%

7% — Spiders

88% Insects

1. Use the percent proportion to find how many species are insects.

2. Express the percent of insects as a decimal. Then multiply the decimal by 854,000.

In Lesson 6-2B, you used a percent proportion to find the missing part, percent, or whole. You can also use a percent equation.

$$\frac{\text{part}}{\text{whole}} = \text{percent}$$ The percent must be written as a decimal or fraction.

$$\frac{\text{part}}{\text{whole}} \cdot \text{whole} = \text{percent} \cdot \text{whole}$$ Multiply each side by the whole.

$$\text{part} = \text{percent} \cdot \text{whole}$$ ◄ This form is called the **percent equation.**

EXAMPLE Find the Part

1 **What number is 12% of 150?**

Estimate 12% of 150 ≈ 0.1 · 150 or 15

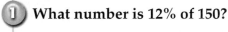
part = percent · whole

$p = 0.12 \cdot 150$ Write the percent equation. 12% = 0.12

$p = 18$ Multiply.

So, 18 is 12% of 150.

Study Tip
Percent Equation
A percent must always be converted to a decimal or a fraction when it is used in an equation.

 CHECK Your Progress

Write an equation for each problem. Then solve. Round to the nearest tenth if necessary.

a. What is 6% of 19?   **b.** Find 72% of 90.

EXAMPLE **Find the Percent**

2 **21 is what percent of 40?**

Estimate $\frac{21}{40} \approx \frac{1}{2}$ or 50%

$$\underbrace{\text{part}} = \underbrace{\text{percent}} \cdot \underbrace{\text{whole}}$$

$21 =$	$n \cdot 40$	Write the percent equation.
$\dfrac{21}{40} =$	$\dfrac{40n}{40}$	Divide each side by 40.
$0.525 = n$		Simplify.

Since n represents the decimal form, the percent is 52.5%.

So, 21 is 52.5% of 40.

Check for Reasonableness 52.5% ≈ 50% ✓

 CHECK Your Progress

Write an equation for each problem. Then solve. Round to the nearest tenth if necessary.

c. 35 is what percent of 70?   **d.** What percent of 125 is 75?

e. What percent of 40 is 9?   **f.** 27 is what percent of 150?

Study Tip

Percent Remember to write the decimal as a percent in your final answer.

EXAMPLE **Find the Whole**

3 **13 is 26% of what number?**

Estimate $\frac{1}{4}$ of 48 = 12

$$\underbrace{\text{part}} = \underbrace{\text{percent}} \cdot \underbrace{\text{whole}}$$

$13 =$	$0.26 \cdot w$	Write the percent equation. 26% = 0.26
$\dfrac{13}{0.26} =$	$\dfrac{0.26w}{0.26}$	Divide each side by 0.26.
$50 = w$		Simplify.

So, 13 is 26% of 50.

Check for Reasonableness 50 is close to 48. ✓

 CHECK Your Progress

Write an equation for each problem. Then solve. Round to the nearest tenth if necessary.

g. 39 is 84% of what number?   **h.** 26% of what number is 45?

i. 14% of what number is 7?   **j.** 24 is 32% of what number?

Real-World EXAMPLE

④ **CELL PHONES** A survey found that 25% of people aged 18–24 gave up their home phone and only use a cell phone. If 3,264 people only use a cell phone, how many people were surveyed?

Words	3,264 people is 25% of what number of people?
Variable	Let n represent the number of people.
Equation	$3{,}264 \;=\; 0.25 \;\cdot\; n$

$3{,}264 = 0.25 \cdot n$ Write the percent equation. 25% = 0.25

$\dfrac{3{,}264}{0.25} = \dfrac{0.25n}{0.25}$ Divide each side by 0.25. Use a calculator.

$13{,}056 = n$ Simplify.

About 13,056 people were surveyed.

✓ CHECK Your Progress

k. POPULATION The Miami-Dade County metropolitan area contains 13.3% of the population of Florida. If the population of Florida is about 18,089,888 people, what is the population of the Miami-Dade County metropolitan area?

Key Concept   **Types of Percent Problems**

Type	Example	Equation
Find the Percent	3 is what percent of 6?	$3 = n \cdot 6$
Find the Part	What number is 50% of 6?	$p = 0.5 \cdot 6$
Find the Whole	3 is 50% of what number?	$3 = 0.5 \cdot w$

✓ CHECK Your Understanding

Examples 1–3
(pp. 317–318)

Write an equation for each problem. Then solve. Round to the nearest tenth if necessary.

1. What number is 88% of 300?
2. What number is 12% of 250?
3. 75 is what percent of 150?
4. 24 is what percent of 120?
5. 3 is 12% of what number?
6. 84 is 60% of what number?

Example 4
(p. 319)

7. **BUSINESS** A local bakery sold 60 loaves of bread in one day. If 65% of these were sold in the afternoon, how many loaves were sold in the afternoon?

= **Step-by-Step Solutions** begin on page R15.
Extra Practice is on page EP15.

Examples 1–3
(pp. 317–318)

Write an equation for each problem. Then solve. Round to the nearest tenth if necessary.

8. What number is 65% of 98?

9. Find 39% of 65.

10. Find 24% of 25.

11. What number is 53% of 470?

12. 9 is what percent of 45?

13. What percent of 96 is 26?

14. What percent of 392 is 98?

15. 30 is what percent of 64?

16. 33% of what number is 1.45?

17. 84 is 75% of what number?

18. 17 is 40% of what number?

19. 80% of what number is 64?

Example 4
(p. 319)

20. BOOKS Ruben bought 6 new books for his collection. This increased his collection by 12%. How many books did he have before his purchases?

21. VIDEO GAMES A store sold 550 video games during the month of December. If this made up 12.5% of their yearly video game sales, about how many video games did the store sell all year?

22. MEASUREMENT The length of Giselle's arm is 27 inches. The length of her lower arm is 17 inches. About what percent of Giselle's arm is her lower arm?

23. LOBSTERS Approximately 0.02% of North Atlantic lobsters are born bright blue in color. Out of 5,000 North Atlantic lobsters, how many would you expect to be blue in color?

Write an equation for each problem. Then solve. Round to the nearest tenth if necessary.

24. Find 135% of 64.

25. What number is 0.4% of 82.1?

26. 450 is 75.2% of what number?

27. What percent of 200 is 230?

28. SALARY Suppose you earn $6 per hour at your part-time job. What will your new hourly rate be after a 2.5% raise?

29 ONLINE VIDEOS About 142 million people in the United States watch online videos. The graph shows what type of videos they watch. Use the graph to answer the questions.

a. About what percent of viewers watch comedy, jokes, and bloopers?

b. About what percent watch news stories?

c. What percent of the viewers watch music videos and movie previews?

Online Video Viewers

Movie previews	39.76
News stories	44.02
Clips on video-sharing sites	46.86
Music videos	51.12
Comedy, jokes, bloopers	52.54

Millions of Viewers

30. **OPEN ENDED** Write a percent problem for which the percent is greater than 100 and the part is known. Use the percent equation to solve your problem to find the whole.

31. **CHALLENGE** If you need to find the percent of a number, explain how you can predict whether the part will be less than, greater than, or equal to the number.

32. **Write MATH** Compare the percent equation and the percent proportion. Then explain when it might be easier to use the percent equation rather than the percent proportion.

NGSSS Practice   MA.7.A.1.2

33. In a survey, 100 students were asked to choose their favorite take-out food. The table shows the results.

Favorite Take-Out Food	
Type of Food	**Percent**
Pizza	40
Sandwiches	32
Fried chicken	28

Based on these data, predict how many out of 1,800 students would choose sandwiches.

  A. 504   C. 680

  B. 576   D. 720

34. If 60% of a number is 18, what is 90% of the number?

  F. 3   H. 27

  G. 16   I. 30

35. Taryn's grandmother took her family out to dinner. If the dinner was $74 and Taryn's dinner was 20% of the bill, how much was Taryn's dinner?

  A. $6.80   C. $9.50

  B. $7.20   D. $14.80

Spiral Review

Find each number. Round to the nearest hundredth if necessary. (Lesson 6-2B)

36. What percent of 15 is 20?

37. 20.5% of what number is 35?

38. What number is 0.5% of 10?

39. **TRAVEL** On a 511-mile trip, Mya drove about 68% on Monday. Determine a reasonable estimate for the number of miles she drove on Monday. (Lesson 6-1C)

40. **HEALTH** Use the graph to predict the height of a 16-year-old. (Lesson 5-3A)

41. **ALGEBRA** Solve the equation $-7y + 18 - 39$. Check your solution. (Lesson 3-3B)

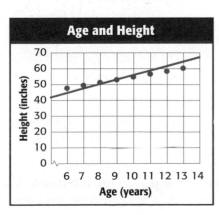

Problem-Solving Investigation

Main Idea Solve problems by determining reasonable answers.

P.S.I. TEAM +

Determine Reasonable Answers

DOUG: My dad and I are at a restaurant. Our bill is $28. We want to leave a tip that is 15% of the bill. I think he should leave $5 for the tip.

YOUR MISSION: Determine whether it is reasonable for Doug's dad to leave $5 as the tip.

Understand	Doug and his dad spent $28. Doug thinks that $5 is about 15% of the bill.
Plan	Make a bar diagram to represent 100%.
Solve	Divide it into ten parts, each representing 10%.

$$\mid\text{-----------------------} \$28 \text{-----------------------}\mid$$

$2.80	$2.80	$2.80	$2.80	$2.80	$2.80	$2.80	$2.80	$2.80	$2.80

So, a 10% tip would be $2.80.
If 10% = $2.80, 5% is $2.80 ÷ 2 or $1.40.
So, a 15% tip would be $2.80 + $1.40 or $4.20. A $5 tip is reasonable.

Check	$28 × 0.15 = $4.20. So, $5 is a reasonable estimate.

Analyze the Strategy

1. Explain how to use mental math to find 15% of a number.

2. **Write MATH** Write two real-world problems involving tips. One should have a reasonable answer and the other should not.

NGSSS

MA.7.A.1.2 Solve percent problems, including problems involving discounts, simple interest, taxes, **tips** and percents of increase or decrease. *Also addresses MA.7.A.3.2.*

- Determine reasonable answers.
- Guess, check, and revise.
- Look for a pattern.
- Choose an operation.

Use the *determine reasonable answers* strategy to solve Exercises 3–6.

3. **TIPS** Brett decides to leave a 20% tip on a restaurant bill of $17.50. How much should he tip the restaurant server?

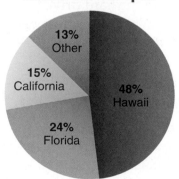

4. **SCHOOL** Of 423 students, 57.6% live within 5 miles of the school. What is a reasonable estimate for the number of students living within 5 miles of the school? Explain.

5. **EXERCISE** A survey showed that 61% of middle school students do some kind of physical activity every day. If there are 828 middle school students in your school, would the number of students who exercise be about 300, 400, or 500? Explain.

6. **TRAVEL** A travel agency surveyed 140 families about their favorite vacation spots. Is 60, 70, or 80 families a reasonable estimate for the number of families that did *not* choose Hawaii?

Favorite Vacation Spots

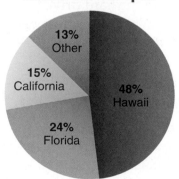

- 13% Other
- 15% California
- 48% Hawaii
- 24% Florida

Use any strategy to solve Exercises 7–13.

7. **COINS** Gavin has 10 coins that total $0.83. What are the coins?

8. **BAKING** Refer to the graph. A pie is set out to cool. Is it reasonable to estimate that the pie will be 90°F after ten minutes of cooling? Explain.

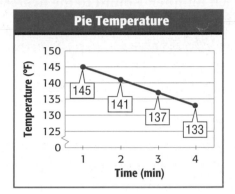

Pie Temperature

- 145
- 141
- 137
- 133

Time (min)

9. **SHOPPING** Deshawn wants to buy a shirt that has a regular price of $41 but is now on sale for 25% off the regular price. Is $25, $30, or $35 the best estimate for the cost of the shirt?

10. **BOWLING** In bowling, you get a spare when you knock down the ten pins in two throws. How many possible ways are there to get a spare?

11. **SAVING** Aliayah saves $11 each month for her class trip. What is a reasonable estimate for the amount of money she will have saved after a year: about $100, $120, or $160? Explain.

12. **FUNDRAISER** During a popcorn sale for a fundraiser, the soccer team gets to keep 25% of the sales. One box of popcorn sells for $1.50 and the team has sold 510 boxes so far. Has the team raised a total of $175? Explain.

13. **MEASUREMENT** How many square yards of carpet are needed to carpet the two rooms described below? Explain.

Room	Dimensions
Living room	15 ft by 18 ft
TV room	18 ft by 20 ft

Find each number. Round to the nearest tenth if necessary. (Lesson 6-1B)

1. Find 17% of 655.

2. What is 235% of 82?

3. What number is 162.2% of 55?

4. **NGSSS PRACTICE** Ayana has 220 coins in her piggy bank. Of those, 45% are pennies. How many coins are NOT pennies? (Lesson 6-1B)

   A. 121   **C.** 109

   B. 116   **D.** 85

Estimate. (Lesson 6-1C)

5. 20% of 392   **6.** 78% of 112   **7.** 30% of 42

Find each number. Round to the nearest tenth if necessary. (Lesson 6-2B)

8. What percent of 84 is 12?

9. 15 is 25% of what number?

10. 85% of 252 is what number?

11. **ANALYZE GRAPHS** Refer to the graph that shows the results of a survey of 200 students' favorite DVDs. (Lesson 6-2C)

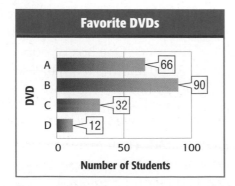

Favorite DVDs

DVD / Number of Students

A — 66
B — 90
C — 32
D — 12

  a. What percent of students preferred DVD A?

  b. Which DVD did about 15% of students prefer?

Write an equation for each problem. Then solve. Round to the nearest tenth if necessary. (Lesson 6-2C)

12. What number is 35% of 72?

13. 16.1 is what percent of 70?

14. 27.2 is 68% of what number?

15. 16% of 32 is what number?

16. 55% of what number is 1.265?

17. 15 is 35% of what number?

18. 12 is what percent of 20?

19. **ANALYZE TABLES** The table shows the costs of owning a dog over an average 11-year lifespan. What percent of the total cost is veterinary bills? (Lesson 6-2C)

Dog Ownership Costs	
Item	**Cost ($)**
Food	4,020
Veterinary bills	3,930
Grooming, equipment	2,960
Training	1,220
Other	2,470

20. **SHOPPING** A desktop computer costs $849.75 and the hard drive is 61.3% of the total cost. What is a reasonable estimate for the cost of the hard drive? (Lesson 6-2D)

21. **NGSSS PRACTICE** A football player has made about 75% of the field goals he has attempted in his career. He attempts 41 field goals in one season. What is a reasonable estimate for the number of field goals he is expected to make? (Lesson 6-2D)

   F. 35   **H.** 25

   G. 30   **I.** 20

6-3 Applying Percents

Explore Percent of Change

Main Idea

Use bar diagrams to solve problems involving percent of change.

NGSSS

MA.7.A.1.2 Solve percent problems, including problems involving discounts, simple interest, taxes, tips and **percents of increase or decrease.**

Get Connected
glencoe.com

ADMISSION The admission price for the state fair has increased by 50% in the last five years. If the admission price was $6 five years ago, what is the current admission price?

ACTIVITY

What do you need to find? current admission price for the state fair after a 50% increase

STEP 1 Draw a bar diagram that will represent 100%. Cut it out and label it.

| price 5 years ago = $6 | 100% |

STEP 2 Draw a second bar diagram that is half the length of the first. It represents 50%. Cut it out and label it.

| increase = $3 | 50% |

STEP 3 Tape the two bars together, end to end. This new bar represents a 50% increase or 150% of the first bar.

| price 5 years ago = $6 | increase = $3 | 150% |

The current admission price for the state fair is $6 + $3 or $9.

Analyze the Results

1. Suppose the price had increased 10%. What would you do differently in Step 2? What is the new admission price?

2. Describe how this process would change to show percent of decrease.

Practice and Apply

3. Model each percent of change with bar diagrams.

   a. 25% increase **b.** 75% increase **c.** 30% decrease **d.** 40% decrease

Main Idea
Find the percent of increase or decrease.

NGSSS

 MA.7.A.1.2 Solve percent problems, including problems involving discounts, simple interest, taxes, tips and **percents of increase or decrease.**

New Vocabulary
percent of change
percent of increase
percent of decrease

Get Connected
glencoe.com

Percent of Change

FOOTBALL The table shows about how many people attended the home games of a high school football team for five consecutive years.

Attendance of Home Games	
Year	Total Attendance (thousands)
2007	16.6
2008	16.4
2009	16.9
2010	17.4
2011	17.6

1. How much did the attendance increase from 2009 to 2010?

2. Write the ratio $\dfrac{\text{amount of increase}}{\text{attendance in 2009}}$. Then write the ratio as a percent. Round to the nearest hundredth.

3. How much did the attendance increase from 2008 to 2009?

4. Write the ratio $\dfrac{\text{amount of increase}}{\text{attendance in 2008}}$. Then write the ratio as a percent. Round to the nearest hundredth.

5. **MAKE A CONJECTURE** Why are the amounts of increase the same but the percents different?

When you subtracted the original amount from the final amount, you found the *amount* of change. When you compared the change to the original amount in a ratio, you found the *percent* of change.

> **Key Concept**   Percent of Change
>
> **Words**   A **percent of change** is a ratio that compares the change in quantity to the original amount.
>
> **Equation** $\text{percent of change} = \dfrac{\text{amount of change}}{\text{orginal amount}}$
>
> $= \dfrac{\text{final amount} - \text{original amount}}{\text{original amount}}$

When the percent of change is positive, then it is called a **percent of increase**. When the percent of change is negative, then it is called a

EXAMPLE **Find Percent of Increase**

① **GASOLINE** Find the percent of change in the cost of gasoline from 1970 to 2008. Round to the nearest whole percent if necessary. Then state whether the percent of change is an *increase* or *decrease*.

1970

2008

Step 1 Find the amount of change.
$3.95 − $1.30 = $2.65

Step 2 Find the percent of change.

$$\text{percent of change} = \frac{\text{amount of change}}{\text{original amount}}$$

$$= \frac{\$2.65}{\$1.30} \qquad \text{Substitution}$$

$$\approx 2.04 \qquad \text{Simplify.}$$

$$\approx 204\% \qquad \text{Write 2.04 as a percent.}$$

The percent of change is 204%. Since the percent of change is positive, this is a percent of *increase*.

 CHECK Your Progress

a. MEASUREMENT Find the percent of change from 10 yards to 13 yards.

> ### Study Tip
>
> **Percents**
> In the percent of change formula, the decimal repesenting the percent of change must be written as a percent.

EXAMPLE **Find Percent of Decrease**

② **DVD RECORDER** Yusuf bought a DVD recorder for $280. Now, it is on sale for $220. Find the percent of change in the price. Round to the nearest whole percent if necessary. Then state whether the percent of change is an *increase* or *decrease*.

Step 1 Find the amount of change.
$220 − $280 = −$60

Step 2 Find the percent of change.

$$\text{percent of change} = \frac{\text{amount of change}}{\text{original amount}}$$

$$= \frac{-\$60}{\$280} \qquad \text{Substitution}$$

$$\approx -0.21 \qquad \text{Simplify.}$$

$$\approx -21\% \qquad \text{Write −0.21 as a percent.}$$

The percent of change is −21%. Since the percent of change is negative, this is a percent of *decrease*.

 CHECK Your Progress

b. MONEY Find the percent of change from $20 to $15.

Examples 1 and 2
(p. 327)

Find each percent of change. Round to the nearest whole percent if necessary. State whether the percent of change is an *increase* or a *decrease*.

1. 30 inches to 24 inches

2. 20.5 meters to 35.5 meters

3. $126 to $150

4. $75.80 to $94.75

5. SOCCER The table shows the number of youth 7 years and older who played soccer from 2000 to 2007.

  a. Find the percent of change from 2004 to 2007. Round to the nearest tenth of a percent. Is it a change of increase or decrease?

  b. Find the percent of change from 2002 to 2004. Round to the nearest tenth of a percent. Is it a change of increase or decrease?

Playing Soccer	
Year	Number (millions)
2000	12.9
2002	13.7
2004	13.3
2006	14.0
2007	13.8

Practice and Problem Solving

● = **Step-by-Step Solutions** begin on page R15.
Extra Practice is on page EP16.

Examples 1 and 2
(p. 327)

Find each percent of change. Round to the nearest whole percent if necessary. State whether the percent of change is an *increase* or a *decrease*.

6. 15 yards to 18 yards

7. 100 acres to 140 acres

8. $12 to $6

9. 48 notebooks to 14 notebooks

10. 125 centimeters to 87.5 centimeters

11 $15.60 to $11.70

12. 1.6 hours to 0.95 hour

13. 132 days to 125.4 days

14. $240 to $320

15. 624 feet to 702 feet

Find each percent of change. Round to the nearest whole percent if necessary. State whether the percent of change is an *increase* or a *decrease*.

16. BOOKS On Monday, Kenya spent 60 minutes reading her favorite book. Today, she spent 45 minutes reading this book.

17. EXERCISE Three months ago, Santos could walk 2 miles in 40 minutes. Today he can walk 2 miles in 25 minutes.

18. SCHOOL Last school year the enrollment of Genoa Middle School was 465 students. This year the enrollment is 525.

19. MONEY Jake had $782 in his checking account. He now has $798.

20. MEASUREMENT Refer to the rectangle at the right. Suppose the side lengths are doubled.

  a. Find the percent of change in the perimeter.

  b. Find the percent of change in the area.

4 in.
2 in.

21. FIND THE DATA Refer to the Data File on pages 2–5. Choose some data and write a real-world problem in which you would find the percent of change.

22. SALES Use the graphic shown to find the percent of change in CD sales from 2008 to 2009.

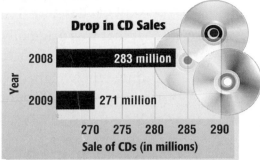

Drop in CD Sales

2008 — 283 million
2009 — 271 million

270 275 280 285 290
Sale of CDs (in millions)

Year

23 SHOES In 2010, shoe sales for a certain company were $25.9 billion. Sales are expected to increase by about 20% from 2010 to 2011. Find the projected amount of shoe sales in 2011.

24. BABYSITTING The table shows how many hours Catalina spent babysitting during the months of April and May.

Month	Hours Worked
April	40
May	32
June	42

a. If Catalina charges $6.50 per hour, what is the percent of change in the amount of money earned from April to May? Is it a change of increase or decrease?

b. What is the percent of change in the amount of money earned from May to June? Round to the nearest percent if needed. Is it a change of increase or decrease?

c. Compare the percent of change from April to May and then May to June. Which is a greater percent of change?

H.O.T. Problems

25. NUMBER SENSE The costs of two different sound systems were decreased by $10. The original costs of the systems were $90 and $60, respectively. Without calculating, which had a greater percent of decrease? Explain.

26. FIND THE ERROR Dario is finding the percent of change from $52 to $125. Find his mistake and correct it.

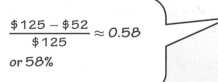

$$\frac{\$125 - \$52}{\$125} \approx 0.58$$

or 58%

27. Write MATH Explain how, when comparing data, two amounts of change can be the same but the percents of change can be different.

28. Which of the following represents the least percent of change?

   A. A coat that was originally priced at $90 is now $72.

   B. A puppy who weighed 6 ounces at birth now weighs 96 ounces.

   C. A child grew from 54 inches to 60 inches in 1 year.

   D. A savings account increased from $500 to $550 in 6 months.

29. **SHORT RESPONSE** A music video Web site received 5,000 comments on a new song they released. After the artist performed the song on television, the number of comments increased by 30% the next day. How many new comments were on the Web site at the end of the next day?

30. Students in a reading program gradually increased the amount of time they read. The first week, they read 20 minutes per day. Each week thereafter, they increased their reading time by 50% until they read an hour per day. In what week of the program did the students begin reading an hour per day?

   F. Week 2   **H.** Week 4

   G. Week 3   **I.** Week 5

31. **GRIDDED RESPONSE** Find the percent of change in the perimeter of the square below if its side length is tripled.

Spiral Review

32. **SURVEY** There are 622 students at Jackson Middle School. About 52.3% of them selected art class as their favorite class. What is a reasonable estimate for the number of students who chose art as their favorite? (Lesson 6-2D)

ALGEBRA Write an equation for each problem. Then solve. Round to the nearest tenth if necessary. (Lesson 6-2C)

33. 30% of what number is 17?   **34.** What is 21% of 62?

35. **SHOPPING** Four pounds of pecans cost $12.75. How much is this per pound? (Lesson 4-1B)

36. **MODELS** On a scale model of a building, 3 inches = 12 feet. If the model is 8 inches tall, how tall is the actual building? (Lesson 4-2B)

Multiply. (Lesson 2-3B)

37. $\frac{1}{2} \cdot 60$ **38.** $\frac{3}{4} \cdot 28$

Add or subtract. (Lesson 2-2D)

39. $3\frac{3}{8} - 1\frac{3}{4}$ **40.** $7\frac{6}{7} + 1\frac{1}{2}$

Main Idea
Solve problems involving sales tax and tips.

NGSSS

MA.7.A.1.2 Solve percent problems, including problems involving discounts, simple interest, **taxes, tips** and percents of increase or decrease. *Also addresses MA.7.A.3.2, MA.7.A.5.1.*

New Vocabulary
sales tax
tip
gratuity

Get Connected
glencoe.com

Sales Tax and Tips

KAYAKS Alonso plans to buy a new kayak that costs $1,849. He lives in Florida where there is a 7.5% sales tax.

1. Calculate the sales tax by finding 7.5% of $1,849. Round to the nearest cent.

2. What will be the total cost including the sales tax?

3. Multiply 1.075 and 1,849. How does the result compare to your answer in Exercise 2?

Sales tax is an additional amount of money charged on items that people buy. The total cost of an item is the regular price plus the sales tax.

EXAMPLE   Find the Total Cost

① **ELECTRONICS** A DVD player costs $140 and the sales tax is 5.75%. What is the total cost of the DVD player?

Method 1   Add sales tax to the regular price.

First, find the sales tax.

5.75% of $\$140 = 0.0575 \times 140$ Write 5.75% as a decimal.
$\qquad\qquad\qquad = 8.05$ The sales tax is $8.05.

Next, add the sales tax to the regular price.
$\$8.05 + \$140 = \$148.05$

Method 2   Add the percent of tax to 100%.

$100\% + 5.75\% = 105.75\%$ Add the percent of tax to 100%.

The total cost is 105.75% of the regular price.

105.75% of $\$140 = 1.0575 \times \$140$ Write 105.75% as a decimal.
$\qquad\qquad\qquad\ = \$148.05$ Multiply.

The total cost of the DVD player is $148.05.

 CHOOSE Your Method

a. **CLOTHES** What is the total cost of a sweatshirt if the regular price is $42 and the sales tax is $5\frac{1}{2}\%$?

A **tip** or **gratuity** is a small amount of money in return for a service. The total price is the regular price of the service plus the tip.

EXAMPLE Find the Tip

2 **TIPPING** A customer wants to tip 15% of the restaurant bill. What will be the total bill with tip?

Sal's Bistro
Check 004322

Herbed Salmon	16.25
Chicken Pasta	15.25
Iced Tea	1.75
Iced Tea	1.75

Total | 35.00

THANK YOU

Method 1   Add the tip to the regular price.

First, find the tip.

15% of $\$35 = 0.15 \times 35$ Write 15% as a decimal.
$\qquad\qquad\quad = 5.25$ The tip is $5.25.

$\$5.25 + \$35 = \$40.25$ Add the tip to the bill.

Method 2   Add the percent of tip to 100%.

$100\% + 15\% = 115\%$ Add the percent of tip to 100%.

The total cost is 115% of the bill.

115% of $\$35 = 1.15 \times \$35$ Write 115% as a decimal.
$\qquad\qquad\quad = \$40.25$ Multiply.

The total cost of the bill with tip is $40.25.

 CHOOSE Your Method

b. TAXICAB Scott wants to tip his taxicab driver. If his commute costs $15 and he wants to give the driver a 20% tip, what is the total cost?

Real-World EXAMPLE

3 **HAIRCUTS** A haircut costs $20. Sales tax is 4.75%. Is $25 sufficient to cover the haircut with tax and a 15% tip?

Sales tax is 4.75% and the tip is 15%, so together they will be 19.75%.

19.75% of $\$20 = 0.1975 \times 20$ Write 19.75% as a decimal.
$\qquad\qquad\qquad = 3.95$ Multiply.

$\$20 + \$3.95 = \$23.95$ Add.

Yes, $25 is sufficient to cover the haircut with tax and tip.

 CHECK Your Progress

c. SPA Find the total cost of a spa treatment of $42 including 6% tax and 20% tip.

Real-World Link · · · ·

In a recent year, the Internal Revenue Service estimated that Americans paid $15.37 billion in tips.

Study Tip

Mental Math 10% of a number can be found by moving the decimal one place to the left.
10% of $20 is $2. So, 20% of $20 is $4.

Examples 1 and 2
(pp. 331–332)

Find the total cost to the nearest cent.

1. $2.95 notebook; 5% tax
2. $46 shoes; 2.9% tax
3. $28 lunch; 15% tip
4. $98 catered dinner; 18% gratuity

Example 3
(p. 332)

5. **MANICURE** Jaimi went to have a manicure that cost $30. She wanted to tip the technician 20% and tax is 5.75%. How much did she spend total for the manicure?

Practice and Problem Solving

● = **Step-by-Step Solutions** begin on page R16.
Extra Practice is on page EP16.

Examples 1 and 2
(pp. 331–332)

Find the total cost to the nearest cent.

6. $58 bill; 20% tip
7. $1,500 computer; 7% tax
8. $99 CD player; 5% tax
9. $13 haircut; 15% tip
10. $43 dinner; 18% gratuity
11. $7.50 meal; 6.5% tax
12. $39 pizza order; 15% tip
13. $89.75 scooter; $7\frac{1}{4}$% tax

Example 3
(p. 332)

14. **PET GROOMING** Toru takes his dog to be groomed. The fee to groom the dog is $75 plus 6.75% tax. Is $80 enough to pay for the service? Explain.

15. **CLEANING** Diana and Sujit clean homes for a summer job. They charge $70 for the job plus 5% for supplies. A homeowner gave them a 15% tip. How much did they receive for the job?

16. **VIDEO GAMES** What is the sales tax of a $178.90 video game system if the tax rate is 5.75%?

17. **RESTAURANTS** A restaurant bill comes to $28.35. Find the total cost if the tax is 6.25% and a 20% tip is left on the amount before tax.

18. **GRAPHIC NOVEL** Refer to the graphic novel frame below. Find the price that a student would pay including the group discount for each amusement park. Which is the best deal?

We are trying to find the cheapest admission for our trip. Refer to the calculations you made on p. 303.

I think we have it! Guess where we are going?

19. CHALLENGE The Leather Depot buys a coat from a supplier for $90 wholesale and marks up the price by 40%. What is the retail price including 7% tax?

20. OPEN ENDED Give an example of the regular price of an item and the total cost including sales tax if the tax rate is 5.75%.

21. Which One Doesn't Belong? In each pair, the first value is the regular price of an item and the second value is the price with gratuity. Identify the pair that does not belong with the other three. Explain.

| $30, $34.50 | $54, $64.80 | $16, $18.40 | $90, $103.50 |

22. **MATH** Describe two methods for finding the total price of a bill that includes a 20% tip. Which method do you prefer? Explain.

NGSSS Practice   MA.7.A.1.2

23. Ms. Taylor bought a water tube to pull behind her boat. The tube cost $87.00 and 9% sales tax was added at the register. Ms. Taylor gave the cashier five $20 bills. How much change should she have received?

A. $4.83

B. $5.17

C. $94.83

D. $117.00

24. Prices for several cell phones are listed in the table below. It shows the regular price p and the price with tax t.

Phone	Regular Price (p)	Price with Tax (t)
Flip phone	$80	$86.40
Slide phone	$110	$118.80
Picture phone	$120	$129.60

Which formula can be used to calculate the price with tax?

F. $t = p \times 0.8$ H. $t = p \times 0.08$

G. $t = p - 0.8$ I. $t = p \times 1.08$

Find each percent of change. Round to the nearest whole percent if necessary. State whether the percent of change is an *increase* or *decrease*. (Lesson 6-3B)

25. 4 hours to 6 hours   **26.** $500 to $456   **27.** 20.5 meters to 35.5 meters

28. FINANCIAL LITERACY Bethany has to pay a 20% handling fee on a book she ordered online that cost $12. Write and solve a percent equation to find the handling fee. (Lesson 6-2C)

Multiply. Write in simplest form. (Lesson 2-3B)

29. $\frac{2}{7} \cdot \frac{4}{5}$ **30.** $\frac{1}{8} \cdot \frac{4}{9}$ **31.** $\frac{6}{11} \cdot \frac{9}{24}$

Main Idea

Solve problems involving discount.

NGSSS

MA.7.A.1.2 Solve percent problems, including problems involving discounts, simple interest, taxes, tips and percents of increase or decrease. *Also addresses MA.7.A.3.2, MA.7.A.5.1.*

New Vocabulary

discount

Get Connected
glencoe.com

Discount

WATER PARKS A pass at a water park is $58. Halfway through the season, the pass is discounted by 20%.

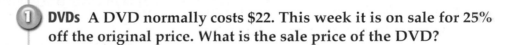

1. Calculate the discount by finding 20% of $58. Round to the nearest cent.

2. What will be the discounted price?

3. Multiply 0.8 and $58. How does the result compare to your answer in Exercise 2?

Discount is the amount by which the regular price of an item is reduced. The sale price is the regular price minus the discount.

Real-World EXAMPLE

① **DVDs** A DVD normally costs $22. This week it is on sale for 25% off the original price. What is the sale price of the DVD?

Method 1   Subtract the discount from the regular price.

First, find the amount of the discount.

$$25\% \text{ of } \$22 = 0.25 \times \$22 \quad \text{Write 25\% as a decimal.}$$
$$= \$5.50 \quad\quad\quad\quad \text{The discount is \$5.50.}$$

Next, subtract the discount from the regular price.
$$\$22 - \$5.50 = \$16.50$$

Method 2   Subtract the percent of discount from 100%.

$$100\% - 25\% = 75\% \quad\quad \text{Subtract the discount from 100\%.}$$

The sale price is 75% of the regular price.

$$75\% \text{ of } \$22 = 0.75 \times \$22 \quad \text{Write 75\% as a decimal.}$$
$$= \$16.50 \quad\quad\quad\quad \text{Multiply.}$$

The sale price of the DVD is $16.50.

 CHOOSE Your Method

a. **CLOTHES** A shirt is regularly priced at $42. It is on sale for 15% off. What is the sale price of the shirt?

EXAMPLE **Find the Sale Price**

2 **BOOGIE BOARDS** A boogie board that has a regular price of $69 is on sale at a 35% discount. What is the sale price with 7% tax?

Step 1 Find the amount of the discount.

$$35\% \text{ of } \$69 = 0.35 \cdot \$69 \quad \text{Write 35\% as a decimal.}$$

$$= \$24.15 \quad \text{The discount is \$24.15.}$$

Step 2 Subtract the discount from the regular price.

$$\$69 - \$24.15 = \$44.85$$

Step 3 The percent of tax is applied after the discount is taken.

$$7\% \text{ of } \$44.85 = 0.07 \cdot 44.85 \quad \text{Write 7\% as a decimal.}$$

$$= 3.14 \quad \text{The tax is \$3.14.}$$

Add the tax to the sale price of the boogie board.

$$\$44.85 + \$3.14 = \$47.99$$

The sale price of the boogie board including tax is $47.99.

✓ CHECK Your Progress

b. MUSIC A CD that has a regular price of $15.50 is on sale at a 25% discount. What is the sale price with 6.5% tax?

EXAMPLE **Find the Original Price**

3 **CELL PHONES** A cell phone is on sale for 30% off. If the sale price is $239.89, what is the original price?

The sale price is 100% − 30% or 70% of the original price.

Words	$239.89 is 70% of what price?
Variable	Let p represent the original price.
Equation	$239.89 = 0.7 \times p$

$239.89 = 0.7p$ Write the equation.

$\dfrac{239.89}{0.7} = \dfrac{0.7p}{0.7}$ Divide each side by 0.7.

$342.70 = p$ Simplify.

The original price is $342.70.

✓ CHECK Your Progress

c. Find the original price if the sale price of the cell phone is $205.50.

Example 1
(p. 335)

Find the sale price to the nearest cent.

1. $210 bicycle; 25% discount

2. $40 sweater; 33% discount

Example 2
(p. 336)

3. $1,575 computer; 15% discount; 4.25% tax

4. $119.50 skateboard; 20% off; 7% tax

Example 3
(p. 336)

5. IN-LINE SKATES A pair of in-line skates is on sale for $90. If this price represents a 9% discount from the original price, what is the original price to the nearest cent?

Practice and Problem Solving

> = **Step-by-Step Solutions** begin on page R16.
> **Extra Practice** is on page EP16.

Examples 1 and 2
(pp. 335–336)

Find the sale price to the nearest cent.

6. $64 jacket; 20% discount

7. $1,200 TV; 10% discount

8. $199 MP3 player; 15% discount

9. $12.25 pen set; 60% discount

10. $4.30 makeup; 40% discount; 6% tax

11 $7.50 admission; 20% off; 5.75% tax

12. $39.60 sweater; 33% discount; 4.5% tax

13. $90.00 skateboard; $33\frac{1}{3}$% off; 8% tax

Example 3
(p. 336)

14. COSMETICS A bottle of hand lotion is on sale for $2.25. If this price represents a 50% discount from the original price, what is the original price to the nearest cent?

15. TICKETS At a movie theater, the cost of admission to a matinee is $5.25. If this price represents a 30% discount from the evening price, find the evening price to the nearest cent.

Find the original price to the nearest cent.

16. calendar: discount, 75%
　　　　sale price, $2.25

17. telescope: discount, 30%
　　　　sale price, $126

18. COMPUTERS The Wares want to buy a new computer. The regular price is $1,049. The store is offering a 20% discount and a sales tax of 5.25% is added after the discount. What is the total cost?

19 **MULTIPLE REPRESENTATIONS** An online store is having a sale on digital cameras. The table shows the regular price and the sale price for the cameras.

Camera Model	Regular Price	Sale Price
A	$97.99	$83.30
B	$102.50	$82.00
C	$75.99	$65.35
D	$150.50	$135.45

　　a. TABLE Copy the table including a column for the discount.

　　b. WORDS Write a verbal rule that can be used to find the percent of decrease for any of the cameras.

　　c. NUMBERS Which model has the best discount?

20. **CHALLENGE** A gift store is having a sale in which all items are discounted 20%. Including tax, Colin paid $21 for a picture frame. If the sales tax rate is 5%, what was the original price of the picture frame?

21. **OPEN ENDED** Give an example of the sale price of an item and the total cost including sales tax if the tax rate is 5.75% and the item is 25% off.

22. **REASONING** Two department stores, The James Store and Ratcliffe's, are having sales. The stores sell the same brand of sneakers. The James Store usually sells them for $50, but has marked them at 40% off. At Ratcliffe's, the sneakers are marked down to 30% off of the usual price of $30. Which store has the better sale price? Explain.

23. **Write MATH** Describe two methods for finding the sale price of an item that is discounted 30%. Which method do you prefer? Explain.

NGSSS Practice   MA.7.A.1.2

24. A computer software store is having a sale. The table shows the regular price r and the sale price s of various items.

Item	Regular Price (r)	Sale Price (s)
A	$5.00	$4.00
B	$8.00	$6.40
C	$10.00	$8.00
D	$15.00	$12.00

Which formula can be used to calculate the sale price?

A. $s = r \times 0.2$ C. $s = r \times 0.8$

B. $s = r - 0.2$ D. $s = r - 0.8$

25. A chair that costs $210 was reduced by 40% for a one-day sale. After the sale, the sale price was increased by 40%. What is the price of the chair?

F. $176.40   H. $205.50

G. $185.30   I. $210.00

26. Carmen paid $10.50 for a T-shirt at the mall. It was on sale for 30% off. What was the original price before the discount?

A. $3.15   C. $15.00

B. $7.35   D. $35.00

27. **RESTAURANTS** Mitchell spent $13 on dinner. He wants to tip the server 15%. About how much money should he leave as the tip? (Lesson 6-3C)

Find the percent of change. Round to the nearest whole percent if necessary. State whether the percent of change is an *increase* or *decrease*. (Lesson 6-3B)

28. 35 birds to 45 birds   29. 60 inches to 38 inches   30. $2.75 to $1.80

Main Idea

Solve problems involving simple interest.

NGSSS

MA.7.A.1.2 Solve percent problems, including problems involving discounts, **simple interest,** taxes, tips and percents of increase or decrease. *Also addresses MA.7.A.3.2.*

New Vocabulary

principal
simple interest

Get Connected
glencoe.com

Financial Literacy: Simple Interest

INVESTING Suni plans to save the $200 she received for her birthday. The table shows the average yearly rates at three different banks.

Bank	Interest Rate
Nation Bank	3%
Federal Credit Union	2.50%
First Bank	2.75%

1. Calculate 2.50% of $200 to find the amount of money Suni can earn in one year at Federal Credit Union.

2. Calculate 2.75% of $200 to find the amount of money Suni can earn in one year at First Bank.

Principal is the amount of money deposited or borrowed. **Simple interest** is the amount paid or earned for the use of money. To find simple interest I, use the following formula.

Interest ⟶
Annual interest rate, written as a decimal.

$$I = prt$$

Principal ⟶
Time, expressed in years.

EXAMPLES Find Interest Earned

CHECKING Arnold has $580 in a savings account that pays 3% interest. How much interest will he earn in each amount of time?

① **5 years**

$I = prt$	Formula for simple interest
$I = 580 \cdot 0.03 \cdot 5$	Replace p with $580, r$ with 0.03, and t with 5.
$I = 87$	Simplify.

Arnold will earn $87 in interest in 5 years.

② **6 months**

6 months $= \dfrac{6}{12}$ or 0.5 year	Write the time as years.
$I = prt$	Formula for simple interest
$I = 580 \cdot 0.03 \cdot 0.5$	$p = \$580, r = 0.03, t = 0.5$
$I = 8.7$	Simplify.

Arnold will earn $8.70 in interest in 6 months.

CHECK Your Progress

a. **SAVINGS** Jenny has $1,560 in a savings account that pays 2.5% simple interest. How much interest will she earn in 3 years?

The formula $I = prt$ can also be used to find the interest owed when you borrow money. In this case, p is the amount of money borrowed and t is the amount of time the money is borrowed.

Real-World Link · · · ·
There are over 250 million registered passenger vehicles in the United States.

> **EXAMPLE** **Find Interest Paid on a Loan**

 LOANS Rondell's parents borrow $6,300 from the bank for a new car. The interest rate is 6% per year. How much simple interest will they pay if they take 2 years to repay the loan?

$I = prt$	Formula for simple interest
$I = 6{,}300 \cdot 0.06 \cdot 2$	Replace p with $6,300, r with 0.06, and t with 2.
$I = 756$	Simplify.

Rondell's parents will pay $756 in interest in 2 years.

 CHECK Your Progress

b. **LOANS** Mrs. Hanover borrows $1,400 at a rate of 5.5% per year. How much simple interest will she pay if it takes 8 months to repay the loan?

> **EXAMPLE** **Find Total Paid on a Credit Card**

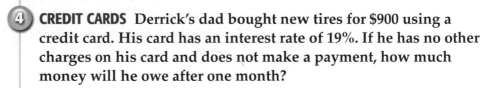 **CREDIT CARDS** Derrick's dad bought new tires for $900 using a credit card. His card has an interest rate of 19%. If he has no other charges on his card and does not make a payment, how much money will he owe after one month?

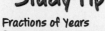

Study Tip

Fractions of Years Remember to express 1 month as $\frac{1}{12}$ year in the formula.

$I = prt$	Formula for simple interest
$I = 900 \cdot 0.19 \cdot \dfrac{1}{12}$	Replace p with $900, r with 0.19, and t with $\frac{1}{12}$.
$I = 14.25$	Simplify.

The interest owed after one month is $14.25. So, the total amount owed would be $900 + $14.25 or $914.25.

CHECK Your Progress

c. **CREDIT CARDS** An office manager charged $425 worth of office supplies on a credit card with an interest rate of 9.9%. How much money will he owe at the end of the month if he makes no other charges on the card and does not make a payment?

Examples 1 and 2
(pp. 339–340)

Find the simple interest earned to the nearest cent for each principal, interest rate, and time.

1. $640, 3%, 2 years
2. $1,500, 4.25%, 4 years
3. $580, 2%, 6 months
4. $1,200, 3.9%, 8 months

Example 3
(p. 340)

Find the simple interest paid to the nearest cent for each loan, interest rate, and time.

5 $4,500, 9%, 3.5 years
6. $290, 12.5%, 6 months

Example 4
(p. 340)

7. **FINANCES** The Masters family financed a computer that cost $1,200. If the interest rate is 19%, how much will the family owe for the computer after one month if no payments are made?

Practice and Problem Solving

 = **Step-by-Step Solutions** begin on page R16.
Extra Practice is on page EP17.

Examples 1 and 2
(pp. 339–340)

Find the simple interest earned to the nearest cent for each principal, interest rate, and time.

8. $1,050, 4.6%, 2 years
9. $250, 2.85%, 3 years
10. $500, 3.75%, 4 months
11. $3,000, 5.5%, 9 months

Example 3
(p. 340)

Find the simple interest paid to the nearest cent for each loan, interest rate, and time.

12. $1,000, 7%, 2 years
13. $725, 6.25%, 1 year
14. $2,700, 8.2%, 3 months
15. $175.80, 12%, 8 months

Example 4
(p. 340)

16. **CREDIT CARDS** Leon charged $75 at an interest rate of 12.5%. How much will Leon have to pay after one month if he makes no payments?

17. **TRAVEL** A family charged $1,345 in travel expenses to a credit card with a 7.25% interest rate. If no payments are made, how much will they owe after one month for their travel expenses?

18. **BANKING** The table shows interest rates that can be earned for various lengths of time.

   a. What is the simple interest earned on $900 for 9 months?

   b. Find the simple interest earned on $2,500 for 18 months.

Home Savings and Loan

Time	Rate
6 months	2.4%
9 months	2.9%
12 months	3.0%
18 months	3.1%

19 **INVESTING** Ramon has $4,200 to invest for college.

   a. If Ramon invests $4,200 for 3 years and earns $630, what is the simple interest rate?

   b. Ramon's goal is to have $5,000 after 4 years. Is this possible if he invests with a rate of return of 6%? Explain.

20. **OPEN ENDED** Suppose you earn 3% on a $1,200 deposit for 5 years. Explain how the simple interest is affected if the rate is increased by 1%. What happens if the time is increased by 1 year?

21. **CHALLENGE** Mrs. Antil deposits $800 in a savings account that earns 3.2% interest annually. At the end of the year, the interest is added to the principal or original amount. She keeps her money in this account for three years without withdrawing any money. Find the total in her account after each year for three years.

22. **MATH** List the steps you would use to find the simple interest on a $500 loan at a 6% interest rate for 18 months. Then find the simple interest.

NGSSS Practice   MA.6.A.3.2, MA.7.A.1.2

23. Jada invests $590 in a money market account. Her account pays 7.2% simple interest. If she does not add or withdraw any money, how much interest will Jada's account earn after 4 years of simple interest?

   A. $75.80

   B. $158.67

   C. $169.92

   D. $220.67

24. Mr. Sprockett borrows $3,500 from his bank to buy a used car. The loan has a 7.4% annual simple interest rate. If it takes Mr. Sprockett two years to pay back the loan, what is the total amount he will be paying?

   F. $3,012

   G. $3,598

   H. $4,018

   I. $4,550

25. **SPORTS** Find the total cost of a $20 volleyball if it is on sale for 33% off.
(Lesson 6-3D)

Find the total cost of each of the following. (Lesson 6-3C)

26. backpack, $25 with 7% tax

27. car, $8,000 with $5\frac{1}{2}$% tax

28. dinner, $50 with 18% tip

29. car wash, $25 with 15% tip

Divide. Write in simplest form. (Lesson 2-3D)

30. $\frac{3}{5} \div \frac{1}{2}$

31. $\frac{4}{7} \div \frac{5}{8}$

32. $2\frac{2}{3} \div 1\frac{1}{4}$

Extend

Spreadsheet: Simple Interest

Main Idea

Use a spreadsheet to calculate simple interest.

NGSSS

 MA.7.A.1.2 Solve percent problems, including problems **involving** discounts, **simple interest,** taxes, tips and percents of increase or decrease.

Get Connected
glencoe.com

A computer spreadsheet is a useful tool for quickly calculating simple interest for different values of principal, rate, and time.

ACTIVITY

SAVINGS Joel plans on opening a "Young Savers" account at his bank. The current rate on the account is 4%. To find the balance at the end of 2 years for different principal amounts, he enters the values B2 = 4 and C2 = 2 into the spreadsheet below.

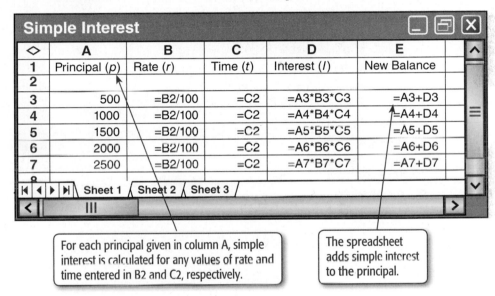

	A	B	C	D	E
1	Principal (*p*)	Rate (*r*)	Time (*t*)	Interest (*I*)	New Balance
2					
3	500	=B2/100	=C2	=A3*B3*C3	=A3+D3
4	1000	=B2/100	=C2	=A4*B4*C4	=A4+D4
5	1500	=B2/100	=C2	=A5*B5*C5	=A5+D5
6	2000	=B2/100	=C2	−A6*B6*C6	=A6+D6
7	2500	=B2/100	=C2	=A7*B7*C7	=A7+D7

Sheet 1 / Sheet 2 / Sheet 3

For each principal given in column A, simple interest is calculated for any values of rate and time entered in B2 and C2, respectively.

The spreadsheet adds simple interest to the principal.

Analyze the Results

1. Why is the rate in column B divided by 100?

2. What is the balance in Joel's account after 2 years if the principal is $1,500 and the simple interest rate is 4%?

3. How much interest does Joel earn in 2 years if his account has a principal of $2,000 and a simple interest rate of 4%?

4. Is the amount of principal proportional to the interest Joel earns if his account earns 4% simple interest over 2 years? Explain.

5. Is the amount of principal proportional to the balance in Joel's account if it earns 4% simple interest over 2 years? Explain.

Problem Solving in Video Game Design

ALL FUN AND GAMES

Are you passionate about computer gaming? You might want to explore a career in video game design. A video game designer is responsible for a game's concept, layout, character development, and game-play. Game designers use math and logic to compute how different parts of a game will work.

Choose a Major

Are you interested in a career as a video game designer? Take some of the following courses in high school.

- Introduction to Computer Literacy
- 3-D Digital Animation
- Introduction to Game Development

Get Connected glencoe.com

NGSSS

MA.7.A.1.2 Solve percent problems, including problems involving discounts, simple interest, taxes, tips and percents of increase or decrease.

Video Game Sales History

Week	Japan Sales ($)	U.S. Sales ($)
1	580,510	1,213,264
2	185,528	415,320
3	149,045	263,825

Real-World Math

Use the information in the circle graph and the table to solve each problem.

1. How many of the top 20 video games sold in 2007 were sports games?

2. Out of the top 20 video games sold in 2007, how many more music games were there than racer games?

3. In Week 1, the total sales for a video game were $2,374,136. What percent of the total sales was from the U.S.? Round to the nearest whole percent.

4. Find the percent of change in sales of the video game from Week 1 to Week 3 in Japan. Round to the nearest whole percent. State whether the percent of change is an *increase* or a *decrease*.

5. Which country had a greater percent decrease in sales from Week 1 to Week 2: Japan or the U.S.? Explain.

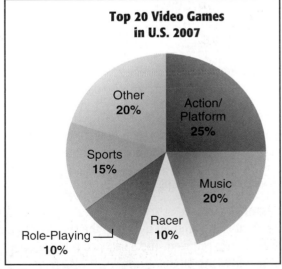

Top 20 Video Games in U.S. 2007

- Other 20%
- Action/Platform 25%
- Music 20%
- Racer 10%
- Role-Playing 10%
- Sports 15%

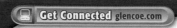

• **STUDY** *TO GO*
• Vocabulary Review
• Multilingual eGlossary

FOLDABLES®
Study Organizer

Be sure the following Key Concepts are noted in your Foldable.

Key Concepts

Percent of a Number (Lesson 6-1)
• To find the percent of a number, first write the percent as either a fraction or decimal and then multiply.

Percent Proportion (Lesson 6-2)

$$\left.\frac{part}{whole} = \frac{n}{100}\right\} percent$$

Percent Equation (Lesson 6-2)

$$part = percent \cdot whole$$

Percent of Change (Lesson 6-3)
• A percent of change is a ratio that compares the change in quantity to the original amount.

$$percent\ of\ change = \frac{amount\ of\ change}{original\ amount}$$

Discount (Lesson 6-3)
• Discount is the amount by which the regular price of an item is reduced. The sale price is the regular price minus the discount.

Sales Tax (Lesson 6-3)
• Sales tax is an additional amount of money charged on items. The total cost of an item is the regular price plus the sales tax.

Key Vocabulary

discount (p. 335)
gratuity (p. 332)
percent equation (p. 317)
percent of change (p. 326)
percent of decrease (p. 326)
percent of increase (p. 326)
percent proportion (p. 312)
principal (p. 339)
sales tax (p. 331)
simple interest (p. 339)
tip (p. 332)

Vocabulary Check

State whether each sentence is *true* or *false*. If *false*, replace the underlined word or number to make a true sentence.

1. The sale price of a discounted item is the regular price <u>minus</u> the discount.

2. A ratio that compares the change in quantity to the original amount is called the <u>percent of change</u>.

3. A <u>percent proportion</u> compares part of a quantity to the whole quantity using a percent.

4. The formula for simple interest is <u>I = prt</u>.

5. One way to find the total bill with tip is to add the percent of tip to <u>10%</u>.

6. The equation part = percent · whole is known as the <u>principal</u> equation.

7. The <u>principal</u> is the amount of money deposited or borrowed.

8. A <u>tax</u> is the amount by which the regular price of an item is reduced.

9. To find a percent of increase, compare the amount of the increase to the <u>new</u> amount.

10. If the new amount is greater than the original amount, then the percent of change is percent of <u>decrease</u>.

Multi-Part Lesson Review

6-1 Percents

Percent of a Number (pp. 300–304)

 MA.7.A.1.2

Find each number. Round to the nearest tenth if necessary.

11. Find 78% of 50.

12. 45.5% of 75 is what number?

13. What is 225% of 60?

14. 0.75% of 80 is what number?

EXAMPLE 1 Find 24% of 200.

24% of 200

$= 24\% \times 200$ Write the expression.

$= 0.24 \times 200$ Write 24% as a decimal.

$= 48$ Multiply.

So, 24% of 200 is 48.

Percent and Estimation (pp. 305–310)

MA.7.A.1.2

Estimate.

15. 25% of 81   **16.** 33% of 122

17. 77% of 38   **18.** 19.5% of 96

Estimate by using 10%.

19. 12% of 77   **20.** 88% of 400

EXAMPLE 2 Estimate 52% of 495.

$52\% \approx 50\%$ or $\frac{1}{2}$, and $495 \approx 500$.

52% of $495 \approx \frac{1}{2} \cdot 500$ or 250.

So, 52% of 495 is about 250.

6-2 Proportions and Equations

The Percent Proportion (pp. 312–316)

MA.7.A.1.2

Find each number. Round to the nearest tenth if necessary.

21. SOCCER A soccer team lost 30% of their games. If they played 20 games, how many did they win?

22. 6 is what percent of 120?

23. Find 0.8% of 35.

24. What percent of 375 is 40?

25. PHONE SERVICE A family pays $21.99 each month for its long distance phone service. This is 80% of the original price of the phone service. What is the original price of the phone service? Round to the nearest cent if necessary.

EXAMPLE 3 What percent of 90 is 18?

$\frac{18}{90} = \frac{n}{100}$ Write the proportion.

$18 \cdot 100 = 90 \cdot n$ Find the cross products.

$\frac{1,800}{90} = \frac{90n}{90}$ Divide each side by 90.

$20 = n$ So, 18 is 20% of 90.

EXAMPLE 4 52 is 65% of what number?

$\frac{52}{w} = \frac{65}{100}$ Write the proportion.

$52 \cdot 100 = w \cdot 65$ Find the cross products.

$\frac{5,200}{65} = \frac{65w}{65}$ Divide each side by 65.

$80 = w$ So, 52 is 65% of 80.

6-2 Proportions and Equations

The Percent Equation (pp. 317–321)

 MA.7.A.1.2

Write an equation for each problem. Then solve. Round to the nearest tenth if necessary.

26. 32 is what percent of 50?

27. 65% of what number is 39?

28. SALONS A salon increased the sales of hair products by about 12.5% this week. If they sold 43 hair products last week, how many did they sell this week?

EXAMPLE 5 27 is what percent of 90?

27 is the part and 90 is the base. Let n represent the percent.

$$\underbrace{\text{part}} = \underbrace{\text{percent}} \cdot \underbrace{\text{base}}$$

$27 = n \cdot 90$ Write an equation.

$\dfrac{27}{90} = \dfrac{90n}{90}$ Divide each side by 90.

$0.3 = n$ The percent is 30%.

So, 27 is 30% of 90.

PSI: Determine Reasonable Answers (pp. 322–323)

 MA.7.A.1.2

Determine a reasonable answer for each problem.

29. CABLE TV In a survey of 1,813 consumers, 18% said that they would be willing to pay more for cable if they got more channels. Is 3.3, 33, or 333 a reasonable estimate for the number of consumers willing to pay more for cable?

EXAMPLE 6 Out of 394 students, 24.8% participate in music programs. What is a reasonable estimate for the number of students who participate in music programs?

$394 \times 0.248 \rightarrow 400 \times 0.25$ or 100 students

6-3 Applying Percents

Percent of Change (pp. 326–330)

 MA.7.A.1.2

Find each percent of change. Round to the nearest whole percent if necessary. State whether the percent of change is an *increase* or *decrease*.

30. original: 172
new: 254

31. original: $200
new: $386

32. original: 75
new: 60

33. original: $49.95
new: $54.95

34. Tyree bought a collectible comic book for $49.62 last year. This year, he sold it for $52.10. Find the percent of change of the price of the comic book. Round to the nearest percent.

EXAMPLE 7 A magazine that originally cost $2.75 is now $3.55. Find the percent of change. Round to the nearest whole percent.

Find the amount of change.
$3.55 - 2.75 = 0.80$

percent of change $= \dfrac{\text{amount of change}}{\text{original amount}}$

$= \dfrac{0.80}{2.75}$ Substitution

≈ 0.29 Simplify.

The percent of change is about 29%. Since the percent of change is positive, this is a percent of *increase*.

6-3 Applying Percents

Sales Tax and Tips (pp. 331–334)

Find the total cost to the nearest cent.

35. $12 haircut; 15% tip

36. $48 dinner; 18% gratuity

37. RESTAURANTS A restaurant bill comes to $42.75. Find the total cost if the tax is 6% and a 15% tip is left on the amount after the tax is added.

EXAMPLE 8 Raymond wants to tip the server for his dinner. If the dinner costs $24 and he wants to give the server a 15% tip, what is the total cost?

15% of 24 = 0.15 × 24	Write 15% as a decimal.
= 3.60	The tip is $3.60.
$24.00 + 3.60 = $27.60	Add the tip and cost of the dinner.

Discount (pp. 335–338)

Find the sale price to the nearest cent.

38. $45 roller blades; 20% discount

39. $15 T-shirt; 25% discount

40. ELECTRONICS A new radio is priced at $30. The store has an end-of-year sale and all their items are 40% off. What is the sale price of the radio?

EXAMPLE 9 A pair of shoes normally costs $40. This week they are on sale for 20% off. What is the sale price of the shoes?

20% of 40 ⟶ 0.20 × 40	Write 20% as a decimal.
= 8.00	The discount is $8.00.
$40 − $8 = $32.00	Subtract the discount from the cost.

Simple Interest (pp. 339–342)

Find the interest earned to the nearest cent for the principal, interest rate, and time.

41. $475, 5%, 2 years

Find the interest paid to the nearest cent for the loan balance, interest rate, and time.

42. $3,200, 8%, 4 years

43. SAVINGS Aleta deposited $450 into a savings account earning 3.75% annual simple interest. How much interest will she earn in 6 years?

EXAMPLE 10 Find the interest earned on $400 at 9% for 3 years.

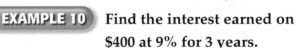

$I = prt$ Simple interest formula

$I = 400 \cdot 0.09 \cdot 3$ $p = \$400, r = 0.09, t = 3$

$I = 108$ Simplify.

The interest earned is $108.

Find each number. Round to the nearest tenth if necessary.

1. Find 55% of 164.

2. What is 355% of 15?

3. Find 25% of 80.

4. **NGSSS** **PRACTICE** Out of 365 students, 210 bought a hot lunch. About what percent of the students did NOT buy a hot lunch?

   A. 35%　　　**C.** 56%

   B. 42%　　　**D.** 78%

Estimate.

5. 18% of 246　　6. 145% of 81

7. 71% of 324　　8. 56% of 65.4

9. **COMMUNICATION** Carla makes a long distance phone call and talks for 50 minutes. Of these minutes, 25% were spent talking to her brother. Would the time spent talking with her brother be about 8, 12, or 15 minutes? Explain your reasoning.

Write an equation for each problem. Then solve. Round to the nearest tenth if necessary.

10. Find 14% of 65.

11. What number is 36% of 294?

12. 82% of what number is 73.8?

13. 75 is what percent of 50?

Find each percent of change. Round to the nearest whole percent if necessary. State whether the percent of change is an *increase* or a *decrease*.

14. $60 to $75

15. 145 meters to 216 meters

16. 48 minutes to 40 minutes

Find the total cost or sale price to the nearest cent.

17. $2,200 computer, $6\frac{1}{2}$% sales tax

18. $16 hat, 55% discount

19. $35.49 jeans, 33% discount

Find the simple interest earned to the nearest cent for each principal, interest rate, and time.

20. $750, 3%, 4 years

21. $1,050, 4.6%, 2 years

22. $2,600, 4%, 3 months

23. **NGSSS** **PRACTICE** Mr. Glover borrows $3,500 to renovate his home. His loan has an annual simple interest rate of 15%. If he pays off the loan after 6 months, about how much will he pay in all?

   F. $3,500

   G. $3,720

   H. $3,763

   I. $4,025

24. **EXTENDED RESPONSE** Use the table below. It shows the results of a survey in which 175 students were asked what type of food they wanted for their class party.

Type of Food	Percent
Subs	32%
Tex-Mex	56%
Italian	12%

   Part A How many of the 175 students chose Italian food for their class party?

   Part B How many students chose Tex-Mex food for the party?

Gridded Response: Percents

When the answer to a gridded-response question is a percent, do not convert the percent to a decimal or fraction. Grid in the percent value without the % symbol.

NGSSS PRACTICE EXAMPLE

Noah took 72 pictures with his new camera. Of those, 54 were taken while he was at summer camp. What percent of Noah's pictures were taken at summer camp?

$$\frac{54}{72} = \frac{n}{100}$$ Write the proportion.

$54 \cdot 100 = 72 \cdot n$ Find the cross products.

$$\frac{5400}{72} = \frac{72n}{72}$$ Simplify and divide each side by 72.

$75 = n$

So, 75% of Noah's pictures were taken at summer camp. Grid in 75.

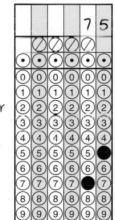

Correct   **NOT Correct**

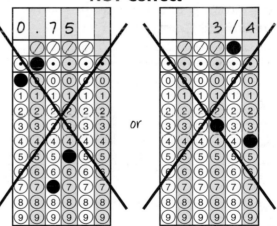

 ## Work on It

Out of the 215 students who play a sport, 86 play more than one sport. What percent of the student athletes play more than one sport? Fill in your answer on a grid like the one shown above.

Test Hint

If your answer will not fit in the response grid, then solve the problem again.

Read each question. Then fill in the correct answer on the answer sheet provided by your teacher or on a sheet of paper.

1. Sarah wants to buy new pillows for her room. Which store offers the best buy on pillows?

Store	Sale Price
A	3 pillows for $40
B	4 pillows for $50
C	2 pillows for $19
D	1 pillow for $11

   A. Store A
   B. Store B
   C. Store C
   D. Store D

2. The graph shows the attendance at a summer art festival from 2002 to 2007. If the trend in attendance continues, which is the best prediction of the attendance at the art festival in 2011?

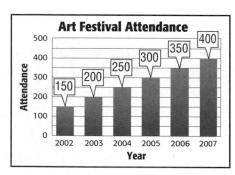

Art Festival Attendance

   F. Fewer than 200
   G. Between 500 and 600
   H. Between 700 and 800
   I. More than 800

3. At their annual car wash, the science club washes 30 cars in 45 minutes. At this rate, how many cars will they wash in 1 hour?
   A. 40
   B. 45
   C. 50
   D. 60

4. **GRIDDED RESPONSE** A necklace regularly sells for $18.00. The store advertises a 15% discount. What is the sale price of the necklace in dollars?

$18.00

5. **GRIDDED RESPONSE** At a middle school, 38% of all seventh graders have taken swimming lessons. There are 250 students in the seventh grade. How many of them have taken swimming lessons?

6. The cost of Ken's car wash was $23.95. If he wants to give his detailer a 15% tip, about how much of a tip should he leave?
   F. $2.40
   G. $3.60
   H. $4.60
   I. $4.80

7. An architect made a model of an office building using a scale of 1 inch equals 3 meters. If the height of the model is 12.5 inches, which of the following represents the actual height of the building?

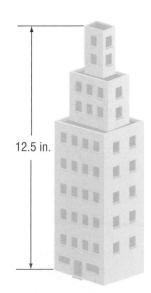
12.5 in.

   A. 40.0 m
   B. 37.5 m
   C. 36.0 m
   D. 28.4 m

8. At a pet store, 38% of the animals are dogs. If there are a total of 88 animals at the pet store, which proportion can be used to find x, the number of dogs at the pet store?

F. $\dfrac{x}{88} = \dfrac{100}{38}$

G. $\dfrac{38}{88} = \dfrac{100}{x}$

H. $\dfrac{x}{88} = \dfrac{38}{100}$

I. $\dfrac{100}{88} = \dfrac{x}{38}$

9. ✎ **GRIDDED RESPONSE** A wrestler competes in 25 matches. Of those matches, he wins 17. What percent of the matches did the wrestler win?

10. **SHORT RESPONSE** The average cost of a 2-bedroom apartment in Grayson was $625 last year. This year, the average cost is $650. What is the percent of increase from last year to this year?

11. What are the coordinates of B?

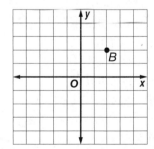

A. $(-2, 2)$

B. $(2, -2)$

C. $(-2, -2)$

D. $(2, 2)$

12. In Nadia's DVD collection, she has 8 action DVDs, 12 comedy DVDs, 7 romance DVDs, and 3 science fiction DVDs. What percent of Nadia's DVD collection is comedies?

F. 25%

G. 30%

H. 35%

I. 40%

13. A salesman needed to sell a four-wheeler. He priced it at $3,500 the first day it was on the market. The second day he reduced the price by 10%. What was the price of the four-wheeler after this reduction?

A. $3850

B. $3465

C. $3150

D. $3000

14. **EXTENDED RESPONSE** Cable Company A increases their rates from $98 a month to $101.92 a month.

Part A What is the percent of increase?

Part B Cable Company B offers their cable for $110 dollars a month but gives a 10% discount for new customers. Describe two ways to find the cost for new customers.

Part C If you currently use Cable Company A, would it make sense to change to Cable Company B? Explain.

NEED EXTRA HELP?														
If You Missed Question...	1	2	3	4	5	6	7	8	9	10	11	12	13	14
Go to Lesson...	4-1B	5-3A	4-1B	6-3D	6-2B	6-1B	4-2B	6-2B	6-2C	6-3B	1-1C	6-2D	6-3D	6-3B
For help with NGSSS...	A.1.6	A.3.1	A.1.6	A.1.2	A.1.2	A.1.2	A.1.6	A.1.2	A.1.2	A.1.2	G.4.3	A.1.2	A.1.2	A.1.2

Data Analysis and Probability

Supporting ★ Idea

Understand how data analysis and probability can be used to represent the population. Construct and analyze histograms, stem-and-leaf plots, and circle graphs.

FOLDABLES® Study Organizer

Make this Foldable to help you organize your notes. Begin with three sheets of notebook paper.

1 Fold 3 sheets of paper in half as shown.

2 Cut a 1" tab along the left edge through one thickness.

3 Glue the 1" tab down. Write the lesson number and title on the front tab.

4 Repeat Steps 2 and 3 for the remaining sheets. Staple them together to form a booklet.

7-1 Statistics

Review Vocabulary

mean (Prior Grade) *media* the sum of the data divided by the number of items in the data set

$$\frac{97 + 75 + 82 + 90}{4} = 86$$

Key Vocabulary

	English	Español
p. 370	stem-and-leaf plot	diagrama de tallo y hojas
p. 375	probability	probabilidad
p. 381	sample space	espacio muestral
p. 410	population	pablación

Multilingual eGlossary glencoe.com

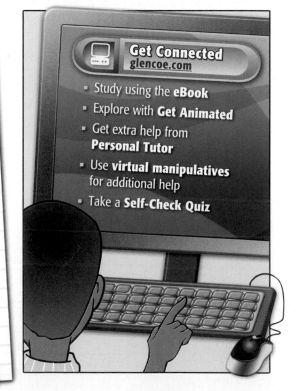

Get Connected
glencoe.com

- Study using the **eBook**
- Explore with **Get Animated**
- Get extra help from **Personal Tutor**
- Use **virtual manipulatives** for additional help
- Take a **Self-Check Quiz**

When Will I Use This?

Jamar and Theresa in **Radio Surveys**

Your Turn!
You will solve this problem in Chapter 7.

Are You Ready for Chapter 7?

You have two options for checking prerequisite skills for this chapter.

Text Option Take the Quick Check below. Refer to the Quick Review for help.

QUICK Check

Find the mean for each data set. Round to the nearest tenth if necessary. (Prior Grade)

1. miles traveled on the weekend: 29, 14, 80, 59, 78, 30, 59, 69, 55, 50

2. points scored in a basketball game: 11, 17, 8, 6, 13, 16, 20, 9

3. number of wins by each team: 10, 8, 9, 11, 5, 7, 13

4. **TEMPERATURE** During the week, the daily low temperatures were 52°F, 45°F, 51°F, 45°F, 47°F, 53°F, and 48°F. What is the mean daily low temperature for the week?

Find the median and mode for each data set. (Prior Grade)

5. number of dogs groomed each week: 65, 56, 57, 75, 76, 66, 65

6. scores earned on a math test: 95, 90, 92, 94, 91, 90, 98, 88, 89, 100

7. prices of books: $10, $18, $11, $6, $6, $5, $10, $11, $46, $7, $6, $8

8. points scored in football games: 21, 35, 14, 17, 28, 14, 7, 21, 14

QUICK Review

EXAMPLE 1

EARNINGS Brianna earned $10, $13, $11, $8, $15, and $21 by helping neighbors clean up around their houses. What is the mean amount Brianna earned helping her neighbors?

To find the mean, add the data values and divide by 6.

$$\frac{10 + 13 + 11 + 8 + 15 + 21}{6} = \frac{78}{6} \text{ or } 13$$

So, Brianna earned a mean amount of $13 helping her neighbors.

EXAMPLE 2

MEASUREMENT Nathaniel found the weekly rainfall totals throughout the months of June and July as shown in the table. Find the median of the data.

Week	1	2	3	4	5	6	7
Rainfall (in.)	8	4	10	9	12	3	7

To find the median, write the data in order from least to greatest.

3, 4, 7, ⑧ 9, 10, 12

↓ median

The median for the data set is 8.

Online Option  Take the Online Readiness Quiz at **glencoe.com**.

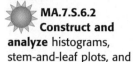

Spreadsheet Lab: Circle Graphs

A type of display used to compare categorical data is a *circle graph*. Circle graphs are useful when comparing parts of a whole.

ACTIVITY

MAGAZINES The spreadsheet below shows the results of a survey in which students were asked their favorite type of magazine. Make a circle graph of the data.

STEP 1 Enter the data in a spreadsheet as shown.

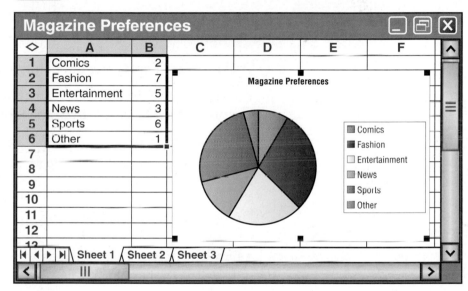

STEP 2 Select the information in cells A1 to B6. Click on the Chart Wizard icon. Choose the Pie chart type. Click Next twice. Enter the title. Then click Next and Finish.

1. **MAKE A CONJECTURE** Use the graph to determine which types of magazines were preferred by $\frac{1}{3}$ and 25% of the students. Explain your reasoning.

2. **COLLECT THE DATA** Collect some data that can be displayed in either a circle or bar graph. Then use a spreadsheet to make both types of displays. When would a bar graph be more useful? a circle graph? Justify your selection.

Main Idea

Construct and analyze circle graphs.

NGSSS

 MA.7.S.6.2 Construct and analyze histograms, stem-and-leaf plots, and **circle graphs.** *Also addresses MA.7.A.3.2.*

New Vocabulary

circle graph

Get Connected
glencoe.com

Circle Graphs

VEGETABLES The students at Pine Ridge Middle School were asked to identify their favorite vegetable. The table shows the results of the survey.

Favorite Vegetable	
Vegetable	**Percent**
Carrots	45%
Green Beans	23%
Peas	17%
Other	15%

1. Explain how you know that each student selected only one favorite vegetable.

2. If 400 students participated in the survey, how many students preferred carrots?

One graph that shows data as parts of a whole is called a **circle graph**. In a circle graph, the percents add up to 100.

EXAMPLE Display Data in a Circle Graph

1. **VEGETABLES** Display the data above in a circle graph.

• There are 360° in a circle. Determine what part of the circle will represent each percent from the table above.

45% of 360° = 0.45 · 360° or 162°

23% of 360° = 0.23 · 360° or 83°   Round to the nearest whole degree.

17% of 360° = 0.17 · 360° or about 61°

15% of 360° = 0.15 · 360° or about 54°

• Draw a circle with a radius as shown. Then use a protractor to draw the first angle, in this case 162°. Repeat this step.

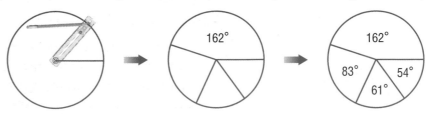

• Label each section of the graph with the category and percent. Give the graph a title.

Check
162° + 83° + 61° + 54° = 360° ✓

Favorite Vegetable

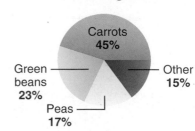

a. **SCIENCE** The table shows the present composition of Earth's atmosphere. Display the data in a circle graph.

Composition of Earth's Atmosphere	
Element	Percent
Nitrogen	78%
Oxygen	21%
Other gases	1%

When constructing a circle graph, you first may need to convert the data to ratios and decimals and then to degrees and percents.

EXAMPLE **Construct a Circle Graph**

2 **ANIMALS** The table shows endangered species in the United States. Make a circle graph of the data.

- Find the total number of species.
  $68 + 77 + 14 + 11 = 170$

- Find the ratio that compares each number with the total. Write the ratio as a decimal rounded to the nearest hundredth.

  mammals: $\frac{68}{170} = 0.40$ birds: $\frac{77}{170} \approx 0.45$

  reptiles: $\frac{14}{170} \approx 0.08$ amphibians: $\frac{11}{170} \approx 0.06$

Species	Number of Species
Mammals	68
Birds	77
Reptiles	14
Amphibians	11

- Find the number of degrees for each section of the graph.

  mammals: $0.40 \cdot 360° = 144°$

  birds: $0.45 \cdot 360° \approx 162°$

  reptiles: $0.08 \cdot 360° \approx 29°$

  amphibians: $0.06 \cdot 360° \approx 22°$

  Because of rounding, the sum of the degrees is 357°.

- Draw the circle graph. Label each piece with the title and percent.

Check After drawing the first three sections, you can measure the last section of a circle graph to verify that the angle has the correct measure.

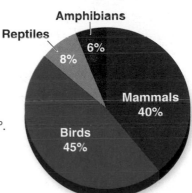

Real-World Link · · · ·
The Carolina Northern and Virginia Northern Flying Squirrel are both endangered. The northern flying squirrel is a small nocturnal gliding mammal that is about 10 to 12 inches in total length and weighs about 3–5 ounces.

 CHECK Your Progress

b. **OLYMPICS** The number of Winter Olympic medals won by the U.S. from 1924 to 2006 is shown in the table. Display the data in a circle graph.

U.S Winter Olympic Medals	
Type	Number
Gold	78
Silver	81
Bronze	59

EXAMPLES Analyze a Circle Graph

AUTOMOBILES The graph shows the percent of automobiles registered in the western United States in a recent year.

U.S. Registered Automobiles in West
Washington 13%
Oregon 6%
Nevada 3%
California 78%

3 Which state had the most registered automobiles?

The largest section of the circle is the one representing California. So, California has the most registered automobiles.

Study Tip

Check for Reasonableness
To check Example 4, you can estimate and solve the problem another way.

78% - 6% ≈ 70%
70% of 24 is 17

Since 17.28 is about 17, the answer is reasonable.

4 If 24 million automobiles were registered in these states, how many more automobiles were registered in California than in Oregon?

California: 78% of 24 million → 0.78×24, or 18.72 million

Oregon: 6% of 24 million → 0.06×24, or 1.44 million

There were 18.72 million − 1.44 million, or 17.28 million more registered automobiles in California than in Oregon.

CHECK Your Progress

c. Which state had the least number of registered automobiles? Explain.

d. What was the total number of registered automobiles in Washington and Oregon?

CHECK Your Understanding

Examples 1 and 2
(pp. 358–359)

Display each set of data in a circle graph.

1.

Blood Types in the U.S.	
Blood Type	**Percent**
O	44
A	42
B	10
AB	4

2.

Favorite Musical Instrument	
Type	**Number of Students**
Piano	54
Guitar	27
Drum	15
Flute	24

Examples 3 and 4
(p. 360)

3. **COLORS** Use the graph that shows the results of a survey.

a. What color is most favored?

b. If 400 people were surveyed, how many more people favored purple than red?

Favorite Color

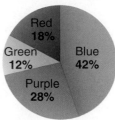

Red 18%
Green 12%
Blue 42%
Purple 28%

Practice and Problem Solving

● = **Step-by-Step Solutions** begin on page R17.
Extra Practice is on page EP17.

Examples 1 and 2
(pp. 358–359)

Display each set of data in a circle graph.

4.

U.S. Steel Roller Coasters	
Type	**Percent**
Sit down	86%
Inverted	8%
Other	6%

5.

U.S. Orange Production	
State	**Orange Production**
California	18%
Florida	81%
Texas	1%

6.

Animals in Pet Store	
Animal	**Number of Pets**
Birds	13
Cats	11
Dogs	9
Fish	56
Other	22

7.

Favorite Games	
Type of Game	**Number of Students**
Card	7
Board	9
Video	39
Sports	17
Drama	8

Examples 3 and 4
(p. 360)

8. **LANDFILLS** Use the circle graph that shows what is in U.S. landfills.

a. What takes up the most space in landfills?

b. About how many times more paper is there than food and yard waste?

c. If a landfill contains 200 million tons of trash, how much of it is plastic?

What is in U.S. Landfills?

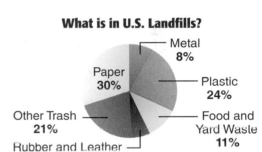

Metal 8%
Paper 30%
Plastic 24%
Other Trash 21%
Food and Yard Waste 11%
Rubber and Leather 6%

9 **MONEY** Use the graph that shows the results of a survey.

Do Americans Favor Common North American Currency?

No 53%
Yes 43%
Don't Know 4%

a. What percent of Americans favor a common North American currency?

b. About how many of the approximately 298 million Americans would say "Don't Know" in response to this survey?

c. About how many more Americans oppose a common currency than favor it?

DATA SENSE For each graph, find the missing values.

10. **Dog Expenses**

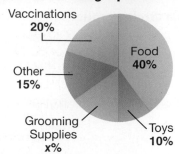

Vaccinations 20%
Other 15%
Food 40%
Grooming Supplies x%
Toys 10%

11. **Family Budget**

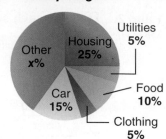

Other x%
Housing 25%
Utilities 5%
Car 15%
Food 10%
Clothing 5%

Select an appropriate type of graph to display each set of data: line graph, bar graph, or circle graph. Then display the data using the graph.

12.

Top 5 Presidential Birth States	
Place	**Presidents**
Virginia	8
Ohio	7
Massachusetts	4
New York	4
Texas	3

13.

Tanya's Day	
Activity	**Percent**
School	25%
Sleep	33%
Homework	12%
Sports	8%
Other	22%

14. **GEOGRAPHY** Use the table.

   a. Display the data in a circle graph.

   b. Use your graph to find which two lakes equal the size of Lake Superior.

   c. Find the median size of the Great Lakes.

Sizes of U.S. Great Lakes	
Lake	**Size (sq mi)**
Erie	9,930
Huron	23,010
Michigan	22,400
Ontario	7,520
Superior	31,820

15. **POLITICS** A group of students was asked whether people their age could make a difference in the political decisions of elected officials. The results are shown in the graph.

   a. How many students participated in the survey?

   b. Write a convincing argument explaining whether or not it is reasonable to say that 50% more students said they could make a difference than those who said they could not make a difference.

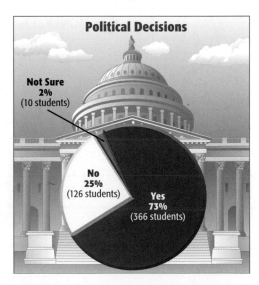

Political Decisions

Not Sure 2% (10 students)
No 25% (126 students)
Yes 73% (366 students)

16. **FIND THE DATA** Refer to the Data File on pages 2–5. Choose some data that can be displayed in a circle graph. Then display the data in a circle graph and write one statement analyzing the data.

17. CHALLENGE The graph shows the results of a survey about students' favorite school subject. About what percent of those surveyed said that math was their favorite subject? Explain your reasoning.

18. COLLECT THE DATA Collect some data from your classmates that can be represented in a circle graph. Then create the circle graph and write one statement analyzing the data.

19. Write MATH The table shows the percent of people who like each type of fruit juice. Can the data be represented in a circle graph? Justify your answer.

Favorite Subject

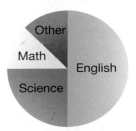

Fruit Juice	Percent
Apple	54%
Grape	48%
Orange	37%
Cranberry	15%

NGSSS Practice   MA.7.S.6.2

20. The graph shows the types of vehicles that crossed a bridge during one month.

Types of Vehicles

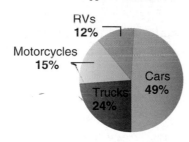

Which of the following shows the number of trucks if 480,000 vehicles cross the bridge each month?

A. 57,600   C. 115,200

B. 72,000   D. 235,200

21. ✎ **GRIDDED RESPONSE** The circle graph shows the results of a survey in which middle school students were asked to name one of their favorite pizza toppings. What percent of the people surveyed named mushrooms as their favorite topping?

Pizza Toppings

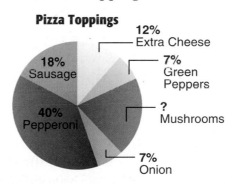

22. VIDEO GAME Sancho buys a video game system for $399 and finances it for 6 months at 10% interest. What is the total amount that Sancho will pay for the game system including interest? (Lesson 6-3E)

Find the cost or sale price to the nearest cent. (Lesson 6-3D)

23. $35.95 sweater, 6% tax

24. $258 television, 14% discount

Main Idea

Display and analyze data in a histogram.

NGSSS

MA.7.S.6.2 Construct and analyze histograms, stem-and-leaf plots, and circle graphs.

New Vocabulary

histogram

Get Connected
glencoe.com

Histograms

BASKETBALL Kylie researched the average ticket prices for NBA basketball games for 30 teams. The frequency table shows the results.

Price Interval ($)	Tally	Frequency
20.00–29.99	I	1
30.00–39.99	IIII IIII I	11
40.00–49.99	IIII IIII	10
50.00–59.99	IIII	5
60.00–69.99	I	1
70.00–79.99	II	2

1. What do you notice about the price intervals in the table?

2. How many tickets were at least $20.00 but less than $50.00?

Data from a frequency table can be displayed as a histogram. A **histogram** is similar to a bar graph and is used to display numerical data that have been organized into equal intervals.

 EXAMPLE **Construct a Histogram**

① **MOVIES** Choose intervals and make a frequency table of the data shown below. Then construct a histogram to represent the data.

Running Time of Movies (minutes)				
135	89	142	219	96
144	104	135	94	155
106	127	134	116	91
118	138	118	110	101

The least value in the data is 89 and the greatest is 219. An interval size of 30 minutes would yield the frequency table at the right.

To construct a histogram, follow these steps.

Step 1 Draw and label a horizontal and vertical axis. Include a title.

Step 2 Show the intervals from the frequency table on the horizontal axis.

Running Time of Movies (minutes)		
Time	Tally	Frequency
81–110	IIII III	8
111–140	IIII III	8
141–170	III	3
171–200		0
201–230	I	1

Step 3 For each time interval, draw a bar whose height is given by its frequency.

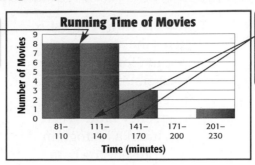

There is no space between bars.

Because all of the intervals are equal, all of the bars have the same width.

Running Time of Movies

CHECK Your Progress

a. SCHOOL The list at the right gives a set of test scores. Choose intervals, make a frequency table, and construct a histogram to represent the data.

Test Scores							
94	85	73	93	75	77	89	80
89	83	79	81	87	85	90	83
88	86	83	91	93	93	92	90
91	88	96	97	98	82	90	100

EXAMPLES Analyze and Interpret Histograms

2 BASEBALL How many Tampa Bay Rays players were at bat at least 400 times in a season?

Five players were at bat 400–499 times, and 2 players were at bat 500–599 times. One player was at bat 600–699 times. Therefore, 5 + 2 + 1 or 8 players were at bat at least 400 times.

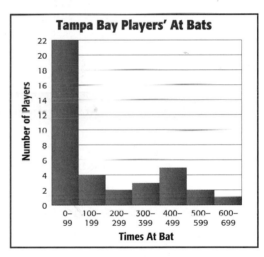

Tampa Bay Players' At Bats

3 BASEBALL What percent of the players were at bat 199 times or fewer?

There were 22 + 4 + 2 + 3 + 5 + 2 + 1 or 39 players at bat. There were 22 + 4 or 26 players that were at bat 199 times or fewer.

$\frac{26}{39} \approx 0.67$ Divide 26 by 39.

So, about 67% of the players were at bat 199 times or fewer.

CHECK Your Progress

b. What was the greatest number of times at bat for any one player?

c. Based on the data above, how many times is a Tampa Bay Rays player most likely to be at bat?

Example 1
(pp. 364–365)

1. POPULATION The list gives the approximate population density for each state. Choose intervals and make a frequency table. Then construct a histogram to represent the data.

U.S. State Population Density (per square mile)									
88	42	189	33	810	6	15	50	10	179
1	703	16	102	175	22	402	36	138	89
45	401	223	103	62	18	165	274	80	75
51	296	170	41	61	138	9	1,003	27	99
217	141	52	542	81	1,135	277	133	66	5

Examples 2 and 3
(p. 365)

2. VOLCANOES Use the histogram at the right.

    a. What percent of the volcanoes are 8,999 feet or less?

    b. How likely is it that any given volcano is at least 15,000 feet tall? Explain your reasoning.

    c. What is the height of the tallest volcano?

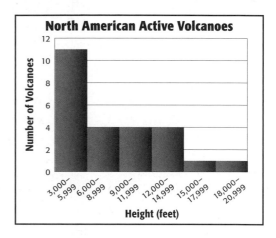

Practice and Problem Solving

● = **Step-by-Step Solutions** begin on page R17.
Extra Practice is on page EP17.

Example 1
(pp. 364–365)

For each problem, choose intervals and make a frequency table. Then construct a histogram to represent the data.

3.

Hours Spent Exercising per Week						
3	0	9	1	4	2	0
3	6	14	4	2	5	3
7	3	0	8	3	10	

4.

Average Speed (mph), Selected Animals						
70	61	50	50	50	45	8
43	42	40	40	40	35	0.17
35	32	32	30	30	30	1.17
30	25	20	9	18	14	200

Examples 2 and 3
(p. 365)

5. COUNTRIES Use the histogram shown.

    a. How many countries have an area less than 401 square kilometers?

    b. What percent of the countries have an area of 201–600 square kilometers?

    c. How likely is it that any given country will have an area greater than 800 square kilometers? Explain.

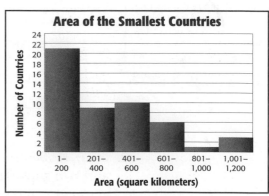

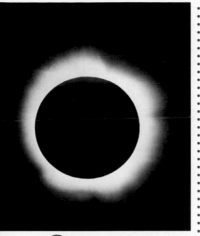

Real-World Link · · · ·

Total solar eclipses occur about 3 times every 4 years.

6. **ECLIPSES** Use the histogram at the right.

   a. What percent of the solar eclipses lasted at least 7 minutes 31 seconds?

   b. How long was the shortest solar eclipse?

   c. What is the duration of a typical solar eclipse during the decade? Explain your reasoning.

   d. How many solar eclipses lasted between 1 second and 5 minutes?

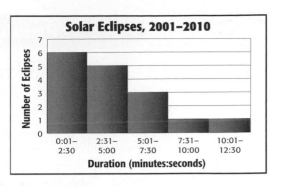

7. **BUILDINGS** Use the histograms shown.

Tall Buildings in Pittsburgh and Seattle

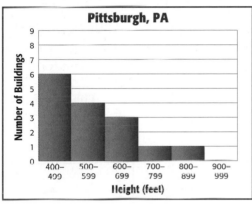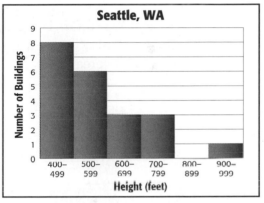

   a. Which city has the tallest building?

   b. Determine which city has more buildings that are 800–899 feet tall.

   c. Determine which city has more buildings that are at least 600 feet tall. What percent of the buildings in that city are at least 600 feet tall?

   d. Which city has more tall buildings? by how many?

8. **COLLECT THE DATA** Conduct a survey of your classmates to determine the number of hours each person spends on the Internet during a typical week. Then choose intervals, make a frequency table, and construct a histogram to represent the data.

9. **RESEARCH** Use the Internet or other resource to find the populations of each county, census division, or parish in your state. Make a histogram using your data. How does your county, census division, or parish compare with others in your state?

10. **OPEN ENDED** Construct a histogram that has a vertical line of symmetry and two gaps. Then construct a histogram that has a vertical line of symmetry and one gap.

11. **CHALLENGE** Describe how the histogram at the right would change if larger intervals, such as 0–9 and 10–19, were used. Describe how it would change if smaller intervals, such as 0–2, 3–5, 6–8, and so on, were used.

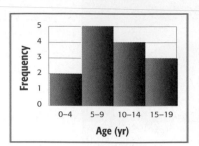

12. **Write MATH** Describe when a histogram might be more useful than a table with individual data. Then describe when a table of data might be more useful.

NGSSS Practice   MA.7.S.6.2

13. **GRIDDED RESPONSE** The graph shows the amount of sugar per serving in various adult cereals.

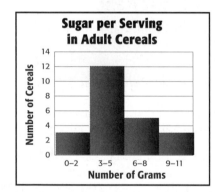

How many kinds of cereal contain 6–8 grams of sugar per serving?

14. **SHORT RESPONSE** A group of mothers reported when their children got their first tooth.

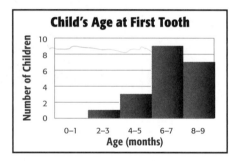

What fraction of the number of children reported got their first tooth when they were six months old or older?

15. **ICE CREAM** The graph shows the results of a survey. (Lesson 7-1B)

   a. Which flavor is most preferred?

   b. If 300 people were surveyed, how many more people favored chocolate over strawberry?

16. **INVESTMENT** Calculate the interest earned on a $400 investment over 2 years at a 6% earning rate. (Lesson 6-3E)

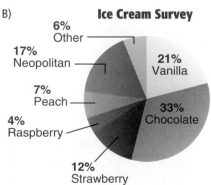

7-1 Statistics

Extend

Graphing Technology: Histograms

Main Idea

Use a graphing calculator to make histograms.

NGSSS

 MA.7.S.6.2 Construct and analyze histograms, stem-and-leaf plots, and circle graphs.

Get Connected
glencoe.com

You can make a histogram using a graphing calculator.

ACTIVITY

The Moapa Middle School basketball team listed each player's average points per game. Make a histogram of the data.

Average Points per Game											
15	3	11	7	4	6	18	1	2	21	10	3
9	2	1	12	24	5	13	20	4	12	1	2

STEP 1 Clear any existing data in list L1 by pressing [STAT] [ENTER] [▲] [CLEAR] [ENTER].

Then enter the data in L1. Input each number and press [ENTER].

STEP 2 Turn on the statistical plot by pressing [2nd] [STAT PLOT] [ENTER] [ENTER].

Select the histogram and L1 as the Xlist by pressing [▼] [▶] [▶] [ENTER] [▼] [2nd] [L1] [ENTER].

STEP 3 Press [WINDOW]. To set the viewing window to be [0, 25] scl: 5 by [0, 12] scl: 1, press [WINDOW] 0 [ENTER] 25 [ENTER] 5 [ENTER] 0 [ENTER] 12 [ENTER] 1 [ENTER] [GRAPH].

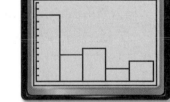

STEP 4 Press [GRAPH] to create the histogram.

Analyze the Results

1. Press [TRACE]. Find the frequency of each interval.

2. Explain why the *x*-values for this data set were chosen as 0 to 25.

3. **COLLECT THE DATA** Use the graphing calculator to make a histogram of your classmates' heights in inches. Analyze the graph to make some conclusions about the data.

Main Idea

Display and analyze data in a stem-and-leaf plot.

NGSSS

MA.7.S.6.2 Construct and analyze histograms, **stem-and-leaf plots,** and circle graphs.

New Vocabulary

stem-and-leaf plot
leaf
stem
outlier

Get Connected
glencoe.com

Stem-and-Leaf Plots

BIRDS The table shows the average mass in grams of sixteen different species of chicks.

Chick Mass (g)			
19	6	7	10
11	13	18	25
21	12	5	12
20	21	11	12

1. Which mass is the lightest?

2. How many of the masses are less than 10 grams?

In a **stem-and-leaf plot**, the data are organized from least to greatest. The digits of the least place value usually form the **leaves**, and the next place-value digits form the **stems**.

EXAMPLE Display Data in a Stem-and-Leaf Plot

① **BIRDS** **Display the data from the table above in a stem-and-leaf plot.**

Step 1 Choose the stems using digits in the tens place, 0, 1, and 2. The least value, 5, has 0 in the tens place. The greatest value, 25, has 2 in the tens place.

Step 2 List the stems from least to greatest in the *Stem* column. Write the leaves, the ones digits, to the right of the corresponding stems.

Stem	Leaf
0	6 7 5
1	9 0 1 3 8 2 2 1 2
2	5 1 0 1

Step 3 Order the leaves and write a *key* that explains how to read the stems and leaves. Include a title.

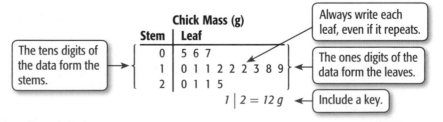

Chick Mass (g)

Stem	Leaf
0	5 6 7
1	0 1 1 2 2 2 3 8 9
2	0 1 1 5

1 | 2 = 12 g

The tens digits of the data form the stems.

Always write each leaf, even if it repeats.

The ones digits of the data form the leaves.

Include a key.

CHECK Your Progress

a. HOMEWORK The number of minutes the students in Mr. Blackwell's class spent doing their homework one night is shown. Display the data in a stem-and-leaf plot.

Homework Time (min)				
42	5	75	30	45
47	0	24	45	51
56	23	39	30	49
58	55	75	45	35

EXAMPLE **Analyze Stem-and-Leaf Plots**

 CHESS The stem-and-leaf plot shows the number of chess matches won by members of the Avery Middle School Chess Team. Find the range, median, and mode of the data.

Chess Matches Won	
Stem	Leaf
0	8 8 9
1	9
2	0 0 2 4 4 8 9
3	1 1 2 4 5 5 6 6 7 7 8
4	0 0 0 3 8 9
5	2 4
6	1

$3 \mid 2 = 32$ wins

range: greatest wins − least wins
= 61 − 8 or 53

median: middle value, 35

mode: most frequent value, 40

✓ **CHECK Your Progress**

b. BIRDS Find the range, median, and mode of the data in Example 1.

Study Tip

Data Sets Remember that measures of central tendency are numbers that describe the center of a data set and include the mean, median, and mode. The range is the difference between the greatest and least numbers in a data set.

The measures of central tendency can be affected by an extreme value, called an **outlier**.

 EXAMPLE **Effect of Outliers**

🌐 **Real-World Link** · · · ·
The University of Florida Gators basketball team finished the 2007–2008 season with a 57.6% shooting average.

 SPORTS The stem-and-leaf plot shows the number of points scored by a college basketball player. Which measure of central tendency is most affected by the outlier?

Basketball Points	
Stem	Leaf
0	2
1	2 2 3 5 8
2	0 0 1 1 3 4 6 6 6 8 9
3	0 1
4	3

$1 \mid 2 = 12$ points

The mode, 26, is not affected by the inclusion of the outlier, 43.

Calculate the mean and median, each without the outlier, 43. Then calculate them including the outlier and compare.

without the outlier

mean: $\dfrac{2 + 12 + \cdots + 31}{19} \approx 20.89$

median: 21

including the outlier

mean: $\dfrac{2 + 12 + 12 + \cdots + 43}{20} = 22$

$\dfrac{21 + 23}{2} = 22$

The mean increased by 22 − 20.89, or 1.11, while the median increased by 22 − 21, or 1. Since 1.11 > 1, the mean is more affected.

✓ **CHECK Your Progress**

c. CHESS Refer to Example 2. If an additional student had 84 wins, which measure of central tendency would be most affected?

Example 1
(p. 370)

Display each set of data in a stem-and-leaf plot.

1.

Height of Trees (ft)				
15	25	8	12	20
10	16	15	8	18

2.

Cost of Shoes ($)				
42	47	19	16	21
23	25	25	29	31
33	34	35	39	48

Examples 2 and 3
(p. 371)

 CAMP The stem-and-leaf plot at the right shows the ages of students in a pottery class.

a. What is the range of the ages of the students?

b. Find the median and mode of the data.

c. If an additional student was 6 years old, which measure of central tendency would be most affected?

Ages of Students

Stem	Leaf
0	9 9 9
1	0 1 1 1 1 2 2 3 3 4

$1 \mid 0 = 10$ years

Practice and Problem Solving

= **Step-by-Step Solutions** begin on page R18.
Extra Practice is on page EP18.

Example 1
(p. 370)

Display each set of data in a stem-and-leaf plot.

4.

Quiz Scores (%)			
70	96	72	91
80	80	79	93
76	95	73	93
90	93	77	91

5.

Low Temperatures (°F)				
15	13	28	32	38
30	31	13	36	35
38	32	38	24	20

6.

Floats at Annual Parade			
151	158	139	103
111	134	133	154
157	142	149	159

7.

School Play Attendance			
225	227	230	229
246	243	269	269
267	278	278	278

Examples 2 and 3
(p. 371)

8. CYCLING The number of Tour de France titles won by eleven countries is shown.

a. Find the range of titles won.

b. Find the median and mode of the data.

c. Which measure of central tendency is most affected by the outlier?

Tour de France Titles Won by Countries

Stem	Leaf
0	8 8 9
1	0 8
2	
3	6

$0 \mid 8 = 8$ titles

9. ELECTRONICS Use the stem-and-leaf plot that shows the costs of various DVD players at an electronics store.

a. What is the range of the prices?

b. Find the median and mode of the data.

c. If an additional DVD player costs $153, which measure of central tendency would be most affected?

Costs of DVD Players

Stem	Leaf
8	2 5 5
9	9 9
10	0 0 2 5 6 8
11	0 0 5 5 5 9 9
12	5 7 7

$11 \mid 5 = \$115$

10. **HISTORY** Refer to the stem-and-leaf plot below.

Ages of Signers of Declaration of Independence

Stem	Leaf
2	6 6 9
3	0 1 3 3 3 4 4 5 5 5 7 7 8 8 9 9
4	0 0 1 1 1 2 2 2 4 5 5 5 5 6 6 6 6 7 8 9
5	0 0 0 0 2 2 3 3 5 7
6	0 0 2 3 5 9
7	0

$3 \mid 1 = 31$ years

a. How many people signed the Declaration of Independence?

b. What was the age of the youngest signer?

c. What is the range of the ages of the signers?

d. Based on the data, can you conclude that the majority of the signers were 30–49 years old? Explain your reasoning.

11. **GYMNASTICS** The scores for 10 girls in a gymnastics event are 9.3, 10.0, 9.9, 8.9, 8.7, 9.0, 8.7, 8.5, 8.8, and 9.3. Analyze a stem-and-leaf plot of the data to draw two conclusions about the scores.

12. **REPTILES** The average lengths of certain species of crocodiles are given in the table. Analyze a stem-and-leaf plot of this data to write a convincing argument about a reasonable length for a crocodile.

Crocodile Average Lengths (ft)			
8.1	16.3	16.3	9.8
16.3	16.3	11.4	6.3
13.6	9.8	19.5	16.0

13. **FIND THE DATA** Refer to the Data File on pages 2–5. Choose some data that can be presented in a stem-and-leaf plot. Then analyze the stem-and-leaf plot to draw two conclusions about the data.

Real-World Link · · · ·
The saltwater crocodile is the largest living reptile. Some measuring 27–30 feet in length have been recorded in the wild.

H.O.T. Problems

14. **FIND THE ERROR** Aisha is analyzing the data in the stem-and-leaf plot below. Find her mistake and correct it.

Cut Ribbon Length

Stem	Leaf
2	6 6 9
3	
4	6
5	3 6

$2 \mid 6 = 26$ in.

There are no pieces of ribbon more than 50 inches in length.

15. **Write MATH** Present the data shown at the right in a line plot and a stem-and-leaf plot. Describe the similarities and differences among the representations. Which representation do you prefer to use? Explain your reasoning.

Fiber in Cereal (g)				
5	5	4	3	3
3	1	1	1	2
1	1	1	1	0

16. Denzell's science quiz scores are 11, 12, 13, 21, and 35. Which stem-and-leaf plot **best** represents this data?

A.

Stem	Leaf
1	1
2	1
3	5

$3 \mid 5 = 35$

B.

Stem	Leaf
1	3
2	1
3	5

$3 \mid 5 = 35$

C.

Stem	Leaf
1	1 2 3
2	1
3	5

$3 \mid 5 = 35$

D.

Stem	Leaf
1	1
2	1 1
3	5

$3 \mid 5 = 35$

17. The stem-and-leaf plot shows the points scored by the Harding Middle School basketball team.

Points Scored

Stem	Leaf
4	7 8 8 8
5	0 0 2 3 7 9
6	1 6
7	
8	4

$4 \mid 7 = 47$

Which one of the following statements is true concerning how the measures of central tendency are affected by the inclusion of the outlier?

F. The mode is most affected.

G. The median is not affected.

H. The mean is most affected.

I. None of the measures of central tendency are affected.

18. MATH Use the histogram that shows the math quiz scores of students. (Lesson 7-1C)

a. How many students earned a quiz score of 80–89?

b. What percent of students earned at least 80?

c. Compare the number of students who earned a score between 60–69 and the students in the 90–100 range.

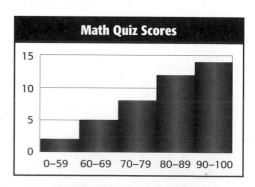

19. Display the data in the table at the right in a circle graph. (Lesson 7-1B)

Multiply. Write in simplest form. (Lesson 2-3B)

20. $\dfrac{2}{3} \times \dfrac{1}{4}$

21. $\dfrac{5}{7} \times 7$

22. $\dfrac{3}{8} \times \dfrac{4}{6}$

23. $\dfrac{11}{34} \times \dfrac{17}{6}$

Activity	Hours Per Day
School	7
Sleep	8
Homework	2
Sports	3
Other	4

Main Idea
Find the probability of a simple event.

NGSSS

MA.7.P.7.1 Determine the outcome of an experiment and predict which events are likely or unlikely, and if the experiment is fair or unfair.

New Vocabulary
outcome
simple event
probability
random
complementary event

Get Connected
glencoe.com

Probability

FOOD A cheesecake has four slices of each type as shown.

1. What fraction of the cheesecake is chocolate? Write in simplest form.

2. Suppose your friend gives you the first piece of cheesecake without asking which type you prefer. Are your chances of getting original the same as getting raspberry?

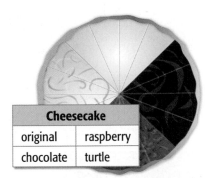

Cheesecake	
original	raspberry
chocolate	turtle

An **outcome** is any one of the possible results of an action. A **simple event** has one outcome or a collection of outcomes. For example, getting a piece of chocolate cheesecake is a simple event. The chance of that event happening is called its **probability**.

Key Concept — Probability

Words	If all outcomes are equally likely, the probability of a simple event is a ratio that compares the number of favorable outcomes to the number of possible outcomes.
Symbols	$P(\text{event}) = \dfrac{\text{number of favorable outcomes}}{\text{number of possible outcomes}}$

Study Tip

Reasonable Answer
The greatest probability of an event occurring is 100%. A possible probability is always between 0% and 100% inclusive. Any calculation over 100% would be unreasonable.

EXAMPLE Find Probability

① What is the probability of rolling an even number on a number cube marked with 1, 2, 3, 4, 5, and 6 on its faces?

$$P(\text{even number}) = \frac{\text{even numbers possible}}{\text{total numbers possible}}$$

$$= \frac{3}{6} \text{ or } \frac{1}{2}$$

The probability of rolling an even number is $\frac{1}{2}$, 0.5, or 50%.

✓ CHECK Your Progress

Use the number cube above to find each probability. Write as a fraction, decimal, and percent.

a. $P(\text{odd number})$ **b.** $P(5 \text{ or } 6)$ **c.** $P(\text{prime number})$

Outcomes occur at **random** if each outcome occurs by chance. For example, the number that results when rolling a number cube is a *random* outcome.

Real-World EXAMPLE

2) TALENT COMPETITION Simone and her three friends were deciding how to pick the song they will sing for their school's talent show. They decide to roll a number cube. The person with the lowest number chooses the song. If her friends rolled a 6, 5, and 2, what is the probability that Simone will get to choose the song?

The possible outcomes of rolling a number cube are 1, 2, 3, 4, 5, and 6.

In order for Simone to be able to choose the song, she will need to roll a 1.

Let $P(A)$ be the probability that Simone chooses the song.

$P(A) = \dfrac{\text{number of favorable outcomes}}{\text{number of possible outcomes}}$

$\qquad = \dfrac{1}{6}$ There are 6 possible outcomes, and 1 of them is favorable.

The probability that Simone will choose the song is $\dfrac{1}{6}$, or about 17%.

Real-World Link · · · ·

Founded in 1842, the New York Philharmonic is the oldest symphony orchestra in the United States. They have performed over 14,000 concerts.

CHECK Your Progress

MUSIC The table shows the numbers of brass instrument players in the New York Philharmonic. Suppose one brass instrument player is randomly selected to be a featured performer. Find the probability of each event. Write as a fraction in simplest form.

New York Philharmonic Brass Instrument Players	
Horn	6
Trombone	4
Trumpet	3
Tuba	1

d. $P(\text{trumpet})$

e. $P(\text{brass})$

f. $P(\text{flute})$

g. $P(\text{horn or tuba})$

The probability that an event will happen can be any number from 0 to 1, including 0 and 1, as shown on the number line below. Notice that probabilities can be written as fractions, decimals, or percents.

Impossible	Unlikely	As likely to happen as not	Likely	Certain
0	$\frac{1}{4}$	$\frac{1}{2}$	$\frac{3}{4}$	1
0	0.25	0.5	0.75	1
0%	25%	50%	75%	100%

In Example 2, either Simone will go first or she will *not* go first. These two events are **complementary events**. The sum of the probabilities of an event and its complement is 1 or 100%. In symbols, $P(A) + P(not\ A) = 1$.

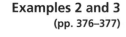
EXAMPLE **Complementary Events**

 TALENT COMPETITION Refer to Example 2. Find the probability that Simone will *not* choose the song.

$P(A) + P(not\ A) = 1$ Definition of complementary events

$\dfrac{1}{6} + P(not\ A) = 1$ Replace $P(A)$ with $\dfrac{1}{6}$.

$-\dfrac{1}{6} \qquad\qquad -\dfrac{1}{6}$ Subtract $\dfrac{1}{6}$ from each side.

$\overline{}$

$P(not\ A) = \dfrac{5}{6}$ $1 - \dfrac{1}{6}$ is $\dfrac{6}{6} - \dfrac{1}{6}$ or $\dfrac{5}{6}$

CHECK Your Progress

SCHOOL Ricardo's teacher uses a spinner similar to the one shown at the right to determine the order in which each group will make their presentation. Use the spinner to find each probability. Write as a fraction in simplest form.

h. $P(not\ \text{group 4})$ **i.** $P(not\ \text{group 1 or group 3})$

CHECK Your Understanding

Example 1
(p. 375)

Use the spinner to find each probability. Write as a fraction in simplest form, a decimal, and a percent.

1. $P(M)$ **2.** $P(Q\ or\ R)$ **3.** $P(\text{vowel})$

Examples 2 and 3
(pp. 376–377)

MARBLES Roberto has a bag that contains 7 blue, 5 purple, 12 red, and 6 orange marbles. Find each probability if he draws one marble at random from the bag. Write as a fraction in simplest form.

4. $P(\text{purple})$ **5** $P(\text{red or orange})$ **6.** $P(\text{green})$

7. $P(not\ \text{blue})$ **8.** $P(not\ \text{red or orange})$ **9.** $P(not\ \text{yellow})$

Example 3
(p. 377)

10. SURVEYS Shanté asked her classmates how many pets they own. The responses are in the table. If a student in her class is selected at random, what is the probability that the student does *not* own 3 or more pets?

Number of Pets	Response
None	6
1–2	15
3 or more	4

Practice and Problem Solving

● = **Step-by-Step Solutions** begin on page R19.
Extra Practice is on page EP18.

Example 1
(p. 375)

A set of 20 cards is numbered 1, 2, 3, . . ., 20. Suppose you pick a card at random without looking. Find the probability of each event. Write as a fraction in simplest form, a decimal, and a percent.

11. $P(1)$
12. $P(3 \text{ or } 13)$
13. $P(\text{multiple of } 3)$

14. $P(\text{even number})$
15. $P(not\ 20)$
16. $P(not \text{ a factor of } 10)$

Examples 2 and 3
(pp. 376–377)

RAFFLE The table shows the number of students in seventh grade who entered in the school drawing to win lunch with the principal. Suppose that only one student is randomly selected to win. Find the probability of each event. Write as a fraction in simplest form.

Lunch Raffle	
Room 8	24
Room 9	20
Room 10	10
Room 11	16
Room 12	14

17. $P(\text{Room } 8)$
18. $P(\text{Room } 9)$

19. $P(\text{Room } 12)$
20. $P(\text{Room } 10)$

21. $P(not \text{ Room } 8)$
22. $P(\text{Room } 11)$

23 $P(not \text{ Room } 10)$
24. $P(\text{Room } 10 \text{ or } 11)$

Example 3
(p. 377)

25. SOUP A cupboard contains 20 soup cans. Seven are tomato, 4 are cream of mushroom, 5 are chicken, and 4 are vegetable. If one can is chosen at random from the cupboard, what is the probability that it is *neither* cream of mushroom *nor* vegetable soup? Write as a percent.

26. VIDEOS In a drawing, one name is randomly chosen from a jar of 75 names to receive free video rentals for a month. If Enola entered her name 8 times, what is the probability that she is *not* chosen to receive the free rentals? Write as a fraction in simplest form.

27. PETS The graph shows the last 33 types of pets that were purchased at a local pet store. What is the probability that a receipt chosen at random from these sales would be for a cat or dog? Express as a percent.

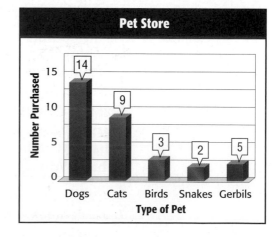

28. GAMES For a certain game, the probability of choosing a card with the number 13 is 0.008. What is the probability of *not* choosing card 13? Describe the likelihood of the event occurring using the number line at the bottom of page 376.

29. WEATHER The forecast for tomorrow says that there is a 40% chance of rain. Describe the complementary event and predict its probability.

30. FLOWERS Tatiana and her brother are each looking for flowers to give their aunt for her birthday. Tatiana likes either red roses or yellow tulips. Her brother likes blue irises, yellow daisies, red tulips, or white gardenias. Suppose Tatiana and her brother each choose one of their favorite flowers at random.

a. What is the probability that Tatiana will choose a yellow flower? a red flower? Describe the likelihood of each event using the number line at the bottom of page 376.

b. What is the probability that her brother will choose a yellow flower? a red flower? Describe the likelihood of each choice.

31 GRAPHIC NOVEL Refer to the graphic novel frame below. Jamar and Theresa found that there were five music genres that students enjoyed: country, classical, hip-hop, oldies, and alternative. If they decided to create a music mix for a school dance and include an equal number of each genre, what would be the probability that any given song would be from the hip-hop genre?

H.O.T. Problems

32. REASONING A *leap year* has 366 days and occurs in non-century years that are divisible by 4. The extra day is added as February 29th. Determine whether each probability is 0 or 1. Explain your reasoning.

a. P(there will be 29 days in February in 2032)

b. P(there will be 29 days in February in 2058)

33. CHALLENGE A bag contains 6 red marbles, 4 blue marbles, and 8 green marbles. How many marbles of each color should be added so that the total number of marbles is 27, but the probability of randomly selecting one marble of each color remains unchanged? Explain your reasoning.

34. Write MATH Marissa has 5 black T-shirts, 2 purple T-shirts, and 1 orange T-shirt. Without calculating, determine whether each of the following probabilities is reasonable if she randomly selects one T-shirt. Explain your reasoning.

a. P(black T-shirt) $= \frac{1}{3}$ **b.** P(orange T-shirt) $= \frac{4}{5}$ **c.** P(purple T-shirt) $= \frac{1}{4}$

35. A bag contains 8 blue marbles, 15 red marbles, 10 yellow marbles, and 3 brown marbles. If a marble is randomly selected, what is the probability that it will be brown?

A. 0.27

C. $0.08\overline{3}$

B. 22%

D. $\frac{3}{8}$

36. The records of a sporting goods store show that 1 out of every 4 balls purchased is a football. What is the probability that a football will NOT be purchased when a ball is purchased?

F. $\frac{1}{1}$

G. $\frac{1}{4}$

H. $\frac{3}{4}$

I. $\frac{1}{25}$

37. What is the probability of the spinner landing on a number less than 3?

A. 25%   **C.** 50%

B. 37.5%   **D.** 75%

38. At a school picnic, students can choose their dessert. The desserts include 8 ice cream sandwiches, 9 chocolate frozen bananas, 12 ice cream cones, 11 frozen pops, 16 push-up sticks, and 14 shaved ice cones. If desserts are chosen at random, what is the probability that the first person in line will choose an ice cream cone?

F. $\frac{6}{29}$

H. $\frac{1}{6}$

G. $\frac{6}{35}$

I. $\frac{1}{12}$

39. AGES The stem-and-leaf plot shows the ages of patients in a waiting room.
(Lesson 7-1E)

a. Find the oldest and youngest ages.

b. What is the median age?

c. Write a statement that describes the data.

Ages

Stem	Leaf
1	2 4 7
2	3
3	1 5
4	6 8
5	2 3 9

1 | 7 = 17 years

40. SCHOOL If you were to conduct a survey of your classmates to determine the number of hours each person spends sleeping during a typical week, what would be reasonable intervals to use to construct a histogram to represent the data? (Lesson 7-1C)

Write each fraction in simplest form. (Previous Course)

41. $\frac{2}{6}$

42. $\frac{6}{8}$

43. $\frac{15}{30}$

44. $\frac{18}{32}$

Main Idea
Find sample spaces and probabilities.

NGSSS

MA.7.P.7.1 Determine the outcome of an experiment and predict which events are likely or unlikely, and if the experiment is fair or unfair.

New Vocabulary
sample space
tree diagram

Get Connected
glencoe.com

Sample Spaces

Explore Here is a probability game for two players.

- Place two green marbles into Bag A. Place one green and one red marble into Bag B.

- Without looking, player 1 chooses a marble from each bag. If both marbles are the same color, player 1 wins a point. If the marbles are different colors, player 2 wins a point. Record your results and place the marbles back in the bag.

- Player 2 then pulls a marble from each bag and records the results. Continue alternating turns until each player has pulled from the bag 10 times. The player with the most points wins.

Now, play the game. Who won? What was the final score?

The set of all of the possible outcomes in a probability experiment is called the **sample space**. A **tree diagram** is a display that represents the sample space.

EXAMPLE   **Find a Sample Space**

1 **ICE CREAM** A vendor sells vanilla and chocolate ice cream. Customers can choose from a waffle or sugar cone. Find the sample space for all possible orders of one scoop of ice cream in a cone.

Make a tree diagram that shows all of the possible outcomes.

Ice Cream	Cone	Sample Space
vanilla	waffle	vanilla, waffle
	sugar	vanilla, sugar
chocolate	waffle	chocolate, waffle
	sugar	chocolate, sugar

CHECK Your Progress

a. **PETS** The animal shelter has both male and female Labradors in yellow, brown, or black. Find the sample space for all possible Labradors available at the shelter.

EXAMPLE **Find Probability**

2 **GAMES** Refer to the Explore at the start of this lesson. Find the sample space. Then find the probability that player 2 wins.

Make a tree diagram to show the sample space.

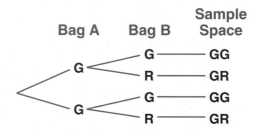

There are 4 equally likely outcomes with 2 favoring each player. So, the probability that player 2 wins is $\frac{2}{4}$, or $\frac{1}{2}$, or 0.5, or 50%.

 **Study Tip**

Fair Game A fair game is one in which each player has an equal chance of winning. This game is a fair game.

CHECK Your Progress

b. **GAMES** Delmar tosses three coins. If all three coins show up heads, Delmar wins. Otherwise, Kara wins. Find the sample space. Then find the probability that Delmar wins.

CHECK Your Understanding

Example 1
(p. 381)

For each situation, find the sample space using a tree diagram.

1 A coin is tossed twice.

2. A pair of brown or black sandals are available in sizes 7, 8, or 9.

3. FOOD Sandwiches can be made with ham or turkey on rye, white, or sourdough breads. Draw a tree diagram to show all the possibilities.

Example 2
(p. 382)

4. GAMES Gerardo spins a spinner with four sections of equal size, labeled A, B, C, and D, twice. If letter A is spun at least once, Gerardo wins. Otherwise, Odell wins. Find the probability that Odell wins.

Practice and Problem Solving

● = **Step-by-Step Solutions** begin on page R19.
Extra Practice is on page EP18.

Example 1
(p. 381)

For each situation, find the sample space using a tree diagram.

5. tossing a coin and spinning the spinner from the choices at the right

6. picking a number from 1 to 5 and choosing the color red, white, or blue

7. choosing a purple, green, black, or silver mountain bike having 10, 18, 21, or 24 speeds

8. choosing a letter from the word SPACE and choosing a consonant from the word MATH

9. CLOTHES Jerry can buy a school T-shirt with either short sleeves or long sleeves in either gray or white and in small, medium, or large. Find the sample space for all possible T-shirts he can buy.

10. FOOD Three-course dinners can be made from the menu shown. Find the sample space for a dinner consisting of an appetizer, entrée, and dessert.

Appetizers	Entrees	Desserts
Soup	Steak	Carrot cake
Salad	Chicken	Apple pie
	Fish	

Example 2
(p. 382)

For each game, find the sample space. Then find the indicated probability.

11. Elba tosses a quarter, a dime, and a nickel. If tails comes up at least twice, Steve wins. Otherwise Elba wins. Find P(Elba wins).

12. Ming rolls a number cube, tosses a coin, and chooses a card from two cards marked A and B. If an even number and heads appears, Ming wins, no matter which card is chosen. Otherwise Lashonda wins. Find P(Ming wins).

13. FAMILIES Mr. and Mrs. Romero are expecting triplets. Suppose the chance of each child being a boy is 50% and of being a girl is 50%. Find each probability.

   a. P(all three children will be boys)

   b. P(at least one boy and one girl)

   c. P(two boys and one girl)

   d. P(at least two girls)

   e. P(the first two born are boys and the last born is a girl)

Real-World Link. • • • •
The average family size in the United States is 2.59 people.

14. GAMES The following is a game for two players. Find the probability that each player wins.

   • Three counters are labeled according to the table at the right.

   • Toss the three counters.

   • If exactly 2 counters match, Player 1 scores a point. Otherwise, Player 2 scores a point.

Counters	Side 1	Side 2
Counter 1	red	blue
Counter 2	red	yellow
Counter 3	blue	yellow

15. **UNIFORMS** The University of Oregon's football team has many different uniforms. The coach can choose from four colors of jerseys and pants: green, yellow, white, and black. There are three helmet options: green, white, and yellow. Also, there are the same four colors of socks and two colors of shoes, black and yellow.

   a. How many jersey/pant combinations are there?

   b. If the coach picks a jersey/pant combination at random, what is the probability he will pick a yellow jersey with green pants?

   c. Use a tree diagram to find all of the possible shoe and sock combinations.

   d. **RESEARCH** Use the Internet or another resource to find the number of jerseys and pants your favorite college or professional sports team has as part of its uniform. How many jersey/pant combinations are there for the team you chose?

H.O.T. Problems

16. **CHALLENGE** Refer to Exercise 14. Do they both have an equal chance of winning? Explain.

17. **FIND THE ERROR** Caitlyn wants to determine the probability of guessing correctly on two true-false questions on her history test. She draws the tree diagram below using C for correct and I for incorrect. Find her mistake and correct it.

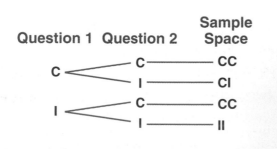

18. **REASONING** In the English language, 13% of the letters used are Es. Suppose you are guessing the letters of a two-letter word in a puzzle. Would you guess an E? Explain.

19. **Write MATH** Describe a game between two players using one coin in which each player has an equal chance of winning.

20. Mr. Zajac will choose one student from each of the two groups below to present their history reports to the class.

Group 1	Group 2
Ava	Mario
Antoine	Brooke
Greg	

Which set shows all the possible choices?

A. {(Ava, Mario), (Antoine, Mario), (Greg, Mario)}

B. {(Ava, Antoine), (Antoine, Greg), (Brooke, Mario)}

C. {(Ava, Mario), (Antoine, Mario), (Greg, Mario), (Ava, Brooke), (Antoine, Brooke), (Greg, Brooke)}

D. {(Brooke, Antoine), (Mario, Greg), (Ava, Brooke), (Mario, Antoine)}

21. **GRIDDED RESPONSE** A coffee shop offers 2 types of coffee: regular and decaffeinated; 3 types of flavoring: vanilla, hazelnut, and caramel; and 2 choices of topping: with or without whipped cream. How many possible choices are there?

22. **SHORT RESPONSE** Miranda needs to get dressed (D), brush her teeth (T), pack her lunch (L), and make her bed (B) before she leaves for school.

She always makes her bed right after she packs her lunch. List all the different combinations of tasks Miranda could do. Use the given letters of each task in your list (D, T, L, B).

Spiral Review

PROBABILITY A spinner is equally likely to stop on each of its regions numbered 1 to 20. Find each probability as a fraction in simplest form. (Lesson 7-2A)

23. a prime number

24. GCF(12, 18)

25. multiple of 2 or 3

26. *not* a multiple of 4

27. factor of 10 or 6

28. *not* an even number

29. GYMNASTICS Display the gymnastic team's scores in a stem-and-leaf plot. (Lesson 7-1E)

Scores			
7.8	8.3	7.6	9.1
7.9	10.0	9.8	8.5
6.9	7.4	9.2	8.6

Find each number. Round to the nearest tenth if necessary. (Lesson 6-1B)

30. 43% of 266

31. 17% of 92

Solve each equation. (Lesson 3-1D)

32. $x + 7 = 10$

33. $m - 2 = 8$

34. $12 + a = 16$

Main Idea

Use multiplication to count outcomes and find probabilities.

NGSSS

MA.7.P.7.1 Determine the outcome of an experiment and predict which events are likely or unlikely, and if the experiment is fair or unfair.

New Vocabulary

Fundamental Counting Principle

Get Connected
glencoe.com

Counting Outcomes

SALES The Shoe Warehouse sells sandals in different colors and styles.

1. According to the table, how many colors of sandals are available?

2. How many styles are available?

3. Draw a tree diagram to find the number of different color and style combinations.

4. Find the product of the two numbers you found in Exercises 1 and 2. How does the number of outcomes compare to the product?

Color	Style
Black	Platforms
Brown	Slides
Tan	Wedges
White	
Red	

In the activity above, you discovered that multiplication, instead of a tree diagram, can be used to find the number of possible outcomes in a sample space. This is called the **Fundamental Counting Principle**.

> ### Key Concept — Fundamental Counting Principle
>
> **Words** If event M has m possible outcomes and event N has n possible outcomes, then event M followed by event N has $m \times n$ possible outcomes.

EXAMPLE Find the Number of Outcomes

1. Find the total number of outcomes when a coin is tossed and a number cube is rolled.

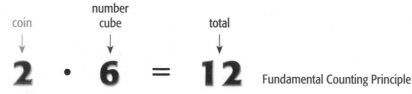

$$2 \cdot 6 = 12 \quad \text{Fundamental Counting Principle}$$

There are 12 different outcomes.

Check Draw a tree diagram to show the sample space.

 CHECK Your Progress

a. Find the total number of outcomes when choosing from bike helmets that come in three colors and two styles.

2 JEANS The Jeans Shop sells young men's jeans in different sizes, styles, and lengths. Find the number of jeans available. Then find the probability of randomly selecting a size 32 × 34 slim fit. Is it likely or unlikely that the size would be chosen?

The Jeans Shop		
Waist Size	Length (in.)	Style

30	30	slim fit
32	32	bootcut
34	34	loose fit
36		
38		

sizes   length   style   total

$$5 \cdot 3 \cdot 3 = 45 \quad \text{Fundamental Counting Principle}$$

There are 45 different types of jeans to choose from. Out of the 45 possible outcomes, only one is favorable. So, the probability of randomly selecting a 32 × 34 slim fit is $\frac{1}{45}$ or about 2%.

It is very unlikely that the size would be chosen at random.

Study Tip

Jean Size In men's jeans, the size is labeled waist × length. So, a 32 × 34 is a 32-inch waist with a 34-inch length.

✓ CHECK Your Progress

b. JEANS If the Jeans Shop adds relaxed fit jeans to its selection, find the number of available jeans. Then find the probability of randomly selecting a 36 × 30 relaxed fit pair of jeans. Is it likely or unlikely that the size would be chosen?

✓ CHECK Your Understanding

Example 1
(p. 386)

Use the Fundamental Counting Principle to find the total number of outcomes in each situation.

1 tossing a quarter, a dime, and a nickel

2. choosing a number on a number cube and picking a marble from the bag at the right

Example 2
(p. 387)

3. CLOTHES Mira has 3 sweaters, 4 blouses, and 6 skirts that coordinate. Find the number of different outfits consisting of a sweater, blouse, and skirt that are possible. Then find the probability of randomly selecting a particular sweater-blouse-skirt outfit. State the probability as a fraction and percent. Is the probability of this event likely or unlikely?

Practice and Problem Solving

= **Step-by-Step Solutions** begin on page R20.
Extra Practice is on page EP19.

Example 1
(p. 386)

Use the Fundamental Counting Principle to find the total number of outcomes in each situation.

Bagels	Cream Cheese
Plain	Plain
Blueberry	Chive
Cinnamon raisin	Sun-dried tomato
Garlic	

4. choosing a bagel with one type of cream cheese from the list shown in the table

5. choosing a number from 1 to 20 and a color from 7 colors

6. picking a month of the year and a day of the week

7. choosing from a comedy, horror, or action movie each shown in four different theaters

8. rolling a number cube and tossing two coins

9. choosing iced tea in regular, raspberry, lemon, or peach flavors; sweetened or unsweetened; and in a glass or a plastic container

Example 2
(p. 387)

10. **ROADS** Two roads, Broadway and State, connect the towns of Eastland and Harping. Three roads, Park, Fairview, and Main, connect the towns of Harping and Johnstown. Find the number of possible routes from Eastland to Johnstown that pass through Harping. Then find the probability that State and Fairview will be used if a route is selected at random. State the probability as a fraction and percent and its likelihood.

11. **APPLES** An orchard makes apple nut bread, apple pumpkin nut bread, and apple buttermilk bread using 6 different varieties of apples, including Fuji. Find the number of possible bread choices. Then find the probability of selecting a Fuji apple buttermilk bread if a customer buys a loaf of bread at random. How likely is the probability of buying this bread at random?

12. **PASSWORDS** Find the number of possible choices for a 2-digit password that is greater than 19. Then find the number of possible choices for a 4-digit Personal Identification Number (PIN) if the digits cannot be repeated.

13. **T-SHIRTS** A store advertises that they have a different T-shirt for each day of the year. The store offers 32 different T-shirt designs and 11 choices of color. Is the advertisement true? Explain.

14. **ANALYZE TABLES** The table shows cell phone options offered by a wireless phone company. If a phone with one payment plan and one accessory is given away at random, predict the probability that it will be Brand B and have a headset. Explain your reasoning.

Phone Brands	Payment Plans	Accessories
Brand A	Individual	Leather case
Brand B	Family	Car mount
Brand C	Business	Headset
	Government	Travel charger

Real-World Link

A popular orchard in Wapato, Washington, grows 7 varieties of apples including Granny Smith and Fuji.

H.O.T. Problems

15. CHALLENGE Determine the number of possible outcomes when tossing one coin, two coins, and three coins. Then determine the number of possible outcomes for tossing n coins. Describe the strategy you used.

16. Which One Doesn't Belong? Identify the choices for events M and N that do not result in the same number of outcomes as the other two. Explain your reasoning.

| 9 drinks, 8 desserts | | 18 shirts, 4 pants | | 10 groups, 8 activities |

17. Write MATH Explain when you might choose to use the Fundamental Counting Principle to find the number of possible outcomes and when you might choose to use a tree diagram.

NGSSS Practice   MA.7.P.7.1

18. A bakery offers white, chocolate, or yellow cakes with white or chocolate icing. There are also 24 designs that can be applied to a cake. If all orders are equally likely, what is the probability that a customer will order a white cake with white icing in a specific design?

A. $\frac{1}{30}$ C. $\frac{1}{120}$

B. $\frac{1}{64}$ D. $\frac{1}{144}$

19. THINK SOLVE EXPLAIN **SHORT RESPONSE** Hat Shack sells 9 different styles of hats in several different colors for 2 different sports teams. If the company makes 108 kinds of hats, how many different colors do they make?

Styles	Colors	Teams
9	?	2

 **Spiral Review**

20. SCHOOL Corinna can choose from 2 geography, 3 history, and 2 statistics classes. Find the sample space for all possible schedules. (Lesson 7-2B)

PROBABILITY Find the probability that the spinner shown at the right will stop on each of the following. Write as a fraction in simplest form. (Lesson 7-2A)

21. a vowel   **22.** red

Order each set of numbers from least to greatest. (Lesson 2-1C)

23. 27%, $\frac{1}{5}$, 0.22, 20.1   **24.** $\frac{19}{20}$, 88%, 0.85, $\frac{3}{4}$

Add. (Lesson 1-2B)

25. $-6 + (-6) + (-6) + (-6)$ **26.** $-11 + (-11) + (11)$

27. $2 + (-2) + (-2) + (2)$ **28.** $-8 + (-8) + (-8)$

Explore Independent and Dependent Events

Main Idea

Explore the probability of independent and dependent events.

NGSSS

 MA.7.P.7.2 Determine, compare, and make predictions **based on experimental** or theoretical **probability of independent or dependent events.**

Get Connected
glencoe.com

Place two red counters and two white counters in a paper bag. Then complete the following activities.

ACTIVITIES

① **STEP 1** Without looking, remove a counter from the bag and record its color. Place the counter back in the bag.

STEP 2 Without looking, remove a second counter and record its color. The two colors are one trial. Place the counter back in the bag.

STEP 3 Repeat until you have 50 trials. Count and record the number of times you chose a red counter followed by a white counter.

② **STEP 1** Without looking, remove a counter from the bag and record its color. This time do not replace the counter.

STEP 2 Without looking, remove a second counter and record its color. The two colors are one trial. Place both counters back in the bag.

STEP 3 Repeat until you have 50 trials. Count and record the number of times you chose a red counter followed by a white counter.

Analyze the Results

1. In Activity 1, how many times did you choose a red counter followed by a white counter?

2. Were the results of Activity 2 the same or different than Activity 1?

3. Explain what caused any differences between Activity 2 and Activity 1.

Main Idea

Find the probability of independent and dependent events.

NGSSS

 MA.7.P.7.2 Determine, compare, and make predictions based on experimental or **theoretical probability of independent or dependent events.**

New Vocabulary

compound event
independent events
dependent events

 Get Connected
glencoe.com

Independent and Dependent Events

SALES A sale advertises that if you buy an item from the column on the left, you get a tote bag free. Suppose you choose items at random.

Type of Item	Tote Bag Colors
T-shirt	green
jacket	red
hat	white
beach towel	
visor	
polo shirt	

1. What is the probability of buying a beach towel? receiving a red tote bag?

2. What is the product of the probabilities in Exercise 1?

3. Draw a tree diagram to determine the probability that someone buys a beach towel and receives a red tote bag.

The combined action of buying an item and receiving a free tote bag is a compound event. A **compound event** consists of two or more simple events. These events are **independent events** because the outcome of one event does not affect the other event.

> ### Key Concept   Probability of Independent Events
>
> **Words**   The probability of two independent events can be found by multiplying the probability of the first event by the probability of the second event.
>
> **Symbols** $P(A \text{ and } B) = P(A) \cdot P(B)$

Vocabulary Link

Everyday Use

Independent not under control by others

Math Use

Independent outcome does not rely on another event

EXAMPLES Independent Events

1. One letter tile is selected and the spinner is spun. What is the probability that both will be a vowel?

$P(\text{selecting a vowel}) = \dfrac{2}{7}$

$P(\text{spinning a vowel}) = \dfrac{2}{6} \text{ or } \dfrac{1}{3}$

$P(\text{both letters are vowels}) = \dfrac{2}{7} \cdot \dfrac{1}{3} \text{ or } \dfrac{2}{21}$

② A spinner and a number cube are used in a game. The spinner has an equal chance of landing on one of five colors: red, yellow, blue, green, or purple. The faces of the cube are labeled 1 through 6. What is the probability of a player spinning blue and then rolling a 3 or 4?

You are asked to find the probability of the spinner landing on blue and rolling a 3 or 4 on a number cube. The events are independent because spinning the spinner does not affect the outcome of rolling a number cube.

First, find the probability of each event.

$$P(\text{blue}) = \frac{1}{5} \longleftarrow \frac{\text{number of ways to spin blue}}{\text{number of possible outcomes}}$$

$$P(3 \text{ or } 4) = \frac{2}{6} \text{ or } \frac{1}{3} \begin{matrix} \longleftarrow \text{number of ways to roll 3 or 4} \\ \longleftarrow \text{number of possible outcomes} \end{matrix}$$

Then, find the probability of both events occurring.

$$P(\text{blue and 3 or 4}) = \frac{1}{5} \cdot \frac{1}{3} \quad P(A \text{ and } B) = P(A) \cdot P(B)$$

$$= \frac{1}{15} \quad \text{Multiply.}$$

The probability is $\frac{1}{15}$.

 CHECK Your Progress

a. A game requires players to roll two number cubes to move the game pieces. The faces of the cubes are labeled 1 through 6. What is the probability of rolling a 2 or 4 on the first number cube and then rolling a 5 on the second?

Vocabulary Link

Everyday Use

Dependent under the control of others

Math Use

Dependent relying on another quantity or action

If the outcome of one event affects the outcome of another event, the events are called **dependent events**.

Key Concept **Probability of Dependent Events**

Words If two events A and B are dependent, then the probability of both events occurring is the product of the probability of A and the probability of B after A occurs.

Symbols $P(A \text{ and } B) = P(A) \cdot P(B \text{ following } A)$

3 **FRUIT** There are 4 oranges, 7 bananas, and 5 apples in a fruit basket. Ignacio selects a piece of fruit at random and then Terrance selects a piece of fruit at random. Find the probability that two apples are chosen.

Since the first piece of fruit is not replaced, the first event affects the second event. These are dependent events.

$P(\text{first piece is an apple}) = \dfrac{5}{16}$ ← number of apples
   ← total pieces of fruit

$P(\text{second piece is an apple}) = \dfrac{4}{15}$ ⎰ number of apples after one apple is removed
   ⎱ total pieces of fruit after one apple is removed

$P(\text{two apples}) = \dfrac{\overset{1}{\cancel{5}}}{\underset{4}{\cancel{16}}} \cdot \dfrac{\overset{1}{\cancel{4}}}{\underset{3}{\cancel{15}}} \text{ or } \dfrac{1}{12}$

 CHECK Your Progress

Refer to the situation above. Find each probability.

b. $P(\text{two bananas})$

c. $P(\text{orange then apple})$

d. $P(\text{apple then banana})$

e. $P(\text{two oranges})$

CHECK Your Understanding

Example 1
(p. 391)

A penny is tossed and a number cube is rolled. Find each probability.

1 $P(\text{tails and 3})$ **2.** $P(\text{heads and odd})$

Example 2
(p. 392)

3. A spinner and a number cube are used in a game. The spinner has an equal chance of landing on 1 of 3 colors: red, yellow, and blue. The faces of the cube are labeled 1 through 6. What is the probability of a player spinning red and then rolling an even number?

Example 3
(p. 393)

A card is drawn at random from the cards shown and not replaced. Then, a second card is drawn at random. Find each probability.

4. $P(\text{two even numbers})$

5. $P(\text{a number less than 4 and then a number greater than 4})$

$\boxed{1}\ \boxed{2}\ \boxed{3}\ \boxed{4}$

$\boxed{5}\ \boxed{6}\ \boxed{7}\ \boxed{8}\ \boxed{9}$

● = **Step-by-Step Solutions** begin on page R21.
Extra Practice is on page EP19.

Example 1
(p. 391)

A number cube is rolled and a marble is selected at random from the bag at the right. Find each probability.

6. P(1 and red) **7.** P(3 and purple)

8. P(even and yellow) **9.** P(odd and *not* green)

10. P(less than 4 and blue) **11.** P(greater than 1 and red)

Example 2
(p. 392)

12. GAMES Corbin is playing a board game that requires rolling two number cubes to move a game piece. He needs to roll a sum of 6 on his next turn and then a sum of 10 to land on the next two bonus spaces. What is the probability that Corbin will roll a sum of 6 and then a sum of 10 on his next two turns?

Example 3
(p. 393)

13. LAUNDRY A laundry basket contains 18 blue socks and 24 black socks. What is the probability of randomly picking 2 black socks from the basket?

Mrs. Ameldo's class has 5 students with blue eyes, 7 with brown eyes, 4 with hazel eyes, and 4 with green eyes. Two students are selected at random. Find each probability.

14. P(two blue) **15** P(green then brown)

16. P(hazel then blue) **17.** P(brown then blue)

18. P(two green) **19.** P(two *not* hazel)

20. MARKETING A discount supermarket has found that 60% of their customers spend more than $75 each visit. What is the probability that the next two customers will each spend more than $75?

21. SCHOOL Use the information below and the table at the right.

At Clearview Middle School, 56% of the students are girls and 44% are boys.

a. If two students are chosen at random, what is the probability that the first student is a girl and that the second student's favorite subject is science?

b. What is the probability that of two randomly selected students, one is a boy and the other is a student whose favorite subject is *not* art or math?

Clearview Middle School	
Favorite Subject	
Art	16%
Language Arts	13%
Math	28%
Music	7%
Science	21%
Social Studies	15%

22. MOVIES You and a friend plan to see 2 movies over the weekend. You can choose from 6 comedy, 2 drama, 4 romance, 1 science fiction, or 3 action movies. You write the movie titles on pieces of paper, place them in a bag, and each randomly select a movie. What is the probability that neither of you selects a comedy? Is this a dependent or independent event? Explain.

23. **MONEY** Donoma had 8 dimes and 6 pennies in her pocket at random. If she took out 1 coin and then a second coin without replacing the first, what is the probability that both coins were dimes? Is this a dependent or independent event? Explain.

24. **POPULATION** Use the information in the table.

Assume that age is *not* dependent on the region.

a. A resident of Lewburg County is picked at random. What is the probability that the person is under 64 years old and from an urban area?

b. What is the probability that the person is less than 18 years old or 65 years or older and from a rural area?

Lewburg County Population	
Demographic Group	**Fraction of the Population**
Under age 18	$\frac{3}{10}$
18 to 64 years old	$\frac{3}{5}$
65 years or older	$\frac{1}{10}$
Rural Area	$\frac{4}{5}$
Urban Area	$\frac{1}{5}$

25 **DOMINOES** A standard set of dominoes contains 28 tiles, with each tile having two sides of dots from 0 to 6. Of these tiles, 7 have the same number of dots on each side. If four players each randomly choose a tile, without replacement, what is the probability that each chooses a tile with the same number of dots on each side?

Real-World Link
The game of dominoes is believed to have originated in 12th century China.

H.O.T. Problems

26. **OPEN ENDED** There are 9 marbles representing 3 different colors. Write a problem where 2 marbles are selected at random without replacement and the probability is $\frac{1}{6}$.

27. **FIND THE ERROR** The spinner below is spun twice. Raul is finding the probability that both spins will result in an even number. Find his mistake and correct it.

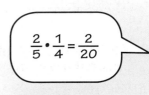

$$\frac{2}{5} \cdot \frac{1}{4} = \frac{2}{20}$$

28. **CHALLENGE** Determine whether the following statement is *true* or *false*. If the statement is false, provide a counterexample.
If two events are independent, then the probability of both events is less than 1.

29. **Write MATH** What is the difference between independent events and dependent events?

30. Mr. Fernandez is holding four straws of different lengths. He has asked four students to each randomly pick a straw to see who goes first in a game. Milo picks first, gets the second longest straw, and keeps it. What is the probability that Felipe will get the longest straw if he picks second?

  A. $\frac{1}{4}$ **C.** $\frac{1}{3}$

  B. $\frac{1}{2}$ **D.** $\frac{1}{5}$

31. Each customer at a sporting goods store gets to spin the arrow on the spinner twice for a discount on their total purchase. If the sections on the spinner are congruent, what is the probability that the spinner will land on a section for $10 off and then on a section for $5 off?

  F. $\frac{3}{8}$ **H.** $\frac{5}{64}$

  G. $\frac{1}{4}$ **I.** $\frac{3}{32}$

32. The spinners below are each spun once.

What is the probability of spinning 2 and white?

  A. $\frac{1}{16}$ **C.** $\frac{2}{5}$

  B. $\frac{1}{4}$ **D.** $\frac{3}{5}$

33. A jar of beads contains 6 aqua beads and 4 black beads. If two beads are selected at random, with replacement, what is the probability that both beads will be aqua?

  F. $\frac{3}{10}$ **H.** $\frac{3}{5}$

  G. $\frac{9}{25}$ **I.** $\frac{9}{10}$

Spiral Review

34. SCHOOL Doli can take 4 different classes first period, 3 different classes second period, and 5 different classes third period. How many different schedules can she have? (Lesson 7-2C)

35. LUNCH Make a tree diagram showing all of the various ways to make a sandwich with the options at the right. (Lesson 7-2B)

Meat	Cheese
turkey	cheddar
ham	Swiss
salami	

Find each percent of change. Round to the nearest whole percent if necessary. State whether the percent of change is an increase or decrease. (Lesson 6-3B)

36. 4 hours to 6 hours   **37.** $500 to $456   **38.** 20.5 meters to 35.5 meters

39. SCALE MODEL A model of a building is; built on a scale of 1 centimeter to 30 centimeters and has a volume of 250 cubic centimeters. What is the volume of the actual building? (Lesson 4-2B)

1. **SOCCER** Display the data in a circle graph. (Lesson 7-1B)

Injuries of High School Girls' Soccer Players	
Position	**Percent**
Halfbacks	37%
Fullbacks	23%
Forward line	28%
Goalkeepers	12%

MALLS The histogram shows the number of stores in the largest malls in the U.S. (Lesson 7-1C)

2. How many malls are represented in the histogram?

3. How many malls have more than 274 stores?

MAMMALS Refer to the stem-and-leaf plot that shows the maximum weight in kilograms of several rabbits. (Lesson 7-1E)

Maximum Weight of Rabbits (kg)	
Stem	Leaf
0	8 9
1	0 2 4 6 8
2	7
3	
4	
5	4 0 | 8 = 0.8 kg

4. Find the range of weights.

5. Find the median and mode of the data.

6. Which measure of central tendency is most affected by the inclusion of the outlier? Explain.

A number cube is rolled. Find each probability. Write as a fraction in simplest form. (Lesson 7-2A)

7. P(an odd number)

8. P(a number *not* greater than 4)

9. P(a number less than 6)

10. P(a multiple of 2)

11. **NGSSS PRACTICE** At a diner, a customer can choose from eggs or pancakes as an entrée and from ham or sausage as a side. Which set shows all the possible choices of one entrée and one side? (Lesson 7-2B)

 A. {(eggs, pancakes), (ham, sausage)}

 B. {(eggs, ham), (eggs, sausage), (pancakes, ham), (pancakes, sausage)}

 C. {(eggs, ham), (eggs, pancakes), (sausage, pancakes)}

 D. {(eggs, ham), (pancakes, sausage)}

12. **NGSSS PRACTICE** How many ways can 6 swimmers come in first, second, or third place? (Lesson 7-2C)

 F. 360 ways   H. 120 ways

 G. 30 ways   I. 720 ways

A box contains 2 yellow, 3 red, 2 blue, 3 purple, and 4 pink marbles. Once a marble is selected, it is *not* replaced. Find each probability. (Lesson 7-2E)

13. P(two purple marbles)

14. P(two yellow marbles)

15. P(a pink marble then a red marble)

16. P(two marbles that are *not* blue)

17. P(two marbles that are neither yellow nor pink)

Wild About Going to Work

If you are an independent person who is interested in wildlife and who enjoys working outdoors, a career as a wildlife technician might be a good fit for you. Wildlife technicians collect data on animal populations and participate in land area surveys to determine the varieties of plants and animals. They must have good written language skills and have a solid background in high school math and science.

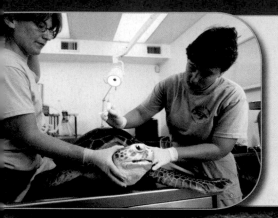

Choose a Major

Are you interested in a career as a wildlife technician? Take some of the following courses in high school.

- Algebra
- Biology
- Geometry
- Natural Resources
- Statistical Methods

Get Connected glencoe.com

Florida's Loggerhead Turtles Nesting Data

Year	Number of Nests, Hillsborough County	Number of Nests, Escambia County
1990	14	27
1991	16	11
1992	22	14
1993	31	37
1994	31	40
1995	56	42
1996	37	62
1997	72	48
1998	71	58
1999	54	73
2000	30	81
2001	15	50
2002	29	22
2003	45	47
2004	26	37
2005	31	23
2006	21	36
2007	21	16

Real-World Math

Use the information in the table to solve each problem.

1. Choose intervals and make a frequency table showing the number of nests in Hillsborough County.

2. Construct a histogram to represent the Hillsborough County data.

3. In what percent of the years were there fewer than 40 loggerhead nests in Hillsborough County?

4. Display the Escambia County data in a stem-and-leaf plot.

5. What were the least and greatest numbers of loggerhead nests in Escambia County?

6. Write a sentence that describes the Escambia County data.

Explore Probability

Main Idea

Investigate experimental probability by conducting a simulation.

NGSSS

MA.7.P.7.2 **Determine, compare, and make predictions based on experimental or theoretical probability** of independent or dependent events.

Get Connected
glencoe.com

A *simulation* is a way of modeling a problem situation. Simulations often mimic events that would be difficult or impractical to perform. In this lab, you will simulate purchasing a box of cereal and getting one of four possible prizes inside.

ACTIVITY

STEP 1 Place four different colored cubes into a paper bag.

STEP 2 Without looking, draw a cube from the bag, record its color, and then place the cube back in the bag.

STEP 3 Repeat steps 1 and 2 until you have drawn a cube from the bag a total of four times.

Analyze the Results

1. Based on your results, predict the probability of getting each cube.

2. What is the theoretical probability of getting each cube?

3. How do your probabilities in Exercises 1 and 2 compare?

4. **MAKE A PREDICTION** Predict the probability of selecting all four cubes in four boxes of cereal.

5. Repeat the simulation above 20 times. Use this data to predict the probability of selecting all four cubes in four choices.

6. Calculate the probability you found in Exercise 5 using the combined data of five different groups. How does this probability compare with your prediction?

7. Describe a simulation that could be used to predict the probability of taking a five-question true/false test and getting all five questions correct by guessing. Choose from two-sided counters, number cubes, coins, or spinners for your model.

8. **COLLECT THE DATA** Conduct 50 trials of the experiment you described in Exercise 7. Then calculate the probability of getting all five questions correct by guessing.

Main Idea

Find and compare experimental and theoretical probabilities.

NGSSS

MA.7.P.7.2 Determine, compare, and make predictions based on experimental or theoretical probability of independent or dependent events. *Also addresses MA.7.A.1.1.*

New Vocabulary

theoretical probability
experimental probability

Get Connected
glencoe.com

Probability Experiments

Explore Follow the steps to determine how many times doubles are expected to turn up when two number cubes are rolled.

Step 1 Use the table to help you find the expected number of times doubles should turn up when rolling two number cubes 36 times. The top row represents one number cube, and the left column represents the other number cube.

	1	2	3	4	5	6
1	1, 1	1, 2	1, 3	1, 4	1, 5	1, 6
2	2, 1	2, 2	2, 3	2, 4	2, 5	2, 6
3	3, 1	3, 2	3, 3	3, 4	3, 5	3, 6
4	4, 1	4, 2	4, 3	4, 4	4, 5	4, 6
5	5, 1	5, 2	5, 3	5, 4	5, 5	5, 6
6	6, 1	6, 2	6, 3	6, 4	6, 5	6, 6

Step 2 Roll two number cubes 36 times. Record the number of times doubles turn up.

1. Compare the number of times you *expected* to roll doubles with the number of times you *actually* rolled doubles.

2. Write the probability of rolling doubles out of 36 rolls using the number of times you *expected* to roll doubles from Step 1. Then write the probability of rolling doubles out of 36 rolls using the number of times you *actually* rolled doubles from Step 2.

In the Explore above, you found both the theoretical probability and the experimental probability of rolling doubles using two number cubes. **Theoretical probability** is based on what *should* happen when conducting a probability experiment. This is the probability you have been using since Lesson 7-2A. **Experimental probability** is based on what *actually* occurred during such an experiment.

Theoretical Probability	**Experimental Probability**
$\dfrac{6}{36}$ ← 6 rolls *should* occur	$\dfrac{n}{36}$ ← *n* rolls *actually* occurred

The theoretical probability and the experimental probability of an event may or may not be the same. As the number of times an experiment is conducted increases, the theoretical probability and the experimental probability should become closer in value.

EXAMPLE **Experimental Probability**

1 When two number cubes are rolled together 75 times, a sum of 9 is rolled 10 times. What is the experimental probability of rolling a sum of 9?

$$P(9) = \frac{\text{number of times a sum of 9 occurs}}{\text{total number of rolls}}$$

$$= \frac{10}{75} \text{ or } \frac{2}{15}$$

The experimental probability of rolling a sum of 9 is $\frac{2}{15}$.

CHECK Your Progress

a. In the above experiment, what is the experimental probability of rolling a sum that is *not* 9?

EXAMPLES **Experimental and Theoretical Probability**

Study Tip

Trials A trial is one experiment in a series of successive experiments.

2 The graph shows the results of an experiment in which a spinner with 3 equal sections is spun sixty times. Find the experimental probability of spinning red for this experiment.

The graph indicates that the spinner landed on red 24 times, blue 15 times, and green 21 times.

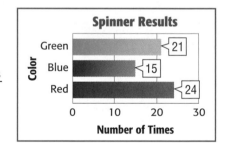

$$P(\text{red}) = \frac{\text{number of times red occurs}}{\text{total number of spins}}$$

$$= \frac{24}{60} \text{ or } \frac{2}{5}$$

The experimental probability of spinning red is $\frac{2}{5}$.

3 Compare the experimental probability you found in Example 2 to its theoretical probability.

The spinner has three equal sections: red, blue, or green. So, the theoretical probability of spinning red is $\frac{1}{3}$. Since $\frac{2}{5} \approx \frac{1}{3}$, the experimental probability is close to the theoretical probability.

CHECK Your Progress

b. Refer to Example 2. If the spinner was spun 3 more times and landed on green each time, find the experimental probability of spinning green for this experiment.

c. Compare the experimental probability you found in Exercise **b** to its theoretical probability.

Theoretical and experimental probability can be used to make predictions about future events.

 Real-World EXAMPLES **Predict Future Events**

④ MEDIA A media buyer examines last year's DVD sales to decide how many DVDs of each type to buy this year. Last year's sales are shown in the table. What is the probability that a person buys a comedy DVD?

DVDs Sold	
Type	**Number**
Action	670
Comedy	580
Drama	450
Horror	300

There were 2,000 DVDs sold and 580 chose comedy. So, the probability is $\frac{580}{2,000}$ or $\frac{29}{100}$.

⑤ Suppose the media buyer expects to sell 5,000 DVDs this year. How many drama DVDs should she buy?

$\frac{450}{2,000} = \frac{x}{5,000}$ Write a proportion.

$450 \cdot 5,000 = 2,000 \cdot x$ Find the cross products.

$2,250,000 = 2,000x$ Multiply.

$1,125 = x$ Divide each side by 2,000.

She should buy about 1,125 drama DVDs.

✓ CHECK Your Progress

   d. What is the probability that a person buys a horror DVD?

   e. If the media buyer expects to sell 3,000 DVDs this year, about how many action movies should she buy?

 Your Understanding

Examples 1–3
(p. 402)

① A coin is tossed 50 times, and it lands on heads 28 times.

   a. Find the experimental probability of the coin landing on heads.

   b. Find the theoretical probability of the coin landing on heads.

   c. Compare the probabilities in Exercises **a** and **b**.

Examples 4 and 5
(p. 403)

2. FOOD Use the table showing the types of muffins that customers bought one morning from their local bakery.

Muffin	Number of People
Blueberry	22
Poppyseed	17
Banana	11

   a. What is the probability that a customer buys a blueberry muffin?

   b. If 100 customers buy muffins tomorrow, about how many would you expect to buy a banana muffin?

Practice and Problem Solving

⬤ = **Step-by-Step Solutions** begin on page R21.
Extra Practice is on page EP19.

Examples 1–3
(p. 402)

3. A number cube is rolled 20 times and lands on 1 two times and on 5 four times.

    a. Find the experimental probability of landing on 5. Compare the experimental probability to the theoretical probability.

    b. Find the experimental probability of *not* landing on 1. Compare the experimental probability to the theoretical probability.

Examples 4 and 5
(p. 403)

4. ZOO Use the graph of a survey of 70 zoo visitors who were asked to name their favorite animal exhibit.

    a. What is the probability that the elephant exhibit is someone's favorite?

    b. What is the probability that the bear exhibit is someone's favorite?

    c. Suppose 540 people visit the zoo. Predict how many people will choose the monkey exhibit as their favorite.

What is Your Favorite Animal Exhibit?		
Exhibit	**Tally**	**Frequency**
Bears	𝖳𝖧𝖫 I	6
Elephants	𝖳𝖧𝖫 𝖳𝖧𝖫 𝖳𝖧𝖫 II	17
Monkeys	𝖳𝖧𝖫 𝖳𝖧𝖫 𝖳𝖧𝖫 𝖳𝖧𝖫 I	21
Penguins	𝖳𝖧𝖫 𝖳𝖧𝖫 III	13
Snakes	𝖳𝖧𝖫 𝖳𝖧𝖫 III	13

    d. Suppose 720 people visit the zoo. Predict how many people will choose the penguin exhibit as their favorite.

5 A spinner with three equal-sized sections marked A, B, and C is spun 100 times.

    a. What is the theoretical probability of landing on A?

    b. The results of the experiment are shown in the table. What is the experimental probability of landing on A? of landing on C?

    c. Make a drawing of what the spinner might look like based on its experimental probabilities. Explain your reasoning.

Section	Frequency
A	24
B	50
C	26

6. GIFTS Use the graph at the right.

    a. What is the probability that a mother will receive a gift of flowers or plants? Write the probability as a fraction.

    b. Out of 400 mothers that receive gifts, predict how many will receive flowers or plants.

Most Popular Mother's Day Gifts

card — 40%
flowers/plants — 28%
dinner/brunch — 8%
gardening items — 8%
apparel — 7%
jewelry — 6%
home décor — 3%

7. **CHALLENGE** The experimental probability of a coin landing on heads is $\frac{7}{12}$. If the coin landed on tails 30 times, find the number of tosses.

8. **REASONING** Twenty sharpened pencils are placed in a box containing an unknown number of unsharpened pencils. Suppose 15 pencils are taken out at random, of which five are sharpened. Based on this, is it reasonable to assume that the number of unsharpened pencils was 40? Explain your reasoning.

9. **Write MATH** Compare and contrast experimental probability and theoretical probability.

NGSSS Practice MA.7.P.7.1

10. The frequency table shows Mitch's record for the last thirty par-3 holes he has played.

Mitch's Golf Results	
Score	Number of Holes
2	4
3	14
4	9
5	3

Based on this record, what is the probability that Mitch will score a 2 or 3 on the next par-3 hole?

A. $\frac{7}{9}$ C. $\frac{3}{10}$

B. $\frac{3}{5}$ D. $\frac{9}{50}$

11. J.R. tossed a coin 100 times and graphed the results.

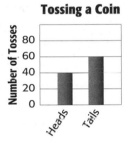

Tossing a Coin

Based on this information, what is the experimental probability of tossing tails on the next toss?

F. $\frac{1}{5}$ H. $\frac{3}{5}$

G. $\frac{2}{3}$ I. $\frac{4}{5}$

Spiral Review

Eight cards numbered 1–8 are shuffled together. A card is drawn at random. It is not replaced. Find each probability. (Lesson 7-2E)

12. P(8 then 4)

13. P(even then odd)

14. **CLOTHES** A pair of jeans comes in 4 different styles, 3 different colors, and 5 different sizes. How many unique outcomes are possible? (Lesson 7-2C)

15. **PROBABILITY** Ella is going to roll a number cube 30 times. How many times should she expect to roll a number greater than 2? (Lesson 7-2A)

7-3 Predictions

Problem-Solving Investigation

Main Idea Solve problems by acting it out.

P.S.I. TEAM +

Act It Out

EDDIE: I've been practicing free throws every day after school. Now I can make an average of 3 out of every 4 free throws I try. I wonder how many times I usually make two free throws in a row.

YOUR MISSION: Act it out to determine the probability that Eddie makes two free throws in a row.

Understand	You know that Eddie makes an average of 3 out of every 4 free throws. You could have Eddie actually make free throws, but that requires a basketball hoop. You could also act it out with a spinner.
Plan	Spin a spinner, numbered 1 to 4, two times. If the spinner lands on 1, 2, or 3, he makes the free throw. If the spinner lands on 4, he doesn't make it. Repeat the experiment 10 times.
Solve	Spin the spinner and make a table of the results.

Trials	1	2	3	4	5	6	7	8	9	10
First Spin	4	1	4	3	1	2	2	1	3	2
Second Spin	2	3	3	2	1	4	1	4	3	3

The circled columns show that six out of the 10 trials resulted in two free throws in a row. So, the probability is 60%.

Check	Repeat the experiment several times to see whether the results agree.

Analyze the Strategy

1. Would the results of the experiment be the same if it were repeated?

2. **Write MATH** Write a problem that can be solved by acting it out. Then solve the problem by acting it out.

NGSSS

MA.7.P.7.2 Determine, compare, and make predictions based on experimental or theoretical **probability** of independent or dependent events.

- Act it out.
- Draw a diagram.
- Use reasonable answers.
- Choose an operation.

Use the *act it out* **strategy to solve Exercises 3–6.**

3. **TESTS** Determine whether using a spinner with four equal sections is a good way to answer a five-question multiple-choice quiz if each question has choices A, B, C, and D. Justify your answer.

4. **BOOKS** There are 6 students in a book club. Two of them order books, and the delivery comes to the classroom teacher. However, the teacher cannot remember which 2 students ordered the books. Is it a good idea for the teacher to randomly pass out the books to any two students? Explain. What is the probability that the teacher will give the books to the correct students?

5. **RUNNING** Six runners are entered in a race. Assuming there are no ties, in how many different ways can first and second places be awarded?

6. **MOVIES** In how many different ways can four friends sit in a row of four seats at the movies if two of the friends insist on sitting next to each other?

Use any strategy to solve Exercises 7–12.

7. FESTIVALS The Student Council will have a booth set up at the town festival. They surveyed 160 students to find out their preference for the booth. The results are shown below. Is 35, 65, or 95 a reasonable answer for the number of students who would prefer a dunking booth? Explain.

Town Festival Survey Results

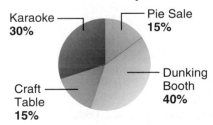

Karaoke 30%
Pie Sale 15%
Craft Table 15%
Dunking Booth 40%

8. **ALGEBRA** The pattern below is known as Pascal's Triangle. Would 1, 6, 10, 10, 6, and 1 be a reasonable conjecture for the numbers in the 6th row? Justify your answer.

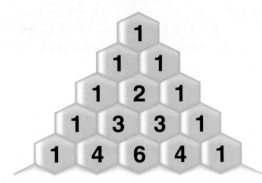

9. **CHESS** A chess tournament is held and 32 students participate. The tournament will be single-elimination, which means if a player loses one match, he or she will be eliminated. How many total games will be played in the tournament?

10. **SCHOOL** Suppose rolling an even number on a number cube corresponds to an answer of *true* and rolling an odd number corresponds to an answer of *false*. Determine whether rolling this number cube is a good way to answer a five-question true-false quiz. Justify your answer.

11. **CABLE** A cable company is running a special for new customers. For the first 3 months they will get a discount of 20% off their regular bill. Would $50, $60, or $70 be a reasonable estimate for the first bill if their regular bill is $95? Explain.

12. **MUSIC** Liseta has an equal number of jazz, country, rap, pop, and R&B songs on her MP3 player. She listens to her MP3 player on random mode on both Wednesday and Thursday nights. What is the probability Liseta will hear a rap song first on Wednesday night?

Explore Fair and Unfair Games

Main Idea

Use experimental and theoretical probabilities to decide whether a game is fair or unfair.

NGSSS

MA.7.P.7.1 Determine the outcome of an experiment and predict which events are likely or unlikely, **and if the experiment is fair or unfair.**
MA.7.P.7.2 Determine, compare, and make predictions based on experimental or theoretical probability of independent or dependent events.

New Vocabulary

fair game
unfair game

Get Connected
glencoe.com

Mathematically speaking, a two-player game is **fair** if each player has an equal chance of winning. A game is **unfair** if there is not such a chance. In this activity, you will analyze two simple games and determine whether each game is fair or unfair.

EXAMPLE Get Animated

1. **In a counter-toss game, players toss three two-color counters. The winner of each game is determined by how many counters land with either the red or yellow side facing up. Play this game with a partner.**

STEP 1 Player 1 tosses the counters. If 2 or 3 chips land red-side up, Player 1 wins. If 2 or 3 chips land yellow-side up, Player 2 wins. Record the results in a table like the one shown below. Place a check in the winner's column for each game.

Game	Player 1	Player 2
1		
2		

STEP 2 Player 2 then tosses the counters and the results are recorded.

STEP 3 Continue alternating the tosses until each player has tossed the counters 10 times.

Analyze the Results

1. Make an organized list of all the possible outcomes resulting from one toss of the 3 counters.

2. Calculate the theoretical probability of each player winning. Write each probability as a fraction and as a percent.

3. **MAKE A CONJECTURE** Based on the theoretical probabilities of each player winning, is this a fair or unfair game? Explain your reasoning.

4. Calculate the experimental probability of each player winning. Write each probability as a fraction and as a percent.

5. Compare the probabilities in Exercises 2 and 4.

6. **GRAPH THE DATA** Make a coordinate graph of the experimental probabilities of Player 1 winning for 5, 10, 15, and 20 games. Graph the ordered pairs (games played, Player 1 wins) using a blue pencil, pen, or marker. Describe how the points appear on your graph.

7. Add to the graph you created in Exercise 6 the theoretical probabilities of Player 1 winning for 5, 10, 15, and 20 games. Graph the ordered pairs (games played, Player 1 wins) using a red pencil, pen, or marker. Connect these red points and describe how they appear on your graph.

8. **MAKE A PREDICTION** Predict the number of times Player 1 would win if the game were played 100 times. Is this a fair or unfair game? Explain.

ACTIVITY

2 **In a number-cube game, players roll two number cubes. Play this game with a partner.**

STEP 1 Player 1 rolls the number cubes. Player 1 wins if the total of the numbers rolled is 5 or if a 5 is shown on one or both number cubes. Otherwise, Player 2 wins. Record the results in a table like the one shown below.

Game	Player 1	Player 2
1		
2		

STEP 2 Player 2 then rolls the number cubes and the results are recorded.

STEP 3 Continue alternating the rolls until each player has rolled the number cubes 10 times.

Analyze the Results

9. Make an organized list of all the possible outcomes resulting from one roll.

10. Calculate the theoretical probability of each player winning and the experimental probability of each player winning. Write each probability as a fraction and as a percent. Then compare these probabilities.

11. **MAKE A CONJECTURE** Based on the theoretical and experimental probabilities of each player winning, is this a fair or unfair game? Explain your reasoning.

12. **Write MATH** If the game is fair, explain how you could change the game so that it is unfair. If the game is unfair, explain how you could change the game to make it fair. Explain.

Main Idea

Predict actions of a larger group by using a sample.

NGSSS

 Preparation for MA.7.S.6.1 Evaluate the reasonableness of a sample to determine the appropriateness of generalizations made about the population.

New Vocabulary

survey
population
sample

 Get Connected
glencoe.com

Use Data to Predict

TELEVISION The circle graph shows the results of a survey in which children ages 8 to 12 were asked whether they have a television in their bedroom.

1. Can you tell how many were surveyed? Explain.

2. Describe how you could use the graph to predict how many students in your school have a television in their bedroom.

A **survey** is designed to collect data about a specific group of people, called the **population**. A smaller group called a **sample** must be chosen. A sample is used to represent a population. If a survey is conducted at random, or without preference, you can assume that the survey represents the population. In this lesson, you will use the results of randomly conducted surveys to make predictions about the population.

Real-World EXAMPLE

1. **TELEVISION** Refer to the graphic above. Predict how many out of 1,725 students would not have a television in their bedroom.

You can use the percent equation and the survey results to predict what part p of the 1,725 students have no TV in their bedroom.

$$\underbrace{part} = \underbrace{percent} \cdot \underbrace{whole}$$

$p = 0.54 \cdot 1,725$ Survey results: 54%

$p = 931.5$ Multiply.

About 932 students do not have a television in their bedroom.

 CHECK Your Progress

a. **TELEVISION** Refer to the same graphic. Predict how many out of 1,370 students have a television in their bedroom.

Real-World Link · · · · ·
A survey found that 85% of people use emoticons on their instant messengers.

2 **INSTANT MESSAGING** Use the information at the left to predict how many of the 2,450 students at Washington Middle School use emoticons on their instant messengers.

You need to predict how many of the 2,450 students use emoticons.

Words	What number of students is 85% of 2,450 students?
Variable	Let n represent the number of students.
Equation	n = 0.85 • 2,450

$n = 0.85 \cdot 2,450$ Write the percent equation.

$n = 2,082.5$ Multiply.

About 2,083 of the students use emoticons.

CHECK Your Progress

b. INSTANT MESSAGING This same survey found that 59% of people use sound on their instant messengers. Predict how many of the 2,450 students use sound on their instant messengers.

CHECK Your Understanding

Example 1
(p. 410)

1 **SPENDING** Use the circle graph that shows the results of a poll to which 60,000 teens responded.

a. How many of the teens surveyed said that they would save their money?

b. Predict how many of the approximately 28 million teens in the United States would buy a music CD if they were given $20.

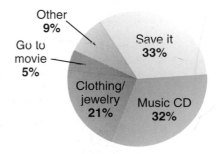

How Would You Spend a Gift of $20?

Other 9%
Go to movie 5%
Save it 33%
Clothing/jewelry 21%
Music CD 32%

Example 2
(p. 411)

2. FOOD Use the bar graph that shows the results of a survey in which students were asked their favorite ice cream flavor.

a. Out of 538 students at Vail Middle School, predict how many prefer strawberry ice cream.

b. Predict how many students prefer chocolate ice cream.

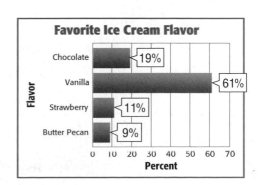

Favorite Ice Cream Flavor

Chocolate 19%
Vanilla 61%
Strawberry 11%
Butter Pecan 9%

Flavor

0 10 20 30 40 50 60 70
Percent

Practice and Problem Solving

⬤ = **Step-by-Step Solutions** begin on page R22.
Extra Practice is on page EP20.

Examples 1 and 2
(pp. 410–411)

3. RECREATION In a survey, 250 people from a town were asked if they thought the town needed a recreation center. The results are shown in the table.

Recreation Center Needed	
Response	**Percent**
Yes	44%
No	38%
Undecided	18%

   a. Predict how many of the 3,225 people in the town think a recreation center is needed.

   b. About how many of the people would be undecided?

4. VOLUNTEERING A survey showed that 90% of teens donate money to a charity during the holidays. Based on that survey, how many teens in a class of 400 will donate money the next holiday season?

Match each situation with the appropriate equation or proportion.

⑤ 27 MP3s is what percent of 238 MP3s?

6. 238% of 27 is what number?

7. 27% of MP3 owners download music weekly. Predict how many MP3 owners out of 238 owners download music weekly.

   a. $n = 27 \cdot 2.38$

   b. $\dfrac{27}{100} = \dfrac{p}{238}$

   c. $\dfrac{27}{238} = \dfrac{n}{100}$

8. CATS Use the graph that shows the percent of cat owners who train their cats in each category.

   a. Out of 255 cat owners, predict how many owners trained their cat not to climb on furniture.

   b. Out of 316 cat owners, predict how many more cat owners have trained their cat not to claw on furniture than have trained their cat not to fight with other animals.

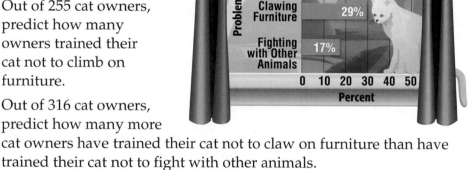

9. FIND THE DATA Refer to the Data File on pages 2–5. Choose some data and write a real-world problem in which you could use the percent proportion or percent equation to make a prediction.

H.O.T. Problems

10. CHALLENGE A survey found that 80% of teens enjoy going to the movies in their free time. Out of 5,200 teens, predict how many said that they do not enjoy going to the movies in their free time.

11. Write MATH Explain how to use a sample to predict what a group of people prefer. Then give an example of a situation in which it makes sense to use a sample.

12. The table shows how students spend time with their family.

How Students Spend Time with Family	
Dinner	34%
TV	20%
Talking	14%
Sports	14%
Taking Walks	4%
Other	14%

Of the 515 students surveyed, about how many spend time with their family at dinner?

A. 17   C. 119

B. 34   D. 175

13. Yesterday, a bakery baked 54 loaves of bread in 20 minutes. Today, the bakery needs to bake 375 loaves of bread. At this rate, predict how long it will take to bake the bread.

F. 1.5 hours   H. 3.0 hours

G. 2.3 hours   I. 3.75 hours

14. Of the 357 students in a freshman class, about 82% plan to go to college. How many students plan on going to college?

A. 224   C. 314

B. 293   D. 325

15. Mr. Freisen surveyed his middle school students to collect information about how much time they spend playing video games each week. The results of his survey are shown in the chart below.

Video Game Time	Percent
Do not play	14%
Around 1–5 hours per week	42%
5–10 hours per week	32%
10 or more hours per week	12%

a. What percent of students play at least 5 hours or more per week?

b. What percent of students play video games during the week?

Spiral Review

16. SPINNERS In how many ways could the colors in the spinner shown be arranged so that red and blue remain in the same place? (Lesson 7-3C)

17. A coin is tossed and a number cube is rolled. Find the probability of tossing tails and rolling an even number. (Lesson 7-3B)

Solve each proportion. (Lesson 4-1D)

18. $\frac{4}{7} = \frac{b}{35}$ **19.** $\frac{18}{9} = \frac{g}{3}$ **20.** $\frac{8.5}{6} = \frac{x}{12}$ **21.** $\frac{2.1}{m} = \frac{3}{4}$

Multiply. (Lesson 1-3C)

22. -4×6 **23.** $5 \times (-8)$ **24.** $-6 \times (-9)$ **25.** 8×3

Main Idea
Predict the actions of a larger group by using a sample.

NGSSS
MA.7.S.6.1 Evaluate the reasonableness of a sample to determine the appropriateness of generalizations made about the population.

New Vocabulary
unbiased sample
simple random sample
stratified random sample
systematic random sample
biased sample
convenience sample
voluntary response sample

Get Connected
glencoe.com

Unbiased and Biased Samples

ENTERTAINMENT The manager of a television station wants to conduct a survey to determine which sport people consider their favorite to watch.

1. Suppose she decides to survey a group of 100 people at a basketball game. Should you assume the results would represent all of the people in the viewing area? Explain.

2. Suppose she decides to survey 100 students at your middle school. Should you assume the results would represent all of the people in the viewing area? Explain.

3. Suppose she decides to call every 100th household in the telephone book. Should you assume the results would represent all of the people in the viewing area? Explain.

What Type of Sports Do You Like to Watch?
Baseball
Basketball
Football
Lacrosse
Soccer

The manager of the television station cannot survey everyone in the viewing area. To get valid results, a sample must be chosen very carefully. An **unbiased sample** is selected so that it accurately represents the entire population. Three ways to pick an unbiased sample are listed below.

Concept Summary — Unbiased Samples

Type	Description	Example
Simple Random Sample	Each item or person in the population is as likely to be chosen as any other.	Each student's name is written on a piece of paper. The names are placed in a bowl, and names are picked without looking.
Stratified Random Sample	The population is divided into similar, non-overlapping groups. A simple random sample is then selected from each group.	Students are picked at random from each grade level at a school.
Systematic Random Sample	The items or people are selected according to a specific time or item interval.	Every 20th person is chosen from an alphabetical list of all students attending a school.

In a **biased sample**, one or more parts of the population are favored over others. Two ways to pick a biased sample are listed below.

Concept Summary — Biased Samples

Type	Description	Example
Convenience Sample	A convenience sample consists of members of a population that are easily accessed.	To represent all the students attending a school, the principal surveys the students in one math class.
Voluntary Response Sample	A voluntary response sample involves only those who want to participate in the sampling.	Students at a school who wish to express their opinions complete an online survey.

EXAMPLES Determine Validity of Conclusions

Determine whether each conclusion is valid. Justify your answer.

1 Every tenth person who walks into a department store is surveyed to determine his or her music preference. Out of 150 customers, 70 stated that they prefer rock music. The manager concludes that about half of all customers prefer rock music.

Since the population is every tenth customer of a department store, the sample is an unbiased, systematic random sample.

2 The customers of a music store are surveyed to determine their favorite leisure time activity. Of these, 85% said that they like to listen to music, so the store manager concludes that most people prefer to listen to music in their leisure time.

The customers of a music store probably like to listen to music in their leisure time. This sample is a biased, convenience sample since all of the people surveyed are in one specific location. The conclusion is not valid.

CHECK Your Progress

a. A radio station asks its listeners to indicate their preference for one of two candidates in an upcoming election. Seventy-two percent of the listeners who responded preferred candidate A, so the radio station announced that candidate A would win the election. Is the conclusion valid? Justify your answer.

A valid sampling method uses unbiased samples. If a sampling method is valid, you can make generalizations about the population.

 Real-World EXAMPLE   **Use Sampling to Predict**

3 **STORES** A store sells 4 styles of pants: jeans, capris, cargos, and khakis. The store workers survey 50 customers at random. The types of survey responses are indicated at the right. If 450 pairs of pants are to be ordered, how many should be jeans?

Type	Number
Jeans	25
Capris	10
Cargos	8
Khakis	7

First, determine whether the sample method is valid. The sample is a simple random sample since customers were randomly selected. Thus, the sample method is valid.

$\frac{25}{50}$ or 50% of the customers prefer jeans. So, find 50% of 450.

$0.5 \times 450 = 225$, so about 225 pairs of jeans should be ordered.

✔ CHECK Your Progress

b. RECREATION An instructor at a swimming pool asked her students if they would be interested in an advanced swimming course, and 60% stated that they would. Are the results valid? If so, suppose there are 870 pool members. How many people can the instructor expect to take the course?

✔ CHECK Your Understanding

Examples 1 and 2 (p. 415)

Determine whether each conclusion is valid. Justify your answer.

1. To determine how much money the average American family spends to cool their home, a survey of 100 Alaskan households are surveyed at random. Of the households, 85 said that they spend less than $75 per month on cooling. The researcher concluded that the average American household spends less than $75 on cooling per month.

2. To determine the most important company benefit, one out of every five employees is chosen at random. Medical insurance was listed as the most important benefit by 67% of the employees. The company managers conclude that medical insurance should be provided to all employees.

Example 3 (p. 416)

3 **GOLF** Zach is trying to decide which of three different golf courses is the best. He randomly surveyed people at a golf store and recorded the results in the table. Are the results valid? If so, suppose Zach surveyed 150 people. How many would be expected to vote for Rolling Meadows?

Course	Number
Whispering Trail	10
Tall Pines	8
Rolling Meadows	7

Practice and Problem Solving

⬤ = **Step-by-Step Solutions** begin on page R22.
Extra Practice is on page EP21.

Examples 1 and 2
(p. 415)

Determine whether each conclusion is valid. Justify your answer.

4. To evaluate the quality of their product, a manufacturer of cell phones checks every 50th phone off the assembly line. Out of 200 phones tested, 4 are defective. The manager concludes that about 2% of the cell phones produced will be defective.

5. To determine whether the students will attend an arts festival at the school, Oliver surveys his friends in the art club. All of his friends plan to attend, so Oliver assumes that all the students at his school will also attend.

6. A magazine asks its readers to complete a questionnaire about popular television actors and send it back to the magazine. The majority of those who replied liked one actor the most, so the magazine decides to write more articles about that actor.

7 To determine what people in California think about a proposed law, 2 people from each county in the state are surveyed at random. Of those surveyed, 42% said that they do not support the proposal. The legislature concludes that the law should not be passed.

Do You Support Proposed Law?	
Yes	30%
No	42%
Not sure	28%

Example 3
(p. 416)

8. COMMUNICATION The Student Council advisor asked every tenth student in the lunch line how they preferred to be contacted with school news. The results are shown in the table. If there are 680 students at the school, how many can be expected to prefer E-mail?

Method	Number
E-mail	16
Newsletter	12
Announcement	5
Telephone	3

9. TRAVEL A random sample of people at a mall shows that 22 prefer to take a family trip by car, 18 prefer to travel by plane, and 4 prefer to travel by bus. Out of 500 people, how many would you expect to say they prefer to travel by plane?

10. GRAPHIC NOVEL Refer to the graphic novel frame to answer Exercises a–b.

We are conducting a survey to see what type of music the young people in our area like. Refer to page 355 to read about it.

Let's think about the types of people that we would be surveying in each situation.

Yeah! We need to make sure that it matches our target audience.

a. Which strategy gives Jamar and Marisol an appropriate sample for valid data?

b. What makes the sample appropriate?

11. **CHALLENGE** How could the wording of a question or the tone of voice of the interviewer affect a survey? Give at least two examples.

12. **Write MATH** Explain how using a survey is one way to determine experimental probability.

NGSSS Practice   **MA.7.S.6.1**

13. Maci surveyed all the members of her softball team about their favorite sport.

Sport	Number of Members
Softball	12
Basketball	5
Soccer	3
Volleyball	8

From these results, Maci concluded that softball was the favorite sport among all her classmates. Which is the best explanation for why her conclusion might NOT be valid?

A. The softball team meets only on weekdays.

B. She should have asked only people who do not play sports.

C. The survey should have been done daily for a week.

D. The sample was not representative of all of her classmates.

14. Ms. Hernandez determined that 60% of the students in her classes brought an umbrella to school when the weather forecast predicted rain. If she has a total of 150 students, which statement does NOT represent Ms. Hernandez's data?

F. On days when rain is forecast, less than $\frac{2}{5}$ of her students bring an umbrella to school.

G. On days when rain is forecast, 90 of her students bring an umbrella to school.

H. On days when rain is forecast, more than $\frac{1}{2}$ of her students bring an umbrella to school.

I. On days when rain is forecast, 60 of her students do not bring an umbrella to school.

 **Spiral Review**

15. **SCHOOL** In a survey of 120 randomly selected students at Jefferson Middle School, 34% stated that science was their favorite class. How many of the 858 students in the school would choose science as their favorite class? (Lesson 7-3E)

16. **PIZZA** A pizza parlor offers thin crust and thick crust, 2 different cheeses, and 4 toppings. Use the *act it out* strategy to determine how many different one-cheese and one-topping pizzas can be ordered. (Lesson 7-3D)

17. **CAR RENTAL** You can rent a car for either $35 a day plus $0.40 per mile or for $20 a day plus $0.55 per mile. Write and solve an equation to find the number of miles that result in the same cost for one day. (Lesson 3-3B)

Get Connected glencoe.com

• **STUDY** TO GO
• Vocabulary Review
• Multilingual eGlossary

FOLDABLES®
Study Organizer

Be sure the following Key Concepts are noted in your Foldable.

7-1
Statistics

Key Concepts

Statistical Displays (Lesson 7-1)
• Circle graphs compare parts to the whole.
• Stem-and-leaf plots list all individual numerical data in an ordered form.
• Histograms show the frequency of data divided into intervals.

Probability (Lesson 7-2)
A tree diagram is a display that represents the sample space.

Uniforms

Pants	Shirts	
blue	yellow ———	blue, yellow
	blue ———	blue, blue
	green ———	blue, green
tan	yellow ———	tan, yellow
	blue ———	tan, blue
	green ———	tan, green

Predictions (Lesson 7-3)
• Theoretical probability is based on what *should* happen when conducting a probability experiment.
• Experimental probability is based on what *actually occurred* during a probability experiment.

Key Vocabulary

circle graph (p. 358)
complementary event (p. 377)
compound event (p. 391)
experimental probability (p. 401)
Fundamental Counting Principle (p. 386)
histogram (p. 364)
independent event (p. 391)
leaf (p. 370)
outcome (p. 375)
population (p. 410)
probability (p. 375)
random (p. 376)
sample (p. 410)
sample space (p. 381)
simple event (p. 375)
stem (p. 370)
stem-and-leaf plot (p. 370)
survey (p. 410)
theoretical probability (p. 401)
tree diagram (p. 381)

Vocabulary Check

State whether each sentence is *true* or *false*. If *false*, replace the underlined word to make a true sentence.

1. <u>Compound events</u> consist of two or more simple events.

2. A <u>random</u> outcome is an outcome that occurs by chance.

3. The Fundamental Counting Principle counts the number of possible outcomes using the operation of <u>addition</u>.

4. Events in which the outcome of the first event does not affect the outcome of the other event(s) are <u>simple events</u>.

5. The <u>sample space</u> of an event is the set of outcomes not included in the event.

6. <u>Stem-and-leaf plots</u> organize data by dividing the digits into leaves and stems.

7. A <u>sample</u> is any one of the possible results of an action.

Multi-Part Lesson Review

7-1 Statistics

Circle Graphs (pp. 358–363)

MA.7.S.6.2

8. **COLORS** The table shows the shades of blue paint sold. Display the data in a circle graph.

Shade	Percent
Navy	35%
Sky/light blue	30%
Aquamarine	17%
Other	18%

EXAMPLE 1 Which pizza was chosen by about twice as many people as supreme?

Pepperoni was chosen by about twice as many people as supreme.

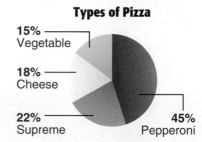

Types of Pizza

15% Vegetable
18% Cheese
22% Supreme
45% Pepperoni

Histograms (pp. 364–368)

MA.7.S.6.2

For Exercises 9–13, use the histogram at the right.

9. How large is each interval?

10. What percent of the runners ran 75 seconds or slower?

11. What was the most likely time?

12. What was the greatest time?

13. **PLANTS** The heights in inches of various types of plants are listed below. Choose intervals and construct a histogram to represent the data.

1, 1, 2, 4, 4, 5, 6, 7, 7, 8, 9, 10, 11, 12, 12, 12, 13, 14, 17, 18, 18, 19, 21, 23, 24

EXAMPLE 2 Choose intervals and construct a histogram to represent the following 400-meter dash times.

| 61 | 71 | 68 | 68 | 69 | 72 | 73 | 61 | 76 | 70 |
| 64 | 64 | 63 | 82 | 68 | 78 | 74 | 80 | 62 | 75 |

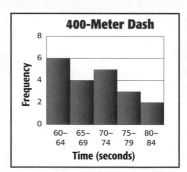

400-Meter Dash

Frequency / Time (seconds)
60–64 65–69 70–74 75–79 80–84

Stem-and-Leaf Plots (pp. 370–374)

MA.7.S.6.2

Display each set of data using a stem-and-leaf plot.

14. hours worked: 29, 54, 31, 26, 38, 46, 23, 21, 32, 37

15. number of points: 75, 83, 78, 85, 87, 92, 78, 53, 87, 89, 91

16. birth dates: 9, 5, 12, 21, 18, 7, 16, 24, 11, 10, 3, 14

EXAMPLE 3 Display the number of pages read in a stem-and-leaf plot: 12, 15, 17, 20, 22, 22, 23, 25, 27, and 35.

The tens digits form the stems, and the ones digits form the leaves.

Pages Read

Stem	Leaf
1	2 5 7
2	0 2 2 3 5 7
3	5

2 | 3 = 23 pages

Probability (pp. 375–380)

A bag of animal crackers contains 5 monkeys, 4 giraffes, 6 elephants, and 3 tigers. Suppose you draw a cracker at random. Find the probability of each event. Write as a fraction in simplest form.

17. P(monkey)

18. P(monkey, giraffe, or elephant)

 MA.7.P.7.1

EXAMPLE 4 What is the probability of rolling a number less than 3 on a number cube? Write as a fraction in simplest form.

$$P(1 \text{ or } 2) = \frac{\text{numbers less than 3}}{\text{total number of possible outcomes}}$$

$$= \frac{2}{6} \quad \text{Two numbers are less than 3.}$$

$$= \frac{1}{3} \quad \text{Simplify.}$$

Sample Spaces (pp. 381–385)

For each situation, find the sample space using a tree diagram.

19. rolling a number cube and tossing a coin

20. choosing from pepperoni, mushroom, or cheese pizza and water, juice, or milk

21. **GAMES** Eliza and Zeke are playing a game in which Zeke spins the spinner shown and rolls a number cube. If the sum of the numbers is less than six, Eliza wins. Otherwise Zeke wins. Find the probability that Zeke wins.

 MA.7.P.7.1

EXAMPLE 5 **GAMES** Ginger and Micah are playing a game in which a coin is tossed twice. If heads comes up exactly once, Ginger wins. Otherwise, Micah wins. Find the sample space. Then find the probability that Ginger wins.

Make a tree diagram.

First Toss	Second Toss	Sample Space
H	H	HH
H	T	HT
T	H	TH
T	T	TT

There are four equally likely outcomes with 2 favoring each player. The probability that Ginger wins is $\frac{2}{4}$ or $\frac{1}{2}$.

Counting Outcomes (pp. 386–389)

Use the Fundamental Counting Principle to find the total number of outcomes in each situation.

22. rolling two number cubes

23. creating an outfit from 6 different shirts and 4 different pants

 MA.7.P.7.1

EXAMPLE 6 Use the Fundamental Counting Principle to find the total number of outcomes for a coin that is tossed four times.

There are 2 possible outcomes, heads or tails, each time a coin is tossed. For a coin that is tossed four times, there are 2 · 2 · 2 · 2 or 16 outcomes.

7-2 Probability (continued)

Independent and Dependent Events (pp. 391–396)

 MA.7.P.7.2

A bag of marbles contains 3 red, 4 blue, and 2 yellow marbles, and 1 green marble. Once selected, a marble is *not* replaced. Find each probability.

24. P(2 yellow)

25. P(red then blue)

26. P(green then red)

27. P(yellow then blue)

EXAMPLE 7 A spinner that is equally divided into eight sections labeled 1–8 is spun and a coin is tossed. What is the probability of spinning an even number and tossing heads?

P(spinning an even number) $= \frac{1}{2}$

P(tossing heads) $= \frac{1}{2}$

P(even and heads) $= \frac{1}{2} \cdot \frac{1}{2} = \frac{1}{4}$

7-3 Predictions

Probability Experiments (pp. 401–405)

 MA.7.P.7.2

A number cube is rolled. The table shows the results of the last 50 rolls.

Find each experimental probability.

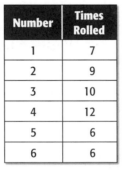

Number	Times Rolled
1	7
2	9
3	10
4	12
5	6
6	6

28. P(five)

29. P(one or two)

30. P(less than 6)

EXAMPLE 8 In an experiment, the same two coins are tossed 50 times. Ten of those times, tails was showing on both coins. Find the experimental probability of tossing two tails.

Since tails were showing 10 out of the 50 tries, the experimental probability is $\frac{10}{50}$ or $\frac{1}{5}$.

PSI: Act It Out (pp. 406–407)

 MA.7.P.7.1

Solve each problem. Use the *act it out* strategy.

31. **FAMILY PORTRAIT** In how many ways can the Maxwell family pose for a portrait if Mr. and Mrs. Maxwell are sitting in the middle and their three children are standing behind them?

32. **AMUSEMENT PARK** In how many ways can 4 friends be seated in 2 rows of 2 seats each on a roller coaster if Judy and Mateo must ride together?

EXAMPLE 9 In how many ways can three females and two males sit in a row of five seats at a concert if the females must sit in the first three seats?

Place five desks or chairs in a row. Have three females and two males sit in any of the seats as long as the females sit in the first three seats. Continue rearranging until you find all the possibilities. Record the results. There are 12 possible arrangements.

Use Data to Predict (pp. 410–413)

CAREERS Use the table that shows the results of a university survey of incoming freshmen.

Career Goal	Percent
Elementary teacher	5.5%
Engineer	6.4%

33. Predict how many of the 3,775 freshmen would choose a career as an elementary teacher.

34. How many of the 3,775 freshmen would you expect to choose a career as an engineer?

35. SHOES A survey showed that 72% of teens bought new athletic shoes for the new school year. Based on that survey, how many teens in a group of 225 bought new athletic shoes for the new school year?

EXAMPLE 10

The circle graph shows the results of a survey to which 150 students at McAuliffe Middle School responded. Predict how many of the 644 students at the school have after-school jobs.

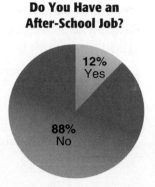

Do You Have an After-School Job?

12% Yes

88% No

Find 12% of 644.

$n = 0.12 \cdot 644$ Write an equation.

$= 77.28$ Multiply.

So, you could predict that about 77 students at McAuliffe Middle School have after-school jobs.

Unbiased and Biased Samples (pp. 414–418)

DANCES Mrs. Jenkins is taking a survey to find how many students would attend a school dance.

36. Describe the sample if Mrs. Jenkins asks every tenth student in the eighth grade.

37. Suppose 7 out of 12 students surveyed said they would attend a school dance. How many out of 350 students would be expected to attend a dance?

EXAMPLE 11 In a survey of store customers, the owners of a grocery store determined that 25 out of 40 customers prefer the store brand oatmeal over the name brand oatmeal. If there is space for 500 boxes of oatmeal, how many store brand containers of oatmeal should the store order?

25 out of 40 or 62.5% of the customers prefer the store brand oatmeal.

Find 62.5% of 500.

$0.625 \times 500 = 312.5$

The store should order about 313 boxes of store brand oatmeal.

1. **NGSSS PRACTICE** The table shows the results of a survey. The results are to be displayed in a circle graph. Which statement about the graph is NOT true?

Favorite Types of Bagel	
Type	**Students**
Blueberry	8
Cinnamon raisin	9
Everything	18
Plain	32

A. About 12% of students chose blueberry as their favorite bagel.

B. The blueberry section on the graph will have an angle measure of about 43°.

C. The everything and plain sections on the circle graph form supplementary angles.

D. Plain bagels were preferred more than any other type of bagel.

2. **GRADES** Make a histogram for the following French test grades: 95, 76, 82, 90, 83, 76, 79, 82, 95, 85, 93, 81, and 63.

Display each data set in a stem-and-leaf plot.

3. 37°, 59°, 26°, 42°, 57°, 53°, 31°, 58°

4. $461, $422, $430, $425, $425, $467, $429

The spinner shown has an equal chance of landing on each number. Find each probability.

5. $P(1 \text{ or } 7)$

6. $P(not \text{ a prime number})$

7. Find the probability of landing on a number greater than 1 and then rolling a number cube and getting an even number.

8. **EMPLOYMENT** The line graph shows the percent of women who had jobs outside the home from 1975 to 2000. Use the graph to predict the number of women who will have jobs outside the home in 2010.

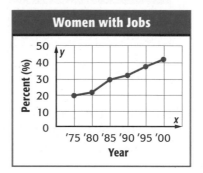

Women with Jobs

Use the Fundamental Counting Principle to find the total number of outcomes in each situation.

9. a 4-digit security code is chosen

10. a number cube is rolled five times

11. **PROBABILITY** A spinner is spun 60 times. The results are shown in the table. What is the experimental probability that the spinner lands on section C? Write as a percent.

Section	Number of Times
A	12
B	17
C	12
D	4
E	15

12. **THINK SOLVE EXPLAIN EXTENDED RESPONSE** A spinner numbered 1–4 is spun and a 6-sided die is rolled. A number on the spinner and the number on the top of the 6-sided die are multiplied and the product is recorded.

Part A List the sample space for this experiment.

Part B How many equally likely outcomes are possible? Are any of them duplicates?

Part C Determine the probability associated with each possible product.

Preparing for Standardized Tests

Multiple Choice: Key Words

When solving multiple-choice questions, pay attention to words like **most**, **least**, and NOT. These words will be boldfaced or uppercase.

 NGSSS PRACTICE EXAMPLE

The manager of a music store estimates that 60 out of every 100 instruments sold are guitars. What is the probability that the next instrument sold is NOT a guitar?

A. $\frac{1}{1}$ **C.** $\frac{3}{5}$

B. $\frac{2}{5}$ **D.** $\frac{1}{60}$

> The key word tells you to find the complement of the event.

$P(\text{a guitar}) = \frac{60}{100}$ or $\frac{3}{5}$

$P(\text{NOT a guitar}) = 1 - \frac{3}{5}$ or $\frac{2}{5}$

The correct answer is B.

Work on It

Joleigh made the spinner below as an interesting way to determine where to go on Saturdays with her friends. What is the probability that on the first spin, the arrow will NOT land on a space for the library?

F. $\frac{1}{6}$ **H.** $\frac{2}{3}$

G. $\frac{1}{3}$ **I.** $\frac{5}{6}$

> **Test Hint**
> Check every answer choice of a multiple-choice question. Each time you find an incorrect answer, cross it off so you remember that you've eliminated it.

Read each question. Then fill in the correct answer on the answer sheet provided by your teacher or on a sheet of paper.

1. The circle graph shows the results of a survey in which students were asked to name their favorite color.

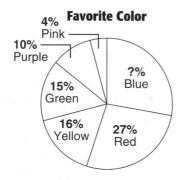

Favorite Color

4% Pink
10% Purple
15% Green
16% Yellow
27% Red
?% Blue

What percent of the students surveyed named blue as their favorite color?

A. 18%   **C.** 28%

B. 23%   **D.** 32%

2. What is $4 \div \frac{1}{3}$?

F. $\frac{1}{12}$ **H.** 7

G. $\frac{4}{3}$ **I.** 12

3. The students in Mrs. Martin's class sell items to raise money for field trips each year. They took a survey to determine which items to sell to other students. The results of the survey are shown in the table. Based on the survey results, what is the probability that a student, selected at random, would buy a drink?

Item	Number of Votes
rings	62
bracelets	27
earrings	21
trading cards	49
snacks	111
small toys	30
drinks	100

A. $\frac{1}{5}$ **C.** $\frac{1}{2}$

B. $\frac{1}{4}$ **D.** $\frac{1}{3}$

4. **GRIDDED RESPONSE** Stacy has a spinner and a number cube pictured below. After spinning and rolling the number cube, she will add the two numbers.

What is the probability that the sum of the numbers from the spinner and number cube will be 3 or 4?

5. **GRIDDED RESPONSE** The table shows the total distance traveled by a boat traveling at a constant rate of speed.

Based on this information, how far will the boat have traveled in miles after 8 hours?

Time (h)	Distance (mi)
2	90
2.5	112.5
3	135
4	180

6. Coach Castillo wanted his team to do a variety of running exercises for practice. To make it more interesting, he used the spinner below to determine which running exercise the team would perform.

What is the probability of landing on 40-yard sprints?

F. $\frac{1}{8}$ **H.** $\frac{1}{5}$

G. $\frac{1}{6}$ **I.** $\frac{1}{4}$

7. Douglas paid $21 for a pair of jeans at the mall. They were on sale for 20% off. What was the original price before the discount?

  A. $4.20   **C.** $26.25

  B. $5.25   **D.** $105.00

8. 🔲 **SHORT RESPONSE** Which point has a coordinate with the greatest absolute value? Explain.

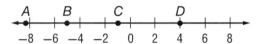

9. A cell phone company charges $35 a month plus $0.30 per text message. Which expression could be used to find the cost for one month of service with b text messages?

  F. $35 + 0.30b$ **H.** $35.30b$

  G. $35b + 0.30$ **I.** $35b + 0.30b$

10. 🔲 **SHORT RESPONSE** Corri needs to get milk (M), eggs (E), bread (B), and cereal (C) at the store. Since the bread is close to the cereal, Corri always picks up the cereal right after getting bread.

List all of the different combinations of ways she can pick up the items she needs. Use the first letter of each item in your list (M, E, B, C).

11. Sierra has 11.5 yards of fabric. She will use 20% of the fabric to make a flag. How many yards of fabric will she use?

  A. 9.2 yd   **C.** 4.5 yd

  B. 8.6 yd   **D.** 2.3 yd

12. Julius made a list of the time in minutes that it took him to get to school each morning.

He used the times to make a stem-and-leaf plot, as shown.

Stem	Leaf
1	4 9
2	0 5 6 8 9

$1 \mid 9 = 19$ minutes

What is the median of this set of times?

  F. 20   **H.** 25

  G. 23   **I.** 26

13. 🔲 **EXTENDED RESPONSE** Molly will travel from Trenton to Mayo by car. Suppose she leaves Trenton on one of three routes: 47 North, 129 North, or 26 West, and arrives in Mayo via either 51 North or 27 West. She does not retrace her steps.

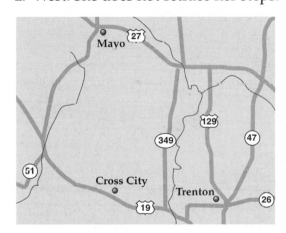

Part A Based on the map, how many different routes could Molly take for her journey? Create a table, list, or tree diagram to show the possibilities.

Part B If Molly chooses one route at random, what is the probability she will drive on US 27?

NEED EXTRA HELP?													
If You Missed Question...	1	2	3	4	5	6	7	8	9	10	11	12	13
Go to Lesson...	7-1B	2-3D	7-3E	7-2E	4-1B	7-2A	6-3D	1-1B	3-3B	7-2B	6-2C	7-1E	7-2C
For help with NGSSS...	S.6.2	A.3.2	S.6.1	P.7.2	A.1.6	P.7.1	A.1.2	A.3.1	A.3.3	P.7.1	A.1.2	S.6.2	P.7.1

Surface Area and Volume

The ★ BIG Idea

Develop an understanding of and use formulas to determine surface areas and volume of three-dimensional shapes.

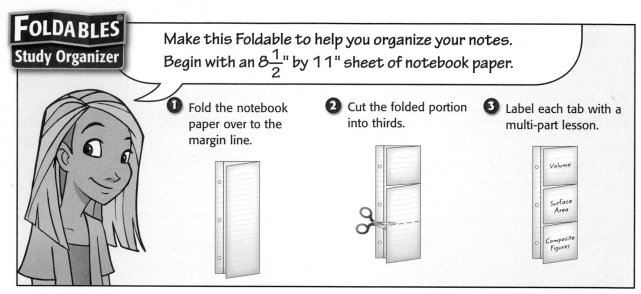

FOLDABLES®
Study Organizer

Make this Foldable to help you organize your notes. Begin with an $8\frac{1}{2}$" by 11" sheet of notebook paper.

1 Fold the notebook paper over to the margin line.

2 Cut the folded portion into thirds.

3 Label each tab with a multi-part lesson.

> Volume
> Surface Area
> Composite Figures

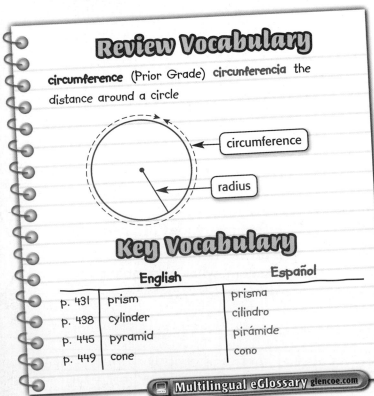

Review Vocabulary

circumference (Prior Grade) **circunferencia** the distance around a circle

circumference

radius

Key Vocabulary

	English	Español
p. 431	prism	prisma
p. 438	cylinder	cilindro
p. 445	pyramid	pirámide
p. 449	cone	cono

Multilingual eGlossary glencoe.com

Get Connected
glencoe.com

- Study using the **eBook**
- Explore with **Get Animated**
- Get extra help from **Personal Tutor**
- Use **virtual manipulatives** for additional help
- Take a **Self-Check Quiz**

When Will I Use This?

Are You Ready for Chapter 8?

You have two options for checking prerequisite skills for this chapter.

Text Option Take the Quick Check below. Refer to the Quick Review for help.

QUICK Check

Find the area of each triangle. (Prior Grade)

1.

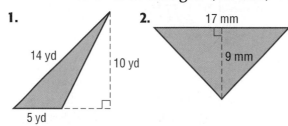

14 yd   10 yd

5 yd

2.

17 mm

9 mm

3. YARD Anita wants to fertilize her triangular-shaped yard. The dimensions of the yard have a height of 35 feet and a base of 50 feet. Find the area of the yard.

Find the area of each circle. Use 3.14 for π. Round to the nearest tenth. (Prior Grade)

4.

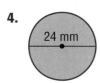

24 mm

5.

11 in.

6. PIZZA Find the area of a circular pizza with a radius of 6 inches.

7. CUPS A manufacturer measures a cup's diameter to determine how much material is needed for a lid. The diameter is 10 centimeters. Find the area of the lid.

QUICK Review

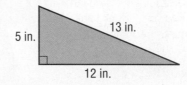

Find the area of the triangle.

5 in.   13 in.

12 in.

$A = \frac{1}{2}bh$ Area of a triangle

$A = \frac{1}{2}(12)(5)$ Replace b with 12 and h with 5.

$A = \frac{1}{2}(60)$ Multiply.

$A = 30$ Multiply.

The area of the triangle is 30 square inches.

EXAMPLE 2

Find the area of the circle. Use 3.14 for π. Round to the nearest tenth.

3 cm

Estimate $3.14 \times (3)^2 = 3 \times 9$ or 27

$A = \pi r^2$ Area of a circle

$A \approx 3.14 \times (3)^2$ Replace π with 3.14 and r with 3.

$A \approx 3.14 \times 9$ Evaluate $(3)^2$.

$A \approx 28.26$ Multiply.

Round to the nearest tenth. The area is about 28.3 square centimeters.

Check $28.3 \approx 27$ ✓

Online Option  **Get Connected** Take the Online Readiness Quiz at **glencoe.com**.

Explore Meaning of Volume

Main Idea
Justify formulas for the volume of prisms.

NGSSS
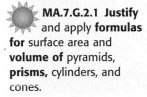
MA.7.G.2.1 **Justify** and apply **formulas for** surface area and **volume of** pyramids, **prisms,** cylinders, and cones.

New Vocabulary
prism

Get Connected
glencoe.com

A cereal box or a box of tissues is shaped like a prism. A **prism** is a three-dimensional figure with at least three rectangular lateral faces and top and bottom faces parallel. The top view of a rectangular prism is shown below.

ACTIVITY

What do you need to find? the volume of several prisms

STEP 1   Build a prism 1 unit high with the same top view as above. Find its volume.

   The prism uses 8 centimeter cubes. So, the volume is 8 cubic centimeters.

STEP 2   Build a prism 2 units high with the same top view as above. Find its volume.

   The prism uses 16 centimeter cubes. So, the volume is 16 cubic centimeters.

Analyze the Results

1. What is the volume if you create a prism that is 10 units high with the same top view as above?

2. Write an expression for the volume of a prism with this top view and height h.

3. What is the area of the top view? Justify your reasoning.

4. Find an object that is a rectangular prism.

   a. Measure the dimensions.

   b. Estimate the volume of the object.

   c. Calculate the volume of the object.

5. **MAKE A CONJECTURE** Write a method for finding the volume of any rectangular prism given its dimensions. Justify your answer using a model or a formula.

Main Idea

Find the volumes of rectangular and triangular prisms.

NGSSS

MA.7.G.2.1 Justify and **apply formulas for** surface area and **volume of** pyramids, **prisms,** cylinders, and cones. *Also addresses MA.7.A.3.2.*

New Vocabulary

volume
rectangular prism
triangular prism

Get Connected
glencoe.com

Volume of Prisms

1. If you observed the Great Pyramid in Egypt or the Inner Harbor and Trade Center in Baltimore from directly above, what geometric shape would you see?

2. If you stood directly in front of each structure, what geometric shape would you see?

The **volume** of a three-dimensional shape is the measure of space occupied by it. It is measured in cubic units such as cubic centimeters (cm^3) or cubic inches (in^3).

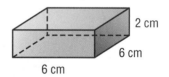

2 cm
6 cm
6 cm

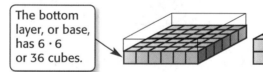

The bottom layer, or base, has 6 · 6 or 36 cubes.

There are two layers.

It takes 2 layers of 36 cubes to fill the box. So, the volume of the box is 72 cubic centimeters.

The figure above is a rectangular prism. A **rectangular prism** is a prism that has rectangular bases.

Key Concept — Volume of a Rectangular Prism

Words	The volume *V* of a rectangular prism is the product of the base *b*, the width *w*, and the height *h*. It is also the area of the base *B* times the height *h*.	**Model**
Symbols	$V = bwh$ or $V = Bh$	

h, *w*, *b*, *B = bw*

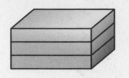
EXAMPLE **Volume of a Rectangular Prism**

1 Find the volume of the rectangular prism.

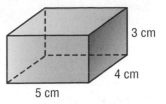

$V = bwh$	Volume of a prism
$V = 5 \cdot 4 \cdot 3$	$b = 5$, $w = 4$, and $h = 3$
$V = 60$	Multiply.

The volume is 60 cubic centimeters or 60 cm^3.

✓ **CHECK Your Progress**

a. Find the volume of the rectangular prism at the right.

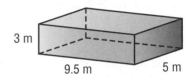

Real-World EXAMPLE Get Animated

2 **MARKETING** A company needs to decide which size lunch box to manufacture. Which lunch box shown will hold more food?

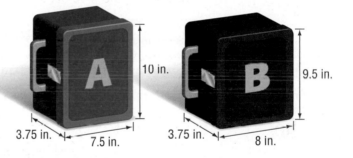

Find the volume of each lunch box. Then compare.

Lunch Box A	**Lunch Box B**
$V = bwh$	$V = bwh$
$V = 7.5 \cdot 3.75 \cdot 10$	$V = 8 \cdot 3.75 \cdot 9.5$
$V = 281.25 \text{ in}^3$	$V = 285 \text{ in}^3$

Since 285 in^3 > 281.25 in^3, Lunch Box B will hold more food.

✓ **CHECK Your Progress**

b. PACKAGING A concession stand serves peanuts in two differently sized containers. Which container holds more peanuts? Justify your answer.

Study Tip

Height Do not confuse the height of the triangular base with the height of the prism.

A **triangular prism** is a prism that has triangular bases. The diagram below shows that the volume of a triangular prism is also the product of the area of the base B and the height h of the prism.

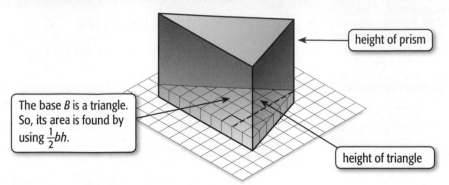

height of prism

The base B is a triangle. So, its area is found by using $\frac{1}{2}bh$.

height of triangle

Key Concept **Volume of a Triangular Prism**

Words The volume V of a triangular prism is the area of the base B times the height h.

Symbols $V = Bh$, where B is the area of the base.

Model

h

B

EXAMPLE **Volume of a Triangular Prism**

Study Tip

Base Before finding the volume of a prism, identify the base. In Example 3, the base is a triangle so you replace B with $\frac{1}{2}bh$.

3 Find the volume of the triangular prism shown.

The area of the triangle is $\frac{1}{2} \cdot 6 \cdot 8$ so replace B with $\frac{1}{2} \cdot 6 \cdot 8$.

$V = Bh$ Volume of a prism

$V = \left(\frac{1}{2} \cdot 6 \cdot 8\right)h$ Replace B with $\frac{1}{2} \cdot 6 \cdot 8$.

$V = \left(\frac{1}{2} \cdot 6 \cdot 8\right)9$ The height of the prism is 9.

$V = 216$ Multiply.

The volume is 216 cubic feet or 216 ft³.

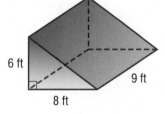

6 ft

8 ft

9 ft

CHECK Your Progress

Find the volume of each triangular prism.

c.

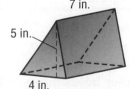

7 in.

5 in.

4 in.

d.

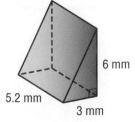

6 mm

5.2 mm

3 mm

Example 1
(p. 433)

Find the volume of each prism. Round to the nearest tenth if necessary.

1.
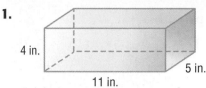
4 in.
11 in.
5 in.

2.
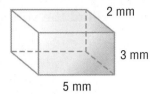
2 mm
3 mm
5 mm

Example 3
(p. 434)

3.
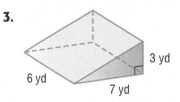
3 yd
6 yd
7 yd

4.
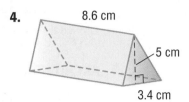
8.6 cm
5 cm
3.4 cm

Example 2
(p. 433)

5. STORAGE One cabinet measures 3 feet by 2.5 feet by 5 feet. A second measures 4 feet by 3.5 feet by 4.5 feet. Which volume is greater? Explain.

Practice and Problem Solving

= **Step-by-Step Solutions** begin on page R23.
Extra Practice is on page EP21.

Examples 1 and 3
(pp. 433–434)

Find the volume of each prism. Round to the nearest tenth if necessary.

6.
6 in.
20 in.
8 in.

7.
10 ft
3 ft
3 ft

8.
4 m
6 m
8 m

9.
12.5 cm
4.2 cm
4.5 cm

10.
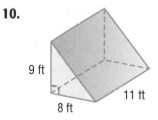
9 ft
8 ft
11 ft

11
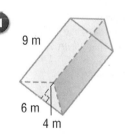
9 m
6 m
4 m

12.
2.8 yd
4.5 yd
6 yd

13.
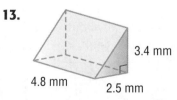
3.4 mm
4.8 mm
2.5 mm

Example 2
(p. 433)

14. PACKAGING A soap company sells laundry detergent in two different containers. Which container holds more detergent? Justify your answer.

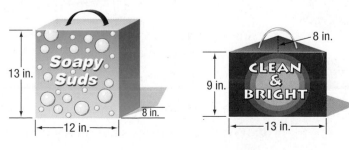

Soapy Suds
13 in.
8 in.
12 in.

CLEAN & BRIGHT
8 in.
9 in.
13 in.

15. TOYS A toy company makes rectangular sandboxes that measure 6 feet by 5 feet by 1.2 feet. A customer buys a sandbox and 40 cubic feet of sand. Did the customer buy too much or too little sand? Justify your answer.

Find the volume of each prism.

16.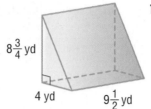
$5\frac{1}{2}$ ft
3 ft $2\frac{1}{4}$ ft

17.
$8\frac{3}{4}$ yd
4 yd $9\frac{1}{2}$ yd

18.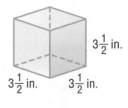
$3\frac{1}{2}$ in.
$3\frac{1}{2}$ in. $3\frac{1}{2}$ in.

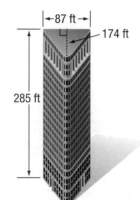
←87 ft→
174 ft
285 ft

19. ARCHITECTURE Use the diagram at the right that shows the approximate dimensions of the Flatiron Building in New York City.

a. What is the approximate volume of the Flatiron Building?

b. The building is 22 stories tall. Estimate the volume of each story.

20. ALGEBRA The base of a rectangular prism has an area of 19.4 square meters and the prism has a volume of 306.52 cubic meters. Write an equation that can be used to find the height h of the prism. Then find the height of the prism.

21 MONEY The diagram shows the dimensions of an office. It costs about $0.11 per year to air condition one cubic foot of space. On average, how much does it cost to air condition the office for one month?

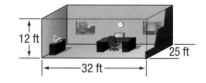
12 ft
32 ft
25 ft

22. GRAPHIC NOVEL Refer to the graphic novel frame below for Exercises a and b.

Refer to page 429 to read all about our dunk tank.

Get Animated

Length	Width	Height	Surface Area	Volume
2	12	4	136	96
4	4	8	144	128
4	7	6	160	168
8	5	4	152	160
10	4	3	124	120

a. Are there any other possibilities for dimensions?

b. Which dimensions are reasonable for a dunk tank? Explain.

23. REASONING Two rectangular prisms are shown at the right. When the dimensions of Prism A are doubled, does the volume also double? Explain your reasoning.

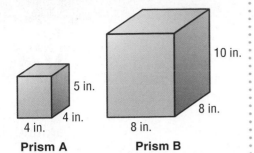

5 in.
4 in.
4 in.
Prism A

10 in.
8 in.
8 in.
Prism B

24. CHALLENGE How many cubic inches are in a cubic foot?

25. Write MATH Explain the similarities and differences in finding the volume of a rectangular prism and a triangular prism.

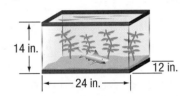

NGSSS Practice   MA.7.G.2.1

26. A fish aquarium is shown below.

14 in.

12 in.

24 in.

What is the volume of the aquarium?

A. 168 in³

C. 2,016 in³

B. 342 in³

D. 4,032 in³

27. The volume of the box below is 1.5 cubic inches. Which of the following are possible dimensions of the box?

PAPER CLIPS

F. 2 in. by 2 in. by 1 in.

G. 1 in. by 1 in. by 1 in.

H. 2 in. by 1.5 in. by 0.5 in.

I. 3 in. by 0.5 in. by 1.5 in.

Spiral Review

28. CARS To determine what kind of vehicle is preferred by most customers, the owner of a dealership surveys every 10th person who enters. Of these, 54% state that they prefer 4-door sedans. Based on these results, if the dealership stocks 150 cars, about how many of them should be 4-door sedans? (Lesson 7-3E)

29. MP3 PLAYERS In a survey, 46% of randomly selected teens said they own an MP3 player. Predict how many of the 850 teens at Harvey Middle School own an MP3 player. (Lesson 7-3E)

30. SPORTS Refer to the table that lists the number of games won by each team in a baseball league. (Lesson 7-1E)

a. Make a stem-and-leaf plot of the data.

b. What is the mean, median, and mode of the data?

Number of Wins					
25	36	46	15	30	53
40	32	17	45	41	31
56	50	52	47	26	40
43	56	51	50	55	50
44	47	53	23	19	

Main Idea

Find the volumes of cylinders.

NGSSS

 MA.7.G.2.1 Justify and apply formulas for surface area and **volume of** pyramids, prisms, **cylinders,** and cones. *Also addresses MA.7.A.3.2.*

New Vocabulary

cylinder

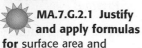 **Get Connected**
glencoe.com

Volume of Cylinders

Explore Set a soup can on a piece of grid paper and trace around the base, as shown below.

1. Estimate the number of centimeter cubes that would fit at the bottom of the container. Include parts of cubes.

2. If each layer is 1 centimeter high, how many layers would it take to fill the cylinder?

3. **MAKE A CONJECTURE** Write a formula that allows you to find the volume of the container. Justify the formula.

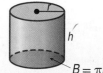

A **cylinder** is a three-dimensional figure with two parallel congruent circular bases. As with prisms, the area of the base of a cylinder tells the number of cubic units in one layer. The height tells how many layers there are in the cylinder.

Key Concept — Volume of a Cylinder

Words   The volume V of a cylinder with radius r is the area of the base B times the height h.

Symbols $V = Bh$, where $B = \pi r^2$
or $V = \pi r^2 h$

Model

h

$B = \pi r^2$

EXAMPLE   Volume of a Cylinder

① **Find the volume of the cylinder. Round to the nearest tenth.**

$V = \pi r^2 h$ Volume of a cylinder

$V = \pi (5)^2 (8.3)$ Replace r with 5 and h with 8.3.

Use a calculator.

[2nd] [π] [X] 5 [x²] [ENTER] 651.8804756

The volume is about 651.9 cubic centimeters.

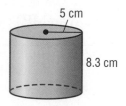

5 cm

8.3 cm

✓ **CHECK Your Progress**

Find the volume of each cylinder. Round to the nearest tenth.

a.
3 in.
1.8 in.

b. 2.4 m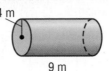
9 m

Study Tip

Circles Recall that the radius is half the diameter.

Real-World EXAMPLE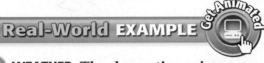

3 cm
13 cm

② **WEATHER** The decorative rain gauge shown has a height of 13 centimeters and a diameter of 3 centimeters. How much water can the rain gauge hold?

$V = \pi r^2 h$	Volume of a cylinder
$V = \pi(1.5)^2 13$	Replace r with 1.5 and h with 13.
$V \approx 91.9$	Simplify.

The rain gauge can hold about 91.9 cubic centimeters.

✓ **CHECK Your Progress**

c. PAINT Find the volume of a cylindrical paint can that has a diameter of 4 inches and a height of 5 inches. Round to the nearest tenth.

✓ CHECK Your Understanding

Example 1
(pp. 438–439)

Find the volume of each cylinder. Round to the nearest tenth.

1.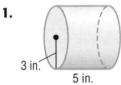
3 in.
5 in.

2. 8 cm
1.5 cm

3 |← 11 ft →|
6.5 ft

Example 2
(p. 439)

4. CONTAINERS A can of concentrated orange juice has the dimensions shown at the right. Find the volume of the can of orange juice to the nearest tenth.

5. CANDLES A scented candle is in the shape of a cylinder. The radius is 4 centimeters and the height is 12 centimeters. Find the volume of the candle to the nearest tenth.

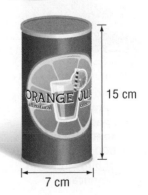
15 cm
7 cm

Practice and Problem Solving

● = **Step-by-Step Solutions** begin on page R23.
Extra Practice is on page EP22.

Example 1
(pp. 438–439)

Find the volume of each cylinder. Round to the nearest tenth.

6.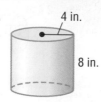
4 in.
8 in.

7.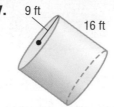
9 ft
16 ft

8.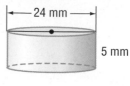
├── 24 mm ──┤
5 mm

9.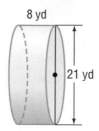
8 yd
21 yd

10.
13.3 cm
2 cm

11.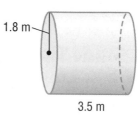
1.8 m
3.5 m

12. diameter = 15 mm
height = 4.8 mm

13 diameter = 4.5 m
height = 6.5 m

14. radius = 6 ft

height = $5\frac{1}{3}$ ft

15. radius = $3\frac{1}{2}$ in.

height = $7\frac{1}{2}$ in.

16. BIRDS A cylindrical bird feeder has a diameter of 4 inches and a height of 18 inches. How much birdseed can the feeder hold? Round to the nearest tenth.

Example 2
(p. 439)

17. WATER BOTTLE What is the volume of a cylindrical water bottle that has a radius of $1\frac{1}{4}$ inches and a height of 7 inches? Round to the nearest tenth.

Find the volume of each cylinder. Round to the nearest tenth.

18.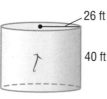
26 ft
40 ft

19.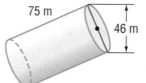
75 m
46 m

20.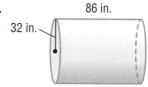
86 in.
32 in.

ESTIMATION Match each cylinder with its approximate volume.

21. radius = 4.1 ft, height = 5 ft

22. diameter = 8 ft, height = 2.2 ft

23. diameter = 6.2 ft, height = 3 ft

24. radius = 2 ft, height = 3.8 ft

a. 91 ft³

b. 48 ft³

c. 111 ft³

d. 264 ft³

25. POTTERY A vase in the shape of a cylinder has a diameter of 11 centimeters and a height of 250 millimeters. Find the volume of the vase to the nearest cubic centimeter. (*Hint*: 1 cm = 10 mm)

Real-World Link
Bird feeders can attract many species of birds. There are over 800 species of birds in North America.

26. BAKING Which will hold more cake batter, the rectangular pan or two round pans? Explain.

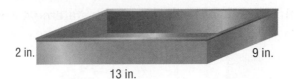

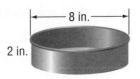

27 **ALGEBRA** Cylinder A has a radius of 4 inches and a height of 2 inches. Cylinder B has a radius of 2 inches. What is the height of Cylinder B if both cylinders have the same volume? Round to the nearest tenth.

28. ANALYZE TABLES The volumes, using 3.14 for π, of four cylinders are shown in the table.

  a. Describe how the radius and the height increase for each successive cylinder.

  b. As the radius and the height increase, how does the volume of each cylinder increase?

Radius (cm)	Height (cm)	Volume (cm³)
2	4	50.24
4	8	401.92
8	16	3,215.36
16	32	25,722.88

H.O.T. Problems

29. CHALLENGE Two equally sized sheets of construction paper are rolled; one along the length and the other along the width, as shown. Which cylinder do you think has the greater volume? Explain.

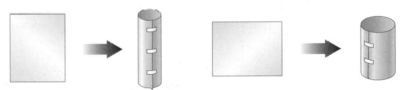

30. OPEN ENDED Draw and label a cylinder that has a larger radius but less volume than the cylinder shown at the right.

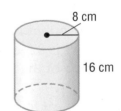

31. NUMBER SENSE What is the ratio of the volume of a cylinder to the volume of a cylinder having twice the height but the same radius?

32. NUMBER SENSE Suppose Cylinder A has the same height but twice the radius of Cylinder B. What is the ratio of the volume of Cylinder B to Cylinder A?

33. **Write MATH** Explain how the formula for the volume of a cylinder is similar to the formula for the volume of a rectangular prism.

34. The oatmeal container shown has a diameter of $3\frac{1}{2}$ inches and a height of 9 inches. Which is closest to the number of cubic inches it will hold when filled?

$3\frac{1}{2}$ in.

9 in.

   A. 32   C. 75.92

   B. 42.78   D. 86.59

35. ✎ **GRIDDED RESPONSE** Jarrod's family stores their sugar in a cylindrical container like the one shown at the right. They regularly fill a sugar dispenser with a volume of 38.9 cubic inches from the container. Assuming the storage container is full, what is the maximum number of times the dispenser can be completely filled?

$7\frac{1}{2}$ in.

8 in.

36. Which statement is true about the volumes of the cylinders shown?

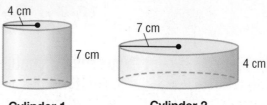

4 cm

7 cm

7 cm

4 cm

Cylinder 1   **Cylinder 2**

   F. The volume of Cylinder 1 is greater than the volume of Cylinder 2.

   G. The volume of Cylinder 2 is greater than the volume of Cylinder 1.

   H. The volumes are equal.

   I. The volume of Cylinder 1 is twice the volume of Cylinder 2.

37. THINK SOLVE EXPLAIN **SHORT RESPONSE** Chenoa is making candles as gifts for her family. She is using the mold at the right. What is the volume of candle wax, in cubic centimeters, that the mold holds? Use 3.14 for π.

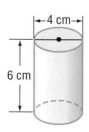

4 cm

6 cm

38. TENTS A tent is in the shape of a triangular prism. On its side, the tent is 8 feet long, 5 feet tall, and 5 feet wide. What is the volume of the tent? (Lesson 8-1B)

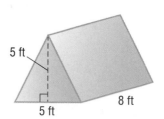

5 ft

5 ft

8 ft

39. CATS A cat food company mailed 250 surveys to cat owners. Of the 185 surveys that were returned, 52% preferred calico cats. The company concluded that about half of cat owners prefer calico cats. Determine whether this conclusion is valid. Justify your answer. (Lesson 7-3E)

Find the total cost to the nearest cent. (Lesson 6-3C)

40. $51.49 stereo; 6% sales tax

41. $38.62 meal; 15% tip

42. $15.95 shirt; 7% sales tax

Explore Volume of Pyramids and Cones

Main Idea

Justify formulas for the volume of pyramids and cones.

NGSSS

 **MA.7.G.2.1 Justify** and apply **formulas for** surface area and **volume of pyramids,** prisms, cylinders, **and cones.**

Get Connected
glencoe.com

MOVIE THEATERS A movie theater offers two different containers of popcorn: a square prism and a square pyramid. They are both 4 inches tall and have a base area of 16 square inches.

In the following Activity, you will compare their volumes.

ACTIVITY
Get Animated

1 **STEP 1** Draw each net onto card stock. Cut out each and tape together. The prism and pyramid will be open. The pyramid is composed of four congruent isosceles triangles with bases of 4 inches and heights of $4\frac{1}{2}$ inches.

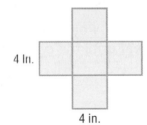
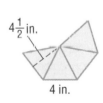

STEP 2 Fill the pyramid with rice. Pour the rice from the pyramid into the prism and repeat until the prism is full. Slide a ruler across the top to level the amount.

Analyze the Results

1. Compare the bases of the prism and pyramid.

2. Compare the heights of the prism and pyramid.

3. How many pyramids of rice did it take to fill the prism?

4. What fraction of the volume of the prism is the volume of the pyramid?

5. Repeat the Activity with a rectangular prism and a rectangular pyramid. The prism and the pyramid should have equal heights and equal bases. What fraction of the volume of the prism is the volume of the pyramid?

6. MAKE A CONJECTURE Explain how you could find the volume of a pyramid given a prism with the same base area and height. Justify your answer.

ACTIVITY

2 **MOVIES** Suppose the movie theater also offers shaved ice in a cylinder and in a cone. The cylinder and the cone have equal heights and equal base areas. Make a model of each container.

STEP 1 Draw each net onto card stock. Cut out each and tape together. For the cone, cut out the radius of the larger circle and overlap until the cone is formed. The cylinder and cone will be open.

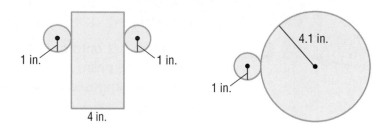

STEP 2 Fill the cone with rice. Pour the rice from the cone into the cylinder and repeat until the cylinder is full.

Analyze the Results

7. Compare the bases and heights of the cylinder and cone.

8. How many cones of rice did it take to fill the cylinder?

9. What fraction of the volume of the cylinder is the volume of the cone?

10. MAKE A CONJECTURE If the cylinder of shaved ice has a volume of 27 ounces, what is the volume of the cone of shaved ice? Justify your answer.

Main Idea

Find the volume of pyramids.

NGSSS

 MA.7.G.2.1 Justify and **apply formulas for** surface area and **volume of pyramids,** prisms, cylinders, and cones. *Also addresses MA.7.A.3.2.*

New Vocabulary

pyramid
lateral face

Get Connected
glencoe.com

Volume of Pyramids

SAND SCULPTURE Dion is helping his brother build a sand sculpture at the beach in the shape of a pyramid. The square pyramid has a base with a length and width of 12 inches each and a height of 12 inches.

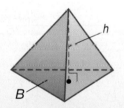

1. What is the area of the base?

2. What is the volume of a square prism with the same dimensions as the pyramid?

A **pyramid** is a three-dimensional shape with one base and triangular **lateral faces**, or any flat surfaces that are not bases. The lateral edges meet at one vertex. The height of a pyramid is the distance from the vertex perpendicular to the base.

🔑 Key Concept   Volume of a Pyramid

Words   The volume V of a pyramid is one third the area of the base B times the height of the pyramid h.

Symbols $V = \frac{1}{3}Bh$

Model

 EXAMPLE   Find the Volume of a Pyramid

1 Find the volume of the pyramid. Round to the nearest tenth.

$V = \frac{1}{3}Bh$ Volume of a pyramid

$V = \frac{1}{3}(3.2 \cdot 1.4)2.8$ $B = 3.2 \cdot 1.4, h = 2.8$

$V \approx 4.2$ Simplify.

2.8 in.

3.2 in.   1.4 in.

The volume is about 4.2 cubic inches.

 CHECK Your Progress

a. Find the volume of a pyramid that has a height of 9 centimeters and a rectangular base with a length of 7 centimeters and a width of 3 centimeters.

You can also use the formula for the volume of a pyramid to find a missing height.

 EXAMPLE **Find the Height of a Pyramid**

QUICK Review

Multiplying Fractions
To find $\frac{1}{3} \cdot \frac{1}{2} \cdot 8 \cdot 3$,
multiply $\frac{1}{3} \cdot \frac{1}{2}$ and $8 \cdot 3$
to get $\frac{1}{6}$ and 24, then
find $\frac{1}{6}$ of 24.

2 A triangular pyramid has a volume of 44 cubic meters. It has an 8-meter base and a 3-meter height. Find the height of the pyramid.

$V = \frac{1}{3}Bh$ Volume of a pyramid

$44 = \frac{1}{3}\left(\frac{1}{2} \cdot 8 \cdot 3\right)h$ $V = 44, B = \frac{1}{2} \cdot 8 \cdot 3$

$44 = 4h$ Multiply.

$\frac{44}{4} = \frac{4h}{4}$ Divide by 4.

$11 = h$ Simplify.

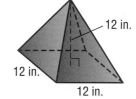

The height of the pyramid is 11 meters.

✓ **CHECK Your Progress**

b. A triangular pyramid has a volume of 840 cubic inches. It has a base of 20 inches and a height of 21 inches. Find the height of the pyramid.

Real-World EXAMPLE

Real-World Link · · · · ·
The U.S. Department of Agriculture recommends that teenagers eat at least three ounces of whole grains, plenty of dark green and orange vegetables, a variety of fruit, calcium-rich foods, lean meats, and a limited intake of oils each day.

3 **SAND SCULPTURES** The sand sculpture from page 445 is shown at the right. Find the volume of the square pyramid.

$V = \frac{1}{3}Bh$ Volume of a pyramid

$V = \frac{1}{3}(12 \cdot 12)12$ $B = 12 \cdot 12, h = 12$

$V = 576$ Simplify.

The volume is 576 cubic inches.

✓ **CHECK Your Progress**

c. MODELS Kamilah is making a model of the Food Guide Pyramid for a class project. The model is a square pyramid with a base edge of 4 inches and a height of 5 inches. Find the volume of plaster needed to make the model. Round to the nearest tenth.

d. STADIUMS The Pyramid Arena in Memphis, Tennessee, is a square pyramid 321 feet tall. The base has 600-foot sides. Find the volume of the pyramid.

Example 1
(p. 445)

Find the volume of each pyramid. Round to the nearest tenth if necessary.

1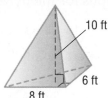

2.

Example 2
(p. 446)

Find the height of each pyramid.

3. square pyramid: volume 1,024 cm³, base edge 16 cm

4. triangular pyramid: volume 48 in³, base edge 9 in., base height 4 in.

Example 3
(p. 446)

5. BUILDINGS The Transamerica Pyramid is the tallest skyscraper in San Francisco. The rectangular base has a length of 175 feet and a width of 120 feet. The height is 853 feet. Find the volume of the building.

Practice and Problem Solving

● = **Step-by-Step Solutions** begin on page R23.
Extra Practice is on page EP22.

Example 1
(p. 445)

Find the volume of each pyramid. Round to the nearest tenth if necessary.

6.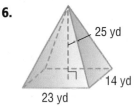

7.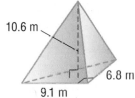

8.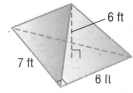

Example 2
(p. 446)

Find the height of each pyramid.

9. rectangular pyramid: volume 448 in³, base edge 12 in., base length 8 in.

10. triangular pyramid: volume 270 cm³, base edge 15 cm, height of base 4 cm

11. square pyramid: volume 297 ft³, area of the base 81 ft²

12. hexagonal pyramid: volume 1,320 ft³, area of the base 120 ft²

Example 3
(p. 446)

13 GLASS A glass pyramid has a height of 4 inches. Its rectangular base has a length of 3 inches and a width of 2.5 inches. Find the volume of glass used to create the pyramid.

14. HISTORY An ancient stone pyramid has a height of 13.6 meters. The edges of the square base are 16.5 meters. Find the volume of the stone pyramid.

15. RESEARCH Use the Internet or another research tool to find information on a pyramid-shaped building. Find the volume of the building.

16. MEASUREMENT A rectangular pyramid has a length of 14 centimeters, a width of 9 centimeters, and a height of 10 centimeters. Explain the effect on the volume if each dimension were doubled.

17. OPEN ENDED A rectangular pyramid has a volume of 160 cubic feet. Find two possible sets of dimensions for the pyramid.

18. CHALLENGE A square pyramid and a cube have the same bases and volumes. How are their heights related? Explain.

19. REASONING The two figures shown have congruent bases. How does the volume of the two square pyramids in Figure B compare to the volume of the square pyramid in Figure A?

Figure A   **Figure B**

NGSSS Practice   MA.7.G.2.1

20. A rectangular pyramid has a volume of 1,560 cubic inches and a base that is 13 inches by 15 inches. What is the height of the pyramid?

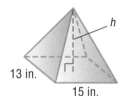

13 in.

15 in.

A. 8 in.   **C.** 30 in.

B. 24 in.   **D.** 48 in.

21. Find the volume of the rectangular pyramid shown. Round to the nearest tenth.

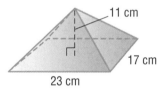

11 cm

17 cm

23 cm

F. 4,301 cm³   **H.** 1,433.7 cm³

G. 2,867.3 cm³   **I.** 716.3 cm³

Find the volume of each cylinder or prism. Round to the nearest tenth.

(Lessons 8-1B and 8-1C)

22.
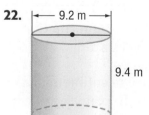

|← 9.2 m →|

9.4 m

23.
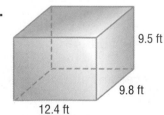

9.5 ft

9.8 ft

12.4 ft

24.
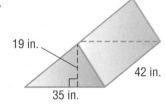

19 in.

42 in.

35 in.

Main Idea
Find the volume of cones.

NGSSS

MA.7.G.2.1 Justify and **apply formulas for** surface area and **volume of** pyramids, prisms, cylinders, and **cones.**

New Vocabulary
cone

Get Connected
glencoe.com

Volume of Cones

CANDLE MAKING Grace and Elle are making candles to donate for a school fundraiser. The mold they are using is 6 inches tall and has a radius of 3 inches.

1. What would be the volume of the candle if it was a cylinder, but had the same dimensions?

2. **MAKE A CONJECTURE** What fraction of the cylinder is the cone?

A **cone** is a three-dimensional figure with one circular base. A curved surface connects the base and vertex.

Key Concept   Volume of a Cone

Words   The volume V of a cone with radius r is one third the area of the base B times the height h.

Model

Symbols $V = \frac{1}{3}Bh$ or $V = \frac{1}{3}\pi r^2 h$

EXAMPLE   Volume of a Cone

1 **Find the volume of the cone. Round to the nearest tenth.**

$V = \frac{1}{3}\pi r^2 h$ Volume of a cone

$V = \frac{1}{3} \cdot \pi \cdot 3^2 \cdot 6$ $r = 3, h = 6$

$V \approx 56.5$ Simplify.

The volume is about 56.5 cubic inches.

6 in.

3 in.

Read Math
The ≈ symbol is read *is about equal to.*

CHECK Your Progress

Find the volume of each cone. Round to the nearest tenth.

a.
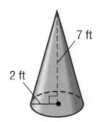
7 ft

2 ft

b.
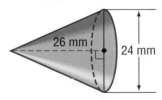
26 mm

24 mm

Real-World EXAMPLE

2 PAPER CUPS A cone-shaped paper cup is filled with water. The height of the cup is 7 centimeters and the diameter is 6 centimeters. If one cubic centimeter is equal to one milliliter, how many milliliters does the paper cup hold?

$V = \frac{1}{3}\pi r^2 h$ Volume of a cone

$V = \frac{1}{3} \cdot \pi \cdot 3^2 \cdot 7$ $r = 3, h = 7$

$V \approx 65.94$ Simplify.

The paper cup holds about 66 milliliters.

✓ CHECK Your Progress

c. TEPEES April is putting together a tepee in her backyard. It is 7.5 feet tall with a radius of 4 feet. What is the tepee's volume to the nearest tenth?

✓ CHECK Your Understanding

Example 1
(p. 449)

Find the volume of each cone. Round to the nearest tenth.

1.

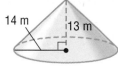

14 m   13 m

2.

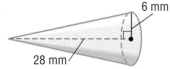

6 mm

28 mm

3 height: 8.4 feet, diameter: 3.5 feet

4. height: 120 millimeters, radius: 45 millimeters

Example 2
(p. 450)

5. FUNNELS Austin is using a funnel to fill a glass bottle with colored sand. The funnel has a height of 4 inches and a diameter of 5 inches. If one cup is about 14.4 cubic inches, about how many cups of sand will fill the funnel at one time? Round to the nearest tenth.

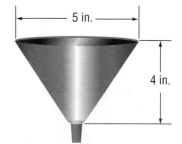

5 in.

4 in.

6. FLOWERS Madison is creating a floral centerpiece by attaching artificial flowers to a foam cone. The height of the cone is 16 inches and the diameter is 5 inches. What is the volume of the foam cone? Round to the nearest tenth.

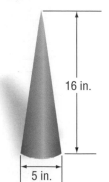

16 in.

5 in.

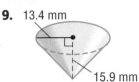
= **Step-by-Step Solutions** begin on page R23.
Extra Practice is on page EP22.

Example 1
(p. 449)

Find the volume of each cone. Round to the nearest tenth.

7.  23 mm · 14 mm

8. 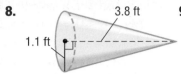 3.8 ft · 1.1 ft

9. 13.4 mm  15.9 mm

10. height: 3.9 yards, radius: 1.7 yards

11. height: 24 centimeters, diameter: 8 centimeters

12. height: 15 inches, diameter: 5 inches

Example 2
(p. 450)

13. HATS A party hat like the one at the right is going to be filled with candy. If one cup is about 14.4 cubic inches, about how many cups of candy will fit in the party hat?

14. ICE Isaiah is making cone-shaped ice cubes by using a mold. The radius of the mold is 1.5 inches and the height is 2 inches. If one cubic inch is about 0.55 ounce, how many ounces will ten cone-shaped ice cubes weigh? Round to the nearest tenth.

15. GEOMETRY The volume of a cone with a 30-millimeter radius is 9,420 cubic millimeters. What is the height of the cone? Round to the nearest tenth.

16. The volume of a cone is 593.46 cubic inches. The radius is 9 inches. Find the height of the cone. Round to the nearest tenth.

17 A cylinder has a radius of 5 centimeters and a height of 12 centimeters. What would the height of a cone need to be if it has the same volume and radius? Round to the nearest tenth.

18. VOLCANOES Mount Rainier, a cone-shaped volcano in Washington, is about 4.4 kilometers tall and about 18 kilometers across its base. Find the volume of Mount Rainier. Round to the nearest tenth.

Find the height of each cone. Round to the nearest tenth.

19. h · 3 m

Volume: 42.39 m³

20. 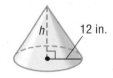 h · 12 in.

Volume: 1,205.76 in³

21.  h · 2.5 yd

Volume: 19.625 yd³

22. GEOMETRY The volume of a cone with a height of 18 millimeters is 471 cubic millimeters. Find the area of the base to the nearest tenth.

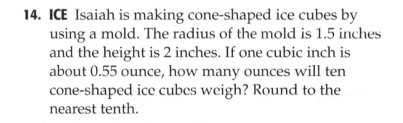
8 in.
Celebrate
7 in.

23. FIND THE ERROR Aisha is finding the volume of rice that will fill a cone-shaped decorative vase. The vase is 6 inches tall with a 4-inch diameter. Find her mistake and correct it.

$$V = \frac{1}{3}\pi r^2 h$$
$$V = \frac{1}{3}\pi \cdot 4 \cdot 4 \cdot 6$$
$$V \approx 100.5 \text{ in}^3$$

24. OPEN ENDED Draw and label two cones with different dimensions but the same volume.

25. Write MATH Which would have a greater effect on the volume of a cone: doubling its radius or doubling its height? Explain.

NGSSS Practice   MA.7.G.2.1

26. Which is closest to the volume of the cone shown?

A. 564.4 cm³

B. 666.7 cm³

C. 886.5 cm³

D. 1,238.2 cm³

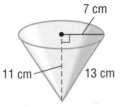

7 cm

11 cm   13 cm

27. Which is closest to the volume of ice cream that the cone can hold?

F. 47.1 in³

G. 23.55 in³

H. 15.7 in³

I. 11.8 in³

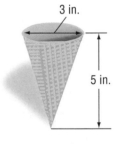

3 in.

5 in.

Spiral Review

Find the volume of each pyramid. Round to the nearest tenth. (Lesson 8-1E)

28.

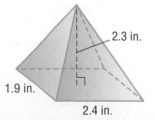

2.3 in.

1.9 in.

2.4 in.

29.

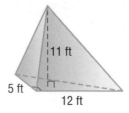

11 ft

5 ft

12 ft

30. Find the volume of a cylinder with a radius of 2.9 meters and a height of 4.9 meters. Round to the nearest tenth. (Lesson 8-1C)

Find the volume of each prism. Round to the nearest tenth if necessary. (Lesson 8-1B)

1.

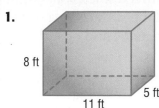

8 ft
11 ft
5 ft

2.

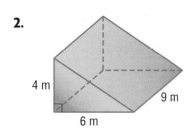

4 m
9 m
6 m

3. **CAKE** A piece of cake is shaped like a triangular prism. The area of the base is 6 square inches and the height is 3 inches. Find the volume of the piece of cake. (Lesson 8-1B)

4. Find the volume of the cylinder. Round to the nearest tenth. (Lesson 8-1C)

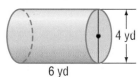

4 yd
6 yd

5. **FOOD** A can of peanuts has a diameter of 4 inches and a height of 4 inches. Find the volume of the peanut can. (Lesson 8-1C)

Find the volume of each pyramid. Round to the nearest tenth. (Lesson 8-1E)

6.

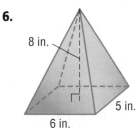

8 in.
5 in.
6 in.

7.

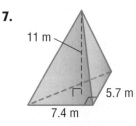

11 m
5.7 m
7.4 m

8. **NGSSS PRACTICE** A triangular pyramid has a triangle base of 24 centimeters, triangle height of 16 centimeters, and a pyramid height of 14 centimeters. Which is closest to the volume of the triangular prism in cubic meters? (Lesson 8-1E)

A. 0.00085 m^3 C. 0.00095 m^3

B. 0.0009 m^3 D. 0.001 m^3

9. Find the volume of the cone. Round to the nearest tenth. (Lesson 8-1F)

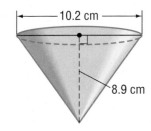

10.2 cm
8.9 cm

10. **TRAFFIC CONE** An engineer wants to make a traffic cone with a diameter of 12 inches and a height of 16 inches. To make the cone, she needs to know its volume. Find the volume of the traffic cone to the nearest tenth. (Lesson 8-1F)

11. **NGSSS PRACTICE** Find the volume of the cone. Round to the nearest tenth. (Lesson 8-1F)

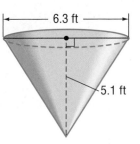

6.3 ft
5.1 ft

F. 212.0 ft^3 H. 53.0 ft^3

G. 172.1 ft^3 I. 52.0 ft^3

Explore   Nets of Three-Dimensional Figures

Main Idea

Find the surface area of prisms and cylinders using models and nets.

NGSSS

MA.7.G.2.1 Justify and apply **formulas for surface area** and volume **of** pyramids, **prisms, cylinders,** and cones.

New Vocabulary

net

Get Connected
glencoe.com

Nets are two-dimensional patterns of three-dimensional figures. When you construct a net, you are decomposing the three-dimensional figure into separate figures. You can use a net to find the surface area of three-dimensional figures such as prisms, pyramids, and cylinders.

ACTIVITY

1   **STEP 1**   Use an empty cereal box. Measure and record the length, width, and height of the box.

     STEP 2   Label the top and bottom faces using a green marker. Label the front and back faces using a blue marker and label the left and right faces using a red marker.

     STEP 3   Carefully cut along three edges of the top face and then cut down each vertical edge.

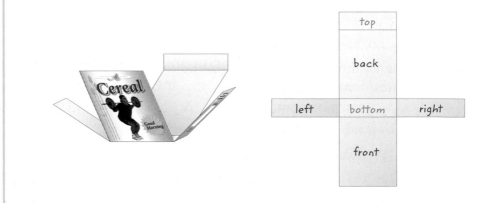

Analyze the Results

1. Name the shape(s) that make up the net.

2. What do you notice about the top and bottom faces, the left and right faces, and the front and back faces?

3. Explain how you could find the total area of the rectangles.

4. **MAKE A CONJECTURE** Write the formula for the surface area of the box using the net. Justify your answer.

ACTIVITY

2 **STEP 1** Use a soup can. Measure and record the height of the can.

STEP 2 Label the top and bottom faces using a blue marker. Label the curved side using a red marker.

STEP 3 Carefully peel off the label of the soup can and tape it to a piece of paper. Trace the top and bottom faces so they are adjacent to the label.

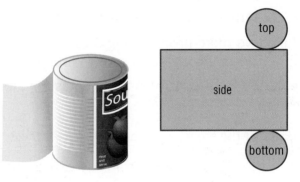

Analyze the Results

5. Name the shapes that make up the net of the container.

6. Find the diameter of the top of the container and use it to find the perimeter or circumference of that face. Find the area of the top and bottom faces.

7. How is the circumference of the top face of the container related to the rectangle?

8. How could the area of the label be found with the circumference of the top face of the container? Calculate the area of the label.

9. Add the area of the label to the sum of the areas of the two circular bases.

10. **MAKE A CONJECTURE** Write a formula for finding the area of all the surfaces of a cylinder given the measures of its height and the diameter of one of its bases.

Practice and Apply

11. **CAKES** Cake decorators use sheets of icing called fondant. Desa is decorating a rectangular cake that is 24 inches by 18 inches by 4 inches. What is the area of the sheet of fondant that she will need to cover the exposed parts of the cake?

12. **FIRE PIT** James is forging a cylindrical iron fire pit. He wants the pit to be 3 feet in diameter and 2 feet high with the bottom closed and the top open. How much iron will be used to forge the pit? Round to the nearest tenth if needed.

Main Idea

Find the surface areas of prisms.

NGSSS

 MA.7.G.2.1 Justify and **apply formulas for surface area** and volume **of** pyramids, **prisms,** cylinders, and cones. *Also addresses MA.7.A.3.2.*

New Vocabulary

surface area

Get Connected
glencoe.com

Surface Area of Prisms

Explore

Use the cubes to build a rectangular prism with a length of 8 centimeters. Count the number of squares on the outside of the prism. The sum is the *surface area*.

1. Record the dimensions, volume, and surface area in a table.

2. Build two more prisms using 8 cubes. For each, record the dimensions, volume, and surface area.

3. Describe the prisms with the greatest and least surface areas.

The sum of the areas of all the surfaces, or faces, of a three-dimensional figure is the **surface area**.

Key Concept   Surface Area of a Rectangular Prism

Words	The surface area *S.A.* of a rectangular prism with base *b*, width *w*, and height *h* is the sum of the areas of its faces.	**Model**
Symbols	$S.A. = 2bh + 2bw + 2hw$	

EXAMPLES   Surface Area of Rectangular Prisms

1 Find the surface area of the rectangular prism.

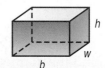

There are three pairs of congruent faces.

- top and bottom
- front and back
- two sides

Faces	Area
top and bottom	$2(5 \cdot 4) = 40$
front and back	$2(5 \cdot 3) = 30$
two sides	$2(3 \cdot 4) = 24$
sum of the areas	$40 + 30 + 24 = 94$

The surface area is 94 square centimeters.

2 Find the surface area of the rectangular prism.

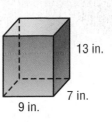

Replace b with 9, w with 7, and h with 13.

$$\text{surface area} = 2bh + 2bw + 2hw$$
$$= 2 \cdot 9 \cdot 13 + 2 \cdot 9 \cdot 7 + 2 \cdot 13 \cdot 7$$
$$= 234 + 126 + 182 \quad \text{Multiply first. Then add.}$$
$$= 542$$

The surface area of the prism is 542 square inches.

Study Tip

Surface Area When you find the surface area of a three-dimensional figure, the units are square units, not cubic units.

✓ **CHECK Your Progress**

Find the surface area of each rectangular prism.

a.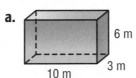

b.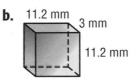

Real-World EXAMPLE

3 **PAINTING** Domingo built a toy box 60 inches long, 24 inches wide, and 36 inches high. He has 1 quart of paint that covers about 87 square feet of surface. Does he have enough to paint the toy box? Justify your answer.

Step 1 Find the surface area of the toy box.

Replace b with 60, w with 24, and h with 36.

$$\text{surface area} = 2bh + 2bw + 2hw$$
$$= 2 \cdot 60 \cdot 36 + 2 \cdot 60 \cdot 24 + 2 \cdot 36 \cdot 24$$
$$= 8,928 \text{ in}^2$$

Step 2 Find the number of square inches the paint will cover.

$$1 \text{ ft}^2 = 1 \text{ ft} \times 1 \text{ ft} \qquad \text{Replace 1 ft with 12 in.}$$
$$= 12 \text{ in.} \times 12 \text{ in.} \quad \text{Multiply.}$$
$$= 144 \text{ in}^2$$

So, 87 square feet is equal to 87×144 or 12,528 square inches.

Since 12,528 > 8,928, Domingo has enough paint.

Study Tip

Consistent Units Since the surface area of the toy box is expressed in inches, convert 87 ft² to square inches so that all measurements are expressed using the same units.

✓ **CHECK Your Progress**

c. **BOXES** The largest corrugated cardboard box ever constructed measured about 23 feet long, 9 feet high, and 8 feet wide. Would 950 square feet of paper be enough to cover the box? Justify your answer.

To find the surface area of a triangular prism, it is more efficient to find the area of each face and calculate the sum of all of the faces rather than using a formula.

Real-World EXAMPLE   **Surface Area of Triangular Prisms**

④ **PACKAGING** Marty is mailing his aunt a package and is using a container that is a triangular prism. The height is 14 inches. The triangular base has a height of 3 inches and a base of 4 inches. How much cardboard is used to create the shipping container?

To find the surface area of the container, find the area of each face and add.

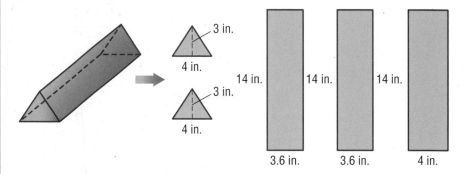

The area of each triangle is $\frac{1}{2} \cdot 4 \cdot 3$ or 6.

The area of two of the rectangles is 14 · 3.6 or 50.4. The area of the third rectangle is 14 · 4 or 56.

The sum of the areas of the faces is 6 + 6 + 50.4 + 50.4 + 56 or 168.8 cubic inches.

CHECK Your Progress

Find the surface area of the triangular prism to the nearest tenth.

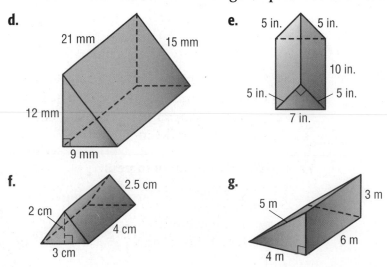

d. 21 mm, 15 mm, 12 mm, 9 mm

e. 5 in., 5 in., 10 in., 5 in., 5 in., 7 in.

f. 2.5 cm, 2 cm, 4 cm, 3 cm

g. 5 m, 3 m, 6 m, 4 m

Examples 1 and 2
(pp. 456–457)

Find the surface area of each rectangular prism. Round to the nearest tenth if necessary.

1.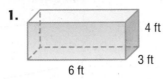
4 ft
3 ft
6 ft

2.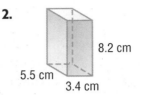
8.2 cm
5.5 cm
3.4 cm

Example 3
(p. 457)

3. **GIFTS** Marsha is wrapping a gift. She places it in a box 8 inches long, 2 inches wide, and 11 inches high. If Marsha bought a roll of wrapping paper that is 1 foot wide and 2 feet long, did she buy enough paper to wrap the gift? Justify your answer.

Example 4
(p. 458)

4. **INSULATION** The attic shown is a triangular prism. Insulation will be placed inside all walls not including the floor. Find the surface area that will be covered with insulation.

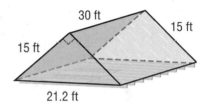
30 ft
15 ft
15 ft
21.2 ft

● = **Step-by-Step Solutions** begin on page R24.
Extra Practice is on page EP23.

Examples 1 and 2
(pp. 456–457)

Find the surface area of each rectangular prism. Round to the nearest tenth if necessary.

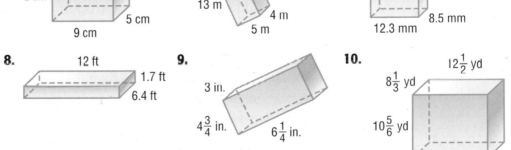

5.
8 cm
5 cm
9 cm

6.
13 m
4 m
5 m

7.
15 mm
8.5 mm
12.3 mm

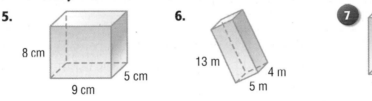

8.
12 ft
1.7 ft
6.4 ft

9.
3 in.
4¾ in.
6¼ in.

10.
12½ yd
8⅓ yd
10⅚ yd

Example 3
(p. 457)

11. **BOOKS** When making a book cover, Anwar adds an additional 20 square inches to the surface area to allow for overlap. How many square inches of paper will Anwar use to make a book cover for a book 11 inches long, 8 inches wide, and 1 inch high?

12. **FENCES** If one gallon of paint covers 350 square feet, will 8 gallons of paint be enough to paint the inside and outside of the fence shown once? Explain.

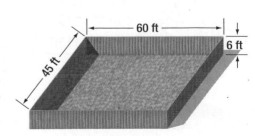
60 ft
6 ft
45 ft

Example 4
(p. 458)

Find the surface area of each triangular prism. Round to the nearest tenth if necessary.

13.
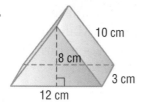
24 m
17.2 m
14 m
10 m

14. 3 ft   4 ft
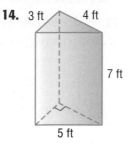
7 ft
5 ft

15.
10 cm
8 cm
3 cm
12 cm

16. 13 in.
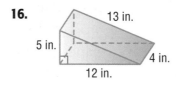
5 in.
4 in.
12 in.

17. MUSIC To the nearest tenth, find the approximate amount of plastic covering the outside of the CD case.

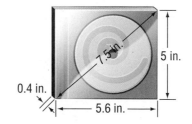
7.5 in.
5 in.
0.4 in.
5.6 in.

18. MEASUREMENT What is the surface area of a rectangular prism that has a length of 6.5 centimeters, a width of 2.8 centimeters, and a height of 9.7 centimeters?

19 ALGEBRA Write a formula for the surface area *S.A.* of a cube in which each side measures *x* units.

20. PACKAGING A company will make a cereal box with whole number dimensions and a volume of 100 cubic centimeters. If cardboard costs $0.05 per 100 square centimeters, what is the least cost to make 100 boxes?

21. GRAPHIC NOVEL Refer to the graphic novel frame below. What dimensions would allow the students to maximize the volume while keeping the surface area at most 160 square feet? Excess metal is permitted. Explain your reasoning.

We are designing a dunk tank. Remember, we want to maximize the volume and minimize the surface area.

22. REASONING The bottom and sides of a pool in the shape of a rectangular prism will be painted blue. The length, width, and height of the pool are 18 feet, 12 feet, and 6 feet, respectively. Explain why the number of square feet to be painted is *not* equivalent to the expression $2(18)(12) + 2(18)(6) + 2(12)(6)$.

23. CHALLENGE The figure at the right is made by placing a cube with 12-centimeter sides on top of another cube with 15-centimeter sides. Find the surface area.

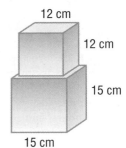

24. **Write MATH** Explain why the surface area of a three-dimensional figure is measured in square units rather than in cubic units.

 NGSSS Practice   MA.7.G.2.1

25. Which of the following expressions represents the surface area of a cube with side length w?

   A. w^3

   B. $6w^2$

   C. $6w^3$

   D. $2w + 4w^2$

26. How much cardboard is needed to make a box with a length of 2.5 feet, a width of 1.6 feet, and a height of 2 feet?

   F. 37.5 square feet

   G. 24.4 square feet

   H. 8 square feet

   I. 6.1 square feet

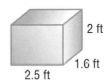

 **Spiral Review**

Find the volume of each cone. Round to the nearest tenth. (Lesson 8-1F)

27.

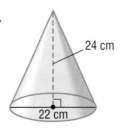

24 cm

22 cm

28.

10.4 yd

3.1 yd

29. LANDSCAPING Pat is digging circular post holes for a new fence. It is recommended that the holes are at least 10 inches across and 18 inches deep. What is the least amount of dirt she is removing for each hole? Round to the nearest tenth. (Lesson 8-1D)

30. SCIENCE A graduated cylinder has an 11-millimeter diameter and is 114 millimeters tall. (Lesson 8-1C)

11 mm

114 mm

   a. What is the volume of the beaker to the nearest tenth?

   b. If 1,000 cubic millimeters equal 1 milliliter, how many milliliters does the beaker hold?

Main Idea

Find the surface area of a cylinder.

NGSSS

 **MA.7.G.2.1** Justify and **apply formulas for surface area** and volume **of** pyramids, prisms, **cylinders,** and cones.

Get Connected
glencoe.com

Surface Area of Cylinders

Explore

Step 1   Trace the top and bottom of the can on grid paper. Then cut out the shapes.

Step 2   Cut a long rectangle from the grid paper. The width of the rectangle should be the same as the height of the can. Wrap the rectangle around the can. Cut off the excess paper so that the edges just meet.

1. Make a net of the cylinder.

2. Name the shapes in the net.

3. How is the length of the rectangle related to the circles?

You can put two circles and a rectangle together to make a cylinder.

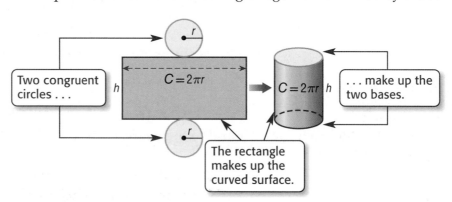

In the diagram above, the length of the rectangle is the same as the circumference of the circle, $2\pi r$. Also, the width of the rectangle is the same as the height of the cylinder.

Key Concept   Surface Area of a Cylinder

Words   The surface area *S.A.* of a cylinder with height h and radius r is the sum of the area of the curved surface and the areas of the circular bases.

Model

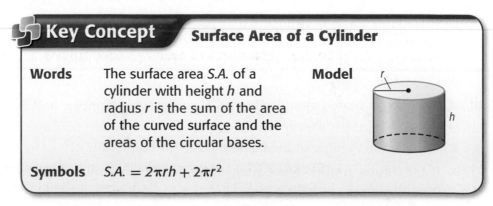

Symbols $S.A. = 2\pi rh + 2\pi r^2$

Surface Area of a Cylinder

1 Find the surface area of the cylinder. Round to the nearest tenth.

2 m

7 m

$$S.A. = 2\pi rh + 2\pi r^2 \qquad \text{Surface area of a cylinder}$$

$$= 2\pi(2)(7) + 2\pi(2)^2 \quad \text{Replace } r \text{ with 2 and } h \text{ with 7.}$$

$$\approx 113.1 \qquad \text{Simplify.}$$

The surface area is about 113.1 square meters.

 CHECK Your Progress

a. Find the surface area of the cylinder. Round to the nearest tenth.

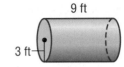
9 ft

3 ft

Real-World EXAMPLE

 Real-World Link · · · ·
Of the 3,000 to 4,000 wooden carousels carved in America between 1885 and 1930, fewer than 150 operate today.

2 **CAROUSELS** A circular fence that is 2 feet high is to be built around the outside of a carousel. The distance from the center of the carousel to the edge of the fence will be 35 feet. How much fencing material is needed to make the fence around the carousel?

The radius of the circular fence is 35 feet. The height is 2 feet.

$$S.A. = 2\pi rh \qquad \text{Curved surface of a cylinder}$$

$$= 2\pi(35)(2) \quad \text{Replace } r \text{ with 35 and } h \text{ with 2.}$$

$$\approx 439.8 \qquad \text{Simplify.}$$

So, about 439.8 square feet of material is needed to make the fence.

CHECK Your Progress

b. **DESIGN** Find the area of the label of a can of tuna with a radius of 5.1 centimeters and a height of 2.9 centimeters. Round to the nearest tenth.

 CHECK Your Understanding

Example 1
(p. 463)

Find the surface area of each cylinder. Round to the nearest tenth.

1
5 mm

2 mm

2.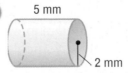
├─11 in.─┤

8 in.

Example 2
(p. 463)

3. STORAGE The height of a water tank is 10 meters, and it has a diameter of 10 meters. What is the surface area of the tank to the nearest tenth?

Practice and Problem Solving

 = **Step-by-Step Solutions** begin on page R24.
Extra Practice is on page EP23.

Example 1
(p. 463)

Find the surface area of each cylinder. Round to the nearest tenth.

4.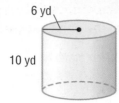
6 yd
10 yd

5.
12.5 m
9 m

6. 3 ft
18 ft

7.
5.6 mm
8.7 mm

8. 5 cm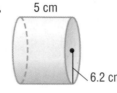
6.2 cm

9.
11½ in.
4 in.

Example 2
(p. 463)

10. CANDLES A cylindrical candle has a diameter of 4 inches and a height of 7 inches. What is the surface area of the candle to the nearest tenth?

11. PENCILS Find the surface area of an unsharpened cylindrical pencil that has a radius of 0.5 centimeter and a height of 19 centimeters. Round to the nearest tenth.

ESTIMATION Estimate the surface area of each cylinder.

12.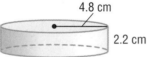
4.8 cm
2.2 cm

13. 8.2 m
3.7 m

14. 12.8 ft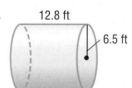
6.5 ft

15 PACKAGING The mail tube shown is made of cardboard and has plastic end caps. Approximately what percent of the surface area of the mail tube is cardboard?

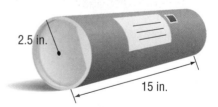
2.5 in.
15 in.

H.O.T. Problems

16. CHALLENGE If the height of a cylinder is doubled, will its surface area also double? Explain your reasoning.

17. Write MATH Write a real-world problem in which you would find the surface area of a cylinder. Then solve the problem.

18. REASONING Which has more surface area, a cylinder with radius 6 centimeters and height 3 centimeters or a cylinder with radius 3 centimeters and height 6 centimeters? Explain your reasoning.

19. Stacey has a cylindrical paper clip holder with the net shown.

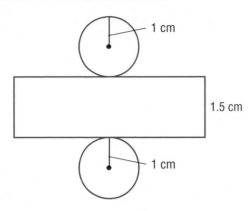

Which is closest to the surface area of the cylindrical paper clip holder?

A. 12.5 cm²

B. 13.5 cm²

C. 14.5 cm²

D. 15.5 cm²

20. The four containers below each hold the same amount of liquid. Which container has the greatest surface area?

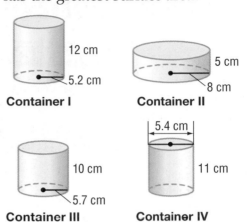

F. Container I

G. Container II

H. Container III

I. Container IV

Spiral Review

Find the volume of each pyramid. Round to the nearest tenth if necessary.
(Lesson 8-1E)

21. rectangular pyramid: base, 12 inches by 5 inches; height, 13 inches

22. rectangular pyramid: base, 28 meters by 4 meters; height, 15 meters

23. hexagonal pyramid: area of base, 212 cm²; height, 17 cm

Find the surface area of each prism. (Lesson 8-2B)

24.

0.8 ft
2.1 ft
3.4 ft

25.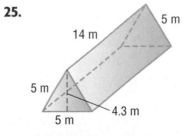

5 m
14 m
5 m
4.3 m
5 m

Graph the function represented by each table. (Lesson 5-1C)

26.

Total Cost of DVD	
DVD	Total Cost ($)
1	12
2	24
3	36
4	48

27.

Convert Weeks to Days	
Weeks	Days
1	7
2	14
3	21
4	28

Extend   Surface Area and Volume

Main Idea

Compare surface area and volume of rectangular prisms and cylinders.

NGSSS

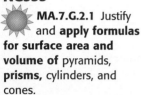 **MA.7.G.2.1** Justify and **apply formulas for surface area and volume of** pyramids, **prisms,** cylinders, and cones.

 Get Connected
glencoe.com

ACTIVITY

Use centimeter cubes to create as many rectangular prisms as possible.

STEP 1   Create a rectangular prism using 8 centimeter cubes. Copy the table below, record the dimensions, and find the surface area and volume of the prism.

2 cm
2 cm
2 cm

Rectangular Prism	Length	Width	Height	Surface Area	Volume
1	2	2	2	24 cm²	8 cm³
2					
3					
4					
5					
6					
7					
8					
9					
10					

STEP 2   Repeat Step 1 for as many rectangular prisms as you can create.

Analyze the Results

1. What do you notice about the volume of each rectangular prism?

2. Which rectangular prism had the greatest surface area? Give the dimensions.

3. Which rectangular prism had the least surface area? Give the dimensions.

4. Compare the two rectangular prisms at the right with the same volume. What is the volume? Which shape has the least amount of surface area?

Shape 1

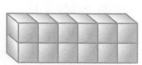
Shape 2

5. **MAKE A CONJECTURE** Though you changed the dimensions of the rectangular prisms, which shape is always going to have the lesser surface area?

Practice and Apply

Compare the two shapes that have the same volume. Then determine which one has a greater surface area. Explain.

6.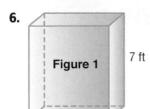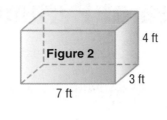

Figure 1   7 ft   6 ft   2 ft

Figure 2   4 ft   7 ft   3 ft

7.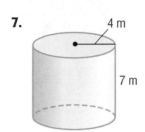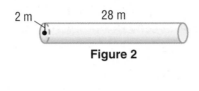

4 m   7 m

Figure 1

2 m   28 m

Figure 2

8. PACKAGING Chandler wants to build a box that will hold as many of his collector's coins as possible. He wants the volume of the box to be 20 cubic inches. The dimensions of possible boxes are given in the table below. Find the surface area of each box. Then determine which box has the least amount of surface area.

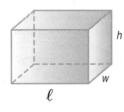

Box	(ℓ)	(w)	(h)	Surface Area	Volume (in³)
1	20	1	1	▨	20
2	4	5	1	▨	20
3	2	2	5	▨	20
4	10	2	1	▨	20

9. CRAFTS Monique sews together pieces of fabric to make gift boxes. If she only uses whole numbers, what are the dimensions of a box with a volume of 50 cubic inches that has the greatest amount of surface area?

10. CONTAINERS Thomas is creating a decorative container to fill with colored sand. What will be the dimensions of the rectangular prism that will hold 100 cubic inches with the least amount of surface area, if he only uses whole numbers? The top of the container is open.

11. BOXES The specifications of a cardboard box indicate that it has the same volume as a rectangular box 4 inches by 10 inches by 12 inches, but with less surface area. What size box would meet these requirements?

12. COOKING Zachariah needs to melt a stick of butter 5 inches by 1 inch by 1 inch in a pan. Explain why cutting the butter into smaller pieces will help the butter melt faster.

Main Idea
Find the surface area of pyramids.

NGSSS
 MA.7.G.2.1 Justify and apply formulas for surface area and volume of pyramids, prisms, cylinders, and cones.

New Vocabulary
slant height
lateral surface area

Get Connected
glencoe.com

Surface Area of Pyramids

Explore

- Copy the following net of a square pyramid onto a piece of paper.

- Cut out the net and tape it together.

1. What shapes make up the net of the square pyramid?

2. What do you notice about the triangular faces of the pyramid?

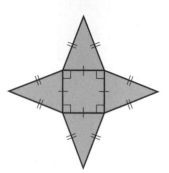

A right square pyramid has a square base and four isosceles triangles that make up the lateral faces. The height of each lateral face is called the **slant height**. The **lateral surface area** of a solid is the sum of the areas of all its lateral faces.

Model of Square Pyramid   **Net of Square Pyramid**

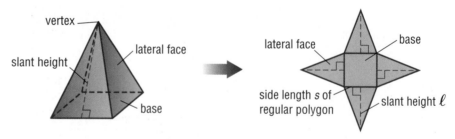

To find the lateral area L of a regular pyramid, refer to the net. The lateral area is the sum of the areas of the triangles.

$L = 4\left(\frac{1}{2}s\ell\right)$ Area of the lateral faces

$L = \frac{1}{2}(4s)\ell$ Commutative Property of Multiplication

$L = \frac{1}{2}P\ell$ The perimeter of the base P is $4s$.

The total surface area of a regular pyramid is the lateral surface area L plus the area of the base B.

$$S.A. = B + \frac{1}{2}P\ell$$

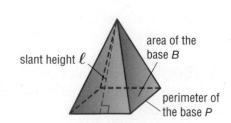

1 Find the total surface area of the pyramid. Round to the nearest tenth.

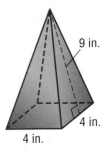

9 in.

4 in.

4 in.

$S.A. = B + \frac{1}{2}P\ell$ Surface area of a pyramid

$S.A. = 16 + \frac{1}{2}(16 \cdot 9)$ $B = 4 \cdot 4, P = 4(4)$ or 16, $\ell = 9$

$S.A. = 88$ Simplify.

The surface area is 88 square inches.

2 Find the total surface area of the pyramid with a base area of 111 square meters.

20 m

16 m

16 m   16 m

$S.A. = B + \frac{1}{2}P\ell$ Surface area of a pyramid

$S.A. = 111 + \frac{1}{2}(48 \cdot 20)$ $B = 111, P = 16 + 16 + 16$ or 48, $\ell = 20$

$S.A. = 591$ Simplify.

The surface area of the pyramid is 591 square meters.

 CHECK Your Progress

a. Find the surface area of a square pyramid that has a slant height of 8 centimeters and a base length of 5 centimeters.

Real-World EXAMPLE

3 **GIFT BOXES** Rachel is making gift boxes in the shape of square pyramids for party favors. They have a slant height of 3 inches and base edges 2.5 inches long. How many square inches of card stock are used to make one gift box?

$S.A. = B + \frac{1}{2}P\ell$ Surface area of a pyramid

$S.A. = 6.25 + \frac{1}{2}(10 \cdot 3)$ $P = 4(2.5)$ or 10, $\ell = 3, B = 2.5^2$ or 6.25

$S.A. = 21.25$ Simplify.

So, 21.25 square inches of card stock are used to make one gift box.

 CHECK Your Progress

b. **PERFUME** Amado purchased a bottle of perfume that is in the shape of a square pyramid. The slant height of the bottle is 4.5 inches and the base is 2 inches. Find the surface area.

Examples 1 and 2
(p. 469)

Find the total surface area of each pyramid. Round to the nearest tenth.

1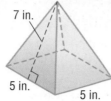
7 in.
5 in.
5 in.

2.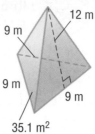
12 m
9 m
9 m
9 m
35.1 m²

Example 3
(p. 469)

3. MONUMENTS The Washington Monument is an obelisk with a square pyramid top. The slant height of the pyramid is 55.5 feet, and the square base has sides of 34.5 feet. Find the lateral area of the pyramid.

Practice and Problem Solving

● = **Step-by-Step Solutions** begin on page R24.
Extra Practice is on page EP24.

Examples 1 and 2
(p. 469)

Find the total surface area of each pyramid. Round to the nearest tenth.

4.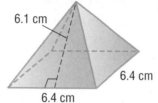
6.1 cm
6.4 cm
6.4 cm

5.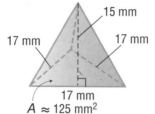
15 mm
17 mm
17 mm
17 mm
A ≈ 125 mm²

6.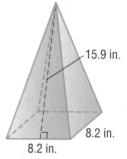
15.9 in.
8.2 in.
8.2 in.

7. The base of a square pyramid has a side length of 27 centimeters. The slant height is 25 centimeters. Find the surface area.

8. A triangular pyramid has a slant height of 0.75 foot. The equilateral triangular base has a perimeter of 1.2 feet and an area of 0.6 square foot. Find the surface area.

9. A square pyramid has a slant height of $4\frac{2}{3}$ feet. The base has side lengths of $2\frac{1}{4}$ feet. Find the surface area.

Example 3
(p. 469)

10. GEMSTONES The gemstone shown has a base that is a square pyramid with sides 3.4 inches long. The slant height of the pyramid is 3.8 inches. Find the surface area of the gemstone.

11 BIRDHOUSES Isaac is building a birdhouse for a class project. The birdhouse is a regular hexagonal pyramid. The base has side lengths of 3 inches and an area of about 24 square inches. The slant height is 6 inches. Find the approximate surface area of the birdhouse.

12. GEOMETRY A square pyramid has a surface area of 175 square inches. The square base has side lengths of 5 inches. Find the slant height of the pyramid.

13. **CHALLENGE** Suppose you could climb to the top of the Great Pyramid of Giza in Egypt. Which path would be shorter, climbing a lateral edge or the slant height? Justify your response.

14. **OPEN ENDED** Draw a square pyramid and a rectangular pyramid. Explain the differences between the two.

15. **Write MATH** Justify the formula for the surface area of a pyramid.

NGSSS Practice MA.7.G.2.1

16. The We Entertain company is constructing a tent in the shape of a square pyramid, without a floor, to be used at a party. Find the number of square feet of fabric that will be required.

    A. 1,500 ft²

    B. 1,700 ft²

    C. 2,250 ft²

    D. 2,550 ft²

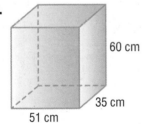

17. Find the surface area of the triangular pyramid shown with a base area of 27.7 square yards.

    F. 39.3 yd²

    G. 117.9 yd²

    H. 171.7 yd²

    I. 213.5 yd²

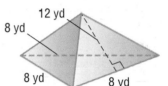

Spiral Review

Find the surface area of each prism. (Lesson 8-2B)

18.

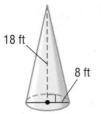

19.

Find the volume of each cone. Round to the nearest tenth. (Lesson 8-1E)

20.

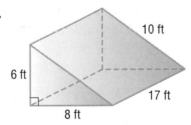

21.

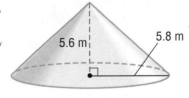

Find the total cost or sale price to the nearest cent. (Lesson 6-3D)

22. $15.99 DVD; 5% tax

23. $12.65 meal; 15% tip

24. $379.59 television; 10% discount

25. $39.95 pants; 30% discount

Extend   Net of a Cone

Main Idea

Justify the formula for the surface area of a cone by using a net.

NGSSS

 MA.7.G.2.1 Justify and apply formulas for surface area and volume **of** pyramids, prisms, cylinders, and **cones.**

Get Connected
glencoe.com

PIÑATAS Corinne is constructing a piñata to use for her sister's birthday. It is in the shape of a cone and will be covered with tissue paper. What is the surface area of the cone that will be covered with tissue paper?

14 cm

6 cm

ACTIVITY   Construct a Net of a Cone

① **STEP 1**   Use a compass to draw two circles slightly touching, one with a radius of 6 centimeters and one with a radius of 14 centimeters.

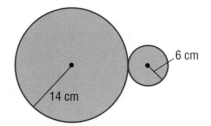

6 cm

14 cm

STEP 2   Only a part of the larger circle is needed to make the cone. Use a proportion to find the part.

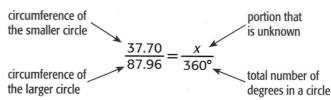

circumference of the smaller circle →   ← portion that is unknown

$$\frac{37.70}{87.96} = \frac{x}{360°}$$

circumference of the larger circle →   ← total number of degrees in a circle

Solve the proportion.

$\dfrac{37.70}{87.96} = \dfrac{x}{360°}$ Write the proportion.

$x(87.96) = 13,572$ Cross multiply. $37.70 \cdot 360 = 13,572$

$\dfrac{x \cdot 87.96}{87.96} = \dfrac{13,572}{87.96}$ Divide each side by 87.96.

$x \approx 154$ Simplify.

You need 154° of the larger circle.

STEP 3   Cut a central angle of 154° from the larger circle and make a cone.

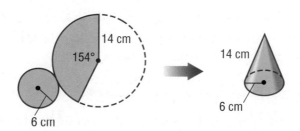

14 cm

154°

6 cm

14 cm

6 cm

The net shows that the surface area of a cone is the sum of its base B and its lateral area $L.A.$ The base B is a circle. The lateral area $L.A.$ is *part* of a larger circle.

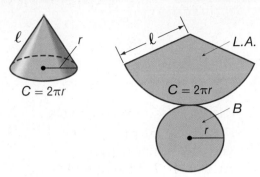

In the following Activity, you will determine the formula for the lateral surface area of a cone.

ACTIVITY Find the Surface Area of a Cone

2 **STEP 1** Use a compass to draw a circle. It represents the lateral surface area.

STEP 2 Draw 3 diameter lines that divide the circle equally into 6 sections.

STEP 3 Cut out the sections and form a figure that resembles a parallelogram.

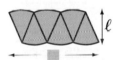

Analyze the Results

1. The circumference of the circle is represented by $2\pi r$. What expression represents the length of the parallelogram in Step 3?

2. **MAKE A CONJECTURE** Use the expression from Exercise 1 to write a formula for the area of the parallelogram, which is the lateral surface area of the cone.

3. **MAKE A CONJECTURE** Write a formula for the total surface area of a cone.

4. Why is only a portion of the larger circle necessary to construct a cone?

5. If the radius of the base is increased while the slant height stays the same, how will that affect the lateral surface area?

6. If a cone's slant height is decreased, which would be affected more: the base or the lateral area? Justify your response.

7. Find the surface area of the piñata that Corinne is covering with tissue paper. Use 3.14 for π.

Staying in Tune

Do you have a love of music and enjoy playing different kinds of instruments? If so, a job as a musical instrument repairer might be the perfect job for you. Instrument repairers are highly skilled craftspeople who use their expertise to diagnose problems with instruments. In addition to knowing how to play all the instruments they repair, they have a strong sense of pitch and good hand-eye coordination. Some technical schools and colleges offer courses in instrument repair technology.

Choose a Major
Are you interested in a career as a musical instrument repairer? Take some of the following courses in high school.

- Ear Training & Sight Singing
- Instrumental Techniques
- Geometry
- Music Theory

💻 **Get Connected** glencoe.com

NGSSS

MA.7.G.2.1 Justify and **apply formulas for surface area and volume of** pyramids, prisms, **cylinders,** and cones.

Real-World Math

Use the information in the table to solve each problem. Round to the nearest tenth if necessary.

diameter

1. The *shell* of a drum is its curved surface. What is the area of the piccolo snare shell?

2. Find the surface area of the standard snare drum.

3. What is the volume of the floor tom drum?

4. About how many square inches greater is the surface area of the floor tom drum than the surface area of the deep snare drum?

5. About how many times greater is the volume of the bass drum than the volume of the piccolo snare drum?

Types of Drums		
Drum	**Diameter (in.)**	**Depth (in.)**
Piccolo Snare	13	3
Standard Snare	14	5.5
Deep Snare	14	6.5
Floor Tom	18	16
Bass	22	18

8-3 Composite Shapes

Problem-Solving Investigation

Main Idea Solve problems by solving a simpler problem.

P.S.I. TEAM +

Solve A Simpler Problem

LIAM: For a service project, I am helping mulch the play area at the community center. We need to know how large the play area is in order to buy the right amount of mulch. The diagram shows the dimensions of the play area.

YOUR MISSION: Find the area of the play area to be mulched.

Understand	You know that the play area is made of two rectangles.	
Plan	Find the area of the two rectangles, and then add.	

Solve	Area of Rectangle 1	Area of Rectangle 2
	$A = \ell w$	$A = \ell w$
	$A = 5 \cdot 10$	$A = 8 \cdot 7$
	$A = 50$	$A = 56$
	The total area is $50 + 56$ or 106 square feet. So, we need to buy enough mulch for at least 106 square feet.	
Check	The play area is less than $13 \cdot 10$ or 130 square feet. So, an answer of 106 square feet is reasonable.	

Analyze the Strategy

1. Why is breaking this problem into simpler parts a good strategy to solve it?

2. **Write MATH** Write a problem that can be solved when broken into simpler parts. Solve the problem and explain your answer.

NGSSS

Preparation for MA.7.G.2.2 Use formulas to find surface areas and volume of three-dimensional composite shapes.

- Solve a simpler problem.
- Eliminate possibilities.
- Draw a diagram.
- Choose an operation.

Use the *solve a simpler problem* strategy for Exercises 3 and 4.

3. WALLPAPER Dora is wallpapering a wall in her house. What is the area that will be wallpapered?

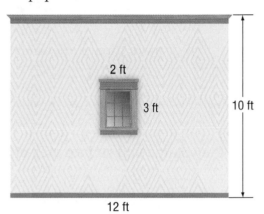

4. CONTINENTS The table lists each continent and its percent of the world's land area. The land area of Earth is 57,505,708 square miles. Find the approximate land area of each continent.

Continent	Percent of Earth's Land
Asia	30
Africa	20.2
North America	16.5
South America	12
Antarctica	8.9
Europe	6.7
Australia/Oceana	5.3

Use any strategy to solve Exercises 5–9.

5. DRIVING Don is driving from New Orleans to Atlanta at a constant speed. The distance is 480 miles. After driving for 6 hours, he is $\frac{3}{4}$ of the way there. How much longer does he have to drive to reach Atlanta?

6. ZOO The table shows the cost of admission.

Ticket	Cost
Adult	$10.50
Child	$7.00
Senior	$8.50

A family spent $33.00 on admission. What combination is possible for the number of tickets that they purchased?

A. 2 adult, 1 child, 1 senior

B. 1 adult, 2 child, 1 senior

C. 1 adult, 1 child, 2 senior

D. 2 adult, 2 child

7. MUSIC On Mondays, you practice piano for 45 minutes. For each successive day of the week, you practice $\frac{1}{3}$ hour more than the day before. How many hours and minutes do you practice the piano on Saturdays?

8. FOUNTAINS Mr. Flores has a circular fountain with a radius of 5 feet. He plans on installing a brick path around the fountain. What will be the area of the path? Use 3.14 for π.

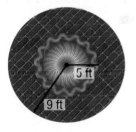

9. VIDEO GAMES The graph shows the results of a survey in which 347 students were asked to name their favorite type of video game. About how many students chose adventure as their favorite type of game?

Favorite Types of Video Games

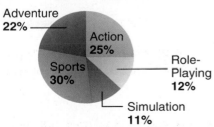

Explore Composite Figures

Main Idea

Explore volume and surface area of composite shapes.

NGSSS

 MA.7.G.2.2 Use formulas to **find surface areas and volume of three-dimensional composite shapes.**

New Vocabulary

composite shape

 Get Connected
glencoe.com

ARCHITECTURE A company made a model of a new factory. The building is composed of rectangular prisms. Create a model of the building using centimeter cubes to find the volume and surface area.

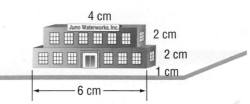

A **composite shape** is made up of two or more three-dimensional shapes.

ACTIVITY

1 **What do you need to find?** the volume and surface area of the model factory

STEP 1 Model the top and bottom rectangular prisms using models.

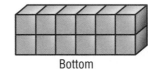

Bottom   Top

STEP 2 Copy and complete the table using the models from Step 1. Count the cubes to find the dimensions.

Rectangular Prism	Length (cm)	Width (cm)	Height (cm)	Volume (cm³)	Surface Area (cm²)
Bottom	6	1	2	▪	▪
Top	4	1	2	▪	▪

STEP 3 Copy the table and use the models from Step 1 to find the total volume of the model.

Analyze the Results

1. How many cubes did it take to create the model? What does this number represent?
2. What is the total surface area of both prisms?
3. What is the total surface area of the model? Explain.

Suppose Mrs. Wendell's class made a model of a house. The model was composed of a rectangular prism and a triangular prism. Create a model of the building using centimeter cubes to find the volume and surface area.

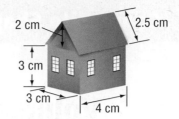

2 cm
2.5 cm
3 cm
3 cm
4 cm

ACTIVITY

2 **What do you need to find?** the volume and surface area of the model house

STEP 1 Model the top and bottom prisms using models.

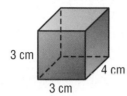
3 cm
4 cm
3 cm

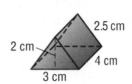
2.5 cm
2 cm
4 cm
3 cm

STEP 2 Copy and complete the tables using the models from Step 1. Count the cubes to find the dimensions.

Rectangular Prism	Length (cm)	Width (cm)	Height (cm)	Volume (cm³)	Surface Area (cm²)
Bottom	4	3	3	▪	▪

Triangular Prism	Length (cm)	Base (cm)	Height (cm)	Volume (cm³)	Surface Area (cm²)
Top	4	3	2	▪	▪

STEP 3 Combine the volume for both prisms to find the total volume of the model.

Analyze the Results

4. What is the total surface area of the model?

5. Describe a real-world situation where it might be necessary to use a model or drawing to find the volume or surface area.

6. **MAKE A CONJECTURE** How could you find the volume and surface area of a composite shape given all the measures?

7. Use the top, side, and front view to build the figure using centimeter cubes. Then make a sketch of the figure. Find the surface area and volume of the figure.

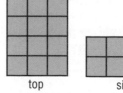
top

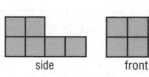
side   front

Main Idea

Find the volume and surface area of composite shapes.

NGSSS

MA.7.G.2.2 Use formulas to find surface areas and volume of three-dimensional composite shapes.

Get Connected
glencoe.com

Volume and Surface Area of Composite Figures

BASKETS The Rockwell family uses the basket shown on their staircase. Mrs. Rockwell would like to make a duplicate for extra storage. She needs to determine the surface area to find how much material she will need and the volume to find how much storage it has.

1. What three-dimensional shapes make up the basket?

2. What method could you use to find the volume and surface area of the basket?

The basket above is made up of two rectangular prisms. The volume of a composite figure can be found by separating the figure into solids whose volumes you know how to find.

EXAMPLE Volume of a Composite Shape

1. **BASKETS** Find the volume of the staircase basket above.

Find the volume of each prism.

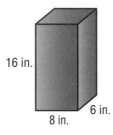

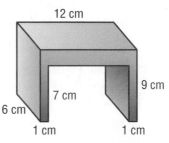

$V = \ell wh$ $\qquad$ $V = \ell wh$

$V = 8 \cdot 6 \cdot 16$ or 768 $\qquad$ $V = 8 \cdot 6 \cdot 8$ or 384

The volume is about $768 + 384$ or 1,152 cubic inches.

CHECK Your Progress

a. Find the volume of the composite shape.

EXAMPLE   Volume of a Composite Shape

Study Tip

Volume The formulas for volume of cylinders and cones are similar:
$V = \pi r^2 h$ for cylinders and $V = \frac{1}{3}\pi r^2 h$ for cones.

2 Find the volume of the composite figure. Round to the nearest tenth.

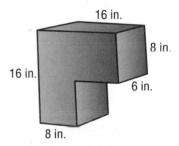

The figure is made up of a cylinder and a cone.

$V = \pi r^2 h + \frac{1}{3}\pi r^2 h$

$V = \pi \cdot 5^2 \cdot 3 + \frac{1}{3} \cdot \pi \cdot 5^2 \cdot 4$

$V \approx 235.5 + 104.7$ or 340.2

The volume of the composite figure is about 340.2 cubic centimeters.

You can also find the surface area of composite figures by finding the areas of the faces that make up the composite figure.

Real-World EXAMPLE   Surface Area of a Composite Shape

Real-World Link · · · ·

Basketry is the weaving of vegetable fibers into containers. Baskets can be made from any wood, vine, leaf, or fiber that is pliable.

3 **BASKETS** Find the surface area of the staircase basket in Example 1.

The basket is made up of three different polygons.

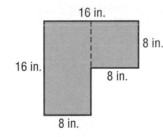

$A = bh + bh$

$A = (8 \cdot 16) + (8 \cdot 8)$

$A = 128 + 64$ or 192

$A = bh$

$A = 6 \cdot 16$

$A = 96$

$A = bh$

$A = 6 \cdot 8$

$A = 48$

The total surface area of the basket is $2(192) + 2(96) + 4(48)$ or 768 square inches.

CHECK Your Progress

Study Tip

To make it easier to see each face, sketch all of the faces and label the dimensions of each.

b. Find the surface area of the composite figure.

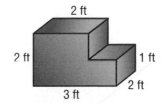

Examples 1 and 2
(pp. 480–481)

Find the volume of each composite figure. Round to the nearest tenth if necessary.

1.

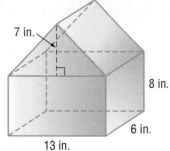

7 in.

8 in.

6 in.

13 in.

2.

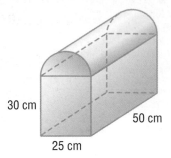

30 cm

50 cm

25 cm

Example 3
(p. 481)

Find the surface area of each composite figure.

3.

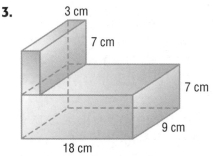

3 cm

7 cm

7 cm

9 cm

18 cm

4.

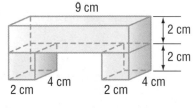

9 cm

2 cm

2 cm

2 cm   4 cm   2 cm   4 cm

5. DIGITAL CAMERA A digital camera is 1 inch by 3 inches by 4 inches. The lens on the front face is 0.5 inch long with a 1-inch diameter. What is the surface area of the digital camera? Round to the nearest tenth.

Practice and Problem Solving

● = **Step-by-Step Solutions** begin on page R25.
Extra Practice is on page EP25.

Examples 1 and 2
(pp. 480–481)

Find the volume of each composite figure. Round to the nearest tenth if necessary.

6.

15 ft

20 ft

20 ft

20 ft

7

0.7 m

0.8 m

1.1 m

1.8 m

8.

2.5 m

3 m

2 m

4 m

Example 3
(p. 481)

Find the surface area of each composite figure. Round to the nearest tenth if necessary.

9.

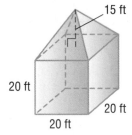

20 m

8 m

5 m

8 m   15 m

8 m   5 m

20 m

10.

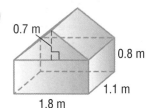

2 m

6 m

6 m

9 m

16 m

11.

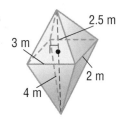

|◄7 m►|

15 m

12. SWIMMING POOLS The swimming pool at the right is being filled with water. Find the number of cubic feet that it will take to fill the swimming pool. (*Hint*: The area of a trapezoid is $a = \frac{1}{2}h(b_1 + b_2)$.)

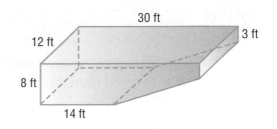

30 ft
12 ft
3 ft
8 ft
14 ft

13. BOXES Charlotte wants to make the box shown. What is the surface area of the box? Round to the nearest tenth.

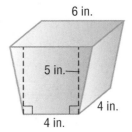

5 in.
11 in.
9 in.
10 in.

14. FOOD A carryout container is shown. The bottom base is a 4-inch square and the top base is a 4-inch by 6-inch rectangle. The height of the container is 5 inches. Find the volume of food that it holds.

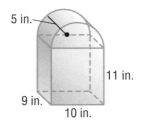

6 in.
5 in.
4 in.
4 in.

15 GEOMETRY Find the volume of the figure at the right in cubic feet. Round to the nearest tenth.

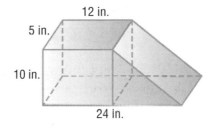

12 in.
5 in.
10 in.
24 in.

H.O.T. Problems

16. OPEN ENDED Draw a composite figure that is made up of a cylinder and two cones. Label its dimensions and find the volume of the figure.

17. CHALLENGE Give an example of a composite solid that has a volume between 250 and 300 cubic units.

18. FIND THE ERROR Seth is finding the surface area of the composite figure shown. Find his mistake and correct it.

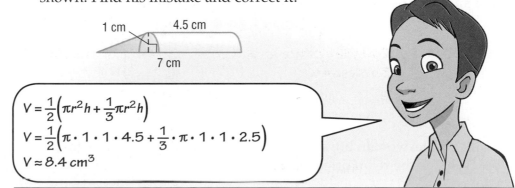

1 cm
4.5 cm
7 cm

$$V = \frac{1}{2}\left(\pi r^2 h + \frac{1}{3}\pi r^2 h\right)$$
$$V = \frac{1}{2}\left(\pi \cdot 1 \cdot 1 \cdot 4.5 + \frac{1}{3} \cdot \pi \cdot 1 \cdot 1 \cdot 2.5\right)$$
$$V \approx 8.4 \text{ cm}^3$$

19. Write MATH How is finding the surface area of a half-cylinder different from finding the surface area of a cylinder?

20. Jaime is covering the decorative wall hanging shown below in felt, including the back and bottom. What is the total area to be covered with felt?

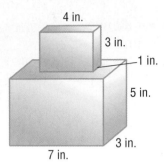

4 in.
3 in.
1 in.
5 in.
3 in.
7 in.

A. 23 in²   **C.** 172 in²

B. 117 in²   **D.** 1,260 in²

21. Which of the following formulas cannot be used to find the volume of the composite figure?

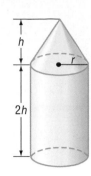

F. $V = 2\pi r^2 h + \frac{1}{3}\pi r^2 h$

G. $V = \frac{7}{3}\pi r^2 h$

H. $V = \pi r^2(2h) + \frac{1}{3}\pi r^2 h$

I. $V = \frac{2}{3}\pi r^2 h$

Spiral Review

22. MONEY Over the weekend, Mr. Lobo spent $534. Of that, about 68% was spent on groceries. About how much money was not spent on groceries? Use the *solve a simpler problem* strategy. (Lesson 8-3A)

Find the surface area of each pyramid. (Lesson 8-2E)

23.

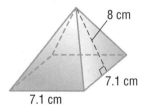

8 cm
7.1 cm
7.1 cm

24.

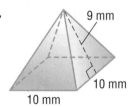

9 mm
10 mm
10 mm

Find the surface area of each cylinder. Round to the nearest tenth. (Lesson 8-2C)

25.

←—14 ft—→
14 ft

26.

8 m
12 m

27. RETAIL A saleswoman buys DVD players for $39.00 and marks them up 25%. What is the retail price? (Lesson 6-2C)

28. SURVEY 70% of the students in Mr. Wade's class have a television in their room. Out of the 30 students in the class, how many do not have a television in their room? (Lesson 6-1B)

FOLDABLES®
Study Organizer

Be sure the following Key Concepts are noted in your Foldable.

Key Concepts

Volume (Lesson 8-1)
- rectangular prism: $V = Bh$, where $B = bh$
- triangular prism: $V = Bh$, where $B = \frac{1}{2}bh$
- cylinder: $V = Bh$, where $B = \pi r^2$

 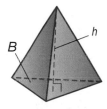

cone   **pyramid**

$$V = \frac{1}{3}Bh$$

Surface Area (Lesson 8-2)
- rectangular prism
  $S.A. = 2bw + 2bh + 2hw$

- cylinder
  $S.A. = 2\pi rh + 2\pi r^2$

- square pyramid
  $S.A. = B + \frac{1}{2}P\ell$

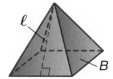

Key Vocabulary

composite shapes (p. 478)   surface area (p. 456)

cone (p. 449)   triangular prism (p. 434)

cylinder (p. 438)   volume (p. 432)

lateral surface area (p. 468)

net (p. 454)

prism (p. 431)

pyramid (p. 445)

rectangular prism (p. 432)

slant height (p. 468)

Vocabulary Check

Choose the correct term to complete each sentence.

1. A (rectangular prism, rectangle) is a three-dimensional figure that has three sets of parallel congruent sides.

2. The (volume, surface area) of a three-dimensional figure is the measure of the space occupied by it.

3. Volume is measured in (square, cubic) units.

4. A (cylinder, prism) is a three-dimensional figure that has two congruent, parallel circles as its bases.

5. The formula for the volume of a (rectangular prism, cone) is $V = \frac{1}{3}Bh$.

6. To find the surface area of a (pyramid, cylinder), you must know the measurements of the height and the radius.

7. The volume of a rectangular prism is found by (adding, multiplying) the length, the width, and the height.

8. The formula for the surface area of a (cylinder, rectangular prism) is $S.A. = 2\pi rh + 2\pi r^2$.

Multi-Part Lesson Review

8-1 Volume

Volume of Prisms (pp. 432–437)

 MA.7.G.2.1

Find the volume of each prism. Round to the nearest tenth if necessary.

9.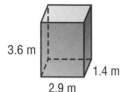
3.6 m
1.4 m
2.9 m

10.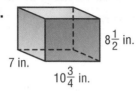
$8\frac{1}{2}$ in.
7 in.
$10\frac{3}{4}$ in.

11. **CEREAL** A box of cereal is 8.5 inches long, 12.5 inches tall, and 3.5 inches wide. What is the maximum amount of cereal the box can contain?

12. **TRUCKS** The dimensions of the bed of a dump truck are length 20 feet, width 7 feet, and height $9\frac{1}{2}$ feet. What is the volume of the bed of the dump truck?

EXAMPLE 1 A local city provides residents with a rectangular container for recycling products. Find the volume of the rectangular container.

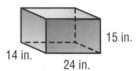
15 in.
14 in.
24 in.

$V = \ell wh$ Volume of a rectangular prism

$V = (24)(14)(15)$ Replace ℓ with 24, w with 14, and h with 15.

$V = 5{,}040$ Multiply.

The volume of the rectangular container is 5,040 cubic inches.

Volume of Cylinders (pp. 438–442)

 MA.7.G.2.1

Find the volume of each cylinder. Round to the nearest tenth.

13.
8.7 km
17 km

14.
15 mm
21.1 mm

15. **CONTAINERS** A can of soup has a diameter of 3.5 inches and a height of 5 inches. Find the volume of the soup can. Round to the nearest tenth.

16. **COOKIES** Mrs. Delagado stores cookies in a cylinder-shaped jar that has a height of 12 inches and a diameter of 10 inches. Find the volume to the nearest cubic inch.

EXAMPLE 2 Marquez stores his toys in a cylinder-shaped can like the one shown below. Find the volume of the can. Round to the nearest tenth.

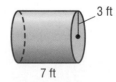
3 ft
7 ft

$V = \pi r^2 h$ Volume of a cylinder

$V = \pi 3^2(7)$ Replace r with 3 and h with 7.

$V \approx 197.8$ Multiply.

The volume of the cylinder-shaped can is 197.8 cubic feet.

Volume of Pyramids (pp. 445–448)

MA.7.G.2.1

Find the volume of each pyramid. Round to the nearest tenth.

17.

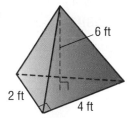

4.7 mm

2 mm   2 mm

18.

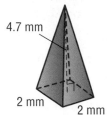

6 ft

2 ft   4 ft

19. CRYSTALS Lelah bought a pyramid-shaped crystal to hang in her room. The rectangular base of the crystal measures 9 centimeters by 8 centimeters and has a height of 12 centimeters. What is the volume of the pyramid-shaped crystal?

EXAMPLE 3 Guilia bought a lawn decoration shaped like the pyramid shown below. Find the volume of the pyramid-shaped decoration. Round to the nearest tenth.

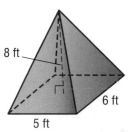

8 ft

6 ft

5 ft

$V = \frac{1}{3}Bh$ Volume of a pyramid

$V = \frac{1}{3}(6 \times 5) \times 8$ Replace B with 6×5 and h with 8.

$V = 80$ Multiply.

The volume of the pyramid-shaped lawn decoration is 80 cubic feet.

Volume of Cones (pp. 449-452)

MA.7.G.2.1

Find the volume of each cone. Round to the nearest tenth.

20.

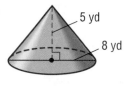

5 yd

8 yd

21.

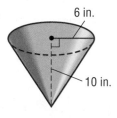

6 in.

10 in.

22. CONTAINER Mr. Corwin built a cone-shaped storage container with a base 15 inches in diameter and a height of 8 inches. What is the volume of the container to the nearest tenth?

EXAMPLE 4 Find the volume of the cone. Round to the nearest tenth.

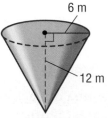

6 m

12 m

$V = \frac{1}{3}\pi r^2 h$ Volume of a cone

$V = \frac{1}{3}\pi 6^2(12)$ Replace r with 6 and h with 12.

$V \approx 452.4$ Simplify.

The volume of the cone is 452.4 cubic meters.

8-2 Surface Area

Surface Area of Prisms (pp. 456–461)

MA.7.G.2.1

Find the surface area of each rectangular prism. Round to the nearest tenth if necessary.

23.

24.

25. MOVING A large wardrobe box is 2.25 feet long, 2 feet wide, and 4 feet tall. How much cardboard was needed to make the box?

EXAMPLE 5 Find the surface area of the rectangular prism.

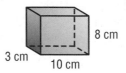

Surface area of rectangular prism

$= 2bh + 2bw + 2hw$

$= 2(10)(8) + 2(10)(3) + 2(8)(3)$ or 268

The surface area is 268 square centimeters.

Surface Area of Cylinders (pp. 462–465)

MA.7.G.2.1

Find the surface area of each cylinder. Round to the nearest tenth.

26.

27.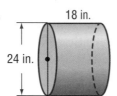

28. DESIGN A can of black beans is $5\frac{1}{2}$ inches high, and its base has a radius of 2 inches. How much paper is needed to make the label on the can? Round to the nearest tenth.

EXAMPLE 6 Find the surface area of the cylinder. Round to the nearest tenth.

Surface area of cylinder

$= 2\pi r^2 + 2\pi rh$

$= 2\pi(2)^2 + 2\pi(2)8$ or 125.7

The surface area is about 125.7 square feet.

Surface Area of Pyramids (pp. 468–471)

MA.7.G.2.1

Find the surface area of each pyramid. Round to the nearest tenth.

29.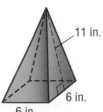

30.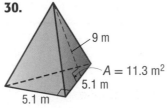

EXAMPLE 7 Find the surface area of the pyramid. Round to the nearest tenth.

Surface area of pyramid

$= B + \frac{1}{2}P\ell$

$= 25 + \frac{1}{2}(20)(7)$ or 95

The surface area is 95 square meters.

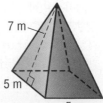

PSI: Solve a Simpler Problem (pp. 476–477)

 MA.7.G.4.1

31. LAND A rectangular plot of land measures 1,450 feet by 850 feet. A contractor wishes to section off a portion of this land to build an apartment complex. If the complex is 425 feet by 550 feet, how many square feet of land will *not* be sectioned off to build it?

32. TRAVEL Mrs. Whitmore left Chicago at 6:45 A.M. and arrived in St. Louis at 11:15 A.M., driving a distance of approximately 292 miles. Find her approximate average speed.

33. SHOPPING Mercedes spent $175.89 over the weekend. Of the money she spent, 40% was spent on shoes. About how much money was *not* spent on shoes?

EXAMPLE 8 A total of 950 residents voted on whether to build a neighborhood playground. Of those that voted, 70% voted for the playground. How many residents voted for the playground?

Find 10% of 950 and then use the result to find 70% of 950.

10% of 950 = 95

Since there are seven 10s in 70%, multiply 95 by 7.

So, 95 × 7 or 665 residents voted for the playground.

Volume and Surface Area of Composite Figures (pp. 480–484)

 MA.7.G.2.2

Find the volume of each composite shape. Round to the nearest tenth if necessary.

34.
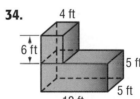

35.
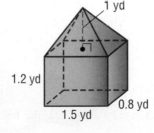

36. MAILBOX Berdina is helping her dad paint a mailbox like the one shown. If one quart of paint covers 40 square feet, how many quarts of paint should they buy?

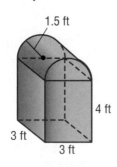

EXAMPLE 9 Joey built a small greenhouse shown below. What is the volume of the greenhouse?

Volume of rectangular prism

$$= bwh$$
$$= (1.5)(0.8)(1.2)$$
$$= 1.44 \text{ yd}^3$$

Volume of pyramid

$$= \frac{1}{3}Bh$$
$$= \frac{1}{3}(1.2)(1)$$
$$= 0.4 \text{ yd}^3$$

1.44 + 0.4 = 1.84 cubic yards

So, there are 1.84 cubic yards in the greenhouse.

Find the volume of each prism and cylinder. Round to the nearest tenth.

1.
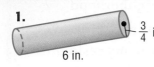
$\frac{3}{4}$ in.
6 in.

2.
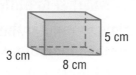
5 cm
3 cm
8 cm

3.
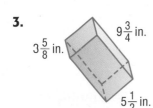
$9\frac{3}{4}$ in.
$3\frac{5}{8}$ in.
$5\frac{1}{2}$ in.

4.
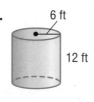
6 ft
12 ft

5. **NGSSS PRACTICE** A cylinder-shaped coffee mug has a radius of 4 centimeters and a height of 10 centimeters. How much coffee is in the mug if it is only half full?

A. 251.3 cm³

B. 149.5 cm³

C. 135.7 cm³

D. 102.0 cm³

6. **DIVING** Scuba diving tanks are made up of cylinders. What is the volume of one tank if it has a radius of 2 inches and a height of 16 inches? Round to the nearest tenth.

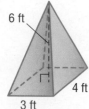

Find the volume of the pyramid and cone. Round to the nearest tenth.

7.

6 ft
4 ft
3 ft

8.
$8\frac{1}{2}$ m
5 m

Find the surface area of each figure. Round to the nearest tenth if necessary.

9.
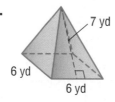
5 cm
3 cm
8 cm

10.
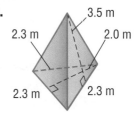
6 ft
12 ft

11.
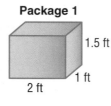
7 yd
6 yd
6 yd

12.
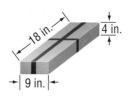
3.5 m
2.3 m
2.0 m
2.3 m
2.3 m

13. **PACKAGING** Mr. Cole is wrapping a gift. What is the least amount of wrapping paper he will need to wrap the box at the right?

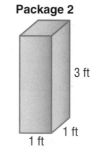
18 in.
4 in.
9 in.

14. **EXTENDED RESPONSE** A packaging company produces the boxes shown below.

Package 1
1.5 ft
1 ft
2 ft

Package 2
3 ft
1 ft
1 ft

Part A Predict which package holds more materials.

Part B Which package has a greater volume?

Part C Which package has the greater surface area?

Part D Help the company produce a package with the same volume as Package 1, but with the least amount of surface area.

CHAPTER 8 Preparing for Standardized Tests

THINK SOLVE EXPLAIN Short-Response Questions: Showing Work

Short-response questions require that you show your work. You may be able to get partial credit even if your answer is not entirely correct.

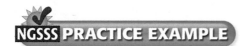

NGSSS PRACTICE EXAMPLE

A cheerleading mat is rolled up to form a cylinder that measures 6 feet long and 3.5 feet in diameter.

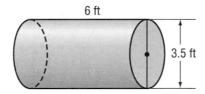

What is the approximate volume, in cubic feet, of the roll? Show your work or explain in words how to determine the answer.

Work Space

Volume (V) of a cylinder $= \pi r^2 h$

radius $= 3.5 \div 2$ or 1.75

$V = \pi(1.75)^2(6)$

$V \approx 57.7$

Volume __57.7__ cubic feet

The formula, steps, and calculations used to find the solution are clearly shown.

Work on It

Chase's cell phone is a rectangular prism 3.3 inches high, 1.7 inches long, and 0.8 inch wide. What is the surface area, in square inches, of Chase's phone?

Test Hint

Be sure to keep your calculations inside the work space provided.

Read each question. Then fill in the correct answer on the answer sheet provided by your teacher or on a sheet of paper.

1. A metal toolbox has a length of 11 inches, a width of 5 inches, and a height of 6 inches. What is the volume of the toolbox?

   A. 22 in^3 C. 210 in^3

   B. 121 in^3 D. 330 in^3

2. A bag contains 5 red, 2 yellow, and 8 blue marbles. Xavier removed one blue marble from the bag and did not put it back. He then randomly removed another marble. What is the probability that the second marble removed was blue?

   F. $\frac{8}{14}$ H. $\frac{7}{15}$

   G. $\frac{8}{15}$ I. $\frac{1}{2}$

3. Evelyn has 3 apples to serve to her friends. If Evelyn serves each friend $\frac{1}{3}$ of a whole apple, how many friends can she serve?

   A. 1   C. 9

   B. 3   D. 12

4. ✎ **GRIDDED RESPONSE** Daniel is designing and building a small storage shed. He wants the dimensions of the shed to be one half the dimensions of the shed shown below.

Storage Shed

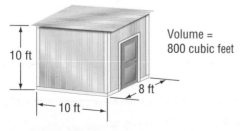

Volume = 800 cubic feet

10 ft

10 ft

8 ft

If the dimensions of the shed above are each divided in half, the volume of Daniel's new storage shed will be what fraction of the volume of the original storage shed?

5. ✎ **GRIDDED RESPONSE** Timea ran 3 miles in 19 minutes. At this rate, how many minutes would it take her to run 5 miles?

6. Wilma made a decorative piece shaped like a square pyramid with the dimensions shown.

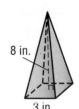

8 in.

3 in.

She wants to double the volume of the piece.
Which of the following square pyramid pieces will have a volume that is twice the volume of Wilma's decorative piece?

F.

8 in.

6 in.

H.

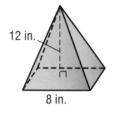

16 in.

3 in.

G.

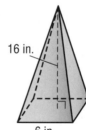

16 in.

6 in.

I.

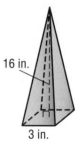

12 in.

8 in.

7. Which line contains the ordered pair (−1, 1)?

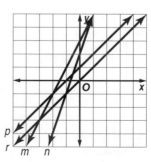

p
r   m   n

   A. line m C. line p

   B. line n D. line r

8. ✏️ **GRIDDED RESPONSE** Solve the equation $b - 5 = -8$. What is the value of b?

9. A tube of caulk comes in a cylindrical-shaped tube. The tube measures 10 inches long and has a 2-inch diameter. What is the approximate volume of caulk, in cubic inches, contained in this tube?

F. 3.14 in^3 **H.** 62.8 in^3

G. 31.4 in^3 **I.** 125.7 in^3

10. **THINK SOLVE EXPLAIN** **SHORT RESPONSE** Compare the surface area of the shapes below that have equal volume. Justify your answer.

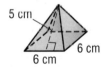

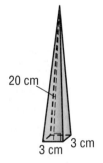

11. What are the coordinates of point H?

A. $(2, 1)$

B. $(1, 2)$

C. $(-1, 2)$

D. $(-1, -2)$

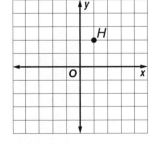

12. Andrea made a tiered cake for a wedding. She wants to cover the outside of each layer with white icing, marked A, B, and C.

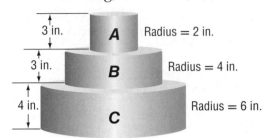

What is the total area of the 3 surfaces to be covered with white icing? The top surface of each layer will not be covered.

F. 289.4 in^2 **H.** 163.5 in^2

G. 263.9 in^2 **I.** 131.9 in^2

13. **THINK SOLVE EXPLAIN** **EXTENDED RESPONSE** A dish company makes small cylindrical dishes with lids that have a radius of 8 centimeters and a height of 6 centimeters. The dishes are shipped in rectangular boxes that are 20 centimeters by 20 centimeters by 16 centimeters. The extra space in the box is filled with packing material to protect the dish.

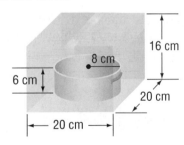

Part A   How much space does the dish take up?

Part B   How much packing material is needed?

Part C   How much material is needed to make the box?

NEED EXTRA HELP?													
If You Missed Question...	1	2	3	4	5	6	7	8	9	10	11	12	13
Go to Lesson...	8-1B	7-2A	2-3D	8-1B	4-1D	8-1E	1-1C	3-1D	8-1C	8-2E	1-1C	8-2C	8-3C
For help with NGSSS...	G.2.1	P.7.1	A.3.2	G.2.1	A.1.1	G.2.1	G.4.3	A.3.3	G.2.1	G.2.1	G.4.3	G.2.1	G.2.1

CHAPTER 9

Measurement and Proportional Reasoning

Supporting ★ Idea

Compare, contrast, and convert units of measure and dimensions.

FOLDABLES®
Study Organizer

Make this Foldable to help you organize your notes. Begin with a sheet of notebook paper.

1 Fold lengthwise to the holes.

2 Cut along the top line and then make equal cuts to form 5 tabs.

3 Label the major topics as shown.

Convert measurements
Convert between systems
Convert rates
Convert area and volume
Similar solids

Review Vocabulary

ratio table (Prior Grade) **tabla de razones** a table with columns filled with pairs of numbers that have the same ratio

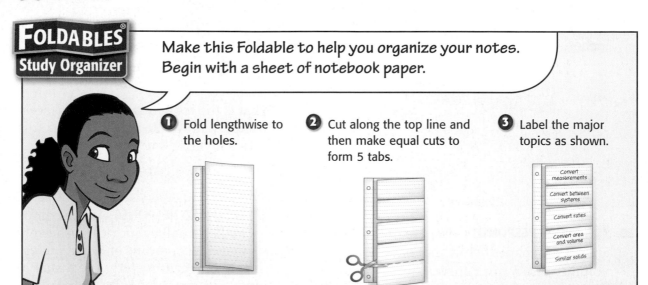

Gallons of Paint	1	2	3	4
Drops of Red	6	12	18	24

+1 +1 +1
+6 +6 +6

Key Vocabulary

	English	Español
p. 501	unit ratio	tasa unitaria
p. 505	metric system	sistema métrico
p. 528	similar solids	sólidos semejantes

Multilingual eGlossary glencoe.com

When Will I Use This?

Trial	1	2	3	4
Distance (m)	0.25	0.50	0.75	1.00
Time (s)	0.13	0.20	0.25	0.27

Your Turn!
You will solve this problem in Chapter 9.

Are You Ready for Chapter 9?

You have two options for checking prerequisite skills for this chapter.

Text Option Take the Quick Check below. Refer to the Quick Review for help.

QUICK Check

Multiply. Write in simplest form.
(Prior Grade)

1. $\frac{2}{3} \times \frac{9}{10}$

2. $\frac{1}{2} \times \frac{6}{7}$

3. $\frac{2}{5} \times \frac{5}{8}$

4. $4 \times \frac{7}{8}$

5. $8 \times \frac{3}{16}$

6. $\frac{2}{3} \times 9$

7. **FRUIT** A farmer planted 6 acres of land with orange trees. During the past year, only $\frac{2}{3}$ of the planted acres produced oranges. How many acres produced oranges?

Multiply. (Prior Grade)

8. 5.8×10

9. $0.9 \times 1,000$

10. 1.04×100

11. $2.4 \times 1,000$

12. 0.03×100

13. 8.15×10

14. **MEASUREMENT** The height of the KVLY Tower in North Dakota in feet can be found by multiplying 2.063 by 1,000. Find the height of the KVLY Tower.

QUICK Review

EXAMPLE 1

Find $\frac{3}{4} \times \frac{2}{9}$.

$\frac{3}{4} \times \frac{2}{9} = \frac{\overset{1}{\cancel{3}} \times \overset{1}{\cancel{2}}}{\underset{2}{\cancel{4}} \times \underset{3}{\cancel{9}}}$ Divide 3 and 9 by their GCF, 3.
Divide 2 and 4 by their GCF, 2.

$= \frac{1}{6}$ Simplify.

EXAMPLE 2

Find $5 \times \frac{3}{10}$.

$5 \times \frac{3}{10} = \frac{\overset{1}{\cancel{5}}}{1} \times \frac{3}{\underset{2}{\cancel{10}}}$ Divide 5 and 10 by their GCF, 5.

$= \frac{3}{2}$ or $1\frac{1}{2}$ Simplify.

EXAMPLE 3

Find 6.3×100.

Method 1   Use paper and pencil.

$$\begin{array}{r} 100 \\ \times\ 6.3 \quad \text{one decimal place} \\ \hline 300 \\ 6,000 \\ \hline 630.0 \quad \text{one decimal place} \end{array}$$

Method 2   Use mental math.

Move the decimal point two places to the right.

$6.3 \times 100 = 6.300$ or 630.

Online Option  Take the Online Readiness Quiz at **glencoe.com**.

Studying Math

Power Notes

Power notes are similar to lesson outlines, but they are simpler to organize. Power notes use the numbers 1, 2, 3, and so on.

Do you ever have trouble organizing your notes? Try using power notes.

Power 1: This is the main idea.
    Power 2: This provides details about the main idea.
        Power 3: This provides details about Power 2.
        and so on…

Here's a sample of power notes from Lesson 9-1B. Notice that you can even add drawings or examples to your power notes.

```
1: The Customary System
   2: Length
      3: Units of Length
         4: inch
         4: foot
            5: 1 foot = 12 inches
            5: 3 feet = 1 yard
         4: yard
         4: mile
      3: Converting Units of Length
         4: from larger to smaller — multiply
         4: from smaller to larger — divide
   2: Weight
```

You can have more than one detail under each power.

Practice

Use power notes to make an outline for each concept.

1. metric system (Lesson 9-1C)

2. convert between systems (Lesson 9-1D)

3. adding and subtracting integers (Lesson 1-2B, 1-2D)

NGSSS
LA.7.3.2.2 The student will draft writing by organizing information into a logical sequence and combining or deleting sentences to enhance clarity.

Explore Units of Measure

Main Idea

Determine the appropriate unit of measure. Compare and contrast units of measure.

NGSSS

  MA.7.G.4.4 Compare, contrast, and convert **units of measure between different measurement systems (US customary or metric (SI)),** dimensions, and derived units **to solve problems.**

Get Connected
glencoe.com

ELEVATORS Elevators have been around since the mid-1800s. All elevators have a maximum weight limit. Is the maximum weight limit of this elevator more likely to be be 3,500 ounces or 3,500 pounds?

In this activity, you will explore different units of measure.

ACTIVITY

STEP 1 Locate the following objects. Estimate their measures. Copy and complete the table.

Object	Estimated Length		Estimated Weight	
Math textbook	▦ inches	▦ centimeters	▦ pounds	▦ kilograms
Pencil	▦ inches	▦ millimeters	▦ ounces	▦ grams
Board eraser	▦ inches	▦ centimeters	▦ ounces	▦ grams
Classroom door	▦ yards	▦ meters	▦ pounds	▦ kilograms
Chair	▦ feet	▦ centimeters	▦ pounds	▦ kilograms

STEP 2 Find the actual measures of two of the objects in the table.

Analyze the Results

1. Would the maximum weight limit of an elevator be measured in ounces or pounds? Explain your reasoning.

2. Compare and contrast your measurements for each object. Are there any units that are similar?

3. **RESEARCH** Use the Internet or another source to research which countries use the customary system of measurement and which countries use the metric system of measurement.

Practice and Apply

Choose the better unit of measure for each object.

4. kilograms or tons

5. cups or milliliters

6. yards or kilometers

7. milligrams or ounces

8. grams or pounds

9. liters or pints

Write the customary and metric units that you would use to measure each of the following.

10. thickness of a coin

11. amount of water in a pitcher

12. length of a skateboard

13. length of a football field

14. thickness of a pencil

15. vanilla used in a cookie recipe

16. bag of sugar

17. distance between two cities

18. gas in the tank of a car

19. MAPS The map shows part of the eastern coast of central Florida.

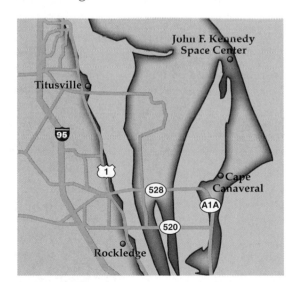

   a. Estimate the map distance in inches between Rockledge and Titusville. Check your measurement with a ruler.

   b. Estimate the map distance in centimeters between Cape Canaveral and the John F. Kennedy Space Center. Check your measurement with a ruler.

20. Which customary unit of length is approximately equal to one meter?

21. Which metric unit of length would you use instead of a mile?

22. COLLECT THE DATA Choose two classmates or family members. Which customary and metric units of length would you use to measure each person's height? Estimate the height of each person. Then measure to check the reasonableness of your estimate.

23. OPEN ENDED Without looking at their labels, estimate the weight or capacity of three packaged food items in your kitchen. Use customary and metric units. Then compare your estimate to the actual weight or capacity.

Main Idea
Change units of measure in the customary system.

NGSSS
MA.7.G.4.4 Compare, contrast, **and convert units of measure** between different measurement systems (**US customary** or metric (SI)), dimensions, and derived units **to solve problems.** *Also addresses MA.7.A.3.2.*

New Vocabulary
unit ratio
dimensional analysis

Get Connected
glencoe.com

Convert Customary Units

ANIMALS The table shows the approximate weights in tons of several large land animals.

Animal	Weight (T)
Grizzly bear	1
White rhinoceros	4
Hippopotamus	5
African elephant	8

One ton is equivalent to 2,000 pounds. You can use a *ratio table* to convert each weight from tons to pounds.

1. Copy and complete the ratio table. The first two ratios are done for you.

Tons	1	4	5	8
Pounds	2,000	8,000	▦	▦

To produce equivalent ratios, multiply the quantities in each row by the same number.

2. Then graph the ordered pairs (tons, pounds) from the table. Label the horizontal axis *Weight in Tons* and the vertical axis *Weight in Pounds*. Connect the points. What do you notice about the graph?

Key Concept   Customary Units

Type of Measure	Larger Unit →		Smaller Unit
Length	1 foot (ft)	=	12 inches (in.)
	1 yard (yd)	=	3 feet
	1 mile (mi)	=	5,280 feet
Weight	1 pound (lb)	=	16 ounces (oz)
	1 ton (T)	=	2,000 pounds
Capacity	1 cup (c)	=	8 fluid ounces (fl oz)
	1 pint (pt)	=	2 cups
	1 quart (qt)	=	2 pints
	1 gallon (gal)	=	4 quarts

Each of the relationships on the previous page can be written as a unit ratio. Like a unit rate, a **unit ratio** is one in which the denominator is 1 unit.

$$\frac{3 \text{ ft}}{1 \text{ yd}} \qquad \frac{2{,}000 \text{ lb}}{1 \text{ T}} \qquad \frac{4 \text{ qt}}{1 \text{ gal}}$$

Notice that the numerator and denominator of each fraction above are equivalent, so the value of each ratio is 1. You can multiply by a unit ratio of this type to *convert* or change from larger units to smaller units.

The process of including units of measurement as factors when you compute is called **dimensional analysis**.

Study Tip

Multiplying by 1 Although the number and units changed in Example 1, because the measure is multiplied by 1, the value of the converted measure is the same as the original.

EXAMPLES **Convert Larger Units to Smaller Units**

① **Convert 20 feet to inches.**

Since 1 foot = 12 inches, the unit ratio is $\frac{12 \text{ in.}}{1 \text{ ft}}$.

$20 \text{ ft} = 20 \text{ ft} \cdot \dfrac{12 \text{ in.}}{1 \text{ ft}}$ Multiply by $\frac{12 \text{ in.}}{1 \text{ ft}}$.

$\phantom{20 \text{ ft}} = 20 \text{ ft} \cdot \dfrac{12 \text{ in.}}{1 \text{ ft}}$ Divide out common units, leaving the desired unit, inches.

$\phantom{20 \text{ ft}} = 20 \cdot 12 \text{ in. or } 240 \text{ in.}$ Multiply.

So, 20 feet = 240 inches.

② **GARDENING** Marco mixes $\frac{1}{4}$ cup of fertilizer with soil before planting each bulb. How many fluid ounces of fertilizer does he use per bulb?

$\dfrac{1}{4} \text{ c} = \dfrac{1}{4} \text{ c} \cdot \dfrac{8 \text{ fl oz}}{1 \text{ c}}$ Since 1 cup = 8 fluid ounces, multiply by $\frac{8 \text{ fl oz}}{1 \text{ c}}$. Then, divide out common units.

$\phantom{\dfrac{1}{4} \text{ c}} = \dfrac{1}{4} \cdot 8 \text{ fl oz or } 2 \text{ fl oz}$ Multiply.

So, 2 fluid ounces of fertilizer are used per bulb.

 CHECK Your Progress

Complete.

a. $36 \text{ yd} = \blacksquare \text{ ft}$ **b.** $\frac{3}{4} \text{ T} = \blacksquare \text{ lb}$ **c.** $1\frac{1}{2} \text{ qt} = \blacksquare \text{ pt}$

To convert from smaller units to larger units, multiply by the reciprocal of the appropriate unit ratio.

Convert Smaller Units to Larger Units

Review Vocabulary

Reciprocal The product of a number and its reciprocal is 1; *Example:* The reciprocal of $\frac{3}{5}$ is $\frac{5}{3}$.
(Lesson 2-3D)

3 **Convert 15 quarts to gallons.**

Since 1 gallon = 4 quarts, the unit ratio is $\frac{4 \text{ qt}}{1 \text{ gal}}$, and its reciprocal is $\frac{1 \text{ gal}}{4 \text{ qt}}$.

$15 \text{ qt} = 15 \text{ qt} \cdot \frac{1 \text{ gal}}{4 \text{ qt}}$ Multiply by $\frac{1 \text{ gal}}{4 \text{ qt}}$.

$= 15 \cancel{\text{ qt}} \cdot \frac{1 \text{ gal}}{4 \cancel{\text{ qt}}}$ Divide out common units, leaving the desired unit, gallons.

$= 15 \cdot \frac{1}{4} \text{ gal}$ or 3.75 gal   Multiplying 15 by $\frac{1}{4}$ is the same as dividing 15 by 4.

4 **COSTUMES** Umeka needs $4\frac{1}{2}$ feet of fabric to make a costume for a play. How many yards of fabric does she need?

$4\frac{1}{2} \text{ ft} = 4\frac{1}{2} \cancel{\text{ ft}} \cdot \frac{1 \text{ yd}}{3 \cancel{\text{ ft}}}$ Since 1 yard = 3 feet, multiply by $\frac{1 \text{ yd}}{3 \text{ ft}}$. Then, divide out common units.

$= \frac{\cancel{9}^{3}}{2} \cdot \frac{1}{\cancel{3}_{1}} \text{ yd}$ Write $4\frac{1}{2}$ as an improper fraction. Then divide out common factors.

$= \frac{3}{2} \text{ yd}$ or $1\frac{1}{2} \text{ yd}$ Multiply.

So, Umeka needs $1\frac{1}{2}$ yards of fabric.

 CHECK Your Progress

Complete.

d. $2{,}640 \text{ ft} = \blacksquare \text{ mi}$ **e.** $100 \text{ oz} = \blacksquare \text{ lb}$ **f.** $3 \text{ c} = \blacksquare \text{ pt}$

g. **FOOD** A 3-pound pork loin can be cut into 10 pork chops of equal weight. How many ounces is each pork chop?

CHECK Your Understanding

Examples 1 and 2
(p. 501)

Complete.

1. $3 \text{ lb} = \blacksquare \text{ oz}$ **2.** $5\frac{1}{3} \text{ yd} = \blacksquare \text{ ft}$ **3** $6.5 \text{ c} = \blacksquare \text{ fl oz}$

4. **FISH** Grouper are members of the sea bass family. A large grouper can weigh $\frac{1}{3}$ ton. How much does a large grouper weigh to the nearest pound?

Examples 3 and 4
(p. 502)

Complete.

5. $12 \text{ qt} = \blacksquare \text{ gal}$ **6.** $28 \text{ in.} = \blacksquare \text{ ft}$ **7.** $15 \text{ pt} = \blacksquare \text{ qt}$

8. **VEHICLES** The world's narrowest electric vehicle is about 35 inches wide and is designed to move down narrow aisles in warehouses. How wide is this vehicle to the nearest foot?

Practice and Problem Solving

= Step-by-Step Solutions begin on page R25.
Extra Practice is on page EP25.

Examples 1–4 (pp. 501–502)

Complete.

9. $18 \text{ ft} = \blacksquare \text{ yd}$

10. $72 \text{ oz} = \blacksquare \text{ lb}$

11. $2 \text{ lb} = \blacksquare \text{ oz}$

12. $4 \text{ gal} = \blacksquare \text{ qt}$

13. $4\frac{1}{2} \text{ pt} = \blacksquare \text{ c}$

14. $3 \text{ c} = \blacksquare \text{ fl oz}$

15. $2 \text{ mi} = \blacksquare \text{ ft}$

16. $1\frac{1}{4} \text{ mi} = \blacksquare \text{ ft}$

17. $5,000 \text{ lb} = \blacksquare \text{ T}$

18. $13 \text{ c} = \blacksquare \text{ pt}$

19. $2\frac{3}{4} \text{ qt} = \blacksquare \text{ pt}$

20. $3\frac{3}{8} \text{ T} = \blacksquare \text{ lb}$

21. **PUMPKINS** One of the largest pumpkins ever grown weighed about $\frac{1}{2}$ ton. How many pounds did the pumpkin weigh?

22. **SKIING** Speed skiing takes place on a course that is $\frac{2}{3}$ mile long. How many feet long is the course?

23. **BOATING** A 40-foot power boat is for sale by owner. How long is the boat to the nearest yard?

24. **BLOOD** A total of 35 pints of blood were collected at a local blood drive. How many quarts of blood were collected?

25. **PUNCH** Will a 2-quart pitcher hold the entire recipe of citrus punch given at the right? Explain your reasoning.

Recipe: Citrus Punch Drink
2 cups orange juice
2 cups grapefruit juice
$\frac{1}{4}$ cup apricot nectar
$\frac{1}{3}$ cup pineapple juice
4 cups ginger ale

26. **WEATHER** On Monday, it snowed a total of 15 inches. On Tuesday and Wednesday, it snowed an additional $4\frac{1}{2}$ inches and $6\frac{3}{4}$ inches, respectively. A weather forecaster says that over the last three days, it snowed about $2\frac{1}{2}$ feet. Is this a valid claim? Justify your answer.

MEASUREMENT Complete the following statements.

27. If $16 \text{ c} = 1 \text{ gal}$, then $1\frac{1}{4} \text{ gal} = \blacksquare \text{ c}$.

28. If $1,760 \text{ yd} = 1 \text{ mi}$, then $880 \text{ yd} = \blacksquare \text{ mi}$.

29. If $36 \text{ in.} = 1 \text{ yd}$, then $2.3 \text{ yd} = \blacksquare \text{ in.}$

30. **MULTIPLE REPRESENTATIONS** Use the graph at the right.

    a. **NUMBERS** What does an ordered pair from this graph represent?

    b. **ALGEBRA** Find the slope of the line.

    c. **MEASUREMENT** Use the graph to find the capacity in quarts of a 2.5-gallon container. Explain your reasoning.

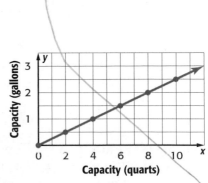

H.O.T. Problems

31. OPEN ENDED Write a problem about a real-world situation in which you would need to convert pints to cups.

CHALLENGE Replace each ● with <, >, or = to make a true sentence. Justify your answers.

32. 16 in. ● $1\frac{1}{2}$ ft

33. $8\frac{3}{4}$ gal ● 32 qt

34. 2.7 T ● 86,400 oz

35.  **MATH** Use multiplication by unit ratios of equivalent measures to convert 5 square feet to square inches. Justify your answer.

NGSSS Practice   MA.5.G.5.2, MA.7.G.4.4

36. Which situation is represented by the graph?

A. conversion of inches to yards

B. conversion of feet to inches

C. conversion of miles to feet

D. conversion of yards to feet

37. How many cups of milk are shown at the right?

F. $\frac{3}{4}$ c

G. $1\frac{1}{4}$ c

H. $2\frac{1}{2}$ c

I. 10 c

Spiral Review

Find the surface area of each composite shape. Round to the nearest tenth if necessary. (Lesson 8-3C)

38.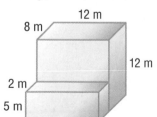

12 m
8 m
12 m
2 m
5 m

39.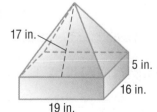

17 in.
5 in.
16 in.
19 in.

40.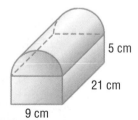

5 cm
21 cm
9 cm

41. SPORTS PROFIT A stadium seats 101,800 people. 22% of the tickets cost $134.87 each and 45% of the tickets cost $67.99 each. The remaining 33% cost only $35.87 each. About how much revenue is made from one game if each seat is sold out? Use the *solve a simpler problem* strategy. (Lesson 8-3A)

Main Idea

Change metric units of length, capacity, and mass.

NGSSS

MA.7.G.4.4 Compare, contrast, and convert units of measure between different measurement systems (US customary or **metric (SI)**), dimensions, and derived units **to solve problems.** *Also addresses MA.7.A.3.2.*

New Vocabulary

metric system
meter
liter
gram
kilogram

Get Connected
glencoe.com

Convert Metric Units

Explore The lengths of two objects are shown below.

Object	Length (millimeters)	Length (centimeters)
Paper clip	45	4.5
CD case	144	14.4

1. Select three other objects. Find and record the width of all three objects to the nearest millimeter and tenth of a centimeter.

2. Compare and contrast the measurements of the objects. Write a rule that describes how to convert from millimeters to centimeters.

3. Measure the length of your classroom in meters. Make a conjecture about how to convert this measure to centimeters. Explain.

The **metric system** is a decimal system of measures. The prefixes commonly used in this system are kilo-, centi-, and milli-.

Prefix	Meaning in Words	Meaning in Numbers
kilo-	thousands	1,000
centi-	hundredths	0.01
milli-	thousandths	0.001

In the metric system, the base unit of *length* is the **meter** (m). Using prefixes, the names of other units of length are formed. Notice that the prefixes tell you how the units relate to the meter.

Unit	Symbol	Relationship to Meter	
kilometer	km	1 km = 1,000 m	1 m = 0.001 km
meter	m	1 m = 1 m	
centimeter	cm	1 cm = 0.01 m	1 m = 100 cm
millimeter	mm	1 mm = 0.001 m	1 m = 1,000 mm

The **liter** (L) is the base unit of *capacity*, the amount of dry or liquid material an object can hold. The **gram** (g) measures *mass*, the amount of matter in an object. The prefixes can also be applied to these units. Whereas the meter and liter are the base units of length and capacity, the base unit of mass is the **kilogram** (kg).

To convert a metric measure of length, mass, or capacity from one unit to another, you can use the relationship between the two units and multiplication by a power of 10.

 EXAMPLES Convert Units in the Metric System

Study Tip

Metric Conversions When converting from a larger unit to a smaller unit, the power of ten being multiplied will be greater than 1.

When converting from a smaller unit to a larger unit, the power of ten will be less than 1.

1 **Convert 4.5 liters to milliliters.**

You need to convert liters to milliliters. Use the relationship $1 \text{ L} = 1,000 \text{ mL}$.

$1 \text{ L} = 1,000 \text{ mL}$ Write the relationship.

$4.5 \times 1 \text{ L} = 4.5 \times 1,000 \text{ mL}$ Multiply each side by 4.5 since you have 4.5 L.

$4.5 \text{ L} = 4,500 \text{ mL}$ To multiply 4.5 by 1,000, move the decimal point 3 places to the right.

2 **Convert 500 millimeters to meters.**

You need to convert millimeters to meters. Use the relationship $1 \text{ mm} = 0.001 \text{ m}$.

$1 \text{ mm} = 0.001 \text{ m}$ Write the relationship.

$500 \times 1 \text{ mm} = 500 \times 0.001 \text{ m}$ Multiply each side by 500 since you have 500 mm.

$500 \text{ mm} = 0.5 \text{ m}$ To multiply 500 by 0.001, move the decimal point 3 places to the left.

✓ **CHECK Your Progress**

Complete.

a. $25.4 \text{ g} = \blacksquare \text{ kg}$ **b.** $158 \text{ mm} = \blacksquare \text{ m}$

Real-World EXAMPLE

Real-World Link · · · · ·
The average mass of a flamingo is 2.95 kilograms.

3 **FLAMINGOS** The only state in which the flamingo is found in the wild is Florida. Use the information at the left to find the average mass of a flamingo in grams.

You are converting kilograms to grams. Since the average mass of a flamingo is 2.95 kilograms, use the relationship $1 \text{ kg} = 1,000 \text{ g}$.

$1 \text{ kg} = 1,000 \text{ g}$ Write the relationship.

$2.95 \times 1 \text{ kg} = 2.95 \times 1,000 \text{ g}$ Multiply each side by 2.95 since you have 2.95 kg.

$2.95 \text{ kg} = 2,950 \text{ g}$ To multiply 2.95 by 1,000, move the decimal point 3 places to the right.

So, the average mass of a flamingo is 2,950 grams.

✓ **CHECK Your Progress**

c. FOOD A bottle contains 1.75 liters of juice. How many milliliters does the bottle contain?

Examples 1 and 2
(p. 506)

Complete. Round to the nearest hundredth if necessary.

1. 3.7 m = ■ cm
2. 550 m = ■ km
3. 1,160 mg = ■ g
4. 2.34 kL = ■ L

Example 3
(p. 506)

5. **SPORTS** How many centimeters does a team of athletes run in a 5-kilometer relay race?

Practice and Problem Solving

● = **Step-by-Step Solutions** begin on page R25.
Extra Practice is on page EP25.

Examples 1 and 2
(p. 506)

Complete. Round to the nearest hundredth if necessary.

6. 720 cm = ■ m
7. 983 mm = ■ m
8. 3.2 m = ■ cm
9. 0.03 g = ■ mg
10. 997 g = ■ kg
11. 82.1 g = ■ kg
12. 9.1 L = ■ mL
13. 130.5 kL = ■ L

Example 3
(p. 506)

14. **WATERFALLS** At 979 meters tall, Angel Falls in Venezuela is the highest waterfall in the world. How many kilometers tall is the waterfall?

15. **FOOD** An 18-ounce jar contains 510 grams of grape jelly. How many kilograms of grape jelly does the jar contain?

16. **CYCLING** Ramon rode his bike a distance of 8 kilometers. How many centimeters did Ramon ride his bike?

17. **BIRDS** A gull can fly at a speed of 35 kilometers per hour. How many meters per hour can a gull fly?

Order each set of measures from least to greatest.

18. 0.02 km, 50 m, 3,000 cm
19. 660 mL, 0.06 L, 6.6 kL
20. 0.32 kg, 345 g, 35,100 mg
21. 2,650 mm, 130 cm, 5 m

22. **ANALYZE TABLES** The table shows the lengths of bridges in the United States. Which bridges are about 1 kilometer in length? Justify your answer.

23 **CARPENTRY** Jacinta needs a 2.5-meter pole for a birdfeeder that she is building. How many centimeters will she need to cut off of a 3-meter pole in order to use it for the birdfeeder?

Bridge	Length (m)
Mackinac, MI	1,158
George Washington, NY	1,067
Tacoma Narrows II, WA	853
Oakland Bay, CA	704
Pennybacker, TX	345
Sunshine Skyway, FL	8,712
Golden Gate, CA	2,780

Real-World Link

The Mackinac Bridge opened on November 1, 1957. It is the longest two-tower suspension bridge between bases in the Western Hemisphere.

24. **BAKING** One recipe for apple pie calls for 0.94 kilogram of apples. Another recipe calls for 950 grams of apples. Which pie requires more apples?

25. FIND THE ERROR Theresa is converting 3.25 kilograms to grams. Find her mistake and correct it.

3.25 kg = 0.00325 g

26. CHALLENGE The metric prefix *giga*– refers to something one billion times larger than the base unit.

   a. How many meters are in one gigameter?

   b. How many millimeters are in one gigameter?

27. Write MATH Explain why it makes sense to multiply by a power of 10 that is greater than 1 when changing from a larger unit to a smaller unit.

NGSSS Practice   MA.7.G.4.4

28. The table shows the mass of four wireless telephones. Find the approximate total mass of the telephones in kilograms.

Telephone Owner	Mass (g)
Claudio	100.4
Al	70.8
Jane	95.6
Corey	120.4

  A. 0.39 kilogram   **C.** 39.0 kilograms

  B. 3.9 kilograms   **D.** 390.0 kilograms

29. Which relationship between the given units of measure is correct?

  F. One gram is $\frac{1}{100}$ of a centigram.

  G. One meter is $\frac{1}{100}$ of a centimeter.

  H. One gram is $\frac{1}{1,000}$ of a kilogram.

  I. One milliliter is $\frac{1}{100}$ of a liter.

30. MEASUREMENT A certain car weighs 3,200 pounds. What is the weight of the car in tons? (Lesson 9-1B)

31. Find the volume of the figure. Round to the nearest tenth. (Lesson 8-3C)

32. Solve the proportion $\frac{3}{5} = \frac{2,016}{x}$. (Lesson 4-1D)

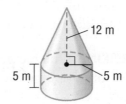

Main Idea
Convert units of measure between the customary and metric systems.

NGSSS

 **MA.7.G.4.4** Compare, contrast, and **convert units of measure between different measurement systems (US customary or metric (SI)), dimensions,** and derived units **to solve problems.** *Also addresses MA.7.A.3.2.*

Get Connected
glencoe.com

Convert Between Systems

RACES Races are often measured in kilometers. A 5K race is 5 kilometers long.

1. How many meters long is the race?

2. One mile is approximately 1.6 kilometers. About how many miles is the race?

To convert measures between customary units and metric units, use the relationships below.

Key Concept — Customary and Metric Relationships

Type of Measure	Customary	→	Metric
Length	1 inch (in.)	≈	2.54 centimeters (cm)
	1 foot (ft)	≈	0.30 meter (m)
	1 yard (yd)	≈	0.91 meter (m)
	1 mile (mi)	≈	1.61 kilometers (km)
Weight/Mass	1 pound (lb)	≈	453.6 grams (g)
	1 pound (lb)	≈	0.4536 kilogram (kg)
	1 ton (T)	≈	907.2 kilograms (kg)
Capacity	1 cup (c)	≈	236.59 milliliters (mL)
	1 pint (pt)	≈	473.18 milliliters (mL)
	1 quart (qt)	≈	946.35 milliliters (mL)
	1 gallon (gal)	≈	3.79 liters (L)

EXAMPLES — Convert Between Measurement Systems

1 **Convert 17.22 inches to centimeters. Round to the nearest hundredth if necessary.**

Since 2.54 centimeters ≈ 1 inch, multiply by $\frac{2.54 \text{ cm}}{1 \text{ in.}}$.

$17.22 \approx 17.22 \text{ in.} \cdot \frac{2.54 \text{ cm}}{1 \text{ in.}}$ Multiply by $\frac{2.54 \text{ cm}}{1 \text{ in.}}$. Divide out common units.

$\approx 43.7388 \text{ cm}$ Simplify.

So, 17.22 inches is approximately 43.74 centimeters.

2 Convert 828.5 milliliters to cups. Round to the nearest hundredth if necessary.

Since 1 cup ≈ 236.59 milliliters, multiply by $\frac{1\text{ c}}{236.59\text{ mL}}$.

$828.5 \text{ mL} \approx 828.5 \cancel{\text{mL}} \cdot \dfrac{1\text{ c}}{236.59 \cancel{\text{mL}}}$ Multiply by $\frac{1\text{ c}}{236.59\text{ mL}}$ and divide out common units.

$\approx \dfrac{828.5\text{ c}}{236.59}$ or 3.5 c   Simplify.

So, 828.5 milliliters is approximately 3.5 cups.

 CHECK Your Progress

Complete. Round to the nearest hundredth if necessary.

a. 7.44 c ≈ ■ mL   **b.** 22.09 lb ≈ ■ kg   **c.** 35.85 L ≈ ■ gal

Real-World Link · · · ·
The National Aquatics Center, also called the Water Cube, built for the 2008 Olympics in Beijing consists of more than 100,000 square meters (or 1.08 million square feet) of plastic foils and is the largest, most complicated, plastic-covered structure in the world.

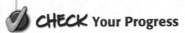 **Real-World EXAMPLE**   **Convert Between Systems**

3 **SWIMMING** An Olympic-size swimming pool is 50 meters long. About how many feet is the length of an Olympic-size swimming pool?

Since 1 foot ≈ 0.30 meter, use the ratio $\frac{1\text{ ft}}{0.30\text{ m}}$.

$50 \text{ m} \approx 50 \text{ m} \cdot \dfrac{1\text{ ft}}{0.30\text{ m}}$ Multiply by $\frac{1\text{ ft}}{0.30\text{ m}}$.

$\approx 50 \cancel{\text{m}} \cdot \dfrac{1\text{ ft}}{0.30 \cancel{\text{m}}}$ Divide out common units, leaving the desired unit, feet.

$\approx \dfrac{50\text{ ft}}{0.30}$ or 166.67 ft   Divide.

An Olympic-size swimming pool is about 166.67 feet.

CHECK Your Progress

d. **POOLS** An NCAA regulation-size swimming pool is 25 yards long. About how many meters is the length of an NCAA regulation-size pool?

CHECK Your Understanding

Examples 1 and 2
(pp. 509–510)

Complete. Round to the nearest hundredth if necessary.

1. 3.7 yd ≈ ■ m   **2.** 11.07 pt ≈ ■ mL   **3** 58.14 kg ≈ ■ lb

4. 3.75 c ≈ ■ mL   **5.** 4.725 m ≈ ■ ft   **6.** 680.4 g ≈ ■ lb

Example 3
(p. 510)

7. **SPORTS** About how many feet does a team of athletes run in a 1,600-meter relay race?

8. **FOOD** Raheem bought 3 pounds of bananas. About how many kilograms did he buy?

Practice and Problem Solving

 = **Step-by-Step Solutions** begin on page R26.
Extra Practice is on page EP26.

Examples 1 and 2
(pp. 509–510)

Complete. Round to the nearest hundredth if necessary.

9. 5 in. ≈ ■ cm   **10.** 15 cm ≈ ■ in.   **11.** 2 L ≈ ■ qt   **12.** 650 lb ≈ ■ kg

13. 4 qt ≈ ■ L   **14.** 10 mL ≈ ■ c   **15.** 63.5 T ≈ ■ kg   **16.** 50 mL ≈ ■ fl oz

17. 54 cm ≈ ■ in.   **18.** 17 mi ≈ ■ km   **19.** 32 gal ≈ ■ L   **20.** 350 lb ≈ ■ kg

21. 19 kg ≈ ■ lb   **22.** 3 T ≈ ■ kg   **23.** 6 in. ≈ ■ cm   **24.** 12 in. ≈ ■ m

Example 3
(p. 510)

25. COMPUTERS A notebook computer has a mass of 2.25 kilograms. About how many pounds does the notebook weigh?

26. TREES A Cabbage Palmetto, the state tree of Florida, has a height of 80 feet. About how many meters is the height of the tree?

27. BUILDINGS As of 2008, the tallest building in the United States was the Willis Tower at 1,451 feet. About how many meters is the height?

28. WATER Which is greater, a bottle containing 64 fluid ounces of water or a bottle containing 2 liters of water?

29. FOOD Which is greater, a 1.5-pound box of raisins or a 650-gram box of raisins?

30. BAKING A bakery uses 900 grams of peaches in a cobbler. How many pounds of peaches is this?

Determine which is greater.

31. 3 gal, 10 L   **32.** 14 oz, 0.4 kg   **33.** 4 mi, 6.2 km

34. Velocity is a rate usually expressed in feet/second or meters/second. How can the units give you a clue as to how you would calculate velocity using the distance a car traveled and the time recorded?

35. GRAPHIC NOVEL Refer to the graphic novel frame below. Convert all of the distances from meters to feet. Round to the nearest hundredth if necessary.

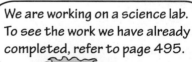

We are working on a science lab. To see the work we have already completed, refer to page 495.

How do I change meters to feet?

36. **NUMBER SENSE** One gram of water has a volume of 1 milliliter. What is the volume of the water if it has a mass of 1 kilogram?

37. **CHALLENGE** The distance from Earth to the Sun is approximately 93 million miles. About how many gigameters is this? Round to the nearest hundredth.

REASONING Order each set of measures from greatest to least.

38. 1.2 cm, 0.6 in., 0.031 m, 0.1 ft

39. 2 lb, 891 g, 1 kg, 0.02 T

40. $1\frac{1}{4}$ c, 0.4 L, 950 mL, 0.7 gal

41. **Write MATH** Explain how to order lengths of objects from shortest to longest if lengths are given in both customary and metric units.

NGSSS Practice   MA.6.A.1.1, MA.7.G.4.4

42. Which of the following measurements is approximately equal to the length of the fork?

6 in.

   A. 2.4 cm   **C.** 24 cm

   B. 15.2 cm   **D.** 152 cm

43. Which of the following is the most appropriate unit to measure the height of a door?

   F. centimeters

   G. inches

   H. meters

   I. miles

Spiral Review

44. **BUILDINGS** A skyscraper is 0.484 kilometer tall. What is the height of the skyscraper in meters? (Lesson 9-1C)

Convert. Round to the nearest tenth if necessary. (Lesson 9-1B)

45. 17 ft = ■ yd

46. 82 in. = ■ ft

47. 3 mi = ■ ft

48. **TEMPERATURE** The table shows record high temperatures in degrees Fahrenheit for Kentucky in July. Construct a stem-and-leaf plot of the data. Determine the range and the mode for the data. (Lesson 7-1E)

July Temperatures				
99	98	96	98	98
97	100	103	103	103
100	95	100	103	105

Main Idea

Convert units of measure between derived units to solve problems.

NGSSS

MA.7.G.4.4 Compare, contrast, and convert units of measure between different measurement systems (US customary or metric (SI)), dimensions, and derived units to solve problems. *Also addresses MA.7.A.1.6.*

New Vocabulary

derived unit

Get Connected
glencoe.com

Convert Rates

TRAINS Some of the fastest passenger trains are located in Japan and France. The table shows various trains and their speeds.

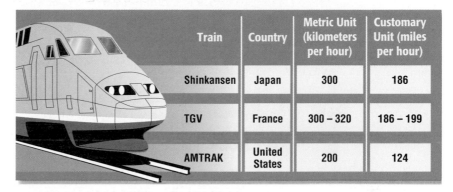

Train	Country	Metric Unit (kilometers per hour)	Customary Unit (miles per hour)
Shinkansen	Japan	300	186
TGV	France	300 – 320	186 – 199
AMTRAK	United States	200	124

1. How many feet are in one mile?

2. How many seconds are in one hour?

You can convert one rate to an equivalent rate by multiplying by a unit ratio or its reciprocal. A **derived unit** is a unit that is derived from a measurement system base unit such as length, mass, or time. Examples include square inches and meters per second.

Real-World EXAMPLE   Convert Rates

 FISH A swordfish can swim at a rate of 60 miles per hour. How many feet per hour is this?

You can use 1 mile = 5,280 feet to convert the rates.

$$\frac{60 \text{ mi}}{1 \text{ h}} = \frac{60 \text{ mi}}{1 \text{ h}} \cdot \frac{5{,}280 \text{ ft}}{1 \text{ mi}} \qquad \text{Multiply by } \frac{5{,}280 \text{ ft}}{1 \text{ mi}}.$$

$$= \frac{60 \text{ mi}}{1 \text{ h}} \cdot \frac{5{,}280 \text{ ft}}{1 \text{ mi}} \qquad \text{Divide out common units.}$$

$$= \frac{60 \cdot 5{,}280 \text{ ft}}{1 \cdot 1 \text{ h}} \qquad \text{Simplify.}$$

$$= \frac{316{,}800 \text{ ft}}{1 \text{ h}} \qquad \text{Simplify.}$$

A swordfish can swim at a rate of 316,800 feet per hour.

 CHECK Your Progress

a. BIRDS A gull can fly at a speed of 22 miles per hour. About how many kilometers per hour can the gull fly?

Real-World EXAMPLE **Convert Rates**

2 WALKING Marvin walks at a speed of 7 feet per second. How many feet per hour is this?

You can use 60 seconds = 1 minute and 60 minutes = 1 hour to convert the rates.

$\dfrac{7 \text{ ft}}{1 \text{ s}} = \dfrac{7 \text{ ft}}{1 \text{ s}} \cdot \dfrac{60 \text{ s}}{1 \text{ min}} \cdot \dfrac{60 \text{ min}}{1 \text{ h}}$　　Multiply by $\frac{60 \text{ s}}{1 \text{ min}}$ and $\frac{60 \text{ min}}{1 \text{ h}}$.

$\quad = \dfrac{7 \text{ ft}}{1 \text{ s}} \cdot \dfrac{60 \text{ s}}{1 \text{ min}} \cdot \dfrac{60 \text{ min}}{1 \text{ h}}$　　Divide out common units.

$\quad = \dfrac{7 \cdot 60 \cdot 60 \text{ ft}}{1 \cdot 1 \cdot 1 \text{ h}}$　　Simplify.

$\quad = \dfrac{25,200 \text{ ft}}{1 \text{ h}}$　　Simplify.

Marvin walks 25,200 feet in 1 hour.

 CHECK Your Progress

b. TRAINS An AMTRAK train travels at 125 miles per hour. Convert the speed to miles per minute.

Study Tip

Unit Rates Make sure the units cancel so that the desired units remain.

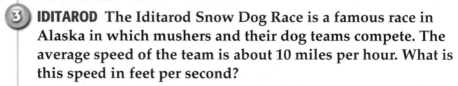 **Real-World EXAMPLE** **Convert Derived Units**

3 IDITAROD The Iditarod Snow Dog Race is a famous race in Alaska in which mushers and their dog teams compete. The average speed of the team is about 10 miles per hour. What is this speed in feet per second?

We can use 1 mile = 5,280 feet, 1 hour = 60 minutes, and 1 minute = 60 seconds to convert the rates.

$\dfrac{10 \text{ mi}}{1 \text{ h}} = \dfrac{10 \text{ mi}}{1 \text{ h}} \cdot \dfrac{5,280 \text{ ft}}{1 \text{ mi}} \cdot \dfrac{1 \text{ h}}{60 \text{ min}} \cdot \dfrac{1 \text{ min}}{60 \text{ s}}$　　Multiply by distance and time unit ratios.

$\quad = \dfrac{10 \text{ mi}}{1 \text{ h}} \cdot \dfrac{5,280 \text{ ft}}{1 \text{ mi}} \cdot \dfrac{1 \text{ h}}{60 \text{ min}} \cdot \dfrac{1 \text{ min}}{60 \text{ s}}$　　Divide out common units.

$\quad = \dfrac{10 \cdot 5,280 \cdot 1 \cdot 1 \text{ ft}}{1 \cdot 1 \cdot 60 \cdot 60 \text{ s}}$　　Simplify.

$\quad = \dfrac{52,800 \text{ ft}}{3,600 \text{ s}}$　　Simplify.

$\quad = \dfrac{14.7 \text{ ft}}{1 \text{ s}}$　　Simplify.

The Iditarod mushing teams travel at an average speed of 14.7 feet per second.

 CHECK Your Progress

c. RUNNING Charlie runs at a speed of 3 meters per second. About how many miles per hour does Charlie run?

Example 1
(p. 513)

1 GO-KARTS A go-kart's top speed is 607,200 feet per hour. How many miles per hour is this?

Example 2
(p. 514)

2. SPORTS A skydiver is falling at about 176 feet per second. About how many feet per minute is this?

Example 3
(p. 514)

3. CYCLING Lorenzo rides his bike at a rate of 2.2 meters per second. About how many miles per hour can Lorenzo ride his bike?

Practice and Problem Solving

= **Step-by-Step Solutions** begin on page R26.
Extra Practice is on page EP26.

Example 1
(p. 513)

4. WATER Water weighs about 8.34 pounds per gallon. About how many ounces per gallon is this?

5. BIRDS A peregrine falcon can fly at over 322 kilometers per hour. How many meters per hour is this?

Example 2
(p. 514)

6. RUNNING The fastest a human has ever run is about 27 miles per hour. How many miles per minute is this?

Example 3
(p. 514)

7. PLUMBING A pipe is leaking at 1.5 cups per day. About how many liters per week is this?

Convert each rate. Round to the nearest tenth if necessary.

8. 20 mi/h = ■ ft/min

9. 16 cm/min = ■ m/h

10. 45 mi/h = ■ ft/s

11. 26 cm/s = ■ m/min

12. 2.5 qt/min = ■ L/h

13. 13 lb/gal = ■ kg/L

14. 7 m/min = ■ yd/h

15. 4.7 g/cm = ■ oz/in.

16. INTERNET The speed at which a certain computer can access the Internet is 2 megabytes per second. How fast is this in megabytes per hour?

17 INSECTS The table shows the speed and number of wing beats per second for various flying insects.

a. What is the speed of a housefly in feet per second?

b. How many times does a dragonfly's wing beat per minute?

c. How many kilometers can a bumblebee travel in one minute?

d. How many times can a honeybee beat its wings in one hour?

	Flying Insects	
Insect	Speed (miles per hour)	Wing Beats per Second
Housefly	4.4	190
Honeybee	5.7	250
Dragonfly	15.6	38
Hornet	12.8	100
Bumblebee	6.4	130

18. **OPEN ENDED** Give an example of a unit rate used in a real-world situation.

19. **FIND THE ERROR** Divya is converting miles per hour to kilometers per minute. Find her mistake and correct it.

$$\frac{65 \text{ mi}}{1 \text{ h}} = \frac{65 \text{ mi}}{1 \text{ h}} \cdot \frac{1.61 \text{ km}}{1 \text{ mi}} \cdot \frac{60 \text{ min}}{1 \text{ h}}$$

$$= \frac{65 \cdot 1.61 \cdot 60}{1}$$

$$= 6,279 \text{ kilometers per minute}$$

20. **Write MATH** Compare and contrast pounds per gallon to kilograms per liter.

---

21. Thirty-five miles per hour is the same rate as which of the following?

    A. 150 feet per minute

    B. 1,500 feet per minute

    C. 2,200 feet per minute

    D. 3,080 feet per minute

22. **THINK SOLVE EXPLAIN** **SHORT RESPONSE** An oil tanker empties at 3.5 gallons per minute. Convert this rate to cups per second. Round to the nearest tenth. Show the steps you used.

Spiral Review

23. **PAPER** Standard sized notebook paper is $8\frac{1}{2}$ inches by 11 inches. What are the dimensions in centimeters? (Lesson 9-1D)

Convert. Round to the nearest hundredth if necessary. (Lessons 9-1B and 9-1C)

24. 34 yd = ■ ft

25. $1\frac{1}{2}$ gal = ■ qt

26. 4.67 m = ■ cm

27. 901 g = ■ kg

Main Idea

Convert units of measure between dimensions including area and volume.

NGSSS

 MA.8.G.5.1 Compare, contrast, and convert units of measure between different measurement systems (US customary or metric (SI)) and **dimensions including** temperature, **area, volume,** and derived units **to solve problems.**

Get Connected
glencoe.com

Convert Units of Area and Volume

CARPETING Jonathan is carpeting his bedroom which is 15 feet long and 12 feet wide. While shopping, he notices carpet is sold in square yards.

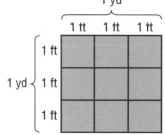

1. How many feet are in one yard?
2. How many yards long is the room?
3. How many yards wide is the room?
4. What is the area of the room in square yards?

You can use the formula for the area of a square, $A = s^2$, to find the number of square feet in one square yard.

EXAMPLES   Convert Area Measurements

1   **Convert one square yard to square feet.**

A square yard is a square with a side length of one yard. You know that one yard is equal to three feet. So, one square yard is a square with side length three feet.

$A = s^2$ Write the formula.

$A = 3^2$ Replace s with 3.

$A = 9$ Simplify.

So, one square yard is equal to 9 square feet.

2   **Convert one square meter to square centimeters.**

A square meter is a square with a side length of one meter. You know that one meter is equal to 100 centimeters. So, one square meter is a square with side length 100 centimeters.

$A = s^2$ Write the formula.

$A = 100^2$ Replace s with 100.

$A = 10,000$ Simplify.

So, one square meter is equal to 10,000 square centimeters.

CHECK Your Progress

Complete.

a. $1 \text{ ft}^2 = \blacksquare \text{ in}^2$

b. $1 \text{ cm}^2 = \blacksquare \text{ mm}^2$

You can use the formula for the volume of a prism, $V = bwh$, to convert cubic units.

EXAMPLE **Convert Volume Measurements**

3 Convert one cubic foot to cubic inches.

A cubic foot is a cube with a side length of one foot or 12 inches.

$V = bwh$	Write the formula.
$V = 12 \cdot 12 \cdot 12$	Replace b, w, and h with 12.
$V = 1{,}728$	Simplify.

So, one cubic foot is equal to 1,728 cubic inches.

1 ft = 12 in.

1 ft = 12 in.

1 ft = 12 in.

CHECK Your Progress

Complete.

c. $1 \text{ yd}^3 = \blacksquare \text{ ft}^3$

d. $1 \text{ cm}^3 = \blacksquare \text{ mm}^3$

The table gives several common measurement conversions for square units and cubic units.

Key Concept	**Measurement Conversions**	
	Customary Units	**Metric Units**
Area	$1 \text{ ft}^2 = 144 \text{ in}^2$	$1 \text{ m}^2 = 10{,}000 \text{ cm}^2$
	$1 \text{ yd}^2 = 9 \text{ ft}^2$	$1 \text{ cm}^2 = 100 \text{ mm}^2$
Volume	$1 \text{ ft}^3 = 1{,}728 \text{ in}^3$	$1 \text{ m}^3 = 1{,}000{,}000 \text{ cm}^3$
	$1 \text{ yd}^3 = 27 \text{ ft}^3$	$1 \text{ cm}^3 = 1{,}000 \text{ mm}^3$

Each relationship in the Key Concept box can be written as a unit ratio. To convert square or cubic units, use the unit ratio or its reciprocal.

Real-World EXAMPLE **Convert Measurements**

4 **CONSTRUCTION** A roof is 25 feet by 35 feet. How many square yards is the roof? Round to the nearest tenth.

The area of the roof is 25 feet × 35 feet or 875 square feet. Use the reciprocal of the unit ratio $\dfrac{9 \text{ ft}^2}{1 \text{ yd}^2}$ to find the number of square yards.

$875 \text{ ft}^2 = 875 \text{ ft}^2 \cdot \dfrac{1 \text{ yd}^2}{9 \text{ ft}^2}$ Multiply by $\dfrac{1 \text{ yd}^2}{9 \text{ ft}^2}$.

$\phantom{875 \text{ ft}^2} = 875 \, \cancel{\text{ft}^2} \cdot \dfrac{1 \text{ yd}^2}{9 \, \cancel{\text{ft}^2}}$ Divide out common units, leaving the desired unit, yards.

$\phantom{875 \text{ ft}^2} = \dfrac{875 \text{ yd}^2}{9}$ or 97.2 yd^2 Divide.

The roof is 97.2 square yards.

 CHECK Your Progress

   e. CEREAL A cereal box holds 320 cubic inches of cereal. How many cubic feet is this? Round to the nearest tenth.

The metric system also relates length, mass, and capacity.

Key Concept **Length, Mass, and Capacity**

Words	Symbols
1 milliliter has the same volume as 1 cubic centimeter.	1 mL = 1 cc
1 milliliter of water is approximately 1 gram.	1 mL ≈ 1 g

EXAMPLE **Convert Volume to Capacity**

5 Convert one cubic meter to milliliters.

A cubic meter is a cube with a side length of one meter or 100 centimeters. Use 1 cc = 1 mL to convert the rates.

$V = b \cdot w \cdot h$ Write the formula.

$V = 100 \cdot 100 \cdot 100$ Replace b, w, and h with 100.

$V = 1{,}000{,}000$ Simplify.

So, one cubic meter is equal to 1,000,000 milliliters.

 CHECK Your Progress

Complete.

   f. $17{,}000 \text{ mm}^3 = \blacksquare \text{ mL}$ **g.** $150 \text{ cc} = \blacksquare \text{ L}$

Examples 1 and 2
(p. 517)

Complete.

1. $3 \text{ ft}^2 = \blacksquare \text{ in}^2$

2. $4 \text{ yd}^2 = \blacksquare \text{ ft}^2$

3. $720 \text{ in}^2 = \blacksquare \text{ ft}^2$

4. $3.2 \text{ m}^2 = \blacksquare \text{ cm}^2$

5. $900 \text{ mm}^2 = \blacksquare \text{ cm}^2$

6. $8 \text{ cm}^2 = \blacksquare \text{ mm}^2$

Examples 3 and 5
(pp. 518–519)

Complete.

7. $0.2 \text{ ft}^3 = \blacksquare \text{ in}^3$

8. $4,320 \text{ in}^3 = \blacksquare \text{ ft}^3$

9. $1.5 \text{ yd}^3 = \blacksquare \text{ ft}^3$

10. $5,600 \text{ mm}^3 = \blacksquare \text{ mL}$

11. $4.1 \text{ m}^3 = \blacksquare \text{ cm}^3$

12. $2 \text{ cm}^3 = \blacksquare \text{ mL}$

Example 4
(p. 519)

13. FENCING A playground is surrounded by chain-link fencing. The dimensions of the playground are 52 feet by 37 feet. How many square yards does the fencing surround? Round to the nearest tenth if necessary.

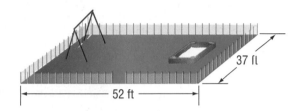

37 ft

52 ft

14. SCUBA DIVING Maria is using a cylindrical oxygen tank while scuba diving. It holds 80 cubic inches of air. How many cubic feet of air is she using? Round to the nearest hundredth if necessary.

Practice and Problem Solving

 = **Step-by-Step Solutions** begin on page R26.
Extra Practice is on page EP26.

Examples 1 and 2
(p. 517)

Complete. Round to the nearest hundredth if necessary.

15. $11.5 \text{ ft}^2 = \blacksquare \text{ in}^2$

16. $1,396.8 \text{ in}^2 = \blacksquare \text{ ft}^2$

17 $216 \text{ ft}^2 = \blacksquare \text{ yd}^2$

18. $14 \text{ yd}^2 = \blacksquare \text{ ft}^2$

19. $7.5 \text{ m}^2 = \blacksquare \text{ cm}^2$

20. $980 \text{ cm}^2 = \blacksquare \text{ m}^2$

21. $5.4 \text{ cm}^2 = \blacksquare \text{ mm}^2$

22. $597 \text{ mm}^2 = \blacksquare \text{ cm}^2$

23. $1 \text{ mi}^2 = \blacksquare \text{ ft}^2$

Examples 3 and 5
(pp. 518–519)

Complete. Round to the nearest hundredth if necessary.

24. $3 \text{ yd}^3 = \blacksquare \text{ ft}^3$

25. $11,232 \text{ in}^3 = \blacksquare \text{ ft}^3$

26. $6.06 \text{ ft}^3 = \blacksquare \text{ in}^3$

27. $280.8 \text{ ft}^3 = \blacksquare \text{ yd}^3$

28. $6,750 \text{ mm}^3 = \blacksquare \text{ cm}^3$

29. $0.45 \text{ m}^3 = \blacksquare \text{ mL}$

30. $7.7 \text{ cm}^3 = \blacksquare \text{ mm}^3$

31. $973,000 \text{ mL} = \blacksquare \text{ m}^3$

32. $1 \text{ yd}^3 = \blacksquare \text{ in}^3$

Example 4
(p. 519)

33. SPORTS Including the end zones, a football field is 360 feet long by 160 feet wide. What is the area of a football field in square yards?

34. GARDENING Tabitha has a small garden. If the garden has an area of 1,512 square inches, what is the area of the garden in square feet?

35. APPLIANCES A refrigerator has 25.3 cubic feet of space. How many cubic yards is this?

36. PARADE A cartoon character was depicted as a balloon in a parade. The balloon contained 2,443 cubic yards of air. How many cubic feet is this?

37. MEDICINE A specific medicine states that a dose is 2 teaspoons. One teaspoon is equal to 5 milliliters. How many cubic centimeters is the dose?

38. How many square yards are in one square mile?

39. One square yard is equal to how many square inches?

40. BOXES Two boxes are shown.

a. What is the difference of their volume, in cubic feet?

b. How many times greater is the volume of Box A than Box B?

c. What conclusion can you draw about the volume of a prism after its dimensions are halved?

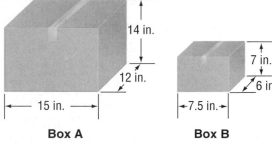

Box A   Box B

41 **SWIMMING POOL** The world's largest swimming pool is located in Chile and has a volume of 250,000 cubic meters. How many cubic yards is this? (*Hint*: 1 meter = 1.1 yards)

42. DOSAGES A liquid allergy medication comes in a bottle containing 4 fluid ounces. How many 5 cubic-centimeter doses are in the bottle? (*Hint*: 1 fl oz = 29.5 mL)

H.O.T. Problems

43. REASONING Alberto measured his bedroom for new carpet. The room is 169 square feet. When he got to the carpet store, all of the prices were given in square yards. Explain how he would convert his calculations to square yards to determine the cost.

44. CHALLENGE The Art Club is tiling a wall 8 feet tall by 10 feet long. Each tile is a 3-inch square and costs $0.59. What is the cost of tiling the wall?

45. FIND THE ERROR Seth is converting the volume of his shed from cubic feet to cubic inches. Find his mistake and correct it.

$$8{,}640 \text{ ft}^3 = 8{,}640 \text{ ft}^3 \times \frac{1 \text{ ft}^3}{1{,}728 \text{ in}^3}$$
$$= \frac{8{,}640 \text{ ft}^3}{1{,}728 \text{ in}^3}$$
$$= 5 \text{ in}^3$$

46. **Write MATH** Compare and contrast one mile with one square mile.

47. Which of the following measurements is NOT equivalent to the other three?

   A. $400{,}000{,}000$ cm^2

   B. $4{,}000$ m^2

   C. 0.04 km^2

   D. $40{,}000{,}000{,}000$ mm^2

48.  **GRIDDED RESPONSE** Two students were asked to design a dog run with an area of 36 feet. The first student made a 9-foot-long by 4-foot-long run. The second student made a square run that was 6 feet on each side. How many more feet of fence will the first student need than the second?

49. **THINK SOLVE EXPLAIN** **EXTENDED RESPONSE** A freight container has the dimensions shown below.

Part A What is the volume of the container in cubic feet?

Part B What is the volume of the container in cubic inches?

Part C What is the volume of the container in cubic meters? Round to the nearest tenth if necessary.

Spiral Review

Complete. Round to the nearest tenth if necessary. (Lesson 9-1E)

50. 24 mi/h $=$ ■ ft/s   **51.** 39 kg/min $=$ ■ g/s   **52.** 8.3 m/h $=$ ■ yd/min

53. WEIGHTLIFTING A barbell weighs 10 pounds. What is its mass in kilograms? Round to the nearest tenth if necessary. (Lesson 9-1D)

54. STORAGE The jar shown is used to store marinara sauce. What is the volume of marinara sauce that can be stored? Round to the nearest tenth if necessary. (Lesson 8-1C)

1.5 in.

4.5 in.

55. FISHERY The table shows the population of various fish kept at a fishery. (Lesson 6-3B)

Fishery Population		
Fish	Month 1	Month 2
Herring	2,300	2,250
Cod	1,250	1,450
Flounder	4,900	4,725

   a. What was the percent of increase of cod from Month 1 to Month 2?

   b. What was the percent of change of herring from Month 1 to Month 2?

   c. Which fish had the greatest percent of change?

Complete. (Lesson 9-1B)

1. 42 ft = ■ yd
2. 9 pt = ■ qt
3. 7,600 lb = ■ T
4. $7\frac{1}{2}$ gal = ■ qt

5. **NGSSS PRACTICE** Which situation is **best** represented by the graph? (Lesson 9-1B)

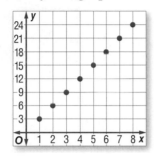

A. conversion of inches to yards

B. conversion of feet to inches

C. conversion of inches to miles

D. conversion of yards to feet

Complete. Round to the nearest hundredth if necessary. (Lessons 9-1B and 9-1C)

6. 12.5 mi = ■ yd
7. 4.75 gal = ■ pt
8. 76 cm = ■ m
9. 31.8 kg = ■ g

10. **MEASUREMENT** Bryant was painting lines on the football field and needed to make sure the lines were correctly spaced. He measured the distance to equal 16 feet. How many yards is this? (Lesson 9-1B)

11. **BUILDINGS** The table shows the heights of buildings in the United States. Which building is 0.366 kilometer in height? (Lesson 9-1C)

Building	Height (m)
Willis Tower	442
Empire State Building	381
Bank of America Tower	366
Aon Center	346

Complete. Round to the nearest hundredth if necessary. (Lesson 9-1D)

12. 11 in. = ■ mm
13. 2.4 T = ■ kg
14. 48 mL = ■ fl oz
15. 30 cm = ■ ft

16. A family is driving 65 miles per hour and enters Canada, where the speed limit is 100 kilometers per hour. How fast should the family drive in miles per hour? (Lesson 9-1E)

17. **NGSSS PRACTICE** Which of the following is the same as 2,088 feet per minute? (Lesson 9-1E)

F. 0.6264 meters per minute

G. 6.264 meters per minute

H. 389.2 meters per minute

I. 626.4 meters per minute

Complete. (Lesson 9-1F)

18. 6 ft^2 = ■ in^2
19. 476 in^2 = ■ ft^2
20. 6 yd^3 = ■ ft^3
21. 2 m^3 = ■ cm^3

22. **CONSTRUCTION** A construction worker ordered 5 cubic yards of concrete to pour a sidewalk. How many cubic feet of sidewalk can he pour? (Lesson 9-1F)

23. What is the volume of the cylinder in cubic centimeters? (Lesson 9-1F)

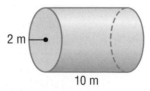

24. Which box has the greater volume? Justify your answer. (Lesson 9-1F)

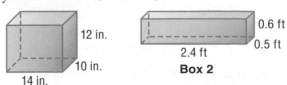

9-2 Similar Solids

Problem-Solving Investigation

Main Idea Solve problems by making a model.

P.S.I. TEAM +

AYITA: I am decorating the school's gymnasium for the spring dance with cubes that will hang from the ceiling. I have 100 square feet of cardboard.

YOUR MISSION: Make a model to find how much cardboard will be needed for each cube if the edge of one cube measures 12 inches.

Understand	You know that each cube is 12 inches long. She has 100 square feet of cardboard.
Plan	Make a cardboard model of a cube with sides 12 inches long. You will also need to determine where to put tabs so that all of the edges are glued together.
Solve	Start with a cube, then unfold it to show the pattern. Five of the edges do not need tabs because they are the fold lines.
	The remaining 7 edges need a tab. Use $\frac{1}{2}$-inch tabs.
	7×12 in. $\times \frac{1}{2}$ in. $\longrightarrow$ 42 in^2 7 tabs
	6×12 in. $\times 12$ in. $\longrightarrow$ + 864 in^2 6 faces
	906 in^2 total area
	Convert 906 square inches to square feet. Then divide the total material by the amount of material needed for one cube.
	$906 \text{ in}^2 \times \dfrac{1 \text{ ft}^2}{144 \text{ in}^2} = 6.3 \text{ ft}^2$ $100 \text{ ft}^2 \div 6.3 \text{ ft}^2 = 15.9$
	So, Ayita has enough cardboard to make 15 cubes.
Check	Make another cube to determine whether all the edges can be glued together using your model.

Analyze the Strategy

1. How can making a model be useful when solving a word problem?

 NGSSS

MA.7.G.2.2 Use formulas to find **surface areas** and volume **of three-dimensional composite shapes.**

- Make a model.
- Draw a diagram.
- Use logical reasoning.
- Choose an operation.

Use the *make a model* strategy to solve Exercises 2–4.

2. **CARS** Fiona counted the number of vehicles in the parking lot at a store. She counted a total of 12 cars and motorcycles. If there was a total of 40 wheels, how many cars and motorcycles were there?

3. **ART** Miguel is making a drawing of his family room for a school project. The room measures 18 feet by 21 feet. He uses a scale of 1 foot = $\frac{1}{2}$ inch. What are the dimensions of the family room on the drawing?

4. **MEASUREMENT** Francis has a photo that measures 10 inches by $8\frac{1}{2}$ inches. The frame he uses is $1\frac{1}{4}$ inches wide. What is the perimeter of the framed picture?

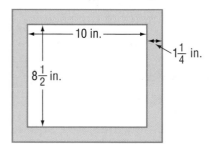

Use any strategy to solve Exercises 5–11.

5. **DONATIONS** Hickory Point Middle School collected money for a local shelter. The school newspaper reported that about $5,000 were collected. Is this estimate reasonable? Explain.

Grade	Dollars Collected
Sixth	1,872
Seventh	2,146
Eighth	1,629

6. **BIRDHOUSES** About how many square inches of the birdhouse will be painted if only the outside of the wood is painted?

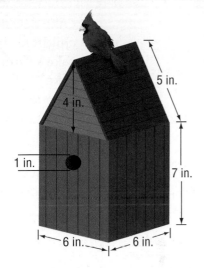

7. **MONEY** At the beginning of the week, Myra had $45.50. She spent $2.75 each of five days on lunch and bought a sweater for $14.95. Tucker repaid her $10 that he owed her. How much money did she have at the end of the week?

8. **BOXES** Juliet is placing 20 cereal boxes that measure 8 inches by 2 inches by 12 inches on a shelf that is 3 feet long and 11 inches deep. What is a possible arrangement for the boxes on the shelf?

9. **MEASUREMENT** A wall measures $15\frac{1}{4}$ feet by $8\frac{3}{4}$ feet and has a window that measures 2 feet by 4 feet. How many square feet of wallpaper are needed to cover the wall?

10. **BASEBALL** A regulation baseball diamond is a square with an area of 8,100 square feet. Suppose it is on a field that is 172 feet wide and 301 feet long. How much greater is the distance around the whole field than the distance around the diamond?

11. **Write MATH** Write a problem that could be solved by making a model. Then solve the problem.

Explore Changes in Scale

Main Idea

Determine how changes in dimensions affect area and volume.

NGSSS

MA.7.G.4.1 **Determine how changes in dimensions affect the** perimeter, area, **and volume of common geometric figures and apply these relationships to solve problems.**

Get Connected
glencoe.com

CAKE DECORATING A cake decorator is making a cake in the shape of a children's board game. The original game is 12 inches by 16 inches. The cake's dimensions will be half as long and half as wide. How does the cake's perimeter and area compare to the game's perimeter and area?

ACTIVITY

1 **What do you need to find?** the change in scale for perimeter and area of the cake

STEP 1 Draw a model of the cake on grid paper where each centimeter represents 1 inch.

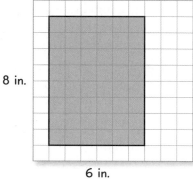

8 in.

6 in.

STEP 2 Find the perimeter of the cake using the grid paper.

8 in. + 8 in. + 6 in. + 6 in. = 28 inches

Compare this to the game's perimeter, 56 inches. Since $\frac{28}{56} = \frac{1}{2}$, the perimeter of the cake is $\frac{1}{2}$ of the perimeter of the board game.

STEP 3 Find the area of the cake.

8 × 6 = 48 square inches

Compare this to the game's area, 192 square inches. Since $\frac{48}{192} = \frac{1}{4}$, the area of the cake is $\frac{1}{4}$ the area of the board game.

Analyze the Results

1. Suppose another cake's dimensions are twice as long and wide as the board game. How do the perimeter and area of the cake compare to the perimeter and area of the game?

2. **MAKE A CONJECTURE** How does changing the dimensions of a figure affect its perimeter? area?

Changing dimensions of a three-dimensional figure also affects the surface area and volume.

ACTIVITY

2 **STEP 1** Find the volume and surface area of one centimeter cube. Then record the data in a table like the one below.

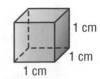

STEP 2 Create a cube with side lengths that are double that of the previous cube. Find the volume and surface area and record the data in the table.

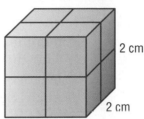

STEP 3 Triple the side lengths of the original centimeter cube. Find the volume and surface area and record the data in the table.

STEP 4 For each cube, write a ratio comparing the side length and the volume. Then write a ratio comparing the side length and the surface area. The first one is done for you.

Side Length (units)	Volume (units³)	Surface Area (units²)	Ratio of Side Length to Volume	Ratio of Side Length to Surface Area
1	$1^3 = 1$	$6 (1^2)$	1 : 1	1 : 6
2				
3				
4				
5				

Practice and Apply

3. **MAKE A CONJECTURE** How does doubling the dimensions of a three-dimensional figure affect the volume of the figure? surface area?

4. **PIZZA** A pizza restaurant advertised the special at the right. The dimensions given are the diameters of each pizza.

   a. What is the area of each pizza? Use $A = 3.14r^2$.

   b. What is the ratio of the area of the personal pizza and the medium pizza?

   c. How does the area of a circle change when the diameter is doubled? tripled?

PIZZA by Pat

5″ personal pizza $3.⁹⁹

10″ medium pizza $9.⁹⁹

15″ family size $14.⁹⁹

Main Idea

Solve problems involving similar solids.

NGSSS

MA.7.G.4.1 Determine how changes in dimensions affect the perimeter, area, and volume of common geometric figures and apply these relationships to solve problems.

New Vocabulary

similar solids

Get Connected
glencoe.com

Changes in Dimensions

MODELS Stephen is creating a model of the Washington Monument for history class. The model will be $\frac{1}{100}$ of the monument's actual size.

1. The pyramid that sits atop the monument's obelisk shape has a height of 55.5 feet. What is the height of the pyramid on the model Stephen is creating?

2. **MAKE A CONJECTURE** Write a sentence about the area of the triangular side of the model compared with the actual monument.

Cubes are **similar solids** because they have the same shape and their corresponding linear measures are proportional.

The cubes at the right are similar. The ratio of their corresponding edge lengths is $\frac{8}{4}$ or 2. The scale factor is 2. How are their surface areas related?

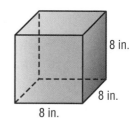

S.A. of Small Cube

$S.A. = 6(4)(4)$

There are 6 faces.

S.A. of Large Cube

$$S.A. = 6(\mathbf{2} \cdot 4)(\mathbf{2} \cdot 4)$$
$$= \mathbf{2} \cdot \mathbf{2}(6)(4 \cdot 4)$$
$$= \mathbf{2}^2(6)(4 \cdot 4)$$

To find the surface area of the large cube, multiply the surface area of the small cube by the *square* of the scale factor, 2^2 or 4. This relationship is true for any similar solids.

Key Concept　　Surface Area of Similar Solids

If Solid X is similar to Solid Y by a scale factor, then the surface area of X is equal to the surface area of Y times the *square* of the scale factor.

EXAMPLES **Surface Area of Similar Solids**

1 The surface area of a rectangular prism is 78 square centimeters. What is the surface area of a similar prism that is 3 times as large?

$S.A. = 78 \times 3^2$ Multiply by the square of the scale factor.

$S.A. = 78 \times 9$ Square 3.

$S.A. = 702 \text{ cm}^2$ Simplify.

2 **MODELS** Refer to page 528. The surface area of the exposed portion of the pyramid atop the Washington Monument is 4,012 square feet. What is the surface area in square inches, to the nearest tenth, of the pyramid on Stephen's model?

$S.A. = 4,012 \times \left(\dfrac{1}{100}\right)^2$ Multiply by the square of the scale factor.

$S.A. = 4,012 \times \dfrac{1}{10,000}$ Square $\dfrac{1}{100}$.

$S.A. = 0.4012 \text{ ft}^2$ Simplify.

$S.A. = 0.4012 \; \cancel{ft} \cdot \cancel{ft} \times \dfrac{12 \text{ in.}}{1 \; \cancel{ft}} \times \dfrac{12 \text{ in.}}{1 \; \cancel{ft}}$ Convert to inches.

$S.A. = 57.8 \text{ in}^2$ Simplify.

The surface area of Stephen's model is 57.8 square inches.

Real-World Link · · · ·
It takes about $4\frac{1}{2}$ pounds of fresh grapes to make one pound of raisins.

 CHECK Your Progress

· · · · · **a. RAISINS** The world's largest box of raisins is located in Kingsburg, California. Its surface area is 352 square feet. If a similar box is smaller than the Kingsburg box by a scale factor of $\dfrac{1}{48}$, what is its surface area?

The volumes of similar solids are also related. Refer to the cubes on page 528.

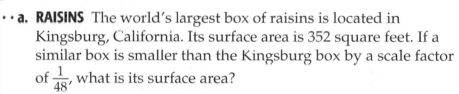

Volume of Small Cube	Volume of Large Cube
$V = 4 \cdot 4 \cdot 4$	$V = (2 \cdot 4)(2 \cdot 4)(2 \cdot 4)$
	$= 2 \cdot 2 \cdot 2(4 \cdot 4 \cdot 4)$
	$= 2^3(4 \cdot 4 \cdot 4)$

The volumes of similar solids are related by the *cube* of the scale factor.

Key Concept   **Volume of Similar Solids**

If Solid X is similar to Solid Y by a scale factor, then the volume of X is equal to the volume of Y times the *cube* of the scale factor.

3 A triangular prism has a volume of 432 cubic yards. If the prism is reduced to one third its original size, what is the volume of the new prism?

$V = 432 \times \left(\dfrac{1}{3}\right)^3$ Multiply by the cube of the scale factor.

$V = 432 \times \dfrac{1}{27}$ Cube $\dfrac{1}{3}$.

$V = 16 \text{ yd}^3$ Simplify.

The volume of the new prism is 16 cubic yards.

 CHECK Your Progress

b. A square pyramid has a volume of 512 cubic centimeters. What is the volume of a square pyramid with dimensions one fourth of the original?

Real-World EXAMPLE

4 **HOCKEY** The standard hockey puck measures as shown at the right. Find the surface area and volume of the giant puck at the left. Use 3.14 for π.

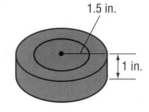

1.5 in.

1 in.

Find the volume and surface area of the standard puck first.

$V = \pi r^2 h$ $S.A. = 2(\pi r^2) + 2\pi rh$

$\approx (3.14)(1.5)^2(1)$ $\approx 2(3.14)(1.5)^2 + 2(3.14)(1.5)(1)$

$\approx 7.065 \text{ in}^3$ $\approx 14.13 + 9.42$

                             $\approx 23.55 \text{ in}^2$

Find the volume and surface area of the giant puck using the scale factor.

$V = V(40)^3$ $S.A. = S.A.(40)^2$

$= (7.065)(40)^3$ $= (23.55)(40)^2$

$= 452{,}160 \text{ in}^3$ $= 37{,}680 \text{ in}^2$

The giant hockey puck has a volume of 452,160 cubic inches and a surface area of 37,680 square inches.

 CHECK Your Progress

c. The dimensions of a rectangular solid are 10 inches by 7 inches by 6 inches. Find the surface area and volume of a solid that is larger by a scale factor of 25 and similar to the original solid.

 Real-World Link · · · ·

The hockey puck that appears to be crashing into the side of the wall at Nationwide Arena in Columbus, Ohio, is about 40 times the actual size of a standard puck.

Example 1
(p. 529)

1. The surface area of a rectangular prism is 35 square inches. What is the surface area of a similar solid that has been enlarged by a scale factor of 7?

Example 2
(p. 529)

2. MODELS The surface area of a ship's hull is about 11,000 square meters. What is the surface area, to the nearest tenth, of the hull of a model ship that is smaller by a scale factor of $\frac{1}{100}$?

Example 3
(p. 530)

3. The volume of a cylinder is about 425 cubic centimeters. What is the volume, to the nearest tenth, of a similar solid that is smaller by a scale factor of $\frac{1}{3}$?

Example 4
(p. 530)

4. ART STUDIO A sink with a sliding lid in Josh's art studio measures 16 inches by 15 inches by 6 inches. A second sink used just for paintbrushes has a similar shape and is smaller by a scale factor of $\frac{1}{2}$. Find the surface area and volume of the second sink.

Practice and Problem Solving

= **Step-by-Step Solutions** begin on page R27.
Extra Practice is on page EP27.

Example 1
(p. 529)

5. The surface area of a rectangular prism is 1,300 square inches. Find the surface area of a similar solid that is larger by a scale factor of 3.

6. The surface area of a triangular prism is 10.4 square meters. What is the surface area of a similar solid that is smaller by a scale factor of $\frac{1}{4}$?

Example 2
(p. 529)

7 FOOD A cereal box has a surface area of 280 square inches. What is the surface area of a similar box that is larger by a scale factor of 1.4?

8. DISPLAYS A glass display box has a surface area of 378 square inches. How many square inches of glass are used to create a glass display box with dimensions one-half the original?

Example 3
(p. 530)

9. A cone has a volume of 9,728 cubic millimeters. What is the volume of a similar cone one-eighth the size of the original?

10. A triangular prism has a volume of 350 cubic meters. If the dimensions are tripled, what is the volume of the new prism?

Example 4
(p. 530)

11. ARCHITECTURE The model of a new apartment building is shown. The architect plans for the building to be 144 times the size of the model. What will be the surface area and volume of the new building when it is completed?

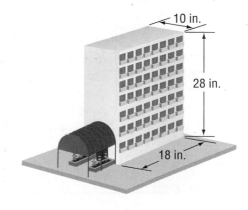

10 in.

28 in.

18 in.

12. The world's largest cube puzzle measures 6 feet on each side. The scale factor between a standard cube puzzle and the largest is $\frac{1}{24}$. Find the surface area and volume of the standard cube puzzle.

13 Two spheres are similar in shape. The scale factor between the smaller sphere and the larger sphere is $\frac{3}{4}$. If the volume of the smaller sphere is 126.9 cubic meters, what is the volume of the larger sphere?

🌐 **Real-World Link**
The world's largest automated cube puzzle solves itself every 30 seconds. The record time a standard cube puzzle was solved in 2008 was 7.08 seconds.

Determine whether each statement is *always*, *sometimes*, or *never* true.

14. Two prisms with equal bases are similar.

15. Similar solids have equal volumes.

16. Two cubes are similar.

17. A prism and pyramid are similar.

18. Find the missing measure for the pair of similar solids.

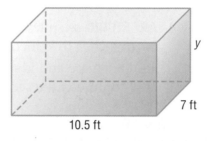
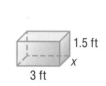

19. Two similar cylinders are shown.

   a. What is the ratio of their radii?

   b. What is the ratio of their surface areas and their volumes?

   c. Find the surface area of Cylinder B.

   d. Find the volume of Cylinder A.

Cylinder A

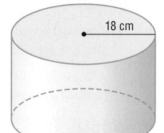

18 cm

S.A. = 5,425.92 cm²

Cylinder B

6 cm

V = 1,130.4 cm³

20. GRAPHIC NOVEL Refer to the graphic novel frame below. Use the distances and times you converted in Lesson 9-1D and the formula $r = \frac{d}{t}$ to calculate the different speeds and express them in miles per hour.

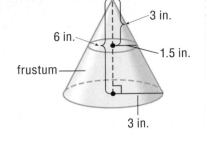

H.O.T. Problems

21. CHALLENGE A *frustum* is the solid left after a cone is cut by a plane parallel to its base and the top cone is removed.

3 in.

6 in.

1.5 in.

frustum

3 in.

a. Is the smaller cone that is removed similar to the original cone? Justify your response.

b. What is the volume of the smaller cone? the larger cone? Use 3.14 for π.

c. What is the ratio of the volume of the smaller cone to the volume of the larger cone?

d. What is the volume of the frustum?

22. Write MATH Explain what happens to the volume of a prism when its dimensions are tripled.

23. For the similar pyramids, find the ratio of the surface area of the larger pyramid to the smaller pyramid.

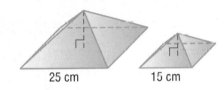

25 cm   15 cm

A. $\frac{5}{3}$ **C.** $\frac{25}{9}$

B. $\frac{25}{15}$ **D.** $\frac{10}{6}$

24. Two similar prisms have volumes of 4 cubic meters and 864 cubic meters, respectively. How many times larger is the second prism?

F. 6 times larger

G. 16 times larger

H. 96 times larger

I. 216 times larger

25. ART Julianna is making a clay figurine of a dog. The dog is 75 centimeters tall. If she uses a scale of 1 centimeter = 10 centimeters, how tall will the clay figurine be? (Lesson 9-2A)

26. SPORTS The table shows the dimensions of the fields used in various sports. (Lesson 9-1F)

a. What is the area of the field hockey field in square feet?

b. What is the difference between the area of the soccer field and the area of the lacrosse field in square feet?

c. If an acre is 43,560 square feet, about how many acres are all four fields combined?

Sport	Length (yards)	Width (yards)
Field hockey	60	100
Football	$53\frac{1}{3}$	120
Lacrosse	60	110
Soccer	70	115

Problem Solving in Culinary Arts

Food for Thought

Do you love cooking and enjoy trying new recipes? You might want to think about a career in the culinary arts. Research chefs use their culinary skills and their knowledge of food science to develop recipes, menus, and products for restaurant chains and food manufacturers. Research chefs are creative and have a passion for cooking and an understanding of food trends, but they must also have strong computer skills, be knowledgeable about new technologies in cooking and food science, and be able to use mathematics to develop their recipes.

Choose a Major

Are you interested in a career as a research chef? Take some of the following courses in high school.

- Algebra
- Commercial Foods and Culinary Arts
- Human Nutrition

Get Connected glencoe.com

NGSSS

MA.7.G.4.4 Compare, contrast, and **convert units of measure between different measurement systems (US customary or metric (SI)),** dimensions, and derived units **to solve problems.**

Raspberry Lemonade

1 (12 fluid ounce) can frozen raspberry
   lemonade concentrate
710 mL water
4 mL lime juice
354 mL lemon-lime flavored carbonated beverage
235 mL crushed ice
125 g fresh raspberries, garnish
225 g fresh mint, garnish

Banana Split Cake

1 (16-ounce) package vanilla wafers, crushed
1 cup margarine, melted
1 (20-ounce) can crushed pineapple, drained
6 bananas
1 (8-ounce) package cream cheese
2 cups confectioners' sugar
1 (12-ounce) container whipped topping
$\frac{1}{4}$ cup chopped walnuts
8 maraschino cherries

Real-World Math

Use the recipes to solve each problem.

1. How many pounds of crushed pineapple are needed for the cake?

2. How many quarts of sugar are needed for the cake?

3. How many liters of water are used to make the lemonade?

4. How many milligrams of fresh mint are used to make the lemonade?

5. About how many grams of whipped topping are used to make the cake?

6. About how many fluid ounces of carbonated beverage are required for lemonade? Round to the nearest fluid ounce.

CHAPTER 9

Study Guide and Review

Get Connected glencoe.com

- STUDY **TO GO**
- Vocabulary Review
- Multilingual eGlossary

FOLDABLES Study Organizer

Be sure the following Key Concepts are noted in your Foldable.

Convert measurements
Convert between systems
Convert rates
Convert area and volume
Similar solids

Key Concepts

Convert Customary Units (Lesson 9-1)
- To convert from larger units to smaller units, multiply by the appropriate unit ratio.
- To convert from smaller units to larger units, multiply by the reciprocal of the appropriate unit ratio.

Convert Metric Units (Lesson 9-1)
- When converting metric units, multiply by the appropriate power of 10.

Convert Between Systems (Lesson 9-1)
- When converting between customary and metric units, use the appropriate unit ratio or relationship.

Convert Rates (Lesson 9-1)
- A unit ratio is a simplified rate whose denominator is 1.

Convert Units of Area and Volume (Lesson 9-1)
- When converting units of area and volume, use the formula that correlates to the figure.

Similar Solids (Lesson 9-2)
- Similar solids have the same shape and their corresponding linear measures are proportional.

Key Vocabulary

derived unit (p. 513)

dimensional analysis (p. 501)

gram (p. 505)

kilogram (p. 505)

liter (p. 505)

meter (p. 505)

metric system (p. 505)

similar solids (p. 528)

unit ratio (p. 501)

Vocabulary Check

Choose the term from the list above that best matches each phrase.

1. the process of including units of measurement as factors when you compute

2. the base unit of capacity

3. a decimal system of measures

4. the base unit of length in the metric system

5. measures mass, which is the amount of matter in an object

6. these have the same shape and their corresponding linear measures are proportional

7. the base unit of mass

8. one in which the denominator is 1 unit

Multi-Part Lesson Review

9-1 Convert Measurements

Convert Customary Units (pp. 500–504)

MA.7.G.4.4

Complete.

9. 4 qt = ■ pt

10. 6 gal = ■ qt

11. 48 oz = ■ lb

12. 9 c = ■ pt

13. **RUNNING** Lenora runs 30,000 feet. How many miles does Lenora run?

14. **ESTIMATION** One bushel of apples weighs about 40 pounds. How many bushels of apples would weigh 1 ton?

EXAMPLE 1 Complete: 32 qt = ■ gal.

Since 1 gallon = 4 quarts, multiply by $\frac{1\text{ gal}}{4\text{ qt}}$.

$32\text{ qt} = 32\text{ qt} \cdot \frac{1\text{ gal}}{4\text{ qt}}$ Multiply by $\frac{1\text{ gal}}{4\text{ qt}}$.

$= \overset{8}{\cancel{32}}\text{ } \cancel{qt} \cdot \frac{1\text{ gal}}{\underset{1}{\cancel{4}\text{ }\cancel{qt}}}$ Divide out common factors and units.

$= 8\text{ gal}$ Multiply.

Convert Metric Units (pp. 505–508)

MA.7.G.4.4

Complete. Round to the nearest hundredth if necessary.

15. 18.25 m = ■ cm

16. 113.6 g = ■ kg

17. 24 L = ■ mL

18. 34 cm = ■ mm

19. **MASS** Kirk found the mass of his textbook to be 1.02 kilograms. What is the mass in grams?

EXAMPLE 2 Complete: 3.8 km = ■ m.

Use the relationship 1 km = 1,000 m.

1 km = 1,000 m

3.8 × 1 km = 3.8 × 1,000 m

3.8 km = 3,800 m

So, 3.8 kilometers is equal to 3,800 meters.

Convert Between Systems (pp. 509–512)

MA.7.G.4.4

Complete. Round to the nearest hundredth if necessary.

20. 18.25 ft ≈ ■ m

21. 113.6 lb ≈ ■ g

22. 24 L ≈ ■ gal

23. 46.8 cm ≈ ■ in.

24. **RUNNING** Justine ran a 10-kilometer race. About how many miles did she run?

25. **BIRDS** The world's largest bird is the ostrich, whose mass can be as much as 156.5 kilograms. What is the approximate weight in pounds?

EXAMPLE 3 Complete: 5.2 mi ≈ ■ km.

Use the relationship 1 mi ≈ 1.61 km.

1 mi ≈ 1.61 km

5.2 × 1 mi ≈ 5.2 × 1.61 km

5.2 mi ≈ 8.372 km

So, 5.2 miles is approximately 8.37 kilometers.

9-1 Convert Measurements (continued)

Convert Rates (pp. 513–516)

Convert each rate. Round to the nearest hundredth.

26. $8\frac{1}{4}$ ft/s = ■ yd/s

27. 105.6 L/h = ■ L/min

28. 52 mi/h ≈ ■ km/min

29. 8.4 lb/min = ■ oz/s

30. AIRPLANE An airplane is traveling at an average speed of 245 meters per second. How many kilometers per second is the plane traveling?

31. RIVER A river is flowing at a rate of 45 feet per minute. About how many meters per second is the water flowing?

EXAMPLE 4 Leo drank an average of 0.1 liter of water per hour. About how many gallons of water did he drink per hour?

Since 1 gallon = 3.79 liters, use the unit ratio $\frac{1 \text{ gal}}{3.79 \text{ L}}$.

$\frac{0.1 \text{ L}}{1 \text{ h}} \approx \frac{0.1 \cancel{L}}{1 \text{ h}} \times \frac{1 \text{ gal}}{3.79 \cancel{L}}$ Multiply by $\frac{1 \text{ gal}}{3.79 \text{ L}}$. Divide out common units.

$\approx \frac{0.03 \text{ gal}}{1 \text{ h}}$ Simplify.

So, Leo drank 0.03 gallon of water per hour.

Convert Units of Area and Volume (pp. 517–522)

Complete. Round to the nearest hundredth if necessary.

32. 0.15 ft^3 = ■ in^3

33. 0.3 m^2 = ■ cm^2

34. 1.64 yd^2 = ■ ft^2

35. 581 mm^3 = ■ cm^3

36. AQUARIUM An aquarium holds 3,456 cubic inches of water. How many cubic feet will the aquarium hold?

37. WRAPPING PAPER A gift needed 4.2 square yards of wrapping paper. How many square feet of wrapping paper were used?

EXAMPLE 5 Convert 16 square feet to square inches.

The area of the square is 4 feet × 4 feet or 16 square feet. Use the ratio $\frac{144 \text{ in}^2}{1 \text{ ft}^2}$ to find the number of square inches.

$16 \text{ ft}^2 = 16 \text{ ft}^2 \times \frac{144 \text{ in}^2}{1 \text{ ft}^2}$ Multiply by $\frac{144 \text{ in}^2}{1 \text{ ft}^2}$.

$= 16 \cancel{\text{ft}^2} \times \frac{144 \text{ in}^2}{1 \cancel{\text{ft}^2}}$ Divide out common units, leaving the desired unit, inches.

$= 2,304 \text{ in}^2$ Simplify.

The area of the square is 2,304 square inches.

PSI: Make a Model (pp. 524–525)

MA.7.G.2.2

Solve the problems by using the *make a model* strategy.

38. FRAMING A painting 15 inches by 25 inches is bordered by a mat that is 3 inches wide. The frame around the mat is 2 inches wide. Find the area of the picture with the frame and mat.

39. DVDs A video store arranges its bestselling DVDs in their front window. In how many different ways can five bestseller DVDs be arranged in a row?

EXAMPLE 6 The bottom layer of a display of soup cans has 6 cans in it. If each layer has one less can than the one below it and there are 4 layers in the display, how many cans are there in the display?

Based on the model, there are 18 cans.

Changes in Dimensions (pp. 528–533)

MA.7.G.4.1

40. The two pyramids are similar. The surface area of the larger pyramid is 108 m². Find the surface area of the smaller pyramid if it is $\frac{3}{4}$ the size of the larger pyramid.

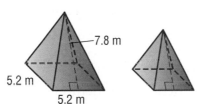

5.2 m

7.8 m

5.2 m

Pyramid 1   **Pyramid 2**

41. GLUE A cylindrical tube of glue has a volume of 22.0 cubic inches and a surface area of 50.3 square inches. What is the surface area and volume of a similar cylinder that is larger by a scale factor of 2?

42. MODEL A model car has a volume of 1,260 cubic centimeters. What is the volume of a similar rectangular prism one sixth the size of the original? Round to the nearest tenth.

EXAMPLE 7 The surface area of the box shown is 32 square centimeters. What is the surface area of a similar box that is larger by a scale factor of 4?

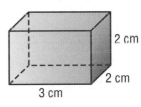

2 cm

2 cm

3 cm

$S.A. = 32 \times 4^2$ or 512

So, the surface area of the similar box that is larger by a scale factor of 4 is 512 square centimeters.

EXAMPLE 8 The volume of the box shown above is 12 cubic centimeters. What is the volume of a similar box that is larger by a scale factor of 4?

$V = 12 \times 4^3$ or 768

So, the volume of the similar box that is larger by a scale factor of 4 is 768 cubic centimeters.

Complete. Round to the nearest hundredth if necessary.

1. 3,600 lb = ■ T   **2.** 21 pt = ■ qt

3. 28 ft = ■ yd   **4.** 0.23 g = ■ mg

5. 0.04 L = ■ mL   **6.** 21 in. = ■ ft

7. **NGSSS PRACTICE** The table shows the volume of four containers. What is the total volume of the four containers in gallons?

Container	Volume (oz)
Cup	10
Pitcher	40
Bowl	35
Jug	50

A. 1.5 gal

B. 1.05 gal

C. 0.15 gal

D. 0.11 gal

Complete. Round to the nearest tenth if necessary.

8. 7.62 yd ≈ ■ m

9. 50.8 lb ≈ ■ kg

10. 3,600 mL ≈ ■ qt

11. 19.25 m ≈ ■ ft

12. **SCIENCE** The population of bacteria in 4 differently sized lab dishes are given. Which dish is closest to 1.4 square feet of the area?

Dish	Bacteria	Area (in²)
1	100	205
2	50	125
3	35	175
4	180	300

13. **ROLLER COASTER** A roller coaster reaches a speed of 112.7 kilometers per hour. About how fast is this in miles per hour?

14. **GARDEN** The garden below measures 30 feet by 45 feet. If the owner wants to apply fertilizer and it will cover 200 square yards, will he have enough? Explain your reasoning.

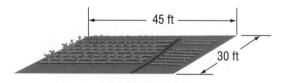

15. **PACKING** The surface area of a packing box is 56 square inches. What is the surface area of a similar box that is larger by a scale factor of 3?

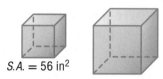

S.A. = 56 in²

16. **THINK SOLVE EXPLAIN** **EXTENDED RESPONSE** Compare the surface area and volume of a prism with dimensions of 2 inches by 2 inches by 2 inches with another prism that is larger by a scale factor of 2, 3, 4, and 5.

2 in.
2 in.
2 in.

Part A Find the surface area and volume of the new prisms.

Part B Compare the surface area to the volume.

Part C Graph the relationship of the side length to the volume and the side length to the surface area.

Part D Do you think that if the solid were another type of shape, like a pyramid, cylinder, or cone, you would get the same results? Why or why not?

Extended Response: Scoring Points

In order to receive all possible points for an extended-response question, an answer must be correct and all work must be shown. An example of a full-credit answer to one part of an extended-response question is shown below.

NGSSS PRACTICE EXAMPLE

Daniela has a corkboard with a 2-centimeter wide frame around it, as shown at the right. She wants to paint the frame in her school colors. How many square inches will Daniela need to paint? Use 1 meter ≈ 39.4 inches.

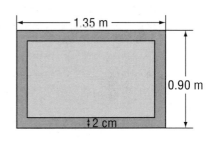

- **Full Credit: 4 points**

$$A = b \cdot h$$
$$A_1 = 1.35 \text{ m} \cdot 0.90 \text{ m} = 1.215 \text{ m}^2$$
$$A_2 = (1.35 \text{ m} - 0.02 \text{ m} - 0.02 \text{ m}) \cdot (0.90 \text{ m} - 0.02 \text{ m} - 0.02 \text{ m})$$
$$A_2 = 1.31 \cdot 0.86 \text{ m} - 1.1266 \text{ m}^2$$
$$A_1 - A_2 = 1.215 \text{ m}^2 - 1.1266 \text{ m}^2 - 0.0884 \text{ m}^2$$
$$1 \text{ m}^2 \approx 1552.36 \text{ in}^2 \rightarrow 0.0884 \text{ m}^2 \cdot \frac{1552.36 \text{ in}^2}{1 \text{ m}^2} \approx 137.2 \text{ in}^2$$

> All work is shown, answer is correct.

- **Partial Credit: 3 points**
  All work is shown, but an incorrect conversion factor is used, so answer is incorrect.

- **Partial Credit: 2 points**
  The steps shown are incorrect, answer is incorrect.

- **Partial Credit: 1 point**
  No work is shown, answer is incorrect.

Work on It

A company sells cylindrical tins of popcorn in two sizes. The large tin has a diameter of 20 centimeters and a height of 25 centimeters. The small tin has a diameter of 12 centimeters and a height of 18 centimeters. How many more cubic inches of popcorn does the larger tin hold than the smaller tin? Use 1 centimeter ≈ 0.39 inch.

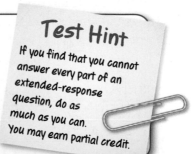

Test Hint

If you find that you cannot answer every part of an extended-response question, do as much as you can. You may earn partial credit.

Read each question. Then fill in the correct answer on the answer sheet provided by your teacher or on a sheet of paper.

1. Dee moves to a new house. Her old bedroom measured 5 meters by 3 meters. Her new bedroom is 2 meters longer and 1 meter wider. How much more area will she have in her new bedroom?

   A. 13 m²   C. 21 m²

   B. 15 m²   D. 30 m²

2. About how many National Basketball Association players scored at least 1,200 points in 2007?

NBA Points Scored

   F. 7   H. 24

   G. 19   I. 50

3. ≡≡≤ **GRIDDED RESPONSE** The diagram below shows two triangular deck areas along two different houses. The base of Deck B is 4 times the base of Deck A.

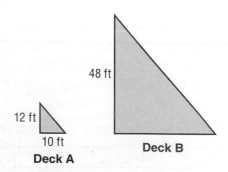

   What is the base, in feet, of Deck B?

4. Courtney ran at a rate of 6.5 miles per hour. At this rate, about how many kilometers can she run in 2 hours?

   A. 10.5 km   C. 21 km

   B. 13 km   D. 24.8 km

5. ≡≡≤ **GRIDDED RESPONSE** Mrs. Black is making 2 pasta salads for a picnic. The first pasta salad requires $4\frac{2}{3}$ cups of pasta and the second pasta salad requires $\frac{1}{3}$ cup more than the first. How many cups of pasta are needed for the second recipe?

6. Amelia carried a package that had a mass of 6.38 kilograms. About how many pounds does the package weigh?

   F. 14.1 lb

   G. 12.9 lb

   H. 9.5 lb

   I. 6.4 lb

7. The table lists interest rates for savings accounts.

Student Savings and Loan	
Time	Rate
6 months	2.9%
12 months	3.5%
18 months	3.65%
24 months	3.7%

   What is the simple interest earned on $1,500 for 18 months?

   A. $21.75

   B. $52.50

   C. $79.24

   D. $82.13

8. ≡≡≤ **GRIDDED RESPONSE** A building is 55 meters tall. About how tall is the building in feet? (1 meter ≈ 39 inches)

9. A shoe store had to increase prices. The table shows the regular price r and the new price n of several shoes. Which of the following formulas can be used to calculate the new price?

Shoe	Regular Price (r)	New Price (n)
A	$25.00	$27.80
B	$30.00	$32.80
C	$35.00	$37.80
D	$40.00	$42.80

F. $n = r - 2.80$ H. $n = r \times 0.1$

G. $n = r + 2.80$ I. $n = r \div 0.1$

10. **THINK SOLVE EXPLAIN** **SHORT RESPONSE** Nancy wanted to make a model of her room. She measured the room and it was 12 feet by 10 feet. She decided to make a model that was $\frac{1}{16}$ as long and $\frac{1}{16}$ as wide as her room. Find the area of the model room. Explain your answer.

11. Nyomi recorded the amount of time she worked each day last week. If she worked 0.75 of her permitted weekly hours, how many hours is she permitted to work?

Time Worked in One Week	
Day	Time (h)
Monday	1
Wednesday	1.25
Friday	1.5
Saturday	3

A. 5 C. 9

B. 6 D. 12

12. What is the volume of the cone in cubic feet? Round to the nearest tenth. Use 3.14 for π.

F. 21.2 ft³

G. 75.8 ft³

H. 84.8 ft³

I. 254.5 ft³

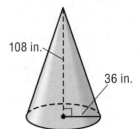

108 in.

36 in.

13. **THINK SOLVE EXPLAIN** **EXTENDED RESPONSE** A movie theater sells popcorn in boxes like the one shown below. The manager wants to sell a new size that is larger by a scale factor of 1.5.

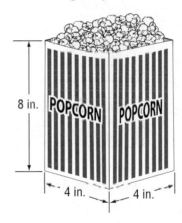

8 in.

4 in.   4 in.

Part A What is the volume of the original popcorn box?

Part B What is the volume of a similar popcorn box that is larger by a scale factor of 1.5?

Part C The surface area of the popcorn box is 144 square inches. What would be the surface area of the similar popcorn box that is larger by a scale factor of 1.5?

NEED EXTRA HELP?													
If You Missed Question...	1	2	3	4	5	6	7	8	9	10	11	12	13
Go to Lesson...	9-2C	7-1C	4-3B	9-1D	2-2D	9-1D	6-3E	9-1D	5-1B	9-2C	3-2B	9-1F	9-2C
For help with NGSSS...	G.4.1	S.6.2	G.4.1	G.4.4	A.3.2	G.4.4	A.1.2	G.4.4	A.1.4	G.4.1	A.3.3	G.4.4	G.4.1

Transformations

Supporting ☆ Idea Predict the results of transformations and draw transformed figures, with and without the coordinate plane.

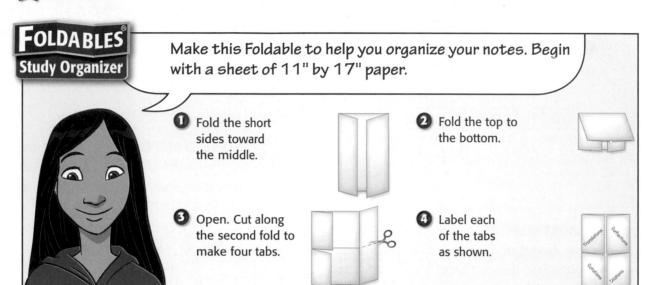

FOLDABLES® Study Organizer

Make this Foldable to help you organize your notes. Begin with a sheet of 11" by 17" paper.

1. Fold the short sides toward the middle.

2. Fold the top to the bottom.

3. Open. Cut along the second fold to make four tabs.

4. Label each of the tabs as shown.

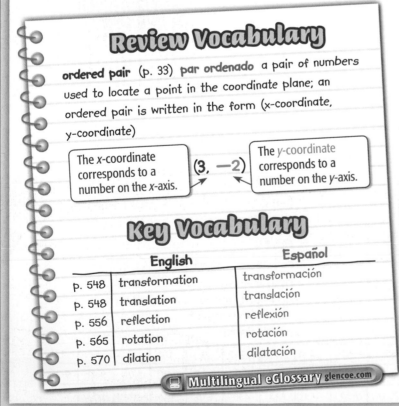

Review Vocabulary

ordered pair (p. 33) **par ordenado** a pair of numbers used to locate a point in the coordinate plane; an ordered pair is written in the form (x-coordinate, y-coordinate)

The *x*-coordinate corresponds to a number on the *x*-axis.

$(3, -2)$

The *y*-coordinate corresponds to a number on the *y*-axis.

Key Vocabulary

	English	Español
p. 548	transformation	transformación
p. 548	translation	translación
p. 556	reflection	reflexión
p. 565	rotation	rotación
p. 570	dilation	dilatación

Multilingual eGlossary glencoe.com

Get Connected glencoe.com

- Study using the **eBook**
- Explore with **Get Animated**
- Get extra help from **Personal Tutor**
- Use **virtual manipulatives** for additional help
- Take a **Self-Check Quiz**

When Will I Use This?

You have two options for checking prerequisite skills for this chapter.

Text Option Take the Quick Check below. Refer to the Quick Review for help.

QUICK Check

Use the coordinate plane to name the ordered pair for each point. (Lesson 1-1C)

1. A **2.** B **3.** C **4.** D

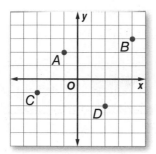

Graph and label each point on a coordinate plane. (Lesson 1-1C)

5. $G(4, -2)$ **6.** $R(-2, -5)$

7. $P(0, -3)$ **8.** $Q(-3, 3)$

Graph each figure and label the missing vertices. (Prior Grade)

9. rectangle with vertices: $B(-3, 3)$, $C(-3, 0)$; side length: 6 units

10. triangle with vertices: $Q(-2, -4)$, $R(2, -4)$; height: 4 units

11. square with vertices: $G(5, 0)$, $H(0, 5)$; side lengths: 5 units

12. parallelogram with vertices: $A(0, 0)$, $B(2, 3)$; base: 4 units

QUICK Review

EXAMPLE 1

Graph and label the point $Z(-3, 2)$.

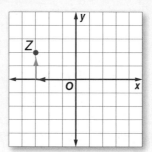

- Start at the origin.
- Move 3 units to the left on the x-axis.
- Then move 2 units up to locate the point.
- Draw a dot and label the dot Z.

EXAMPLE 2

Two vertices of a rectangle are $J(3, 2)$ and $K(1, 2)$. The side length is 4 units. Graph the rectangle and label the other two vertices.

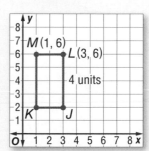

Online Option 🖳 **Get Connected** Take the Online Readiness Quiz at **glencoe.com**.

Explore Congruency in Translations

Main Idea

Identify and draw a figure for a translation.

NGSSS

MA.7.G.4.2 Predict the results of transformations and draw transformed figures, with and without the coordinate plane.

Get Connected
glencoe.com

STENCILING Lauren is stenciling her room using a geometric pattern. She wants to make sure that when she slides the stencil, the resulting figures are *congruent*. Congruent figures have the same size and shape.

ACTIVITY

STEP 1   Cut a triangle out of a piece of cardstock. Label its angles 1, 2, and 3.

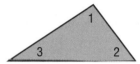

STEP 2   Place the triangle on a piece of notebook paper as shown. Trace the triangle on the paper. Label the vertices *X*, *Y*, and *Z*.

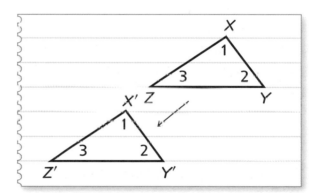

STEP 3   Slide the triangle to another place on the paper without turning it. Trace the triangle again. Label the vertices of this triangle *X'*, *Y'*, and *Z'* so that they correspond to the vertices of the first triangle.

Analyze the Results

1. Use a centimeter ruler to measure the distance between *X* and *X'*, *Y* and *Y'*, and *Z* and *Z'*. What seems to be true about the distance each point in △*XYZ* moved?

2. Compare and contrast △*XYZ* and △*X'Y'Z'*. Use the word *congruent* in your comparison.

3. **MAKE A PREDICTION** Suppose you want to slide the triangle to a third position without turning it. What would it look like?

Main Idea

Predict the results of translations and draw translations on the coordinate plane.

NGSSS

 MA.7.G.4.2 Predict the results of transformations and draw transformed figures, with and without the coordinate plane. *Also addresses MA.7.G.4.3.*

New Vocabulary

transformation
translation
congruent figures

Get Connected
glencoe.com

Translations in the Coordinate Plane

Step 1 Trace a parallelogram-shaped pattern block onto a coordinate grid. Label the vertices *ABCD*.

Step 2 Slide the pattern block over 5 units to the right and 2 units down.

Step 3 Trace the figure in its new position. Label the vertices *A′*, *B′*, *C′*, and *D′*.

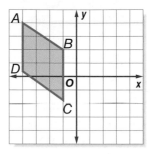

1. Trace the horizontal and vertical path between corresponding vertices. What do you notice?

2. Add 5 to each *x*-coordinate of the vertices of the original figure. Then subtract 2 from each *y*-coordinate of the vertices of the original figure. What do you notice?

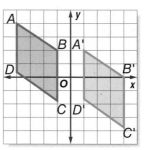

A **transformation** maps one figure onto another. When you move the figure without turning it, the motion is called a **translation**, or slide. When translating a figure, every point of the original figure is moved the same distance and in the same direction.

Key Concept — Translations in the Coordinate Plane

Words	When a figure is translated, the *x*-coordinate of the image changes the value of the horizontal translation, while the *y*-coordinate changes the value of the vertical translation.	**Model** 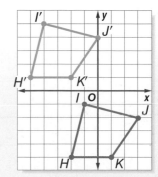
Symbols	$(x, y) \longrightarrow (x + a, y + b)$	

The original figure and the translated figure, or *image*, are congruent. **Congruent figures** have the same size and same shape and the corresponding sides and angles have equal measures.

Draw a Translation

1 Copy trapezoid *WXYZ* at the right on graph paper. Then draw the image of the figure after a translation 4 units left and 2 units down.

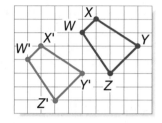

Step 1 Move each vertex of the trapezoid 4 units left and 2 units down.

Step 2 Connect the new vertices to form the image.

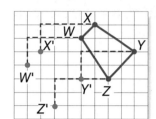

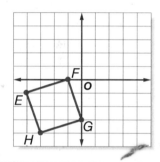

✓ **CHECK Your Progress**

a. Copy square *EFGH* at the right on graph paper. Then draw the image of the figure after a translation 5 units right and 3 units up.

A *positive* integer describes a translation right or up on a coordinate plane. A *negative* integer describes a translation left or down.

Find Coordinates of a Translation

2 Triangle *LMN* has vertices *L*(−1, −2), *M*(6, −3), and *N*(2, −5). Find the vertices of △*L'M'N'* after a translation 6 units left and 4 units up. Then graph the figure and its translated image.

The vertices can be found by adding −6 to the *x*-coordinates and 4 to the *y*-coordinates.

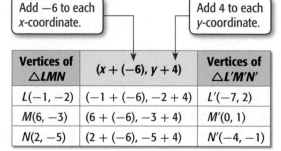

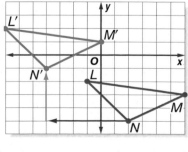

Add −6 to each x-coordinate.	Add 4 to each y-coordinate.

Vertices of △*LMN*	(*x* + (−6), *y* + 4)	Vertices of △*L'M'N'*
L(−1, −2)	(−1 + (−6), −2 + 4)	*L'*(−7, 2)
M(6, −3)	(6 + (−6), −3 + 4)	*M'*(0, 1)
N(2, −5)	(2 + (−6), −5 + 4)	*N'*(−4, −1)

Use the vertices of △*LMN* and of △*L'M'N'* to graph each triangle.

CHECK Your Progress

b. Triangle *TUV* has vertices $T(6, -3)$, $U(-2, 0)$, and $V(-1, 2)$. Find the vertices of $\triangle T'U'V'$ after a translation of 3 units right and 4 units down. Then graph the figure and its translated image.

Real-World EXAMPLE **Find Coordinates of a Translation**

3 **ANIMATION** An animator wants to move a character in a movie 4 units left and 6 units up. If the character had original coordinates at $A(2, -1)$, $B(4, -1)$, $C(4, -5)$, and $D(2, -5)$, find the new vertices of the character after the translation. Then graph the figure and its translated image.

The vertices can be found by subtracting 4 from the *x*-coordinates and adding 6 to the *y*-coordinates.

ABCD	(x − 4, y + 6)	A'B'C'D'
$A(2, -1)$	$(2 - 4, -1 + 6)$	$A'(-2, 5)$
$B(4, -1)$	$(4 - 4, -1 + 6)$	$B'(0, 5)$
$C(4, -5)$	$(4 - 4, -5 + 6)$	$C'(0, 1)$
$D(2, -5)$	$(2 - 4, -5 + 6)$	$D'(-2, 1)$

Use the vertices of the character to graph the character at *ABCD* and *A'B'C'D'*.

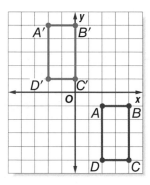

CHECK Your Progress

c. A triangular wall decoration has vertices $X(-3, -1)$, $Y(-3, -3)$, and $Z(-1, -2)$. Find the vertices of the decoration after a translation of 5 units right and 3 units up. Then graph the decoration and its translated image.

In Example 3, the figure was translated 4 units left and 6 units up. This translation can be described as $(x, y) \longrightarrow (x - 4, y + 6)$. In Check Your Progress **c**, the figure was translated 5 units right and 3 units up. This translation can be described as $(x, y) \longrightarrow (x + 5, y + 3)$.

Example 1
(p. 549)

1. Translate △ABC 3 units left and 3 units down. Graph △A'B'C'.

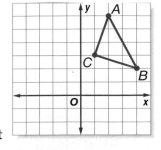

Example 2
(p. 549)

Quadrilateral *DEFG* has vertices *D*(1, 0), *E*(−2, −2), *F*(2, 4), and *G*(6, −3). Find the vertices of *D'E'F'G'* after each translation. Then graph the figure and its translated image.

2. 4 units right, 5 units down

3. 6 units right

Example 3
(p. 550)

4. **MAPS** Julio is in Colorado exploring part of the Denver Zoo as shown. He starts at the felines exhibit and travels 3 units to the right and 5 units up. At which exhibit is Julio located?

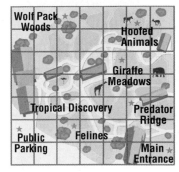

Practice and Problem Solving

● = **Step-by-Step Solutions** begin on page R28.
Extra Practice is on page EP28.

Example 1
(p. 549)

5. Translate △HIJ 2 units right and 6 units down. Graph △H'I'J'.

6. Translate rectangle *KLMN* 1 unit left and 3 units up. Graph rectangle *K'L'M'N'*.

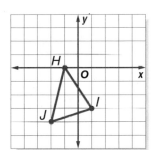

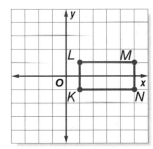

Example 2
(p. 549)

Triangle *PQR* has vertices *P*(0, 0), *Q*(5, −2), and *R*(−3, 6). Predict the vertices of *P'Q'R'* after each translation. Then graph the figure and its translated image.

7 6 units right, 5 units up

8. 8 units left, 1 unit down

9. 3 units left

10. 9 units down

Example 3
(p. 550)

11. **GAMES** When playing the game shown at the right, the player can move horizontally or vertically across the board. Describe each of the following as a translation in words and as an ordered pair.

a. green player

b. orange player

12. GRAPHIC NOVEL Refer to the graphic novel frame below. List the five steps the girls should take and identify any transformations used in the dance steps.

13 Parallelogram *RSTU* is translated 3 units right and 5 units up. Then the translated figure is translated 2 units left. Graph the resulting parallelogram.

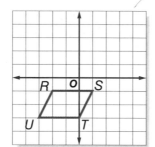

14. Triangle *ABC* is translated 2 units left and 3 units down. Then the translated figure is translated 3 units right. Graph the resulting triangle.

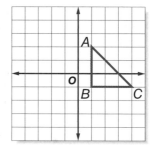

H.O.T. Problems

15. CHALLENGE What are the coordinates of the point (x, y) after being translated m units left and n units up?

16. Which One Doesn't Belong? Identify the transformation that is not the same as the other three. Explain your reasoning.

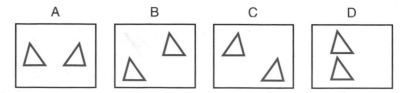

17. Write MATH Triangle *ABC* is translated 4 units right and 2 units down. Then the translated image is translated 7 units left and 5 units up. Describe the final translated image in words.

2 **STEP 1** Use a straightedge and a pencil to draw a quadrilateral on a piece of tracing paper. Label its vertices *A*, *B*, *C*, and *D*.

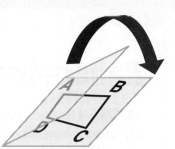

STEP 2 Fold the tracing paper so that quadrilateral *ABCD* is on the inside. Trace the quadrilateral onto the folded side.

STEP 3 Unfold the paper. Label the vertices *A'*, *B'*, *C'*, and *D'* as shown.

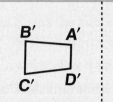

Analyze the Results

7. Use a ruler to measure the distance between *A* and *A'*, *B* and *B'*, *C* and *C'*, and *D* and *D'*. Note also the distance between each vertex and the fold line. From your measurements, what can you conclude about the fold line?

8. Use a protractor to measure ∠*A* and ∠*A'*, ∠*B* and ∠*B'*, ∠*C* and ∠*C'*, and ∠*D* and ∠*D'*. What can you conclude about corresponding angles?

9. Compare and contrast quadrilaterals *ABCD* and *A'B'C'D'*. Use the word *congruent* in your comparison.

10. **MAKE A PREDICTION** Write a sentence that would be true for any figure and the resulting figure when the original figure is flipped over a line.

Practice and Apply

Copy each figure. Draw the resulting figure when each figure is flipped over line ℓ.

11.

12.
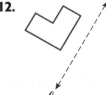

13.
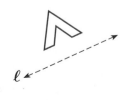

PART ⟩ A B

Main Idea

Predict the results of reflections and graph reflections on a coordinate plane.

NGSSS

 MA.7.G.4.2 Predict the results of transformations and draw transformed figures, with and without the coordinate plane. *Also addresses MA.7.G.4.3.*

New Vocabulary

reflection
line of reflection
image

Get Connected
glencoe.com

Reflections in the Coordinate Plane

NATURE The surface of the water in the art shown acts like a mirror by producing an image of the flamingo.

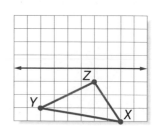

1. Compare the shape and size of the bird on either side of the line of symmetry.

2. Compare the perpendicular distance from the line of symmetry to each of the points shown. What do you observe?

3. The points *A*, *B*, and *C* appear *clockwise* on the bird. How are these points oriented on the other side of the line of symmetry?

The mirror image produced by flipping a figure over a line is called a **reflection**. This line is called the **line of reflection**. A reflection is one type of transformation. In mathematics, an **image** is the position of a figure after a transformation. The image of point *A* is written as *A'*.

EXAMPLE **Draw a Reflection**

1. **Copy △*JKL* at the right onto graph paper. Then draw the image of the figure after a reflection over the given line.**

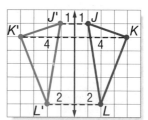

Step 1 Count the number of units between each vertex and the line of reflection.

Step 2 For each vertex, plot a point the same distance away from the line on the other side.

Step 3 Connect the new vertices to form the image of △*JKL*, △*J'K'L'*.

CHECK Your Progress

a. Copy the figure onto a piece of graph paper. Then draw the image of the figure after a reflection over the given line.

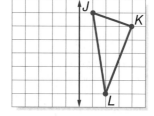

Reflect a Figure Over an Axis

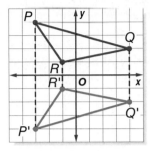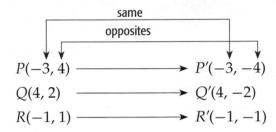

2 Graph △*PQR* with vertices *P*(−3, 4), *Q*(4, 2), and *R*(−1, 1). Then graph the image of △*PQR* after a reflection over the *x*-axis, and write the coordinates of its vertices.

The coordinates of the vertices of the image are *P′*(−3, −4), *Q′*(4, −2), and *R′*(−1, −1). Examine the relationship between the coordinates of each figure.

same
opposites

$P(-3, 4) \longrightarrow P'(-3, -4)$

$Q(4, 2) \longrightarrow Q'(4, -2)$

$R(-1, 1) \longrightarrow R'(-1, -1)$

Notice that the *y*-coordinate of a point reflected over the *x*-axis is the opposite of the *y*-coordinate of the original point.

3 Graph quadrilateral *ABCD* with vertices *A*(−4, 1), *B*(−2, 3), *C*(0, −3), and *D*(−3, −2). Then graph the image of *ABCD* after a reflection over the *y*-axis and write the coordinates of its vertices.

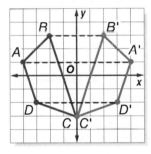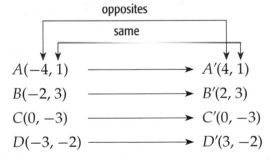

The coordinates of the vertices of the image are *A′*(4, 1), *B′*(2, 3), *C′*(0, −3), and *D′*(3, −2). Examine the relationship between the coordinates of each figure.

opposites
same

$A(-4, 1) \longrightarrow A'(4, 1)$

$B(-2, 3) \longrightarrow B'(2, 3)$

$C(0, -3) \longrightarrow C'(0, -3)$

$D(-3, -2) \longrightarrow D'(3, -2)$

Notice that the *x*-coordinate of a point reflected over the *y*-axis is the opposite of the *x*-coordinate of the original point.

✓ CHECK Your Progress

Graph △*FGH* with vertices *F*(1, −1), *G*(5, −3), and *H*(2, −4). Then graph the image of △*FGH* after a reflection over the given axis and write the coordinates of its vertices.

b. *x*-axis   **c.** *y*-axis

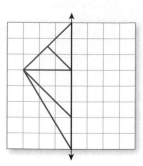

EXAMPLE Use a Reflection

④ **KITES** Copy and complete the kite shown so that the completed figure has a vertical line of symmetry.

Find the distance from each vertex on the figure to the line of reflection.

Then plot a point that same distance away on the opposite side of the line. Connect vertices as appropriate.

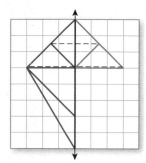 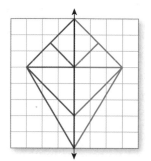

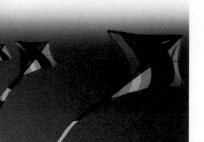
CHECK Your Progress

d. ART Copy and complete the animal shown so that the completed picture has horizontal line symmetry.

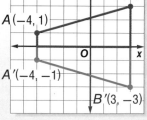

🧩 Key Concept   Reflections in the Coordinate Plane

Words	When a figure is reflected over the *x*-axis, the *x*-coordinate of the image is the same, while the *y*-coordinate is multiplied by −1.	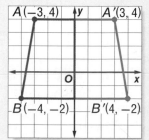
Symbols	$(a, b) \longrightarrow (a, -b)$	
Words	When a figure is reflected over the *y*-axis, the *y*-coordinate of the image is the same, while the *x*-coordinate is multiplied by −1.	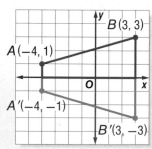
Symbols	$(a, b) \longrightarrow (-a, b)$	

Examples 1–3
(pp. 556–557)

Graph the figure with the given vertices. Then graph the image of the figure after a reflection over the x-axis and y-axis and write the coordinates of the image's vertices.

1. △ABC with vertices A(3, 5), B(4, 1), and C(1, 2)

2. △WXY with vertices W(−1, −2), X(0, −4), and Y(−3, −5)

Example 4
(p. 558)

3. **HOT TUBS** Copy and complete the hot tub design shown so that the completed design has vertical line symmetry.

Practice and Problem Solving

● = **Step-by-Step Solutions** begin on page R28.
Extra Practice is on page EP28.

Examples 1–3
(pp. 556–557)

Copy each figure onto graph paper. Then draw the image of the figure after a reflection over the given line.

4.
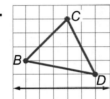

5.
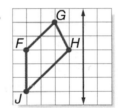

Graph the figure with the given vertices. Then graph the image of the figure after a reflection over the given axis and predict the coordinates of the image's vertices.

6. triangle ABC with vertices A(−1, −1), B(−2, −4), and C(−4, −1); x-axis

7. triangle FGH with vertices F(3, 3), G(4, −3), and H(2, 1); y-axis

8. square JKLM with vertices J(−2, 0), K(−1, −2), L(−3, −3), and M(−4, −1); y-axis

9. quadrilateral PQRS with vertices P(1, 3), Q(3, 5), R(5, 2), and S(3, 1); x-axis

Example 4
(p. 558)

10. **CARS** The drawing shows the left half of a car. Copy the drawing onto grid paper. Then draw the right side of the car so that the completed drawing has a vertical line of symmetry.

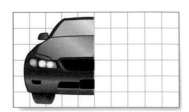

11. **ART** The top half of a Ukrainian decorative egg is shown. Copy the figure onto a piece of paper. Then draw the egg design after it has been reflected over a horizontal line.

12. ARCHITECTURE Describe in what ways the symmetry of the Fogong Monastery, shown below at the left, is similar to that of the Eiffel Tower in Paris, France, shown below at the right.

13. FIND THE DATA Refer to the Data File on pages 2–5. Choose an image that illustrates a reflection.

14. FLAGS Flags of some countries have line symmetry. Of the flags shown below, which flags have line symmetry? Copy and draw all lines of symmetry.

| Nigeria | Ghana | Japan | Mexico |

15 MUSIC Use the photo at the left to determine how many lines of symmetry the body of a violin has.

For Exercises 16–19, use the graph at the right.

16. Identify the pair(s) of figures for which the *x*-axis is the line of reflection.

17. For which pair(s) of figures is the line of reflection the *y*-axis?

18. What type of transformation do figures *B* and *C* represent?

19. Describe the possible transformation(s) required to move figure *A* onto figure *D*.

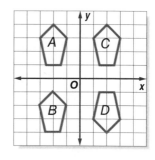

Copy each figure onto graph paper. Then draw the image of the figure after a reflection over the given line.

20.
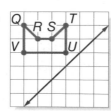

21.
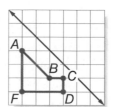

22. **OPEN ENDED** Draw a right triangle ABC in the first quadrant of a coordinate plane. Then draw the image after a reflection over the x-axis.

23. **CHALLENGE** Suppose point K with coordinates $(7, -2)$ is reflected so that the coordinates of its image are $(7, 2)$. Without graphing, which axis was this point reflected over? Explain your reasoning.

24. **Write MATH** Find the coordinates of the point (x, y) after it has been reflected over the x-axis. Then find the coordinates of the point (x, y) after it has been reflected over the y-axis. Explain your reasoning.

25. **FIND THE ERROR** Marisol is finding the new coordinates of the image of a triangle with vertices $A(1, 1)$, $B(4, 1)$, and $C(1, 5)$ after a reflection over the x-axis. Find her mistake and correct it.

> The vertices of triangle $A'B'C'$ are $A'(-1, 1)$, $B'(-4, 1)$, and $C'(-1, 5)$.

NGSSS Practice   MA.7.G.4.2

26. Which of the following is the reflection of $\triangle ABC$ with vertices $A(1, -1)$, $B(4, -1)$, and $C(2, -4)$ over the x-axis?

A. 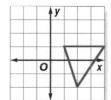 B. 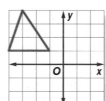 C. 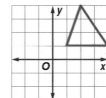 D.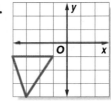

Spiral Review

27. **GEOMETRY** Triangle FGH has vertices $F(-3, 7)$, $G(-1, 5)$, and $H(-2, 2)$. Graph the figure and its image after a translation 4 units right and 1 unit down. Write the ordered pairs for the vertices of the image. (Lesson 10-1B)

28. **MEASUREMENT** Marela's bedroom is modeled in the figure to the right. She plans on knocking down a wall to double her room size. She plans on painting the new room. How many square feet of wall space will she have to cover in the new room? (Lesson 8-2B)

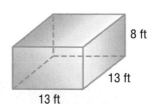

8 ft
13 ft
13 ft

1. Translate $\triangle ABC$ 4 units right and 1 unit up. Graph $\triangle A'B'C'$. (Lesson 10-1B)

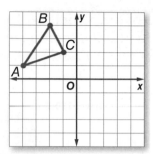

2. **NGSSS PRACTICE** If point D is translated 5 units right and 2 units down, what will be the coordinates of point D in its new position? (Lesson 10-1B)

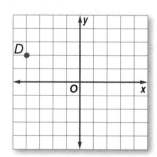

A. $(-9, 0)$ C. $(1, 0)$
B. $(0, -9)$ D. $(0, 9)$

Determine whether each figure has line symmetry. If so, copy the figure and draw all lines of symmetry. (Lesson 10-2B)

3.

4.

5.

6.

Rectangle $MNPQ$ has vertices $M(1, 2)$, $N(6, 2)$, $P(1, 5)$, and $Q(6, 5)$. Find the vertices of $M'N'P'Q'$ after each translation. (Lesson 10-1B)

7. 7 units left, 2 units up

8. 5 units down

9. 4 units left, 6 units down

10. 1 unit right, 4 units down

11. **NGSSS PRACTICE** If $\triangle RST$ is reflected over the x-axis and translated 4 units to the right, which is the resulting image of point R? (Lesson 10-2B)

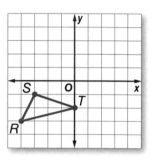

F. $(-4, 3)$ H. $(1, 1)$
G. $(0, 3)$ I. $(4, 2)$

Graph each figure and its reflection over the x-axis. Then find the coordinates of the reflected image. (Lesson 10-2B)

12. $ABCD$ with vertices $A(-2, -2)$, $B(-5, -5)$, $C(2, -5)$, and $D(4, -1)$

13. $WXYZ$ with vertices $W(-7, 6)$, $X(-3, 6)$, $Y(-3, 3)$, and $Z(-7, 3)$

14. GHJ with vertices $G(0, 1)$, $H(3, 6)$, and $J(6, 1)$

15. MNP with vertices $M(-1, -2)$, $N(-5, -4)$, and $P(-2, -6)$

16. **CAR** Identify the number of lines of symmetry in the drawing. (Lesson 10-2B)

Explore Rotational Symmetry and Rotations

Main Idea

Identify rotational symmetry.

NGSSS

MA.7.G.4.2 Predict the results of transformations and draw transformed figures, with and without the coordinate plane.

New Vocabulary

rotational symmetry
angle of rotation

Get Connected
glencoe.com

FAMILY BADGES Kamon are Japanese badges used to signify a specific family. If the badge at the right is turned 72°, it will be identical to the original figure.

A figure has **rotational symmetry** if it can be rotated a certain number of degrees about its center and still look like the original. The **angle of rotation** is the degree measure that the figure is rotated.

 ACTIVITY

1 **STEP 1** Cut a square out of cardstock. Label the four vertices A, B, C, and D. Use a ruler and protractor to make sure the angles and sides are congruent. Lay the square on a piece of patty paper. Trace around the square.

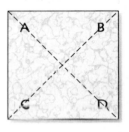

STEP 2 Find the center of the square by drawing the two diagonals shown on the diagram. Place a pin at the center and turn the square clockwise until it matches the original, ignoring the letters.

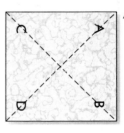

STEP 3 Continue turning the square, noting the angles at which it matches the original, until the vertices are back to their original position.

Analyze the Results

1. How many times did the figure match itself?

2. Describe the relationship between the number of times the figure matched itself and the angle of rotation.

3. **MAKE A PREDICTION** Predict the results of a 90° turn of the figure.

2 **STEP 1** Trace and cut out the figure at the right on a piece of cardstock. Lay a piece of patty paper on the figure.

STEP 2 Place a pin where the red dot indicates on the figure. Turn the figure clockwise one quarter turn or 90°. Trace the turned figure.

STEP 3 Turn the figure clockwise another quarter turn to 180° and trace the figure. Repeat another clockwise quarter turn to 270° and trace.

Analyze the Results

4. Did the figure match itself at any rotation?

5. Does the figure have rotational symmetry?

6. Compare and contrast the figure using line symmetry and rotational symmetry. Does the figure have either?

7. **MAKE A PREDICTION** Predict what the resulting figure will look like with a counterclockwise turn of 45°.

Practice and Apply

Determine whether each figure has rotational symmetry. Write *yes* or *no*. If *yes*, name its angle(s) of rotation.

8.

9.

10.

Show each figure after clockwise turns of 45°, 60°, 90°, 180°, and 270°.

11.

12.

13.

14. **DESIGN** Copy and complete the design shown so that the completed figure has rotational symmetry with 90°, 180°, and 270° as its angles of rotation.

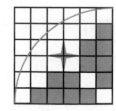

Main Idea
Predict the results of a rotation and graph rotations on a coordinate plane.

NGSSS

 MA.7.G.4.2 Predict the results of transformations and draw transformed figures, with and without the coordinate plane. *Also addresses MA.7.G.4.3.*

New Vocabulary
rotation

Get Connected
glencoe.com

Rotations in the Coordinate Plane

Explore

Step 1 Draw and label triangle *ABC* with vertices *A*(−4, 1), *B*(−4, 6), and *C*(−1, 1).

Step 2 Attach a piece of tracing paper to the coordinate plane with a fastener at the origin of the graph. Trace the triangle. Label the vertices *A′*, *B′*, and *C′*.

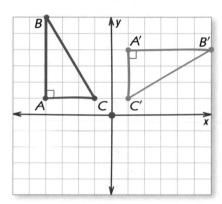

Step 3 Turn the tracing paper clockwise 90° so that the original *y*-axis is on top of the original *x*-axis.

1. Describe the transformation that occurred from triangle *ABC* to triangle *A′B′C′*.

2. What are the coordinates of triangle *A′B′C′*?

A **rotation** is a transformation in which a figure is turned around a fixed point.

Key Concept — Rotations in the Coordinate Plane

Words When a figure is rotated around a point, neither the size nor the shape of the figure changes.

Models

90° Rotation	180° Rotation	270° Rotation

The rotation of a figure is based on a circle, so it can be anywhere from 0° to 360°. A rotation can be a clockwise or counterclockwise turn. Unless otherwise indicated, the rotation is about the origin.

EXAMPLE **Rotate a Figure Clockwise**

 Triangle *RST* has vertices *R*(1, 3), *S*(4, 4), and *T*(2, 1). Graph the figure and its image after a clockwise rotation of 90° about the origin. Then name the coordinates of the vertices for triangle *R′S′T′*.

Step 1 Graph triangle *RST* on a coordinate plane.

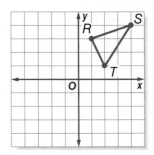

Read Math

Clockwise To rotate the figure the same way the hands on a clock rotate.

Step 2 Sketch $\overline{RO}$ connecting point *R* to the origin. Sketch another segment, $\overline{R'O}$, so that the angle between points *R*, *O*, and *R′* measures 90° and the segment is congruent to $\overline{RO}$.

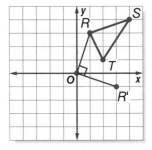

Counterclockwise To rotate the figure the opposite direction of the way the hands on a clock rotate.

Step 3 Repeat Step 2 for points *S* and *T*. Then connect the vertices to form triangle *R′S′T′*.

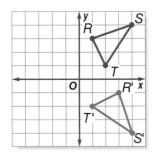

So, the coordinates of the vertices of triangle *R′S′T′* are *R′*(3, −1), *S′*(4, −4), and *T′*(1, −2).

 CHECK Your Progress

a. Triangle *XYZ* has vertices *X*(−5, 4), *Y*(−1, 2), and *Z*(−3, 1). Graph the figure and its image after a counterclockwise rotation of 180° about the origin. Then name the coordinates of the vertices for triangle *X′Y′Z′*.

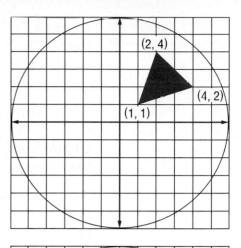

2 LANDSCAPING A landscaper is designing a circular garden that has rotational symmetry. The isosceles triangle represents a decorative stone. Find the coordinates of the vertices of the triangles after rotations of 90°, 180°, and 270° counterclockwise.

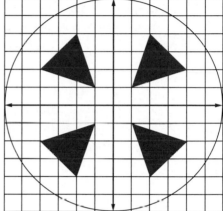

Real-World Link · · · · ·

Landscape designers often use coordinate geometry and algebra as they serve their clients.

Draw each of the three rotations of the isosceles triangle.

List the vertices:
90°: (−1, 1), (−4, 2), (−2, 4)
180°: (−1, −1), (−4, −2), (−2, −4)
270°: (1, −1), (4, −2), (2, −4)

 CHECK Your Progress

b. The landscaper would like to add marigolds to the circular garden. If the marigold plants are located at (2, 1) and (3, 1), rotate the points to find the other three locations for each planting.

CHECK Your Understanding

Example 1
(p. 566)

Graph triangle *ABC* and its image after each rotation. Then name the coordinates of the vertices for triangle *A'B'C'*.

1 90° counterclockwise

2. 180° clockwise

3. 270° counterclockwise

4. 270° clockwise

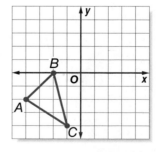

Example 2
(p. 567)

5. GEOMETRY Parallelogram *EFGH* has coordinates *E*(1, 1), *F*(3, 1), *G*(4, 4), and *H*(2, 4). Find the coordinates of the image after a clockwise rotation of 180°. Then graph the original image to check your work.

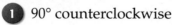

Practice and Problem Solving

● = **Step-by-Step Solutions** begin on page R29.
Extra Practice is on page EP29.

Example 1
(p. 566)

Triangle *PQR* has vertices *P*(1, −5), *Q*(2, −1), and *R*(5, −4). Graph the figure and its image after each rotation. Then predict the coordinates of the vertices for triangle *P′Q′R′*.

6. 270° clockwise

7 180° counterclockwise

8. 90° counterclockwise

9. 90° clockwise

Quadrilateral *FGHJ* has vertices *F*(1, 1), *G*(2, 5), *H*(5, 3), and *J*(4, 0). Graph the figure and its image after each rotation. Then name the coordinates of the vertices for quadrilateral *F′G′H′J′*.

10. 90° clockwise

11. 270° clockwise

12. 270° counterclockwise

13. 180° clockwise

Example 2
(p. 567)

14. Quadrilateral *TUVW* represents a bed in Chantal's bedroom and has vertices *T*(−3, 0), *U*(−3, 2), *V*(−1, 0) and *W*(−1, 2). Chantal would like to rotate her bed 180° clockwise to see if she likes the new placement. What are the coordinates of the final image?

15. The triangle at the right represents the placement of Tyra's tricycle on the driveway. Plot the tricycle after a counterclockwise rotation of 270° about the origin.

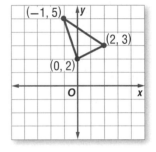

16. GEOMETRY The right isosceles triangle *PQR* has vertices *P*(3, 3), *Q*(3, 1), and *R*(■, ■) and is rotated 90° counterclockwise about the origin. Find the missing vertex of the triangle. Then graph the triangle and its image.

17. GRAPHIC NOVEL Refer to the graphic novel frame below. The last step is shown on grid 6. The girls make a clockwise rotation of 90° and begin the dance again. Expand your grid and mark the ending spot of the second series.

Refer to the graphic novel on page 545 to see about the new dance we are learning.

Ok, now that we finished the first series, we turn 90 degrees clockwise and start all over again.

Isn't that a rotation like we learned in math class?

OPEN ENDED Use the information on line symmetry on page 554 and the following information.

18. Draw a figure that has line symmetry but not rotational symmetry.

19. Draw a figure that has both line symmetry and rotational symmetry.

20. Is it possible for a figure to have rotational symmetry, but not line symmetry? Justify your response with a drawing or an explanation.

CHALLENGE Triangle *JKL* has vertices *J*(−4, −1), *K*(−1, −2), and *L*(−5, −5). Graph the figure and its image after each rotation about the origin. Then give the coordinates of the vertices for triangle *J'K'L'*.

21. 540° clockwise

22. 450° counterclockwise

23. 720° counterclockwise

24. 630° counterclockwise

25. **Write MATH** Describe what information is needed to rotate a figure.

 **NGSSS Practice**   MA.5.G.5.1, MA.7.G.4.2

26. Which figure shows the letter F after a rotation of 270° clockwise?

A.

C.

B.

D.

27. **EXTENDED RESPONSE** Triangle *XYZ* has vertices *X*(2, −2), *Y*(5, 0), and *Z*(3, −4)

Part A What are the coordinates of point *Y'* after a clockwise rotation of 180°?

Part B What are the coordinates of *Y'* after a counterclockwise rotation of 90°?

Spiral Review

Graph quadrilateral *ABCD* and its resulting image after each transformation. (Lessons 10-1C and 10-2B)

28. reflection over the *y*-axis

29. translation 2 units right, 3 units up

30. reflection over the *x*-axis

31. translation 3 units left, 4 units up

32. reflection over the *x*-axis, then over the *y*-axis

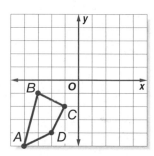

Main Idea

Graph dilations on a coordinate plane.

NGSSS

MA.7.G.4.2 Predict the results of transformations and draw transformed figures, with and without the coordinate plane.

New Vocabulary

dilation
center
enlargement
reduction

Get Connected
glencoe.com

Dilations

Explore The figure shown is drawn on 0.5-centimeter grid paper, so each square is 0.5-by-0.5 centimeter. Redraw the figure using squares that are 1-by-1 centimeter. Use point A as your starting point.

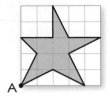

1. Measure and compare corresponding lengths on the original and new figure. Describe the relationship between these measurements. How does this relate to the change in grid size?

The image produced by enlarging or reducing a figure is called a **dilation**. The **center** of the dilation is a fixed point used for measurement when altering the size of the figure.

A dilation image is similar to the original figure. The ratio of a length on the image to a length on the original figure is the scale factor of the dilation.

EXAMPLE Draw a Dilation

① Copy polygon *ABCD* onto graph paper. Then draw the image of the figure after a dilation with center *A* by a scale factor of 2.

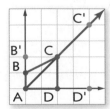

Step 1 Draw ray *AB*, or $\overrightarrow{AB}$, extending it to the edges of the grid.

Step 2 Use a ruler to locate point *B′* on $\overrightarrow{AB}$ so that *AB′* = 2(*AB*).

Step 3 Repeat Steps 1 and 2 for points *C′* and *D′*. Then draw polygon *A′B′C′D′* where *A* = *A′*.

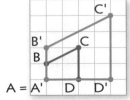

CHECK Your Progress

a. Draw and label a large triangle *XYZ* on grid paper. Then draw the image of △*XYZ* after a dilation with center *X* and scale factor $\frac{1}{4}$.

Study Tip

Dilations on a Coordinate Plane The ratio of the x- and y-coordinates of the vertices of an image to the corresponding values of the coordinates of the vertices of the original figure is the same as the scale factor of the dilation.

EXAMPLE **Graph a Dilation**

2) Graph △JKL with vertices J(3, 8), K(10, 6), and L(8, 2). Then graph its image △J′K′L′ after a dilation with a scale factor of $\frac{1}{2}$.

To find the vertices of the dilation, multiply each coordinate in the ordered pairs by $\frac{1}{2}$. Then graph both images on the same axes.

$$J(3, 8) \rightarrow \left(3 \cdot \frac{1}{2}, 8 \cdot \frac{1}{2}\right) \rightarrow J'\left(\frac{3}{2}, 4\right)$$

$$K(10, 6) \rightarrow \left(10 \cdot \frac{1}{2}, 6 \cdot \frac{1}{2}\right) \rightarrow K'(5, 3)$$

$$L(8, 2) \rightarrow \left(8 \cdot \frac{1}{2}, 2 \cdot \frac{1}{2}\right) \rightarrow L'(4, 1)$$

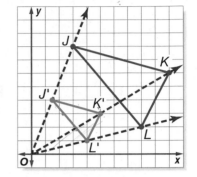

Check for Reasonableness Draw lines through the origin and each of the vertices of the original figure. The vertices of the dilation should lie on those same lines. ✓

CHECK Your Progress

Find the coordinates of the image of △JKL after a dilation with each scale factor. Then graph △JKL and △J′K′L′.

b. scale factor: 3   **c.** scale factor: $\frac{1}{3}$

Key Concept   **Dilations in the Coordinate Plane**

Words   A dilation with a scale factor of *a* will be:

- an **enlargement**, or an image larger than the original, if *a* > 1,
- a **reduction**, or an image smaller than the original, if 0 < *a* < 1, or
- the same as the original figure if *a* = 1.

Model

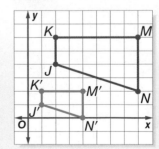

To find the coordinates of the vertices of an image after a dilation with center (0, 0), multiply the x- and y-coordinates by the scale factor.

Symbols   (x, y) → (ax, ay)

EXAMPLE **Find and Classify a Scale Factor**

3 Quadrilateral *V′Z′X′W′* is a dilation of quadrilateral *VZXW*. Find the scale factor of the dilation and classify it as an *enlargement* or a *reduction*.

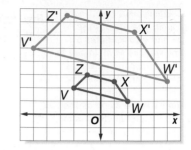

Write a ratio of the *x*- or *y*-coordinate of one vertex of the dilation to the *x*- or *y*-coordinate of the corresponding vertex of the original figure. Use the *y*-coordinates of *V*(−2, 2) and *V′*(−5, 5).

$$\frac{y\text{-coordinate of point } V'}{y\text{-coordinate of point } V} = \frac{5}{2} \quad \text{Verify by using other coordinates.}$$

The scale factor is $\frac{5}{2}$. Since $\frac{5}{2} > 1$, the dilation is an enlargement.

CHECK Your Progress

d. Triangle *A′B′C′* is a dilation of △*ABC*. Find the scale factor of the dilation and classify it as an *enlargement* or a *reduction*.

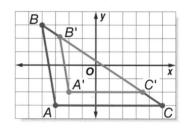

Real-World EXAMPLE

4 **EYES** An optometrist dilates a patient's pupils by a factor of $\frac{5}{3}$. If the pupil has a diameter of 5 millimeters before dilation, find the new diameter after the pupil is dilated.

$a = \frac{5}{3}(5)$ Write the equation.

$a \approx 8.33$ Multiply.

The pupil will be about 8.3 millimeters in diameter after dilation.

CHECK Your Progress

e. **COMPUTERS** Padma uses an image of her dog as the wallpaper on her computer desktop. The original image is 5 inches high and 7 inches wide. If her computer scales the image by a factor of $\frac{5}{4}$, what are the dimensions of the dilated image?

Before Dilation

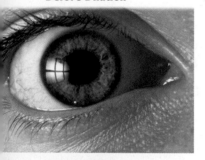

After Dilation

Real-World Link · · · ·

An optometrist will often dilate the pupils to better examine a patient's retina, the layer of nerve tissue that receives and transmits images to the brain.

Example 1
(p. 570)

Copy △ABC on graph paper. Then draw the image of the figure after the dilation with the given center and scale factor.

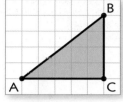

1. center: *A*, scale factor: $\frac{1}{2}$

2. center: *C*, scale factor: $\frac{3}{2}$

Example 2
(p. 571)

Triangle *JKL* has vertices *J*(−4, 2), *K*(−2, −4), and *L*(3, 6). Find the vertices of *J′K′L′* after a dilation with the given scale factor. Then graph △*JKL* and △*J′K′L′*.

3. scale factor: 3

4. scale factor: $\frac{1}{4}$

Example 3
(p. 572)

5. On the graph, $\overline{A'B'}$ is a dilation of $\overline{AB}$. Find the scale factor of the dilation and classify it as an *enlargement* or a *reduction*.

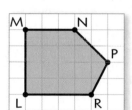

Example 4
(p. 572)

6. **GRAPHIC DESIGN** Jacqui designed a 6-inch by $7\frac{1}{2}$-inch logo for her school. The logo is to be reduced by a scale factor of $\frac{1}{3}$ and used to make face paintings. What are the dimensions of the dilated image?

Practice and Problem Solving

● = Step-by-Step Solutions begin on page R31.
Extra Practice is on page EP29.

Example 1
(p. 570)

Copy each figure on graph paper. Then draw the image of the figure after the dilation with the given center and scale factor.

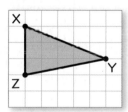

7. center: *X*, scale factor: $\frac{7}{3}$

9 center: *L*, scale factor: $\frac{3}{4}$

8. center: *Z*, scale factor: $\frac{2}{3}$

10. center: *N*, scale factor: 2

Example 2
(p. 571)

Find the vertices of polygon *H′J′K′L′* after polygon *HJKL* is dilated using the given scale factor. Then graph polygon *HJKL* and polygon *H′J′K′L′*.

11. *H*(−1, 3), *J*(3, 2), *K*(2, −3), *L*(−2, −2); scale factor 2

12. *H*(0, 2), *J*(3, 1), *K*(0, −4), *L*(−2, −3); scale factor 3

13. *H*(−6, 2), *J*(4, 4), *K*(7, −2), *L*(−2, −4); scale factor $\frac{1}{2}$

14. *H*(−8, 4), *J*(6, 4), *K*(6, −4), *L*(−8, −4); scale factor $\frac{3}{4}$

Example 3
(p. 572)

On each graph, one figure is a dilation of the other. Find the scale factor of each dilation and classify it as an enlargement or a reduction.

15.

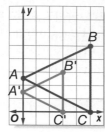

16.

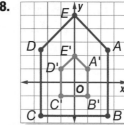

17.

18.

Example 4
(p. 572)

19. PUBLISHING To place a picture in his class newsletter, Joquin must reduce the picture by a scale factor of $\frac{3}{10}$. Find the dimensions of the reduced picture if the original is 15 centimeters wide and 10 centimeters high.

20. PROJECTION An overhead projector transforms the image on a transparency so that it is shown enlarged by a scale factor of 3.5 on a screen. If the original image is 3 inches long by 4 inches wide, find the dimensions of the projected image.

21 BARN ART Scott Hagan painted the Ohio bicentennial logo on one barn in each of Ohio's 88 counties. Each logo measured about 20 feet by 20 feet. Although Hagan drew each logo freehand, they are amazingly similar. If the original logo on which each painting was based measured 5 inches by 5 inches, what is the scale factor from the original logo to one of Hagan's paintings? Justify your answer.

22. DRAWING Artists use dilations to create the illusion of distance and depth. If you stand on a sidewalk and look in the distance, the parallel sides appear to converge and meet at a point. This is called the vanishing point.

   a. Which figure appears to be closer? Explain your reasoning.

   b. Draw a figure similar to the one shown at the right. Measure the larger rectangle. Above the horizon, draw a similar figure that is $\frac{7}{5}$ the size of that rectangle.

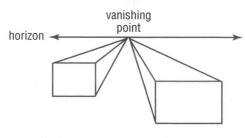

H.O.T. Problems

23. **OPEN ENDED** Graph a triangle and its image after a dilation with a scale factor greater than 1. Graph the resulting image after a dilation with a scale factor between 0 and 1. Predict the scale factor from the original to the final image. Explain your reasoning and verify your prediction.

24. **CHALLENGE** Describe the image of a figure after a dilation with a scale factor of −2.

25. **Write MATH** Write a general rule for finding the new coordinates of any ordered pair (x, y) after a dilation with a scale factor of k.

NGSSS Practice   MA.6.A.2.1, MA.7.G.4.2

26. Square A is similar to square B.

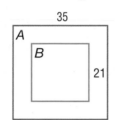

What scale factor was used to dilate square A to square B?

A. $\frac{1}{7}$

B. $\frac{3}{5}$

C. $\frac{5}{3}$

D. 7

27. Quadrilateral $LMNP$ was dilated to form quadrilateral $WXYZ$.

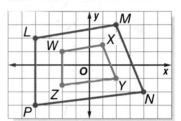

Which number best represents the scale factor used to change quadrilateral $LMNP$ into quadrilateral $WXYZ$?

F. 3

G. 2

H. $\frac{1}{2}$

I. $\frac{1}{3}$

Graph $\triangle XYZ$ and its image after each rotation. Then give the coordinates of the vertices for $\triangle X'Y'Z'$. (Lesson 10-3B)

28. 180° clockwise

29. 90° counterclockwise

30. 90° clockwise

31. **GEOMETRY** Graph $\triangle JKL$ with vertices $J(-1, -4)$, $K(1, 1)$, and $L(3, -2)$ and its reflection over the x-axis. Write the ordered pairs for the vertices of the new figure. (Lesson 10-2B)

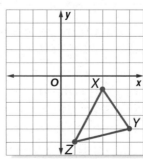

PART > A > B

Problem-Solving Investigation

Main Idea Solve problems using the *work backward* strategy.

P.S.I. TEAM +

Work Backward

TENISHA: At the parade yesterday, I saw that the soccer team's float ended at Abbey and Davidson. The float traveled 3 blocks west on Monroe, 2 blocks north on Nelson, 4 blocks west on Main, and 2 blocks north on Davidson.

YOUR MISSION: Work backward to find the starting point of the soccer team's float in the parade.

Understand	You know the translations involved.
Plan	Start at the end of the parade and work backward.
Solve	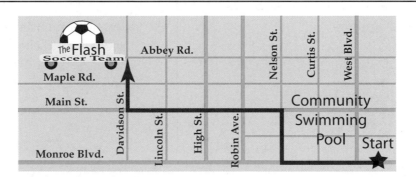
Check	Start at the community swimming pool and translate 3 blocks west, 2 blocks north, 4 blocks west, and 2 blocks north. This takes you to where the float ended. So, the starting point of the float is the community swimming pool. ✓

Analyze the Strategy

1. Explain when you would use the *work backward* strategy to solve a real-world problem involving transformations.

 NGSSS
MA.7.A.5.2 Solve non-routine problems by working backwards. *Also addresses MA.7.G.4.2.*

- Work backward.
- Guess, check, and revise.
- Determine reasonable answers.
- Choose an operation.

Use the *work backward* strategy to solve Exercises 2–5.

2. BEDROOM Bradley moved his bedroom around as shown. He rotated his bed 90° counterclockwise and translated it 14 units to the right and 4 units down. Graph and find the vertices of the bed before it was moved.

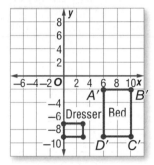

3. If the triangle at the right was translated up and rotated 180° about vertex *S*, draw the original triangle and describe the transformations.

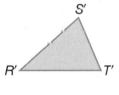

4. The rectangle below was reflected over the *y*-axis. Find the original coordinates of the rectangle.

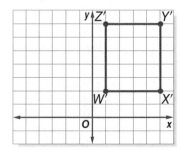

5 Jackie's mom gave her money before she left for her school field trip. Jackie spent half of the money on admission to a museum. She spent $\frac{2}{3}$ of what she had left on lunch. She brought $2.50 back to her mom. How much did Jackie's mom originally give her?

Use any strategy to solve Exercises 6–10.

6. MONEY Cole has $2.58 in coins. If he has quarters, dimes, nickels, and pennies, how many of each coin does he have?

7. FENCING Mr. Hernandez will build a fence to enclose a rectangular yard for his horse. If the area of the yard to be enclosed is 1,944 square feet and the length of the yard is 54 feet, how much fencing is needed?

8. ART Victor draws a right triangle so that one of the acute angles measures 55°. Without measuring, describe how Victor can determine the measure of the other acute angle in the triangle. Then find the angle measure.

9. GEOMETRY Refer to quadrilateral *ABCD*.

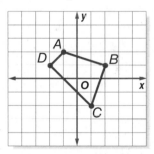

a. Describe the translation that will move *A* to the point (2, −2). Then graph quadrilateral *A′B′C′D′* using this translation.

b. Find the coordinates of the vertices of quadrilateral *ABCD* after a reflection over the *y*-axis. Then graph the reflection.

10. **Write MATH** Write a transformation problem that could be solved by working backward. Then write the steps you would take to find the solution to your problem.

AN ANIMATION SENSATION!

Have you ever wondered how they make animated movies look so realistic? Computer animators use computer technology and apply their artistic skills to make inanimate objects come alive. If you are interested in computer animation, you should practice drawing, study human and animal movement, and take math classes every year in high school. Tony DeRose, a computer scientist at an animation studio said, "Trigonometry helps rotate and move characters, algebra creates the special effects that make images shine and sparkle, and calculus helps light up a scene."

Choose a Major
Are you interested in a career as a computer animator? Take some of the following courses in high school.

- 2-D Animation
- Algebra
- Calculus
- Trigonometry

Get Connected glencoe.com

Figure 1

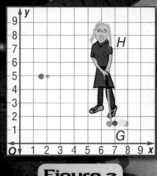

Figure 2

Figure 3

Real-World Math

Use Figures 1–3 to solve each problem.

1. In Figure 1, the car is translated 8 units left and 5 units down so that it appears to be moving. What are the coordinates of A' and B' after the translation?

2. In Figure 1, the car is translated so that A' has coordinates $(-7, 2)$. Describe the translation as an ordered pair. Then find the coordinates of point B'.

3. In Figure 1, the car is reflected over the x-axis in order to make its reflection appear in a pond. What are the coordinates of A' and B' after the reflection?

4. In Figure 2, the artist uses rotation to show the girl's golf swing. Describe the coordinates of G' if the golf club is rotated 90° clockwise about point H.

5. The character in Figure 3 is enlarged by a scale factor of $\frac{5}{2}$. What are the coordinates of Q' and R' after the dilation?

6. The character in Figure 3 is reduced in size by a scale factor of $\frac{2}{3}$. What is the number of units between S' and T', the width of the character's face, after the dilation?

🖵 **Get Connected** glencoe.com

• **STUDY** *TO GO*
• Vocabulary Review
• Multilingual eGlossary

FOLDABLES Study Organizer

Be sure the following Key Concepts are noted in your Foldable.

Key Concepts

Translations (Lesson 10-1)
• When translating a figure, every point in the original figure is moved the same distance in the same direction.

Reflections (Lesson 10-2)
• When reflecting a figure, every point in the original figure is the same distance from the line of reflection as its corresponding point on the original figure.

Rotations (Lesson 10-3)
• A rotation occurs when a figure is rotated, or turned, about a point such as the origin.

Dilations (Lesson 10-4)
• The image produced by enlarging or reducing a figure is called a dilation.

Key Vocabulary

angle of rotation (p. 563)	line symmetry (p. 554)
center (p. 570)	reduction (p. 571)
congruent figures (p. 548)	reflection (p. 556)
dilation (p. 570)	rotation (p. 565)
enlargement (p. 571)	rotational symmetry (p. 563)
image (p. 556)	transformation (p. 548)
line of reflection (p. 556)	translation (p. 548)
line of symmetry (p. 554)	

Vocabulary Check

State whether each sentence is *true* or *false*. If *false*, replace the underlined word or number to make a true sentence.

1. The point (3, −2) when translated up 3 units and to the left 5 units becomes <u>(6, −7)</u>.

2. The image produced by enlarging or reducing a figure is called a <u>dilation</u>.

3. A <u>rotation</u> is a mirror image of the original figure.

4. A <u>reduction</u> is the motion where a figure is moved without being turned.

5. Figures that match exactly when folded in half have <u>line symmetry</u>.

6. <u>Rotational symmetry</u> is the degree measure of the angle through which the figure is rotated.

7. <u>Congruent figures</u> have the same size and same shape, and the corresponding sides and angles have equal measures.

Multi-Part Lesson Review

10-1 Translations

Translations in the Coordinate Plane (pp. 548–553)

MA.7.G.4.2

Triangle *PQR* has coordinates *P*(4, −2), *Q*(−2, −3), and *R*(−1, 6). Find the coordinates of *P'Q'R'* after each translation. Then graph each translation.

8. 6 units left, 3 units up

9. 4 units right, 1 unit down

10. 3 units left

11. 7 units down

12. Square *ABCD* has vertices *A*(−4, −4), *B*(−1, −4), *C*(−4, −1), and *D*(−1, −1). Find the coordinates of square *A'B'C'D'* after a translation 5 units right and 2 units up. Then graph the figure and its translated image.

EXAMPLE 1 Find the coordinates of △*G'H'I'* after a translation 2 units left and 4 units up.

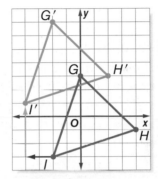

The vertices of △*G'H'I'* are *G'*(−2, 7), *H'*(2, 3), and *I'*(−4, 1).

10-2 Reflections

Reflections in the Coordinate Plane (pp. 556–561)

MA.7.G.4.2

Find the coordinates of each figure after a reflection over the given axis. Then graph the figure and its reflected image.

13. △*RST* with coordinates *R*(−1, 3), *S*(2, 6), and *T*(6, 1); *x*-axis

14. parallelogram *ABCD* with coordinates *A*(1, 3), *B*(2, −1), *C*(5, −1), and *D*(4, 3); *y*-axis

15. rectangle *EFGH* with coordinates *E*(4, 2), *F*(−2, 2), *G*(−2, 5), and *H*(4, 5); *x*-axis

16. square *WXYZ* with coordinates *W*(−3, 0), *X*(−1, 0), *Y*(−1, 2), and *Z*(−3, 2); *y*-axis

EXAMPLE 2 Find the coordinates of △*C'D'E'* after a reflection over the *y*-axis. Then graph its reflected image.

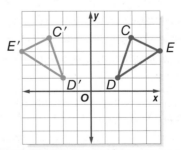

The vertices of △*C'D'E'* are *C'*(−3, 4), *D'*(−2, 1), and *E'*(−5, 3).

10-3 Rotations

Rotations in the Coordinate Plane (pp. 565–569)

 MA.7.G.4.2

Refer to Example 3. Rotate △*XYZ* about the origin and graph its image. Then find the coordinates of △*X′Y′Z′*.

17. 270° clockwise

18. 180° counterclockwise

19. 360° counterclockwise

20. **PAPER FOLDING** Magdalene created the design below out of construction paper. Determine whether the design has rotational symmetry. Write *yes* or *no*. If yes, name its angle(s) of rotation.

EXAMPLE 3 Rotate △*XYZ* in a 90° clockwise rotation about the origin and graph its image. Then find the coordinates of △*X′Y′Z′*.

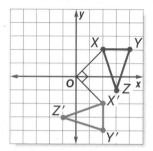

Point *X* becomes *X′*(2, −2).

Point *Y* becomes *Y′*(2, −4).

Point *Z* becomes *Z′*(−1, −3).

10-4 Dilations

Dilations (pp. 570–575)

 MA.7.G.4.2

21. Segment *C′D′* with endpoints *C′*(−8, 20) and *D′*(4, 16) is a dilation of segment *CD* with endpoints *C*(−2, 5) and *D*(1, 4). Find the scale factor of the dilation and classify it as an *enlargement* or a *reduction*.

22. **GEOMETRY** Triangle *ABC* has vertices *A*(−3, −6), *B*(6, 3), and *C*(9, −3). Find the vertices of its image for a dilation with a scale factor of $\frac{1}{3}$. Then graph △*ABC* and its dilation.

EXAMPLE 4 Segment *XY* has endpoints *X*(−4, 1) and *Y*(8, −2). Find the endpoints of its image for a dilation with a scale factor of $\frac{3}{4}$.

Multiply each coordinate in the ordered pair by $\frac{3}{4}$.

$$X(-4, 1) \rightarrow \left(-4 \cdot \frac{3}{4}, 1 \cdot \frac{3}{4}\right) \rightarrow X'\left(-3, \frac{3}{4}\right)$$

$$Y(8, -2) \rightarrow \left(8 \cdot \frac{3}{4}, -2 \cdot \frac{3}{4}\right) \rightarrow Y'\left(6, -1\frac{1}{2}\right)$$

PSI: Work Backward (pp. 576–577)

MA.7.A.5.2

Solve. Use the *work backward* strategy.

23. **PARKING** Mr. Tetto moved his car and parked it in the 3rd row, 5 places from the end. His car was parked 5 rows away and 2 places closer to the end. Where was Mr. Tetto originally parked?

24. **PHOTO** Elias got a photo of his parents enlarged for their anniversary. He increased the photo 3 times the original size. If the new photo is 9 inches by 12 inches, what was the size of the original?

25. **FINANCIAL LITERACY** Ben has a paper route to earn extra money. Each month he saves half of his paycheck and then divides the rest between the four weeks of the month. He spends $\frac{3}{5}$ of his weekly pay on lunches. If he spends $15 on lunches in a week, how much is his monthly paycheck?

EXAMPLE 5   Millie has money from her birthday to spend at the art supply store. She spends $\frac{1}{3}$ of the amount on a sketch pad. She then splits the remainder evenly between pencils and paints. If the pencils cost her $10, how much did she have to spend originally?

By working backward, we can determine the original amount of money Millie had to spend. If she spent $10 on pencils, she also spent $10 on paints. The pencils and paints account for $\frac{2}{3}$ of the money if she spent $\frac{1}{3}$ on the sketch pad. We can write an equation to find the total amount.

$$\frac{2}{3}x = 20 \qquad \text{Write the equation.}$$

$$\left(\frac{3}{2}\right)\frac{2}{3}x = \left(\frac{3}{2}\right)20 \qquad \text{Multiplication Property of Equality}$$

$$x = 30 \qquad \text{Simplify.}$$

Millie had $30 to spend at the art supply store.

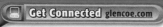

• Chapter Test

1. **ALGEBRA** Square *ABCD* is shown. What are the vertices of *A′B′C′D′* after a translation 2 units right and 2 units down? Graph the translated image.

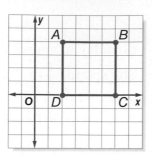

2. **GEOMETRY** Draw a figure with one line of symmetry. Then draw a figure with no lines of symmetry.

NATURE Determine whether each figure has line symmetry. If it does, trace the figure and draw all lines of symmetry. If not, write *none*.

3.
4.
5.

6. **NATURE** Which figure above has rotational symmetry? Name its angle(s) of rotation.

7. **NGSSS PRACTICE** A portion of an archway is shown. Which of the following shows the completed archway with vertical line symmetry?

A.

C.

B.

D.

Graph △JKL with vertices J(2, 3), K(−1, 4), and L(−3, −5). Then graph its image and write the coordinates of its vertices after each transformation.

8. reflection over the *x*-axis

9. translation 2 units left and 5 units up

10. **CHESS** Describe the translation of the letter *B* from its original location to its new location shown in red, if each individual square has a side length of 1 inch.

11. **GEOMETRY** Triangle *ABC* has vertices *A*(1, 1), *B*(−2, 4), and *C*(−3, −2). Find the vertices of its image after a dilation with a scale factor of 2. Then graph △*ABC* and its dilation.

12. **THINK SOLVE EXPLAIN** **EXTENDED RESPONSE** Polygon *HJKL* has vertices *H*(−2, 3), *J*(−3, 1), *K*(−2, −4) and *L*(3, 1).

Part A Graph polygon *HJKL*. What are the vertices of polygon *H′J′K′L′* if it is reflected over the *x*-axis?

Part B Find the vertices of polygon *H″J″K″L″* after polygon *H′J′K′L′* is dilated using a scale factor of 2. Then graph polygon *H′J′K′L′* and polygon *H″J″K″L″*.

Part C Identify at least two things you notice about the relationship between polygon *HJKL* and polygon *H″J″K″L″*.

Multiple Choice: Make a Drawing

You are not required to show your work for multiple-choice questions. However, you are allowed to write on the test book to help you solve problems. Doing so will help keep you from making careless errors.

NGSSS PRACTICE EXAMPLE

Triangle *LMN* has vertices at *L*(−4, −1), *M*(−2, 5), and *N*(1, 2). Triangle *HJK* has one vertex at *H*(0, −3) and one vertex at *J*(2, 3) and represents a slide of triangle *LMN*. Which point would be *K*, the third vertex of triangle *HJK*?

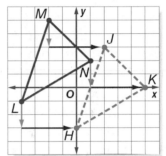

A. (5, 0)   **C.** (−1, 2)

B. (5, 2)   **D.** (−1, −5)

On the figure provided in the test book, graph vertices *H*(0, −3) and *J*(2, 3), as shown above. You can see that these vertices are 2 units down and 4 units right from the corresponding vertices in triangle *LMN*.

If you translate vertex *N* 2 units down and 4 units right, you get the coordinates of vertex *K*, (5, 0). The correct answer is A.

Work on It

Chloe is creating a design by reflecting the figure below across the *x*-axis. What would be the reflected location of point *Q*?

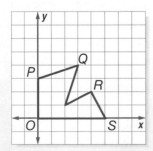

Test Hint

Sometimes it is necessary to make a completely new drawing. Use the white space in the test book to make the drawing.

F. (−2, 4)   **H.** (3, −4)

G. (4, 3)   **I.** (3, −5)

Read each question. Then fill in the correct answer on the answer sheet provided by your teacher or on a sheet of paper.

1. △ABC is translated 2 units right and 2 units down. What are the coordinates of A′?

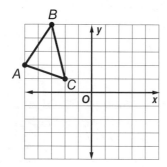

A. (0, −1)

B. (−3, 0)

C. (−1, 3)

D. (0, −3)

2. Seth has $858.60 in his savings account. He plans to spend 15% of his savings on a bicycle. Which of the following represents the amount Seth plans to spend on the bicycle?

F. $182.79

G. $171.72

H. $128.79

I. $122.79

3. Rectangle M is similar to rectangle N.

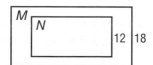

What scale factor was used to dilate rectangle M to rectangle N?

A. $\frac{1}{4}$

B. $\frac{1}{3}$

C. $\frac{2}{3}$

D. $1\frac{1}{2}$

4. **THINK SOLVE EXPLAIN** **SHORT RESPONSE** The figure shown was transformed from Quadrant I to Quadrant IV. What type of transformation was applied?

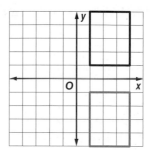

5. **GRIDDED RESPONSE** How many square feet of wrapping paper will Ashton need to cover the box shown?

1.5 ft

1.2 ft

3.4 ft

6. Carrie rotated a puzzle piece 180° clockwise around vertex C to see if she could use it.

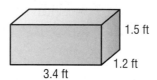

Which image represents the position of the puzzle piece after the 180° clockwise rotation?

F.

H.

G.

I.

7. The table at the right shows the possible outcomes when tossing two fair coins at the same time.

1st Coin	2nd Coin
H	H
H	T
T	H
T	T

Which of the following must be true?

A. The probability that both coins have the same outcome is $\frac{1}{4}$.

B. The probability of getting at least one tail is higher than the probability of getting two heads.

C. The probability that exactly one coin will turn up heads is $\frac{3}{4}$.

D. The probability of getting at least one tail is lower than the probability of getting two tails.

8. **GRIDDED RESPONSE** A manager took an employee to lunch. If the lunch was $48 and she left a 20% tip, how much money did she spend on lunch?

9. Which of the following groups does NOT contain equivalent fractions, decimals, and percents?

F. $\frac{9}{20}$, 0.45, 45%

G. $\frac{3}{10}$, 0.3, 30%

H. $\frac{7}{8}$, 0.875, 87.5%

I. $\frac{1}{100}$, 0.1, 1%

10. **SHORT RESPONSE** Alfonzo drew half of a star on a coordinate plane. If the drawing was reflected across the y-axis, what would be the reflected location of point B?

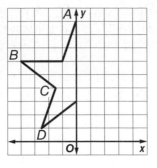

11. Which drawing best represents a reflection over the vertical line segment in the center of the rectangle?

A.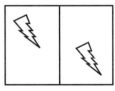

C.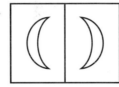

B.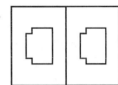

D.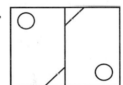

12. **EXTENDED RESPONSE** Graph $\triangle XYZ$ with vertices $X(2, 1)$, $Y(7, 3)$, and $Z(3, 6)$.

Part A Translate $\triangle XYZ$ 3 units left and 4 units down. Identify the coordinates of each new vertex.

Part B Find the vertices of $\triangle X'Y'Z'$ after a dilation with a scale factor of $\frac{1}{2}$. Then graph the dilation.

Part C Rotate the dilated figure 270° clockwise around the origin. Draw the rotation.

NEED EXTRA HELP?												
If You Missed Question...	1	2	3	4	5	6	7	8	9	10	11	12
Go to Lesson...	10-1B	6-1B	10-4A	10-2B	8-2B	10-3B	7-2A	6-3C	2-1C	10-2B	10-2B	10-4A
For help with NGSSS...	G.4.2	A.1.2	G.4.2	G.4.2	G.2.1	G.4.2	P.7.1	A.1.2	A.5.1	G.4.2	G.4.2	G.4.2

NGSSS Review

Throughout the school year, you may be required to take several tests, and you may have many questions about them. Here are some answers to help you get ready.

How Should I Study?

The good news is that you've been studying all along—a little bit every day. Here are some of the ways your textbook has been preparing you.

- **Every Day** Each lesson had practice questions that covered the NGSSS.
- **Every Week** The Mid-Chapter Check and Practice Test had several practice questions.
- **Every Month** The NGSSS Practice pages at the end of each chapter had even more questions similar to those on tests.

Are There Other Ways to Review?

Absolutely! The following pages contain even more practice for NGSSS.

Tips for SUCCESS

Prepare

☑ Go to bed early the night before the test. You will think more clearly after a good night's rest.

☑ Become familiar with common formulas and when they should be used.

☑ Think positively.

During the Test

☑ Read each problem carefully. Underline key words and think about different ways to solve the problem.

☑ Watch for key words like NOT. Also look for order words like **least, greatest, first, last,** and **best**.

☑ Answer questions you are sure about first. If you do not know the answer to a question, skip it and go back to that question later.

☑ Check your answer to make sure it is reasonable.

☑ Make sure that the number of the question on the answer sheet matches the number of the question in your test booklet.

Whatever you do...

☑ Don't try to do it all in your head. If no figure is provided, draw one.

☑ Don't rush. Try to work at a steady pace.

☑ Don't give up. Some problems may seem hard to you, but you may be able to figure out what to do if you try another strategy.

Practice by Big Idea

The ☆**BIG Idea 1** Develop an understanding of and apply proportionality, including similarity.

Read each question. Then fill in the correct answer on the sheet provided by your teacher or on a sheet of paper.

QUICK Check	QUICK Review

1. Randy pedals his bicycle at a constant rate of 15 feet per second. Which linear equation represents his total distance traveled y after x seconds? (MA.7.A.1.4)

   A. $y = x + 15$

   B. $y = x - 15$

   C. $y = 15x$

   D. $y = 15 \div x$

> **STRATEGY** Use the proportional relationship to write a function.

How far does Randy travel in 1 second? 2 seconds? 3 seconds?

Which function models this data?

For more help with using linear functions to model proportional relationships, see page 247.

2. A jacket that normally sells for $85 is being discounted 20% during a sale. What is the sale price of the jacket? (MA.7.A.1.2)

   F. $17

   G. $43

   H. $68

   I. $102

> **STRATEGY** Use the percent proportion to find the sale price.

Set up and solve a proportion for the sale price p.

$$\frac{p}{85} = \frac{80}{100}$$

For more help with solving percent problems, see page 312.

3. Look at the equations below. Which equation does NOT represent a proportional relationship? (MA.7.A.1.5)

   A. $y = 4 \cdot x$

   B. $y = (-1.5)x$

   C. $y = x$

   D. $y = 9 \div x$

> **READING HINT** As one quantity changes in a *proportional relationship,* the other quantity changes by a constant amount.

Use the process of elimination to find the equation that does not represent a proportional relationship.

For more help with distinguishing direct variation from other relationships, see page 273.

4. ✏️ **GRIDDED RESPONSE** Cirilo read 28 pages in 8 minutes. How many minutes would it take him to read 49 pages? (MA.7.A.1.1)

> **STRATEGY** Find the unit rate for the ratio.

How many pages are read each minute?

For more help with distinguishing between situations that are proportional and not proportional, see page 202.

5. The Florida state flag at Glenview Middle School has the dimensions shown below.

4 ft

6 ft

Bruno is sketching a scale drawing of the flag. If his drawing is 15 inches long, how wide will it be? (MA.7.A.1.6)

  F. 8 inches

  G. 10 inches

  H. 12 inches

  I. 14 inches

> **STRATEGY** Set up and solve a proportion for the missing side.

What is the ratio of length to width for the actual flag? Compare this to the ratio of length to width for Bruno's drawing of the flag.

For more help with scale drawings, see page 216.

6. ✏️ **GRIDDED RESPONSE** Triangles *ABC* and *RST* are similar. The ratio of their corresponding sides is 4 : 3.

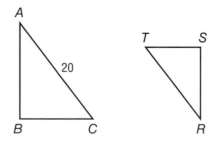

What is the length of *RT*? (MA.7.A.1.3)

> **STRATEGY** Set up a proportion to find the missing side length.

You know the ratio of the corresponding sides of the triangles. Compare this to the ratio of side $\overline{AB}$ to side $\overline{RT}$.

For more help with similar figures, see page 223.

Practice on Your Own

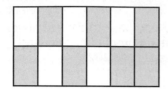

7. What percent of the figure below is shaded? (MA.7.A.1.2)

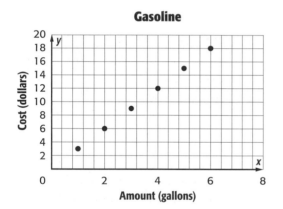

A. $3\frac{1}{3}\%$

B. $41\frac{2}{3}\%$

C. 50%

D. $58\frac{1}{3}\%$

8. The graph shows the cost y of gasoline for x gallons. What is the unit rate of the gasoline? (MA.7.A.1.4)

Gasoline

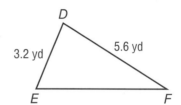

F. $18 per gallon

G. $15 per gallon

H. $9 per gallon

I. $3 per gallon

9. Look at the equations below. Which equation represents a proportional relationship? (MA.7.A.1.5)

A. $y = \frac{1}{x}$

B. $y = x + 5$

C. $y = 3x$

D. $y = 3x + 5$

10. Trent is driving at a constant speed. If he drives 110 miles in 2 hours, how far will he drive in 5 hours? (MA.7.A.1.6)

F. 55 miles

G. 215 miles

H. 245 miles

I. 275 miles

11. **GRIDDED RESPONSE** Triangle ABC is similar to triangle DEF below. What is the value of x in yards? (MA.7.A.1.3, MA.7.A.1.1)

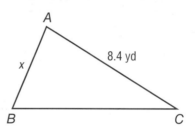

12. Which of the following does NOT represent a direct variation? (MA.7.A.1.5)

A. Julio earns $9 for every hour that he works.

B. Meliah travels 12.5 miles each hour that she spends biking.

C. Victoria has $25. She decides to save $5 each week.

D. A restaurant owner earns $4.75 in profit for each dinner that he sells.

13. Which parallelogram below is similar to parallelogram *RSTU*? (MA.7.A.1.3)

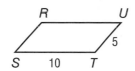

F.

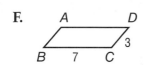

G.

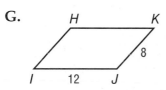

H.

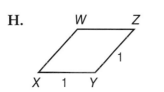

I.

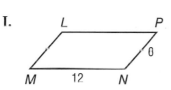

14. ☰☰✎ **GRIDDED RESPONSE** Jakeem used a scale drawing to build a model airplane. Based on the drawing below, what is the actual length of the plane's wingspan in feet? (MA.7.A.1.6)

Scale
$\frac{1}{2}$ inch = 20 feet

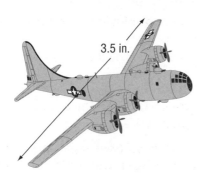

3.5 in.

15. ☰☰✎ **GRIDDED RESPONSE** The receipt below shows Camille's total dinner bill before tip. If she wants to leave a 20% tip on the total bill for the waiter, how much tip should she leave? (MA.7.A.1.2)

La Bamba Restaurant

Burrito $5.80
Rice $3.25
Soda $1.35

Subtotal................$10.40
Tax (5%) $0.52

Total....................$10.92

16. ☰☰✎ **GRIDDED RESPONSE** Kody purchased 4 books for $30. How much would Kody pay for 7 books if each book costs the same? (MA.7.A.1.1)

17. The table below shows the number of words Luis types in different amounts of time. If the relationship is proportional, how many words will he type in 8 minutes? (MA.7.A.1.1)

Typing Speed	
Minutes	**Words**
2	70
5	175
8	?
12	420

A. 35

B. 140

C. 280

D. 350

Practice by Big Idea

☆BIG Idea 2 Develop an understanding of and use formulas to determine surface areas and volumes of three-dimensional shapes.

Read each question. Then fill in the correct answer on your answer document. If a correct answer is *not here,* mark the letter for "Not here."

QUICK Check	QUICK Review

1. Alex is creating sand art in a clear plastic pyramid. The square pyramid is 6 inches along its base and has a height of 4 inches.

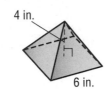

4 in.

6 in.

What is the volume of the pyramid in cubic inches? (MA.7.G.2.1)

A. 48 in³   C. 144 in³

B. 84 in³   D. 270 in³

> **READING HINT** Recall that the *volume* of a pyramid can be found by multiplying $\frac{1}{3}$ by the product of the area of the base and the height.

The volume of the pyramid can be found by multiplying $\frac{1}{3}$ by the product of 36 · 4.

For more help with finding the volume of a pyramid, see page 445.

---

2. ✏️ **GRIDDED RESPONSE** What is the surface area in square units of the solid shown below? (MA.7.G.2.1)

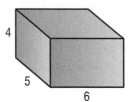

4

5

6

> **READING HINT** The *surface area* of a three-dimensional solid is the sum of the areas of all of the faces.

Find the area of all 6 faces of the rectangular solid. Then add these values.

For more help with finding the surface area of rectangular solids, see page 456.

---

3. How much paper to the nearest square centimeter is needed to make the paper cup below? (MA.7.G.2.1)

8 cm

10 cm

F. 80 cm²

G. 130 cm²

H. 302 cm²

I. 400 cm²

> **STRATEGY** The surface area of a cylinder is the sum of the rectangular curved surface and the two circular bases. A cup would only include one circular base.

For more help with finding the surface area of cylinders, see page 462.

4. ✏️ **GRIDDED RESPONSE** Oscar has a toy rocket that is made of a cylinder and a cone. The total height of the rocket's body is 24 centimeters. The height of the nose cone is 8 centimeters. The diameter of the rocket is 4 centimeters. What is the total volume of the rocket's body in cubic centimeters? Round to the nearest tenth. (MA.7.G.2.2)

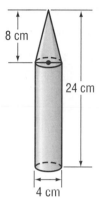

8 cm

24 cm

4 cm

▶ **STRATEGY** Break the composite figure into two simpler shapes.

Use the formula $V = \pi r^2 h$ for the volume of the cylinder.

Use the formula $V = \frac{1}{3}\pi r^2 h$ for the volume of the nose cone.

Add the volumes to find the total volume.

For more help with finding the volume of three-dimensional composite shapes, see page 480.

5. Aiyanna builds a structure using blocks as shown. If each block is a cube that measures 4 centimeters on each side, what is the total volume of the block structure? (MA.7.G.2.2)

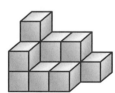

A. 16 cm^3

B. 512 cm^3

C. 768 cm^3

D. 1216 cm^3

▶ **READING HINT** Recall that the *volume* of a rectangular prism can be found by multiplying the length, width, and height.

First determine the number of cubes in the structure. The volume of each cube can be found by finding the product of 4 · 4 · 4.

For more help with finding the volume of a rectangular prism, see page 432.

NGSSS Review

Practice on Your Own

6. The chemical tank shown below is full of liquid chlorine to treat a swimming pool.

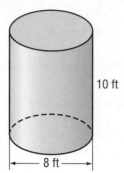

10 ft

8 ft

How much liquid does it hold?
($V = \pi r^2 h$. Use $\pi = 3.14$.) (MA.7.G.2.1)

F. 2009.6 cubic feet

G. 502.4 cubic feet

H. 251.2 cubic feet

I. 125.6 cubic feet

7. A rectangular prism has a volume of 3228.75 cubic centimeters. It has a base length of 20.5 centimeters and a height of 10.5 centimeters. What is the width?
(MA.7.G.2.1)

A. 10.5 cm

B. 15 cm

C. 15.5 cm

D. 20.5 cm

8. ≡≡✎ **GRIDDED RESPONSE** A shipping crate has dimensions 6 feet by 4 feet by 5.5 feet.

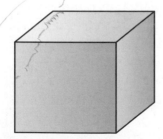

What is the volume of the shipping crate in cubic feet? (MA.7.G.2.1)

9. A cylindrical box of oats has a radius of 2.5 inches and a volume of 235.5 cubic inches. What is the height of the box? (Use 3.14 for π.) (MA.7.G.2.1)

F. 5 in.

G. 10 in.

H. 12 in.

I. 24 in.

10. Arthur stacks boxes for storage in the pattern shown below.

If each box is a 2-foot cube, what is the total volume of the box structure?
(MA.7.G.2.2)

A. 48 ft³

B. 56 ft³

C. 72 ft³

D. 144 ft³

11. ≡≡✎ **GRIDDED RESPONSE** A pyramid has a square base measuring 10 inches on each side. If the height of the pyramid is 18 inches, what is the volume in cubic inches? (MA.7.G.2.1)

12. ≡≡✎ **GRIDDED RESPONSE** A gift is shipped in a special box shown below.

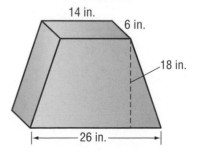

14 in.

6 in.

18 in.

26 in.

Find the volume of the box in cubic inches. (MA.7.G.2.2)

13. Elio is wrapping a gift in the box shown below.

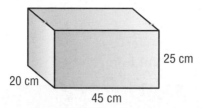

25 cm
20 cm
45 cm

How much wrapping paper will he need to completely cover the box? (MA.7.G.2.1)

F. 5050 cm²

G. 7140 cm²

H. 14 230 cm²

I. 22 500 cm²

14. ✎ **GRIDDED RESPONSE** Curtis is building the birdhouse shown below. The hole in the front of the birdhouse has a diameter of 10 centimeters. What is the minimum amount of paint in square centimeters needed to cover the outside of the birdhouse? (Neglect the hole.) (MA.7.G.2.2)

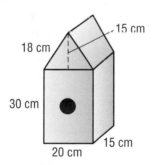

15 cm
18 cm
30 cm
15 cm
20 cm

15. ✎ **GRIDDED RESPONSE** Prisca is icing the sides and top of a cake made of two stacked square cakes shown below.

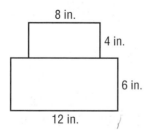

8 in.
4 in.
6 in.
12 in.

How many square inches of icing are needed? (MA.7.G.2.2)

16. A machinist has a cylindrical piece of steel that is 6 millimeters high and has a diameter of 20 millimeters. He creates a washer by drilling out a 12-millimeter cylinder from the center of the metal stock. What is the volume of the finished washer to the nearest tenth in cubic millimeters? (Use π = 3.14.) (MA.7.G.2.2)

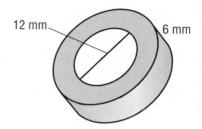

12 mm
6 mm

A 678.2 mm³

B 720.0 mm³

C 1205.8 mm³

D 1884.0 mm³

17. A cup filled with shaved ice is shaped like a cone with a diameter of 10 centimeters and a height of 14 centimeters. How much ice does the cup hold? (Use 3.14 for π and round to the nearest tenth.) (MA.7.G.2.1)

F. 167.5 cm³

G. 366.3 cm³

H. 508.2 cm³

I. 4396.0 cm³

18. ✎ **GRIDDED RESPONSE** What is the surface area in square centimeters of the solid shown below? Use 3.14 for π. Round to the nearest tenth. (MA.7.G.2.1)

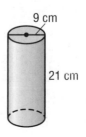

9 cm
21 cm

Practice by Big Idea

☆**BIG Idea** 3 Develop an understanding of operations on all rational numbers and solve linear equations.

Read each question. Then fill in the correct answer on your answer document. If a correct answer is *not here*, mark the letter for "Not here."

QUICK Check	QUICK Review
1. ✎ **GRIDDED RESPONSE** During a visit to his favorite bookstore, Carlos bought 3 hardback books priced at $14.99 each and 4 paperback books priced at $7.99 each. Find the total of Carlos's purchase in dollars before tax is included. (MA.7.A.3.2)	**STRATEGY** Record your answer carefully in the grid. Be sure to put the decimal point in the proper place. Place one digit in each box. Using the order of operations, multiply to find the cost of the hardback books and the cost of the paperback books. Then add to find the total. For more help with multiplying and adding decimals, see page 80.

2. Consider the equation below. Which of the following equations is equivalent to it? (MA.7.A.3.4)
 	
$$-7x + (-4) = -18$$
 	
  A. $-7x = -18$
  B. $-7x = -14$
  C. $-7x = -22$
  D. $7x = -14$
	STRATEGY Use the properties of equality to find an equivalent equation.
	
	What is the result when you subtract (-4) from each side of the equation?
	
	For more help with using the properties of equality to identify equivalent equations, see page 172.

3. If a represents a negative number and b represents a negative number, what is true about the product of a and b? (MA.7.A.3.1)
 	
  F. The product will be zero.
  G. The product will be negative.
  H. The product will be positive.
  I. The sign of the product cannot be determined without knowing the values of a and b.
	READING HINT Use the rules of integers to predict the sign of the product. The word *product* indicates multiplication.
	
	Recall the rules for multiplying integers. Are there set rules for the sign of the answer? If so, use them to predict the sign of the product of a negative number and a negative number.
	
	For more help with multiplying integers, see page 56.

4. Simplify the expression below.
(MA.7.A.3.1)

$$9 + 8(11 - 6) \div 2^2$$

  A. 12.25

  B. 19

  C. 21.25

  D. 81

> **STRATEGY** Use the order of operations to simplify the expression.

Do all operations within grouping symbols first. Next, evaluate any powers and then multiply and divide in order from left to right. Finally, add and subtract in order from left to right.

For more help with evaluating expressions, see page 126.

---

5. ≡≡ **GRIDDED RESPONSE** The sum of a number x and 15 is 54. What is the value of x? (MA.7.A.3.3)

> **READING HINT** Look for key words in the problem statement to help you write an equation. The word *sum* implies addition.

First, write an expression for the sum of a number x and 15. Then set this expression equal to 54. Subtract 15 from both sides of the equation.

For more help with writing algebraic equations, see page 150.

---

6. What value of a makes the equation below true? (MA.7.A.3.3)

$$\frac{1}{4}a - \frac{2}{3} = \frac{7}{12}$$

  F. $-\dfrac{13}{15}$ **H.** $\dfrac{12}{5}$

  G. $-\dfrac{7}{8}$ **I.** 5

> **STRATEGY** Use the properties of equality to solve for a.

First add $\dfrac{2}{3}$ to each side of the equation. Then multiply each side by $\dfrac{4}{1}$.

For more help with solving equations, see page 162.

---

7. During last week's track practice, Kiera practiced $2\frac{1}{4}$ hours on hurdles, $1\frac{1}{2}$ hours on sprinting, and $2\frac{3}{4}$ hours on relays. Find the total amount of time that Kiera practiced last week. (MA.7.A.3.2)

  A. $3\frac{3}{4}$ hours   **C.** $6\frac{1}{2}$ hours

  B. 5 hours   **D.** 9 hours

> **STRATEGY** Record your answer carefully in the grid. Be sure to put the decimal point in the proper place. Place one digit in each box.

Find a common denominator for all 3 types of practice, then add to find the total.

For more help with multiplying and adding fractions, see page 98.

Practice on Your Own

8. Keith works in an electronics store. His monthly sales for the first three months of the year are listed in the table below.

Month	Sales
January	$2,840
February	$2,245
March	$3,175

If Keith's sales commission rate is 0.125, how much commission did he make during the 3-month period? (MA.7.A.3.2)

F. $878.25

G. $946.80

H. $990.10

I. $1,032.50

9. ≣≣ **GRIDDED RESPONSE** The difference between a number n and 17 is 25. What is the value of n? (MA.7.A.3.3)

10. Refer to the number line below.

Which two points have the same absolute value? (MA.7.A.3.1)

A. points U and R

B. points S and T

C. points W and T

D. points V and R

11. Which is the simplified form of the expression below? (MA.7.A.3.1)

$$|4 - 15| + |-6 + 2|$$

F. -4

G. -11

H. -15

I. 15

12. Consider the equation below. Which of the following equations is equivalent to it? (MA.7.A.3.4)

$$\frac{x+3}{7} = -\frac{1}{2}$$

A. $x + 3 = -\frac{7}{2}$

B. $x + 3 = 6\frac{1}{2}$

C. $x + 3 = 7\frac{1}{2}$

D. $x + 3 = \frac{7}{2}$

13. ≣≣ **GRIDDED RESPONSE** Simplify the expression below. (MA.7.A.3.1)

$$2(7 + 5) - 4^2$$

14. Lilian is putting up a wallpaper border on two walls of her room. The walls are $12\frac{3}{8}$ feet and $11\frac{1}{4}$ feet long. The border is 30 feet long. How much border will she have left over? (MA.7.A.3.2)

F. $6\frac{3}{8}$ ft

G. $7\frac{1}{2}$ ft

H. 20 ft

I. $23\frac{5}{8}$ ft

15. ≣≣ **GRIDDED RESPONSE** Suppose it takes Martin 2.5 hours to drive 120 miles. What is his average rate of speed in miles per hour? Use $d = rt$. (MA.7.A.3.3)

16. What is the value of m in the equation below? (MA.7.A.3.3)

$$\frac{m}{3} - 5 = 4$$

A. 27   **C.** -3

B. 3   **D.** -27

17. **GRIDDED RESPONSE** Alexi needs $200 to buy a used computer. She has $75 and can save $25 per week. The equation $25w + 75 = 200$ shows this relationship. For how many weeks must Alexi save to have the money she needs? (MA.7.A.3.3)

18. Which operation would you need to perform in order to show that Equation 1 is equivalent to Equation 2? (MA.7.A.3.4)

Equation 1

$$5(x + 3) = 20x$$

Equation 2

$$x + 3 = 4x$$

F. multiply both sides of Equation 1 by 5

G. divide both sides of Equation 1 by 5

H. subtract 5 from both sides of Equation 1

I. add 5 to both sides of Equation 1

19. Which value of a makes the equation below true? (MA.7.A.3.3)

$$3a + 9 = -18$$

A. 9

B. 3

C. −3

D. −9

20. **GRIDDED RESPONSE** It takes Dennis $1\frac{1}{2}$ hours to mow the lawn, $\frac{2}{3}$ of an hour to trim, and $\frac{1}{4}$ hour to clean up.

What is the total time in hours it takes Dennis to finish the lawn? (MA.7.A.3.1)

21. Which expression is equivalent to $\frac{5^6 \cdot 3^3}{5^5 \cdot 3^2}$? (MA.7.A.3.2)

F. $\frac{1}{5} \cdot \frac{1}{3}$

G. $\frac{15^9}{15^7}$

H. $5 \cdot 3$

I. $5^2 \cdot 3^2$

22. Elian's mother is 12 years older than twice Elian's age. The equation

$$2a + 12 = m$$

where a represents Elian's age and m represents his mother's age can be used to find Elian's age. If his mother is 36 years old, how old is Elian? (MA.7.A.3.3)

A. 6

B. 12

C. 18

D. 36

23. **GRIDDED RESPONSE** Simplify the expression below. (MA.7.A.3.1)

$$(-2)^3 - (-5)(-8)$$

24. Which property best describes the steps taken in solving the equation shown below? (MA.7.A.3.4)

Step 1 $5x + 4 = 3x - 12$

Step 2 $2x + 4 = -12$

F. The Distributive Property

G. The Additive Identity Property

H. The Multiplication Property of Equality

I. The Subtraction Property of Equality

Practice by Supporting Idea

⭐ **Supporting Idea** *Geometry and Measurement*

Read each question. Then fill in the correct answer on your answer document. If a correct answer is *not here,* mark the letter for "Not here."

QUICK Check	QUICK Review

1. If Amy reflects the figure across the *x*-axis, what will be the result?

(MA.7.G.4.2)

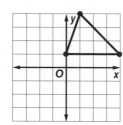

▶ **READING HINT** A *reflection* is the flip of a figure over a line of symmetry.

Find the *x*-axis. Imagine flipping the figure over this line. What will be the result?

For more help with predicting the results of transformations, see page 556.

A.

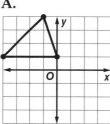

C.

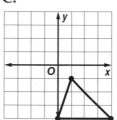

B.

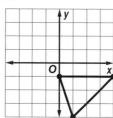

D.

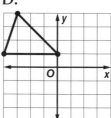

2. ▤✎ **GRIDDED RESPONSE** A computer monitor is 400 millimeters wide. Find the monitor's width in centimeters.

(MA.7.G.4.4)

▶ **STRATEGY** Set up and solve a proportion to convert the units.

1 cm = 10 mm

Solve the proportion $\dfrac{1 \text{ cm}}{10 \text{ mm}} = \dfrac{x \text{ cm}}{400 \text{ mm}}$.

For more help with unit conversions, see page 505.

3. What are the coordinates of point *H*?

(MA.7.G.4.3)

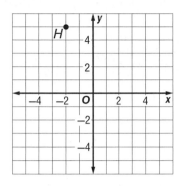

F. $H(-5, 2)$

G. $H(2, -5)$

H. $H(5, -2)$

I. $H(-2, 5)$

STRATEGY   Find the coordinates of the ordered pair.

An ordered pair is of the form (x, y).

Moving *right* or *up* on a coordinate plane is in a positive direction.

Moving *left* or *down* is in a negative direction.

For more help with identifying the coordinates of an ordered pair, see page 33.

---

4. Esther is driving 40 miles per hour. If 1 mile is about 1.6 kilometers, what is her speed in kilometers per hour?

(MA.7.G.4.4)

A. about 70 km/h

B. about 64 km/h

C. about 52 km/h

D. about 25 km/h

STRATEGY   Set up and solve a proportion to find the unit conversion.

$1 \text{ mi} \approx 1.6 \text{ km}$

Solve the proportion $\dfrac{1 \text{ mi}}{1.6 \text{ km}} = \dfrac{40 \text{ mi}}{x \text{ km}}$.

For more help with converting between customary units and metric units, see page 509.

---

5. ✐ **GRIDDED RESPONSE** Suppose the dimensions of a rectangular prism are doubled. How many times as great is the volume of the larger prism than the volume of the original prism?

(MA.7.G.4.1)

STRATEGY   Use a model to help you find the answer.

Sketch a simple rectangular prism and label its dimensions. Find the volume.

Find the volume after doubling the dimensions. Compare the two volumes.

For more help with finding changes in volume when the dimensions of a figure are changed, see page 528.

Practice on Your Own

6. Which of the following shows segment *RS* being translated down 6 units and right 2 units to form segment *R'S'*? (MA.7.G.4.2)

F.

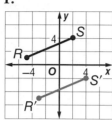

H.

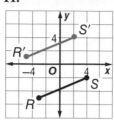

G.

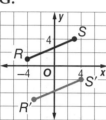

I.

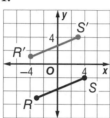

7. ✍ **GRIDDED RESPONSE** Amal's father needs 6 cubic yards of concrete to build the foundation for a new patio. How many cubic feet is this? (MA.7.G.4.4)

8. Which point on the coordinate grid has coordinates (3, −5)? (MA.7.G.4.3)

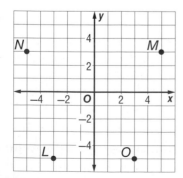

A. point *L*

B. point *M*

C. point *N*

D. point *O*

9. A square has a vertex located at *P*(−4, 7). If the square is reflected over the *y*-axis, what are the coordinates of *P'*? (MA.7.G.4.2)

F. (4, 7)

G. (−4, −7)

H. (4, −7)

I. (−4, 7)

10. Blythe is mailing a gift box to his brother. The box has a volume of 6555 cubic centimeters. If 1 inch equals approximately 2.54 centimeters, about how many cubic inches is the volume of the box? (MA.7.G.4.4)

A. 10 740 in^3

B. 1016 in^3

C. 850 in^3

D. 400 in^3

11. ✍ **GRIDDED RESPONSE** Mali walked to the post office and then to the library. When she returned home, her pedometer indicated she walked a total of 5.5 miles. How many kilometers did she walk? Round to the nearest hundredth if necessary. (MA.7.G.4.4)

12. Describe the single transformation that maps image A onto image B. (MA.7.G.4.2)

Image A

Image B

F. A clockwise rotation of 90°.

G. A dilation.

H. A counterclockwise rotation of 90°.

I. A translation.

13. Mr. Eckinrode uses 80 feet of fencing to enclose a square area in which his puppy can play. Suppose he doubles the amount of fencing to 160 feet. How many times as great is the area of the puppy's enclosure? (MA.7.G.4.1)

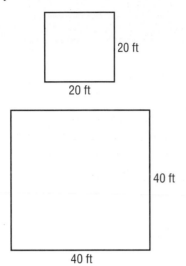

20 ft

20 ft

40 ft

40 ft

A. The area is 2 times larger.

B. The area is 4 times larger.

C. The area is 8 times larger.

D. Not here

14. About how many cubic centimeters are in 4 cubic inches? (MA.7.G.4.4)

$$1 \text{ in}^3 \approx 16.4 \text{ cm}^3$$

F. about 0.24 cm^3

G. about 1.75 cm^3

H. about 52.3 cm^3

I. about 65.6 cm^3

15. ≣≣✎ **GRIDDED RESPONSE** Televisions are measured by the diagonal distance across the screen. Find the measure of a 52-inch television to the nearest centimeter. (MA.7.G.4.4)

16. ≣≣✎ **GRIDDED RESPONSE** Suppose the volume of a solid figure is 121.5 cubic units. If its dimensions are scaled by the same factor, the volume is 4.5 cubic units. What is the scale factor? Show your work. (MA.7.G.4.1)

17. A landscape architect wants to place a circular flower garden in the center of the rectangular yard shown on the grid below.

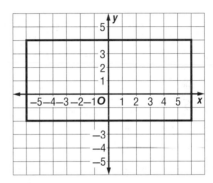

What are the coordinates of the center of the garden? (MA.7.G.4.3)

A. $(1, 0)$

B. $(-1, 0)$

C. $(0, 1)$

D. $(0, -1)$

18. ≣≣✎ **GRIDDED RESPONSE** A manatee can swim as slowly as 89.4 centimeters per second. What is this rate of speed in miles per hour? (MA.7.G.4.4)

19. In what quadrant does the point $(-2, -2)$ lie on the coordinate plane? (MA.7.G.4.3)

F. I

G. II

H. III

I. IV

Practice by Supporting Idea

⭐ Supporting Idea *Number and Operations*

Read each question. Then fill in the correct answer on your answer document. If a correct answer is *not here*, mark the letter for "Not here."

QUICK *Check*	QUICK *Review*
1. Which of the following is equivalent to $\frac{9}{4}$? (MA.7.A.5.1) **A.** 0.444 **B.** 1.8 **C.** 2.25 **D.** 2.75	**STRATEGY** As you examine each choice, put a check beside the ones that are NOT equivalent. The one without a check is the correct answer. To write a fraction as a decimal, divide the numerator by the denominator. For more help with expressing rational numbers as terminating decimals, see page 80.
2. Which of the following is equivalent to $\frac{2}{3}$? (MA.7.A.5.1) **F.** 0.6666 **G.** $0.\overline{6}$ **H.** 0.3333 **I.** $0.\overline{3}$	**STRATEGY** Divide the numerator by the denominator. If a number keeps repeating when you divide two numbers, it is a repeating decimal. For more help with writing rational numbers as repeating decimals, see page 80.
3. ✎ **GRIDDED RESPONSE** Enrico spent one half of his Saturday earnings on a video game and half of the remaining amount on a CD. After he spent $5.85 on lunch, he had $8.15 left. How much in dollars did Enrico earn on Saturday? (MA.7.A.5.2)	**STRATEGY** Work backward to solve the problem. First write an equation to show how Enrico spent his money. Let m = Enrico's earnings. Then let $\frac{1}{2}m$ = the cost of the video game and $\frac{1}{2}\left(\frac{1}{2}\right)m$ = the cost of the CD. Write and solve an equation to find Enrico's earnings on Saturday. For more help with working backward to solve problems, see page 144.

4. Kristen is meeting some friends at 8:30 P.M. She will spend an hour and a half on her homework and then 45 minutes on dinner. What is the latest Kristen can start her homework and still meet her friends on time? (MA.7.A.5.2)

A. 5:45 P.M.

B. 6:15 P.M.

C. 6:30 P.M.

D. 6:45 P.M.

> **STRATEGY** Work backward to solve the problem.

Begin with the time that Kristen will meet her friends. Undo the steps described in the problem to work backward to the latest time she can start her homework.

For more help with working backward to solve problems, see page 144.

5. An elevator begins on Mireya's floor and then follows the sequence of moves below.

- down 3 floors
- down 5 floors
- up 6 floors
- down 2 floors
- up 7 floors
- down 4 floors
- down 2 floors

If the elevator ends on the 5th floor, what is Mireya's floor? (MA.7.A.5.2)

F. 8th floor

G. 9th floor

H. 10th floor

I. 11th floor

> **STRATEGY** Work backward to solve the problem.

Begin with the floor where the elevator stops. Then use inverses to undo the moves in the table to work backward to Mireya's floor.

For more help with working backward to solve problems, see page 144.

6. In a recent year, the Miami Dolphins made 21 field goals out of 24 attempts. Write this ratio as a decimal. (MA.7.A.5.1)

A. 0.65

B. 0.$\overline{6}$

C. 0.875

D. 1.$\overline{142857}$

> **READING HINT** The question asks you to write the ratio as a decimal.

To write a ratio as a decimal, first write the ratio as a fraction. Then divide the numerator by the denominator.

For more help with writing ratios as fractions, see page 196.

Practice on Your Own

7. During a recent game, the basketball coach kept free throw statistics.

Free Throw Shooting	
Attempts	**Made**
28	21

Express Delaney's successful free throw rate as a decimal. (MA.7.A.5.1)

F. 0.675

G. 0.7

H. 0.7125

I. 0.75

8. Which point on the number line represents the repeating decimal 0.14666... ? (MA.7.A.5.1)

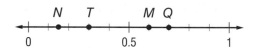

A. point *M*

B. point *N*

C. point *Q*

D. point *T*

9. During a recent food drive, the seventh grade collected 120 pounds of food. Mrs. James's class was the first to turn in their food. Miss Wheeler's class doubled the first donation. The principal tripled what Mrs. James's class collected. How much food did Mrs. James's class turn in? (MA.7.A.5.2)

F. 15 pounds

G. 25 pounds

H. 20 pounds

I. 30 pounds

10. ✎ **GRIDDED RESPONSE** LaBron has some pennies, nickels, dimes, and quarters. He has twice as many nickels as pennies. The number of dimes that LaBron has is 4 more than the number of nickels. He has half as many quarters as dimes. If LaBron has 5 quarters, how many pennies does he have? (MA.7.A.5.2)

11. Which decimal represents the portion of the figure below that is shaded? (MA.7.A.5.1)

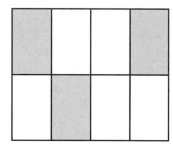

A. 0.3

B. $0.\overline{3}$

C. 0.35

D. 0.375

12. Which decimal below is NOT repeating? (MA.7.A.5.1)

F. $0.\overline{5}$

G. 0.123456789

H. $0.516\overline{4}$

I. $0.561\overline{982}$

13. ✎ **GRIDDED RESPONSE** Lexie spent $7.50 on a movie ticket. Then she spent $3.50 on popcorn and one fourth of what was left on a soft drink. She has $6 left. How much money, in dollars, did she bring with her to the movie theater? (MA.7.A.5.2)

14. How can you express the average of the quiz scores below as a decimal? (MA.7.A.5.1)

Quiz Scores		
8	9	6
7	10	8
8	7	5
9	10	8

A. $7.08\overline{3}$

B. $7.58\overline{3}$

C. $7.8\overline{3}$

D. $7.91\overline{6}$

15. The table below shows the daily change in the price of a share of stock last week. If the stock was trading at $32.59 per share at the end of Friday, what was the price at the beginning of trading Monday? (MA.7.A.5.2)

Stock Tracker	
Day	**Change in Price**
Mon.	+ $0.78 per share
Tues.	+ $1.13 per share
Wed.	− $0.21 per share
Thur.	+ $0.65 per share
Fri.	− $1.74 per share

F. $33.20 per share

G. $32.56 per share

H. $31.98 per share

I. $31.70 per share

16. ✍ **GRIDDED RESPONSE** The Richards Middle School baseball team won 13 games out of 19 games played. Write this ratio as a decimal to the nearest hundredth. (MA.7.A.5.1)

17. ✍ **GRIDDED RESPONSE** Wendy is writing a paper for English class. It is required that the final summary is $\frac{1}{3}$ of the total word count. Her final summary is 200 words. How many words are in the entire paper? (MA.7.A.5.2)

18. Rei wins 8 prizes at a carnival. Five of the prizes are stuffed animals. Which number shows a decimal that represents the portion of the prizes that are stuffed animals? (MA.7.A.5.1)

A. 0.5

B. 0.625

C. 0.75

D. 0.875

19. ✍ **GRIDDED RESPONSE** Elan, Zoe, and Kate created a puzzle for their friends.

- Elan: I am 9 years younger than twice Zoe's age.
- Zoe: If you take my age and multiply it by 0.4, the result is 2 less than Kate's age.
- Kate: I am 6 years old.

How old is Elan? (MA.7.A.5.2)

20. Haley is buying a video game system that is on sale for $\frac{2}{3}$ of its original price. She uses a $50 gift card to help pay for the system. Before tax, the total was $292. Which is the original price of the video game system? (MA.7.A.5.2)

F. $363

G. $488

H. $513

I. $567

Practice by Supporting Idea

☆ Supporting Idea Data Analysis

Read each question. Then fill in the correct answer on your answer document. If a correct answer is *not here,* mark the letter for "Not here."

QUICK Check

1. The stem-and-leaf plot shows the ages of the employees at a company. Which of the following best describes the data? (MA.7.S.6.1 and MA.7.S.6.2)

Employee Ages

Stem	Leaf
2	4 6 7 8
3	0 1 3 4 6 9
4	2 4 5 8
5	1 3 7
6	2 5

$4 \mid 2 = 42$ years

A. The most common age is 33 years old.

B. Ten of the employees have worked at the company for at least 5 years.

C. Half of the employees are younger than 39 years old.

D. The range of ages is 24 years.

2. ✎ **GRIDDED RESPONSE** The stem-and-leaf plot shows the price of cellular phones. What is the median price? (MA.7.S.6.2)

Phone Prices

Stem	Leaf
3	2 3 5 7
4	0 1 4 6 8
5	2 9
6	4 5

$3 \mid 2 = \$32$

QUICK Review

STRATEGY Use the process of elimination to find the correct answer.

Evaluate each answer choice for reasonableness. Eliminate choices that are unreasonable.

For more help with evaluating generalizations for reasonableness, see page 370.

READING HINT The *median* is the middle number when the data are arranged from least to greatest.

The data are already arranged from least to greatest. Count the number of phones. Find the middle price.

For more help with analyzing a stem-and-leaf plot, see page 370.

3. 🖎 **GRIDDED RESPONSE** The histogram below shows the times of runners in a 100-yard dash. How many more runners had a time between 11.1 and 12 seconds than between 10.1 and 11 seconds? Show your work. (MA.7.S.6.2)

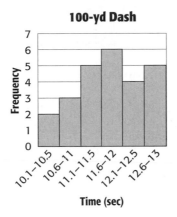

100-yd Dash

Time (sec)

> **STRATEGY** Analyze the data in the histogram to solve the problem.

Find the bars that represent times between 11.1 and 12 seconds.

Find the bars that represent times between 10.1 and 11 seconds.

Compare these values.

For more help with analyzing histograms, see page 364.

4. The table shows the quiz scores that students earned in Mrs. Clayton's math class. Which of the following is true? (MA.7.S.6.1)

Quiz Scores			
10	7	9	8
7	8	5	6
10	9	10	7
6	8	8	8

F. The median score is 9.

G. The range of the scores is 4.

H. The mean score is 7.

I. The mode score is 8.

> **STRATEGY** Use the process of elimination to find the correct answer.

Evaluate each answer choice for reasonableness. Eliminate choices that are unreasonable.

For more help with evaluating generalizations for reasonableness, see page 410.

Practice on Your Own

5. ✎ **GRIDDED RESPONSE** Eighty student athletes were surveyed about their favorite team sport. The results are shown in the circle graph. How many students said they like playing a sport other than baseball, basketball, or soccer? (MA.7.S.6.2)

Favorite Sports

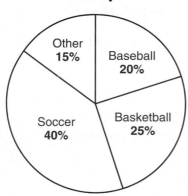

6. The principal at Linden Middle School wants to know what newspaper features students would like in their school paper. Which of these groups would be the best to survey in order to get accurate information? (MA.7.S.6.1)

A. the journalism class

B. the teachers and staff

C. parents

D. every fifth student in the lunch line

7. Which of the following could be found using a histogram? (MA.7.S.6.2)

F. the lowest data value

G. the median

H. the number of data values

I. the range of data values

8. The stem-and-leaf plot shows the final exam scores of the students in a science class.

Test Scores

Stem	Leaf
6	7 9
7	2 4 7 7 8
8	0 1 3 3 3 5 6 7 8 9
9	1 3 4 5 6
10	0

$8 \mid 6 = 86\%$

What is the range of the test scores? (MA.7.S.6.2)

A. 33

B. 42

C. 83

D. 87

9. A candy company recorded that out of 500 candies packaged, three were not wrapped correctly. How many candies would you expect to be wrapped incorrectly out of a shipment of 1200? (MA.7.S.6.1)

F. 5

G. 7

H. 9

I. 11

10. ✎ **GRIDDED RESPONSE** The table shows the results of a survey about favorite ice cream flavors. In a circle graph, what would be the measure of the angle, in degrees, representing strawberry ice cream? (MA.7.S.6.2)

Favorite Ice Cream	
Flavor	**Respondents**
Vanilla	56
Strawberry	15
Chocolate	79

11. Students in Mr. Howell's science class took a trip to the zoo and collected data on the animals they saw. Colleen made a histogram of the top running speeds of animals.

Top Running Speeds

Which table represents the data Colleen used to make her histogram? (MA.7.S.6.2)

A.

Running Speed	
Speed (mph)	Number of Animals
0–10	3
11–20	5
21–30	6
31–40	4
41–50	3
51–60	2

C.

Running Speed	
Speed (mph)	Number of Animals
0–10	4
11–20	5
21–30	6
31–40	4
41–50	3
51–60	2

B.

Running Speed	
Speed (mph)	Number of Animals
0–10	4
11–20	5
21–30	6
31–40	4
41–50	2
51–60	1

D.

Running Speed	
Speed (mph)	Number of Animals
0–10	3
11–20	5
21–30	6
31–40	4
41–50	3
51–60	2

12. Frida surveyed the debate team about their favorite class.

Favorite Class	
Activity	Respondents
Math	5
Science	3
Spanish	7
Language Arts	15

Based on these results, she concluded that 50% of the students in the school would list Language Arts as their favorite class. Which is the best explanation for why her conclusion might NOT be valid? (MA.7.S.6.1)

F. The survey should have been done on a different day.

G. She should have surveyed the teachers as well as the students.

H. The team is too small.

I. The team is not a fair representation of the entire student body.

13. The class of 2016 at Broadway Middle School consists of 560 students. The gender information is shown in the circle graph below. How many students are female? (MA.7.S.6.2)

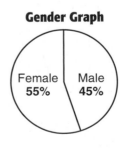

Gender Graph

A. 45

B. 55

C. 252

D. 308

Practice by Supporting Idea

⭐ **Supporting Idea** Probability

Read each question. Then fill in the correct answer on your answer document. If a correct answer is *not here,* mark the letter for "Not here."

QUICK Check	QUICK Review
1. A probability experiment consists of first tossing a coin and then rolling a six-sided number cube. How many outcomes are possible? (MA.7.P.7.1) A. 8 B. 12 C. 16 D. 64	**READING HINT** An outcome is one possible result of a probability event. For example, when a coin is tossed, heads is an outcome. Create a tree diagram to determine all possible outcomes in the sample space. For more help with determining the outcomes of an experiment, see page 386.
2. What is the probability of tossing heads on a coin and rolling an odd number on a six-sided number cube? (MA.7.P.7.2) F. $\frac{1}{12}$　　H. $\frac{1}{6}$ G. $\frac{1}{4}$　　I. $\frac{1}{2}$	**STRATEGY** Compare the number of favorable outcomes with the total number of outcomes. How many possible outcomes are there? How many outcomes involve flipping heads and rolling an odd number? For more help with finding the probability of independent events, see page 391.
3. Suppose Jay spins each spinner once. What is the likelihood of him spinning an A and a 2? (MA.7.P.7.1) 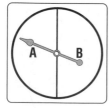  A. equally likely B. likely C. unlikely D. not enough information to determine	**STRATEGY** List the sample space of outcomes. How many outcomes are there? How many of them involve spinning an A and a 2? For more help with determining the likelihood of events, see page 375.

4. The table shows the coins that Tyrell has in a piggy bank. Suppose he selects a coin at random, does not replace it, and then selects another coin without looking. What is the probability Tyrell will select a nickel, then a quarter? (MA.7.P.7.2)

Coin	Number
Penny	6
Nickel	2
Dime	8
Quarter	4

F. $\dfrac{2}{95}$ H. $\dfrac{3}{70}$

G. $\dfrac{1}{50}$ I. $\dfrac{1}{10}$

> **STRATEGY** Find the probability of dependent events.

The second event depends on the first event.

Find the probability that Tyrell selects a nickel. Then find the probability that he selects a quarter, given that he already selected a nickel.

Multiply the probabilities.

For more help with determining the probability of dependent events, see page 391.

---

5. Rebecca has a bag with 3 red marbles, 3 yellow marbles, and 4 blue marbles. She picks a marble out of the bag, replaces it, and picks another. What is the probability Rebecca picked two blue marbles? (MA.7.P.7.2)

A. $\dfrac{2}{15}$ C. $\dfrac{1}{5}$

B. $\dfrac{4}{25}$ D. $\dfrac{2}{5}$

> **STRATEGY** Compare the number of favorable outcomes with the total number of outcomes.

How many possible outcomes are there?

How many outcomes represent a matching pair of gloves?

For more help with determining the probability of dependent events, see page 393.

---

6. A bowl of candy contains 6 candies with nuts and 4 candies without nuts. A piece of candy is selected at random and is not replaced. Then a second piece of candy is selected at random. What is the probability that the first piece will have nuts and the second piece will not? (MA.7.P.7.2)

F. $\dfrac{6}{25}$ H. $\dfrac{4}{9}$

G. $\dfrac{4}{15}$ I. $\dfrac{3}{5}$

> **STRATEGY** Compare the number of favorable outcomes with the total number of outcomes.

How many possible outcomes are there?

How many outcomes have one of each type of candy?

For more help with determining the probability of dependent events, see page 393.

Practice on Your Own

7. The histogram shows the ages of the people in a movie theater. Based on these results, how many people between the ages of 10 and 29 would you expect to be in a crowd of 400 moviegoers? (MA.7.P.7.2)

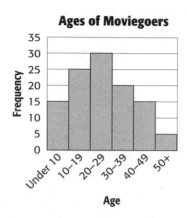

Ages of Moviegoers

A. 55

B. 110

C. 175

D. 200

8. Use the tree diagram to find the probability of flipping 2 or more heads when 3 coins are flipped. (MA.7.P.7.1)

Coin 1	Coin 2	Coin 3

H — H — H
H — H — T
H — T — H
H — T — T
T — H — H
T — H — T
T — T — H
T — T — T

F. 25%

G. 50%

H. 60%

I. 75%

9. François and Mindy are playing a board game using the spinner below. On a turn, a player gains 1 point if they spin a letter in their name.

Which of the following best describes the likelihood of a player scoring a point on their turn? (MA.7.S.6.1)

A. It is equally likely that François and Mindy will score a point.

B. It is more likely that François will score a point.

C. It is more likely that Mindy will score a point.

D. It is unlikely that either player will score a point.

10. In Exercise 7, how would you describe the likelihood that a randomly selected moviegoer is under 10 years old or between the ages of 40 and 49? (MA.7.P.7.1)

F. It is more likely that a moviegoer is under 10.

G. It is more likely that a moviegoer is age 40 to 49.

H. It is equally likely that a moviegoer is under 10 or age 40 to 49.

I. Not here

11. ✎ **GRIDDED RESPONSE** At the local arcade, students can choose 2 activities for $5. For the first activity, the student can choose bowling, miniature golf, or go-kart racing. For the second activity, the student may choose to play one of 6 video games available. How many possibilities are there? (MA.7.P.7.1)

12. ✎ **GRIDDED RESPONSE** James is playing a game at the school carnival. There are 8 marbles in a bag and 2 are red, 2 are blue, 2 are green, and 2 are yellow. James wins a prize if the first marble he chooses is red and the second marble he chooses is blue. If the first marble is not replaced, what is the probability of James winning a prize? (MA.7.P.7.2)

13. Mara spins the spinner below 50 times and records the results in a table. What is the experimental probability of spinning a vowel? (MA.7.P.7.2)

| Letter Frequency | | | | |
A	B	C	D	F
8	11	9	9	13

A. 0.21

B. 0.35

C. 0.42

D. 0.48

14. In Exercise 13, how many times would you expect to spin a letter E in 50 spins based on theoretical probability? (MA.7.P.7.2)

F. 25

G. 10

H. 5

I. 1

15. What is the probability of rolling a number greater than 2 using a standard number cube? (MA.7.P.7.1)

A. $\frac{2}{3}$

B. $\frac{1}{3}$

C. $\frac{2}{5}$

D. $\frac{1}{6}$

16. Amos and Angie are using the board below to play a game. On each player's turn, he or she tosses a chip onto the board. The sections are divided so the chip lands in either a shaded section or an unshaded section on each toss.

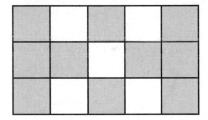

Angie scores a point if the chip lands on a shaded section. Amos scores a point if the chip lands on an unshaded section. Which of the following best describes the game? (MA.7.P.7.1)

F. The game is fair because each player has an equal chance of scoring a point.

G. The game is unfair because Amos has a better chance of scoring a point.

H. The game is unfair because Angie has a better chance of scoring a point.

I. The game is fair because each player has a 30% chance of scoring a point.

Problem-Solving Projects

Are We Similar?

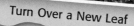
Turn Over a New Leaf

Stand Up and Be Counted!

When will I ever use this?

Have you ever said that? Did you wonder when you would use the math you are learning?

The Problem-Solving Projects apply the math you have learned so far in school. You'll see math in everyday events. Try them!

Be True to Your School

Math Genes

PROJECT 1 — Are We Similar?

Las Vegas is famous for its themed hotels. How is the Statue of Liberty at the New York New York hotel similar to the one in New York City? Head to your school or local library to find out. In this project, you will be reading books or stories about the concept of similarity. Don't forget to bring your math thinking cap and your library card. You'll want to check out this adventure!

What You'll Do

Go to a local library and locate books and stories about similarity. Identify careers that use similarity. Brainstorm other places in life that you use similarities. Create a poster to share your findings with the class.

Materials:

- library books about similarity
- poster board

Procedure

1. Take a trip to your local or school library to research information about similarity and the construction of buildings. Look at the different ways buildings are constructed and how the design team incorporates outside influences. As you research, make a list of jobs that use similarity.

2. Select one famous building or statue. Find the actual measurements and draw a smaller version of it using a scale factor. Some ideas are:
   - Eiffel Tower
   - Leaning Tower of Pisa
   - Stonehenge
   - Statue of Liberty
   - Colosseum
   - Golden Gate Bridge

Technology Tips
- You can use a **computer projector** to help enlarge the scale drawing for your poster.

3. Create a poster that contains key facts about similarity and building design. It should include your scale drawing and any calculations you used throughout the project. Share your poster with the class.

Making the Connection

Use the information collected about similarity as needed to help in these investigations.

Art VA.A.1.3.1

Create an art project that involves similarity. Where is similarity used in your artwork?

Science SC.7.N.1.2

Research objects found in nature that are similar. What makes the objects similar? Does their similarity have an impact on their roles in nature?

Language Arts LA.7.3.1.1, LA.7.3.2.2

Write an essay about a career that uses similarity. Include such information as the type of degree needed, work conditions, and possible industries for that career.

Congratulations!

We hope you enjoyed your experience with construction and buildings! Now that you have gained knowledge about similarities and the jobs that use it, you may find yourself using similarity to earn a living! Keep up the good work and it will take you great places.

PROJECT 2 — Turn Over a New Leaf

You have been selected to join a team of botanists that will be studying leaves. In this project, you will be collecting and analyzing leaves to find out why they are all flat. You'll investigate the relationship between the volume and surface area of a leaf. So, put on your hiking shoes, and don't forget to bring along your geometry and measurement tools. You're about to go on a nature hike.

What You'll Do

Collect a variety of differently sized leaves. Record the characteristics of each leaf, and then calculate the volume and surface area. After finding the measurements, you will analyze and compare the data. Finally, you will research the anatomy of leaves.

Materials:

- 10 leaves
- centimeter ruler
- Internet

Procedure

1. **Get Connected** Gather 10 leaves from outside your school or neighborhood. Record your measurements and observations in a table, like the one found at <u>connectED.mcgraw-hill.com</u>. Trace the leaf on centimeter grid paper and estimate the leaf's area.

2. Estimate each leaf's surface area and volume and record it in the table. Find the ratio of the surface area of the leaf to its volume. Write a few sentences comparing the data presented in the table for the different types of leaves.

3. Use the Internet and research why leaves are flat and why surface area and volume ratios are important to a leaf. Write 1–2 paragraphs discussing the information you found about the anatomy of leaves.

4. Create a graphic organizer that will summarize all of your information and data. Use this in a presentation for your class. Include leaf samples and the calculations that go along with your work.

> ▶ **Technology Tips**
>
> • Use a **spreadsheet** to calculate the surface area and volume.
>
> • Use **publishing software** to make your graphic organizer.

Making the Connection

Use the information collected about leaves as needed to help in these investigations.

Science SC.7.N.1.1

Write a brochure detailing facts about the leaves you found and the trees they come from. Be sure to include the names of the leaves and trees and the volume and surface area of the leaves.

Art VA.A.1.3.4

Draw the leaves you have collected. Use a technique that will help to make the leaves look realistic.

Language Arts LA.7.3.1.1, LA.7.3.2.2

In the fall, many people rake leaves and place them in bags for yard waste. These bags are then collected curbside. Research and write an essay describing what happens to these bags of yard waste.

Congratulations!

You have successfully completed your botanist tasks! Using your mathematical tools, you have witnessed the power and importance of mathematics in the real world. Surface area and volume are all around us in all that we do. Keep up the good work!

Turn Over a New Leaf **593**

PROJECT 3 Stand Up and Be Counted!

Every 10 years, the U.S. Census counts the U.S. population. How does the U.S. Census affect the number of members in the House of Representatives from each state? You're on a mission to find out! Don't forget to bring your math tool kit. This adventure will appeal to your "census."

What You'll Do

Research the history of the United States Census. Find the population of the United States in the years 2000 and 2010. Also, find the number of members in the House of Representatives for each state. Examine the relationship between population and the number of House of Representatives members. Finally, create a presentation of your findings.

Materials:

- Internet

Procedure

1. Use the Internet to research the United States Census. Write a paragraph explaining how the Census works and the process of finding populations.

2. **Get Connected** Find the population for each of the fifty United States in the years 2000 and 2010. Also find the number of members in the House of Representatives for each state. Go to <u>connectED.mcgraw-hill.com</u> to obtain a recording sheet for this information.

3. Select 10 states and examine the relationship between each state's population and its number of members in the House of Representatives. Write an equation that can be used to approximate the number of House of Representatives members based on a state's population.

5. Create a presentation that includes the following:
   - information about the U.S. Census
   - completed recording sheet
   - equation about the relationship between population and number of members in the House of Representatives

▶ **Technology Tips**

- Use a **spreadsheet** to examine the relationships in Procedure 3.

- Use **publishing software** to make your presentation in the form of a booklet, newspaper article, or magazine article.

Projects

Making the Connection

Use the information collected about the United States Census and the House of Representatives as needed to help in these investigations.

Language Arts LA.7.3.1.1, LA.7.3.2.2

Research and write an essay about one aspect of the U.S. Census. Some questions to consider are: Why is the U.S. Census taken? How could the U.S. Census become more accurate? How are the results used?

Social Studies SS.7.C.3.4, SS.7.C.3.8

Research the history of the House of Representatives. Some questions to consider are: Why was it established? When was it established? How many members did it originally have? Who were some of the first members?

Congratulations!

Only a sophisticated and intelligent student could complete such a challenging task! You have successfully completed your job. As you can see, it is important for everyone to be able to analyze and properly display information. You have proven your ability to graph data, find and interpret information, and research real-life problems. We hope you have enjoyed learning about the people that make up our nation.

PROJECT 4 — Be True to Your School

Have you ever wondered what it takes to design a mascot or logo for your school? Is there symmetry involved? If so, what kind(s)? Are transformations used? Which one(s)? In this project, you will design a creative mascot or logo for your school. You will *draw* upon your understanding of transformations, symmetry, coordinate graphs, and integers. Are you ready to begin? 1-2-3 DRAW!

What You'll Do

You have been hired to design a mascot or logo for your school. You will need to find the amount it will cost to make the mascot or logo. You will then create a presentation that displays your mascot or logo to share with your class.

Materials:

- Internet

Procedure

1. Brainstorm about 5 to 8 different ideas. Then narrow down your list to your number one choice. Create drawings and coordinate grids with illustrations of your design.

2. Use the Internet to estimate the cost of your mascot or logo. You will need to look up the materials that are needed to assemble the design. Create a table that includes all of the materials and the cost per unit of each item.

3. Write your cost and profit equations.

4. Create a presentation to share your design with the rest of the class. Include the following in your presentation:
   • drawings and coordinate grids with your design
   • a 1–2 paragraph explanation of your design, including any transformations
   • your cost and profit equations

▶ **Technology Tips**

• Use **geometry software** to create possible logos or mascots.

• Use a **computer projector** to display your design for your presentation.

Making the Connection

Use the information from your design as needed to help in these investigations.

Science SC.7.N.1.5

Research symmetry and where it is found in nature. What effect does symmetry have on objects in nature?

Art VA.A.1.3.4

Create an art project that uses symmetry and transformations. Include an explanation of where you used them and how they enhanced the artwork.

Language Arts LA.7.5.2.3, LA.7.4.3.1

Suppose the school principal is deciding between your design and another student's to become the school's new mascot or logo. Write a speech that you can present to the principal that will encourage him or her to choose your design.

Congratulations!

Congratulations on completing your quest! Was your design a hit? Do you think it could actually be bought in real life? Who knows, maybe you'll really start your own design company one day. Now that you have some of the math tools needed to make such a venture successful, we are sure your designs will be booming.

PROJECT 5 Math Genes

What's math have to do with genetics? Well, you're about to find out. You'll research basic genetics and learn how to use a Punnett Square. Then you'll create sample genes for pet traits. You'll make predictions based on the pets' traits to determine the traits of their offspring. Put on your lab coat and grab your math tool kit to begin this adventure.

What You'll Do

Use the Internet to research the Punnett Square and its role in genetics. Then you will use what you learned to practice problems involving a Punnett Square. Next you will collect and record some specific information about pets. Finally, you will analyze and calculate different statistics based on your data.

Materials:

- Internet
- poster board

Procedure

1. Use the Internet to research and find definitions of the following words: alleles, dominant, genotype, heterozygous, homozygous, phenotype, Punnett Square, and recessive.

2. Locate and read different descriptions of the Punnett Square on the Internet. Find four different scenarios that can be represented using a Punnett Square. Print these four scenarios and then explain how the Punnett Square represents them.

3. **Get Connected** Create sample genes for pet traits. Go to connectED.mcgraw-hill.com to get the recording sheet for the information you will create. Complete the table for 4 different pets and the possible characteristics of each pet. Write 1–2 paragraphs describing how the Punnett Square is used in genetics and how math is involved with the Punnett Square.

4. Create a poster board containing information about the data you have gathered about genetics and pet traits. Include a table displaying your data.

Making the Connection ·······························

Use the information collected about genetics as needed to help in these investigations.

Language Arts LA.7.3.1.1, LA.7.3.2.2

Research the theories of genetics. Write an essay that explains how genes work and what it means for a trait to be dominant or recessive.

Science SC.7.L.15.2, SC.7.L.16.2

Explain how a Punnett Square can be used to determine the probability of inheriting certain features from parents.

Health HE.7.B.2.1, HE.7.B.2.4

Select a health condition or disease and research how genetics may play a part in the disease. Write 1–2 paragraphs explaining how genetics may influence someone's risk of getting the disease and steps that can be taken to reduce the risk factors.

Congratulations!

Great work! Did you find out some interesting things about pet traits? We hope you enjoyed your experience in the amazing world of genetics and saw the large role mathematics plays in understanding this world.

Geometry and Spatial Reasoning

The ☆BIG Idea

Analyze two- and three-dimensional figures by using distance and angles.

Study Organizer

Make this Foldable to help you organize your notes. Begin with 7 sheets of $8\frac{1}{2}$" by 11" paper.

1 Fold a sheet of paper in half lengthwise. Cut a 1" tab along the left edge through one thickness.

2 Glue the 1" tab down. Write the title of the lesson on the front tab.

3 Repeat Steps 1 and 2 for the remaining sheets of paper. Staple together to form a booklet.

Angle Relationships

Angle Relationships

Review Vocabulary

formula (p. 157) **fórmula** an equation that shows a relationship among certain quantities

$$A = bw$$

w

b

Key Vocabulary

English	Español
p. 616	triangle	triángulo
p. 624	quadrilateral	cuadrilátero
p. 642	square root	raíz cuadrada
p. 655	Pythagorean Theorem	Teorema de Pitagoras

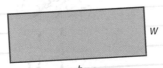 Multilingual eGlossary glencoe.com

 **Get Connected**
glencoe.com

- Study using the **eBook**
- Explore with **Get Animated**
- Get extra help from **Personal Tutor**
- Use **virtual manipulatives** for additional help
- Take a **Self-Check Quiz**

When Will I Use This?

Dario, Hiroshi, and Caitlyn in
Billiard Angles

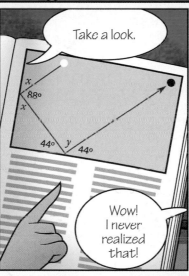

Are You Ready for Chapter 11?

You have two options for checking prerequisite skills for this chapter.

Text Option Take the Quick Check below. Refer to the Quick Review for help.

QUICK Check

Multiply or divide. Round to the nearest hundredth if necessary. (Prior Grade)

1. 412×0.23 **2.** 177×0.82

3. 634×1.09 **4.** 801×0.07

5. $32.9 \div 18$ **6.** $58.3 \div 21$

7. $210.5 \div 38$ **8.** $87.4 \div 41$

9. CELL PHONE Beverly paid a total of $422.88 per year for her cell phone plan. She pays her cell phone bill each month with 12 equal payments. How much does she pay each month?

10. CANDY Patricio bought a package of candy bars for $3.74. The package had a total of 8 candy bars. What was the cost per candy bar?

Solve each equation. (Lesson 3-1D)

11. $114 + c + 19 = 180$

12. $90 = 65 + b$

13. $180 = 27 + v + 98$

14. $46 + t = 90$

15. READING Janis read 41 pages on Wednesday and 58 pages on Thursday. If the book is 180 pages long, how many pages does she have left to read?

QUICK Review

EXAMPLE 1

Find 0.42×240.

$$
\begin{array}{r}
240 \\
\times\ 0.42 \quad \leftarrow \text{two decimal places} \\
\hline
480 \\
+\ 9600 \\
\hline
100.80 \quad \leftarrow \text{two decimal places}
\end{array}
$$

So, $0.42 \times 240 = 100.8$.

EXAMPLE 2

Find $48.3 \div 14$.

$$
\begin{array}{r}
3.45 \\
14\overline{)48.30} \\
-42 \\
\hline
63 \\
-56 \\
\hline
70 \\
-70 \\
\hline
0
\end{array}
$$

Place the decimal point.

Annex a zero and continue dividing.

So, $48.3 \div 14 = 3.45$.

EXAMPLE 3

Solve $39 + f = 90$.

$$
\begin{array}{rr}
39 + f = & 90 \\
-39 & -39 \\
\hline
f = & 51
\end{array}
$$

Write the equation.

Subtract 39 from each side.

Check

$39 + f = 90$

$39 + 51 = 90$

$90 = 90$ ✔

Online Option  Take the Online Readiness Quiz at **glencoe.com**.

 # Reading Math

The Language of Mathematics

Sometimes everyday or scientific usage can give you clues to the mathematical meaning of words. Here are some examples.

> Many of the words you use in math are also used in everyday language.

Usage	Example
Some words are used in English and in mathematics, but have distinct meanings.	leg
Some words are used in science and in mathematics, but the meanings are different.	$x + 4 = -2$ $x = -6$ solution
Some words are used only in mathematics.	hypotenuse

Practice

Explain how the mathematical meaning of each word compares to its everyday meaning.

1. factor

2. rational

Explain how the mathematical meaning of each word compares to its meaning in science.

3. radical

4. variable

Some words are used in English and in mathematics, but the mathematical meaning is more precise. Explain how the mathematical meaning of each word is more precise than the everyday meaning.

5. similar

6. real

 NGSSS
LA.7.1.6.5 The student will relate new vocabulary to familiar words.

Main Idea

Classify and determine the measure of angles.

NGSSS

MA.8.G.2.2 Classify and determine the measure of angles, including angles created when parallel lines are cut by transversals.

New Vocabulary

angle
vertex
degrees
right angle
acute angle
obtuse angle
straight angle
vertical angles
adjacent angles
complementary angles
supplementary angles

Get Connected
glencoe.com

Angle Relationships

BIKE RAMPS The angle of descent of a bike ramp is shown.

1. The ramp has an angle of descent. Draw an angle with a measure between 45° and 90°.

2. Some ramps have an angle of descent that is 90°, known as a vertical angle of descent. Draw a vertical angle of descent.

An **angle** has two sides that share a common endpoint called a **vertex**. Angles are measured in units called **degrees**. If a circle were divided into 360 equal-size parts, each part would have an angle measure of 1 degree (1°).

An angle can be named in several ways. The symbol for angle is ∠.

EXAMPLE   Naming Angles

1. **Name the angle at the right.**

   - Use the vertex as the middle letter and a point from each side.
     ∠LMN or ∠NML

   - Use the vertex only.
     ∠M

   - Use a number.
     ∠1

   The angle can be named in four ways: ∠LMN, ∠NML, ∠M, or ∠1.

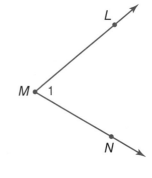

Angles are classified according to their measure.

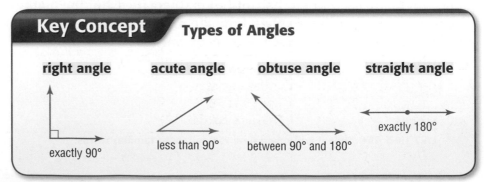

Key Concept   **Types of Angles**

right angle	acute angle	obtuse angle	straight angle
exactly 90°	less than 90°	between 90° and 180°	exactly 180°

EXAMPLES **Classify Angles**

Classify each angle as *acute, obtuse, right,* or *straight.*

② The angle is less than 90°, so it is an acute angle.

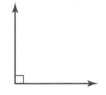

③ The angle is between 90° and 180°, so it is an obtuse angle.

CHECK Your Progress

a.

b.

c.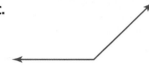

Pairs of angles can also be classified by their relationship.

Review Vocabulary

Congruent Having the same measure. *Example:* Angle *A* is congruent to Angle *B* ($\angle A \cong \angle B$).

Read Math

Angle Measure The notation $m\angle 1$ is read *the measure of angle 1.*

Key Concept **Pairs of Angles**

Words	Models	Symbols
When two lines intersect, they form two pairs of opposite angles, called **vertical angles**, that are congruent.	$\angle 1$ and $\angle 2$, $\angle 3$ and $\angle 4$	$\angle 1 \cong \angle 2$ $\angle 3 \cong \angle 4$
Two angles that share a vertex and a common side and do not overlap are called **adjacent angles**.		$m\angle ABC = m\angle 5 + m\angle 6$
If the sum of the measures of two angles is 90°, they are called **complementary angles**.		$m\angle 7 + m\angle 8 = 90°$
If the sum of the measures of two angles is 180°, they are called **supplementary angles**.		$m\angle 9 + m\angle 10 = 180°$

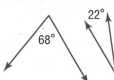

EXAMPLES   Classify Angles

Identify each pair of angles as *complementary*, *supplementary*, or *neither*.

④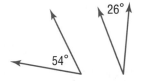

⑤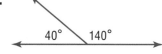

$68° + 22° = 90°$

The angles are complementary.

∠1 and ∠2 form a straight angle. So, the angles are supplementary.

 CHECK Your Progress

d.

e.

Study Tip

Complementary and Supplementary Angles
Two angles do not need to be adjacent angles in order to be complementary or supplementary.

Real-World EXAMPLE   Find a Missing Angle Measure

⑥ **SIDEWALKS** The two adjacent angles in the sidewalk form a straight line. Find the missing angle measure.

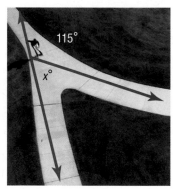

Write an equation.

first angle		second angle		
115	+	x	=	180

Solve the equation.

$$115 + x = 180 \quad \text{Write the equation.}$$
$$\underline{-115 \quad\quad = -115} \quad \text{Subtract 115 from each side.}$$
$$x = 65 \quad \text{Simplify.}$$

So, the value of x is 65.

 CHECK Your Progress

f. **ALGEBRA** Find the value of x.

g. Find the measure of ∠3.

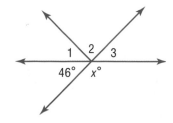

Examples 1–3
(pp. 604–605)

Name each angle in four ways. Then classify the angle as *acute*, *right*, *obtuse*, or *straight*.

1.
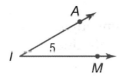

2.
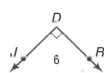

Examples 4 and 5
(p. 606)

Identify each pair of angles as *complementary*, *supplementary*, or *neither*.

3.
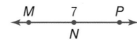

4.

Example 6
(p. 606)

5. **BRACES** The picture shows a support brace for a gate. Find the value of *x*.

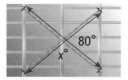

Practice and Problem Solving

= **Step-by-Step Solutions** begin on page R33.
Extra Practice is on page EP30.

Examples 1–3
(pp. 604–605)

Name each angle in four ways. Then classify the angle as *acute*, *right*, *obtuse*, or *straight*.

6.
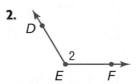

7
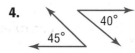

8.

9.

Examples 4 and 5
(p. 606)

Identify each pair of angles as *complementary*, *supplementary*, or *neither*.

10.
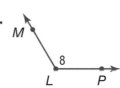

11.
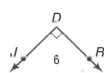

12.
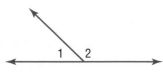

13.

Example 6
(p. 606)

14. **LEAVES** What is the measure of the angle between the veins of the leaf, *x*?

15. **ALGEBRA** If ∠X and ∠Y are complementary and the measure of ∠X is 37°, what is the measure of ∠Y?

16. **ALGEBRA** What is the measure of ∠S if ∠S and ∠T are supplementary and the measure of ∠T is 109°?

Use the figure at the right to name the following.

⓱ a pair of congruent angles

18. a pair of supplementary angles

19. a straight angle

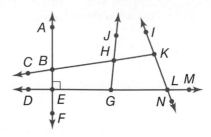

In each diagram describe an angle that might be considered *acute, obtuse, right,* **or** *straight.*

20.

21.

![H.O.T. Problems]

22. **CHALLENGE** Determine whether the statement is *true* or *false*. If the statement is true, draw a diagram to support it. If the statement is false, explain why.

    An obtuse angle and an acute angle are always supplementary.

23. **CHALLENGE** Angles K and O are supplementary. If $m∠K = 3x + 10$ and $m∠O = 10x - 12$, find the measure of each angle.

24. **REASONING** Explain the statement below.

    If two angles are right angles, they must be supplementary.

25. **Which One Doesn't Belong?** Identify the term that does not belong with the other three. Justify your response.

    | acute | right | complementary | obtuse |

26. **Write MATH** Describe the difference between complementary and supplementary angles.

27. Which word best describes the angle marked in the figure?

A. acute   C. right

B. obtuse   D. straight

28. Which statement is true?

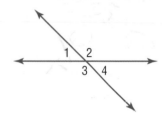

F. ∠1 and ∠2 are complementary.

G. ∠3 and ∠4 are complementary.

H. ∠1 and ∠4 are supplementary.

I. ∠1 and ∠2 are supplementary.

29. What is the value of x?

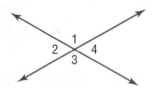

A. 38

B. 52

C. 142

D. not enough information

30. In the diagram, ∠2 is an acute angle.

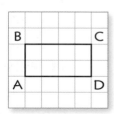

Which conclusion is NOT true?

F. $m\angle 2 + m\angle 4 = 180°$

G. $m\angle 2 + m\angle 3 = 180°$

H. $m\angle 1 + m\angle 4 = 180°$

I. $m\angle 3 + m\angle 4 = 180°$

Copy rectangle ABCD on graph paper. Then draw the image of the figure after the dilation with the given center and scale factor. (Lesson 10-4A)

31. center: A; scale factor: 2

32. center: A; scale factor: $\frac{1}{4}$

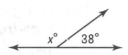

Determine whether each figure has rotational symmetry. Write _yes_ or _no_. If yes, name its angle(s) of rotation. (Lesson 10-3B)

33.

34.

35.

Main Idea

Analyze the relationships of angles formed by two parallel lines and a transversal.

NGSSS

 MA.8.G.2.2 Classify and determine the measure of angles, including angles created when parallel lines are cut by transversals.

New Vocabulary

parallel lines
transversal
perpendicular lines
alternate interior angles
alternate exterior angles
corresponding angles

Get Connected
glencoe.com

Parallel Lines

Explore Draw two vertical lines on a sheet of notebook paper. Then draw another line that intersects both lines. Label the angles as shown.

1. Measure angles 1 and 5. Record the measures.

2. Make a conjecture about the measure of angles 2 and 6.

3. Measure angles 2 and 6 to verify your conjecture.

4. What angle(s) appear congruent to angle 1?

5. What angle(s) appear congruent to angle 2?

Lines in a plane that never intersect are **parallel lines**. When two parallel lines are intersected by a third line, this line is called a **transversal**. Lines that meet or cross each other to form right angles are **perpendicular lines**.

Key Concept   **Transversals and Angles**

If a pair of parallel lines is intersected by a transversal, these pairs of angles are congruent.

Alternate interior angles are on opposite sides of the transversal and inside the parallel lines.

$$\angle 3 \cong \angle 5, \angle 4 \cong \angle 6$$

Alternate exterior angles are on opposite sides of the transversal and outside the parallel lines.

$$\angle 1 \cong \angle 7, \angle 2 \cong \angle 8$$

Corresponding angles are in the same position on the parallel lines in relation to the transversal.

$$\angle 1 \cong \angle 5, \angle 2 \cong \angle 6, \angle 3 \cong \angle 7, \angle 4 \cong \angle 8$$

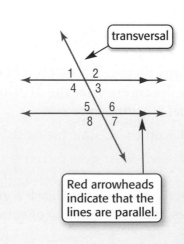

Red arrowheads indicate that the lines are parallel.

EXAMPLES Classify Angles

Classify the pair of angles as *alternate interior, alternate exterior,* or *corresponding angles.*

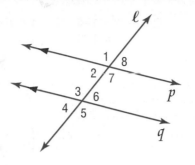

1 ∠1 and ∠5

2 ∠1 and ∠3

3 ∠4 and ∠8

4 ∠3 and ∠7

✓ CHECK Your Progress

a. ∠2 and ∠6 **b.** ∠5 and ∠7

Read Math

Parallel Lines Read $p \parallel q$ as *p is parallel to q.*

EXAMPLE Find Measures of Angles

In the figure, $p \parallel q$ and $m\angle 3 = 95°$. Find the angle measure.

5 $m\angle 7$

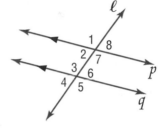

∠3 and ∠7 are alternate interior angles.

$m\angle 7 = m\angle 3 = 95°$

✓ CHECK Your Progress

In the figure, $m\angle 4 = 85°$. Find each measure.

c. $m\angle 8$ **d.** $m\angle 2$

EXAMPLE Use Angle Relationships

6 **ALGEBRA** In the figure, $r \parallel s$. Find the value of y. Explain your reasoning.

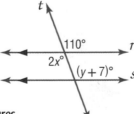

The angles with measures $(y + 7)°$ and 110° are corresponding angles, so they are congruent.

$(y + 7) = 110$ Congruent angles have equal measures.

$y + 7 = 110$

$\underline{-7 = -7}$ Subtract 7 from each side.

$y = 103$ Simplify.

✓ CHECK Your Progress

e. Find the value of x. Explain your reasoning.

Examples 1–4
(p. 611)

In the figure, $\ell \parallel m$ and k is a transversal. Classify each pair.

1. $\angle 2$ and $\angle 3$ 2. $\angle 1$ and $\angle 3$ 3. $\angle 4$ and $\angle 5$

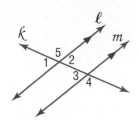

Example 5
(p. 611)

In the figure, $p \parallel q$ and ℓ is a transversal. If $m\angle 8 = 120°$, find each measure.

4. $m\angle 1$ 5. $m\angle 3$ 6. $m\angle 5$

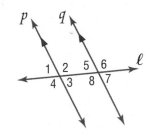

Example 6
(p. 611)

7. **SWIMMING** A swimmer crosses the lanes in a pool and swims from point A to point B, as shown in the figure. What is the value of x? Explain your reasoning.

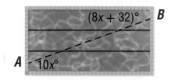

8. **ALGEBRA** Find the value of x in the figure at the right. Explain your reasoning.

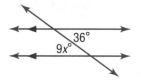

Practice and Problem Solving

 = **Step-by-Step Solutions** begin on page R33.
Extra Practice is on page EP30.

Examples 1–4
(p. 611)

Classify each pair of angles shown in the figure.

9. $\angle 1$ and $\angle 5$ 10. $\angle 3$ and $\angle 5$

11. $\angle 6$ and $\angle 4$ 12. $\angle 7$ and $\angle 1$

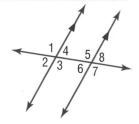

Example 5
(p. 611)

In the figure, if $m\angle 2 = 74°$, find each measure.

13 $m\angle 8$ 14. $m\angle 6$

15. $m\angle 4$ 16. $m\angle 1$

17. **FURNITURE** In the chair, $m\angle 4 = 106°$. Find $m\angle 6$ and $m\angle 3$.

Example 6
(p. 611)

18. **DRIVING** Ambulances cannot safely make turns of less than 70°. The angle at the southeast corner of Delaven and Elmwood is 108°. Can an ambulance safely turn the northeast corner of Bidwell and Elmwood? Explain your reasoning.

Example 6
(p. 611)

In the figure, $m\angle 7 = 96°$. Find each measure.
Explain your reasoning.

19. $m\angle 2$ **20.** $m\angle 5$

21. $m\angle 4$ **22.** $m\angle 8$

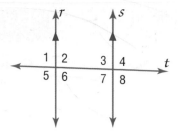

ALGEBRA Find the value of x in each figure.

23.

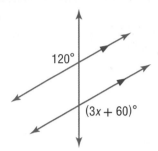

120°

$(3x + 60)°$

24.

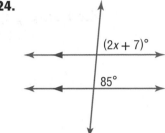

$(2x + 7)°$

85°

25 **ESCALATORS** The escalator shown transports people from one floor to another. The floors are parallel and the escalator makes a 45° angle with the floor. Find the value of x.

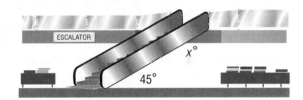

ESCALATOR

$x°$

45°

26. FLAGS The national flag of Bosnia is shown. If $m\angle 1 = 135°$, what is $m\angle 2$? Explain how you found your answer.

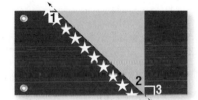

27. ALGEBRA A transversal intersects two parallel lines and forms adjacent angles 5 and 6. If $m\angle 5 = (7x - 11)°$ and $m\angle 6 = (3x + 1)°$, find the measures of the angles.

28. GRAPHIC NOVEL Refer to the graphic novel frame below for Exercises a and b.

We are learning how to use geometry to play billiards. Refer to page 601 for the drawing.

So, if we know that the ball bounces off the wall at an 88 degree angle, then we can find the angles the path makes with the wall of the table.

Find the measure of the given angles.

a. $\angle x$ **b.** $\angle y$

29. **CHALLENGE** Suppose two parallel lines are cut by a transversal. How are the interior angles on the same side of the transversal related?

30. **REASONING** Determine whether the following statement is *sometimes*, *always*, or *never* true. Explain your reasoning.

    Vertical angles are supplementary.

31. **OPEN ENDED** Draw a pair of adjacent, supplementary angles. Label the angle measures.

32. **Write MATH** Summarize the angle relationships that are formed by parallel lines and a transversal. Describe which angles are congruent.

NGSSS Practice   MA.8.G.2.2

33. Bryan is building a swing set. He is building the end of the set as shown in the figure using parallel lines as braces. What is the value of w?

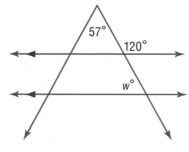

    A. 120   **C.** 60

    B. 63   **D.** 57

34. Which of the following statements is true if two parallel lines are cut by a transversal?

    F. Adjacent angles are complementary.

    G. Vertical angles are adjacent.

    H. Alternate interior angles are supplementary.

    I. Corresponding angles are congruent.

35. **GRIDDED RESPONSE** Angles x and y are supplementary. Angle x has a measure of 88°. What is the measure of $\angle y$ in degrees?

Spiral Review

Find the measure of each missing angle. (Lesson 11-1A)

36.

117° x

37.

x
42°

38.
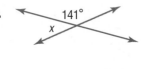
141°
x

39. **ADVERTISEMENT** Toni designed a 4-inch by 6-inch advertisement for the local cable company. The design is to be enlarged by a scale factor of 4 and used to display on signs. What are the dimensions of the dilated image? (Lesson 10-4A)

Explore Triangles

Main Idea

Demonstrate that the sum of the angles in a triangle is 180°.

NGSSS

MA.8.G.2.3 Demonstrate that the sum of the angles in a triangle is 180-degrees and apply this fact to find unknown measure of angles, and the sum of angles in polygons.

Get Connected
glencoe.com

CONSTRUCTION Natasha is helping her dad build a deck for their backyard. The supports for the deck are triangular. What is the sum of the measures of the three angles of each triangle?

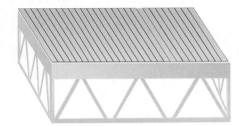

ACTIVITY Get Animated

STEP 1 Use a straightedge to draw a triangle with three acute angles. Label the angles *A*, *B*, and *C*. Cut out the triangle.

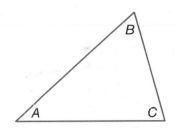

STEP 2 Cut off the regions around the corners.

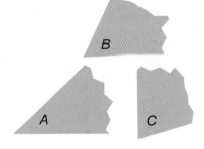

STEP 3 Place the corners together at a common meeting point.

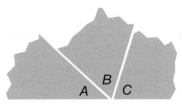

Analyze the Results

1. What kind of angle is formed where the three vertices meet?

2. **MAKE A CONJECTURE** Repeat the activity with another triangle. Make a conjecture about the sum of the measures of the angles of any triangle.

3. *True* or *false*: A triangle can have more than one obtuse angle. Justify your response.

Main Idea

Identify and classify triangles.

NGSSS

 MA.8.G.2.3 Demonstrate that **the sum of the angles in a triangle is 180-degrees and apply this fact to find unknown measure of angles,** and the sum of angles in polygons.

New Vocabulary

triangle
congruent segments
acute triangle
right triangle
obtuse triangle
scalene triangle
isosceles triangle
equilateral triangle

Get Connected
glencoe.com

Triangles

Explore

RAMPS Frederick is building a ramp for his grandmother. She cannot go up an incline greater than 12°.

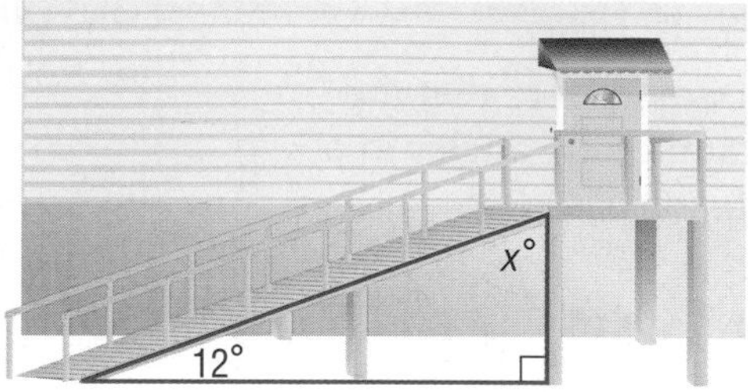

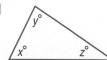

1. What kind of triangle is shown in the figure?

2. Make a prediction about the relationship between the 12° angle and the unknown angle.

A **triangle** is a figure with three sides and three angles. The symbol for triangle is △.

Key Concept   Angles of a Triangle

Words   The sum of the measures of the angles of a triangle is 180°.

Model

Algebra $x + y + z = 180$

EXAMPLE   Find a Missing Measure

1   **ALGEBRA** Find $m\angle Z$.

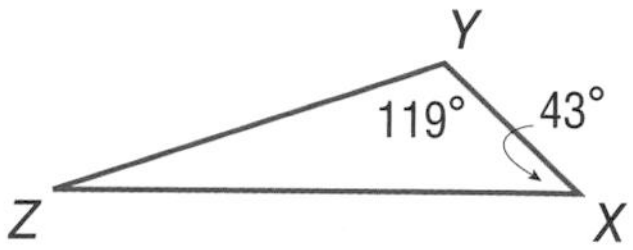

The sum of the angle measures in a triangle is 180°.

$$m\angle Z + 43° + 119° = \quad 180° \quad \text{Write the equation.}$$

$$m\angle Z + 162° = \quad 180° \quad \text{Simplify.}$$

$$\underline{ -162° = -162°} \quad \text{Subtract 162° from each side.}$$

$$m\angle Z \qquad = \quad 18°$$

So, $m\angle Z$ is 18°.

CHECK Your Progress

   a. ALGEBRA In △ABC, if $m\angle A = 25°$ and $m\angle B = 108°$, what is $m\angle C$?

2 **FLAGS** The Alabama state flag is shown. What is the missing measure in the triangle?

To find the missing measure, write and solve an equation.

$$x + 110 + 35 = 180$$ The sum of the measures is 180.

$$x + 145 = 180$$ Simplify.

$$-145 = -145$$ Subtract 145 from each side.

$$x = 35$$

The missing measure is 35°.

✓ **CHECK Your Progress**

b. BICYCLES The frame of a bicycle shows a triangle. What is the missing measure?

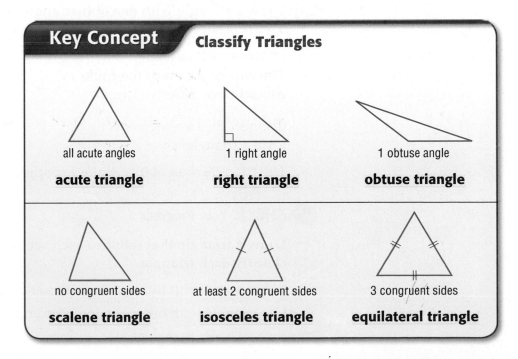

Real-World Link · · · ·
The "Superflag" has been shown at many sporting events, parades, and national celebrations. It measures 40 feet by 72 feet.

Every triangle has at least two acute angles. One way you can classify a triangle is by using the third angle. Another way to classify triangles is by their sides. Sides with the same length are **congruent segments**.

Read Math

Congruent Segments
The marks on the sides of the triangle indicate that those sides are congruent.

Key Concept   **Classify Triangles**

all acute angles	1 right angle	1 obtuse angle
acute triangle	**right triangle**	**obtuse triangle**

no congruent sides	at least 2 congruent sides	3 congruent sides
scalene triangle	**isosceles triangle**	**equilateral triangle**

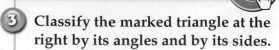

3 Classify the marked triangle at the right by its angles and by its sides.

The triangle on the side of a house has one obtuse angle and two congruent sides. So, it is an obtuse isosceles triangle.

CHECK Your Progress

c.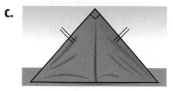

d.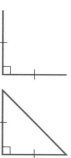

EXAMPLES Draw Triangles

4 Draw a triangle with one right angle and two congruent sides. Then classify the triangle.

Draw a right angle. The two segments should be congruent.

Connect the two segments to form a triangle.

The triangle is a right isosceles triangle.

5 Draw a triangle with one obtuse angle and no congruent sides. Then classify the triangle.

Draw an obtuse angle. The two segments of the angle should have different lengths.

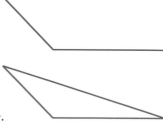

Connect the two segments to form a triangle.

The triangle is an obtuse scalene triangle.

CHECK Your Progress

Draw a triangle that satisfies each set of conditions below. Then classify each triangle.

e. a triangle with three acute angles and three congruent sides

f. a triangle with one right angle and no congruent sides

Example 1
(p. 616)

Find the value of *x*.

1.
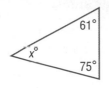
61°
x°
75°

2.
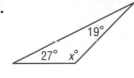
19°
27° *x*°

3.

45°
x°

4. **ALGEBRA** Find *m∠T* in △*RST* if *m∠R* = 37° and *m∠S* = 55°.

Example 2
(p. 617)

5. **BILLIARDS** A triangle is used in the game of pool to rack the pool balls. Find the missing measure of the triangle.

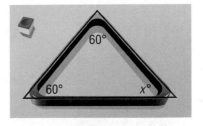
60°
60° *x*°

Example 3
(p. 618)

NATURE Classify the marked triangle in each object by its angles and by its sides.

6.

7.

8.

Examples 4 and 5
(p. 618)

DRAWING TRIANGLES Draw a triangle that satisfies each set of conditions. Then classify each triangle.

9. a triangle with three acute angles and two congruent sides

10. a triangle with one obtuse angle and two congruent sides

● = **Step-by-Step Solutions** begin on page R33.
Extra Practice is on page EP31.

Examples 1 and 2
(pp. 616–617)

Find the value of *x*.

11.

33° *x*°
29°

12.
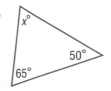
x°
30°

13.
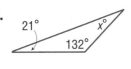
21°
x°
132°

14.
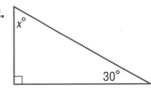
x°
50°
65°

15.

x°
34° 56°

16.
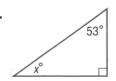
53°
x°

17 **ALGEBRA** Find *m∠Q* in △*QRS* if *m∠R* = 25° and *m∠S* = 102°.

18. **ALGEBRA** In △*EFG*, *m∠F* = 46° and *m∠G* = 34°. What is *m∠E*?

Example 3
(p. 618)

Classify the marked triangle in each object by its angles and by its sides.

19.

20.

21.

22.

23.

24.

25. **ART** The sculpture at the right is entitled *Texas Triangles*. It is located in Lincoln, Massachusetts. What type of triangle is shown: *acute, right,* or *obtuse*?

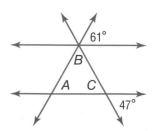

26. **ARCHITECTURE** Use the photo at the left to classify the side view of the Transamerica building by its angles and by its sides.

Examples 4 and 5
(p. 618)

DRAWING TRIANGLES Draw a triangle that satisfies each set of conditions. Then classify each triangle.

27. a triangle with three acute angles and no congruent sides

28. a triangle with one obtuse angle and two congruent sides

29. a triangle with three acute angles and three congruent sides

30. a triangle with one right angle and no congruent sides

Find the value of x for each triangle with the given angle measures.

31. $80°, 20.5°, x°$

32. $75°, x°, 50.2°$

33. $x°, 10.8°, 90°$

34. $45.5°, x°, 105.6°$

35. $x°, 140.1°, 18.6°$

36. $110.2°, x°, 35.6°$

37. **GEOMETRY** Triangle *ABC* is formed by two parallel lines and two transversals. Find the measure of each interior angle *A*, *B*, and *C* of the triangle.

ALGEBRA Find the value of x in each triangle.

38.

39.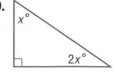

40.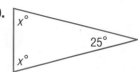

41. CHALLENGE Apply what you know about triangles to find the missing angle measures in the figure.

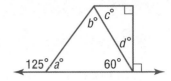

42. OPEN ENDED Draw an acute scalene triangle. Describe the angles and sides of the triangle.

43. REASONING Determine whether each statement is *sometimes*, *always*, or *never* true. Justify your answer.

a. It is possible for a triangle to have two right angles.

b. It is possible for a triangle to have two obtuse angles.

44. Write MATH An equilateral triangle not only has three congruent sides, but also has three congruent angles. Based on this, explain why it is impossible to draw an equilateral triangle that is either right or obtuse.

NGSSS Practice MA.8.G.2.3

45. How would you find $m\angle R$?

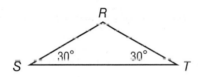

A. Add 30° to 180°.

B. Subtract 60° from 180°.

C. Subtract 30° from 90°.

D. Subtract 180° from 60°.

46. Which of the following is an acute triangle?

F.    H.

G.    I.

Spiral Review

Use the diagram to find the measure of each angle. (Lesson 11-1B)

47. $\angle 1$ **48.** $\angle 2$

49. $\angle 3$ **50.** $\angle 4$

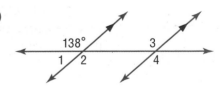

Classify each pair of angles as *complementary*, *supplementary*, or *neither*. (Lesson 11-1A)

51. 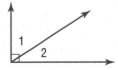   **52.** 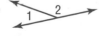   **53.**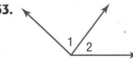

Problem-Solving Investigation

Main Idea Solve problems by using logical reasoning.

P.S.I. TEAM +

Use Logical Reasoning

ANTON: I know that at least two sides of an isosceles triangle are congruent. It also looks like two of the angles in an isosceles triangle are congruent.

YOUR MISSION: Use logical reasoning to find if the angles in an isosceles triangle are congruent.

Understand	Isosceles triangles have at least two congruent sides. We need to find if there is a relationship between the angles.
Plan	Draw several isosceles triangles and measure their angles.
Solve	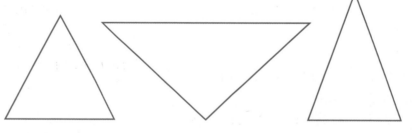 In each triangle, two angles are congruent. So, it seems like an isosceles triangle has two congruent angles.
Check	Try drawing several more isosceles triangles and measuring their angles. Although this is not a proof, it is likely your conclusion is valid. ✓

Analyze the Strategy

1. When you use *inductive reasoning*, you make a rule after seeing several examples. When you use *deductive reasoning*, you use a rule to make a decision. Explain the type of reasoning Anton used to solve the problem.

⋯⋯⋯⋯⋯⋯⋯⋯⋯⋯⋯⋯⋯⋯⋯⋯⋯⋯⋯⋯⋯⋯⋯⋯⋯⋯⋯⋯⋯⋯⋯⋯⋯⋯

 NGSSS
MA.8.G.2.3 Demonstrate that **the sum of the angles in a triangle is 180-degrees and apply this fact to find unknown measure of angles,** and the sum of angles in polygons.

Mixed Problem Solving

Extra Practice is on page EP31.

- Choose an operation.
- Look for a pattern.
- Use a graph.
- Use logical reasoning.

Use the *logical reasoning* strategy to solve Exercises 2–5. Justify your responses.

2. Explain how the *look for a pattern* strategy is similar to inductive reasoning.

3. **GEOMETRY** Draw several scalene triangles and measure their angles. What do you notice about the measures of the angles of a scalene triangle?

4. **HOUSE NUMBERS** Orlondo's house number contains four digits. The digits are 5, 8, 3, and 2. If his house number is odd, divisible by 3, and the middle two numbers are divisible by 5, what is his house number?

5. **FRUIT** Maya, Rashanda, and Perry each brought either a mango, a banana, or an orange with their lunch. If Perry did not bring a banana and Maya brought a mango, what type of fruit did each student bring?

Use any strategy to solve Exercises 6–14.

6. **GEOMETRY** Draw several rectangles and measure their diagonals. Find a relationship between the diagonals of a rectangle.

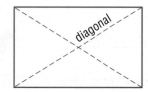

7. **MONEY** Corelia has twice as many quarters in her purse as dimes and half as many nickels as dimes. If she has 12 quarters in her purse, what is the total amount of money she has?

8. **ALGEBRA** Find the next three numbers in the pattern below.

71, 64, 57, 50, ■, ■, ■

9. **MEASUREMENT** The large square has been divided into 9 squares. The lengths of the squares are given. Find the area of the entire square.

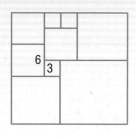

10. **READING** Sonia read 10 pages of a 150-page book on Monday. She plans to read twice as many pages each day than she did the previous day. On what day will she finish the book?

11. **SUPPLIES** Bianca has $55 to buy school supplies. She bought a backpack for $23.50, a combination lock for $6.25, and 4 binders that are $3.99 each. If mechanical pencils are $2.50 per pack, how many packs can she buy?

12. **BOWLING** Cristofer and three friends are going bowling and they have a total of $70 to spend. They buy a pizza, four beverages, and each rent bowling shoes. How many games can they bowl if they all bowl the same number of games?

Bowling Costs	
Item	**Price**
Pizza	$15.75
Beverage	$1.50
Shoe rental	$3.50
Game	$4.00

13. **STATISTICS** Dave has earned scores of 73, 85, 91, and 82 on the first four out of five math tests. What is the minimum score Dave needs to earn on the fifth test to have a test average of at least 82?

14. **ALLOWANCE** Samantha earns $520 in allowance yearly. Her parents promise to give her a $60 raise each year. At this rate, what will her yearly allowance be in 4 years?

Main Idea

Classify quadrilaterals and find missing angle measures in quadrilaterals.

NGSSS

 MA.8.G.2.3 Demonstrate that **the sum of the angles in a triangle is 180-degrees and apply this fact to find unknown measure of angles, and the sum of angles in polygons.**

New Vocabulary

quadrilateral
rectangle
square
parallelogram
rhombus
trapezoid

Get Connected
glencoe.com

Quadrilaterals

Explore The figure below is a **quadrilateral**, since it has four sides and four angles.

Step 1 Draw a quadrilateral.

Step 2 Pick one vertex and draw the diagonal to the opposite vertex.

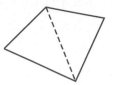

1. What shapes were formed when you drew the diagonal? How many figures were formed?

2. **MAKE A CONJECTURE** Use the relationship among the angle measures in a triangle to find the sum of the angle measures in a quadrilateral. Explain.

3. Find the measure of each angle of your quadrilateral. Compare the sum of these measures to the sum you found in Exercise 2.

The angles of a quadrilateral have a special relationship.

Key Concept | **Angles of a Quadrilateral**

Words The sum of the measures of the angles of a quadrilateral is 360°.

Model 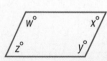   **Symbols** $w + x + y + z = 360$

EXAMPLE **Find Angle Measures**

1. Find the value of x in the quadrilateral.

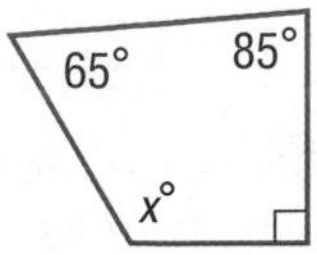

Since the sum of the angle measures in a quadrilateral is 360°, $x + 65 + 85 + 90 = 360$.

$$x + 65 + 85 + 90 = 360 \quad \text{Write the equation.}$$

$$x + 240 = 360 \quad \text{Add 65, 85, and 90.}$$

$$\underline{-240 = -240} \quad \text{Subtract 240 from each side.}$$

$$x = 120$$

So, the value of x is 120.

CHECK Your Progress

Find the value of x.

a.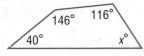

b.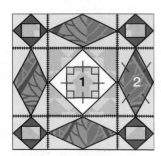

Key Concept — Classifying Quadrilaterals

Quadrilateral	Figure	Characteristics
Rectangle		• Opposite sides congruent • All angles are right angles • Opposite sides parallel
Square		• All sides congruent • All angles are right angles • Opposite sides parallel
Parallelogram		• Opposite sides congruent • Opposite sides parallel • Opposite angles congruent
Rhombus		• All sides congruent • Opposite sides parallel • Opposite angles congruent
Trapezoid		• Exactly one pair of opposite sides parallel

Read Math

Congruent Angles The red arcs show congruent angles.

Real-World EXAMPLE — Classify Quadrilaterals

2 **QUILTS** Classify the quadrilaterals labeled 1 and 2 in the quilt piece.

Figure 1 is a square. Figure 2 is a rhombus.

 CHECK Your Progress

c. LOGOS Classify the quadrilaterals used in the logo below.

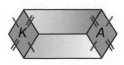

You can use the properties of quadrilaterals to find a missing measure.

Find a Missing Measure

3 **What is the value of x in the parallelogram at the right?**

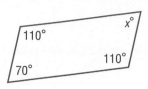

Opposite angles of a parallelogram are congruent. So, $x = 70$.

Check You know the angles in a quadrilateral add to 360°. Since $70° + 110° + 70° + 110° = 360°$, the answer is reasonable. ✔

CHECK Your Progress

d. Find the measure in degrees of $\angle P$ in the rhombus.

e. Find the measure in degrees of $\angle Q$ in the rhombus.

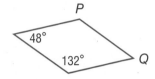

CHECK Your Understanding

Example 1 Find the value of x in each quadrilateral.
(p. 624)

1.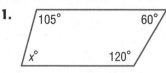

2.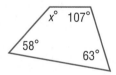

Example 2 **3** **SIGNS** Classify each quadrilateral.
(p. 625)

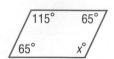

Example 3 **4.** Find the value of x in the parallelogram.
(p. 626)

5. In the quadrilateral shown, $\angle ABC$ is congruent to $\angle ADC$. What is the measure of $\angle ABC$?

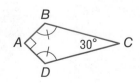

Practice and Problem Solving

= **Step-by-Step Solutions** begin on page R34.
Extra Practice is on page EP31.

Examples 1 and 3
(pp. 624, 626)

Find the value of *x* in each quadrilateral.

6.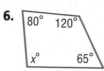
80° 120°
x° 65°

7.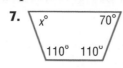
x° 70°
110° 110°

8.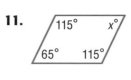
x°
98° 105°

9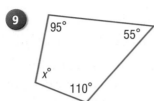
95° 55°
x° 110°

10.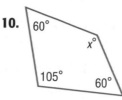
60°
x°
105° 60°

11.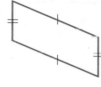
115° *x*°
65° 115°

Example 2
(p. 625)

Classify each quadrilateral.

12.

13.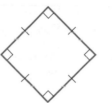

14.

15.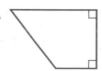

16.

17.

18. FLAGS Many aircraft display the shape of the American flag slightly distorted to indicate motion. Classify each quadrilateral.

19. SIGNS Classify each quadrilateral.

Real-World Link

A tangram is an ancient Chinese puzzle consisting of 7 geometric shapes.

20. TANGRAM Refer to the seven tangram pieces shown at the left. Classify the polygons numbered 3 and 5.

Find the value of *x* in each quadrilateral.

21.
100.4° 90.3°
x° 78.5°

22.
122.8°
x° *x*°
122.8°

23.
2*x*° 2*x*°
2*x*° 2*x*°

Lesson 11-2 Polygons **627**

24. SORTING Lana sorted a set of quadrilaterals into two categories according to a certain rule. The shapes that followed the rule were put in Set A and the shapes that did not follow the rule were put in Set B. What rule did Lana use to sort the quadrilaterals?

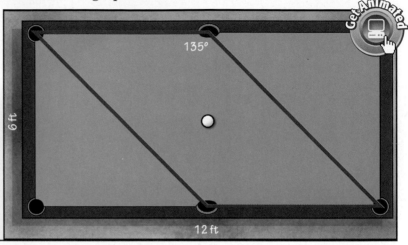

25. GRAPHIC NOVEL Refer to the graphic novel below for Exercises a and b.

Look at this parallelogram that can be formed using the pockets as vertices.

a. Draw a diagram of the parallelogram on a piece of paper. Find and label the other 3 angles of the parallelogram.

b. Draw a diagram of the pool table. What other polygons can you draw using the pockets as vertices?

H.O.T. Problems

26. OPEN ENDED Describe two different real-world items that are shaped as quadrilaterals. Then classify those quadrilaterals.

27. NUMBER SENSE Three of the angle measures of a quadrilateral are congruent. Without calculating, determine if the measure of the fourth angle in each of the following situations is greater than, less than, or equal to 90°. Explain your reasoning.

a. The three congruent angles each measure 89°.

b. The three congruent angles each measure 90°.

c. The three congruent angles each measure 91°.

CHALLENGE Determine whether each statement is *sometimes*, *always*, or *never* true. Explain your reasoning.

28. A rhombus is a square.

29. A quadrilateral is a parallelogram.

30. A rectangle is a square.

31. A square is a rectangle.

32. Write MATH Make a diagram that shows the relationship between each of the following shapes: rectangle, parallelogram, square, rhombus, quadrilateral, and trapezoid. Then write a few sentences that explain your diagram.

33. The drawing shows the shape of Hinto's patio.

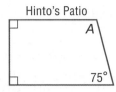

Hinto's Patio

A

75°

Find the measure of ∠A.

A. 75°   C. 165°

B. 105°   D. 195°

34. Identify the name that does NOT describe the quadrilateral shown.

F. quadrilateral   H. trapezoid
G. rectangle   I. parallelogram

35. A parallelogram is shown below. Find the measure of ∠M to the nearest degree.

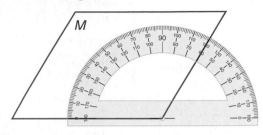

M

A. 30°
B. 60°
C. 120°
D. 150°

Spiral Review

36. REASONING Neva, Sophie, and Gustav have a turtle, a dog, and a hamster for a pet, but not in that order. Sophie's pet lives in a glass aquarium and does not have fur. Neva never has to give her pet a bath. Who has what pet? Use the *logical reasoning* strategy. (Lesson 11-2C)

Find the value of x in each triangle. (Lesson 11-2B)

37.

45°

x°

30°

38.

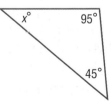

x°   95°

45°

39.

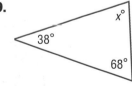

x°

38°

68°

Classify each pair of angles as *complementary*, *supplementary*, or *neither*. (Lesson 11-1A)

40.

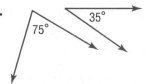

35°

75°

41.

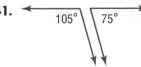

105°   75°

42.

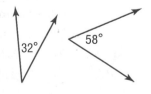

32°   58°

Find the sales tax or discount to the nearest cent. (Lesson 6-3C and 6-3D)

43. $54 jacket; 7% sales tax

44. $23 hat; 15% discount

Main Idea

Find the sum of the angle measures of a polygon and the measure of an interior angle of a regular polygon.

NGSSS

 MA.8.G.2.3 Demonstrate that **the sum of the angles in a triangle is 180-degrees and apply this fact to find unknown measure of angles, and the sum of angles in polygons.**

New Vocabulary

polygon
pentagon
hexagon
heptagon
octagon
nonagon
decagon
equilateral
equiangular
regular polygon

 Get Connected glencoe.com

Polygons and Angles

POOLS Prairie Pools designs and builds swimming pools in various shapes and sizes. The shapes of five swimming pool styles are shown in their catalog.

Aquarius   Kidney   Roman   Oval   Rustic

1. In the pool catalog, the Aquarius and Roman styles are listed under Group A. The remaining pools are listed under Group B. Describe one difference between the shapes of the pools in the two groups.

2. Create your own drawing of the shape of a pool that would fit into Group A. Do the same for Group B.

A **polygon** is a simple, closed figure formed by three or more straight line segments. A *simple figure* does not have lines that cross each other. You have drawn a *closed figure* when your pencil ends up where it started.

Polygons	Not Polygons
△ ⋁ ✛ ▭	⋈ ▭ ◯ ⬭
• Line segments are called sides. • Sides meet only at their endpoints. • Points of intersection are called vertices.	• Figures with sides that cross each other. • Figures that are open. • Figures that have curved sides.

A polygon can be classified by the number of sides it has.

Words	pentagon	hexagon	heptagon	octagon	nonagon	decagon
Number of Sides	5	6	7	8	9	10
Models	⬠	⧖	⇨	✦	⮨	⬍

An **equilateral** polygon has all sides congruent. A polygon is **equiangular** if all of its angles are congruent. A **regular polygon** is equilateral and equiangular, with all sides and all angles congruent.

EXAMPLES **Classify Polygons**

Determine whether each figure is a polygon. If it is, classify the polygon and state whether it is regular. If it is *not* a polygon, explain why.

The figure has 6 congruent sides and 6 congruent angles. It is a regular hexagon.

The figure is not a polygon since it has a curved side.

✓ CHECK Your Progress

a.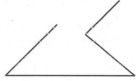

b.

The sum of the measures of the angles of a triangle is 180°. You can use this relationship to find the measures of the angles of polygons.

Study Tip

Diagonals A diagonal is a line segment that joins two nonconsecutive vertices in a polygon.

EXAMPLE **Find the Sum of the Angles of a Polygon**

 Find the sum of the angle measures of the polygon.

Draw all of the diagonals from one vertex as shown and count the number of triangles formed.

Find the sum of the angle measures in the polygon.

$$4 \times 180° = 720°$$

So, the sum of the angle measures of a hexagon is 720°.

✓ CHECK Your Progress

c. pentagon

d. octagon

Key Concept — Interior Angle Sum of a Polygon

Words The sum of the measures of the angles of a polygon is $(n - 2)180$, where n represents the number of sides.

Symbols $S = (n - 2)180$

Real-World EXAMPLE

4 **PICTURE FRAME** Bryan is building a picture frame in the shape of a regular pentagon. Find the measure of each angle of the regular pentagon.

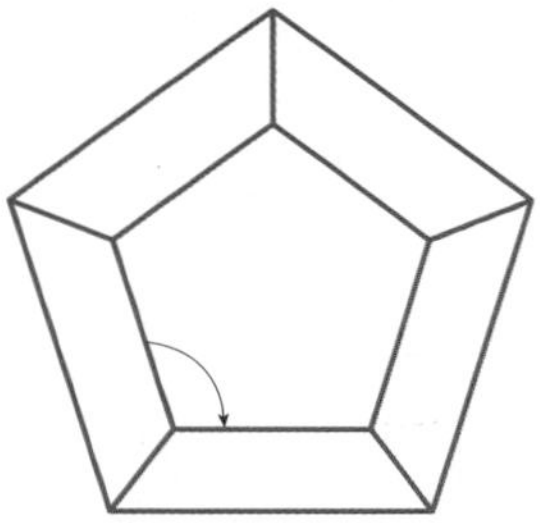

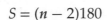

Step 1 Find the sum of the measures of the angles.

$S = (n - 2)180$ Write the formula.

$S = (5 - 2)180$ A pentagon has 5 sides. Replace n with 5.

$S = (3)180$ or 540 Simplify.

The sum of the measures of the angles is 540°.

Step 2 Divide 540 by 5, the number of interior angles, to find the measure of one angle. So, the measure of one angle of a regular pentagon is 540° ÷ 5 or 108°.

Each angle of a regular pentagon measures 108°.

CHECK Your Progress

e. SIGNS A stop sign is a regular octagon. What does each angle measure in a regular octagon?

CHECK Your Understanding

Examples 1 and 2 (p. 631)
Determine whether each figure is a polygon. If it is, classify the polygon and state whether it is regular. If it is *not* a polygon, explain why.

1.

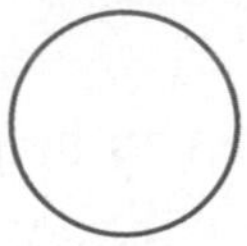

2.

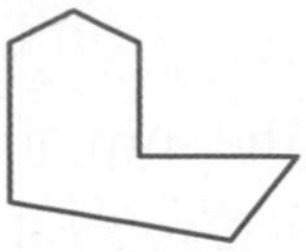

3.

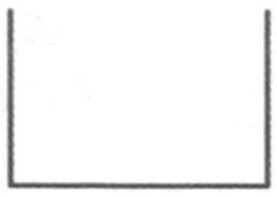

Example 3 (p. 631)
Find the sum of the angle measures of each polygon.

4. quadrilateral

5 heptagon

Example 4 (p. 632)
6. SOCCER A soccer ball is made up of regular pentagons and hexagons. What is the measure of each angle of a regular hexagon?

Practice and Problem Solving

● = **Step-by-Step Solutions** begin on page R35.
Extra Practice is on page EP32.

Examples 1 and 2
(p. 631)

Determine whether each figure is a polygon. If it is, classify the polygon and state whether it is regular. If it is *not* a polygon, explain why.

7.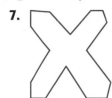

8.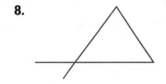

9.

10.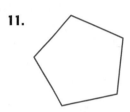

11.

12.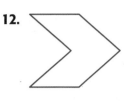

Example 3
(p. 631)

Find the sum of the angle measures of each polygon.

13. nonagon

14. decagon

15. 12-sided polygon

16. 20-sided polygon

Example 4
(p. 632)

17. MIRROR The mirror shown is a regular octagon. What is the measure of each angle of the mirror?

18. GEOMETRY Find the measure of each angle of a regular triangle.

ART The patterns below are made up of polygons. Classify the polygons that are used to create each pattern.

19.

20.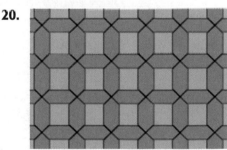

21 TECHNOLOGY Use a calculator to find the measure of each of the angles of a regular 20-sided, 50-sided, and 100-sided polygon. What do you notice about the measure of each angle? Explain why the measure of each angle can never be more than 180°.

22. ALGEBRA Each interior angle of a regular polygon measures 156°. Find the number of sides.

Find the value of each variable.

23.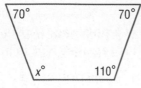

24.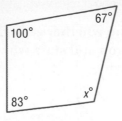

25.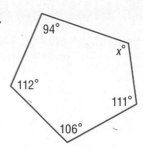

26.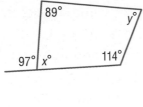

27.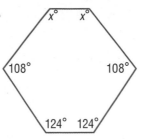

28.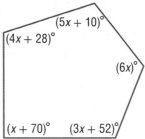

29. ⟳ **MULTIPLE REPRESENTATIONS** Find the sum of the angles of regular polygons with 3, 4, 5, 6, 7, 8, 9, 10, 12, and 15 sides.

   a. TABLE Record your results in a table.

   b. GRAPH Graph your results as ordered pairs (number of sides, sum of angles). Draw a line through the points.

   c. WORDS Describe the graph. What does the slope represent? Is there a *y*-intercept? *x*-intercept?

30. ALPHABET Which letters shown below are *not* considered polygons?

ABCDEFGHIJKLMNOPQRSTUVWXYZ

⬤ **H.O.T. Problems** ·

OPEN ENDED Sketch each of the following figures. Include tick marks to show congruent parts if needed.

31. equiangular quadrilateral

32. equilateral pentagon

33. equilateral quadrilateral with a right angle

34. CHALLENGE When a side of a polygon is extended, an *exterior angle* is formed. Find the sum of the exterior angles of the pentagon.

35. **Write** **MATH** Devion drew a regular polygon and measured one of its interior angles. Explain why it is impossible for his angle measure to be 145°.

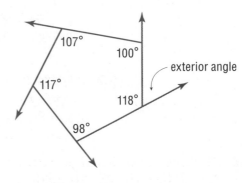

36. What is the measure of ∠1?

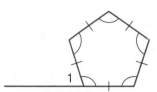

    A. 60°   **C.** 108°

    B. 72°   **D.** 120°

37. Find the measure of each angle of a regular nonagon.

    F. 140°

    G. 145°

    H. 150°

    I. 155°

38. Which statement is true about polygons?

    A. A polygon is classified by the lengths of its sides.

    B. The sides of a polygon overlap.

    C. A polygon is formed by 4 or more line segments.

    D. A regular polygon has equal sides and equal angles.

39. Which polygon is represented by the part shaded gray in the design shown?

    F. hexagon   **H.** octagon

    G. heptagon   **I.** nonagon

Classify each quadrilateral using the name that *best* describes it. (Lesson 11-2D)

40. 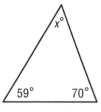   **41.**    **42.**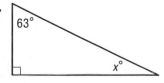

Find the value of *x*. (Lesson 11-2B)

43.    **44.** 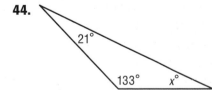   **45.**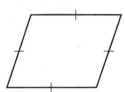

46. VEHICLES A car dealer advertises that they have a different vehicle for each day of the year. The car dealer offers 28 different models of vehicles and 14 different choices of color. Is the advertisement true? Explain. (Lesson 7-2B)

Tessellations

SHIRTS Justin bought a shirt for the new school year. He chose a shirt with patterns in the design. He would like to figure out what types of polygons are used in the shirt's pattern.

Patterns formed by repeating figures that fill a plane without gaps or overlaps are called **tessellations**. A **regular tessellation** is made from one regular polygon.

Main Idea

Recognize a tessellation and create tessellations using transformations.

NGSSS

MA.8.G.2.3 Demonstrate that the sum of angles in a triangle is 180-degrees and **apply this fact to find unknown measure of angles, and the sum of angles in polygons.**

New Vocabulary

tessellation
regular tessellation

Get Connected
glencoe.com

ACTIVITY Get Animated

① **STEP 1** Cut a regular hexagon out of a piece of cardstock. Use a protractor and ruler to check that the angles and sides are congruent.

STEP 2 Place the hexagon on a piece of paper and trace the shape. Translate the figure so that its image is adjacent to the original. Trace the image.

STEP 3 Trace the shape so that the entire paper is covered with hexagons with no gaps or overlaps.

Analyze the Results

1. What is the measure of one angle of a regular hexagon? Find the sum of the measures of the angles around each vertex. Explain.

2. What other regular polygons will tessellate? Explain your reasoning.

ACTIVITY

2 **STEP 1** Draw a square on the back of an index card. Then draw a triangle on the inside of the square and a trapezoid on the bottom of the square as shown.

STEP 2 Cut out the square. Then cut out the triangle and slide it from the right side of the square to the left side of the square. Cut out the trapezoid and slide it from the bottom to the top of the square.

STEP 3 Tape the figures together to form a pattern.

STEP 4 Trace this pattern onto a sheet of paper as shown to create a tessellation.

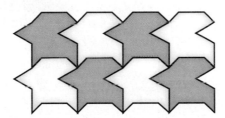

Practice and Apply

Create a tessellation using each pattern.

3.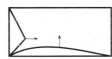

4.

5.

Analyze the Results

6. Design and describe your own tessellation pattern.

7. Explain how congruent figures are used in a tessellation.

8. Some tessellations are formed using combinations of two or three different regular polygons. These are called *semi-regular tessellations*. Identify the regular polygons used in the semi-regular tessellation at the right. Predict the sum of the measures of the angles around each vertex. Check by finding the actual sum.

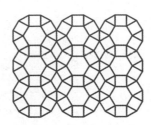

Problem Solving in Bicycle Design

Bikes Have the Right Angles

The design of a bicycle depends on the bike's intended use. For example, road-racing bikes are designed for speed, mountain bikes for stability, and BMX bikes for maneuverability. One way that a bicycle designer makes a bicycle faster, more stable, or more maneuverable is by changing the angles of the bicycle's frame. To have a career designing bicycles, you should be creative, have technical knowledge of bicycles, and have a good understanding of geometry, measurement, and proportion.

Choose a Major

Are you interested in a career as a bicycle designer? Take some of the following courses in high school.

- Art
- Geometry
- Computer Aided Drafting
- Physics

Get Connected glencoe.com

NGSSS

MA.8.G.2.2 Classify and determine the measure of angles including angles created when parallel lines are cut by a transversal.

Bicycle Angles

Type of Bicycle	Head Angle	Seat Tube Angle
Cyclo-cross	72°	74.5°
Mountain	71.5°	73°
Road Sport	73°	75°

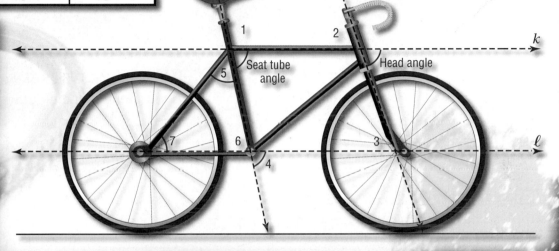

Real-World Math

Use the diagram and the table to solve each problem, assuming *k* is parallel to ℓ. Explain your reasoning.

1. Sometimes, ∠2 in the diagram is described as the head angle. Explain why this is mathematically correct.

2. In the cyclo-cross bike described in the table, what is the measure of ∠1?

3. In the mountain bike, what is the measure of ∠3?

4. In the road sport bike, what is the measure of ∠4?

5. In a bike, the measure of ∠1 is 107°. Is it a cyclo-cross bike, a mountain bike, or a road sport bike?

6. In a bike, the measure of ∠5 is 50° and the measure of ∠6 is 64°. What is the measure of ∠7?

Name each angle in four ways. Then classify the angle as *acute*, *right*, *obtuse*, **or** *straight*. (Lesson 11-1A)

1.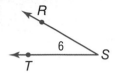

2.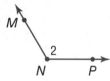

3.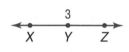

4.

5. **NGSSS PRACTICE** If ∠B and ∠C are supplementary and the measure of ∠B is 53°, what is the measure of ∠C? (Lesson 11-1A)

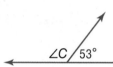

A. 37°   **B.** 127°   **C.** 130°   **D.** 133°

In the figure, find each measure if $m\angle 4 = 117°$. (Lesson 11-1B)

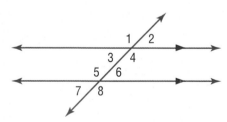

6. $m\angle 1$ **7.** $m\angle 8$

8. $m\angle 3$ **9.** $m\angle 6$

10. **BAR JOISTS** A company produces bar joists for large buildings. If $m\angle 1 = 45°$, what is $m\angle 2$? (Lesson 11-1B)

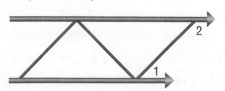

Find the value of *x*. (Lesson 11-2B)

11.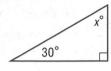

12.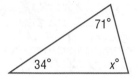

13. **NGSSS PRACTICE** Which of the following is NOT a scalene triangle? (Lesson 11-2B)

F.

H.

G.

I.

Classify each quadrilateral. (Lesson 11-2D)

14.

15.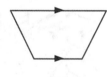

Find the value of *x* **in each quadrilateral.** (Lesson 11-2D)

16.

17.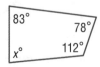

18.

19.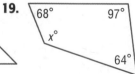

Find the sum of the angle measures of each polygon. (Lesson 11-2E)

20. hexagon

21. octagon

22. 16-sided figure

23. 22-sided figure

Main Idea

Find squares of numbers and square roots of perfect squares.

NGSSS

 Preparation for MA.8.A.6.2 Make reasonable approximations of square roots and mathematical expressions that include square roots, and use them to estimate solutions to problems and to compare mathematical expressions involving real numbers and radical expressions.

New Vocabulary

square
perfect squares
square root
radical sign

Get Connected
glencoe.com

Square Roots

Explore A square with an area of 36 square units is shown.

1. Using tiles, try to construct squares with areas of 4, 9, and 16 square units.

2. Try to construct squares with areas of 12, 18, and 20 square units.

3. Which of the areas form squares?

4. What is the relationship between the lengths of the sides and the areas of these squares?

5. Using your square tiles, create a square that has an area of 49 square units. What are the lengths of the sides of the square?

The area of the square at the right is $5 \cdot 5$ or 25 square units. The product of a number and itself is the **square** of that number. So, the square of 5 is 25.

5 units 25 units^2
5 units

EXAMPLES Find Squares of Numbers

1. Find the square of 3.

$3 \cdot 3 = 9$ Multiply 3 by itself.

9 units^2 3 units
3 units

2. Find the square of 28.

Method 1 Use paper and pencil.	Method 2 Use a calculator.
$\begin{array}{r} 28 \\ \times\ 28 \\ \hline 224 \\ +\ 560 \\ \hline 784 \end{array}$ Multiply 28 by itself. Annex a zero.	28 x^2 ENTER 784

 CHOOSE Your Method

Find the square of each number.

a. 8   b. 12   c. 23

Numbers like 9, 16, and 225 are called square numbers or **perfect squares** because they are squares of whole numbers.

The factors multiplied to form perfect squares are called **square roots**. A **radical sign**, $\sqrt{}$, is the symbol used to indicate a square root.

Key Concept   Square Root

Words	A square root of a number is one of its two equal factors.

Examples	**Numbers**	**Algebra**
	$4 \cdot 4 = 16$, so $\sqrt{16} = 4$.	If $x \cdot x$ or $x^2 = y$, then $\sqrt{y} = x$.

EXAMPLES   **Find Square Roots**

3   Find $\sqrt{81}$.

$9 \cdot 9 = 81$, so $\sqrt{81} = 9$.   What number times itself is 81?

4   Find $\sqrt{225}$.

2nd [$\sqrt{}$] 225 ENTER 15

So, $\sqrt{225} = 15$.

 CHECK Your Progress

Find each square root.

   d. $\sqrt{64}$ **e.** $\sqrt{289}$

Real-World EXAMPLE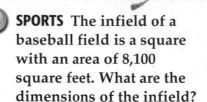

5   **SPORTS** The infield of a baseball field is a square with an area of 8,100 square feet. What are the dimensions of the infield?

The infield is a square. By finding the square root of the area, 8,100, you find the length of one side of the infield.

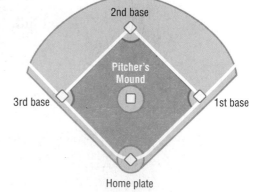

$90 \cdot 90 = 8,100$, so $\sqrt{8,100} = 90$.

The dimensions of the infield are 90 feet by 90 feet.

 CHECK Your Progress

   f. **SPORTS** The largest ring in amateur boxing is a square with an area of 400 square feet. What are the dimensions of the ring?

Examples 1 and 2
(p. 641)

Find the square of each number.

1. 6   **2.** 10   **3** 17   **4.** 30

Examples 3 and 4
(p. 642)

Find each square root.

5. $\sqrt{9}$ **6.** $\sqrt{36}$ **7.** $\sqrt{121}$ **8.** $\sqrt{169}$

Example 5
(p. 642)

9. ROAD SIGNS Historic Route 66 from Chicago to Los Angeles is known as the Main Street of America. If the area of a Route 66 sign measures 576 square inches and the sign is a square, what are the dimensions of the sign?

● = **Step-by-Step Solutions** begin on page R35.
Extra Practice is on page EP32.

Practice and Problem Solving

Examples 1 and 2
(p. 641)

Find the square of each number.

10. 4   **11.** 1   **12.** 7   **13.** 11

14. 16   **15.** 20   **16.** 18   **17.** 34

Examples 3 and 4
(p. 642)

Find each square root.

18. $\sqrt{4}$ **19.** $\sqrt{16}$ **20.** $\sqrt{49}$ **21.** $\sqrt{100}$

22. $\sqrt{144}$ **23.** $\sqrt{256}$ **24.** $\sqrt{529}$ **25.** $\sqrt{625}$

Example 5
(p. 642)

26. MEASUREMENT Roslyn's bedroom is shaped like a square. What are the dimensions of the room if the area of the floor is 196 square feet?

27. SPORTS For the floor exercise, gymnasts perform their tumbling skills on a mat that has an area of 1,600 square feet. How much room does a gymnast have to run along one side of the mat?

28. GEOGRAPHY Refer to the squares in the diagram. They represent the approximate areas of Florida, North Carolina, and Pennsylvania.

    a. What is the area of North Carolina in square miles?

    b. How much larger is Florida than Pennsylvania?

    c. The water areas of Florida, North Carolina, and Pennsylvania are 11,881 square miles, 5,041 square miles, and 1,225 square miles, respectively. Make a similar diagram comparing the water areas of these states.

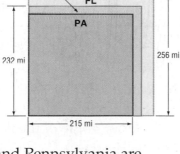

29 MEASUREMENT A chessboard has an area of 324 square inches. There is a 1-inch border around the 64 squares on the board. What is the length of one side of the region containing the small squares?

30. **OPEN ENDED** Write a number whose square is between 100 and 150.

31. **CHALLENGE** Use the diagram shown.

   a. Could the area of the dog's pen be made larger using the same amount of fencing? Explain.

   6 ft

   14 ft

   b. Describe the largest rectangular pen area possible using the same amount of fencing. How do the perimeter and area compare to the original pen?

32. **Write MATH** Explain why raising a number to the second power is called *squaring* the number.

 Practice   **MA.7.G.4.1, MA.8.A.6.2**

33. Which model represents the square of 4?

   A.   C.

   B.   D.

34. Which measure can be the area of a square if the measure of the side length is a whole number?

   F. 836 sq ft

   G. 949 sq ft

   H. 1,100 sq ft

   I. 1,225 sq ft

35. **CONSTRUCTION** Li-Chih is building a gazebo. He would like the base to be a regular octagon. What is the measure of each interior angle of the octagonal floor? (Lesson 11-2E)

Classify each quadrilateral. (Lesson 11-2D)

36.    37. 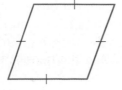   38.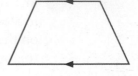

Main Idea
Estimate square roots.

NGSSS
MA.8.A.6.2 Make reasonable approximations of square roots and mathematical expressions that include square roots, and use them to estimate solutions to problems and to compare mathematical expressions involving real numbers and radical expressions.
MA.8.A.6.4 Perform operations on real numbers (including integer exponents, **radicals,** percents, scientific notation, absolute value, rational numbers, and irrational numbers) **using multi-step and real world problems.**

New Vocabulary
irrational number

Get Connected
glencoe.com

Estimate Square Roots

 **Explore** Estimate the square root of 27.

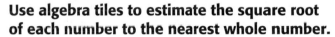

- Arrange 27 tiles into the largest square possible.

- Add tiles to make the next larger square.

- The square root of 27 is between 5 and 6. Since 27 is much closer to 25 than 36, the square root of 27 is closer to 5 than 6.

Use algebra tiles to estimate the square root of each number to the nearest whole number.

1. 40   2. 28   3. 85   4. 62

5. Describe another method that you could use to estimate the square root of a number.

The square root of a perfect square is an integer. You can estimate the square root of a number that is *not* a perfect square.

EXAMPLE   **Estimate a Square Root**

① **Estimate $\sqrt{78}$ to the nearest whole number.**

List some perfect squares.

1, 4, 9, 16, 25, 36, 49, 64, 81, …

$64 < 78 < 81$ 78 is between the perfect squares 64 and 81.

$\sqrt{64} < \sqrt{78} < \sqrt{81}$ Find the square root of each number.

$8 < \sqrt{78} < 9$ $\sqrt{64} = 8$ and $\sqrt{81} = 9$

So, $\sqrt{78}$ is between 8 and 9. Since 78 is much closer to 81 than to 64, the best whole number estimate is 9.   Verify with a calculator.

 CHECK Your Progress

a. Estimate $\sqrt{50}$ to the nearest whole number.

Not all numbers are perfect squares. These numbers have square roots that are irrational. A number that cannot be expressed as the quotient of two integers is an **irrational number**.

$$\text{Irrational Numbers:} \quad 0.636336333\ldots, \sqrt{2}, \pi$$

Real-World EXAMPLE

 SCIENCE Physicist and mathematician Galileo performed an experiment by dropping stones from the edge of the Leaning Tower of Pisa. The formula $t = \dfrac{\sqrt{h}}{4}$ represents the time t in seconds that it takes an object to fall from a height of h feet. If the tower is 180 feet, estimate the time it took the stones to hit the ground.

First estimate the value of $\sqrt{180}$.

$169 \; < \; 180 \; < \; 196$ 169 and 196 are the closest perfect squares.

$13^2 \; < \; 180 \; < \; 14^2$ $169 = 13^2$ and $196 = 14^2$

$\sqrt{13^2} \; < \sqrt{180} < \sqrt{14^2}$ Find the square root of each number.

$13 \; < \sqrt{180} < \quad 14$ Simplify.

Since 180 is closer to 169 than 196, the best whole number estimate for $\sqrt{180}$ is 13. Use this value to evaluate the expression.

$$t = \frac{\sqrt{h}}{4} \approx \frac{13}{4} \text{ or } 3.25$$

So, stones dropped from the Leaning Tower of Pisa would take about 3.25 seconds to hit the ground.

CHECK Your Progress

b. Estimate the time for an object to fall if dropped from the observation deck of the Eiffel Tower at 311 feet.

CHECK Your Understanding

Example 1
(p. 645)

Estimate each square root to the nearest whole number.

1. $\sqrt{39}$ **2.** $\sqrt{106}$ **3.** $\sqrt{90}$ **4.** $\sqrt{140}$

5. MEASUREMENT The diagram shows the floor plan of a square kitchen. What is the approximate length of one side of the kitchen floor to the nearest whole number?

Example 2
(p. 646)

6. SPEED A vehicle's speed can be estimated based on the length of the skid marks made by the car tires using the formula $s = \sqrt{24m}$, where s represents the speed in miles per hour and m represents the length of the skid in feet. A car leaves a mark that is 10 feet long. Estimate the speed of the vehicle.

Practice and Problem Solving

 = **Step-by-Step Solutions** begin on page R35.
Extra Practice is on page EP32.

Example 1
(p. 645)

Estimate each square root to the nearest whole number.

7. $\sqrt{11}$ 8. $\sqrt{20}$ 9. $\sqrt{35}$ 10. $\sqrt{65}$

11 $\sqrt{89}$ 12. $\sqrt{116}$ 13. $\sqrt{137}$ 14. $\sqrt{409}$

15. **MEASUREMENT** The bottom of a square baking pan has an area of 67 square inches. What is the approximate length of one side of the pan?

16. **ALGEBRA** What whole number is closest to $\sqrt{m - n}$ if $m = 45$ and $n = 8$?

Example 2
(p. 646)

17. **ARCHITECTURE** The Parthenon in Athens, Greece, contains the *golden rectangle* proportion repeatedly. The length of the longer side divided by the length of the shorter side is equal to $\dfrac{1 + \sqrt{5}}{2}$. Estimate the value of the ratio.

18. **BASEBALL** In Little League, the field is a square with sides of 60 feet. The expression $\sqrt{(s^2 + s^2)}$ represents the distance *across* a square of side length s. Second base and home plate are in opposite corners across the field. Estimate the distance the catcher at home base would have to throw the ball to reach the second baseman.

Estimate each square root to the nearest whole number.

19. $\sqrt{925}$ 20. $\sqrt{2,480}$ 21. $\sqrt{1,610}$ 22. $\sqrt{6,500}$

Find each square root to the nearest tenth.

23. $\sqrt{0.25}$ 24. $\sqrt{0.49}$ 25. $\sqrt{1.96}$ 26. $\sqrt{2.89}$

ALGEBRA Estimate each expression to the nearest whole number if $a = 8$ and $b = 3.7$.

27. $\sqrt{a + b}$ 28. $\sqrt{6b - a}$

29 **STAMPS** The Special Olympics commemorative stamp is square in shape with an area of 1,008 square millimeters.

   a. Find the length of one side of the postage stamp to the nearest tenth.

   b. What is the length of one side in centimeters?

30. **ALGEBRA** The formula $D = 1.23 \times \sqrt{h}$ can be used to estimate the distance D in miles you can see from a point h feet above Earth's surface. Use the formula to find the distance D in miles that you can see from the top of a 120-foot hill. Round to the nearest tenth.

31. **FIND THE DATA** Refer to the Data File on pages 2–5. Choose some data and write a real-world problem in which you would estimate a square root.

32. Which One Doesn't Belong? Identify the number that does not have the same characteristic as the other three. Explain your reasoning.

$\sqrt{5}$	π	$\sqrt{81}$	0.535335333...

33. OPEN ENDED Select three numbers with square roots between 4 and 5.

34. NUMBER SENSE Explain why 8 is the best whole number estimate for $\sqrt{71}$.

CHALLENGE A cube root of a number is one of three equal factors of that number. Estimate the cube root of each number to the nearest whole number.

35. $\sqrt[3]{9}$ **36.** $\sqrt[3]{26}$ **37.** $\sqrt[3]{120}$ **38.** $\sqrt[3]{500}$

39. 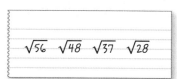 **MATH** Apply what you know about numbers to explain why $\sqrt{30}$ is an irrational number.

NGSSS Practice   MA.6.G.4.3, MA.8.A.6.2

40. Reina wrote four numbers on a piece of paper. She then asked Tyron to select the number closest to 5. Which number should he select?

$\sqrt{56}$ $\sqrt{48}$ $\sqrt{37}$ $\sqrt{28}$

A. $\sqrt{56}$ C. $\sqrt{37}$

B. $\sqrt{48}$ D. $\sqrt{28}$

41. Which of the following is an irrational number?

F. $\sqrt{25}$ H. -13

G. $\sqrt{7}$ I. $\dfrac{4}{5}$

42. THINK SOLVE EXPLAIN **EXTENDED RESPONSE** The area of a square is 169 square inches.

Part A What is the length of a side?

Part B What is the perimeter of the square?

Find the square of each number. (Lesson 11-3A)

43. 11   **44.** 14   **45.** 18

Determine whether each figure is a polygon. If it is, classify the polygon and state whether it is regular. If it is *not* a polygon, explain why. (Lesson 11-2E)

46.

47.
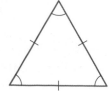

Main Idea

Identify and classify numbers in the real number system. Compare mathematical expressions involving real numbers.

NGSSS

MA.8.A.6.2 Make reasonable approximations of square roots and mathematical expressions that include square roots, and use them to estimate solutions to problems and to compare mathematical expressions involving real numbers and radical expressions.
MA.8.A.6.4 Perform operations on real numbers (including integer exponents, **radicals,** percents, scientific notation, absolute value, **rational numbers, and irrational numbers)** using multi-step and real world problems.

New Vocabulary

real number

Get Connected
glencoe.com

The Real Number System

GYMNASTICS In gymnastics, the floor exercise routine is performed on a mat with the dimensions shown. Most routines have 4 or 5 tumbling passes that run along the diagonal of the mat.

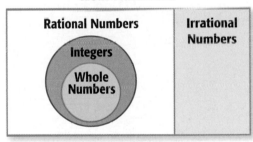

1. The length and width of the mat is 40 feet. Is 40 a rational number? Explain.

2. The length of the diagonal is $\sqrt{3,200}$ feet. Can this square root be written as a rational number? Explain.

Using a calculator, the decimal value of $\sqrt{3,200}$ is 56.56854249. Although the calculator only shows a limited number of places, this number never terminates and never repeats. It is an irrational number.

Rational and irrational numbers make up the set of **real numbers**. The graphic organizer below shows the various sets of real numbers.

Real Numbers

Rational Numbers	Irrational Numbers
Integers	
Whole Numbers	

EXAMPLES Classify Numbers

Name all sets of numbers to which each real number belongs.

1 0.34343434...   The decimal ends in a repeating pattern. It is a rational number because it is equivalent to $\frac{34}{99}$.

2 $\sqrt{49}$ Since $\sqrt{49} = 7$, it is a whole number, integer, and rational number.

3 π The number π is considered an irrational number because it never ends and never repeats.

CHECK Your Progress

a. $\sqrt{35}$ b. $-3\frac{1}{3}$ c. 45

Real numbers follow the properties that hold true for whole numbers, integers, and rational numbers.

	Key Concept	Real Number Properties

Property	Arithmetic	Algebra
Commutative	$3.2 + 2.5 = 2.5 + 3.2$ $5.1 \cdot 2.8 = 2.8 \cdot 5.1$	$a + b = b + a$ $a \cdot b = b \cdot a$
Associative	$(2 + 1) + 5 = 2 + (1 + 5)$ $(3 \cdot 4) \cdot 6 = 3 \cdot (4 \cdot 6)$	$(a + b) + c = a + (b + c)$ $(a \cdot b) \cdot c = a \cdot (b \cdot c)$
Distributive	$2(3 + 5) = 2 \cdot 3 + 2 \cdot 5$	$a(b + c) = a \cdot b + a \cdot c$
Identity	$\sqrt{8} + 0 = \sqrt{8}$ $\sqrt{7} \cdot 1 = \sqrt{7}$	$a + 0 = a$ $a \cdot 1 = a$
Additive Inverse	$4 + (-4) = 0$	$a + (-a) = 0$
Multiplicative Inverse	$\frac{2}{3} \cdot \frac{3}{2} = 1$	$\frac{a}{b} \cdot \frac{b}{a} = 1$, where $a, b \neq 0$

EXAMPLE **Graph Real Numbers**

4 Find $\sqrt{7}$ and $-\sqrt{11}$ to the nearest tenth. Then graph $\sqrt{7}$ and $-\sqrt{11}$ on a number line.

$\sqrt{7} \approx 2.645751311\ldots$ or about 2.6   Use a calculator.

$-\sqrt{11} \approx -3.31662479\ldots$ or about -3.3 Use a calculator.

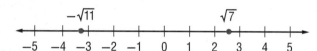

CHECK Your Progress

Find each square root to the nearest tenth. Then graph the square root on a number line.

d. $\sqrt{12}$ **e.** $-\sqrt{8}$ **f.** $\sqrt{63}$

EXAMPLES **Compare Real Numbers**

Replace each ● with $<$, $>$, or $=$ to make a true sentence.

5 $\sqrt{13}$ ● $3\frac{3}{5}$

Write each number as a decimal.

$\sqrt{13} \approx 3.605551275\ldots$ $3\frac{3}{5} = 3.6$

Since $3.605551275\ldots > 3.6$, $\sqrt{13} > 3\frac{3}{5}$.

6 $1.\overline{2}$ $\sqrt{1.44}$

Write $\sqrt{1.44}$ as a decimal.

$\sqrt{1.44} = 1.2$

$1.\overline{2} = 1.222222222\ldots$

Since $1.222222222\ldots > 1.2$, $1.\overline{2} > \sqrt{1.44}$.

 CHECK Your Progress

Replace each ● with $<$, $>$, or $=$ to make a true sentence.

g. -2.3 ● $\sqrt{6}$ **h.** $\frac{14}{2}$ ● $\sqrt{48}$

i. $\sqrt{0.16}$ ● $\frac{2}{5}$ **j.** $1\frac{1}{3}$ ● $1.\overline{3}$

Real-World EXAMPLE

7 **SIGHTSEEING** On a clear day, the number of miles a person can see to the horizon is $1.23\sqrt{h}$ where h is the height of the person from the ground. The observation deck in the crown of the Statue of Liberty is 266 feet high. How far can a visitor see on a clear day in New York City from the statue?

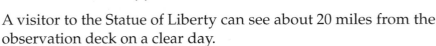

Use a calculator to approximate the distance a person can see.

$d = 1.23\sqrt{h}$ Write the equation.

$= 1.23\sqrt{266}$ Replace h with 266.

$\approx 1.23(16.3)$ Simplify.

≈ 20 Multiply.

A visitor to the Statue of Liberty can see about 20 miles from the observation deck on a clear day.

CHECK Your Progress

k. SKYSCRAPERS How far can a person see on a clear day from the top of the 1,451-foot tall Willis Tower in Chicago? Round to the nearest whole number.

l. MEASUREMENT Estimate the perimeter of a square with area 170 square inches to the nearest whole number.

Examples 1–3
(p. 649)

Name all sets of numbers to which each real number belongs.

1. $0.123112233111\ldots$ **2.** $\sqrt{100}$ **3.** $-\dfrac{4}{9}$

Example 4
(p. 650)

Find each square root to the nearest tenth. Then graph the square root on a number line.

4. $\sqrt{15}$ **5.** $-\sqrt{21}$

Examples 5 and 6
(pp. 650–651)

Replace each ⬤ with <, >, or = to make a true sentence.

6. $5\dfrac{1}{5}$ ⬤ $\sqrt{27}$ **7.** $-6.\overline{7}$ ⬤ $-\sqrt{46}$

Example 7
(p. 651)

8. MEASUREMENT Estimate the perimeter of a square with area 150 square centimeters to the nearest whole number.

Practice and Problem Solving

⬤ = **Step-by-Step Solutions** begin on page R35.
Extra Practice is on page EP33.

Examples 1–3
(p. 649)

Name all sets of numbers to which each real number belongs.

9 0.9 **10.** 5 **11.** $-\sqrt{25}$ **12.** $3.\overline{25}$

13. $\sqrt{324}$ **14.** $2.525225222\ldots$ **15.** $\dfrac{3}{5}$ **16.** -2

Example 4
(p. 650)

Find each square root to the nearest tenth. Then graph the square root on a number line.

17. $\sqrt{75}$ **18.** $\sqrt{80}$ **19.** $-\sqrt{29}$ **20.** $-\sqrt{8}$

Examples 5 and 6
(pp. 650–651)

Replace each ⬤ with <, >, or = to make a true sentence.

21. $4\dfrac{2}{3}$ ⬤ $4.\overline{6}$ **22.** $-\sqrt{30}$ ⬤ -5

23. $3 + \sqrt{5}$ ⬤ 6 **24.** $0.262626\ldots$ ⬤ $\dfrac{26}{99}$

Example 7
(p. 651)

25. MEASUREMENT Use the formula from Example 7 to determine how far someone could see on a clear day from the top of the St. Louis Arch observation area at 630 feet. Round to the nearest tenth if necessary.

26. SEISMIC WAVES The speed of a tsunami can be measured by the formula $s = \sqrt{9.61d}$, where s is the speed of the wave in meters per second and d is the depth of the ocean in meters where the earthquake occurs. What is the speed of a tsunami if an earthquake occurs at a depth of 458 meters? Round to the nearest tenth.

27 TRACK AND FIELD To find the height h in feet that a pole vaulter can reach, coaches can use the formula $v = 8\sqrt{h}$, where v is the velocity of the pole vaulter in feet per second. Suppose a vaulter reached a height of 10 feet. About how fast was she running? Round to the nearest tenth.

28. **OPEN ENDED** Give an example of a number that is a rational number but not an integer.

29. **Which One Doesn't Belong?** Identify the number that does not belong with the other three. Explain your reasoning.

| 3.8 | −3.8 | $3\frac{4}{55}$ | $\sqrt{3.88}$ |

30. **Write MATH** Explain the difference between rational and irrational numbers. Give an example of each.

NGSSS Practice MA.8.A.6.2

31. For what value of x is $\sqrt{x} > x$?

    A. 0.8   C. 5.8

    B. 4   D. 16

32. Which number is represented by the point graphed on the number line?

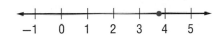

    F. $\sqrt{4}$ H. $\sqrt{14}$

    G. $\sqrt{9}$ I. $\sqrt{17}$

Spiral Review

Estimate each square root to the nearest integer. (Lesson 11-3B)

33. $-\sqrt{35}$ 34. $\sqrt{119}$ 35. $-\sqrt{78}$ 36. $\sqrt{27}$

37. Imani is playing a review game in math class. She needs to pick the card that is labeled with the number closest to 8. Which should she pick? (Lesson 11-3A)

| $\sqrt{25}$ | $\sqrt{16}$ | $\sqrt{100}$ | $\sqrt{49}$ |

38. The figure represents a top view of a school playground. What is the value of x? (Lesson 11-2D)

Lesson 11-3 The Pythagorean Theorem **653**

Explore The Pythagorean Theorem

Main Idea

Validate the Pythagorean Theorem using models.

NGSSS

MA.8.G.2.4
Validate and apply **Pythagorean Theorem** to find distances in real world situations or between points in the coordinate plane.

Get Connected
glencoe.com

BOATING The Jenkins family has a sailboat that they use on a nearby lake. About how far is it from one dock to the other?

The situation can be modeled with squares.

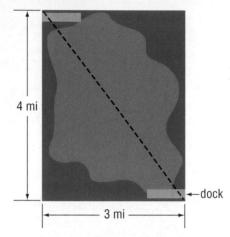

ACTIVITY

STEP 1 Use grid paper or tiles to make squares with sides of 3, 4, and 5 units.

STEP 2 Form a right triangle as shown.

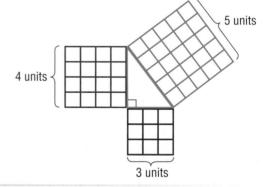

Analyze the Results

1. Compare the sum of the areas of the smaller squares with the area of the largest square.

2. Draw a right triangle with sides 5, 12, and 13 units in length on grid paper. Find the areas of the three squares. What do you notice about the two smaller squares?

3. **MAKE A CONJECTURE** Refer to the diagrams at the right. What can you conclude about the squares of the lengths of the sides of a right triangle?

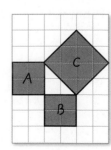

Main Idea

Find length using the Pythagorean Theorem.

NGSSS

MA.8.G.2.4 Validate and **apply Pythagorean Theorem to find distances in real world situations** or between points in the coordinate plane.

New Vocabulary

leg
hypotenuse
Pythagorean Theorem

Get Connected
glencoe.com

The Pythagorean Theorem

ROLLER COASTERS Engineers use triangles to build structures because they provide the most stable support to handle heavy weights. Roller coasters are built using triangles. The roller coaster in the photo is an example of this type of structure.

1. What type of triangle is created by the support beams of the roller coaster?

2. If the horizontal bar of the triangle is 6 feet and the vertical bar of the triangle is 10 feet, will the diagonal bar be more or less than 10 feet?

In a right triangle, the sides have special names.

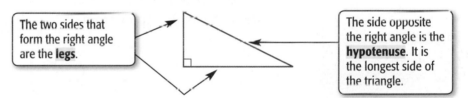

The two sides that form the right angle are the **legs**.

The side opposite the right angle is the **hypotenuse**. It is the longest side of the triangle.

The **Pythagorean Theorem** describes the relationship between the length of the hypotenuse and the lengths of the legs.

Key Concept Pythagorean Theorem

Words In a right triangle, the square of the length of the hypotenuse equals the sum of the squares of the lengths of the legs.

Model

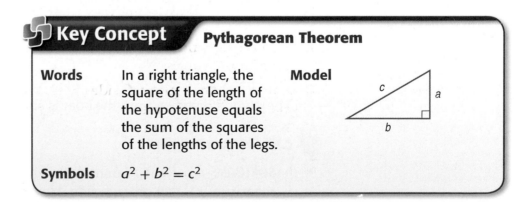

Symbols $a^2 + b^2 = c^2$

When using the Pythagorean Theorem, you will encounter equations that involve square roots. If $n^2 = a$, then $n = \pm\sqrt{a}$. The notation $\pm\sqrt{}$ indicates both the positive and negative square root of a number.

EXAMPLE   **Find the Length of the Hypotenuse**

1 Find the length of the hypotenuse of the triangle.

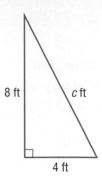

$a^2 + b^2 = c^2$ Pythagorean Theorem

$8^2 + 4^2 = c^2$ Replace a with 8 and b with 4.

$64 + 16 = c^2$ Evaluate 8^2 and 4^2.

$80 = c^2$ Add.

$\pm\sqrt{80} = c$ Definition of square root

$\pm 8.9 \approx c$ Simplify.

8 ft c ft   4 ft

The length of the hypotenuse is about 8.9 feet.

> **Study Tip**
>
> **Check for Reasonableness**
> You can eliminate −8.9 as a solution because the length of a side of a triangle cannot be a negative number.

✓ **CHECK Your Progress**

a. Find the length of the hypotenuse of a right triangle with legs 5 yards and 7 yards. Round to the nearest tenth.

Real-World EXAMPLE

Real-World Link · · · · ·
Equipment needed for scuba diving weighs between 60 and 75 pounds.

2 **SCUBA DIVING** A scuba diver dove 14 feet below the surface. Then he swam 16 feet horizontally. How far is the diver from his boat?

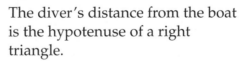

The diver's distance from the boat is the hypotenuse of a right triangle.

$a^2 + b^2 = c^2$ Pythagorean Theorem

$14^2 + 16^2 = x^2$ Replace c with x, a with 14, and b with 16.

$196 + 256 = x^2$ Evaluate 14^2 and 16^2.

$452 = x^2$ Add.

$\pm\sqrt{452} = x$ Definition of square root

$\pm 21.3 \approx x$ Simplify.

The diver's distance from the boat is about 21.3 feet.

✓ **CHECK Your Progress**

b. **SOFTBALL** A softball diamond is a square measuring 60 feet on each side. How far does a player on second base throw when she throws from second base to home? Round to the nearest tenth.

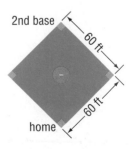

2nd base   60 ft   60 ft   home

You can also use the Pythagorean Theorem to find the measure of a leg if the measure of the other leg and the hypotenuse are known.

EXAMPLE   **Find the Length of a Leg**

③ Find the missing measure of the triangle. Round to the nearest tenth if necessary.

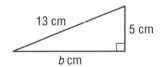

The missing measure is the length of a leg.

$a^2 + b^2 = c^2$	Pythagorean Theorem
$5^2 + b^2 = 13^2$	Replace a with 5 and c with 13.
$25 + b^2 = 169$	Evaluate 13^2 and 5^2.
$\underline{-25 \qquad = -25}$	Subtract 25 from each side.
$b^2 = 144$	Simplify.
$b = \pm\sqrt{144}$	Definition of square root
$b = 12$	Simplify.

The length of the leg is 12 centimeters.

Study Tip

Check for Reasonableness
The hypotenuse is always the longest side in a right triangle. Since 12 < 13, the answer is reasonable.

✓ **CHECK Your Progress**

c.

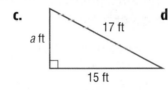

d.

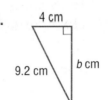

e. $b = 7$ in., $c = 25$ in.

Real-World **EXAMPLE**

④ **FLAGS** Mr. Thomson created a flag in the shape of a rectangle for his home. What is the length of the flag?

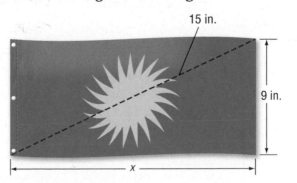

15 in.

9 in.

Use the Pythagorean Theorem to find the length of the side.

(continued on next page)

$$a^2 + b^2 = c^2 \qquad \text{Pythagorean Theorem}$$
$$9^2 + b^2 = 15^2 \qquad \text{Replace } a \text{ with 9 and } c \text{ with 15.}$$
$$81 + b^2 = 225 \qquad \text{Evaluate.}$$
$$b^2 = 144 \qquad \text{Simplify.}$$
$$b = \pm\sqrt{144} \qquad \text{Definition of square root}$$
$$b = \pm 12 \qquad \text{Simplify.}$$

The length is about 12 inches.

✓ CHECK Your Progress

f. POOLS The diagonal of a square pool measures 28.284 feet. What is the length of the pool?

28.284 ft

✓ CHECK Your Understanding

Examples 1 and 3
(pp. 656–657)

Find the missing measure of each triangle. Round to the nearest tenth if necessary.

 1.

c mm
10 mm
24 mm

2.
19 in.   a in.
31 in.

3. $b = 21$ cm, $c = 28$ cm, $a = $ ■

4. $a = 11$ yd, $b = 12$ yd, $c = $ ■

Examples 2 and 4
(pp. 656–658)

5. ARCHITECTURE What is the length of the fence gate shown at the right? Round to the nearest tenth.

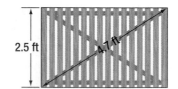
2.5 ft
4.7 ft

6. PARKS A company designed a public play area in the shape of a rectangle. The play area will include a pathway as shown. What is the width of the play area?

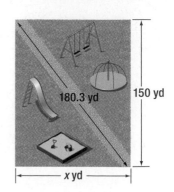
180.3 yd
150 yd
x yd

Practice and Problem Solving

= **Step-by-Step Solutions** begin on page R36.
Extra Practice is on page EP33.

Examples 1 and 3
(pp. 656–657)

Find the missing measure of each triangle. Round to the nearest tenth if necessary.

7.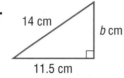

8.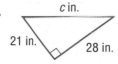

9.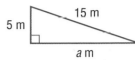

10.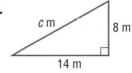

11.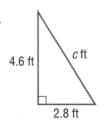

12.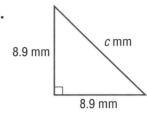

13. $a = 2.4$ yd, $c = 3.7$ yd, $b = $ ▪

14. $b = 8.5$ m, $c = 10.4$ m, $a = $ ▪

15. $a = 7$ in., $b = 24$ in., $c = $ ▪

16. $a = 13.5$ mm, $b = 18$ mm, $c = $ ▪

Examples 2 and 4
(pp. 656–658)

MEASUREMENT For Exercises 17 and 18, find each distance to the nearest tenth.

17.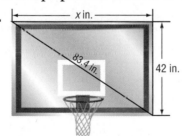

18.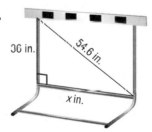

SPORTS For Exercises 19 and 20, find the length or width of each piece of sports equipment. Round to the nearest tenth.

19.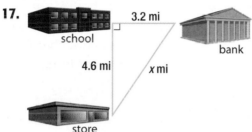

20.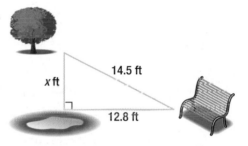

21 **MEASUREMENT** A barn door is 10 feet wide and 15 feet tall. A square plank 16 feet on each side must be taken through the doorway. Can the plank fit through the doorway? Justify your answer.

22. MEASUREMENT On a weekend trip around California, Sydney left her home in Modesto and drove 75 miles east to Yosemite National Park, then 70 miles south to Fresno, and finally 110 miles west to Monterey Bay. About how far is she from her starting point? Justify your answer with a drawing.

23. FIND THE ERROR Dario is writing an equation to find the missing measure of the triangle below. Find his mistake and correct it.

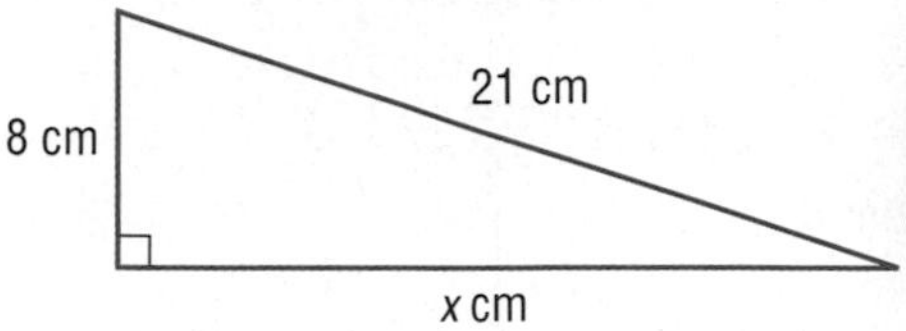

$$x^2 = 21^2 + 8^2$$

21 cm

8 cm

_x_ cm

24. **Write MATH** Write a problem about a real-world situation in which you would use the Pythagorean Theorem.

25. Which triangle has sides a, b, and c so that the relationship $a^2 + b^2 = c^2$ is true?

A.

C.

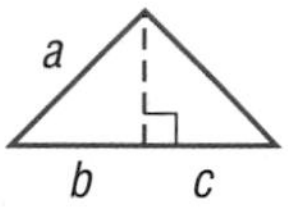

B.

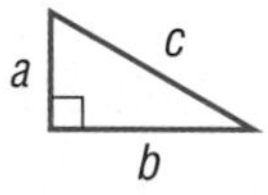

D.

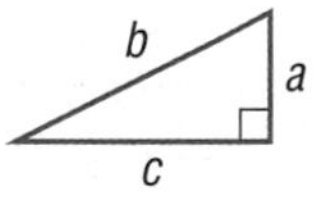

26. An isosceles right triangle has legs that are each 8 inches long. About how long is the hypotenuse?

F.   12.8 inches

G.   11.3 inches

H.   8 inches

I.   4 inches

Spiral Review

Replace each ● with <, >, or = to make a true sentence. (Lesson 11-3C)

27. $\sqrt{42}$ ● $6.\overline{5}$

28. $2\frac{2}{9}$ ● $2.\overline{2}$

29. $-8.4\overline{3}$ ● $\sqrt{72}$

30. $\sqrt{64}$ ● $\frac{16}{2}$

31. Estimate the length of a square table with a diagonal length of $\sqrt{119}$ feet to the nearest whole number. (Lesson 11-3B)

Complete. (Lesson 9-1B)

32. 21 ft = ■ yd

33. 9 c = ■ pt

34. $4\frac{1}{2}$ T = ■ lb

35. 7,000 lb = ■ T

36. 2 gal = ■ qt

37. $3\frac{1}{3}$ ft = ■ in.

Main Idea
Find the distance between two points on the coordinate plane.

NGSSS

MA.8.G.2.4
Validate and **apply Pythagorean Theorem to find distances** in real world situations or **between points in the coordinate plane.**

Get Connected
glencoe.com

Distance on the Coordinate Plane

MAPS A map of a state park is shown at the right. Points A and B represent the locations of two visitor's centers.

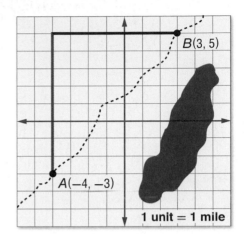

B(3, 5)

A(−4, −3)

1 unit = 1 mile

1. What do the red and blue lines on the graph represent?

2. What type of triangle is formed by the lines?

3. What are the lengths of the red and blue lines?

In the map above, the red and blue lines are the legs and the trail is the hypotenuse of a right triangle. You can use the Pythagorean Theorem to find the distance between points A and B.

Real-World EXAMPLE

Distance on the Coordinate Plane

1. Find the distance between $(-3, -4)$ and $(4, 4)$ using the Pythagorean Theorem. Round to the nearest tenth if necessary.

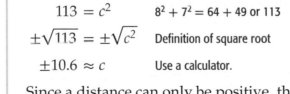

(4, 4)

C

(−3, −4)

$$a^2 + b^2 = c^2 \qquad \text{Pythagorean Theorem}$$

$$8^2 + 7^2 = c^2 \qquad \text{Replace } a \text{ with 8 and } b \text{ with 7.}$$

$$113 = c^2 \qquad 8^2 + 7^2 = 64 + 49 \text{ or } 113$$

$$\pm\sqrt{113} = \pm\sqrt{c^2} \qquad \text{Definition of square root}$$

$$\pm 10.6 \approx c \qquad \text{Use a calculator.}$$

Since a distance can only be positive, the points are about 10.6 units apart.

CHECK Your Progress

a. Find the distance between the points $(-3, 2)$ and $(4, -1)$. Round to the nearest tenth if necessary.

Recall that the values of square roots can be positive or negative. Since distance cannot be negative, only the positive square root is used.

Distance on the Coordinate Plane

2 Brent and Chico leave school. Brent travels 4 blocks east and 3 blocks north. Chico travels 6 blocks south and 8 blocks west. How many blocks apart are they?

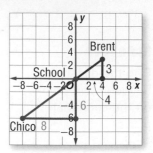

Count the number of blocks east and north that Brent walks to make a right triangle.

$$a^2 + b^2 = c^2$$
$$4^2 + 3^2 = x^2$$
$$25 = x^2$$
$$\pm\sqrt{25} = x$$
$$\pm 5 = x$$

Brent is 5 blocks from school.

Count the number of blocks south and west that Chico walks to make a right triangle.

$$a^2 + b^2 = c^2$$
$$8^2 + 6^2 = y^2$$
$$100 = y^2$$
$$\pm\sqrt{100} = y$$
$$\pm 10 = y$$

Chico is 10 blocks from school.

So, Brent and Chico are 15 blocks away from one another.

CHECK Your Progress

b. Two planes left the airport. One plane flew north 50 miles before turning west and flying 120 miles. The other plane flew east 80 miles before turning south and flying 150 miles. How far apart are the planes?

CHECK Your Understanding

Example 1
(p. 661)

Find the distance between the two points using the Pythagorean Theorem. Round to the nearest tenth if necessary.

1.
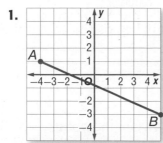

2.

3
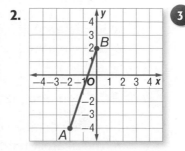

Example 2
(p. 662)

4. ARCHAEOLOGY An archaeologist creates a coordinate system to record where artifacts were discovered. A unit on the grid represents 10 feet. Find the distance between two artifacts found at $(-2, 4)$ and $(-1, -6)$ on the grid. Round to the nearest tenth if necessary.

Practice and Problem Solving

● = **Step-by-Step Solutions** begin on page R36.
Extra Practice is on page EP33.

Example 1
(p. 661)
Find the distance between the two points using the Pythagorean Theorem. Round to the nearest tenth.

5.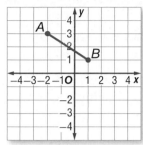

6.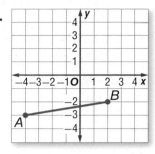

7.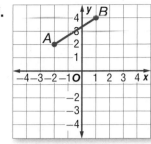

8.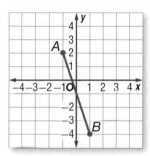

9.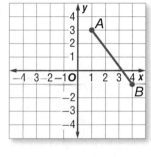

10.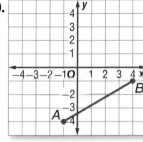

Example 2
(p. 662)

11. LANDSCAPING Patrick set up a coordinate system with units of feet to locate the positions of his flowers. He planted a morning glory plant at (2, 3) and a goldenrod plant at (−3, 8). How far apart are the two plants? Round to the nearest tenth if necessary.

12. BUTTERFLY EXHIBIT Isabelle is looking at a map of the butterfly exhibit that is laid out on a coordinate plane. Isabelle is at (0, 0). The Monarch Butterflies are at (−2, 7) and the Pearl Crescents are at (3, 6). Is Isabelle closer to the Monarchs or the Pearl Crescents?

13. Find the perimeter of △XYZ with vertices X(3, −8), Y(−1, −1), and Z(0, 4) to the nearest tenth.

14. Find the perimeter of △EFG with vertices E(0, 0), F(0, 4), and G(3, 0).

15. GEOGRAPHY On a map of Florida, Key West is located at (1.5, 0.5) and Tampa is located at (4.5, 7.5). Each unit on the map equals 32 miles. What is the distance to the nearest mile between the cities?

16. GEOMETRY Square ABCD is graphed on the coordinate plane. What is the length of each side? the area? Round to the nearest tenth.

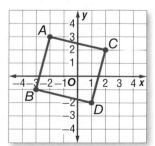

17 GOLF Marcel's golf ball landed 5 feet to the right and 7 feet below the hole. What is the distance between the hole and where the shot landed on the green? Round to the nearest tenth.

18. **CHALLENGE** A line segment has a length of 13 units. One endpoint is located at $(1, -2)$. What is the value of y for the other endpoint if it is located at $(13, y)$?

19. **OPEN ENDED** Give the coordinates of the endpoints of a line segment that is neither horizontal nor vertical and has a length of 13 units.

20. **Write MATH** Given two points (x_1, y_1) and (x_2, y_2), the distance d between the points can be found using the formula $d = \sqrt{(x_2 - x_1)^2 + (y_2 - y_1)^2}$. This is called the Distance Formula. How is the Distance Formula related to the Pythagorean Theorem?

NGSSS Practice   MA.8.G.2.4

21. **THINK SOLVE EXPLAIN** **SHORT RESPONSE** What is the distance between points L and M?

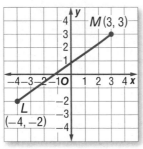

22. What is the perimeter of $\triangle FGH$?

A. 10 units

B. 12.5 units

C. 17.1 units

D. 25 units

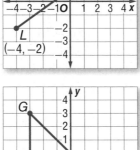

23. What is the distance between R and S in quadrilateral $RSTU$? Round to the nearest tenth.

F. 3.2 units

G. 4.9 units

H. 5.1 units

I. 7.1 units

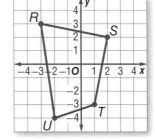

24. Find the perimeter of the triangle with vertices $P(0, 0)$, $Q(0, 6)$, and $R(5, 2)$.

A. 17.8 units   C. 21.5 units

B. 19.2 units   D. 23.9 units

Find the missing measure of each triangle. Round to the nearest tenth if necessary. (Lesson 11-3E)

25.

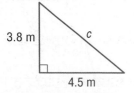

3.8 m   c   4.5 m

26.

32 ft   a   41 ft

27.

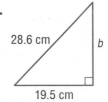

28.6 cm   b   19.5 cm

Replace each ● with $<$, $>$, or $=$ to make a true sentence. (Lesson 11-3C)

28. $\sqrt{35}$ ● 6

29. $-4\frac{2}{7}$ ● $-\sqrt{19}$

30. $0.\overline{64}$ ● $\frac{64}{99}$

31. $\sqrt{49}$ ● $6\frac{5}{6}$

FOLDABLES®
Study Organizer

Be sure the following Key Concepts are noted in your Foldable.

Angle Relationships

Key Concepts

Angle Relationships (Lesson 11-1)
• Two angles are adjacent if they have the same vertex, share a common side, and do not overlap.
• Two angles are vertical if they are opposite angles formed by the intersection of two lines.
• Two angles are complementary if the sum of their measures is 90°.
• Two angles are supplementary if the sum of their measures is 180°.

Triangles and Quadrilaterals (Lesson 11-2)
• The sum of the measures of the angles of a triangle is 180°.
• The sum of the measures of the angles of a quadrilateral is 360°.

The Real Number System (Lesson 11-3)
• An irrational number is a number that cannot be written as a fraction.

The Pythagorean Theorem (Lesson 11-3)
• In a right triangle, the square of the length of the hypotenuse equals the sum of the squares of the lengths of the legs.

Key Vocabulary

adjacent angles (p. 605)

alternate exterior angles (p. 610)

alternate interior angles (p. 610)

complementary angles (p. 605)

equiangular (p. 631)

equilateral (p. 631)

hypotenuse (p. 655)

irrational number (p. 646)

leg (p. 655)

perfect squares (p. 641)

Pythagorean Theorem (p. 655)

quadrilateral (p. 624)

real number (p. 649)

regular polygon (p. 631)

square root (p. 642)

supplementary angles (p. 605)

transversal (p. 610)

triangle (p. 616)

Vocabulary Check

State whether each sentence is *true* or *false*. If *false*, replace the underlined word or number to make a true sentence.

1. Either of the two sides that form the right angle of a right triangle is called a <u>hypotenuse</u>.

2. An <u>irrational number</u> is a number that cannot be expressed as the quotient of two integers.

3. The <u>Pythagorean Theorem</u> can be used to find the length of the hypotenuse of a right triangle if the measures of both legs are known.

4. Rational numbers include <u>only positive</u> numbers.

5. Two angles with measures adding to 180° are called <u>complementary angles</u>.

6. An angle with a measure of less than 90° is called a <u>right angle</u>.

Multi-Part Lesson Review

11-1 Line and Angle Relations

Angle Relationships (pp. 604–609)

MA.8.G.2.2

Identify each pair of angles as *complementary*, *supplementary*, or *neither*.

7.
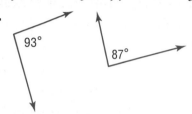

93°
87°

8.
67°
26°

EXAMPLE 1 Refer to the figure below. Identify a pair of adjacent angles.

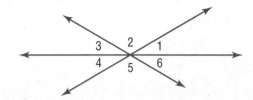

∠1 and ∠2 are adjacent angles.

EXAMPLE 2 Find the value of x.

$$x + 40 = 180$$
$$\underline{-40 = -40}$$
$$x = 140$$

$x°$ $40°$

Parallel Lines (pp. 610–614)

MA.8.G.2.2

If $m\angle 4 = 67°$, find each measure.

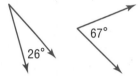

9. $m\angle 1$

10. $m\angle 5$

11. $m\angle 7$

12. $m\angle 2$

1 2
3 4

5 6
7 8

EXAMPLE 3 In the figure, $s \parallel t$. Find the value of x.

$$4x = 108$$
$$\frac{4x}{4} = \frac{108}{4}$$
$$x = 27$$

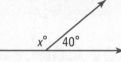

s 108°

t $4x°$

11-2 Polygons

Triangles (pp. 616–621)

MA.8.G.2.3

Find the value of x.

13.
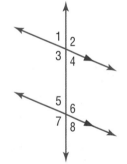

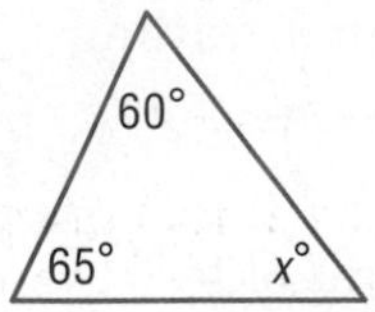

60°
65° $x°$

14.
45°
$x°$

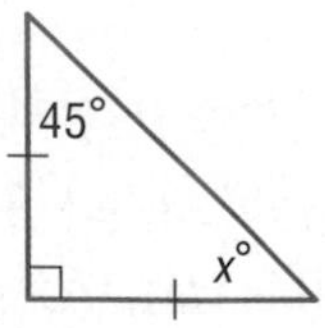

EXAMPLE 4 Find the value of x.

$$x + 64 + 67 = 180$$
$$x + 131 = 180$$
$$\underline{-131 = -131}$$
$$x = 49$$

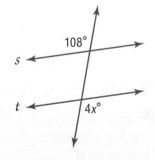

$x°$
64° 67°

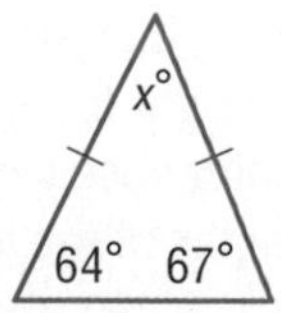

PSI: Logical Reasoning (pp. 622–623)

MA.8.G.2.3

15. SPORTS Donnie, Annie, Dean, and Barbara play volleyball, field hockey, golf, and soccer but not in that order. Use the clues given below to find the sport each person plays.

- Donnie does not like golf, volleyball, or soccer.
- Neither Dean nor Annie likes golf.
- Dean does not like soccer.

16. FOOD Angelo's Pizza Parlor makes square pizzas. After baking, the pizzas are cut along one diagonal into two triangles. Classify the triangles made.

EXAMPLE 5 Todd, Virginia, Elaine, and Jesse are siblings. Todd was born after Jesse, but before Virginia. Elaine is the oldest. Who is the youngest in the family?

Use logical reasoning to determine the youngest in the family.

You know that Elaine is the oldest, so she is first on the list. Todd was born after Jesse, but before Virginia. So, Jesse was second and then Todd was born. Virginia is the youngest of the family.

Quadrilaterals (pp. 624–629)

MA.8.G.2.3

Find the value of x in each quadrilateral.

17.
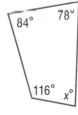
84° 78°
116° $x°$

18.
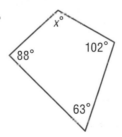
$x°$
88° 102°
63°

Classify each quadrilateral.

19.

20.

21. KITE Identify the quadrilateral outlined.

EXAMPLE 6 Find the value of x in the quadrilateral shown.

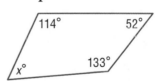
114° 52°
$x°$ 133°

The sum of the angle measures in a quadrilateral is 360°.

$x + 114 + 52 + 133 = 360$

$\qquad x + 299 = 360$ Add 114, 52, and 133.

$\qquad 61 + 299 = 360$ You know that $61 + 299 = 360$.

So, the value of x is 61.

EXAMPLE 7 Classify the quadrilateral shown.

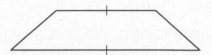

The quadrilateral has exactly one pair of parallel sides, so it is a trapezoid.

11-2 **Polygons** (continued)

Polygons and Angles (pp. 630–635)

MA.8.G.2.3

Determine whether the figure is a polygon. If it is, classify the polygon and state whether it is regular. If it is *not* a polygon, explain why.

22.

23.

24. ALGEBRA Find the sum of the measures of a regular 15-sided polygon.

EXAMPLE 8 Determine whether the figure is a polygon. If it is, classify the polygon and state whether it is regular. If it is *not* a polygon, explain why.

Since the polygon has 8 congruent sides and 8 congruent angles, it is a regular octagon.

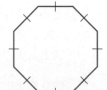

11-3 **The Pythagorean Theorem**

Square Roots (pp. 641–644)

MA.8.A.6.2

Find each square root.

25. $\sqrt{81}$ **26.** $\sqrt{324}$

27. MEASUREMENT The area of a certain kind of ceramic tile is 25 square inches. What is the length of one side?

EXAMPLE 9 Find the square root of 441.

$21 \cdot 21 = 441$, so $\sqrt{441} = 21$.

Estimate Square Roots (pp. 645–648)

MA.8.A.6.2

Estimate each square root to the nearest whole number.

28. $\sqrt{6}$ **29.** $\sqrt{99}$ **30.** $\sqrt{48}$

31. $\sqrt{76}$ **32.** $\sqrt{19}$ **33.** $\sqrt{52}$

Graph each square root on a number line.

34. $\sqrt{61}$ **35.** $\sqrt{132}$

36. $\sqrt{444}$ **37.** $\sqrt{12}$

38. SWIMMING POOL The bottom of Julieta's square swimming pool has an area of 118 square feet. What is the approximate length of one of the sides?

EXAMPLE 10 Estimate $\sqrt{29}$ to the nearest whole number.

$25 < 29 < 36$ 29 is between the perfect squares 25 and 36.

$\sqrt{25} < \sqrt{29} < \sqrt{36}$ Find the square root of each number.

$5 < \sqrt{29} < 6$ $\sqrt{25} = 5$ and $\sqrt{36} = 6$

So, $\sqrt{29}$ is between 5 and 6. Since 29 is closer to 25 than to 36, the best whole number estimate is 5.

11-3 **The Pythagorean Theorem** (continued)

The Real Number System (pp. 649–653)

Name all sets of numbers to which each real number belongs.

39. $-\sqrt{31}$ **40.** $0.\overline{7}$

41. 5.72 **42.** -29

43. MEASUREMENT The area of a square dance floor is 450 square feet. To the nearest hundredth, what is the perimeter of the dance floor?

EXAMPLE 11 Name all sets of numbers to which $-\sqrt{23}$ belongs.

$$-\sqrt{23} \approx -4.795831523$$

Since the decimal does not terminate or repeat, it is an irrational number.

The Pythagorean Theorem (pp. 655–660)

MA.8.G.2.4

Find the missing measure of each triangle. Round to the nearest tenth if necessary.

44. 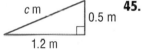 **45.**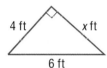

46. COMMUNICATION Find the length of the wire x that is attached to the telephone poles. Round to the nearest tenth.

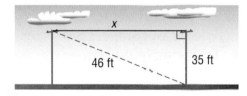

EXAMPLE 12 Find the missing measure of the triangle.

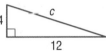

Use the Pythagorean Theorem to solve for c.

$$a^2 + b^2 = c^2 \quad \text{Pythagorean Theorem}$$
$$4^2 + 12^2 = c^2 \quad a = 4 \text{ and } b = 12$$
$$16 + 144 = c^2 \quad \text{Evaluate.}$$
$$160 = c^2 \quad \text{Add.}$$
$$\pm\sqrt{160} = \sqrt{c^2} \quad \text{Definition of square root}$$
$$\pm 12.6 \approx c \quad \text{Simplify.}$$

Since length cannot be negative, it is about 12.6 centimeters.

Distance on the Coordinate Plane (pp. 661–664)

MA.8.G.2.4

Graph each set of ordered pairs. Then find the distance between the two points using the Pythagorean Theorem. Round to the nearest tenth if necessary.

47. $(0, 4)$ and $(3, -2)$

48. $(3, 4)$ and $(1, 0)$

49. $(4, 0)$ and $(0, -3)$

50. $(-3, 3)$ and $(3, -2)$

EXAMPLE 13 Graph and find the distance between points $(2, 1)$ and $(-1, 3)$.

$$a^2 + b^2 = c^2$$
$$3^2 + 2^2 = c^2$$
$$9 + 4 = c^2$$
$$\sqrt{13} = c^2$$
$$\pm\sqrt{13} = c$$
$$\pm 3.6 \approx c$$

The distance is about 3.6 units.

Chapter 11 Study Guide and Review **669**

Name each angle in four ways. Then classify each angle as *acute, obtuse, right,* **or** *straight.*

1.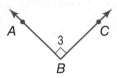

2.

3. ALGEBRA Find the value of *x* in the figure at the right.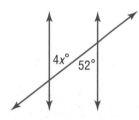

ALGEBRA Find the missing measure in each triangle with the given angle measures.

4. 75°, 25.5°, *x*°

5. 23.5°, *x*°, 109.5°

6. **NGSSS PRACTICE** Which quadrilateral does NOT have opposite sides congruent?

   A. parallelogram

   B. square

   C. trapezoid

   D. rectangle

Determine whether the figure is a polygon. If it is, classify the polygon and state whether it is regular. If it is *not* **a polygon, explain why.**

7.

8.

Find each square root.

9. $\sqrt{121}$

10. $\sqrt{900}$

Estimate each square root to the nearest whole number.

11. $\sqrt{500}$ **12.** $\sqrt{95}$ **13.** $\sqrt{265}$

Graph each square root on the number line.

14. $\sqrt{570}$ **15.** $\sqrt{7}$ **16.** $\sqrt{84}$

Replace each ● **with <, >, or = to make a true sentence.**

17. $\sqrt{34}$ ● $\frac{12}{2}$ **18.** $6\frac{1}{3}$ ● $6.\overline{3}$

Find the missing measure of each right triangle. Round to the nearest tenth if necessary.

19. *a* = 5 m, *b* = 4 m

20. *b* = 12 in., *c* = 14 in.

21. *a* = 7 in., *c* = 13 in.

Find the distance between the points below using the Pythagorean Theorem. Round to the nearest tenth.

22. (−6, 1) and (3, 5)   **23.** (0, 5) and (−5, −6)

24. **THINK SOLVE EXPLAIN** **EXTENDED RESPONSE** In the figure below, $\overline{EF}$ is parallel to $\overline{HJ}$, $m\angle 1 = 113°$, $m\angle 2 = 29°$, and $m\angle 3 = 119°$. Use your knowledge of parallel lines to answer the following questions.

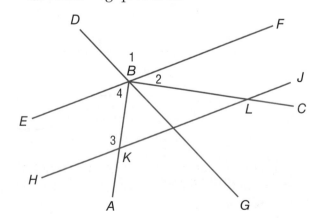

Part A Find the measure of ∠4.

Part B Find the measure of all angles in △*KBL*.

Part C Classify △*KBL* and explain your reasoning.

Short Response: Review Formulas

Basic formulas that you need to answer the test questions will be provided on a reference sheet in the test booklet. However, it is a good idea to review common formulas *before* the test so that you are familiar with how to use them.

NGSSS PRACTICE EXAMPLE

A rectangular garden has a brick path running diagonally through it as shown in the diagram.

Part A $ABCD$ is reflected over the y-axis and the new area is added to the original garden. Vertices A and D stay the same. What are the coordinates of the other two vertices of the larger garden?

New Coordinates   (3, 6), (3, −2)

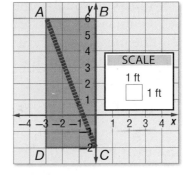

Part B A new brick path is made so that it runs diagonally through the larger garden from point A to the new vertex. What is the length of the new brick path?

$$a^2 + b^2 = c^2$$
$$(8)^2 + (6)^2 = c^2$$
$$64 + 36 = c^2$$
$$100 = c^2$$
$$\pm\sqrt{100} = c$$
$$10 = c$$

Don't forget to write the formula and show your work.

Length of Path   10 feet

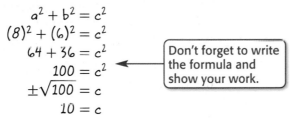

Work on It

Refer to the diagram above. Garden $FGHJ$ is the same size and shape as garden $ABCD$. It is 4 units down and 5 units to the right of $ABCD$.

Part A What are the coordinates of garden $FGHJ$?

Part B Garden $FGHJ$ also has a diagonal path, which runs from F to H. To the nearest tenth of a foot, calculate the length of the path.

Test Hint

Before beginning the test, quickly review the list of formulas in the test booklet so that you know which ones are available.

Read each question. Then fill in the correct answer on the answer sheet provided by your teacher or on a sheet of paper.

1. A flashlight is aimed at a mirror and the angle at which the light hits the mirror is equal to the angle at which the beam is reflected from the mirror. What is the measure of the angle at which the light is reflected from the mirror?

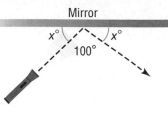

A. 30°   **C.** 45°

B. 40°   **D.** 80°

2. Two buses leave the bus station. One bus travels 4 blocks east and then 3 blocks north. The second bus travels 6 blocks south and then 8 blocks west.

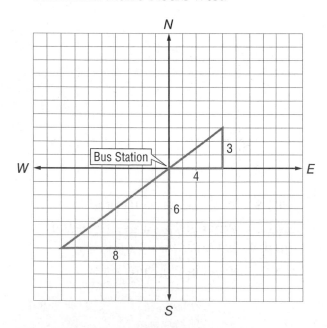

How far apart, in blocks, are the buses?

F. 11   **H.** 13.1

G. 12   **I.** 15

3. A manager took an employee to lunch. If the lunch was $48 and she left a 20% tip, how much money did she spend on lunch?

A. $68.00   **C.** $55.80

B. $57.60   **D.** $38.40

4. **GRIDDED RESPONSE** Toby has $860 in his savings account. He plans to spend 15% of his savings on a bicycle. How much does Toby plan to spend on the bicycle in dollars?

5. **GRIDDED RESPONSE** Adalina made a food pyramid for science class. In degrees, what angle did Adalina use to make the angle marked x in the diagram?

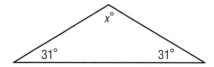

6. The table below shows all the possible outcomes when tossing two fair coins at the same time.

1st coin	2nd coin
H	H
H	T
T	H
T	T

Which of the following must be true?

F. The probability that both coins have the same outcome is $\frac{1}{4}$.

G. The probability of getting at least one tail is higher than the probability of getting two heads.

H. The probability that exactly one coin will turn up heads is $\frac{3}{4}$.

I. The probability of getting at least one tail is lower than the probability of getting two tails.

7. The wallpaper design below is a regular hexagon. What is the measure, in degrees, of ∠G in the design?

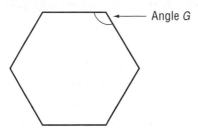

— Angle G

A. 90   **C.** 110

B. 100   **D.** 120

8. Which of the following groups does NOT contain equivalent fractions, decimals, and percents?

F. $\frac{7}{20}$, 0.35, 35%

G. $\frac{8}{10}$, 0.8, 80%

H. $\frac{5}{6}$, 0.8, 80%

I. $\frac{1}{100}$, 0.01, 1%

9. ✎ **GRIDDED RESPONSE**
Find the surface area of the paint can in square inches. Round to the nearest tenth.

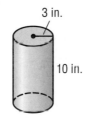

3 in.

10 in.

10. **THINK SOLVE EXPLAIN** **SHORT RESPONSE**
Srecko built a bike ramp. What is the height h of the bike ramp? Round your answer to the nearest tenth.

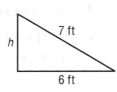

7 ft

h

6 ft

11. Lydie runs an average of 6.3 meters per second during sprints. How many feet per second does she run?

A. 21 feet per second

B. 25.1 feet per second

C. 30.7 feet per second

D. 36.9 feet per second

12. Kazuki found the side of a right triangle to equal $\sqrt{17}$ feet. Which point is closest to $\sqrt{17}$ on the number line?

W X Y   Z

0 1 2 3 4 5 6 7 8 9 10

F. W   **H.** Y

G. X   **I.** Z

13. **THINK SOLVE EXPLAIN** **EXTENDED RESPONSE** In the drawing, line m is parallel to line n.

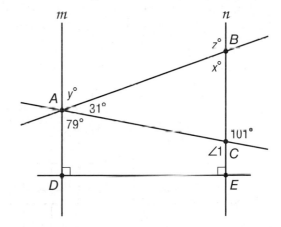

Part A What is the value of y?

Part B What is the value of x in the quadrilateral $ABED$?

Part C What is the value of z?

NEED EXTRA HELP?													
If You Missed Question...	1	2	3	4	5	6	7	8	9	10	11	12	13
Go to Lesson...	11-A	11-3F	6-3C	6-1B	11-2B	7-2A	11-2E	2-1C	8-2C	11-3E	9-1D	11-3B	11-2D
For help with NGSSS...	8.G.2.2	8.G.2.4	A.1.2	A.1.2	8.G.2.3	P.7.1	8.G.2.3	A.5.1	G.2.1	8.G.2.4	G.4.4	8.A.6.2	8.G.2.3

Statistics

Supporting ☆ Idea Select, organize, and construct appropriate data displays to convey information about relationships.

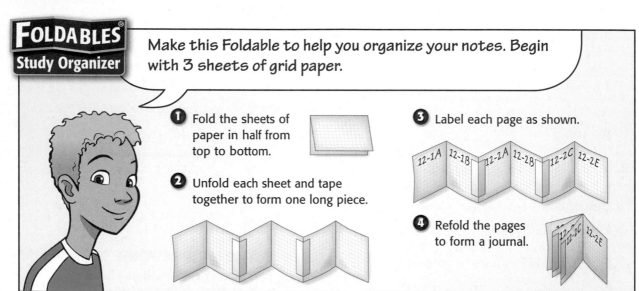

FOLDABLES® Study Organizer

Make this Foldable to help you organize your notes. Begin with 3 sheets of grid paper.

1 Fold the sheets of paper in half from top to bottom.

2 Unfold each sheet and tape together to form one long piece.

3 Label each page as shown.

12-1A 12-1B 12-2A 12-2B 12-2C 12-2E

4 Refold the pages to form a journal.

12-2C 12-2E

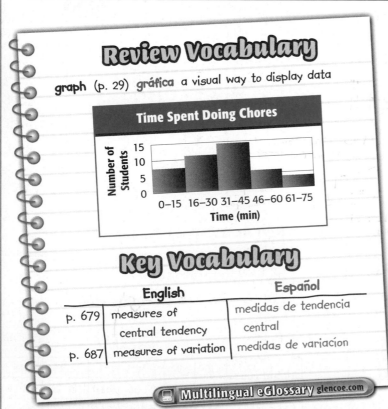

Review Vocabulary

graph (p. 29) **gráfica** a visual way to display data

Time Spent Doing Chores

Number of Students (15, 10, 5, 0)
Time (min): 0–15 16–30 31–45 46–60 61–75

Key Vocabulary

	English	Español
p. 679	measures of central tendency	medidas de tendencia central
p. 687	measures of variation	medidas de variación

Multilingual eGlossary glencoe.com

Get Connected glencoe.com

- Study using the **eBook**
- Explore with **Get Animated**
- Get extra help from **Personal Tutor**
- Use **virtual manipulatives** for additional help
- Take a **Self-Check Quiz**

When Will I Use This?

 Blake, Hannah, and Jamar in
Record Highs

Are You Ready for Chapter 12?

You have two options for checking prerequisite skills for this chapter.

Text Option Take the Quick Check below. Refer to the Quick Review for help.

QUICK Check

1. CHORES About how many more students spend 31–45 minutes on chores than students who spend 0–15 minutes? (Lesson 7-1C)

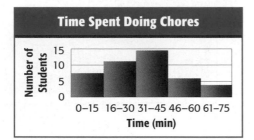

Time Spent Doing Chores

2. CROPS Display the data set in a stem-and-leaf plot. (Lesson 7-1E)

Height of Crops (in.)

40	51	68	57	55
50	57	51	67	41
67	57	48	58	67

3. READING How many students read at least 50 pages?

Pages Read by Students

Stem	Leaf
3	1 5 5 7 7 9
4	2 4 4 6 6 8 8
5	0 0 0 3 4 6 6 7
6	1 6 7 8 8

6 | 1 = 61 pages

QUICK Review

EXAMPLE 1

TEMPERATURE Refer to the histogram.

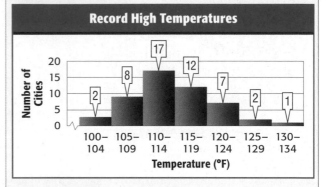

Record High Temperatures

How many cities had a record high temperature of 120°F or higher?

There were 7 + 2 + 1 or 10 cities that had a record high temperature of 120°F or higher.

EXAMPLE 2

TESTS Display the data set of scores on a science test in a stem-and-leaf plot.

Test Scores

76	80	73	81	76
84	72	99	79	80

Test Scores

Stem	Leaf
7	2 3 6 6 9
8	0 0 1 4
9	9

8 | 1 = 81

Put the tens place digit in the stem. Then list each ones place digit next to its corresponding ten in the leaf.

Online Option  **Get Connected** Take the Online Readiness Quiz at **glencoe.com**.

Writing Math

Describe Data

What can you write about the data displayed in the table below?

When you *describe* something, you represent it in words.

TAKEOUT The table shows the menu for Lombardo's Restaurant.

Takeout	Price ($)
Main Dish	8.00
Side Dish	2.50
Dessert	4.00

• The price of a dessert is $4.00.

• The price of a main dish is twice as much as the price of a dessert.

• A side dish is the least expensive item.

• If you buy one of each item, the cost is more than $10.

All of these statements describe the data. In what other ways can you describe the data?

Practice

1. **ADVERTISING** The table shows the results of a survey in which teens were asked to which types of advertising they pay attention. Describe the data.

Type of Advertising	Percent of Teens
Television	80
Magazine	62
Product in a movie	48
E-mail	24

2. **SPORTS** The table shows the number of participants ages 7–17 for each sport. Describe the data.

Sport	Number (millions)
Karate	8.1
Roller hockey	2.7
Snowboarding	9.3
Golf	11.4

3. **Write MATH** Collect some real-world data. Select and make an appropriate display. Then have a classmate describe your data.

NGSSS
LA.7.3.2.2 **The student will draft writing by organizing information into a logical sequence** and combining or deleting sentences to enhance clarity.

Explore Changes in Data Values

Main Idea

Explore how changes in data values affect mean, median, and mode.

NGSSS

MA.8.S.3.2
Determine and describe how changes in data values impact measures of central tendency.

Get Connected
glencoe.com

FISHING Quin and four of his friends went fishing on a Saturday morning. Each bucket shows the number of fish that each person caught.

There are many ways to describe this data.

ACTIVITY

STEP 1 Place counters in five cups to represent the five buckets of fish. Find the mode.

STEP 2 Rearrange the cups from least to greatest to find the amount of counters in the middle cup.

STEP 3 Move the counters among the cups so that each cup has the same number of counters to find the average.

Analyze the Results

1. Was there a number of fish that occurred the most times for the data set? Explain your reasoning.

2. Would your answer to Exercise 1 change if you included a sixth friend who caught 9 fish?

3. How many counters are in the middle cup after you rearrange the cups from least to greatest? Compare this to your answer if you were to include the sixth friend who caught 9 fish.

4. How many counters are in each cup after moving the counters? How many counters would be in each cup if a sixth friend caught 9 fish?

Main Idea

Determine and describe how changes in data values impact measures of central tendency.

NGSSS

MA.8.S.3.2 Determine and describe how changes in data values impact measures of central tendency.

New Vocabulary

measures of central tendency
mean
median
mode

Get Connected
glencoe.com

Measures of Central Tendency

HURRICANES The number of Atlantic hurricanes that formed each year is shown in the table.

1. Which number appears most often?

2. If you list the data in order from least to greatest, which number(s) is in the middle?

3. Suppose the total number of hurricanes is the same, but each year has an equal number of hurricanes. Find that number.

4. If you had to give one number that best represents the data, which would you choose? Explain.

Atlantic Hurricanes	
Year	Number of Hurricanes
2007	6
2006	5
2005	15
2004	9
2003	7
2002	4
2001	9
2000	8

Measures of central tendency are used to describe data.

- The **mean** is the sum of the data divided by the number of items in the data set.

- The **median** is the middle number in a data set when the data are ordered from least to greatest.

- The **mode** is the number(s) that appear most often in a data set. There can be more than one mode.

Real-World EXAMPLE   **Find the Mean**

1. **TESTS** Mr. Kennon removes the lowest test score for each student at the end of the grading period. Louisa received grades of 81, 75, 55, 89, 94, 73, and 86. Compare the mean of Louisa's scores before and after Mr. Kennon drops the lowest grade.

With lowest test: $\dfrac{81 + 75 + 55 + 89 + 94 + 73 + 86}{7} = \dfrac{553}{7}$ or 79

Without lowest test: $\dfrac{81 + 75 + 89 + 94 + 73 + 86}{6} = \dfrac{498}{6}$ or 83

By dropping the lowest test, Louisa's mean score increases.

CHECK Your Progress

a. **HURRICANES** Refer to the table above. How does the mean number of hurricanes change if the number of hurricanes in 2005 is not included?

Effect of Extreme Values

2 MUSIC DOWNLOADS
The number of songs
downloaded during
one week are shown
in the table. Which
measure is affected the most by Saturday's downloads?

Music Downloads						
S	M	T	W	TH	F	S
5	2	3	0	6	4	36

With Saturday's Downloads

Mean $\dfrac{5 + 2 + 3 + 0 + 6 + 4 + 36}{7} = \dfrac{56}{7}$ or 8

Median   0, 2, 3, ④, 5, 6, 36
Mode   no mode

Without Saturday's Downloads

Mean $\dfrac{5 + 2 + 3 + 0 + 6 + 4}{6} = \dfrac{20}{6}$ or $3\dfrac{1}{3}$

Median   0, 2, ③, ④, 5, 6

3.5

Mode   no mode

Study Tip

Mode If every value
occurs once, then there is
no mode, not a mode of 0.

So, Saturday's downloads affect the mean and the median. The mean is affected the most in this example.

CHECK Your Progress

b. LIBRARIES The number of library
books returned at Edison Middle
School is shown in the table.
Which measure is affected the
most by Thursday's returned books?

Library Books Returned				
M	T	W	TH	F
35	23	18	5	29

The table lists some guidelines for using each measure of central tendency.

Key Concept   **Mean, Median, and Mode**

Measure	Most Useful When...
Mean	the data set has no extreme values
Median	the data set has extreme values there are no big gaps in the middle of the data
Mode	the data set has many identical numbers

Choose an Appropriate Measure

③ **EXERCISE** The following set of data shows the number of push-ups Rufio did in one minute for the past 5 days: 24, 21, 28, 27, and 26. Which measure of central tendency best represents the data? Justify your selection and then find the measure.

Since the data set has no extreme values or numbers that are identical, the mean would best represent the data.

Mean $\frac{24 + 21 + 28 + 27 + 26}{5} = \frac{126}{5}$ or 25.2

The measure 25.2 push-ups best represents the data.
The median, 26, is also appropriate.

Real-World Link · · · · ·
Roy Berger of Canada currently holds the record for the most push-ups in one minute at 138.

✓ **CHECK Your Progress**

c. **CLOTHING** The following set of data shows the costs of pairs of jeans for various stores: $25.99, $29.99, $34.99, $19.99, $45.99. Which measure of central tendency best represents the data? Justify your selection and then find the measure.

✓ CHECK Your Understanding

Example 1
(p. 679)

Describe how the mean, median, and mode for each data set will change if the extreme value is dropped. Round to the nearest tenth if necessary.

1. number of states visited: 4, 0, 3, 19, 2, 0, 5, 7

2. inches of rainfall: 3.5, 2.8, 1.4, 1.2, 12.5, 2.3, 0.4

3.

Number of Calories in Vegetables
(1 serving)

12	6	15	14	5	18	14
20	24	10	19	55	14	19

Example 2
(p. 680)

4. **RETAIL** A department store recorded the time, in minutes, it took to help customers: 4, 3.5, 18, 1.5, 2.5, 5, 4.5, 6, 2.5, 3.5. Which measure is affected the most by the extreme value?

Example 3
(p. 681)

5. **VIDEO GAMES** The table shows the cost of various video games. Which measure of central tendency best represents the data? Justify your selection and then find the measure.

Video Game Prices			
$28	$19	$14	$31
$15	$29	$37	$22

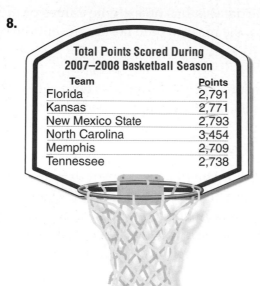

Practice and Problem Solving

● = **Step-by-Step Solutions** begin on page R36.
Extra Practice is on page EP34.

Example 1
(p. 679)

Describe how the mean, median, and mode for each data set will change if the extreme value is dropped. Round to the nearest tenth if necessary.

6. scores earned on a math test: 87, 71, 95, 98, 48, 74, 83, 92, 87, 79

7 ages of professional football players: 25, 23, 23, 27, 39, 27, 23, 31, 26, 28

8.

Total Points Scored During 2007–2008 Basketball Season

Team	Points
Florida	2,791
Kansas	2,771
New Mexico State	2,793
North Carolina	3,454
Memphis	2,709
Tennessee	2,738

9.

Gas Mileage of Various Vehicles

Vehicles

compact	28
hybrid	47
sedan	24
sports	21
SUV	17

0   10   20   30   40   50
Gas Mileage (miles per gallon)

Example 2
(p. 680)

10. HEIGHT The heights of plants, in inches, are 13, 4, 6, 9, 11, 23, and 7. Which measure is affected the most by the extreme value?

11. TEST SCORES Patty had scores of 90, 95, 65, 90, and 85 on five math tests. Which measure is affected the most by the extreme value?

Example 3
(p. 681)

12. STUDENTS The ages of the students in Ms. Watson's seventh-grade class are given in the table. Which measure of central tendency best represents the ages? Justify your selection and then find the measure.

Ages of Students

12	13	12	12	12
12	14	12	12	12
13	12	12	13	12
12	12	13	11	12

13. The number of weeks that songs have been on the Top 20 Country Songs list is shown in the table. Would the mean, median, or mode best represent the data? Explain.

Top 20 Country Songs

6	14	17	24	28
8	15	20	25	31
9	15	20	25	36
13	16	22	26	43

14. INCOME The five employees at Burger Bun each earn $8.50 per hour. The assistant manager earns $14.00 per hour. How would each measure of central tendency change if the manager's pay of $18.55 per hour was included?

15. The mean of a set of fifteen numbers is 5.2. What is the sum of the fifteen numbers?

16. GRAPHIC NOVEL Refer to the graphic novel frame below. Compare and contrast the mean, median, and mode of the data from the two cities. Round to the nearest tenth if necessary.

17. FIND THE DATA Refer to the Data File on pages 2–5. Choose some data with extreme values and then describe it using the mean, median, and mode. Remove the extreme value and describe the changes in the mean, median, and mode.

18. GYMNASTICS Rama needs an average score of 9.5 from 5 judges to win a gymnastics meet. The mean score from 4 judges was 9.48. What is the lowest score Rama can get from the 5th judge and still win?

19. MINERALS The Mohs Hardness Scale is used to identify the hardness of a mineral. A mineral with a hardness of 1 on the scale, such as talc, is the softest, while a mineral with a hardness of 10, such as a diamond, is the hardest. What is the mean hardness of a group of minerals with the following hardness levels: 3, 5, 8, 2, 1, 1, 7, 3, 9, 2, 3, 10?

20. SCIENCE Mr. Gallaher's science class was observing the effects of fertilizer on plants. The results are shown in the table. Find the mean for each data set to the nearest tenth. Compare your results with the mean of all the data. How does combining the data affect the mean?

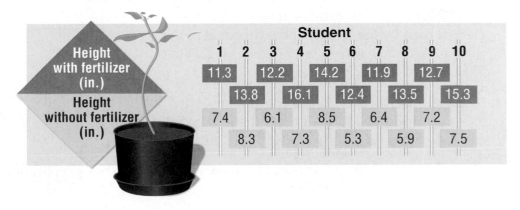

21. OPEN ENDED Write a data set with at least four numbers that has a mean of 5 and a median that is not 5.

22. REASONING Suppose you are ordering school T-shirts for next year. You are ordering only one color and decide to look at the sales figures from this year to make your decision. If the figures are given according to size, should you find the mean, median, or mode for the data? Explain.

23. CHALLENGE The range of a data set is the difference between the greatest and least values. A set of three numbers has a mean of 40, a median of 41, and a range of 9. What are the three numbers?

24. Write MATH Explain why the mean is the measure of central tendency that is most affected by extreme values.

NGSSS Practice   MA.6.S.6.1, MA.8.S.3.2

25. A group of 99 students were asked how many siblings they each have. The results are shown in the table.

Siblings	
zero	5
one	37
two	28
three	29

If the 100th student answered 5 siblings, which measure below would be most affected?

   A. mean   **C.** mode

   B. median   **D.** none of them

26. SHORT RESPONSE Vicki went fishing and caught 6 fish that weighed 7.3 pounds, 5.1 pounds, 8.8 pounds, 4.5 pounds, 5.6 pounds, and 2.4 pounds. She put the smallest fish back in the lake at the end of the day. What is the difference in the mean, median, and mode of the six fish compared to the mean, median, and mode of the five fish she kept?

Spiral Review

Find the distance between the given points using the Pythagorean Theorem. Round to the nearest tenth if necessary. (Lesson 11-3F)

27. $(-3, -2)$ and $(0, 2)$ **28.** $(-1, 4)$ and $(2, -3)$ **29.** $(-3, 1)$ and $(2, 4)$

30. TELEVISION The size of a flat screen television is determined by the length of the diagonal of the screen. A 42-inch screen is 35 inches long. What is its height to the nearest inch? (Lesson 11-3E)

31. Triangle ABC has vertices at coordinates $A(1, 2)$, $B(-1, 4)$, and $C(-2, 1)$. What are the new coordinates after $\triangle ABC$ is dilated by a factor of 2? (Lesson 10-4A)

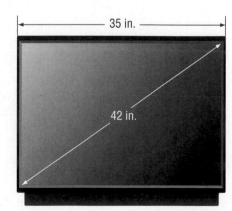

35 in.

42 in.

Extend

Spreadsheet Lab: Mean, Median, Mode

Main Idea

Use technology to calculate the mean, median, and mode of a set of data.

NGSSS

 MA.8.S.3.2 Determine and describe how changes in data values impact measures of central tendency.

Get Connected
glencoe.com

ALLOWANCE Mrs. Jenson's seventh-grade class was surveyed about how much allowance each student receives each week. The results are shown in the table. Make a spreadsheet for the data and find the mean, median, and mode.

Allowance Per Week ($)				
15	10	11	9	12.50
28	12	10	10	15

ACTIVITY

STEP 1 Open a new spreadsheet. Create four columns labeled DATA, MEAN, MEDIAN, and MODE.

Spreadsheet sample ☐ ☐ ☒

Use =AVERAGE (A2:A11) to find the mean.

Use =MEDIAN (A2:A11) to find the median.

Use =MODE (A2:A11) to find the mode.

	A	B	C	D
1	DATA	MEAN	MEDIAN	MODE
2	28	13.25	11.5	10
3	15			
4	15			
5	12.5			
6	12			
7	11			
8	10			
9	10			
10	10			
11	9			

Sheet 1 / Sheet 2 / Sheet 3 /

STEP 2 Enter each allowance amount in the DATA column.

STEP 3 In cell B2, enter =AVERAGE(A2:A11). In cell C2, enter =MEDIAN(A2:A11). In cell D2, enter =MODE(A2:A11). Each of these will find the mean, median, and mode of the data set.

Analyze the Results

1. What data value is an extreme for the set? Explain your reasoning.

2. Describe how the measures of central tendency would change if the extreme value was not included in the data set.

1. **TREES** The heights, in meters, of several trees are 7.6, 6.8, 1.5, 7.0, 7.9, and 6.8. Describe how the mean, median, and mode will change if the extreme value is removed. (Lesson 12-1B)

2. **NGSSS PRACTICE** The table shows the average April rainfall for 12 cities. If the value 4.2 is added to this list, which of the following would be true? (Lesson 12-1B)

Average Rainfall (in.)					
0.5	0.6	1.0	1.0	2.5	3.7
2.6	3.3	2.0	1.4	0.7	0.4

   A. The mode would increase.

   B. The mean would increase.

   C. The mean would decrease.

   D. The median would decrease.

3. **QUIZ** Cedro had quiz scores of 9, 10, 7, 7, 2, 6, 9, 10, 10, and 8. Which measure of central tendency would Cedro want the teacher to use to compute his final grade? Explain. (Lesson 12-1B)

Describe how the mean, median, and mode for each data set will change if the extreme value is dropped. Round to the nearest tenth if necessary. (Lesson 12-1B)

4. hours of sleep each week: 41, 58, 57, 53, 56

5. number of students per class: 21, 24, 26, 21, 25, 8, 28, 23

6. number of text messages per day: 41, 43, 47, 52, 57, 46, 56, 43, 78, 49

7. **ARCHITECTURE** The number of floors in Miami skyscrapers are shown in the table. If the Four Seasons Hotel is not included in the list, how will each measure of central tendency change? (Lesson 12-1B)

Miami Skyscrapers	
Building	**Number of Floors**
50 Biscayne Tower	55
Alfred I. Dupont Building	21
Bank of America Tower	28
Carbonell Condominiums	40
Four Seasons Hotel Miami	70
Grand Doubletree	42
Latitude on the River	44
Miami Center	34
Wachovia Financial Center	55

8. **NGSSS PRACTICE** The table shows the pace for a half marathon. What measure of central tendency is affected the most by the extreme value? (Lesson 12-1B)

Pace for Half Marathon (mph)				
6.7	7.1	7.5	7.6	3.3
7.4	7.2	7.4	7.1	7.4
6.8	6.9	7.3		

   F. mean

   G. median

   H. mode

   I. no effect

9. **MOWING** Paco spent 5 hours, 6 hours, 5 hours, and 7 hours mowing lawns over the past four weeks. If he spent 15 hours mowing the fifth week, how would that affect the mean, median, and mode? (Lesson 12-1B)

Main Idea
Find the measures of variation of a set of data.

NGSSS

Preparation for MA.8.S.3.1 Select, organize and construct appropriate data displays, including box and whisker plots, scatter plots, and lines of best fit to convey information and make conjectures about possible relationships.

New Vocabulary
measures of variation
range
quartile
lower quartile
upper quartile
interquartile range
outlier

Get Connected
glencoe.com

Measures of Variation

SURVEYS Jamie asked her classmates how many glasses of water they drink on a typical day.

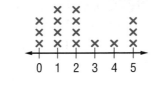

Glasses of Water Consumed

1. What is the median of the data set?

2. Organize the data into two groups: the top half and the bottom half. How many data values are in each group?

3. What is the median of each group?

4. Find the difference between the two numbers from Exercise 3.

Measures of variation are used to describe the distribution of the data. The **range** is the difference between the greatest and least data values. **Quartiles** are values that divide the data set into four equal parts.

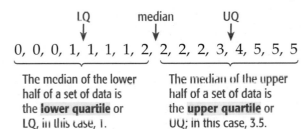

LQ   median   UQ

$$0, 0, 0, 1, 1, 1, 1, 2, \; 2, 2, 2, 3, 4, 5, 5, 5$$

The median of the lower half of a set of data is the **lower quartile** or LQ, in this case, 1.

The median of the upper half of a set of data is the **upper quartile** or UQ; in this case, 3.5.

So, one half of the data lie between the lower quartile and upper quartile. This is called the **interquartile range**.

Key Concept · Measures of Variation

Upper and Lower Quartiles

The upper and lower quartiles are the medians of the upper half and lower half of a set of data, respectively.

14,   18,   19,   20,   24,   29,   31

↑ lower quartile   ↑ median   ↑ upper quartile

Interquartile Range

The range of the middle half of the data. It is the difference between the upper quartile and the lower quartile; in this case, 29 − 18 or 11. The interquartile range is 29 − 18 or 11.

Range

The difference between the greatest and least data values; in this case, 31 − 14 or 17.

EXAMPLE **Find Measures of Variation**

1 **SPEED** Find the measures of variation for the data.

Range 70 − 1 or 69 mph

Quartiles

Order the numbers from least to greatest.

Animal Speeds	
Animal	**Speed (mph)**
cheetah	70
lion	50
cat	30
elephant	25
mouse	8
spider	1

```
      lower half   median   upper half
      ⎧‾‾‾‾‾‾⎫    ↓     ⎧‾‾‾‾‾‾⎫
   1     8    25 ' 30    50    70
      ↑        ↑        ↑
      LQ    25 + 30            UQ
            ─────── = 27.5
               2
```

Interquartile Range 50 − 8 or 42   UQ − LQ

The range is 69, the median is 27.5, the lower quartile is 8, the upper quartile is 50, and the interquartile range is 42.

Study Tip

Interquartile Range If the interquartile range is low, the middle data are grouped closely together.

✔️ **CHECK** Your Progress

a. SPORTS Determine the measures of variation for the data in the table.

Basketball Scores				
64	61	67	59	60
58	57	71	56	62

An **outlier** is a data value that is either much *greater* or much *less* than the median. If a data value is more than 1.5 times the value of the interquartile range beyond the quartiles, is an outlier.

EXAMPLE **Find Outliers**

2 **ELECTIONS** The ages of candidates in an election are 23, 48, 49, 55, 57, 63, and 72. Name any outliers in the data.

Find the interquartile range.
  63 − 48 = 15

Multiply the interquartile range by 1.5.
  15 × 1.5 = 22.5

Subtract 22.5 from the lower quartile and add 22.5 to the upper quartile.
  48 − 22.5 = 25.5   63 + 22.5 = 85.5

The limits for the outliers are between 25.5 and 85.5. The only age beyond this is 23. So, it is the only outlier.

✔️ **CHECK** Your Progress

b. BRIDGES The lengths, in feet, of various bridges are 88, 251, 275, 354, and 1,121. Name any outliers in the data set.

 Real-World Link · · · ·

The 26th Amendment to the United States Constitution lowered the voting age to 18.

3 **SCIENCE** The table shows a set of scores on a science test in two different classrooms. Compare and contrast their measures of variation.

Find the measures of variation for both rooms.

	Room A	Room B
Range	$100 - 65 = 35$	$98 - 63 = 35$
Median	80	81
UQ	$\dfrac{87 + 92}{2} = 89.5$	$\dfrac{87 + 93}{2} = 90$
LQ	$\dfrac{67 + 72}{2} = 69.5$	$\dfrac{65 + 73}{2} = 69$
Interquartile Range	$89.5 - 69.5 = 20$	$90 - 69 = 21$

Room A	Room B
72	63
100	93
67	79
84	83
65	98
78	87
92	73
87	81
80	65

Both classrooms have a range of 35, but Room B has an interquartile range of 21 while Room A's interquartile range is 20. There are slight differences in the medians as well as upper and lower quartiles.

 CHECK Your Progress

c. WEATHER Temperatures for the first half of the year are given for Antelope, Montana, and Augusta, Maine. Compare and contrast the measures of variation of the two cities.

Month	Antelope, MT	Augusta, ME
January	21	28
February	30	32
March	42	41
April	58	55
May	70	66
June	79	75

 CHECK Your Understanding

Examples 1 and 2
(p. 688)

1. WIND SPEED The average wind speeds for several cities in Florida are given in the table.

a. Find the range of the data.

b. Find the median and the upper and lower quartiles.

c. Find the interquartile range.

d. Identify any outliers in the data.

Wind Speed	
Florida City	**Speed (mph)**
Daytona Beach	8.5
Key West	10.9
Miami	9.2
Orlando	8.5
Tallahassee	6.2
Tampa	8.3
Vero Beach	8.3

Example 3
(p. 689)

2. TREES The heights of several types of palm trees, in feet, are 40, 25, 15, 22, 50, and 30. The heights of several types of pine trees, in feet, are 60, 75, 45, 80, 75, and 70. Compare and contrast the measures of variation of both kinds of trees.

● = **Step-by-Step Solutions** begin on page R37.
Extra Practice is on page EP34.

Examples 1 and 2
(p. 688)

③ GOLF COURSES The table shows the number of golf courses in various states.

a. Find the range of the data.

b. Find the median and the upper and lower quartiles.

c. Find the interquartile range.

d. Name any outliers in the data.

Number of Golf Courses	
California	1,117
Florida	1,465
Georgia	513
Iowa	437
Michigan	1,038
New York	954
North Carolina	650
Ohio	893
South Carolina	456
Texas	1,018

4. INTERNET The table shows the countries with the most Internet users.

a. Find the range of the data.

b. Find the median and the upper and lower quartiles.

c. Find the interquartile range.

d. Name any outliers in the data.

Millions of Internet Users	
China	99.8
Germany	41.88
India	36.97
Japan	78.05
South Korea	31.67
United Kingdom	33.11
United States	185.55

Example 3
(p. 689)

5. EXERCISE The table shows the number of minutes of exercise for each person. Compare and contrast the measures of variation for both weeks.

Minutes of Exercise		
	Week 1	Week 2
Tanika	45	30
Tasha	40	55
Tyrone	45	35
Uniqua	55	60
Videl	60	45
Wesley	90	75

6. FOOTBALL The table shows the top 7 teams in the National Football Conference (NFC) and the American Football Conference (AFC).

a. Which conference had a greater range of penalties?

b. Find the measures of variation for each conference.

Penalties During 2007 Season			
NFC		AFC	
Dallas Cowboys	104	New England Patriots	78
Arizona Cardinals	137	Indianapolis Colts	67
Green Bay Packers	113	Jacksonville Jaguars	76
New Orleans Saints	68	San Diego Chargers	94
New York Giants	77	Cleveland Browns	114
Seattle Seahawks	59	Pittsburgh Steelers	80
Minnesota Vikings	86	Houston Texans	82

c. Compare the modes and the interquartile ranges for each conference.

d. Describe the number of penalties for each conference using the measures of central tendency and variation.

Real-World Link
The average twelve year old should spend about one hour a day doing moderate to intense physical activity.

For each data set, find the median, the upper and lower quartiles, and the interquartile range.

7. daily attendance at the water park: 346, 250, 433, 369, 422, 298

8. texts per day: 24, 53, 38, 12, 31, 19, 26

9. cost of admission: $13.95, $24.59, $19.99, $29.98, $23.95, $28.99

10. **SCIENCE** The table shows the number of known moons for each planet in our solar system. Use the measures of variation to describe the data.

Known Moons of Planets			
Mercury	0	Jupiter	63
Venus	0	Saturn	34
Earth	1	Uranus	27
Mars	2	Neptune	13

11. **BIKE RIDING** Lucy and Dena are training for a bike race and recorded their mileage for a week. Find the measures of variation of each person's mileage. Which measures of variation show the girls' similarities in their training? the differences? Explain.

	Monday	Tuesday	Wednesday	Thursday	Friday	Saturday	Sunday
Lucy	7 mi	3 mi	5 mi	8 mi	6 mi	10 mi	9 mi
Dena	6 mi	4 mi	6 mi	8 mi	11 mi	9 mi	7 mi

H.O.T. Problems

12. **FIND THE ERROR** Hiroshi was finding the measures of variation of the following set of data: 89, 93, 99, 110, 128, 135, 144, 152, and 159. Find his mistake and correct it.

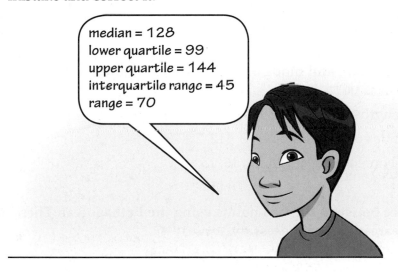

median = 128
lower quartile = 99
upper quartile = 144
interquartile range = 45
range = 70

13. **OPEN ENDED** Create a list of data with at least six numbers that has an interquartile range of 15 and two outliers.

14. **Write MATH** Explain why the median is not affected by very high or very low values in the data.

15. The number of games won by 10 chess players is given.

$$13, 15, 2, 7, 5, 9, 11, 10, 12, 11$$

Which of the following statements is NOT supported by these data?

A. Half of the players won more than 10.5 games and half won less than 10.5 games.

B. The range of the data is 13 games.

C. There are no outliers.

D. One fourth of the players won more than 7 games.

16. The 2007 normal monthly precipitation amounts in inches for Key West, Florida, are given in the table. What values, if any, are outliers?

Jan	Feb	Mar	Apr	May	June
0.65	1.39	0.63	2.16	2.82	4.21
July	Aug	Sept	Oct	Nov	Dec
3.22	1.20	9.31	11.25	0.70	0.80

F. 9.31

G. 11.25

H. 9.31 and 11.25

I. There are no outliers.

17. Which of the following sets of data has an interquartile range of 10?

A. 3, 4, 9, 16, 17, 24, 31

B. 41, 43, 49, 49, 50, 53, 55

C. 12, 14, 17, 19, 19, 20, 21

D. 55, 56, 56, 57, 58, 59, 62

Find the mean, median, and mode of each data set. Round to the nearest tenth if necessary. (Lesson 12-1B)

18. high jump lengths in feet: 14, 16.7, 12, 9, 15.9, 9

19. number of miles of coastline: 22, 43, 112, 28, 73, 19

20. ages of family members: 42, 39, 18, 16, 13

Find the distance between the two points using the Pythagorean Theorem. Round to the nearest tenth if necessary. (Lesson 11-3F)

21. (0, 3) and (−5, −1)   **22.** (−9, 1) and (2, 8)   **23.** (4, −5) and (−3, −6)

24. Find the volume of the triangular prism shown. If the prism is reduced to one third its original size, what is the volume of the new prism? Round to the nearest tenth if necessary. (Lesson 9-2C)

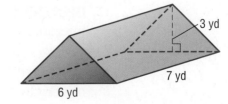

Main Idea

Display and interpret data in box-and-whisker plots.

NGSSS

MA.8.S.3.1 Select, **organize and construct appropriate data displays, including box and whisker plots,** scatter plots, and lines of best fit **to convey information and make conjectures about possible relationships.**

New Vocabulary

box-and-whisker plot

Get Connected
glencoe.com

Box-and-Whisker Plots

FOOTBALL The line plot shows the number of touchdowns scored by each of the 16 teams in the National Football Conference in a recent year.

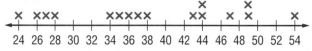

1. Find the median, quartiles, and range of the data.

2. What percent of the teams scored less than 30 touchdowns?

3. What percent of the teams scored more than 37 touchdowns?

The medians and quartiles divide the data into four equal parts. The line plot shows that there are four pieces of data in each part.

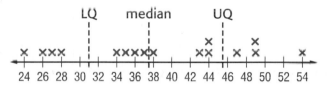

A **box-and-whisker plot** is a diagram that is constructed using the median, quartiles, and extreme values. A *box* is drawn around the quartile values, and the *whiskers* extend from each quartile to the extreme values. The median is marked with a vertical line. The figure below is a box-and-whisker plot of the football data.

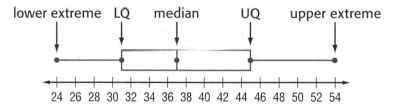

You can see all the pieces of data in a line plot, but in the box-and-whisker plot you can see only the median, quartiles, and extreme values. Box-and-whisker plots separate data into four parts. Even though the parts may differ in length, each contains 25% of the data.

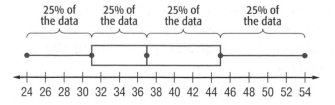

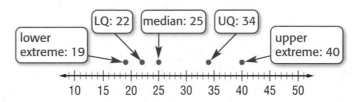

Real-World EXAMPLE **Construct a Box-and-Whisker Plot**

1 **DRIVING** The list below shows the speeds of eleven cars. Draw a box-and-whisker plot of the data.

25 35 27 22 34 40 20 19 23 25 30

Step 1 Order the numbers from least to greatest. Then draw a number line that covers the range of the data.

10 15 20 25 30 35 40 45 50

Step 2 Find the median, the extremes, and the upper and lower quartiles. Mark these points above the number line.

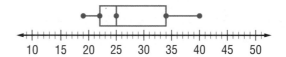

LQ: 22   median: 25   UQ: 34

lower extreme: 19   upper extreme: 40

10 15 20 25 30 35 40 45 50

Step 3 Draw the box so that it includes the quartile values. Draw a vertical line through the box at the median value. Extend the whiskers from each quartile to the extreme data points.

10 15 20 25 30 35 40 45 50

 CHECK Your Progress

a. Draw a box-and-whisker plot of the data set below.
{$20, $25, $22, $30, $15, $18, $20, $17, $30, $27, $15}

Real-World EXAMPLES **Interpret Data**

DRIVING Refer to the box-and-whisker plot in Example 1.

2 **Half of the drivers were driving faster than what speed?**

Half of the drivers were driving faster than 25 miles per hour.

3 **What does the box-and-whisker plot's length tell about the data?**

The length of the left half of the box-and-whisker plot is short. This means that the speeds of the slowest half of the cars are concentrated. The speeds of the fastest half of the cars are spread out.

CHECK Your Progress

b. What percent were driving faster than 34 miles per hour?

Double Box-and-Whisker Plots

④ The double box-and-whisker plot below shows the daily attendance of two fitness clubs. Compare and contrast the range and variance of the attendance at Super Fit versus Athletic Club.

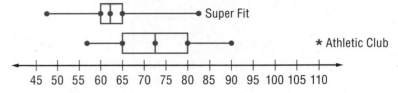

Super Fit had an attendance between 48 and 82. The Athletic Club had an attendance between 57 and 110. The attendance at the Athletic Club varies more than the attendance at Super Fit.

CHECK Your Progress

c. **SPORTS** The number of games won in each conference of the National Football League is displayed below. Compare and contrast the range and variance of each conference.

National Football League Wins, 2007

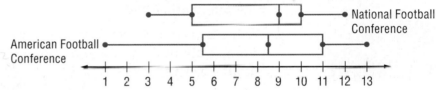

CHECK Your Understanding

Examples 1–3
(p. 694)

1. **EARTH SCIENCE** Use the table.

   a. Make a box-and-whisker plot of the data.

Depth of Recent Earthquakes (km)						
5	15	1	11	2	7	3
9	5	4	9	10	5	7

   b. What percent of the earthquakes were between 4 and 9 kilometers deep?

   c. Write a sentence explaining what the length of the box-and-whisker plot means.

Example 4
(p. 695)

2. **GAS MILEAGE** Use the box-and-whisker plots shown.

   Average Gas Mileage for Various Sedans and SUVs

   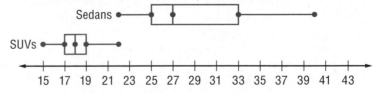

   a. Which types of vehicles tend to be less fuel-efficient?

   b. Compare the most fuel-efficient SUV to the least fuel-efficient sedan.

Practice and Problem Solving

= **Step-by-Step Solutions** begin on page R37.
Extra Practice is on page EP34.

Example 1
(p. 694)

Draw a box-and-whisker plot for each set of data.

3 {65, 92, 74, 61, 55, 35, 88, 99, 97, 100, 96}

4. {26, 22, 31, 36, 22, 27, 15, 36, 32, 29, 30}

5.

Height of Waves (in.)		
80	51	77
72	55	65
42	78	67
40	81	68
63	73	59

6.

Cost of MP3 Players ($)	
95	55
105	100
85	158
122	174
165	162

Examples 2 and 3
(p. 694)

7. GEOGRAPHY The table shows the length of coastline for the 13 states along the Atlantic Coast.

Length of Coastline (mi)	
28	130
580	127
100	301
228	40
31	187
192	112
13	

  a. Make a box-and-whisker plot of the data.

  b. What percent of the coastline states have coastlines greater than 210 miles?

  c. Half of the states have a coastline less than how many miles?

  d. Write a sentence describing what the length of the box-and-whisker plot tells about the number of miles of coastline for states along the Atlantic coast.

Real-World Link
The total lengths of U.S. coastlines are shown below.
Atlantic Coast:
  2,069 mi
Gulf Coast:
  1,631 mi
Pacific Coast:
  7,623 mi
Arctic Coast:
  1,060 mi

8. TESTS Use the box-and-whisker plot. It summarizes the scores of a recent math test.

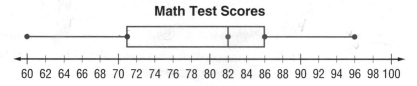

Math Test Scores

60 62 64 66 68 70 72 74 76 78 80 82 84 86 88 90 92 94 96 98 100

  a. What was the greatest test score?

  b. Explain why the median is not in the middle of the box.

  c. What percent of the scores were between 71 and 96?

  d. Half of the scores were higher than what score?

Example 4
(p. 695)

9. NUTRITION The amount of food energy in Calories for fruits and vegetables is displayed. How does the food energy of fruits compare to vegetables?

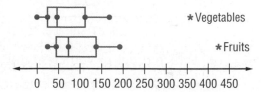

★Vegetables

★Fruits

0   50 100 150 200 250 300 350 400 450

Main Idea
Analyze line graphs and scatter plots to make predictions and conclusions.

NGSSS
MA.8.S.3.1 Select, **organize and construct appropriate data displays, including** box and whisker plots, **scatter plots, and lines of best fit to convey information and make conjectures about possible relationships.**

New Vocabulary

scatter plot
line of best fit

Get Connected
glencoe.com

Scatter Plots and Lines of Best Fit

Explore

- Pour 1 cup of water into a drinking glass.

- Measure the height of the water and record it in a table like the one shown.

- Place 5 marbles in the glass. Measure the height of the water. Record.

- Continue adding marbles, 5 at a time, until there are 20 marbles in the glass. After each time, measure and record the height of the water.

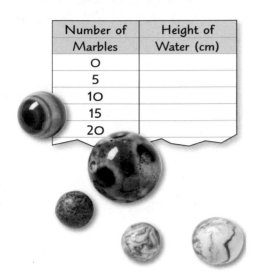

Number of Marbles	Height of Water (cm)
0	
5	
10	
15	
20	

1. By how much did the water's height change after each addition of marbles?

2. Predict the height of the water when 30 marbles are in the drinking glass. Explain how you made your prediction.

3. Test your prediction by placing 10 more marbles in the glass.

4. Graph the ordered pairs you recorded in the table on a coordinate plane.

A **scatter plot** shows the relationship between a set of data with two variables graphed as ordered pairs on a coordinate plane. Like line graphs, scatter plots are useful for making predictions because they show trends in data.

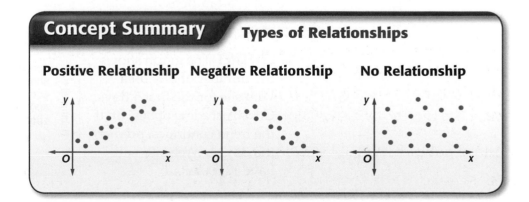

Concept Summary   Types of Relationships

Positive Relationship   **Negative Relationship**   **No Relationship**

EXAMPLE **Identify a Relationship**

① Explain whether the scatter plot of the data for school commute times shows a *positive, negative,* or *no* relationship.

As the distance increases, the time increases. Therefore, the scatter plot shows a positive relationship.

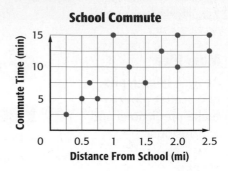

School Commute

✓ **CHECK** Your Progress

a. GRADES The graph shows the scores on a recent math test. Explain whether the scatter plot shows a *positive, negative* or *no* relationship.

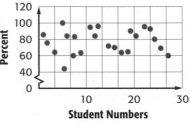

Student Grades on Math Test

The **line of best fit** is a line that is very close to most of the data points in a scatter plot.

EXAMPLE **Use a Line Graph to Predict**

② **SUMMER CAMP** The graph shows the enrollment at a summer camp for the past several years. Construct a line of best fit. If the trend continues, what will be the enrollment in 2012?

Draw the line that is close to most of the data points. If the trend continues, the enrollment in 2012 will be about 175 campers.

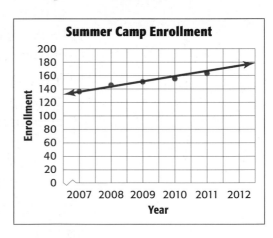

Summer Camp Enrollment

✓ **CHECK** Your Progress

b. INTERNET The graph shows the number of hits on a Web site for the first 5 days. Construct a line of best fit. If the trend continues, predict the day the Web site will have 12,000 hits.

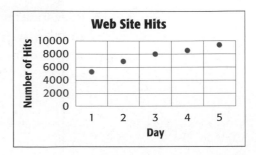

Web Site Hits

EXAMPLE **Use a Scatter Plot to Predict**

3 **NASCAR** The scatter plot shows the earnings for the winning driver of the Daytona 500 from 1996 to 2008. Predict the winning earnings for the 2012 Daytona 500.

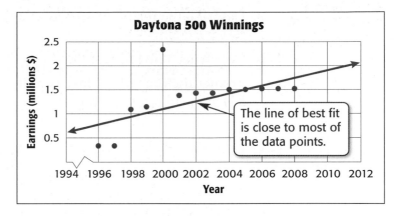

The predicted winning earnings for 2012 will be about $2,000,000.

CHECK Your Progress

c. NASCAR Predict the winning earnings for 2014.

CHECK Your Understanding

Examples 1 and 2
(p. 700)

1. POPULATION Port St. Lucie is a fast growing city in Florida. The graph shows its increase in population.

   a. Describe the relationship between the two variables.

   b. Construct a line of best fit.

   c. If the trend continues, what will be the population in 2010?

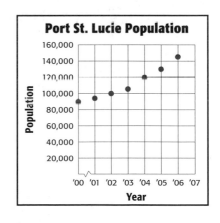

Example 3
(p. 701)

2. PICNICS The scatter plot shows the number of people who attended a neighborhood picnic each year. What is the expected attendance for 2010?

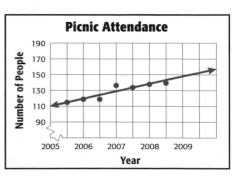

Practice and Problem Solving

= **Step-by-Step Solutions** begin on page R38.
Extra Practice is on page EP35.

Examples 1 and 2
(p. 700)

3 **MONUMENTS** Use the graph that shows the time it takes Ciro to climb the Statue of Liberty.

a. Describe the relationship between the two variables.

b. Construct a line of best fit.

c. Predict the time it will take Ciro to climb 354 steps to reach the top.

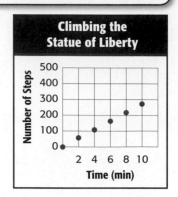

Example 3
(p. 701)

4. **SCHOOL** Use the graph that shows the times students spent studying for a test and their test scores.

a. What score should a student who studies for 50 minutes be expected to earn?

b. If a student scored 90 on the test, about how much time can you assume the student spent studying?

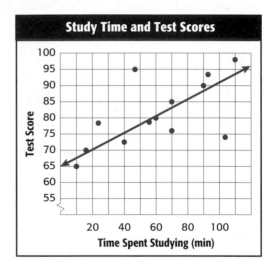

5. **SLEEP** Use the table that shows the relationship between hours of sleep and scores on a math test.

a. Display the data in a scatter plot.

b. Describe the relationship, if any, between the two variables.

c. Predict the test score for someone that sleeps for 5 hours.

Hours of Sleep	Math Test Score
9	96
8	88
7	76
6	71

6. **BASEBALL** Use the table at the right.

a. Make a scatter plot of the data to show the relationship between at bats and hits.

b. Predict the number of hits if 500 at bats occurred.

c. Describe the trend in the data.

Player	At Bats	Hits
C. Guzman	403	126
I. Kinsler	398	134
D. Pedroia	395	124
J. Reyes	394	119
I. Suzuki	391	119
M. Young	391	118
O. Cabrera	385	104
D. Lee	382	117

7 SCHOOLS Use the graph that shows the number of voters in Clinton County for several years.

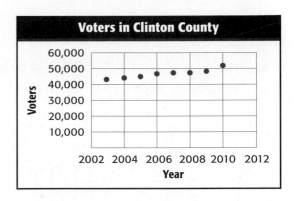

a. Describe the relationship, if any, between the two sets of data.

b. If the trend continues, what will be the average number of voters in 2011?

8. POPULATION The graph at the right shows the population of San Diego, California, from 1980 to 2005. Construct the line of best fit and estimate the population in 1995 from the graph.

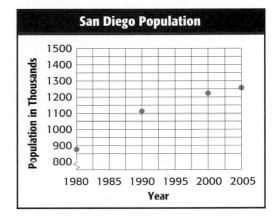

9. RESEARCH Use the Internet or another source to find a real-world example of a scatter plot. Write a description of what the graph displays and extend the graph to show where the data will be in the future.

10. PETS What can you conclude about the relationship between pet owner age and number of pets in the scatter plot at the right?

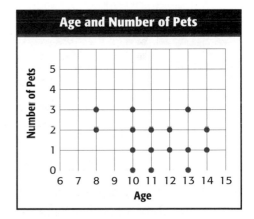

H.O.T. Problems

11. OPEN ENDED Name two sets of data that can be graphed on a scatter plot.

12. Which One Doesn't Belong? Identify the term that does not have the same characteristics as the other three. Explain your reasoning.

| line plot | mode | bar graph | scatter plot |

13. Write MATH Explain how a graph can be used to make predictions.

14. The number of laps Gaspar has been swimming each day is shown.

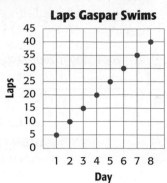

Laps Gaspar Swims

If the trend shown in the graph continues, what is the best prediction for the number of laps he will swim on day 10?

A. 50

B. 65

C. 75

D. 100

15. The number of people at the pool at different times during the day is shown.

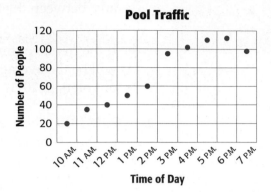

Pool Traffic

If an extra lifeguard is needed when the number of people at the pool exceeds 100, between which hours is an extra lifeguard needed?

F. 10:00 A.M.–12:00 P.M.

G. 12:00 P.M.–3:00 P.M.

H. 2:00 P.M.–5:00 P.M.

I. 4:00 P.M.–6:00 P.M.

 **Spiral Review**

16. PHONE CALLS Use the box-and-whisker plot.
(Lesson 12-2B)

Number of Phone Calls per Week

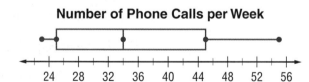

a. What is the median?

b. What are the upper and lower quartiles?

c. Use the measures of variation to describe the data.

Find the median, upper and lower quartiles, and interquartile range for the following data sets. (Lesson 12-2A)

17. stopping distances, in feet: 89, 90, 74, 81, 68

18. swimming pool water temperature, °F: 76, 90, 88, 84, 82, 78

In the diagram at the right, identify each pair of angles as *complementary*, *supplementary*, or *neither*. (Lesson 11-1B)

19. ∠1 and ∠3

20. ∠4 and ∠5

21. ∠1 and ∠2

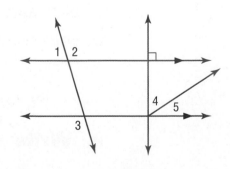

12-2 Statistical Displays

Main Idea

Select, organize, and construct appropriate data displays.

NGSSS

 **MA.8.S.3.1 Select, organize and construct appropriate data displays, including box and whisker plots, scatter plots,** and lines of best fit **to convey information and make conjectures about possible relationships.**

Get Connected
glencoe.com

Select an Appropriate Display

RECYCLING Ms. Stevens's class weighed the total amount of paper that was recycled each week during a ten-week period. The following graphs are four ways they displayed the weekly weights of paper.

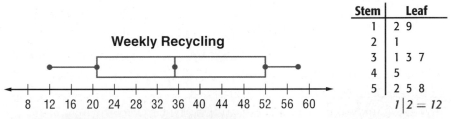

Weekly Recycling

Stem	Leaf
1	2 9
2	1
3	1 3 7
4	5
5	2 5 8

$1|2 = 12$

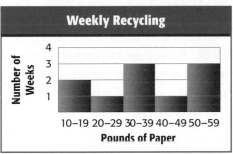

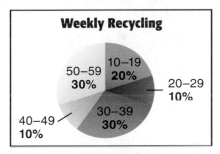

1. Which display(s) shows how many weeks the class collected exactly 31 pounds of paper?

2. Which display(s) most easily shows the number of weeks the class collected between 30 and 39 pounds of paper?

When deciding what type of display to use, ask these questions.

What type of information is given? What do you want the display to show? How will the display be analyzed?

> **EXAMPLE**   **Select an Appropriate Display**
>
> ① **SPORTS** Select an appropriate display to show the number of boys of different age ranges that participate in athletics.
>
> Since the display will show an interval, a histogram would be an appropriate display to represent this data.
>
> **CHECK Your Progress**
>
> **a.** Select an appropriate display for the percent of students in each grade at a middle school.

Concept Summary — Statistical Displays

Type of Display	Best Used to...
Bar Graph	show the number of items in specific categories
Box-and-Whisker Plot	show measures of variation for a set of data; also useful for very large sets of data
Circle Graph	compare parts of the data to the whole
Histogram	show frequency of data divided into equal intervals
Line Graph	show change over a period of time
Scatter Plot	show the relationship between a set of data with two variables graphed as ordered pairs
Stem-and-Leaf Plot	list all individual numerical data in condensed form
Venn Diagram	show how elements of two data sets are related

Real-World Link · · · ·

For every one bushel of corn, it takes 3–5 days to produce 2.8 gallons of ethanol.

Real-World EXAMPLE — Construct an Appropriate Display

② ETHANOL Select an appropriate type of display to compare the percent of ethanol production by state. Justify your reasoning. Then construct the display. What can you conclude from your display?

Ethanol Production by State						
State	Iowa	Nebraska	Illinois	Minnesota	Indiana	Other
Gallons per Year (millions)	3,534	1,665	1,135	1,102	1,074	5,098

You are asked to compare parts to a whole. A circle graph would be an appropriate display to compare the percents.

Indiana, Minnesota, and Illinois produce about the same amount of ethanol.

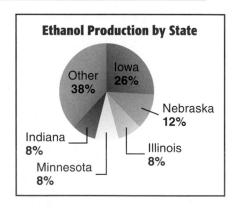

CHECK Your Progress

b. MUSICALS The table lists the ticket prices for school musicals during recent years. Select an appropriate display to predict the price of a ticket in 2012. Justify your reasoning. Then construct the display. What can you conclude from your display?

Ticket Prices	
Year	Price ($)
2008	5.00
2009	5.50
2010	6.50
2011	7.00

Example 1
(p. 705)

Select an appropriate display for each situation. Justify your reasoning.

1. the temperatures for the past week

2. the number of people who have different kinds of pets

3. the percent of different ways electricity is generated

Example 2
(p. 706)

4. **TELEVISION** Select an appropriate display to show a relationship between the number of hours of television watched and test scores. Justify your reasoning. Then construct the display. What can you conclude from your display?

Hours of Television Watched	Test Score
4	78
7	67
1	92
3	81
8	61

5. **SANDWICHES** The prices of sandwiches at a restaurant are $4.50, $5.59, $3.99, $2.50, $4.99, $3.75, $2.99, $3.29, and $4.19. Select an appropriate display to determine how many sandwiches range from $3.00 to $3.99. Justify your reasoning. Then construct the display. What can you conclude from your display?

● = **Step-by-Step Solutions** begin on page R38.
Extra Practice is on page EP35.

Example 1
(p. 705)

Select an appropriate display for each situation. Justify your reasoning.

6. the number of students that favor chocolate, vanilla, or both as a flavor of frosting

7. the median age of members in a community band

8. the resale value of a car over time

9. the percent of people that drink 0, 1, 2, 3, or more than 3 glasses of water a day

Example 2
(p. 706)

Select an appropriate display for each situation. Justify your reasoning. Then construct the display. What can you conclude from your display?

10.

Favorite Movies	
Type of Movie	**Number of People**
Comedy	48
Action	17
Drama	5
Horror	2

11.

Temperature (°F)	Depth of Ice (inches)
10	5.1
13	4.5
19	3.8
25	2.8
30	1.1

12.

Age Group	**Number of Texts per Day**
11–15	25
16–20	23
21–25	17
26–30	10

13.

Number of Push-ups			
56	28	28	54
55	28	25	23
54	53	23	20
57	52	17	10
28	56	51	19

14. **GRAPHIC NOVEL** Refer to the graphic novel frame below. What are the two best types of displays to use for this data? Explain.

15. **FIND THE DATA** Refer to the Data File on pages 2–5. Choose some data and then construct an appropriate display.

16. **SURVEY** A survey asked teens which subject they felt was most difficult. Of those who responded, 25 said English, 39 said social studies, 17 said English and social studies equally, and 13 said neither subject. Construct an appropriate display of the data.

17. **HOME RUNS** The number of home runs hit by each player of a high school baseball team is shown in the table. Construct an appropriate display of the data so that each individual value is still represented.

Home Runs						
10	22	15	11	24	12	8
21	13	16	22	10	14	21

H.O.T. Problems

18. **FIND THE ERROR** Raul created the following circle graph from the table. Find his mistake and correct it.

Colors of Cars in a Parking Lot	
Silver	31
Blue	24
White	24
Black	23
Red	23
Gray	22
Brown	17
Other	16

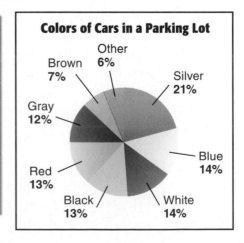

19. **Write MATH** Explain how a scatter plot and line graph are related. Give similarities and differences between each.

20. Moira surveyed 25 of her classmates to find out how many E-mails they received. Which of the following displays gives the most detail about the data?

A.

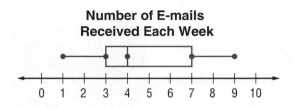

Number of E-mails Received Each Week

C.

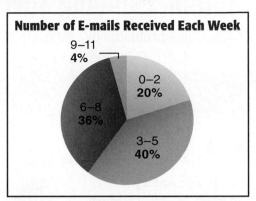

B.

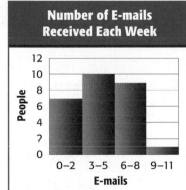

D.

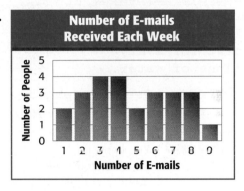

21. SPORTS Waylon is the student manager of the boys' soccer team. He recorded the height and weight of the players and listed them in the table. Make a scatter plot of the data. Determine what a player who is 68 inches tall might weigh. (Lesson 12-2C)

Height (in.)	64	64	67	70	66	69	71	66
Weight (lb)	135	141	148	158	133	147	164	142

22. SPORTS The table below shows the number of goals scored by the leading scorer for each NHL team in a recent season. (Lesson 12-2B)

NHL Leading Goal Scorers by Team									
32	43	36	40	39	40	34	27	40	36
40	23	31	32	25	26	33	45	18	24
39	46	31	35	38	33	30	25	31	56

a. Make a box-and-whisker plot of the data.

b. What percent of the teams had a top scorer with 40 or more goals?

Problem-Solving Investigation

Main Idea Solve problems by using a graph.

P.S.I. TEAM +

Use a Graph

TESS: I recently purchased a saltwater aquarium. I need to add 1 tablespoon of sea salt for every 5 gallons of water.

Sea Salt Requirements						
Tablespoons of Sea Salt	1	2	3	4	5	6
Capacity of Tank (gallons)	5	10	15	20	25	30

YOUR MISSION: Use a graph to predict the number of tablespoons of salt required for a 50-gallon saltwater fish tank.

Understand	You know the number of gallons of the tank. You need to predict the number of tablespoons of sea salt.	
Plan	Organize the data in a graph so you can easily see any trends.	
Solve	Continue the graph with a dotted line in the same direction until you align horizontally with 50 gallons. Graph a point. Find what value of sea salt corresponds with the point. Ten tablespoons are required for a 50-gallon tank.	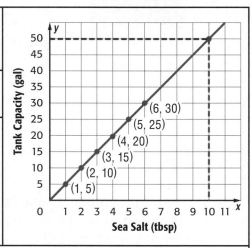
Check	Find the unit rate of tablespoons of sea salt per gallon of water. Multiply the unit rate by the number of gallons to find the number of tablespoons of sea salt.	

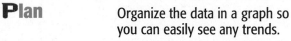

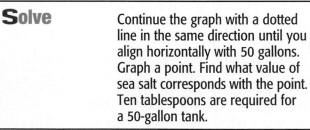

$$\frac{0.2 \text{ tbsp salt}}{1 \text{ gal water}} \times \frac{50 \text{ gal water}}{1} = 10 \text{ tbsp salt} \checkmark$$

Analyze the Strategy

1. Suppose the tank holds 32 gallons. Predict how much sea salt is required.

 NGSSS

MA.8.S.3.1 Select, organize, and construct appropriate data displays including box and whisker plots, scatter plots, and **lines of best fit to convey information and make conjectures about possible relationships.**

- Use a graph.
- Solve a simpler problem.
- Look for a pattern.
- Choose an operation.

Use a graph to solve Exercises 2–4.

2. **CALORIES** The table shows the average number of Calories burned while sleeping for various hours.

Calories Burned While Sleeping	
Hours	**Calories**
6	386
7	450
8	514
9	579

   a. Make a graph of the data.

   b. If the trend continues, about how many Calories are burned by sleeping for 10 hours?

3. **ADVERTISING** A local newspaper charges $14.50 for every three lines of a classified ad. Predict the cost of a 7-line ad.

4. **GAS PRICES** The table shows the price of a gallon of gas from July 2007 to May 2008. Make a graph of the data. Predict the price of a gallon of gas for December 2008.

Monthly Gas Prices for 2007–2008	
Month	**Price per Gallon ($)**
Jul 2007	3.02
Aug 2007	2.75
Sept 2007	2.81
Oct 2007	2.76
Nov 2007	3.06
Dec 2007	3.04
Jan 2008	3.10
Feb 2008	2.98
Mar 2008	3.27
Apr 2008	3.31
May 2008	3.80

Use any strategy to solve Exercises 5–9.

5. **WOODWORKING** Two workers can make two chairs in two days. How many chairs can 8 workers working at the same rate make in 20 days?

6. **POSTAGE** The table shows the postage stamp rate from 1975 to 2008. Make a graph of the data. Predict the year the postage rate will reach $0.50.

Postage Stamp Rates	
Year	**Cost ($)**
1975	0.13
1978	0.15
1981	0.20
1985	0.22
1988	0.25
1991	0.29
1995	0.32
1999	0.33
2001	0.34
2002	0.37
2006	0.39
2007	0.41
2008	0.42

7. **ANATOMY** Each human hand has 27 bones. There are 6 more bones in the fingers than in the wrist. There are 3 fewer bones in the palm than in the wrist. How many bones are in each part of the hand?

8. **ALLOWANCE** Tia used half of her allowance to buy a ticket for the class play. Then she spent $1.75 on an ice cream cone. Now she has $2.25 left. How much is her allowance?

9. **Write MATH** Explain the importance of constructing an accurate graph when predicting future trends.

Problem Solving in Environmental Science

Thinking Green

Are you concerned about protecting the environment? If so, you should think about a career in environmental science. **Environmental engineers apply** engineering principles along with biology and chemistry to develop solutions for improving the air, water, and land. They are involved in pollution control, recycling, and waste disposal. Environmental engineers also determine methods for conserving resources and for reducing environmental damage caused by construction and industry.

Choose a Major
Are you interested in a career as an environmental engineer? Take some of the following courses in high school.

- Algebra
- Biology
- Environmental Science
- Florida's Environmental History
- Flora and Fauna of Florida

 Get Connected glencoe.com

NGSSS

MA.8.S.3.2 Determine and describe how changes in data values impact measures of central tendency. *Also addresses MA.8.S.3.1.*

Percent of Materials That Are Recycled				
Florida County	Aluminum Cans (%)	Glass (%)	Newspapers (%)	Plastic Bottles (%)
Brevard	10	8	55	8
Broward	15	13	41	7
Dade	4	17	28	15
Duval	31	17	81	7
Hillsborough	14	21	38	23
Lee	48	16	66	53
Orange	12	29	33	16
Palm Beach	24	8	57	11
Pinellas	16	4	29	9
Polk	6	26	22	8

Real-World Math

Use the information in the table to solve each problem. Round to the nearest tenth if necessary.

1. Find the mean, median, and mode of the percent of recycled glass data.

2. If Lee County is removed from the recycled aluminum cans data, which changes the most: the mean, median, or mode? Does this make sense? Explain your reasoning.

3. Find the range, quartiles, and interquartile range of the percent of recycled newspapers data.

4. Find any outliers in the percent of recycled plastic bottles data.

5. Make a box-and-whisker plot of the percent of recycled glass data.

6. Refer to the box-and-whisker plot you made in Exercise 5. Compare the parts of the box and the lengths of the whiskers. What does this tell you about the data?

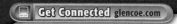

FOLDABLES® Study Organizer

Be sure the following Key Concepts are noted in your Foldable.

Key Concepts

Measures of Central Tendency (Lesson 12-1)

• The mean of a set of data is the sum of the data divided by the number of items in the set.

• The median of a set of data is the middle number of the ordered data if there is an odd number of values, or the mean of the middle two numbers if there is an even number of values.

• The mode of a set of data is the number or numbers that occur most often. If there are two or more numbers that occur most often, all of them are modes.

Measures of Variation (Lesson 12-2)

• The range of a set of data is the difference between the greatest and the least numbers in the set.

• The interquartile range is the range of the middle half of the data. It is the difference between the upper quartile and the lower quartile.

Statistical Displays (Lesson 12-2)

• Box-and-whisker plots use a number line to show the distribution of a set of data.

• Scatter plots show a relationship between a set of data with two variables.

Key Vocabulary

box-and-whisker plot (p. 693)

interquartile range (p. 687)

line of best fit (p. 700)

lower quartile (p. 687)

mean (p. 679)

measures of central tendency (p. 679)

measures of variation (p. 687)

median (p. 679)

mode (p. 679)

outlier (p. 688)

quartiles (p. 687)

range (p. 687)

scatter plot (p. 699)

upper quartile (p. 687)

Vocabulary Check

State whether each sentence is *true* or *false*. If *false*, replace the underlined word or number to make a true sentence.

1. The <u>range</u> is the difference between the greatest and the least values in a set of data.

2. The <u>mode</u> divides a set of data in half.

3. The interquartile range is one of the <u>measures of central tendency</u>.

4. A(n) <u>scatter plot</u> shows a relationship between a set of data with two variables.

5. The median of the bottom half of a data set is the <u>lower quartile</u>.

6. The <u>mean</u> is the arithmetic average of a set of data.

7. The number or item that appears most often in a set of data is the <u>mode</u>.

8. The <u>range</u> is the middle number of the ordered data, or the mean of the middle two numbers.

9. A(n) <u>variation</u> is a piece of data that is more than 1.5 times the value of the interquartile range beyond the quartiles.

Multi-Part Lesson Review

12-1 Measures of Central Tendency

Measures of Central Tendency (pp. 679–684)

Describe how the mean, median, and mode for each data set will change if the extreme value is dropped. Round to the nearest tenth if necessary.

10. number of siblings: 2, 3, 1, 3, 4, 3, 8, 0, 2

11. 89°, 46°, 93°, 100°, 72°, 86°, 74°

12. **MONEY** Which measure of central tendency best represents the amount of money students spent on clothing?

$$\$21, \$75, \$48, \$52, \$65$$

13. **CANNED FOOD DRIVE** Mrs. Warner's homeroom collected 21 cans on Monday, 7 cans on Tuesday, 42 cans on Wednesday, 23 cans on Thursday, and 19 cans on Friday. Select the appropriate measure of central tendency to describe the data. Justify your answer.

 MA.8.S.3.2

EXAMPLE 1 **PLANTS** Karrie measured the plants she was growing for a science fair. They were 3 inches, 4 inches, 2 inches, 2 inches, 5 inches, 7 inches, and 16 inches. Describe how the mean, median, and mode of the plant height will change after Karrie removes the extreme value.

Mean $\dfrac{3 + 4 + 2 + 2 + 5 + 7 + 16}{7} = \dfrac{39}{7}$ or 5.6

$\dfrac{3 + 4 + 2 + 2 + 5 + 7}{6} = \dfrac{23}{6}$ or 3.8

The mean decreases from 5.6 inches to 3.8 inches.

Median 2, 2, 3, ④, 5, 7, 16
2, 2, ③, ④, 5, 7
$3 + 4 = 7 \div 2 = 3.5$

The median decreases from 4 inches to 3.5 inches.

Mode The mode is 2 for both data sets.

12-2 Statistical Displays

Measures of Variation (pp. 687–692)

Find the measures of variation and any outliers for each data set.

14. number of miles ran each week: 14, 5, 4, 3, 5, 5, 6, 5, 4, 6, 3

15. number of hours spent burning music CDs each week: 2, 3, 2, 4, 1, 4, 1, 2

16. **BOWLING** The number of times Brittany's friends have been to the bowling alley over the last six months is 6, 3, 7, 2, 5, 6, 1, and 8. Use the measures of variation to describe this data.

 MA.8.S.3.1

EXAMPLE 2 **BAND** The number of hours Jake spent practicing for a band competition is listed below. Find the measures of variation for the data set.

11, 9, 3, 9, 4, 9, 5, 5, 6, 10, 9

Range $11 - 3$ or 8

Median 3, 4, 5, 5, 6, ⑨, 9, 9, 9, 10, 11

Lower Quartile 3, 4, ⑤, 5, 6

Upper Quartile 9, 9, ⑨, 10, 11

Interquartile Range $9 - 5$ or 4

12-2 Statistical Displays (continued)

Box-and-Whisker Plots (pp. 693–698)

Construct a box-and-whisker plot for each set of data.

17. number of fish caught: 0, 3, 4, 8, 9, 9, 9, 11, 13

18. number of hours spent reading books: 2, 8, 11, 9, 7, 10, 8, 8

19. **POSTERS** The number of posters various students have in their rooms is 3, 2, 1, 0, 2, 3, 4, 2, 5, 0, and 2. Construct a box-and-whisker plot for the data. What do the lengths of the parts of the plot tell you?

20. **STATES** The number of states students have visited on vacation is 2, 11, 7, 8, 12, 13, 9, 8, 10, 15, and 11. Construct a box-and-whisker plot for the data. What do the lengths of the parts of the plot tell you?

EXAMPLE 3 **TRAINS** The lengths in hours of various train rides are listed below. Draw a box-and-whisker plot for the data set.

4, 1, 2, 3, 6, 2, 3, 2, 5, 8, 4

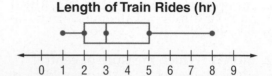

Length of Train Rides (hr)

EXAMPLE 4 Explain what the length of the plot above says about the length of train rides.

Because the box portion is fairly short, the majority of the data is close together in value.

Scatter Plots and Lines of Best Fit (pp. 699–704)

SPORTS Use the graph showing the number of hours practiced per day and the total wins in a season.

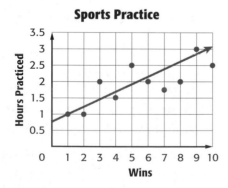

Sports Practice

21. Describe the relationship between the two data sets.

22. Predict the number of wins if a team practices less than 1 hour each day.

EXAMPLE 5 **GARDENS** The scatter plot below shows the heights of flowers and the amount of water received each week.

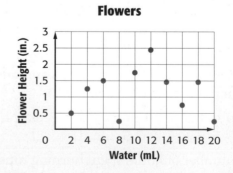

Flowers

Describe the relationship between the two data sets.

The graph shows no obvious patterns. So, there is no relationship.

Select an Appropriate Display (pp. 705–709)

 MA.8.S.3.1

23. **CALORIES** Select an appropriate display to show individual students' Calorie consumption during lunch in numerical order.

24. **PHONE CALLS** Is a circle graph an appropriate display to represent the number of phone calls made each day? Justify your answer.

25. **FRUIT** The prices per pound of fruit at a store are $0.99, $0.50, $0.75, $2.25, $0.89, $1.50, $1.39, $0.79, $1.29, and $2.09. Select an appropriate display to determine how many fruit prices range from $0.50 to $0.99. Justify your reasoning. Then construct the display. What can you conclude from your display?

EXAMPLE 6 **OLYMPICS** Select an appropriate display for the number of Olympic sprinters compared to the total number of athletes.

An appropriate display would be a circle graph because you are comparing a part to the whole.

PSI: Use a Graph (pp. 710–711)

 MA.8.A.1.3

26. **HOCKEY** The graph shows the number of points scored in the first twelve hockey games. What is the average number of points scored so far this season?

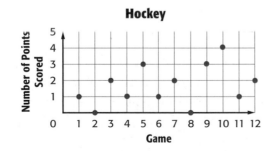

EXAMPLE 7 **TESTS** The graph shows the number of hours spent studying for a test and the resulting test score. Find the average test score. Round to the nearest tenth.

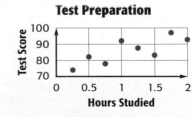

Add the test scores: $73 + 83 + 79 + 91 + 88 + 84 + 96 + 93$ or 687.

Divide: $\frac{687}{8}$ or 85.9

So, the average test score was 85.9.

1. **INSECTS** The lengths in inches of several insects are given below. Describe how the mean, median, and mode will change if the extreme value is dropped. Round to the nearest tenth if necessary.

0.75, 1.24, 0.95, 8.6, 1.18, 1.3

2. **BASEBALL** Miley's baseball team's statistics are shown in the table at the right. What effect does Wyatt's batting average have on the overall team average?

Cyclones Season Statistics	
Player	**Batting Average**
Anakin	0.463
Bredt	0.436
Demario	0.378
Earnest	0.450
Jimmie	0.413
Jorje	0.426
Miley	0.410
Ralph	0.500
Taro	0.365
Will	0.320
Wyatt	0.105

3. Refer to the table.

Daily Activities	
Activity Type	**Average Time (min)**
Cardio	21
Clean room	15
Dishes	12
Download music	20
E-mail	18
Homework	56
Trash	11

a. What is the range of the data?

b. Find the median, upper and lower quartiles, and the interquartile range for the data.

c. Identify any outliers.

d. Use the measures of variation to describe the data in the table.

4. **NGSSS PRACTICE** Refer to the data below. Which of the following statements is true concerning the measures of central tendency?

41, 45, 42, 38, 77, 44, 36, 43

A. The mode is most affected by the inclusion of the extreme number.

B. The median is not affected by the inclusion of the extreme number.

C. The mean is most affected by the inclusion of the extreme number.

D. None of the measures of central tendency are affected by the inclusion of the extreme number.

5. **EMPLOYMENT** The graph shows the percent of women who work out after work. Predict the number of women who will work out after work in 2015.

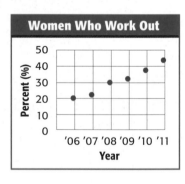

6. **EXTENDED RESPONSE** Ronan asked his friends how many CDs they own. Below is the data Ronan collected from his friends.

0, 0, 3, 5, 6, 8, 9, 15, 15, 15, 18, 20, 20, 28, 31

Part A Construct a box-and-whisker plot with the data set given above.

Part B What is the greatest amount of CDs owned by Ronan's friends?

Part C Explain why the median is not in the middle of the box.

Short Response: Drawing Graphs

When drawing statistical graphs for short-response questions, be sure to include all necessary labels and information in order to receive full credit for that part of the question.

 **PRACTICE EXAMPLE**

The average depths and maximum depths of different lakes around the world are shown below.

Depths of Lakes

Average Depth (m)	149	72	40	72	19	86	50	107	138
Maximum Depth (m)	406	281	84	446	64	224	230	281	267

Construct a scatter plot to display the data.

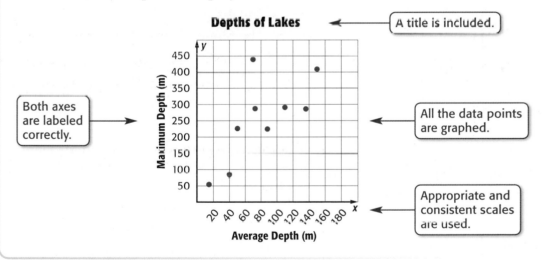

A title is included.

Both axes are labeled correctly.

All the data points are graphed.

Appropriate and consistent scales are used.

 Work on It

Refer to the table of data above. Then construct a box-and-whisker plot showing the average depths of the lakes.

Test Hint

You will often use graphs that you draw to answer other parts of extended-response questions. Double-check your work.

Read each question. Then fill in the correct answer on the answer sheet provided by your teacher or on a sheet of paper.

1. Ed's Used Cars bought 5 used cars for $6,400 each. They later bought another used car for $4,600. What measure of central tendency would best represent the cost of each car?

   A. none

   B. mean

   C. median

   D. mode

2. In the figure below, $s \parallel t$ and $m\angle 1 = 65°$. What is $m\angle 7$?

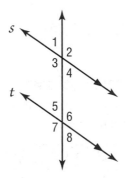

   F. 65°

   G. 115°

   H. 125°

   I. 145°

3. Triangle ABC has vertices $A(1, -2)$, $B(6, 1)$, and $C(3, -4)$. If triangle ABC is reflected over the y-axis and translated 3 units up, which is the resulting image of point A?

   A. $(-1, -2)$

   B. $(-3, -4)$

   C. $(-1, 1)$

   D. $(-3, -1)$

4. **GRIDDED RESPONSE** Neela has 11.5 yards of fabric. She will use 20% of the fabric to make a flag. How many yards of fabric will she use?

5. **GRIDDED RESPONSE** A patio blueprint has a key that shows 1 inch is equal to 12 feet. If the owner wants the length to be 30 feet, how many inches will the length be on the blueprint?

6. The number of ringtones that twelve middle school students have on their cell phones is 14, 8, 7, 6, 5, 5, 10, 11, 8, 8, 6, and 7. Which of the following statements is NOT supported by these data?

   F. Half of the ringtones are below 7.5 and half are above 7.5.

   G. The range of the data is 9 ringtones.

   H. An outlier of the data is 11 ringtones.

   I. About one fourth of the ringtones that the students have are at or above 9.

7. Which box-and-whisker plot represents the data set 8, 12, 21, 15, 20, 9, 16, 14, and 25?

   A.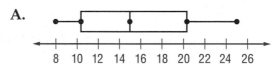

   B.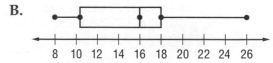

   C.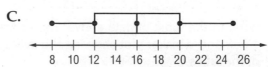

   D.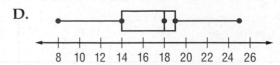

8. Katherine polled 21 classmates to find out the average number of hours each spends watching television each week. Which of the following displays would be most appropriate to show the individual student responses?

F.
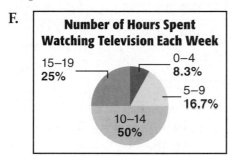

Number of Hours Spent Watching Television Each Week

15–19 25%   0–4 8.3%   5–9 16.7%   10–14 50%

G.
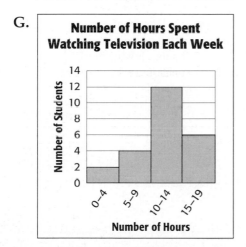

Number of Hours Spent Watching Television Each Week

H. Number of Hours Spent Watching Television Each Week

Stem	Leaf
0	0 3 5 7 8 8
1	0 0 1 2 2 2 3 4 4 4 4 4 5 6 6 8 8 9

1 | 2 = 12

I.   **Number of Hours Spent Watching Television Each Week**

0 2 4 6 8 10 12 14 16 18 20

9. **GRIDDED RESPONSE**
How many pints of liquid are shown at the right? Round your answer to the nearest hundredth.

10. **SHORT RESPONSE**
Find the surface area of the pyramid. Round your answer to the nearest tenth.

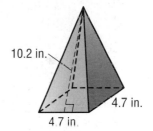

10.2 in. 4.7 in. 4.7 in.

11. **EXTENDED RESPONSE** The table shows how values of a painting increased over ten years.

Year	Value	Year	Value
1997	$350	2002	$1,851
1998	$650	2003	$2,151
1999	$950	2004	$2,451
2000	$1,200	2005	$2,752
2001	$1,551	2006	$3,052

Part A Select and make an appropriate display of the data.

Part B Use the graph to predict what the value of the painting will be in 2010.

NEED EXTRA HELP?

If You Missed Question...	1	2	3	4	5	6	7	8	9	10	11
Go to Lesson...	12-1B	11-1B	10-2B	6-1B	4-2B	12-2A	12-2B	12-2D	9-1B	8-2E	12-2C
For help with NGSSS...	8.S.3.2	8.G.2.2	8.G.4.2	A.1.2	A.1.6	8.S.3.1	8.S.3.1	8.S.3.1	G.4.4	G.2.1	8.S.3.1

Inequalities, Functions, and Monomials

The ☆BIG Idea

Analyze and represent linear fuctions and solve linear equations and systems of linear equations.

FOLDABLES®
Study Organizer

Make this Foldable to help you organize your notes. Begin with 4 sheets of grid paper.

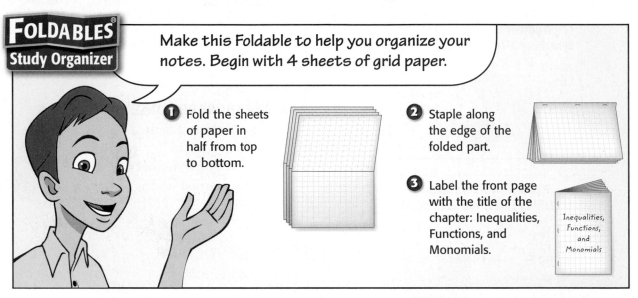

① Fold the sheets of paper in half from top to bottom.

② Staple along the edge of the folded part.

③ Label the front page with the title of the chapter: Inequalities, Functions, and Monomials.

Inequalities, Functions, and Monomials

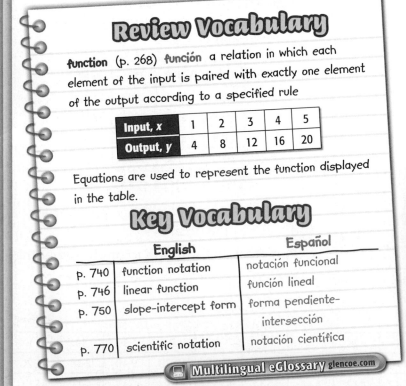

Review Vocabulary

function (p. 268) **función** a relation in which each element of the input is paired with exactly one element of the output according to a specified rule

Input, x	1	2	3	4	5
Output, y	4	8	12	16	20

Equations are used to represent the function displayed in the table.

Key Vocabulary

	English	Español
p. 740	function notation	notación funcional
p. 746	linear function	función lineal
p. 750	slope-intercept form	forma pendiente-intersección
p. 770	scientific notation	notación científica

🔲 **Multilingual eGlossary** glencoe.com

🖥 **Get Connected**
glencoe.com

- Study using the **eBook**
- Explore with **Get Animated**
- Get extra help from **Personal Tutor**
- Use **virtual manipulatives** for additional help
- Take a **Self-Check Quiz**

When Will I Use This?

Are You Ready for Chapter 13?

You have two options for checking prerequisite skills for this chapter.

Text Option Take the Quick Check below. Refer to the Quick Review for help.

QUICK Check

Graph the function represented by each situation. (Prior Grade)

1. **FOOD** Jessica is doing a health project about fat content in food. She found that there are 14.1 grams of fat in one serving of salted peanuts. The equation $f = 14.1p$ describes how much fat f is in p servings of peanuts. Represent this function by a graph.

2. **PENCILS** Germain is purchasing pencils that cost $0.20 each. The equation $c = 20p$ describes the cost of p pencils. Represent this function by a graph.

Graph each equation.

3. $y = x + 3$

4. $y = -3x - 4$

QUICK Review

EXAMPLE 1

JOBS Donald makes $7.50 an hour working at a local restaurant. The equation $m = 7.50h$ describes how much money m he earns for working h hours. Represent this function by a graph.

Step 1 Select any four values for h. Select only positive numbers because h represents time. Make a function table.

Step 2 Graph the ordered pairs and draw a line through the points.

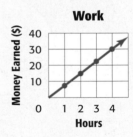

Find the rate of change using the graph. (Lesson 4-1B)

5. The graph shows the amount of homework problems completed each minute. Use the graph to find the rate of change.

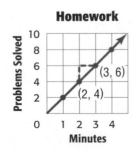

EXAMPLE 2

Find the slope of the line between the points (1, 7.5) and (2, 15).

$$\text{Slope} = \frac{\text{change in } y}{\text{change in } x} \quad \text{Definition of slope}$$

$$= \frac{15 - 7.5}{2 - 1} \quad \text{Use (2, 15) and (1, 7.5).}$$

$$= \frac{7.5}{1} \quad \begin{array}{l} \leftarrow \text{ dollars} \\ \leftarrow \text{ hours} \end{array}$$

Online Option (Get Connected) Take the Online Readiness Quiz at **glencoe.com**.

Studying Math

Definition Map

A *definition map* can help you visualize the parts of a good definition. Ask yourself these questions about the vocabulary terms.

- What is it? (Category)
- What can it be compared to? (Comparisons)
- What is it like? (Properties)
- What are some examples? (Illustrations)

What do you do when you come across a word you do not know?

Here is a definition map for *linear function*.

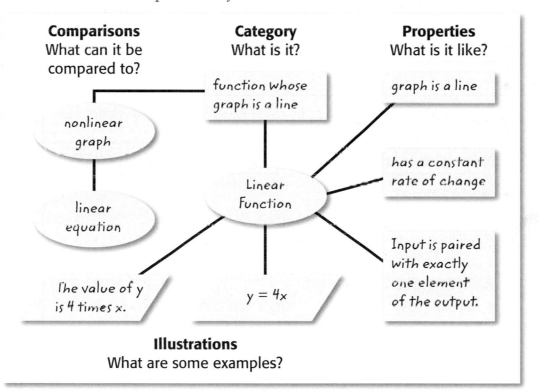

Comparisons
What can it be compared to?

nonlinear graph

linear equation

Category
What is it?

function whose graph is a line

Linear Function

$y = 4x$

Properties
What is it like?

graph is a line

has a constant rate of change

Input is paired with exactly one element of the output.

The value of y is 4 times x.

Illustrations
What are some examples?

Practice

Make a definition map for each term.

1. reflection (p. 556)
2. surface area (p. 456)
3. rational number (p. 80)
4. percent (p. 300)

NGSSS
LA.7.1.6.5 The student will relate new vocabulary to familiar words.

Problem-Solving Investigation

Main Idea Solve problems using the *guess, check, and revise* strategy.

P.S.I. TEAM +

Guess, Check, and Revise

DEVON: My soccer team held a car wash to help pay for a trip to a tournament. We charged $5 for a car and $7 for an SUV. After the first hour we had washed at least 10 vehicles and earned at least $58.

YOUR MISSION: Use guess, check, and revise to find several possibilities of how many of each type of vehicle were washed.

Understand	You know car washes are $5 for cars and $7 for SUVs. At least ten vehicles were washed for at least $58.
Plan	Make a guess and check it. Adjust the guess until you get the correct answer.
Solve	Make a guess.
	5 cars and **5** SUVs $5(5) + 7(5) = \$60$ one possibility
	Adjust the number of SUVs downward.
	5 cars and **4** SUVs $5(5) + 7(4) = \$49$ too low
	Adjust the number of cars upward.
	6 cars and **4** SUVs $5(6) + 7(4) = \$58$ another possibility
	So, 6 cars and 4 SUVs were washed.
Check	Six cars cost $30, and four SUVs cost $28. Since $\$30 + \$28 \geq \$58$, and $25 + 35 \geq \$58$, both guesses are correct. ✓

Analyze the Strategy

1. Explain why you should keep a careful record of each of your guesses.

NGSSS

MA.8.A.6.4 Perform operations on real numbers (including integer exponents, radicals, percents, scientific notation, absolute value, **rational numbers,** and irrational numbers) **using multi-step and real world problems.**

Mixed Problem Solving

Extra Practice is on page EP36.

- Guess, check, and revise.
- Find a pattern.
- Choose an operation.

Use the *guess, check, and revise* strategy to solve Exercises 2–5.

2. **TICKET SALES** The goal for ticket sales for the school basketball game was at least $1,625. Adult tickets were $7 and student tickets were $3. Find several possibilities for how many adult and student tickets were sold.

3. **NUMBERS** A number is multiplied by 6. Then 4 is added to the product. The result is 82. What is the number?

4. **ANALYZE TABLES** Bella is transferring her home videos onto a DVD. Suppose the DVD holds at most 60 minutes. Which videos should Bella select to have the maximum time on the DVD without going over?

Video	Time
birthday	25 min 15 s
family picnic	18 min 10 s
holiday	15 min 20 s
vacation	19 min 20 s

5. **MONEY** Eldora has $1.60 in change in her purse. If she has an equal number of nickels, dimes, and quarters, how many of each does she have?

Use any strategy to solve Exercises 6–12.

6. **BRIDGES** The total length of wire used in the cables supporting the Golden Gate Bridge in San Francisco is about 80,000 miles. This is 5,300 miles longer than three times the distance around Earth at the Equator. What is the distance around Earth at the Equator?

7. **GEOMETRY** What are the next two figures in the pattern?

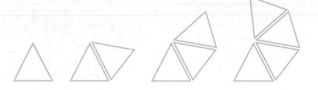

8. **ALGEBRA** What are the next two numbers in the pattern?

$$-16, 32, -64, 128, -256, \blacksquare, \blacksquare$$

9. **FRUIT** Angelo places 4 apples and 3 oranges into each fruit basket he makes. If he has used 24 apples and 18 oranges, how many fruit baskets has he made?

10. **ANALYZE TABLES** The table gives the average snowfall, in inches, for Valdez, Alaska, for the months of October through April.

Month	Snowfall
October	11.6
November	40.3
December	73.0
January	65.8
February	59.4
March	52.0
April	22.7

How many total inches of snowfall could a resident of Valdez expect to receive from October to April?

11. **ROLLER COASTERS** The Jackrabbit roller coaster can handle 1,056 passengers per hour. The coaster has 8 vehicles. If each vehicle carries 4 passengers, how many runs are made in one hour?

12. **Write MATH** Write a problem that could be solved by guess, check, and revise. Then write the steps you would take to find the solution to your problem.

Main Idea

Solve inequalities by using the Addition and Subtraction Properties of Inequality.

NGSSS

 MA.8.A.4.2 Solve and graph one- and two-**step inequalities in one variable.**
MA.8.A.6.4 Perform operations on real numbers (including integer exponents, radicals, percents, scientific notation, absolute value, **rational numbers,** and irrational numbers) **using multi-step and real world problems.**

Get Connected
glencoe.com

Solve Inequalities by Addition or Subtraction

Explore On the balance below, the paper bag may contain some blocks.

The blocks and bag on the scale model an inequality because the two sides are not equal.

The model shows the inequality $x + 2 < 5$. The side with the bag and 2 blocks weighs less than the side with 5 blocks.

1. How many blocks would be in the bag if the left side balanced the right side? Assume that the paper bag weighs nothing.

2. Explain how you determined your answer to Exercise 1.

3. What numbers of blocks can be in the bag to make the left side weigh *less than* the right side?

4. Write an inequality to represent your answer to Exercise 3.

Solving an inequality means finding values for the variable that make the inequality true. In the example above, any number less than 3 is a solution. The solution is written as the inequality $x < 3$.

You can solve inequalities by using the Properties of Inequality.

Key Concept Addition and Subtraction Properties of Inequality

Words When you add or subtract the same number from each side of an inequality, the inequality remains true.

Symbols For all numbers a, b, and c,
1. if $a > b$, then $a + c > b + c$ and $a - c > b - c$.
2. if $a < b$, then $a + c < b + c$ and $a - c < b - c$.

Examples

$$2 < 4 \qquad\qquad 6 > 3$$
$$2 + 3 < 4 + 3 \qquad 6 - 4 > 3 - 4$$
$$5 < 7 \qquad\qquad 2 > -1$$

These properties are also true for $a \geq b$ and $a \leq b$.

Inequalities				

Words	• is less than
	• is fewer than
		• is greater than
		• is more than
		• exceeds
			• is less than or
			  equal to
			• is no more than
			• is at most
				• is greater than
				  or equal to
				• is no less than
				• is at least

Symbols	$<$	$>$	$\leq$	$\geq$

EXAMPLES **Solve Inequalities Using Subtraction and Addition**

 Solve $x + 3 > 10$.

$$x + 3 > 10 \qquad \text{Write the inequality.}$$
$$x + 3 - 3 > 10 - 3 \qquad \text{Subtract 3 from each side.}$$
$$x > 7 \qquad \text{Simplify.}$$

Therefore, the solution is $x > 7$.

 Solve $-6 \geq n - 5$.

$$-6 \geq n - 5 \qquad \text{Write the inequality.}$$
$$-6 + 5 \geq n - 5 + 5 \qquad \text{Add 5 to each side.}$$
$$-1 \geq n \qquad \text{Simplify.}$$

The solution is $-1 \geq n$ or $n \leq -1$.

CHECK Your Progress

a. $a - 3 < 8$ **b.** $14 + y \geq 7$

> **Study Tip**
>
> **Checking Solutions**
> To check Example 1, write the inequality, replace x with a value in the solution set, and check to see if the result is a true statement.
>
> $x + 3 > 10$
> $8 + 3 \overset{?}{>} 10$
> $11 > 10$ ✓

EXAMPLE **Graph Solutions of Inequalities**

 Solve $a + \frac{1}{2} < 2$. Graph the solution set on a number line.

$$a + \frac{1}{2} < 2 \qquad \text{Write the inequality.}$$
$$a + \frac{1}{2} - \frac{1}{2} < 2 - \frac{1}{2} \qquad \text{Subtract } \tfrac{1}{2} \text{ from each side.}$$
$$a < \frac{4}{2} - \frac{1}{2} \qquad \text{Rename 2 as a fraction with a denominator of 2.}$$
$$a < \frac{3}{2} \text{ or } 1\frac{1}{2} \qquad \text{Simplify.}$$

The solution is $a < 1\frac{1}{2}$.   Check your solution.

Graph the solution.

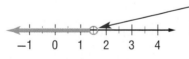

Place an open dot at $1\frac{1}{2}$. Draw a line and an arrow to the left.

> **Study Tip**
>
> **Open and Closed Dots**
> When graphing inequalities, an open dot is used when the value should not be included in the solution, as with $>$ and $<$ inequalities. A closed dot indicates the value is included in the solution, as with $\leq$ and $\geq$ inequalities.

CHECK Your Progress

c. $h + 4 > 4$ **d.** $x - 6 \leq 4$

④ STATE FAIRS Dylan has $18 to ride go-karts and play games at the state fair. If the go-karts cost $5.50, what is the most he can spend on games?

We need to find the greatest amount of money Dylan can spend on games.

Let x represent the amount Dylan can spend on games. Write an inequality to represent the problem.

Words	Cost of go-kart	plus	cost of games	must be less than or equal to	total amount.
Symbols	5.50	+	x	≤	18
Inequality	5.5	+	x	≤	18

$$5.5 + x \leq 18 \qquad \text{Write the inequality. } (5.50 = 5.5)$$

$$5.5 - 5.5 + x \leq 18 - 5.5 \qquad \text{Subtract 5.5 from each side.}$$

$$x \leq 12.5 \qquad \text{Simplify.}$$

Check by choosing an amount less than or equal to $12.50, such as $10. Then Dylan would spend $5.50 + $10 or $15.50 in all. Since $15.50 < $18, the answer is reasonable.

So, the most Dylan can spend on games is $12.50.

 CHECK Your Progress

e. SAVINGS Shane is saving money for a ski trip. He has $62.50, but his goal is to save at least $100. Write and solve an inequality to determine the least amount Shane needs to save to reach his goal.

 **Your Understanding**

Examples 1 and 2
(p. 729)

Solve each inequality.

1. $c + 4 < 8$ **2.** $14 + t \geq 5$ **3.** $y - 9 < 11$

4. $10 > x + 5$ **⑤** $c + 4 \geq 17$ **6.** $t - 7 < 25$

Example 3
(p. 729)

Solve each inequality. Graph the solution set on a number line.

7. $6 + h \geq 12$ **8.** $15 - y < 8$ **9.** $-7 \leq n + 9$

Example 4
(p. 730)

10. ELEVATORS An elevator must weigh less than 2,800 pounds. Write and solve an inequality that describes how much weight the elevator can gain if its current weight is 2,375 pounds.

Practice and Problem Solving

• = **Step-by-Step Solutions** begin on page R40.
Extra Practice is on page EP36.

Examples 1 and 2
(p. 729)

Solve each inequality.

11. $-3 < n - 8$ **12.** $h - 16 \leq -24$ **13.** $y - 6 \geq -13$

14. $3 \leq m + 1.4$ **15.** $x + 0.7 > -0.3$ **16.** $w - 8 \geq 5.6$

Example 3
(p. 729)

Solve each inequality. Graph the solution set on a number line.

17. $-11 > t + 7$ **18.** $m + 5 \geq -1$ **19.** $-21 < a - 16$

20. $t - 6.2 < 4$ **21.** $n - \frac{1}{5} \leq \frac{3}{10}$ **22.** $6 > x + 3\frac{1}{3}$

Example 4
(p. 730)

Write an inequality and solve each problem.

23. Four more than a number is more than 13.

24. The sum of a number and 19 is at least 8.

25. Eight less than a number is less than 10.

26. The difference between a number and 21 is no more than 14.

27. SOCCER The high school soccer team can have no more than 26 players. Write and solve an inequality to determine how many more players can make the team if the coach has already chosen 17 players.

28. CARS There were a total of 125 cars at a car dealership. A salesperson sold 68 of the cars in one month. Write and solve an inequality that describes how many more cars, at most, the salesman has left to sell.

29 CELL PHONES Lalo has 1,500 minutes per month on his cell phone plan. How many more minutes can he use if he has already talked for 785 minutes?

30. TRANSPORTATION A certain minivan has a maximum carrying capacity of 1,100 pounds. If the luggage weighs 120 pounds, what is the maximum weight allowable for passengers?

31. WEATHER Refer to the diagram below.

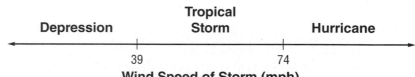

Types of Storms

Depression — Tropical Storm — Hurricane

39   74

Wind Speed of Storm (mph)

a. A hurricane has winds that are at least 74 miles per hour. Suppose a tropical storm has winds that are 42 miles per hour. Write and solve an inequality to find how much the winds must increase before the storm becomes a hurricane.

b. A *major storm* has wind speeds that are at least 110 miles per hour. Write and solve an inequality that describes how much greater these wind speeds are than the slowest hurricane.

32. REASONING Compare and contrast the solutions of $a - 3 = 15$ and $a - 3 \geq 15$.

33. OPEN ENDED Write an addition inequality with the solution set graphed below.

16 18 20 22 24

34. Write MATH Explain when you would use addition and when you would use subtraction to solve an inequality.

---

35. Which inequality represents a temperature that is equal to or less than 42°?

   A. $t \geq 42$

   B. $t > 42$

   C. $t \leq 42$

   D. $t < 42$

36. Which inequality represents the graph below?

$$-5\ -4\ -3\ -2\ -1\ \ 0\ \ 1\ \ 2\ \ 3\ \ 4\ \ 5$$

   F. $x > 3$

   G. $x \geq 3$

   H. $x < 3$

   I. $x \leq 3$

37. Arlo has $25 to spend on a T-shirt and shorts for gym class. The shorts cost $14. Use the inequality $14 + t \leq 25$, where t represents the cost of the T-shirt. What is the most Arlo can spend on the T-shirt?

   A. $9   **C.** $11

   B. $10.99   **D.** $11.50

38. THINK SOLVE EXPLAIN SHORT RESPONSE Write and solve an inequality for the following sentence: Jan has $50 in her savings account and needs to save at least $268 for camp this summer. What is the least amount that she can save to meet her goal?

 **Spiral Review**

39. SHOPPING A grocery store sells hot dog buns in packages of 8 and 12. How many 8-packs and 12-packs could you buy if you needed 44 hot dog buns? Use the *guess, check, and revise* strategy. (Lesson 13-1A)

40. MUSIC A survey asked teens what they liked most about a song; 59% said the sound and 41% said the lyrics. Select an appropriate type of display for this situation. (Lesson 12-2D)

41. ALGEBRA The table shows the time needed to complete 4 art projects. If the pattern continues, how much time is needed to complete the fifth art project? (Lesson 5-1B)

Project	1	2	3	4	5
Time (min)	8	25	42	59	?

Main Idea

Solve inequalities by using the Multiplication or Division Properties of Inequality.

NGSSS

 MA.8.A.4.2 Solve and graph one- and two-step inequalities in one variable.

MA.8.A.6.4 Perform operations on real numbers (including integer exponents, radicals, percents, scientific notation, absolute value, **rational numbers,** and irrational numbers) **using multi-step and real world problems.**

Get Connected
glencoe.com

Study Tip

Reading Math The inequality $c > 0$ means that c is a positive number.

Solve Inequalities by Multiplication or Division

SCIENCE An astronaut in a space suit weighs about 300 pounds on Earth, but only 50 pounds on the Moon.

weight on Earth   weight on Moon
       300   >   50

If the astronaut and space suit each weighed half as much, would the inequality still be true?

Location	Weight of Astronaut (lb)
Earth	300
Moon	50
Pluto	67
Mars	113
Neptune	407
Jupiter	796

1. Divide each side of the inequality 300 > 50 by 2. Is the inequality still true? Explain by using an inequality.

2. Would the weight of 5 astronauts be greater on Pluto or on Earth? Explain by using an inequality.

The examples above demonstrate how you can solve inequalities by using the Multiplication and Division Properties of Inequality.

Key Concept	**Multiplication and Division Properties of Inequality, Positive Number**
Words	When you multiply or divide each side of an inequality by a positive number, the inequality remains true.
Symbols	For all numbers a, b, and c, where $c > 0$, 1. if $a > b$, then $ac > bc$ and $\frac{a}{c} > \frac{b}{c}$. 2. if $a < b$, then $ac < bc$ and $\frac{a}{c} < \frac{b}{c}$.

These properties are also true for $a \geq b$ and $a \leq b$.

EXAMPLES Multiply or Divide by a Positive Number

 Solve $8x \leq 40$.

$$8x \leq 40 \quad \text{Write the inequality.}$$
$$\frac{8x}{8} \leq \frac{40}{8} \quad \text{Divide each side by 8.}$$
$$x \leq 5 \quad \text{Simplify.}$$

The solution is $x \leq 5$. You can check this solution by substituting 5 or a number less than 5 into the inequality.

Solve $\frac{d}{2} > 7$.

$\frac{d}{2} > 7$ Write the inequality.

$2\left(\frac{d}{2}\right) > 2(7)$ Multiply each side by 2.

$d > 14$ Simplify.

The solution is $d > 14$. You can check this solution by substituting a number greater than 14 into the inequality.

CHECK Your Progress

a. $4x < 40$ **b.** $6 \geq \frac{x}{7}$

Key Concept   **Multiplication and Division Properties of Inequality, Negative Number**

Words   When you multiply or divide each side of an inequality by a negative number, the inequality symbol must be reversed for the inequality to remain true.

Study Tip

Reading Math The inequality $c < 0$ means that c is a negative number.

Symbols   For all numbers a, b, and c, where $c < 0$,

   1. if $a > b$, then $ac < bc$ and $\frac{a}{c} < \frac{b}{c}$.

   2. if $a < b$, then $ac > bc$ and $\frac{a}{c} > \frac{b}{c}$.

Examples

$7 > 1$ $-4 < 16$

$-2(7) < -2(1)$ Reverse the symbols. $\frac{-4}{-4} > \frac{16}{-4}$

$-14 < -2$ $1 > -4$

These properties are also true for $a \geq b$ and $a \leq b$.

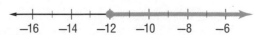 **EXAMPLE**   **Multiply or Divide by a Negative Number**

 Solve $\frac{x}{-3} \leq 4$. Graph the solution set on a number line.

$\frac{x}{-3} \leq 4$ Write the inequality.

$-3\left(\frac{x}{-3}\right) \geq -3(4)$ Multiply each side by -3 and reverse the symbol.

$x \geq -12$ Simplify.

Graph the solution, $x \geq -12$.

 CHECK Your Progress

c. $\frac{k}{-2} < 9$ **d.** $-6a \geq -78$

Some inequalities involve more than one operation. To solve the inequality, work backward to undo the operations, just as you did to solve multi-step equations.

 EXAMPLE **Solve a Multi-Step Inequality**

④ **Solve $\frac{6}{7}x + 15 > 9$. Graph the solution set on a number line.**

$$\frac{6}{7}x + 15 > 9 \qquad \text{Write the inequality.}$$

$$\frac{6}{7}x + 15 - 15 > 9 - 15 \qquad \text{Subtract 15 from each side.}$$

Step 1 Undo the addition.

$$\frac{6}{7}x > -6 \qquad \text{Simplify.}$$

$$\frac{7}{6} \cdot \frac{6x}{7} > \frac{-6}{1} \cdot \frac{7}{6} \qquad \text{Multiply each side by } \frac{7}{6}.$$

Step 2 Undo the multiplication.

$$x > -7 \qquad \text{Simplify.}$$

Graph the solution, $x > -7$.

0 1 2 3 4 5 6 7 8 9 10 11

✓ **CHECK Your Progress**

e. $3x + 4 \le 31$ **f.** $16 - 3c > 14$

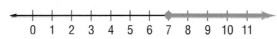 **Real-World EXAMPLE** **Write an Inequality**

⑤ **JOBS** Ling earns $8 per hour working at the zoo. Write and solve an inequality that can be used to find how many hours she must work in a week to earn at least $120.

Let x represent the number of hours worked.

Words	Amount earned per hour	times	number of hours	is at least	amount earned each week.
Variable	8	•	x	$\ge$	120
Inequality	8		x	$\ge$	120

$$8x \ge 120$$

$$\frac{8x}{8} \ge \frac{120}{8} \qquad \text{Divide each side by 8.}$$

$$x \ge 15 \qquad \text{Simplify.}$$

 ✓ **CHECK Your Progress**

g. **EARNINGS** Elisa delivers pizzas. Her average tip is $1.50 for each pizza that she delivers. Write and solve an inequality to represent how many pizzas she must deliver to earn at least $21 in tips.

CHECK Your Understanding

Examples 1 and 2
(pp. 733–734)

Solve each inequality.

1. $5x > 15$

2. $\frac{2}{3} < \frac{4}{5}y$

3. $9h \geq 63$

4. $\frac{h}{6} \leq 8$

Example 3
(p. 734)

5. $-7y > 28$

6. $-3n \leq -21$

7 $\frac{t}{-4} < -11$

8. $\frac{x}{-5} \geq -6$

Example 4
(p. 735)

Solve each inequality. Then graph the solution set on a number line.

9. $y + 1 \geq 4y + 4$

10. $16 - 2c < 14$

11. $-6.1n \geq 3.9n + 5$

12. $-4 \leq \frac{x}{4} - 6$

Example 5
(p. 735)

13. POOL MEMBERSHIP A pool charges $4 each time you visit, or you can buy a 3-month membership for $100. Write and solve an inequality to find how many times a person should use the pool so that a 3-month membership is less expensive than paying each time.

Practice and Problem Solving

● = **Step-by-Step Solutions** begin on page R40.
Extra Practice is on page EP37.

Examples 1 and 2
(pp. 733–734)

Solve each inequality. Check your solution.

14. $6y < 18$

15. $4x \geq 36$

16. $12n \leq 48$

17. $20 < 5t$

18. $60 \leq \frac{m}{3}$

19. $\frac{h}{9} > 9$

Example 3
(p. 734)

20. $-3s \geq 33$

21. $-7y < 35$

22. $-56 \leq -8x$

23. $-10n > -20$

24. $\frac{w}{-5} \geq 9$

25. $\frac{t}{-2} < 6$

26. $\frac{m}{-14} \leq -4$

27. $\frac{s}{-6} > -16$

28. $\frac{x}{-4} \geq -8$

Example 4
(p. 735)

Solve each inequality. Graph the solution set on a number line.

29. $4x + 3 < 19$

30. $7h + 1 \geq -6$

31. $-6y + 6 \leq -8 + y$

32. $9 + \frac{n}{-2} > 5$

33. $\frac{t}{5} - 6 \leq -11$

34. $44 + 4x < 11 + x$

Example 5
(p. 735)

35. CARNIVAL Each game at a carnival costs $0.50, or you can pay $15 and play an unlimited amount of games. Write and solve an inequality to find how many times a person should play a game so that the unlimited game play for $15 is less expensive than paying each time.

36. BASEBALL At a baseball game you can get a single hot dog for $2. You have $10 to spend. Write and solve an inequality to find the number of hot dogs you can buy.

Write an inequality for each sentence. Then solve the inequality.

37 Five times a number decreased by seven is less than -52.

38. The product of a number and 4 minus three is at least -15.

39. FIND THE ERROR Caitlyn solved $-6x \leq 24$. Find her mistake and correct it.

$$-6x \leq 24$$
$$\frac{-6x}{-6} \leq \frac{24}{-6}$$
$$x \leq -4$$

40. CHALLENGE You score a 15, 16, 17, 14, and 19 out of 20 on tests. What must you score on the sixth test to have an average of at least 16 points?

41. Write MATH Explain when you should not reverse the inequality symbol when solving an inequality.

 Practice   MA.6.A.3.1, MA.8.A.4.2

42. Which inequality represents *five more than twice a number is less than ten*?

A. $(5 + 2)n < 10$ C. $10 < 2n + 5$

B. $2n - 5 < 10$ D. $5 + 2n < 10$

43. Which sentence represents the following inequality?

$$\frac{x}{5} - 3 \leq 8$$

F. The difference of a number and 5 increased by 3 is at most 8.

G. The quotient of a number and 5 decreased by 3 is at most 8.

H. The quotient of a number and 5 decreased by 3 is 8.

I. The quotient of a number and 5 decreased by 3 is at least 8.

44. EXTENDED RESPONSE Use the table to answer the questions below.

Karl's scores on the first five science tests are shown in the table.

Test	Score
1	85
2	84
3	90
4	95
5	88

Part A Write an inequality that represents how to find the score he must receive on the sixth test to have an average score of more than 88.

Part B Solve the inequality to determine the lowest score he can receive in order to have an average score of more than 88.

Solve each inequality. Check your solution. (Lesson 13-1B)

45. $20 < -9 + k$

46. $22 \leq -15 + y$

47. $6 + x < -27$

48. $n - 4 \leq -11$

49. MEASUREMENT The perimeter of a rectangle is 42 inches and its area is 104 square inches. Find the dimensions of the rectangle. Use the *guess, check, and revise* strategy. (Lesson 13-1A)

Getting Back in the Game

If you play sports, you know how common injuries are. If you would like to use your experiences to help other athletes someday, you should think about becoming an athletic trainer! An **athletic trainer** specializes in preventing, recognizing, managing, and rehabilitating injuries that result from physical activity. To have a career in athletic training, you should have good communication skills, technical knowledge of how the human body is constructed and how it works, and a good understanding of sports.

Choose a Major

Are you interested in a career as an athletic trainer? Take some of the following courses in high school.

- Algebra
- Anatomy and Physiology
- Biology
- Care and Prevention of Athletic Injuries
- Geometry

 **Get Connected** glencoe.com

Sports-Related Injuries in Youth

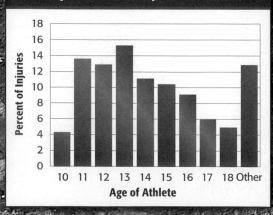

Where Athletic Trainers Work	
Industry	**Number Employed**
Colleges and universities	3,260
General medical and surgical hospitals	2,500
Offices of other health practitioners	1,980
Elementary and secondary schools	1,270

Real-World Math

Use the graph and table to solve each problem.

1. According to the graph, in which age groups did athletes receive more than 12% of the total injuries?

2. Thirteen-year-olds had more than what percent of the sports-related injuries?

3. Complete and then write an inequality:

   Fourteen-year-olds received less than ▇ percent p of the total injuries.

4. Was the percent of injuries received by 15-year-olds *more than double* or *less than double* the percent of injuries received by 17-year-olds?

5. The number of athletic trainers working in elementary and secondary schools is more than twice the number working in the spectator sports industry. How many trainers work in the spectator sports industry? Write and solve an inequality.

6. The number of trainers who work for colleges and universities is less than 1.2 times the number that work in recreation facilities such as golf courses, ski resorts, and fitness centers. How many trainers work in recreation facilities? Write an inequality and solve.

Main Idea

Complete function tables.

NGSSS

 MA.8.A.1.1 Create and interpret tables, graphs, and models to represent, analyze, and solve problems related to linear equations, including analysis of **domain, range** and the difference between discrete and continuous data.

New Vocabulary

function notation

Get Connected
glencoe.com

Function Notation

VACATION For vacation, your family rents a van that costs $49 per day.

1. If your family rented the van for 6 days, what would be the total cost?

2. Explain how to find the total cost of a 9-day rental.

Days	Cost
1	$49
2	$98
3	$147
4	$196

The total cost depends on, or is a function of, the number of days the van is rented. Recall that a relationship that assigns exactly one output value for each input value is called a function. A function that is written as an equation can also be written in a form called **function notation**.

$$f(x) = 49x$$

The *input x* is any real number.

f(x) is read *the function of x*, or more simply, *f of x*. It is the *output*.

To find the value of a function for a certain number, replace the variable with the number in the function notation and evaluate the expression.

EXAMPLE **Find a Function Value**

1. Find $f(8)$ if $f(x) = x - 4$.

   $f(x) = x - 4$ Write the function.

   $f(8) = 8 - 4$ or 4   Substitute 8 for *x*.

   So, $f(8) = 4$.

 CHECK Your Progress

Find each function value.

a. $f(2)$ if $f(x) = x - 3$ **b.** $f(4)$ if $f(x) = 3x + 14$

EXAMPLE Make a Function Table

② Complete the function table for $f(x) = x + 3$. Then state the domain and range of the function.

Input	Rule	Output
x	f(x) = x + 3	f(x)
−2		
−1		
0		
1		

Substitute each value of x, or the input, into the function rule. Then simplify to find the output.

The domain is $\{-2, -1, 0, 1\}$.

The range is $\{1, 2, 3, 4\}$.

Input	Rule	Output
x	f(x) = x + 3	f(x)
−2	−2 + 3	1
−1	−1 + 3	2
0	0 + 3	3
1	1 + 3	4

 CHECK Your Progress

Copy and complete each function table. Then state the domain and range of the function.

c. $f(x) = x - 4$

x	x − 4	f(x)
−3		
−2		
−1		
0		

d. $f(x) = 3x$

x	3x	f(x)
−3		
−2		
−1		
0		

Real-World EXAMPLE

③ **FINANCIAL LITERACY** Darius withdrew $20 from his checking account 6 different times during the last month. On his bank statement, he was charged $2 for each withdrawal. Write a function to represent the amount of money m he was charged for all of the withdrawals w. Then determine how much money it cost him to withdraw money from his account over the past month.

$f(x) = -2x$ Write the function.

$f(6) = -2(6)$ or -12 Substitute 6 for x into the function rule.

So, Darius spent $12 in the past month withdrawing money from his bank account.

 CHECK Your Progress

Find each function value.

e. $f(-3)$ if $f(x) = 2x + 1$

f. $f(-5)$ if $f(x) = 3(x) - 5$

Example 1
(p. 740)

Find each function value.

1. $f(5)$ if $f(x) = x + 8$

2. $f(3)$ if $f(x) = 6x + 2$

Example 2
(p. 741)

Copy and complete each function table. Then state the domain and range of the function.

3. $f(x) = x - 3$

x	x − 3	f(x)
2		
4		
6		
8		

4. $f(x) = 4x - 1$

x	4x − 1	f(x)
1		
2		
3		
4		

5. $f(x) = 2x + 6$

x	2x + 6	f(x)
−1		
1		
3		
5		

Example 3
(p. 741)

6. MUSIC Kira bought a subscription to download an unlimited number of songs for $30 per month. She can also buy music videos for $1 each. Write a function that can be used to represent Kira's total cost to buy x videos. What is the cost if she buys 6 videos?

Practice and Problem Solving

● = **Step-by-Step Solutions** begin on page R40.
Extra Practice is on page EP37.

Example 1
(p. 740)

Find each function value.

7. $f(4)$ if $f(x) = x - 3$

8. $f(7)$ if $f(x) = 6x$

9. $f(3)$ if $f(x) = x + 15$

10. $f(2)$ if $f(x) = 5x + 7$

11 $f(6)$ if $f(x) = 3x - 20$

12. $f(-9)$ if $f(x) = 8x - 13$

Example 2
(p. 741)

Copy and complete each function table. Then state the domain and range of the function.

13. $f(x) = x - 7$

x	x − 7	f(x)
−5		
−4		
−3		
−2		

14. $f(x) = 3x - 10$

x	3x − 10	f(x)
5		
8		
10		
12		

15. $f(x) = 8 + 6x$

x	8 + 6x	f(x)
−4		
−2		
2		
4		

16. $f(x) = x + 3$

x	x + 3	f(x)
3		
6		
9		
12		

17. $f(x) = 9x$

x	9x	f(x)
−5		
−3		
−1		
4		

18. $f(x) = 7x - 4$

x	7x − 4	f(x)
−8		
−6		
−4		
−2		

Example 3 (p. 741)

19. SWIMMING Ellis swam 10 laps before swim practice. During practice he swam x laps. Write a function to represent the total number of laps given that he swam laps before practice. What is the total number of laps if he swam 20 laps during practice?

20. JOBS A waitress makes $8 an hour. Write a function to represent the total amount the waitress earned in x hours. At this rate, how much money does she make in 8 hours?

Find each function value.

21. $f(6)$ if $f(x) = 3x + \frac{1}{2}$

22. $f(3)$ if $f(x) = 5x + \frac{1}{5}$

23. BAKING Mrs. Link is making a cake for her son's birthday. She spent 25 minutes prepping before putting it in the oven. Write a function that represents the total time given bake time x in minutes and the 25 minutes of prep time. Make a function table showing the total time for baking times 10, 15, 20, and 25 minutes. How long did it take to make the cake if the bake time was 20 minutes?

Real-World Link
While swimming, the resistance of the water is equal to more than ten times the resistance of air.

H.O.T. Problems

24. GRAPHIC NOVEL Refer to the graphic novel frame below. Write an inequality stating the height restrictions for each coaster. If Seth is 61 inches tall, which coasters can he ride?

25. OPEN ENDED Write a function rule. Solve for 3 different values of x.

26. CHALLENGE Write the function rule for each function table.

a.

x	$f(x)$
2	10
4	20
6	30
8	40

b.

x	$f(x)$
−3	−9
−1	−7
1	−5
3	−3

c.

x	y
1	4
2	7
3	10
4	13

d.

x	y
−8	−66
−7	−58
−6	−50
−5	−42

27. Write MATH Write a situation that can be represented by the function $f(x) = 35 - 0.99x$. Explain your reasoning.

28. The equation $c = 14t$ represents c, the total cost of t tickets for a Major League Baseball game. Which table contains values that satisfy this equation?

A.

Cost of Baseball Tickets				
t	1	2	3	4
c	$14	$28	$42	$56

B.

Cost of Baseball Tickets				
t	1	2	3	4
c	$14	$30	$48	$68

C.

Cost of Baseball Tickets				
t	1	2	3	4
c	$28	$42	$56	$70

D.

Cost of Baseball Tickets				
t	1	2	3	4
c	$14	$18	$22	$26

29. Lucio received a $50 gift certificate to the movie rental store. The cost of renting a movie is $4.95. Which table **best** describes b, the balance remaining after he rents m movies?

F.

m	b
1	$45
2	$40
3	$35
4	$30

H.

m	b
2	$40.10
4	$30.20
6	$20.30
8	$10.40

G.

m	b
0	$50
3	$35
6	$20
9	$5

I.

m	b
1	$49.95
2	$49.90
3	$49.85
4	$49.80

Spiral Review

30. MUSIC Choose an appropriate display for the data. Then make the display. Justify your reasoning. (Lesson 12-2D)

Adult Audience of Oldies Radio					
Age	18 to 24	25 to 34	35 to 44	45 to 54	55 or older
Percent of Audience	10%	14%	29%	33%	14%

31. RUNNING The table shows the time it took Dale to run each mile of a 5-mile run. (Lesson 12-2C)

a. Make a scatter plot of the data.

b. Describe the relationship, if any, between the two sets of data.

c. Suppose the trend continues. Predict the time it would take Dale to run a sixth mile.

Mile	Time
1	4 min 19 s
2	4 min 28 s
3	4 min 39 s
4	4 min 54 s
5	5 min 1 s

Multiply. (Lesson 1-3C)

32. -4×6

33. $5 \times (-8)$

34. $-6 \times (-9)$

35. 8×3

Main Idea

Represent linear functions using function tables and graphs.

NGSSS

 MA.8.A.1.1 Create and interpret tables, graphs, and models **to represent, analyze, and solve problems related to linear equations, including** analysis of domain, range and **the difference between discrete and continuous data.**

New Vocabulary

x-intercept
y-intercept
linear function
discrete data
continuous data

Get Connected
glencoe.com

Represent Linear Functions

HOT AIR BALLOON A hot air balloon travels at the wind speed of the air around it. In the United States, that is about 7 miles per hour on average. If x represents the hours traveled at this speed, the function rule for the distance traveled is $y = 7x$.

Input	Rule	Output	(Input, Output)
x	$7x$	y	(x, y)
1	7(1)	7	(1, 7)
2	7(2)		
3			
4			

1. Copy and complete the function table.

2. Graph the ordered pairs (x, y) on a coordinate plane. What do you notice?

Functions can be represented in words, in a table, as an equation, with a graph, and as ordered pairs. The **x-intercept** is where the graph crosses the x-axis. The **y-intercept** is where the graph crosses the y-axis.

EXAMPLE Graph a Function

1. Graph $y = x + 3$ using the x- and y-intercepts.

   Use intercepts.

   Step 1 Find the x-intercept.

   To find the x-intercept, let $y = 0$.

   $y = x + 3$

   $0 = x + 3$ Replace y with 0.

   $\underline{-3 \qquad -3}$ Subtract 3 from each side.

   $-3 = x$

   Since $x = -3$ when $y = 0$, graph the ordered pair $(-3, 0)$.

   Step 2 Find the y-intercept.

   To find the y-intercept, let $x = 0$.

   $y = x + 3$

   $y = 0 + 3$ Replace x with 0.

   $y = 3$ Simplify.

   Since $y = 3$ when $x = 0$, graph the ordered pair $(0, 3)$.

   Step 3 Connect the points with a line.

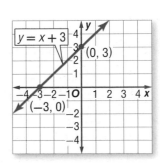

2 **REFRESHMENTS** Student Council sells refreshments at the soccer game. Nachos are $2 and hot dogs are $1. The cost of x orders of nachos and y hot dogs is $2x + y$. Grant has $6 to spend. Graph $2x + y = 6$ to find how many orders of nachos and hot dogs Grant can buy.

$$2x + y = 6 \qquad \text{Write the equation.}$$

$$2x - 2x + y = 6 - 2x \qquad \text{Subtract 2x from each side.}$$

$$y = 6 - 2x \qquad \text{Simplify.}$$

The equation $y = 6 - 2x$ represents a function. Choose values for x and substitute them to find y. Then graph the ordered pairs (x, y).

x	6 − 2x	y	(x, y)
0	6 − 2(0)	6	(0, 6)
1	6 − 2(1)	4	(1, 4)
2	6 − 2(2)	2	(2, 2)
3	6 − 2(3)	0	(3, 0)

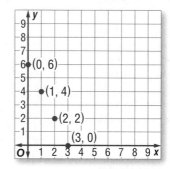

Grant can buy 0 nachos and 6 hot dogs, 1 nacho and 4 hot dogs, 2 nachos and 2 hot dogs, or 3 nachos and 0 hot dogs.

CHECK Your Progress

a. SCHOOL SUPPLIES The school bookstore sells spiral notebooks x for $3 and pocket folders y for $1. Graph the function $3x + y = 10$ to find the number of each that can be bought with $10.

Review Vocabulary

Linear Relationship Relationships that have straight-line graphs. (Lesson 5-1B)

A function in which the graph of the solutions forms a straight line is called a **linear function**. Therefore, $y = x + 3$ is a *linear equation*.

Concept Summary **Represent Functions**

Words The value of y is one less than the corresponding value of x.

Equation $y = x - 1$ **Ordered Pairs** $(0, -1), (1, 0), (2, 1), (3, 2)$

Table

x	y
0	−1
1	0
2	1
3	2

Graph

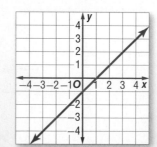

When solutions of a function are only integer values, the solutions represent **discrete data**. **Continuous data** can take on any real number value. You can determine if data that model real-world situations are discrete or continuous by considering what numbers are reasonable.

Discrete Data	Continuous Data
the number of students in a classroom	the size of the classroom
the number of hamburgers bought at a restaurant	the amount of money the hamburgers cost

EXAMPLES · Discrete and Continuous Data

PETS Marisela has a fish tank that measures 4 feet long, 2 feet wide, and 3 feet high. She currently has 6 fish. Every two weeks she uses a portion of her paycheck to buy a new fish.

3 **a. How many fish will Marisela have after 8 weeks?**

Make a table and graph. Marisela will have 10 fish after 8 weeks.

Week	Number of Fish
0	6
2	7
4	8
6	9
8	10

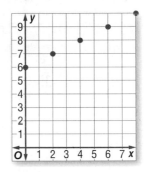

Study Tip

Graphs Graphs of discrete functions are represented by dots or dashed lines. Continuous functions are represented by solid lines.

b. Is part a an example of discrete or continuous data?

Marisela must buy a whole number of fish. She cannot buy part of a fish. The graph shows that the points are connected with a dashed line. Therefore, this is an example of discrete data.

4 **a. Marisela is filling the fish tank with water, and the level of the water increases by three inches every minute. How long will it take to fill the tank?**

The tank is 3 feet or 36 inches high. The level increases 3 inches per minute. So, it will take 12 minutes to fill the tank.

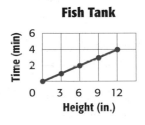

Fish Tank

b. Is part a an example of discrete or continuous data?

Make a graph. The graph shows that the tank fills continuously. Therefore, this is an example of continuous data.

 CHECK Your Progress

SAVINGS Kareem is mowing lawns to earn money. He deposits $50 in his savings account every Friday. He already had $200.

b. How much money will Kareem have after 24 weeks?

c. Is this situation continuous or discrete?

Example 1
(p. 745)

Graph each function.

1. $y = x + 8$

2. $y = -2x - 4$

3. $y = -\frac{1}{2}x + 7$

Example 2
(p. 746)

4. TOYS Dolls come in packages of 4 and action figures come in packages of 2. Graph the function $4x + 2y = 16$ to find the number of dolls x and action figures y you can get if you want 16 total toys.

Examples 3 and 4
(p. 747)

5. FOOD A restaurant tracks how many chicken dinners they sell at $5.95 each.

    a. How much will 12 chicken dinners cost altogether?

    b. Is this situation continuous or discrete?

Practice and Problem Solving

● = **Step-by-Step Solutions** begin on page R41.
Extra Practice is on page EP37.

Example 1
(p. 745)

Graph each function.

6. $y = 5x$

7 $y = -x + 3$

8. $y = 5x - 2$

9. $y = \frac{3}{4}x + 4$

Example 2
(p. 746)

10. CANDY Chocolate bars cost $1 each and giant lollipops cost $2 each. Graph the function $x + 2y = 15$ to determine how many chocolate bars x and lollipops y Drew can buy for $15.

Examples 3 and 4
(p. 747)

11 JOBS Gretchen worked for three hours and earned $28.50.

    a. At this rate, how much would she earn after working 7 hours?

    b. Is this situation continuous or discrete?

12. GRAPHIC NOVEL Refer to the graphic novel frame below. Graph the inequalities on a number line.

13. **OPEN ENDED** Give two examples of continuous data and two examples of discrete data.

14. **CHALLENGE** Name the coordinates of three points that satisfy the function at the right. Then give the function rule.

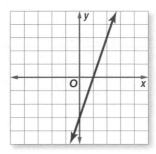

15. **Write MATH** Write a problem that has both discrete and continuous data.

NGSSS Practice MA.8.A.1.2

16. Which line graphed below **best** represents the table of values for the ordered pairs (x, y)?

x	−2	0	2	4
y	1	0	−1	−2

A.

C.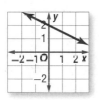

B.

D.

17. The graph shows the line $y = 3x + 1$.

Which table of ordered pairs contains only points on this line?

F.
x	−2	−1	0	1
y	−9	−6	−3	0

G.
x	−3	−2	−1	0
y	−6	−3	0	3

H.
x	−2	−1	0	1
y	−5	−2	1	4

I.
x	0	1	2	3
y	−1	0	1	2

Find each function value. (Lesson 13-2A)

18. $f(2)$ if $f(x) = 3x - 7$

19. $f(-3)$ if $f(x) = 15x + 3$

20. $f(6)$ if $f(x) = 7x - 2$

Choose an appropriate type of display for each situation. (Lesson 12-2D)

21. the amount of each pizza topping sold relative to total sales

22. the number of students attending a sporting event by specific grade level

23. **SHOPPING** Nora bought a pair of running shoes discounted by 35%. The original price of the shoes was $89.90. Find the discounted price to the nearest cent. (Lesson 6-3D)

$89.90

Main Idea

Determine slopes and y-intercepts of lines. Graph linear equations using the slope and y-intercept.

NGSSS

 MA.8.A.1.2 Interpret the slope and the x- and y-intercepts when graphing a linear equation for a real world problem.

New Vocabulary

slope-intercept form

Slope-Intercept Form

Explore Compare and contrast these two situations.

Pizza Place charges $5 for each medium pizza, with no delivery charge. The cost for any number of medium pizzas is shown in the graph.

Pizza Place charges $5 for each medium pizza, but has a $10 delivery charge.

1. Write an equation that represents the cost of the pizza and delivery charge in the second situation.

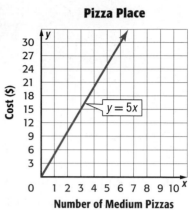

Pizza Place

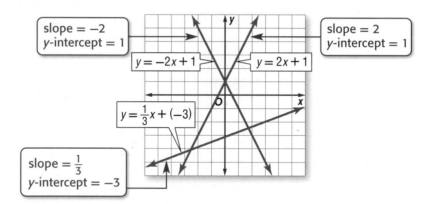

The equations above are written in the form $y = mx + b$, where m is the slope and b is the y-intercept. It is called **slope-intercept form**.

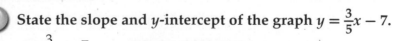

$$y = mx + b$$
slope ⟋   ⟍ y-intercept

Study Tip

Different Forms Both equations below are written in slope-intercept form.

$y = x + (-2)$

$y = x - 2$

EXAMPLE   **Find the Slope and y-intercept**

1. State the slope and y-intercept of the graph $y = \frac{3}{5}x - 7$.

$y = \frac{3}{5}x - 7$ Write the original equation.

$y = \frac{3}{5}x + (-7)$ Write the equation in the form $y = mx + b$.

$y = mx + b$ $m = \frac{3}{5}, b = -7$

The slope of the graph is $\frac{3}{5}$, and the y-intercept is -7.

EXAMPLE Graph an Equation

2 Graph $y = -\frac{1}{2}x - 4$ using the slope and y-intercept.

Step 1 Find the slope and y-intercept.

$$\text{slope} = -\frac{1}{2} \qquad y\text{-intercept} = -4$$

Step 2 Graph the y-intercept.

Step 3 Write the slope $-\frac{1}{2}$ as $\frac{-1}{2}$.

Use it to locate a second point on the line.

$$m = \frac{-1}{2} \quad \begin{array}{l} \leftarrow \text{change in } y\text{: down 1 unit} \\ \leftarrow \text{change in } x\text{: right 2 units} \end{array}$$

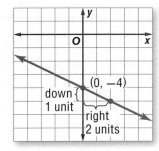

Step 4 Draw a line through the two points.

Step 5 Check by locating another point on the line and substituting the coordinates into the original equation.

✓ CHECK Your Progress

a. Graph $y = \frac{1}{3}x - 2$ using the slope and y-intercept.

Real-World EXAMPLE Interpret the Slope and y-intercept

3 **READING** Naomi has read 25 pages of her book. She plans to read 15 pages each day until she finishes the book. The total number of pages read y can be represented by $y = 15x + 25$, where x is the number of days. Graph the equation. Explain what the y-intercept represents.

Step 1 First, find the slope and the y-intercept.

$$\text{slope} = 15$$
$$y\text{-intercept} = 25$$

Step 2 Plot the point at $(0, 25)$. Then go up 15 and right 1 and plot another point.

Step 3 Connect these points and extend the line.

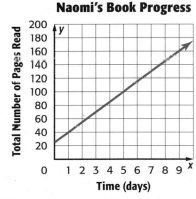

Naomi's Book Progress

The y-intercept represents the initial 25 pages that Naomi had already read.

✓ CHECK Your Progress

b. **AIRPLANE** A remote-controlled airplane flying 45 feet in the air is falling. The altitude of the airplane can be represented by $y = -x + 45$, where x is the time in seconds. Graph the equation. Explain what the x-intercept represents.

Example 1
(p. 750)

State the slope and y-intercept for the graph of each equation.

1. $y = x + 7$

2. $y = -\frac{2}{3}x + \frac{1}{6}$

3. $-5x + y = 8$

Example 2
(p. 751)

Graph each equation using the slope and y-intercept.

4. $y = 2x + 4$

5 $y = -\frac{1}{4}x + \frac{1}{6}$

6. $y = -3x + 1$

Example 3
(p. 751)

7. AMUSEMENT PARK Reynaldo is going to go to an amusement park. The cost of admission is $25 per person. It costs $2 for every ride. The total cost y for riding x number of rides can be represented by the equation $y = 25 + 2x$.

    a. Graph the equation to find how much it will cost to ride 8 rides.

    b. Explain what the slope and y-intercept represent.

Practice and Problem Solving

● = **Step-by-Step Solutions** begin on page R41.
Extra Practice is on page EP38.

Example 1
(p. 750)

State the slope and y-intercept for the graph of each equation.

8. $y = 4x - 8$

9. $y = -3x + 7$

10. $y = \frac{3}{4}x - \frac{1}{6}$

11. $y = -\frac{3}{8}x - \frac{5}{8}$

12. $y - 4x = 6$

13. $2x + y = 9$

Example 2
(p. 751)

Graph each equation using the slope and y-intercept.

14. $y = 5x + 3$

15. $y = -4x - 7$

16. $y = \frac{1}{3}x + 2$

17. $y = -\frac{4}{3}x - 4$

18. $y - 4x = 2.5$

19 $6.5 = 3x + y$

Example 3
(p. 751)

20. COOKING Mrs. Brooks needs to make 325 cookies for a bake sale. She can make 50 cookies in one hour. The equation for the number of cookies she has left to make is $y = 325 - 50x$, where x is the number of hours she baked.

    a. Graph the equation to find how many cookies Mrs. Brooks still needs to make after 4 hours.

    b. Explain what the slope and y-intercept represent.

21. SEWING Heather is buying fabric to make a blanket. It costs 5 dollars to cut the fabric and 3 dollars for every foot of fabric she gets. The total cost y for getting x feet of fabric can be represented by the equation $y = 5 + 3x$.

    a. Graph the equation to find the total cost for 5 feet of fabric.

    b. Explain what the y-intercept represents.

22. **OPEN ENDED** Draw the graph of a line that has an *x*-intercept but no *y*-intercept.

23. **FIND THE ERROR** Aisha is finding the slope and *y*-intercept of $3x + 4y = 5$. Find her mistake and correct it.

> The slope of $3x + 4y = 5$ is 3 and the y-intercept is 4.

24. **Write MATH** Write a linear equation involving sports. Describe how the slope and *y*-intercept would appear in these three different representations of the problem: table, equation, and graph.

NGSSS Practice   MA.7.A.1.4, MA.8.A.1.2

25. Which equation below is $2x + 3y = 6$ in slope-intercept form?

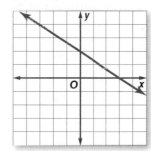

  A. $y = -\frac{2}{3}x - 2$ **C.** $y = -\frac{3}{2}x + 2$

  B. $y = -\frac{2}{3}x + 2$ **D.** $y = -\frac{3}{2}x - 2$

26. Darnell spent $5 on lunch each day at school. On Friday, he bought ice cream for $2. The total cost for each week *y* for his lunches *x* can be represented by the equation $y = 5x + 2$. What is the slope and *y*-intercept of the equation?

  F. $5; -2$

  G. $2; 5$

  H. $-5; 2$

  I. $5; 2$

Graph each function. (Lesson 13-2B)

27. $y = 3x$ **28.** $y = x - 4$ **29.** $y = 2x + 1$ **30.** $y = 4x + 3$

31. TEMPERATURE The function used to convert a Celsius temperature *C* to a Fahrenheit temperature *F* is $F = \frac{9}{5}C + 32$. Convert 20° Celsius to Fahrenheit. (Lesson 13-2A)

Solve each inequality. Graph the solution set on a number line. (Lesson 13-1B)

1. $3 + b \geq 8$

2. $s - 7 \leq 3$

3. $2.9 + g < 10.7$

4. $k - 1.5 > 3.1$

5. **GIRAFFE** A male giraffe can grow up to 5 meters tall. Write and solve an inequality that describes how many meters a young giraffe can expect to grow if it is currently 1.8 meters tall. (Lesson 13-1B)

Solve each inequality. Graph the solution set on a number line. (Lesson 13-1C)

6. $\frac{n}{4} > -3$

7. $5m \geq 25$

8. $-6t < 24$

9. $\frac{r}{-3} \geq -7$

10. **NGSSS PRACTICE** You want to purchase a video game system for $299. You have already saved $165 and can set aside $25 per week. Which inequality can be used to find the number of weeks it will take to save at least $299? (Lesson 13-1C)

A. $25w + 165 \geq 299$

B. $25w + 165 \leq 299$

C. $25 + 165w \geq 299$

D. $25w + 165 < 299$

Find each function value. (Lesson 13-2A)

11. $f(5)$ if $f(x) = x + 2$

12. $f(9)$ if $f(x) = 3x - 23$

13. $f(2)$ if $f(x) = 12 + 4x$

14. $f(-6)$ if $f(x) = 2x + 12$

15. **NGSSS PRACTICE** Which equation describes the function represented by the table? (Lesson 13-2A)

x	y
−3	−7
0	−4
3	−1
6	2

F. $y = 2x - 5$

G. $y = x + 4$

H. $y = 2x + 5$

I. $y = x - 4$

Graph each function. (Lesson 13-2B)

16. $y = x + 4$

17. $y = 3x - 2$

State the slope and y-intercept for the graph of each equation. (Lesson 13-2C)

18. $y = 5x + 4$

19. $y = -4x - 2$

20. $y = \frac{4}{5}x + \frac{1}{5}$

21. $y + 3x = 8$

22. **THINK SOLVE EXPLAIN** **EXTENDED RESPONSE** Use the graph below. (Lesson 13-2C)

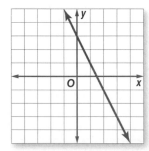

Part A What is the slope and y-intercept of the line?

Part B Describe how the slope and y-intercept appear on the graph.

Part C Use the slope and y-intercept to write the equation of the line in slope-intercept form.

 **Graphs of Nonlinear Functions**

Main Idea

Explore the difference between linear and nonlinear functions.

NGSSS

✸ **MA.8.A.1.6**
Compare the graphs of linear and nonlinear functions for real-world situations.

Get Connected
glencoe.com

SAVINGS Katrina received $200 for her birthday. She kept it in a piggy bank. Each year on her birthday she puts another $20 into the piggy bank. Carson also received $200 for his birthday. He deposited it in a savings account that earns 10% interest each year. Neither person makes any withdrawals. Who will have the most money after 5 years?

ACTIVITY

What do you need to find? who will have the most money in the bank after 5 years

STEP 1   Make a table representing Katrina's money for each year. Complete the table.

Katrina		
Year	Rule	Amount
0	$200 + 20x$	$200
1		
2		
3		
4		
5		

STEP 2   Make a table representing Carson's money for each year. Complete the table below.

Carson		
Year	Rule	Amount
0	200	$200
1	200(110%)	$220
2	220(110%)	
3		
4		
5		

Carson's money is a percent of the original amount. Each year, 10% of the current balance is added to the account. Therefore, he has the current balance (100%) plus the added amount (10%). So, the new amount can be found by multiplying the current amount by 110%.

STEP 3   Graph the ordered pairs (year, amount) from both tables on the same coordinate plane.

Analyze the Results

1. Who has more money after 5 years?

2. Find the rates of change in Katrina's and Carson's money between consecutive years.

3. Compare and contrast the rates of change in Step 3.

4. Explain why the function describing Katrina's money is linear and Carson's is not.

5. Give an example of real-world data that would not be linear when graphed.

Practice and Apply

6. **PATENTS** The table at the right shows the years in which the first six million patents were issued. Graph the data and describe the function as linear or nonlinear. Explain why.

Year	Number of Patents Issued
1911	1 million
1936	2 million
1961	3 million
1976	4 million
1991	5 million
1999	6 million
2007	7 million

7. **INCOME** The table below shows a person's salary for the first five years they are with a company. Graph the data and describe the function as linear or nonlinear.

Year	1	2	3	4	5
Salary	$40,000	$41,600	$43,264	$44,995	$46,794

8. **SALES** The table at the right shows the number of cars sold by a particular salesperson. The salesperson's current number of sales for the year is recorded in the second column.

   a. Complete the table if the rate of change is constant.

   b. Graph the data and describe the function as linear or nonlinear. If it is linear, determine the slope of the line.

   c. How many cars did the salesperson sell for the year?

Month	Number of Cars Sold this Year
January	3
February	6
March	9
April	
May	
June	
July	
August	
September	
October	
November	
December	

9. **E-MAIL** The table below shows the pattern of an E-mail tree.

   a. Complete the table if the pattern continues.

   b. Graph the data and describe the function as linear or nonlinear. If it is linear, determine the slope of the line.

   c. How many E-mails were sent out in the 7th round?

Round	1	2	3	4	5	6	7
Number of E-Mails	2	4	8				

Main Idea

Determine whether a function is linear or nonlinear.

NGSSS

MA.8.A.1.6 Compare the graphs of linear and non-linear functions for real-world situations.

New Vocabulary

nonlinear function

Get Connected
glencoe.com

Linear and Nonlinear Functions

DECKS The sum of the lengths of three sides of a new deck is 40 feet. Suppose x represents the width of the deck and the length is $40 - 2x$.

1. Write an expression to represent the area of the deck.

2. Copy and complete the table at the right.

Width (x)	Length (40 − 2x)	Area
6	■	■
8	■	■
10	■	■
12	■	■
14	■	■

3. Graph the points with ordered pairs that are (width, area). Do the points fall along a straight line? Explain.

In Chapter 5, you learned that linear functions have graphs that are straight lines and represent a constant rate of change. **Nonlinear functions** have graphs that are *not* straight lines.

EXAMPLE **Identify Functions Using Tables**

Determine whether each table represents a *linear* or *nonlinear* function. Explain.

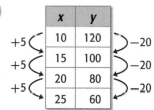

x	y
10	120
15	100
20	80
25	60

+5 ... −20

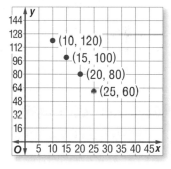

As x increases by 5, y decreases by 20. So this is a linear function.

Graph the points on a coordinate plane. The points fall in a line. The function is linear. ✓

Study Tip

Recall that the equation for a linear function can be written in the form $y = mx + b$. Therefore, you can determine whether a function is linear by looking at its equation.

EXAMPLES **Identify Functions Using Equations**

Determine whether each equation or table represents a *linear* or *nonlinear* function. Explain.

2 $y = 10x$

This function is linear because it can be written as $y = 10x + 0$.

3 $y = \dfrac{3}{x}$

This function is nonlinear because x is in the denominator and cannot be written in the form $y = mx + b$.

Study Tip

Identifying Linear Equations Always examine an equation after it has been solved for y to see that the power of x is 1 or 0. Then check to see that x does not appear in the denominator.

4

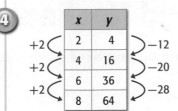

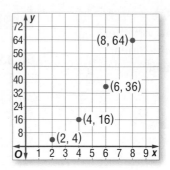

As x increases by 2, y increases by a different amount each time.

Graph the points on a coordinate plane. The points do not fall in a line. The function is nonlinear. ✓

CHECK Your Progress

Determine whether each table or equation represents a *linear* or *nonlinear* function. Explain.

a. $y = \dfrac{x}{5}$ **b.** $y = 3x^3 + 1$ **c.** $y = 7x$

d.

x	0	3	6	9
y	5	10	15	20

e.

x	0	2	4	8
y	2	4	8	16

CHECK Your Understanding

Examples 1–4
(pp. 757–758)

Determine whether each equation or table represents a *linear* or *nonlinear* function. Explain.

1 $y = 4x^3$ **2.** $y = -\dfrac{x}{6}$

3.

x	0	1	2	3
y	5	10	15	20

4.

x	2	4	6	8
y	1	3	6	10

5. RUNNING The table shows the amount of time it takes Neka to run 4 laps around a track. Is the time a linear function of the laps run? Explain.

Laps	1	2	3	4
Time (seconds)	66	69	72	75

= **Step-by-Step Solutions** begin on page R42.
Extra Practice is on page EP38.

Examples 1–4
(pp. 757–758)

Determine whether each equation or table represents a *linear* or *nonlinear* function. Explain.

6. $y = \frac{x}{4} + 6$

7. $y = 0.25x$

8. $y = 3x^2 + 5$

9. $y = 6x^3$

10. $y = \frac{8}{x}$

11. $y = \frac{3}{x} + 0.25$

12.

x	0	1	2	3
y	1	3	7	12

13.

x	2	4	6	8
y	1	4	7	10

14.

x	1	2	3	4
y	14	10	6	2

15.

x	5	10	15	20
y	−2	−8	−14	−20

16.

x	3	6	9	12
y	1	5	10	12

17.

x	4	8	12	16
y	0	1	3	5

18. BAKING Noriko is baking cakes for a cake walk. Use the table to determine whether the cakes made are a linear function of the hours they are baked. Explain.

Time (h)	1	2	3	4
Cakes	3	6	9	12

19. SWIMMING The table shows the number of laps a swimmer swims in x minutes. Use the table to determine whether the laps are a linear function of the number of minutes.

Time (min)	2	4	6	8
Laps	4	7	8	10

20. Determine whether each equation or table represents a *linear* or *nonlinear* function. Explain.

a. $y + 4x - 7$

b. $xy = 7$

c. $y - 4^x$

d.

x	2	4	6	8
y	5	10	15	20

e.

x	0.5	1	1.5	2
y	7	10	14	19

21 BASKETBALL The table shows the amount of baskets made during each quarter of a basketball game. Use the table to determine if the number of baskets made is a linear function of the number of quarters.

Quarter	1	2	3	4
Baskets	15	30	45	60

22. WEATHER The table shows the amount of rainfall from a 4-hour storm. Use the table to determine whether the rainfall in inches is a linear function of the number of hours.

Time (h)	1	2	3	4
Rainfall (in.)	4	8	12	16

23. SCHOOL The table shows the number of hours a student studies in each grade over a week. Use the table to determine whether the amount of studying is a linear function of the grade.

Grade	8	9	10	11
Time Spent Studying (h)	2	4	8	9

24. OPEN ENDED Give an example of a table that shows a linear function.

25. CHALLENGE Does the graph of $x = 5$ represent a linear function? Explain your reasoning.

26. Which One Doesn't Belong? Identify the function that is linear. Explain your reasoning.

| $y = x^3 + 7$ | $y = x^7 + 3$ | $y = 7x^3$ | $y = 3x + 7$ |

27. Write MATH Write a nonlinear equation and then explain why it is not linear.

NGSSS Practice　　MA.8.A.1.6

28. Which equation represents a linear function?

   A. $y = \frac{1}{2}x$

   B. $3xy = 12$

   C. $x^2 - 1 = y$

   D. $y = x(x + 4)$

29. Determine which equation represents a nonlinear function if $a > 1$.

   F. $y = ax$

   G. $y = \frac{x}{a}$

   H. $y = a^x$

   I. $y = a + x$

 **Spiral Review**

30. Use the graph at the right. (Lesson 13-2C)

   a. State the slope and y-intercept of the graph.

   b. Write the equation of the line in slope-intercept form.

   c. Find the y value when x is 16.

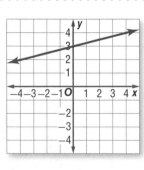

31. JOBS Callie charges $20 plus $5 per half hour to mow a lawn. (Lesson 13-2B)

   a. How much will Callie earn if she spends 3.5 hours mowing a lawn?

   b. Is the situation continuous or discrete?

32. FAMILY At Vito's family reunion, $\frac{4}{5}$ of the people are 18 years of age or older. Half of the remaining people are under 12 years old. If 20 children are under 12 years old, how many people are at the reunion? Use the *draw a diagram* strategy. (Lesson 2-3C)

Main Idea
Multiply and divide monomials.

NGSSS
MA.8.A.6.3 Simplify real number expressions using the laws of exponents.

New Vocabulary
monomial

Get Connected
glencoe.com

Multiply and Divide Monomials

EARTHQUAKES For each increase on the Richter scale, an earthquake's vibrations, or *seismic waves*, are 10 times greater. So, an earthquake of magnitude 4 has seismic waves that are 10 times greater than that of a magnitude 3 earthquake.

Richter Scale	Times Greater than Magnitude 3 Earthquake	Written Using Powers
4	$10 \times 1 = 10$	10^1
5	$10 \times 10 = 100$	$10^1 \times 10^1 = 10^2$
6	$10 \times 100 = 1,000$	$10^1 \times 10^2 = 10^3$
7	$10 \times 1,000 = 10,000$	$10^1 \times 10^3 = 10^4$
8	$10 \times 10,000 = 100,000$	$10^1 \times 10^4 = 10^5$

1. Examine the exponents of the powers in the last column. What do you observe?

2. **MAKE A CONJECTURE** Write a rule for determining the exponent of the product when you multiply powers with the same base. Test your rule by multiplying 2^2 and 2^4 using a calculator.

Recall that exponents are used to show repeated multiplication. You can use the definition of an exponent to find a rule for multiplying powers with the same base.

$$2^3 \cdot 2^4 = \overbrace{(2 \cdot 2 \cdot 2)}^{3 \text{ factors}} \cdot \overbrace{(2 \cdot 2 \cdot 2 \cdot 2)}^{4 \text{ factors}}$$

$$\underbrace{}_{7 \text{ factors}}$$

$$= 2^7$$

Notice the sum of the original exponents is the exponent in the final product.

> **Key Concept** **Product of Powers**
>
> **Words** To multiply powers with the same base, add their exponents.
>
> **Symbols** $a^m \cdot a^n = a^{m+n}$
>
> **Example** $3^2 \cdot 3^4 = 3^{2+4}$ or 3^6

Multiply Powers

 Find $7^3 \cdot 7$. Express using exponents.

$7^3 \cdot 7 = 7^3 \times 7^1$ $7 = 7^1$ **Check** $7^3 \cdot 7 = (7 \cdot 7 \cdot 7)(7)$

$\qquad = 7^{3+1}$ The common base is 7. $\qquad\qquad = 7 \cdot 7 \cdot 7 \cdot 7$ or 7^4 ✓

$\qquad = 7^4$ Add the exponents.

✅ **CHECK Your Progress**

Simplify. Express using exponents.

a. $5^3 \cdot 5^4$

b. $\left(\frac{1}{2}\right)^2 \cdot \left(\frac{1}{2}\right)^9$

Study Tip

Common Misconception
When multiplying powers, do not multiply the bases.
$3^2 \cdot 3^4 = 3^6$, not 9^6.

A **monomial** is a number, variable, or product of a number and one or more variables. Monomials can also be multiplied using the rule for the product of powers.

EXAMPLES **Multiply Monomials**

Find each product.

 $x^5 \cdot x^2$

$x^5 \cdot x^2 = x^{5+2}$ The common base is x.

$\qquad = x^7$ Add the exponents.

③ $(-4n^3)(2n^6)$

$(-4n^3)(2n^6) = (-4 \cdot 2)(n^3 \cdot n^6)$ Use the Commutative and Associative Properties.

$\qquad\qquad = (-8)(n^{3+6})$ The common base is n.

$\qquad\qquad = -8n^9$ Add the exponents.

QUICK Review

Properties
Commutative Property of Multiplication
$\quad a \cdot b = b \cdot a$
Associative Property of Multiplication
$\quad (ab)c = a(bc)$

✅ **CHECK Your Progress**

Simplify. Express using exponents.

c. $-3m(-8m^4)$

d. $5^2x^2y^4 \cdot 5^3xy^3$

You can also write a rule for finding quotients of powers.

$$\frac{2^6}{2^1} = \frac{2 \cdot 2 \cdot 2 \cdot 2 \cdot 2 \cdot 2}{2}$$ ← 6 factors
  ← 1 factor

$$= \frac{2 \cdot 2 \cdot 2 \cdot 2 \cdot 2 \cdot \overset{1}{\cancel{2}}}{\underset{1}{\cancel{2}}}$$ Divide out common factors.

$$= 2^5$$ ← 5 factors   Simplify.

Compare the difference between the original exponents and the exponent in the final quotient. This relationship is stated in the following Key Concept box.

EXAMPLES   **Divide Powers**

Find each quotient.

4 $\dfrac{5^7}{5^4}$

$\dfrac{5^7}{5^4} = 5^{7-4}$ The common base is 5.

$\quad\quad = 5^3$ Subtract the exponents.

5 $\dfrac{y^5}{y^3}$

$\dfrac{y^5}{y^3} = y^{5-3}$ The common base is y.

$\quad\quad = y^2$ Subtract the exponents.

 CHECK Your Progress

Simplify. Express using exponents.

e. $\dfrac{7^6}{7^2}$ **f.** $\dfrac{9c^7}{3c^2}$

Real-World Link · · · ·
In 2007, there were over two hundred million personal computers in homes across the United States. It is expected that the number will double by the year 2014.

Real-World EXAMPLE

6   **COMPUTERS** The table compares the processing speeds of a specific type of computer in 1999 and in 2008. Find how many times faster the computer was in 2008 than in 1999.

Year	Processing Speed (instructions per second)
1999	10^3
2008	10^9

Write a division expression to compare the speeds.

$\dfrac{10^9}{10^3} = 10^{9-3}$ The common base is 10.

$\quad\quad = 10^6$ Subtract the exponents.

So, the computer was 10^6 or one million times faster in 2008 than in 1999.

 CHECK Your Progress

g. **FOOD** A candy store owner has 3^8 chocolate bars and 3^6 packages of sour candy. How many times as many chocolate bars does the candy store owner have than packages of sour candy?

CHECK Your Understanding

Example 1
(p. 762)

Simplify. Express using exponents.

1. $6^5 \cdot 6^4$

2. $3^3 \cdot 3^2$

3. $\left(\frac{2}{3}\right)^4\left(\frac{2}{3}\right)^5$

Examples 2 and 3
(p. 762)

4. $m^4 \cdot m^8$

5. $-4c^2(3c^6)$

6. $4^3x^4y^6 \cdot 4^2x^3y$

Examples 4 and 5
(p. 763)

7 $\dfrac{4^7}{4^3}$

8. $\dfrac{x^8}{x^6}$

9. $\dfrac{6t^4}{3t}$

Example 6
(p. 763)

10. SURVEY A school surveyed people who like fruit and vegetables. Of the students surveyed, 2^6 like vegetables and 2^4 like fruit. How many times as many students prefer vegetables over fruit?

Practice and Problem Solving

● = **Step-by-Step Solutions** begin on page R42.
Extra Practice is on page EP38.

Example 1
(p. 762)

Simplify. Express using exponents.

11. $5^6 \cdot 5^4$

12. $3^7 \cdot 3^8$

13. $\left(\frac{1}{5}\right)^3\left(\frac{1}{5}\right)^2$

14. $4^3 \cdot 4^4$

15. $7 \cdot 7^7$

16. $\left(\frac{3}{4}\right)\left(\frac{3}{4}\right)^4$

Examples 2 and 3
(p. 762)

17. $n^2 \cdot n$

18. $4b^3 \cdot 5b^4$

19. $3j^3k^4 \cdot 6jk^9$

20. $t^6 \cdot t^3$

21. $(7h^3)(2h^8)$

22. $(-7m^3n^7p^9)(-8m^4n^5p^4)$

23. $(6x^5)(4x^7)$

24. $(-5f)(8f^6)$

25. $(-6p^9)(-7p^7)$

Examples 4 and 5
(p. 763)

26. $\dfrac{5^4}{5}$

27. $\dfrac{8^8}{8^3}$

28. $\dfrac{6^7}{6^4}$

29. $\dfrac{c^6}{c^3}$

30. $\dfrac{h^8}{h^4}$

31. $\dfrac{x^8}{x^7}$

32. $\dfrac{36g^8}{4g^3}$

33. $\dfrac{50n^7}{5n^2}$

34. $\dfrac{x^3 \cdot y^6 \cdot z^9}{x \cdot y^4 \cdot z^3}$

Example 6
(p. 763)

35. FISH The number of fish in a school of fish is 4^3. If the number of fish in the school increased by 4^2 times the original number of fish, how many fish are now in the school?

36. MUSIC Jon has 5^4 songs on his computer. His friend has 5^2 times the number of songs he has. How many songs does his friend have?

37 POWERS OF TEN Use the information in the table.

a. How many times greater is one trillion than one million?

b. How many times greater is one quintillion than one billion?

Power of Ten	U.S. Name
10^3	One thousand
10^6	One million
10^9	One billion
10^{12}	One trillion
10^{15}	One quadrillion
10^{18}	One quintillion

38. **CHALLENGE** What is twice 2^{20}? Write using exponents.

39. **NUMBER SENSE** Is $\dfrac{4^{200}}{4^{199}}$ *greater than*, *less than*, or *equal to* 4? Explain your reasoning.

40. **Write MATH** Does $3^2 + 3^5$ have the same value as $3^2 \cdot 3^5$? Explain.

NGSSS Practice   **MA.8.A.6.3**

41. Multiply $7xy$ and $x^{14}z$.

   A. $7x^{15}yz$

   B. $7x^{15}y$

   C. $7x^{13}yz$

   D. $x^{15}yz$

42. Find the quotient of $a^5 \div a$.

   F. a^5

   G. a^4

   H. a^6

   I. a

43. **THINK SOLVE EXPLAIN** **SHORT RESPONSE** What is the area of the rectangle?

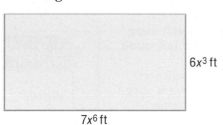

$6x^3$ ft

$7x^6$ ft

Spiral Review

Determine whether each equation represents a *linear* or *nonlinear* function. Explain. (Lesson 13-3B)

44. $y = x - 3$ 45. $y = 2x^3 + 3$ 46. $x + y = -7$ 47. $y = -5x^2$

State the slope and *y*-intercept for the graph of each equation. (Lesson 13-2C)

48. $y = x - 5$ 49. $y = \dfrac{1}{3}x + 6$ 50. $2x + 3y = 9$ 51. $x + 4y = 12$

52. **TRAVEL** Andre needs to be at the train station by 5:30 P.M. It takes him $\dfrac{1}{3}$ hour to pack and $1\dfrac{1}{4}$ hours to get to the station. Find the latest time he should begin packing. Use the *work backward* strategy. (Lesson 3-1A)

53. **SCHOOL** Josefina did $\dfrac{1}{5}$ of her homework in class and $\dfrac{1}{3}$ more on the bus. What fraction of her homework does she still need to do? (Lesson 2-2C)

Main Idea
Write expressions using negative exponents.

NGSSS

MA.8.A.6.4 Perform operations on real numbers (including integer exponents, radicals, percents, scientific notation, absolute value, rational numbers, and irrational numbers) **using multi-step and real-world problems.**

MA.8.A.6.3 Simplify real number expressions using the law of exponents.

Get Connected
glencoe.com

Negative Exponents

Explore Copy the table at the right.

1. Describe the pattern of the powers in the first column. Continue the pattern by writing the next two values in the table.

2. Describe the pattern of values in the second column. Then complete the second column.

3. Determine how 3^{-1} should be defined.

Power	Value
2^6	64
2^5	32
2^4	16
2^3	8
2^2	4
2^1	2
2^0	■
2^{-1}	■

Key Concept   Negative Exponents

Words   Any nonzero number to the negative n power is the multiplicative inverse of its nth power.

Symbols $a^{-n} = \dfrac{1}{a^n}$, for $a \neq 0$ and any integer n

Example $5^{-4} = \dfrac{1}{5^4}$

EXAMPLES   Use Positive Exponents

Write each expression using a positive exponent.

(1) 6^{-2}

$6^{-2} = \dfrac{1}{6^2}$ Definition of negative exponent

(2) x^{-5}

$x^{-5} = \dfrac{1}{x^5}$ Definition of negative exponent

 CHECK Your Progress

a. 5^{-6}

b. t^{-6}

EXAMPLES   Use Negative Exponents

Write each expression using a negative exponent.

(3) $\dfrac{1}{9} = \dfrac{1}{3^2}$ Definition of exponent

$= 3^{-2}$ Definition of negative exponent

(4) $\dfrac{1}{d^5} = \dfrac{1}{d \cdot d \cdot d \cdot d \cdot d}$ Definition of exponent

$= d^{-5}$ Definition of negative exponent

 CHECK Your Progress

c. $\dfrac{1}{16}$

d. $\dfrac{1}{t^6}$

EXAMPLES   Perform Operations with Exponents

⑤ Simplify $x^3 \cdot x^{-5}$.

Method 1 Product of Powers

$$x^3 \cdot x^{-5} = x^{3+(-5)}$$
$$= x^{-2}$$

Method 2 Definition of Power

$$x^3 \cdot x^{-5}$$
$$= x \cdot x \cdot x \cdot \frac{1}{x \cdot x \cdot x \cdot x \cdot x}$$
$$= \cancel{x^1} \cdot \cancel{x^1} \cdot \cancel{x^1} \cdot \frac{1}{\cancel{x_1} \cdot \cancel{x_1} \cdot \cancel{x_1} \cdot x \cdot x}$$
$$= \frac{1}{x \cdot x} \text{ or } x^{-2}$$

⑥ Simplify $\dfrac{g^5}{g^2}$.

Method 1 Quotient of Powers

$$\frac{g^5}{g^2} = g^{5-2}$$
$$= g^3$$

Method 2 Definition of Power

$$\frac{g^5}{g^2} = \frac{\cancel{g^1} \cdot \cancel{g^1} \cdot g \cdot g \cdot g}{\cancel{g^1} \cdot \cancel{g^1}}$$
$$= g^3$$

 CHOOSE Your Method

e. $\dfrac{x^{-7}}{x^{-1}}$

f. $c^{-4} \times c^3$

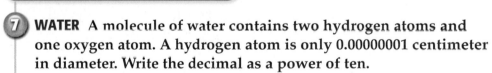 **Real-World EXAMPLE**

Real-World Link · · · ·
A single drop of water contains about 10^{20} molecules.

⑦ **WATER** A molecule of water contains two hydrogen atoms and one oxygen atom. A hydrogen atom is only 0.00000001 centimeter in diameter. Write the decimal as a power of ten.

The digit 1 is in the 100-millionths place.

$$0.00000001 = \frac{1}{100,000,000} \quad \text{Write the decimal as a fraction.}$$
$$= \frac{1}{10^8} \quad \quad 100,000,000 = 10^8$$
$$= 10^{-8} \quad \quad \text{Definition of negative exponent}$$

A hydrogen atom is 10^{-8} centimeter in diameter.

 CHECK Your Progress

g. **MEASUREMENT** A unit of measure called a *micron* equals 0.001 millimeter. Write this number using a negative exponent.

Examples 1 and 2
(p. 766)

Write each expression using a positive exponent.

1. 5^{-2} 2. $(-7)^{-1}$ **3** t^{-10} 4. n^{-2}

Examples 3 and 4
(p. 766)

Write each fraction as an expression using a negative exponent other than −1.

5. $\dfrac{1}{3^4}$ 6. $\dfrac{1}{x^2}$ 7. $\dfrac{1}{49}$ 8. $\dfrac{1}{8}$

Examples 5 and 6
(p. 767)

Simplify each expression.

9. $h^4 \cdot h^{-2}$ 10. $n^{-6} \cdot n^{-1}$ 11. $\dfrac{r^5}{r^4}$ 12. $\dfrac{s^{-8}}{s^{-3}}$

Example 7
(p. 767)

13. **MEASUREMENTS** A unit of measure called a *microgram* equals 0.000001 gram. Write this number using a negative exponent.

Practice and Problem Solving

 = **Step-by-Step Solutions** begin on page R42.
Extra Practice is on page EP39.

Examples 1 and 2
(p. 766)

Write each expression using a positive exponent.

14. 4^{-1} 15. 5^{-3} 16. $(-6)^{-2}$ 17. $(-3)^{-3}$

18. 3^{-5} 19. 10^{-4} 20. p^{-1} 21. a^{-10}

22. d^{-3} 23. q^{-4} 24. $2s^{-5}$ 25. x^{-2}

Examples 3 and 4
(p. 766)

Write each fraction as an expression using a negative exponent other than −1.

26. $\dfrac{1}{9^4}$ 27. $\dfrac{1}{5^5}$ 28. $\dfrac{1}{b^3}$ 29. $\dfrac{1}{k^2}$

30. $\dfrac{1}{1,000}$ 31. $\dfrac{1}{81}$ 32. $\dfrac{1}{27}$ 33. $\dfrac{1}{16}$

Example 5–7
(p. 767)

Simplify each expression.

34. $d^3 \cdot d^4$ 35. $g^{-4} \cdot g^2$ 36. $3m^7 \cdot 2m^{-2}$ 37. $5v^{-2} \cdot 3v^{-3}$

38. $\dfrac{f^8}{f^2}$ 39. $\dfrac{k^{-9}}{k^{-8}}$ 40. $\dfrac{36b^5}{6b^3}$ 41. $\dfrac{81c^{-6}}{9c^{-2}}$

Write each decimal using a negative exponent.

42. 0.1 43. 0.01 44. 0.0001 45. 0.00001

46. **ANIMALS** A common flea 2^{-4} inch long can jump about 2^3 inches high. How many times its body size can a flea jump?

47 **MEDICINE** Which type of molecule in the table has a greater mass? How many times greater is it than the other type?

Molecule	Mass (kg)
Penicillin	10^{-18}
Insulin	10^{-23}

48. **OPEN ENDED** Write a convincing argument that $3^0 = 1$ using the fact that $3^4 = 81$, $3^3 = 27$, $3^2 = 9$, and $3^1 = 3$.

49. **REASONING** Order 8^{-8}, 8^3, and 8^0 from greatest to least. Explain your reasoning.

50. **FIND THE ERROR** Theresa is finding 3^{-2}. Find her mistake and correct it.

$$3^{-2} = -3^2 = -9$$

51. **CHALLENGE** Compare and contrast x^{-n} and x^n. Then give a numerical example to show the relationship.

52. **MATH** Explain the difference between $(-4)^2$ and $\frac{1}{4^2}$.

53. Which is 15^{-5} written as a fraction?

   A. $\frac{1}{5^5}$ C. $\frac{1}{15}$

   B. $\frac{1}{15^5}$ D. $-\frac{1}{15^5}$

54. **SHORT RESPONSE** Rewrite the numbers with negative exponents so they have positive exponents.

Negative Exponents	m^{-5}	$b^{-3} \cdot b^{-1}$	$\frac{x^{-5}}{x^{-3}}$
Positive Exponents	■	■	■

ALGEBRA Simplify. Express your answer using exponents. (Lesson 13-4A)

55. $3^6 \cdot 3$ 56. $x^2 \cdot x^4$ 57. $\frac{5^5}{5^2}$ 58. $(n^4)(-2n^3)$

59. **MEASUREMENT** The volume V of a sphere is equal to four-thirds pi times the cube of its radius. Is the volume of a sphere a *linear* or *nonlinear* function of its radius? Explain. (Lesson 13-3B)

60. **PROBABILITY** A spinner is spun 20 times, and it lands on the color red 5 times. What is the experimental probability of *not* landing on red? (Lesson 7-3B)

Main Idea

Express numbers in scientific notation and in standard form.

NGSSS

MA.8.A.6.1 Use exponents and scientific notation to write large and small numbers and vice versa and to solve problems.
MA.8.A.6.4 Perform operations on real numbers (including integer exponents, radicals, percents, **scientific notation,** absolute value, rational numbers, and irrational numbers) **using multi-step and real world problems.**

New Vocabulary

scientific notation

Get Connected
glencoe.com

Scientific Notation

More than 425 million pounds of gold have been discovered in the world. If all this gold were in one place, it would form a cube seven stories on each side.

1. Write 425 million in standard form.
2. Complete: $4.25 \times \underline{} = 425$ million.

When you deal with very large numbers like 425,000,000, it can be difficult to keep track of the zeros. You can express numbers such as this in **scientific notation** by writing the number as the product of a factor and a power of 10.

Key Concept — **Scientific Notation**

Words	A number is expressed in scientific notation when it is written as the product of a factor and a power of 10. The factor must be greater than or equal to 1 and less than 10.
Symbols	$a \times 10^n$, where $1 \le a < 10$ and n is an integer
Example	$425{,}000{,}000 = 4.25 \times 10^8$

EXAMPLE **Express Large Numbers in Standard Form**

 Express 2.16×10^5 in standard form.

$2.16 \times 10^5 = 2.16 \times 100{,}000$ $10^5 = 100{,}000$

$ = 216{,}000$ Move the decimal point 5 places.

 CHECK Your Progress

Express each number in standard form.

a. 7.6×10^6 **b.** 3.201×10^4

Scientific notation is also used to express very small numbers. Study the pattern of products at the right. Notice that multiplying by a negative power of 10 moves the decimal point to the left the same number of places as the absolute value of the exponent.

$1.25 \times 10^2 = 125$
$1.25 \times 10^1 = 12.5$
$1.25 \times 10^0 = 1.25$
$1.25 \times 10^{-1} = 0.125$
$1.25 \times 10^{-2} = 0.0125$
$1.25 \times 10^{-3} = 0.00125$

EXAMPLE **Express Small Numbers in Standard Form**

2 Express 5.8×10^{-3} in standard form.

$$5.8 \times 10^{-3} = 5.8 \times 0.001 \qquad 10^{-3} = 0.001$$

$$= 0.0058 \qquad \text{Move the decimal point 3 places.}$$

✔ **CHECK Your Progress**

c. 4.7×10^{-5} **d.** 9×10^{-4}

To write a number in scientific notation, place the decimal point after the first nonzero digit. Then find the power of 10.

EXAMPLES **Express Numbers in Scientific Notation**

Express each number in scientific notation.

3 1,457,000

$$1,457,000 = 1.457 \times 1,000,000 \qquad \text{The decimal point moves 6 places.}$$

$$= 1.457 \times 10^6 \qquad \text{The exponent is positive.}$$

4 0.00063

$$0.00063 = 6.3 \times 0.0001 \qquad \text{The decimal point moves 4 places.}$$

$$= 6.3 \times 10^{-4} \qquad \text{The exponent is negative.}$$

✔ **CHECK Your Progress**

e. 35,000   **f.** 0.00722

Compare the exponents to compare numbers in scientific notation. With positive numbers, any number with a greater exponent is greater. If the exponents are the same, compare the factors.

 Real-World EXAMPLE **Compare Numbers in Scientific Notation**

5 **OCEANS** The Atlantic Ocean has an area of 3.18×10^7 square miles. The Pacific Ocean has an area of 6.4×10^7 square miles. Which ocean has the greater area?

$$3.18 < 6.4 \quad \longrightarrow \quad 3.18 \times 10^7 < 6.4 \times 10^7$$

So, the Pacific Ocean has the greater area.

✔ **CHECK Your Progress**

g. Replace ● with <, >, or = to make 4.13×10^{-2} ● 5.0×10^{-3} a true sentence.

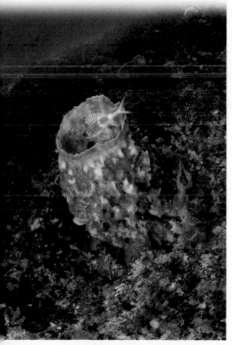

Real-World Link · · · · ·

At the deepest point in the ocean, the pressure is greater than 8 tons per square inch and the temperature is only a few degrees above freezing.

Examples 1 and 2
(pp. 770–771)

Express each number in standard form.

1. 3.754×10^5 **2.** 8.34×10^6

3. 1.5×10^{-4} **4.** 2.68×10^{-3}

Examples 3 and 4
(p. 771)

Express each number in scientific notation.

5 4,510,000   **6.** 0.00673

7. 0.000092   **8.** 11,620,000

9. PHYSICAL SCIENCE Light travels 300,000 kilometers per second. Write this number in scientific notation.

Example 5
(p. 771)

10. TECHNOLOGY The distance between tracks on a CD and DVD are shown in the table. Which disc has the greater distance between tracks?

Disc	Distance (mm)
CD	1.6×10^{-3}
DVD	7.4×10^{-4}

Replace each ● with <, >, or = to make a true sentence.

11. 2.3×10^5 ● 1.7×10^5 **12.** 0.012 ● 1.4×10^{-1}

Practice and Problem Solving

● = **Step-by-Step Solutions** begin on page R43.
Extra Practice is on page EP39.

Examples 1 and 2
(pp. 770–771)

Express each number in standard form.

13. 6.1×10^4 **14.** 5.72×10^6 **15.** 3.3×10^{-1} **16.** 5.68×10^{-3}

17. 9.014×10^{-2} **18.** 1.399×10^5 **19.** 2.505×10^3 **20.** 7.4×10^{-5}

21. SPIDERS The diameter of a spider's thread is 1×10^{-3} inch. Write this number in standard form.

22. DINOSAURS The *Giganotosaurus* dinosaur weighed about 1.4×10^4 pounds. Write this number in standard form.

Examples 3 and 4
(p. 771)

Express each number in scientific notation.

23. 499,000   **24.** 2,000,000   **25.** 0.006   **26.** 0.0125

27. 50,000,000   **28.** 39,560   **29.** 0.000078   **30.** 0.000425

31. CHESS The number of possible ways that a player can play the first four moves in a chess game is 3 billion. Write this number in scientific notation.

32. SCIENCE A particular parasite is approximately 0.025 inch long. Write this number in scientific notation.

Example 5
(p. 771)

33. SPORTS Use the table. Determine which category in each pair had a greater amount of sales.

a. golf or tennis

b. camping or golf

Category	Sales ($)
Camping	1.547×10^9
Golf	3.243×10^9
Tennis	3.73×10^8

Example 5
(p. 771)

Replace each ● with <, >, or = to make a true sentence.

34. 1.8×10^3 ● 1.9×10^{-1}

35. 5.2×10^2 ● $5,000$

36. 0.00701 ● 7.1×10^{-3}

37. 6.49×10^4 ● 649×10^2

38. MEASUREMENT The table at the right shows the values of different prefixes that are used in the metric system. Write the units attometer, gigameter, kilometer, nanometer, petameter, and picometer in order from greatest to least measure.

Metric Measures	
Prefix	**Meaning**
atto	10^{-18}
giga	10^9
kilo	10^3
nano	10^{-9}
peta	10^{15}
pico	10^{-12}

39. NUMBER SENSE Write the product of 0.00004 and 0.0008 in scientific notation.

40. NUMBER SENSE Order 6.1×10^4, 6,100, 6.1×10^{-5}, 0.0061, and 6.1×10^{-2} from least to greatest.

41 PHYSICAL SCIENCE The table shows the maximum amounts of lava in cubic meters per second that erupted from four volcanoes.

Volcanic Eruptions	
Volcano, Year	**Eruption Rate (m³/s)**
Mount St. Helens, 1980	2×10^4
Ngauruhoe, 1975	2×10^3
Hekla, 1970	4×10^3
Agung, 1963	3×10^4

a. How many times greater was the Mount St. Helens eruption than the Ngauruhoe eruption?

b. How many times greater was the Hekla eruption than the Ngauruhoe eruption?

Write each number in standard form.

42. $(8 \times 10^0) + (4 \times 10^{-3}) + (3 \times 10^{-5})$

43. $(4 \times 10^4) + (8 \times 10^3) + (3 \times 10^2) + (9 \times 10^1) + (6 \times 10^0)$

44. 🔄 MULTIPLE REPRESENTATIONS A square piece of property has a side of 3,250 feet.

a. ALGEBRA Write an equation to represent the area of the property in square feet.

b. ALGEBRA Solve the equation in **part a** to find the area of the property.

c. NUMBERS Express the area in scientific notation.

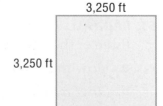
3,250 ft

3,250 ft

H.O.T. Problems

45. CHALLENGE Convert the numbers in each expression to scientific notation. Then evaluate the expression. Express in scientific notation and in decimal notation.

a. $\dfrac{(420,000)(0.015)}{0.025}$

b. $\dfrac{(0.078)(8.5)}{0.16(250,000)}$

46. REASONING Which is a better estimate for the number of times per year that a person blinks: 6.25×10^{-2} times or 6.25×10^{6} times? Explain your reasoning.

47. OPEN ENDED Describe a real-world value or measure using numbers in scientific notation and in standard form.

48. Write MATH Explain the relationship between a number in standard form and the sign of the exponent when the number is written in scientific notation.

NGSSS Practice   MA.8.A.6.1

49. Which shows 0.00000029 in scientific notation?

A. 2.9×10^{7}

B. 2.9×10^{6}

C. 2.9×10^{-6}

D. 2.9×10^{-7}

50. The average width of a strand of thread is 2.2×10^{-4} meter. Which expression represents this number in standard form?

F. 22,000 meters

G. 220,000 meters

H. 0.00022 meter

I. 0.000022 meter

51. Evaluate each expression. (Lesson 13-4B)

a. 5^{-3}

b. 3^{-6}

52. MEASUREMENT Find the area of a rectangle with a length of $9xy^2$ and a width of $4x^2y$. (Lesson 13-4A)

53. RAINFALL The table shows the average annual precipitation for three of the driest locations on Earth. (Lesson 2-2C)

a. How much more rain does Iquique get per year than Arica?

b. How much more annual rain does Callao get than Iquique?

Location	Precipitation (in.)
Arica, Chile	$\dfrac{3}{100}$
Iquique, Chile	$\dfrac{1}{5}$
Callao, Peru	$\dfrac{12}{25}$

FOLDABLES® Study Organizer

Be sure the following Key Concepts are noted in your Foldable.

Inequalities, Functions, and Monomials

Key Concepts

Inequality Properties (Lesson 13-1)
- When you add, subtract, multiply, or divide by the same positive number on each side of an inequality, the inequality remains true.
- When you multiply or divide each side of an inequality by a negative number, the direction of the symbol must be reversed for the inequality to be true.

Functions (Lesson 13-2)
- A function is a relationship in which one value is dependent upon another.
- Functions can be represented by words, equations, tables, ordered pairs, and graphs.

Slope-Intercept Form (Lesson 13-2)
- An equation written in slope-intercept form is written as $y = mx + b$, where m is the slope and b is the y-intercept.

Powers and Scientific Notation (Lesson 13-4)
- A number is expressed in scientific notation when it is written as the product of a factor and a power of 10. The factor must be greater than or equal to 1 and less than 10.

Key Vocabulary

discrete data (p. 747)

function notation (p. 740)

linear function (p. 746)

monomial (p. 762)

nonlinear function (p. 757)

scientific notation (p. 770)

slope-intercept form (p. 750)

x-intercept (p. 745)

y-intercept (p. 745)

Vocabulary Check

Choose the correct term or number to complete each sentence.

1. Data that can take on any real number value is called (continuous, discrete) data.

2. The number that is expressed using an exponent is a (rational number, power).

3. A (linear function, nonlinear function) has a constant rate of change.

4. The slope formula is $\left(\dfrac{y_2 - y_1}{x_2 - x_1}, \dfrac{x_2 - x_1}{y_2 - y_1}\right)$.

5. The graph of a linear function is a (straight, curved) line.

6. To divide powers with the same base, (add, subtract) the exponents.

7. The number 4.05×10^8 is written in (scientific notation, standard notation).

8. The (x-intercept, y-intercept) has the coordinates $(0, b)$.

9. The number 5^4 is a(n) (exponent, power).

10. The (Product of Powers, Quotient of Powers) states that when dividing powers with the same base, subtract their exponents.

Multi-Part Lesson Review

13-1 Inequalities

PSI: Guess, Check, and Revise (pp. 726–727)

 MA.8.A.6.4

Solve. Use the *guess, check, and revise* strategy.

11. **TRAVEL** Lucinda is driving away from Redding at 50 miles per hour. When she is 100 miles away, Javon leaves Redding driving at 60 miles per hour in the same direction. After how many hours will Javon pass Lucinda?

12. **FARMING** A farmer sells a bushel of soybeans for $5 and a bushel of corn for $3. If he hopes to earn $164 and plans to sell 40 bushels in all, how many bushels of soybeans does he need to sell?

EXAMPLE 1 Find two numbers with a product of 30 and a difference of 13.

Make a guess and check to see if it is correct. Then adjust the guess until it is correct.

5 and 6 $5 \cdot 6 = 30$ and $6 - 5 = 1$
incorrect

3 and 10 $3 \cdot 10 = 30$ and $10 - 3 = 7$
incorrect

2 and 15 $2 \cdot 15 = 30$ and $15 - 2 = 13$
correct

The two numbers are 2 and 15.

Solve Inequalities by Addition or Subtraction (pp. 728–732)

 MA.8.A.4.2

Solve each inequality. Check your solution.

13. $m + 3 < 9$ 14. $4 \geq 6 + n$

15. $x + \frac{3}{4} \leq 5$ 16. $-1\frac{1}{3} < g - 5$

17. **LIFTING** An athlete is training for sports and is lifting 120 pounds on the bench press. The athlete can lift a maximum of 180 pounds. Write and solve an inequality to determine how much additional weight the athlete can lift.

EXAMPLE 2 Solve $x + 5 \geq 7$. Check your solution.

$x + 5 \geq 7$ Write the inequality.
$x + 5 - 5 \geq 7 - 5$ Subtract 5 from each side.
$x \geq 2$ Simplify.

Check $x + 5 \geq 7$ Write the inequality.

$2 + 5 \overset{?}{\geq} 7$ Replace x with a number greater than or equal to 2.

$7 \geq 7$ ✓   This statement is true.

Solve Inequalities by Multiplication or Division (pp. 733–737)

 MA.8.A.4.2

Solve each inequality.

18. $\frac{p}{3} < 6$ 19. $\frac{w}{2.4} \leq 3$

20. $-0.9d > 6.3$ 21. $-42 \leq 6y$

22. **SOCCER** Jody wants to spend less than $18.75 on new socks. Each pack costs $6. Write and solve an inequality to find the maximum number of packs she can buy.

EXAMPLE 3 Solve $-3k \leq 33$. Check your solution.

$-3k \leq 33$ Write the inequality.

$\frac{-3k}{-3} \geq \frac{33}{-3}$ Divide each side by -3 and reverse the symbol.

$k \geq -11$ Simplify.

The solution is $k \geq -11$. You can check this solution by substituting -11 or a number greater than -11 into the inequality.

Linear Functions

Function Notation (pp. 740–744)

MA.8.A.1.1

Find each function value.

23. $f(-4)$ if $f(x) = 2x - 5$

24. $f(7)$ if $f(x) = -3x$

25. $f(3)$ if $f(x) = \frac{1}{3}x + 8$

26. Complete the function table for $f(x) = 7x - 2$. Then state the domain and range of the function.

x	7x − 2	f(x)
−2		
0		
1		
3		

EXAMPLE 4 Complete the function table for $f(x) = 4x + 3$. Then state the domain and range of the function.

x	4x + 3	f(x)
−2	4(−2) + 3	−5
0	4(0) + 3	3
1	4(1) + 3	7
3	4(3) + 3	15

Domain: $\{-2, 0, 1, 3\}$

Range: $\{-5, 3, 7, 15\}$

Representing Linear Functions (pp. 745–749)

MA.8.A.1.1

Graph each function.

27. $y = -x - 3$ **28.** $y = \frac{2}{3}x + 4$

29. DRINKS A regular drink x costs $1.25 and a large drink y costs $2.50. Graph the function $1.25x + 2.5y = 10$ to determine how many of each type of drink Hank can buy with $10.

EXAMPLE 5 Graph $y = 5 + 2x$.

x	5 + 2x	y
−1	5 + 2(−1)	3
0	5 + 2(0)	5
2	5 + 2(2)	9
3	5 + 2(3)	11

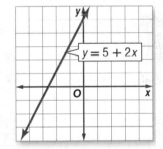

Slope-Intercept Form (pp. 750–753)

MA.8.A.1.2

State the slope and y-intercept for the graph of each equation.

30. $y = 4x - 2$ **31.** $y = -\frac{1}{6}x + 3$

32. $y + 3x = 7$ **33.** $8x + y = -10$

34. MONEY June has saved $75 mowing lawns. She saves an additional $15 for each lawn she mows. The equation for the amount of money y June has saved is $y = 75 + 15x$, where x is the number of lawns she mowed. Graph the equation.

EXAMPLE 6 State the slope and y-intercept of the graph of $y = -\frac{3}{5}x + 7$.

$y = -\frac{3}{5}x + 7$ Write the equation.

$y = mx + b$

The slope of the graph is $-\frac{3}{5}$, and the y-intercept is 7.

13-3 Nonlinear Functions

Linear and Nonlinear Functions (pp. 757–760)

Determine whether each equation or table represents a *linear* or *nonlinear* function. Explain.

35. $y - 6x = 8$ **36.** $y = x^2 + 2$

37.

Time (h)	3	4	5	6
Number of Miles	165	220	280	335

EXAMPLE 7 Determine whether the table represents a *linear* or *nonlinear* function.

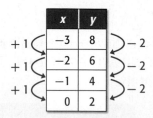

As x increases by 1, y decreases by 2. The rate of change is constant, so this function is linear.

13-4 Monomials

Multiply and Divide Monomials (pp. 761–765)

Simplify. Express using exponents.

38. $6 \cdot 6^3$ **39.** $b^4 \cdot b^3$

40. $-3m^5(4m^7)$ **41.** $\left(\frac{2}{5}s^3\right) \times \left(\frac{2}{5}s^5\right)$

42. $\dfrac{3^7}{3^2}$ **43.** $\dfrac{c^8}{c}$

44. $\dfrac{24t^6}{3t^4}$ **45.** $\dfrac{-42g^9}{6g^8}$

46. PHONE CALLS A telemarketer makes 3^3 phone calls each day. Suppose the number of phone calls increases by 3 times that number. How many phone calls will be made after the increase?

47. MEASUREMENT The area of a master bedroom is 2^8 square feet. The area of a bathroom is 2^6 square feet. How many times greater is the area of the master bedroom?

EXAMPLE 8 Find $3 \cdot 3^5$. Express using exponents.

$3 \cdot 3^5 = 3^1 \cdot 3^5$ $3 = 3^1$

$= 3^{1+5}$ The common base is 3.

$= 3^6$ Add the exponents.

EXAMPLE 9 Find $2b^2 \cdot 6b^4$.

$2b^2 \cdot 6b^4 = (2 \cdot 6)b^{2+4}$ Commutative and

$= 12b^6$ Associative Properties

EXAMPLE 10 Simplify $\dfrac{7^5}{7^2}$. Express using exponents.

$\dfrac{7^5}{7^2} = 7^{5-2}$ The common base is 7.

$= 7^3$ Simplify.

Monomials (continued)

Negative Exponents (pp. 766–769)

MA.8.A.6.4

Write each expression using a positive exponent.

48. 6^{-3} **49.** 3^{-5}

50. b^{-4} **51.** m^{-2}

Write each fraction as an expression using a negative exponent other than -1.

52. $\dfrac{1}{5^2}$ **53.** $\dfrac{1}{64}$

54. $\dfrac{1}{x^4}$ **55.** $\dfrac{1}{h^8}$

EXAMPLE 11 Write 4^{-3} using a positive exponent.

$4^{-3} = \dfrac{1}{4^3}$ Definition of negative exponent

EXAMPLE 12 Write m^{-5} using a positive exponent.

$m^{-5} = \dfrac{1}{m^5}$ Definition of negative exponent

EXAMPLE 13 Write $\dfrac{1}{16}$ as an expression using a negative exponent.

$\dfrac{1}{16} = \dfrac{1}{2^4}$ Definition of exponent

$\quad\;\; = 2^{-4}$ Definition of negative exponent

Scientific Notation (pp. 770–774)

MA.8.A.6.1

Express each number in standard form.

56. 5.7×10^{-4} **57.** 2.08×10^3

58. 9.35×10^6 **59.** 7.6×10^{-5}

60. INSECTS The giant weta is the largest known insect, having a mass of about 7.1×10^1 grams. Write this mass in standard form.

Express each number in scientific notation.

61. 0.00027   **62.** 0.0000196

63. 10,400,000   **64.** 780,000

EXAMPLE 14 Write 6.5×10^{-5} in standard form.

$6.5 \times 10^{-5} = 0.000065$ Move the decimal point 5 places.

EXAMPLE 15 Write 3.06×10^6 in standard form.

$3.06 \times 10^6 = 3,060,000$ Move the decimal point 6 places.

EXAMPLE 16 Write 0.00016 in scientific notation.

$0.00016 = 16 \times 0.0001$ Move the decimal point 4 places.

$\quad\quad\;\;\; = 1.6 \times 10^{-4}$ Since $0 < 0.00016 < 1$, the exponent is negative.

Solve each inequality. Check your solution.

1. $-6 < \dfrac{r}{5}$ **2.** $3x \geq -27$

3. $6h - 6 < 30$ **4.** $9 - 2c \leq 55$

Find each function value.

5. $f(4)$ if $f(x) = 7x$

6. $f(-6)$ if $f(x) = x + 12$

7. $f(9)$ if $f(x) = 4x - 6$

8. $f\left(\dfrac{2}{3}\right)$ if $f(x) = 4x + \dfrac{1}{3}$

9. AQUARIUM Talia needs to add algae control to her fish tank. The instructions tell her to add 2 drops for every 1 gallon of water. Write a function to represent the amount of algae treatment t needed for g gallons of water. Then determine how much algae treatment is needed for her 10-gallon aquarium.

10. NGSSS PRACTICE
The graph shows the line $y = 6x + 2$.

Which table of ordered pairs contains only points on this line?

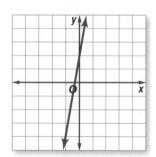

A.

x	−2	−1	0	1
y	−5	−3	4	6

B.

x	−3	−2	−1	0
y	−20	−14	−8	2

C.

x	0	1	2	3
y	2	8	16	24

D.

x	−1	0	1	2
y	−4	2	8	14

State the slope and y-intercept for the graph of each equation.

11. $y = 9x - 6$ **12.** $8 = \dfrac{3}{2}x + y$

Determine whether each table represents a *linear* or *nonlinear* function. Explain.

13.

x	4	8	12	16
y	25	20	15	10

14.

x	−3	0	3	6
y	−3	0	4	8

Simplify. Express using exponents.

15. $c^7 \times c^{-2}$ **16.** $4g^2 \times 3g^{-5}$

Express each number in standard form.

17. 5.034×10^6 **18.** 1.57×10^{-4}

19. EXTENDED RESPONSE The Drama Club held a fundraiser in the school auditorium. They hoped to raise $2,500 for charity. The Parent Group donated $300 to help with costs. They sold event tickets for $6.00.

Part A Copy and complete the table.

Number of tickets sold (x)	0	5	10	15	20	25
Amount of money made ($)	▪	▪	▪	▪	▪	▪

Part B Graph the data.

Part C The total amount made is given by the equation $y = 300 + 6x$. Identify the slope and y-intercept of the graph. Explain their meaning.

Part D Is this data discrete or continuous? Explain your reasoning.

Part E How many tickets must be sold to raise $2,500? Write and solve an inequality.

 **Gridded Response: Negative Numbers**

When the answer to a gridded-response question is a negative number, use the negative sign in the answer grid.

NGSSS PRACTICE EXAMPLE

The chart at the right shows how the temperature of Earth's atmosphere changes as the altitude increases. If the pattern in the chart continues, what would be the temperature in degrees Fahrenheit at an altitude of 30,000 feet?

Earth's Atmosphere	
Altitude (feet)	Temperature (degrees Fahrenheit)
10,000	23
15,000	5
20,000	−13
25,000	−31

+ 5000, + 5000, + 5000 — 18, − 18, − 18

As the altitude increases by 5,000 feet, the temperature decreases by 18°F. So, at 30,000 feet, the temperature would be −31 − 18 or −49°F. Grid in −49.

Correct

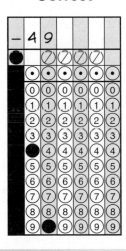

NOT Correct

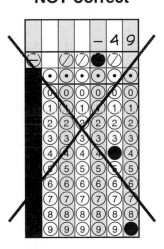

 Work on It

The morning temperature in Anchorage, Alaska, was −15°F. It increased by about 2 degrees each hour. This can be represented by $t = -15 + 2n$, where n is the number of hours and t is the temperature. According to the equation, what is the temperature after 5 hours? Fill in an answer grid.

Test Hint

To grid negative numbers, always start the answer in the left answer box of the grid.

Read each question. Then fill in the correct answer on the answer sheet provided by your teacher or on a sheet of paper.

1. Which statement is NOT true about the slope of line $\overleftrightarrow{AC}$?

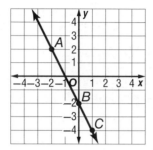

A. The slope is positive.

B. The slope between point A and point C is equal to the slope between point B and point C.

C. The slope of line $\overleftrightarrow{AC}$ is -2.

D. The slope is the same between any two points.

2. If $n - 5 > 27$, then n could be which of the following values?

F. 21

G. 22

H. 32

I. 33

3. Sarita has 3 apples to serve to her friends. If Sarita serves each friend $\frac{1}{3}$ of a whole apple, how many friends can she serve?

A. 1

B. 3

C. 9

D. 12

4. 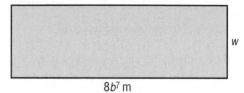 **SHORT RESPONSE** The area of the rectangle shown below is $32b^{12}$ square meters. If the base of the rectangle is $8b^7$ meters, what is the height of the rectangle?

$8b^7$ m

5. **GRIDDED RESPONSE** The square notepad paper shown has an area of 81 square centimeters. What are the dimensions of the notepad paper?

6. A homeowner tracked the value of a home using a scatter plot.

Lifetime Value of Home

Which description best represents the relationship of the home's value?

F. negative trend

G. no trend

H. positive trend

I. cannot be determined

7. If point *B* is translated 5 units right and 2 units down, what will be the coordinates of point *B* in its new position?

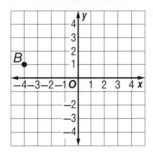

A. $(-2, -4)$ **C.** $(1, -3)$

B. $(1, -1)$ **D.** $(-1, 1)$

8. The Indian River flows with speeds of about 1.7 meters per second. How many feet per second is this?

F. 5.7   **H.** 7.3

G. 6.5   **I.** 8.6

9. ✎ **GRIDDED RESPONSE** The diameter of Saturn measures 7.46×10^4 miles. What is this distance in miles in standard notation?

10. ▦ **SHORT RESPONSE** A model car is shown below. The term 2^{-6} represents the scale size of the car. What is 2^{-6} in standard form?

11. The table shows the results from a survey of thirty middle school students.

Favorite After-School Activity	Number of Students
Sleep	3
Sports	13
Video games	10
Reading	4

Based on this survey, what is the probability that a student will play video games or read?

A. $\dfrac{7}{15}$ **C.** $\dfrac{7}{30}$

B. $\dfrac{8}{15}$ **D.** $\dfrac{2}{5}$

12. ▦ **EXTENDED RESPONSE** The table summarizes the depth of the water in Jeremiah's cylindrical pool as he refills it with water.

x time (minutes)	y depth (inches)
0	6
10	8
20	10
30	12

Part A   State whether the data represents a *linear* or *nonlinear* function. Justify your response.

Part B   Using words, describe the relationship between the depth of the water and the number of minutes Jeremiah has been filling the pool.

Part C   Create a graph of the situation.

Part D   Write an equation in slope-intercept form to represent the function.

NEED EXTRA HELP?												
If You Missed Question...	1	2	3	4	5	6	7	8	9	10	11	12
Go to Lesson...	13-2B	13-1B	2-3D	13-4A	11-3A	12-2C	10-1B	9-1D	13-4C	13-4B	7-3B	13-2C
For help with NGSSS...	8.A.1.1	8.A.4.2	7.A.3.2	8.A.6.3	8.A.6.2	8.S.3.1	7.G.4.2	7.G.4.4	8.A.6.1	8.A.6.4	7.P.7.2	8.A.1.2

Student Handbook

How to Use the Student Handbook

The Student Handbook is the additional skill and reference material found at the end of books. The Student Handbook can help answer these questions.

What if I need more practice?

You, or your teacher, may decide that working through some additional problems would be helpful. The **Extra Practice** section provides these problems for each lesson so you have ample opportunity to practice new skills.

What if I forget a vocabulary word?

The **English-Spanish-Haitian Creole Glossary** provides a list of new vocabulary words used throughout the textbook. It provides a definition in English, Spanish, and Haitian Creole as well as the page number(s) where the word can be found.

What if I need to check a homework answer?

The answers to the odd-numbered problems are included in **Selected Answers and Solutions**. Check your answers to make sure you understand how to solve all of the assigned problems. Fully worked out solutions to selected problems are also included in this section.

What if I need to find something quickly?

The **Index** alphabetically lists the subjects covered throughout the entire textbook and the pages on which each subject can be found.

What if I forget a formula?

Inside the back cover of your math book is a **Mathematics Reference Sheet** with formulas that are used in the book.

Extra Practice

Multi-Part Lesson 1-1
PARTS A B

PAGES 28–32

Write an integer for each situation.

1. seven degrees below zero **2.** a loss of 3 pounds **3.** a loss of 20 yards

4. a profit of $25 **5.** 112°F above 0 **6.** 2,830 feet above sea level

Graph each set of integers on a number line.

7. $\{-2, 0, 2\}$ **8.** $\{1, 3, 5\}$ **9.** $\{-2, -5, 3\}$ **10.** $\{7, -1, 4\}$

ALGEBRA Evaluate each expression.

11. $|1|$ **12.** $|-8|$ **13.** $|0|$ **14.** $|-82|$

15. $|64|$ **16.** $|-128|$ **17.** $|-22| + 5$ **18.** $|-40| - 8$

19. $|-18| + |10|$ **20.** $|-7| + |-1|$ **21.** $|98| - |-5|$ **22.** $|-49| - |-10|$

PART C

PAGES 33–37

Write the ordered pair for each point graphed at the right. Then name the quadrant or axis on which each point is located.

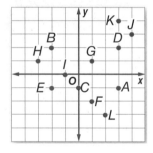

1. A **2.** B **3.** C

4. D **5.** E **6.** F

7. G **8.** H **9.** I

10. J **11.** K **12.** L

On graph paper, draw a coordinate plane. Then graph and label each point.

13. $N(-4, 3)$ **14.** $K(2, 5)$ **15.** $W(-6, -2)$ **16.** $X(5, 0)$

17. $Y(4, -4)$ **18.** $M(0, -3)$ **19.** $Z(-2, 0.5)$ **20.** $S(-1, -3)$

21. $A(0, 2)$ **22.** $C(-2, -2)$ **23.** $E(0, 1)$ **24.** $G(1, -1)$

Multi-Part Lesson 1-2
PARTS A B

PAGES 38–44

Add.

1. $-4 + 8$ **2.** $14 + 16$ **3.** $-7 + (-7)$

4. $-9 + (-6)$ **5.** $-18 + 11$ **6.** $-36 + 40$

7. $42 + (-18)$ **8.** $-42 + 29$ **9.** $18 + (-32)$

ALGEBRA Evaluate each expression if $a = 6$, $b = -2$, $c = -6$, and $d = 3$.

10. $-96 + a$ **11.** $b + (-5)$ **12.** $c + (-32)$

13. $d + 98$ **14.** $-120 + b$ **15.** $-120 + c$

16. $5 + b$ **17.** $a + d$ **18.** $c + a$

Multi-Part Lesson 1-2 (continued)
PARTS C D

PAGES 45–50

Subtract.

1. $3 - 7$
2. $-5 - 4$
3. $-6 - 2$
4. $8 - 13$
5. $6 - (-4)$
6. $12 - 9$
7. $-2 - 23$
8. $63 - 78$
9. $0 - (-14)$
10. $15 - 6$
11. $18 - 20$
12. $-5 - 8$

ALGEBRA Evaluate each expression if $k = -3$, $p = 6$, $n = 1$, and $d = -8$.

13. $55 - k$
14. $p - 7$
15. $d - 15$
16. $n - 12$
17. $-51 - d$
18. $k - 21$
19. $n - k$
20. $-99 - k$
21. $p - k$
22. $d - (-1)$
23. $k - d$
24. $n - d$

Multi-Part Lesson 1-3
PARTS A B

PAGES 52–55

Solve using the *look for a pattern* strategy.

1. **NUMBERS** Determine the next three numbers in the pattern below.

   $15, 21, 27, 33, 39, \ldots$

2. **TIME** Determine the next two times in the pattern below.

   2:30 A.M., 2:50 A.M., 3:10 A.M., 3:30 A.M., …

3. **MONEY** The table shows Abigail's savings. If the pattern continues, what will be the total amount in week 6?

Week	Total ($)
1	$400
2	$800
3	$1,200
4	$1,600
5	$2,000
6	▪

4. **SCIENCE** A single rotation of Earth takes about 24 hours. Copy and complete the table to determine the number of hours in a week.

Number of Days	Number of Hours
1	24
2	48
3	72
4	▪
5	▪
6	▪
7	▪

PART C

PAGES 56–60

Multiply.

1. $5(-2)$
2. $6(-4)$
3. $4(21)$
4. $-11(-5)$
5. $-6(5)$
6. $-50(0)$
7. $-5(-5)$
8. $-4(8)$
9. $(-6)^2$
10. $(-2)^2$
11. $(-4)^3$
12. $(-5)^3$

ALGEBRA Evaluate each expression if $a = -5$, $b = 2$, $c = -3$, and $d = 4$.

13. $-2d$
14. $6a$
15. $3ab$
16. $-12d$
17. $-4b^2$
18. $-5cd$
19. a^2
20. $13ab$

Multi-Part Lesson 1-3 (continued)

PART D

PAGES 61–65

Divide.

1. $4 \div (-2)$ **2.** $16 \div (-8)$ **3.** $-14 \div (-2)$ **4.** $\dfrac{32}{8}$

5. $18 \div (-3)$ **6.** $-18 \div 3$ **7.** $8 \div (-8)$ **8.** $0 \div (-1)$

9. $-25 \div 5$ **10.** $\dfrac{-14}{-7}$ **11.** $-32 \div 8$ **12.** $-56 \div (-8)$

13. $-81 \div 9$ **14.** $-42 \div (-7)$ **15.** $121 \div (-11)$ **16.** $-81 \div (-9)$

ALGEBRA Evaluate each expression if $a = -2$, $b = -7$, $x = 8$, and $y = -4$.

17. $-64 \div x$ **18.** $\dfrac{16}{y}$ **19.** $x \div 2$ **20.** $\dfrac{a}{2}$

21. $ax \div y$ **22.** $\dfrac{bx}{y}$ **23.** $2y \div 1$ **24.** $\dfrac{x}{ay}$

25. $-y \div a$ **26.** $x^2 \div y$ **27.** $\dfrac{ab}{1}$ **28.** $\dfrac{xy}{a}$

Multi-Part Lesson 2-1

PARTS A B

PAGES 79–84

Write each fraction or mixed number as a decimal. Use bar notation if the decimal is a repeating decimal.

1. $\dfrac{16}{20}$ **2.** $\dfrac{30}{120}$ **3.** $1\dfrac{7}{8}$ **4.** $\dfrac{1}{6}$

5. $\dfrac{11}{40}$ **6.** $5\dfrac{13}{50}$ **7.** $\dfrac{55}{300}$ **8.** $1\dfrac{1}{2}$

9. $\dfrac{5}{9}$ **10.** $2\dfrac{3}{4}$ **11.** $\dfrac{9}{11}$ **12.** $4\dfrac{1}{9}$

Write each decimal as a fraction or mixed number in simplest form.

13. 0.26 **14.** 0.75 **15.** 0.4 **16.** 0.1

17. 4.48 **18.** 9.8 **19.** 0.91 **20.** 11.15

PART C

PAGES 85–90

Replace each ● with $<$, $>$, or $=$ to make a true sentence. Use a number line if necessary.

1. $-\dfrac{1}{5}$ ● $-\dfrac{3}{5}$ **2.** $-\dfrac{7}{8}$ ● $-\dfrac{5}{8}$ **3.** $-\dfrac{1}{6}$ ● $-\dfrac{5}{6}$ **4.** $-\dfrac{3}{4}$ ● $-\dfrac{1}{4}$

5. $-2\dfrac{1}{4}$ ● $-2\dfrac{2}{8}$ **6.** $-4\dfrac{3}{7}$ ● $-4\dfrac{2}{7}$ **7.** $-1\dfrac{4}{9}$ ● $-1\dfrac{8}{9}$ **8.** $-3\dfrac{4}{5}$ ● $-3\dfrac{2}{5}$

9. $\dfrac{7}{9}$ ● $\dfrac{3}{5}$ **10.** $\dfrac{14}{25}$ ● $\dfrac{3}{4}$ **11.** $\dfrac{8}{24}$ ● $\dfrac{20}{60}$ **12.** $\dfrac{5}{12}$ ● $\dfrac{4}{9}$

13. $\dfrac{18}{24}$ ● $\dfrac{10}{18}$ **14.** $\dfrac{4}{6}$ ● $\dfrac{5}{9}$ **15.** $\dfrac{11}{49}$ ● $\dfrac{12}{42}$ **16.** $\dfrac{5}{14}$ ● $\dfrac{2}{6}$

Order each set of numbers from least to greatest.

17. $70\%, 0.6, \dfrac{2}{3}$ **18.** $0.8, \dfrac{17}{20}, 17\%$ **19.** $\dfrac{61}{100}, 0.65, 61.5\%$

20. $0.\overline{42}, \dfrac{3}{7}, 42\%$ **21.** $2.15, 2.105, 2\dfrac{7}{50}$ **22.** $7\dfrac{1}{8}, 7.81, 7.18$

Multi-Part Lesson 2-2

PART A

PAGES 91–95

Add or subtract. Write in simplest form.

1. $\frac{5}{11} + \frac{9}{11}$

2. $\frac{5}{8} - \frac{1}{8}$

3. $\frac{7}{10} + \frac{7}{10}$

4. $\frac{9}{12} - \frac{5}{12}$

5. $\frac{2}{9} + \frac{1}{9}$

6. $\frac{1}{4} + \frac{3}{4}$

7. $\frac{17}{21} + \left(-\frac{13}{21}\right)$

8. $-\frac{8}{13} + \left(-\frac{11}{13}\right)$

9. $\frac{13}{28} - \frac{9}{28}$

10. $\frac{15}{16} + \frac{13}{16}$

11. $-\frac{4}{35} - \left(-\frac{17}{35}\right)$

12. $\frac{3}{8} + \left(-\frac{5}{8}\right)$

13. $\frac{8}{15} - \frac{2}{15}$

14. $-\frac{3}{10} + \frac{7}{10}$

15. $\frac{5}{6} - \frac{7}{6}$

16. $\frac{7}{24} + \frac{7}{24}$

17. $-\frac{29}{9} - \left(-\frac{26}{9}\right)$

18. $\frac{3}{7} - \frac{4}{7}$

PARTS B C

PAGES 96–103

Add or subtract. Write in simplest form.

1. $\frac{1}{4} - \frac{3}{12}$

2. $\frac{3}{7} + \frac{6}{14}$

3. $\frac{1}{4} + \frac{3}{5}$

4. $\frac{4}{9} + \frac{1}{2}$

5. $\frac{5}{7} - \frac{4}{6}$

6. $\frac{3}{4} - \frac{1}{6}$

7. $\frac{3}{5} + \frac{3}{4}$

8. $\frac{2}{3} - \frac{1}{8}$

9. $\frac{9}{10} + \frac{1}{3}$

10. $-\frac{3}{4} + \frac{7}{8}$

11. $\frac{3}{8} + \frac{7}{12}$

12. $\frac{3}{5} - \frac{2}{3}$

13. $\frac{2}{5} + \left(-\frac{2}{7}\right)$

14. $-\frac{3}{5} - \left(-\frac{5}{6}\right)$

15. $-\frac{7}{12} - \frac{3}{4}$

Evaluate each expression if $a = \frac{2}{3}$ and $b = \frac{7}{12}$.

16. $\frac{1}{5} + a$

17. $a - \frac{1}{2}$

18. $b + \frac{7}{8}$

19. $\frac{7}{8} - a$

20. $a + b$

21. $a - b$

PART D

PAGES 104–108

Add or subtract. Write in simplest form.

1. $2\frac{1}{3} + 1\frac{1}{3}$

2. $5\frac{2}{7} - 2\frac{3}{7}$

3. $6\frac{3}{8} + 7\frac{1}{8}$

4. $2\frac{3}{4} - 1\frac{1}{4}$

5. $5\frac{1}{2} - 3\frac{1}{4}$

6. $2\frac{2}{3} + 4\frac{1}{9}$

7. $7\frac{4}{5} + 9\frac{3}{10}$

8. $3\frac{3}{4} + 5\frac{5}{8}$

9. $10\frac{2}{3} + 5\frac{6}{7}$

10. $17\frac{2}{9} - 12\frac{1}{3}$

11. $6\frac{5}{12} + 12\frac{5}{12}$

12. $7\frac{1}{4} + 15\frac{5}{6}$

13. $6\frac{1}{8} + 4\frac{2}{3}$

14. $7 - 6\frac{4}{9}$

15. $8\frac{1}{12} + 12\frac{6}{11}$

16. $7\frac{2}{3} + 8\frac{1}{4}$

17. $12\frac{3}{11} + 14\frac{3}{13}$

18. $21\frac{1}{3} + 15\frac{3}{8}$

19. $19\frac{1}{7} + 6\frac{1}{4}$

20. $9\frac{2}{5} - 8\frac{1}{3}$

21. $18\frac{1}{4} - 3\frac{3}{8}$

22. $1\frac{1}{8} + 2\frac{1}{12}$

23. $2\frac{1}{12} - 1\frac{1}{8}$

24. $10 - \frac{2}{3}$

Extra Practice

Multi-Part Lesson 2-3

PARTS A B

PAGES 110–117

Multiply. Write in simplest form.

1. $\frac{2}{3} \times \frac{3}{5}$
2. $\frac{1}{6} \times \frac{2}{5}$
3. $\frac{4}{9} \times \frac{3}{7}$
4. $\frac{5}{12} \times \frac{6}{11}$

5. $\frac{3}{8} \times \frac{8}{9}$
6. $\frac{2}{5} \times \frac{5}{8}$
7. $\frac{7}{15} \times \frac{3}{21}$
8. $\frac{5}{6} \times \frac{15}{16}$

9. $\frac{2}{3} \times \frac{3}{13}$
10. $\frac{4}{9} \times \frac{1}{6}$
11. $3 \times \frac{1}{9}$
12. $5 \times \frac{6}{7}$

13. $\frac{3}{5} \times 15$
14. $3\frac{1}{2} \times 4\frac{1}{3}$
15. $\frac{4}{5} \times 2\frac{3}{4}$
16. $6\frac{1}{8} \times 5\frac{1}{7}$

17. $2\frac{2}{3} \times 2\frac{1}{4}$
18. $\frac{7}{8} \times 16$
19. $5\frac{1}{5} \times 2\frac{1}{2}$
20. $7 \times \frac{1}{14}$

21. $22 \times \frac{3}{11}$
22. $8\frac{2}{3} \times 1\frac{1}{2}$
23. $4 \times 6\frac{1}{2}$
24. $\frac{1}{2} \times 10\frac{2}{3}$

25. $\frac{2}{3} \times 21\frac{1}{3}$
26. $\frac{7}{8} \times \frac{8}{7}$
27. $21 \times \frac{1}{2}$
28. $11 \times \frac{1}{4}$

PART C

PAGES 118–119

Use the *draw a diagram* strategy to solve the following problems.

1. **TESTS** The scores on a test are found by adding or subtracting points as shown below. If Salazar's score on a 15-question test was 86 points, how many of his answers were correct, incorrect, and blank?

Answer	Points
Correct	+8
Incorrect	−4
Blank	−2

2. **GAMES** Six members of a video game club are having a tournament. In the first round, every player will play a video game against every other player. How many games will be in the first round of the tournament?

3. **PLAYS** In a play, $\frac{2}{5}$ of the cast members are 21 years of age or older. One-third of the remaining cast members are under age 21. If 5 people are under 21 years old, how many people are in the cast?

PART D

PAGES 120–125

Divide. Write in simplest form.

1. $\frac{2}{3} \div \frac{3}{2}$
2. $\frac{3}{5} \div \frac{2}{5}$
3. $\frac{7}{10} \div \frac{3}{8}$

4. $\frac{5}{9} \div \frac{2}{5}$
5. $4 \div \frac{2}{3}$
6. $8 \div \frac{4}{5}$

7. $9 \div \frac{5}{9}$
8. $\frac{2}{7} \div 2$
9. $\frac{1}{14} \div 7$

10. $15 \div \frac{3}{5}$
11. $\frac{9}{14} \div \frac{3}{4}$
12. $\frac{7}{8} \div 10$

13. $16 \div \frac{3}{4}$
14. $\frac{3}{8} \div 2\frac{1}{2}$
15. $5\frac{1}{2} \div 2\frac{1}{2}$

16. $3\frac{1}{4} \div 5\frac{1}{2}$
17. $12\frac{5}{6} \div 2\frac{1}{6}$
18. $7\frac{1}{2} \div 3\frac{1}{2}$

EP6 Extra Practice

Multi-Part Lesson 2-3 (continued)

PART E

PAGES 126–129

Write each power as a product of the same factor.

1. 13^4
2. 9^6
3. 1^7
4. 12^2
5. 5^8
6. 15^4

Evaluate each expression.

7. 5^6
8. 17^3
9. 2^{12}
10. 3^5
11. 1^4
12. 5^3
13. 10^2
14. 2^8
15. 8^2
16. 7^4
17. 20^3
18. 42^3

Write each product in exponential form.

19. $2 \cdot 2 \cdot 2 \cdot 2 \cdot 2$
20. $3 \cdot 3$
21. $1 \cdot 1 \cdot 1 \cdot 1 \cdot 1 \cdot 1$
22. $18 \cdot 18 \cdot 18 \cdot 18$
23. $9 \cdot 9 \cdot 9 \cdot 9 \cdot 9 \cdot 9 \cdot 9 \cdot 9$
24. $10 \cdot 10 \cdot 10 \cdot 10 \cdot 10 \cdot 10$

Multi-Part Lesson 3-1

PARTS A B

PAGES 144–147

Use the *work backward* strategy to solve each problem.

1. **NUMBERS** A number is divided by 2. Then 4 is added to the quotient. Next, the sum of these numbers is multiplied by 3. The result is 21. Find the number.

2. **MONEY** Holly spent $13.76 on a birthday present for her mom. She also spent $3.25 on a snack for herself. If she now has $7.74, how much money did she have initially?

3. **DVDS** Jeffrey rented 2 times as many DVDs as Paloma last month. Paloma rented 4 fewer than Robbie, but 4 more than Sanjay. Robbie rented 9 DVDs. How many DVDs did each person rent?

4. **TIME** A portion of a shuttle bus schedule is shown. What is the earliest time after 9 A.M. when the bus departs?

Departs	Arrives
8:55 A.M.	9:20 A.M.
?	10:08 A.M.
10:31 A.M.	10:56 A.M.
11:19 A.M.	11:44 A.M.

5. **FOOD** After four days, 0.5 pound of lunch meat was left in the refrigerator. If half this amount was eaten on each of the previous four days, how much lunch meat was initially in the refrigerator?

PARTS C D

PAGES 148–155

Solve each equation. Check your solution.

1. $r - 3 = 14$
2. $t + 3 = 21$
3. $s + 10 = 23$
4. $7 + a = -10$
5. $14 + m = 24$
6. $-9 + n = 13$
7. $s - 2 = -6$
8. $6 + f = 71$
9. $x + 27 = 30$
10. $k - 9 = -3$
11. $j + 12 = 11$
12. $-42 + v = -42$
13. $s + 1.3 = 18$
14. $x + 7.4 = 23.5$
15. $p + 3.1 = 18$
16. $w - 3.7 = 4.63$
17. $m - 4.8 = 7.4$
18. $x - 1.3 = 12$
19. $y + 3.4 = 18$
20. $7.2 + g = 9.1$
21. $z - 12.1 = 14$
22. $v - 18 = 13\frac{7}{10}$
23. $w - \frac{1}{10} = \frac{8}{25}$
24. $r + 6\frac{7}{10} = 1\frac{1}{5}$

Multi-Part Lesson 3-2
PARTS A B
PAGES 156–161

Solve each equation. Check your solution.

1. $2m = 18$
2. $-42 = 6n$
3. $72 = 8k$
4. $-20r = 20$
5. $420 = 5s$
6. $325 = 25t$
7. $-14 = -2p$
8. $18q = 36$
9. $40 = 10a$
10. $100 = 20b$
11. $416 = 4c$
12. $45 = 9d$
13. $0.5m = 3.5$
14. $1.8 = 0.6x$
15. $0.4y = 2$
16. $1.86 = 6.2z$
17. $-8x = 24$
18. $8.34 = 2r$
19. $1.67t = 10.02$
20. $243 = 27a$
21. $0.9x = 4.5$
22. $\frac{r}{7} = -8$
23. $\frac{w}{7} = 8$
24. $\frac{y}{12} = -6$
25. $\frac{c}{-4} = 10$
26. $\frac{s}{9} = 8$
27. $\frac{m}{8} = 5$

PARTS C D
PAGES 162–168

Find the multiplicative inverse of each number.

1. $\frac{2}{3}$
2. $\frac{5}{4}$
3. 1
4. 10
5. $\frac{1}{7}$
6. $\frac{9}{16}$
7. $1\frac{1}{3}$
8. $3\frac{3}{4}$
9. $7\frac{3}{8}$
10. $6\frac{2}{5}$
11. $33\frac{1}{3}$
12. $66\frac{2}{3}$

Solve each equation. Check your solution.

13. $\frac{a}{13} = 2$
14. $\frac{8}{9}x = 24$
15. $\frac{3}{8}r = 36$
16. $\frac{3}{4}t = \frac{1}{2}$
17. $16 = \frac{h}{4}$
18. $\frac{m}{8} = 12$
19. $\frac{5}{8}n = 45$
20. $10 = \frac{b}{10}$
21. $\frac{1}{7}x = 7$
22. $5 = \frac{1}{5}y$
23. $\frac{4}{3}m = 28$
24. $\frac{2}{3}z = 20$
25. $\frac{c}{9} = 81$
26. $\frac{m}{9} = 9$
27. $16 = \frac{4}{9}f$
28. $\frac{15}{8}x = 225$

Multi-Part Lesson 3-3
PARTS A B
PAGES 170–176

Solve each equation. Check your solution.

1. $3x + 6 = 6$
2. $2r - 7 = -1$
3. $-10 + 2d = 8$
4. $2b + 4 = -8$
5. $5w - 12 = 3$
6. $5t - 4 = 6$
7. $2q - 6 = 4$
8. $2g - 3 = -9$
9. $15 = 6y + 3$
10. $3s - 4 = 8$
11. $18 - 7f = 4$
12. $13 + 3p = 7$
13. $7.5r + 2 = -28$
14. $4.2 + 7z = 2.8$
15. $-9m - 9 = 9$
16. $32 + 0.2c = 1$
17. $5t - 14 = -14$
18. $-0.25x + 0.5 = 4$
19. $5w - 4 = 8$
20. $4d - 3 = 9$
21. $2g - 16 = -9$
22. $4k + 13 = 20$
23. $7 = 5 - 2x$
24. $8z + 15 = -1$
25. $92 - 16b = 12$
26. $14e + 14 = 28$
27. $1.1j + 2 = 7.5$

Multi-Part Lesson 3-3 (continued)
PARTS C D
PAGES 177–181

Express each equation as another equivalent equation. Justify your answer.

1. $x - 6 = -3x + 10$ **2.** $2x + 7 = x - 6$ **3.** $5x - 3 = 18 + 2x$

Solve each equation. Check your solution.

4. $11x - 7 = 5 - x$ **5.** $2 - 8x = 10x + 20$ **6.** $17 - 3x = 2 + 2x$

7. $4x - 5 = 2x + 11$ **8.** $\frac{x}{2} + 4 = \frac{5}{2}x - 6$ **9.** $7 - 4x = x + 12$

10. $-1 + 8x = 4x + 5$ **11.** $-6 - 5x = 12 - x$ **12.** $6x + 11 = 4x + 10$

13. $3 + \frac{x}{6} = -2 + x$ **14.** $-9x + 7 = 25 - 3x$ **15.** $-42 + 3x = 12 - 3x$

Multi-Part Lesson 4-1
PARTS A B
PAGES 195–201

Find each unit rate. Round to the nearest hundredth if necessary.

1. $240 for 4 days

2. 250 people in 5 buses

3. 500 miles in 10 hours

4. $18 for 24 pounds

5. 32 people in 8 cars

6. $4.50 for 3 dozen

7. 245 tickets in 5 days

8. 12 classes in 4 semesters

9. 60 people in 4 rows

10. 48 ounces in 3 pounds

11. 20 people in 4 groups

12. 1.5 pounds for $3.00

13. 45 miles in 60 minutes

14. $5.50 for 10 disks

15. 360 miles on 12 gallons

16. $8.50 for 5 yards

17. 24 cups for $1.20

18. 160 words in 4 minutes

19. $60 for 5 books

20. $24 for 6 hours

PART C
PAGES 202–205

1. POPCORN Fun Center rents popcorn machines for $20 per hour. In addition to the hourly charge, there is a rental fee of $32. Is the number of hours you rent the popcorn machine proportional to the total cost?

2. BAKING Mrs. Govin is making cakes for the school bake sale. She needs 2 cups of sugar for every cake she makes. Is the number of cakes Mrs. Govin makes proportional to the number of cups of sugar?

3. MUSIC At a local music store, CDs cost $11.99 including tax. Is the number of CDs purchased proportional to the cost of the CDs?

4. SAVINGS Jean has $280 in her savings account. Starting next week, she will deposit $30 in her account every week. Is the amount of money in her account proportional to the number of weeks?

Multi-Part Lesson 4-1 (continued)
PARTS D E

PAGES 206–211

Solve each proportion.

1. $\dfrac{x}{15} = \dfrac{4}{5}$ **2.** $\dfrac{a}{11} = \dfrac{24}{8}$ **3.** $\dfrac{19}{p} = \dfrac{16}{32}$ **4.** $\dfrac{5}{t} = \dfrac{0.5}{0.3}$

5. $\dfrac{5}{19} = \dfrac{c}{57}$ **6.** $\dfrac{3.6}{3} = \dfrac{b}{2.5}$ **7.** $\dfrac{18}{4.5} = \dfrac{8}{f}$ **8.** $\dfrac{36}{7} = \dfrac{a}{21}$

9. $\dfrac{9}{8} = \dfrac{36}{a}$ **10.** $\dfrac{b}{126} = \dfrac{3}{14}$ **11.** $\dfrac{n}{6} = \dfrac{1}{4}$ **12.** $\dfrac{7}{9} = \dfrac{c}{54}$

13. $\dfrac{2}{3} = \dfrac{a}{12}$ **14.** $\dfrac{7}{8} = \dfrac{c}{16}$ **15.** $\dfrac{3}{7} = \dfrac{21}{d}$ **16.** $\dfrac{2}{5} = \dfrac{18}{x}$

17. $\dfrac{3}{5} = \dfrac{n}{21}$ **18.** $\dfrac{5}{12} = \dfrac{b}{5}$ **19.** $\dfrac{4}{36} = \dfrac{2}{y}$ **20.** $\dfrac{16}{8} = \dfrac{y}{12}$

Multi-Part Lesson 4-2
PART A

PAGES 212–213

Use the *draw a diagram* strategy to solve the problem.

1. PICTURE FRAMES Mr. Francisco has 4 picture frames that he wants to hang on the wall. In how many different ways can he hang the picture frames in a row on the wall?

2. PONDS Carter is filling the pond in his backyard. After 2 minutes and 20 seconds, the pond is only $\frac{1}{7}$ full. If the pond can hold 280 gallons, how much longer will it take to fill the pond?

3. MARCHING BAND The marching band is in formation on the field. In the first row, there are 10 band members. Each additional row has 6 more members in it than the previous row. If there are a total of 6 rows, how many band members are there?

PARTS B C

PAGES 214–221

On a map, the scale is 1 inch = 50 miles. For each map distance, find the actual distance.

1. 5 inches   **2.** 12 inches

3. $2\frac{3}{8}$ inches   **4.** $\frac{4}{5}$ inch

5. $2\frac{5}{6}$ inches   **6.** 3.25 inches

7. 4.75 inches   **8.** 5.25 inches

On a scale drawing, the scale is $\frac{1}{2}$ inch = 2 feet. Find the dimensions of each room in the scale drawing.

9. 14 feet by 18 feet   **10.** 32 feet by 6 feet

11. 3 feet by 5 feet   **12.** 20 feet by 30 feet

13. A photograph was enlarged from 5.5 inches by 7 inches to 11 inches by 14 inches. Find the scale factor of the enlargement.

Multi-Part Lesson 4-3

PART A

Find the value of x in each pair of similar figures.

1.

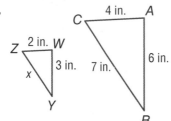

2.

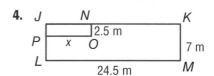

3.

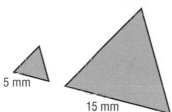

4.

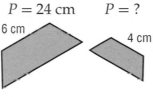

PARTS B C

For each pair of similar figures, find the perimeter of the second figure.

1. $P = 15$ $P = ?$

5 mm

15 mm

2. $P = 24$ cm $P = ?$

6 cm

4 cm

3. $P = 42$ in. $P = ?$

12 in.   8 in.

Multi-Part Lesson 5-1

PARTS A B

Copy and complete each function table. Then identify the domain and range.

1.

x	2x	y
0		
1		
2		
3		

2.

x	3x + 1	y
1		
2		
3		
4		

3.

x	x − 2	y
3		
4		
5		
6		

4.

x	x + 0.1	y
2		
3		
4		
5		

Multi-Part Lesson 5-1 (continued)

PARTS C D

PAGES 253–258

Graph the function represented by the table.

1.

Total Cost of Tennis Balls	
Number of Tennis Balls	**Total Cost ($)**
3	6
4	8
5	10
6	12

2.

Convert Gallons to Quarts	
Gallon	**Quarts**
1	4
2	8
3	12
4	16

Graph each equation.

3. $y = 3x$

4. $y = 2x + 3$

5. $y = -x$

6. $y = 0.5x + 2$

7. $y = -x + 3$

8. $y = 0.25x + 6$

Multi-Part Lesson 5-2

PARTS A B

PAGES 259–263

For Exercises 1 and 2, find the rate of change for each table.

1.

Age (yr)	Height (in.)
9	54
10	56
11	58
12	60

2.

Time (h)	Temperature (°C)
0	0
4	3
8	6
12	9

3. **MOVIE RENTALS** The graph shows the cost of renting movies. Use the graph to find the rate of change.

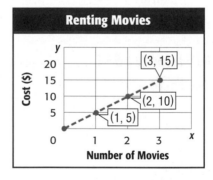

Renting Movies

PARTS C D

PAGES 264–268

1. The table below shows the number of apples y per basket x. Find the slope of the line.

Baskets	2	4	6	8
Apples	10	20	30	40

2. Find the slope of the line and describe what happens when the amount of flour decreases.

Baking Cookies

Multi-Part Lesson 5-3

PART **A** **PAGES 270–271**

WEATHER For Exercises 1–3, solve by using the graph.

1. In which month is the average high temperature about twice as high as the average low temperature for January?

2. What is the approximate difference between the average high temperature and the average low temperature each month?

3. Predict the high and low temperatures for June based on the data given on the graph.

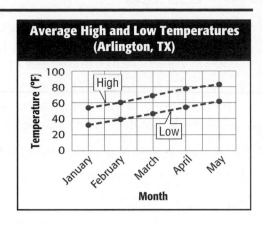

Average High and Low Temperatures (Arlington, TX)

CLUBS For Exercises 4–6, use the table that shows the math club membership from 2001 to 2006.

4. Make a graph of the data.

5. Describe how the number of math club memberships changed from 2001 to 2006.

6. What is a reasonable prediction for the membership in 2007 if this membership trend continues?

Math Club Membership

Year	Number of Students
2001	20
2002	21
2003	30
2004	34
2005	38
2006	45

PARTS **B** **C**

PAGES 272–278

TRAVEL Use the graph to answer Exercises 1 and 2.

1. The number of miles traveled varies directly with the number of hours traveled. What is the rate of speed in miles per hour?

2. Going at the rate shown, what distance would one travel in 39 hours?

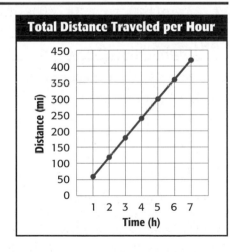

Total Distance Traveled per Hour

3. **GAS MILEAGE** Dustin's car can travel about 100 miles on 3 gallons of gas. Assuming that the distance traveled remains constant to the amount of gas used, how many gallons of gas would be needed to travel 650 miles?

4. **MONEY** Determine whether the linear function shown is a direct variation. If so, state the constant of variation.

Years, x	2	3	4	5
Savings, y	$2,154	$3,231	$4,308	$5,385

Multi-Part Lesson 5-3 (continued)

PARTS D E

1. The cost to print programs for football season varies inversely as the number of programs printed. If 1,250 programs are printed, the cost is $2.00 each. Find the cost per program if 2,000 programs are printed.

2. The base b of a parallelogram varies inversely as the height h. What is the base of a parallelogram when the height is 3.2 meters if the base is 9.3 meters when the height is 1.4 meters?

Solve. Assume that y varies inversely as x.

3. Suppose $x = 3$ when $y = 8$. Find x when $y = -4$.

4. Find x when $y = 25$ if $x = 50$ when $y = 2$.

5. If $x = 16$ when $y = 3$, find x when $y = 2$.

6. Find y when $x = 4.5$ if $y = 2.4$ when $x = 1.5$.

7. Suppose $y = -\frac{3}{4}$ when $x = \frac{1}{6}$. Find x when $y = -\frac{5}{12}$.

8. If $y = -9$ when $x = -3.2$, find y when $x = -1.5$.

Multi-Part Lesson 6-1

PARTS A B

Find each number. Round to the nearest tenth if necessary.

1. 5% of 40	**2.** 10% of 120	**3.** 12% of 150	**4.** 12.5% of 40
5. 75% of 200	**6.** 13% of 25.3	**7.** 250% of 44	**8.** 0.5% of 13.7
9. 600% of 7	**10.** 1.5% of $25	**11.** 81% of 134	**12.** 43% of 110
13. 61% of 524	**14.** 100% of 3.5	**15.** 20% of 58.5	**16.** 45% of 125.5
17. 23% of 500	**18.** 80% of 8	**19.** 90% of 72	**20.** 32% of 54

PART C

Estimate by using fractions.

1. 28% of 48	**2.** 99% of 65	**3.** 445% of 20
4. 9% of 81	**5.** 73% of 240	**6.** 65.5% of 75
7. 48.2% of 93	**8.** 39.45% of 51	**9.** 287% of 122
10. 53% of 80	**11.** 414% of 72	**12.** 59% of 105

Estimate by using 10%.

13. 30% of 42	**14.** 70% of 104	**15.** 90% of 152	**16.** 67% of 70
17. 78% of 92	**18.** 12% of 183	**19.** 51% of 221	**20.** 23% of 504
21. 81% of 390	**22.** 41% of 60	**23.** 59% of 178	**24.** 22% of 450

Estimate.

25. 50% of 37	**26.** 18% of 90	**27.** 300% of 245
28. 1% of 48	**29.** 70% of 300	**30.** 35% of 35
31. 60.5% of 60	**32.** $5\frac{1}{2}$% of 100	**33.** 40.01% of 16
34. 80% of 62	**35.** 45% of 119	**36.** 14.81% of 986

Multi-Part Lesson 6-2

PARTS A B

PAGES 311–316

Find each number. Round to the nearest tenth if necessary.

1. What number is 25% of 280?
2. 38 is what percent of 50?
3. 54 is 25% of what number?
4. 24.5% of what number is 15?
5. What number is 80% of 500?
6. 12% of 120 is what number?
7. Find 68% of 50.
8. What percent of 240 is 32?
9. 99 is what percent of 150?
10. Find 75% of 1.
11. What number is $33\frac{1}{3}$% of 66?
12. 50% of 350 is what number?
13. What percent of 450 is 50?
14. What number is $37\frac{1}{2}$% of 32?
15. 95% of 40 is what number?
16. Find 30% of 26.
17. 9 is what percent of 30?
18. 52% of what number is 109.2?
19. What number is 65% of 200?
20. What number is 15.5% of 45?

PART C

PAGES 317–321

Write an equation for each problem. Then solve. Round to the nearest tenth if necessary.

1. Find 45% of 50.
2. 75 is what percent of 300?
3. 16% of what number is 2?
4. 75% of 80 is what number?
5. 5% of what number is 12?
6. Find 60% of 45.
7. 90 is what percent of 95?
8. $28\frac{1}{2}$% of 64 is what number?
9. Find 46.5% of 75.
10. What number is 55.5% of 70?
11. 80.5% of what number is 80.5?
12. $66\frac{2}{3}$% of what number is 40?
13. Find 122.5% of 80.
14. 250% of what number is 75?

PART D

PAGES 322–323

Solve each problem using the *reasonable answers* strategy.

1. **SKIING** Emil skied for 13.5 hours and estimated that he spent 30% of his time on the ski lift. Did he spend about 4, 6, or 8 hours on the ski lift?

2. **CLASS TRIP** The class trip at Wilson Middle School costs $145 per student. A fundraiser earns 38% of this cost. Will each student have to pay about $70, $80, or $90?

3. **GAS MILEAGE** Holden's car gets 38 miles per gallon and has 2.5 gallons of gasoline left in the tank. Can he drive for 85, 95, or 105 more miles before he runs out of gas?

4. **DINING** At a restaurant, the total cost of a meal is $87.50. Dawn wants to leave a 20% tip. Should she leave a total of $95, $105, or $115?

Multi-Part Lesson 6-3
PARTS A B

PAGES 325–330

Find each percent of change. Round to the nearest whole percent if necessary. State whether the percent of change is an *increase* or *decrease*.

1. 450 centimeters to 675 centimeters
2. 77 million to 200.2 million
3. 500 albums to 100 albums
4. 350 yards to 420 yards
5. 3.25 meters to 2.95 meters
6. $65 to $75
7. 180 dishes to 160 dishes
8. 450 pieces to 445.5 pieces
9. 700 grams to 910 grams
10. 55 women to 11 women
11. 412 children to 1,339 children
12. 464 kilograms to 20 kilograms
13. 24 hours to 86 hours
14. 16 minutes to 24 minutes

PART C

PAGES 331–334

Find the total cost to the nearest cent.

1. $45 sweater; 6% tax
2. $29 shirt; 7% tax
3. $145 coat; 6.25% tax
4. $12 meal; 4.5% tax
5. $105 skateboard; $7\frac{1}{2}$% tax
6. $12,500 car; $3\frac{3}{4}$% tax
7. $49.95 gloves; $5\frac{1}{4}$% tax
8. $525 stereo; 6% tax
9. Find the 20% tip for a $62 meal.
10. Find the original cost of the food if the bill is $38 including a 20% tip.

PART D

PAGES 335–338

Find the sale price to the nearest cent.

1. $18.99 CD; 15% discount
2. $199 ring; 10% discount
3. $19 purse; 25% discount
4. $899 computer; 20% discount
5. $599 TV; 12% discount
6. $210 watch; 20% discount

Find the percent of discount to the nearest percent.

7. sneakers: regular price, $72 sale price, $60
8. dress shirt: regular price, $90 sale price, $22.50
9. portable game player: regular price, $125 sale price, $100
10. car: regular price, $25,000 sale price, $22,000
11. hiking boots: regular price, $139 sale price, $113.98
12. airline tickets: regular price, $556 sale price, $500.40
13. CD: regular price, $15 sale price, $9
14. computer: regular price, $600 sale price, $450

Multi-Part Lesson 6-3 (continued)
PARTS E F

PAGES 339–343

Find the simple interest earned to the nearest cent for each principal, interest rate, and time.

1. $2,000, 8%, 5 years
2. $500, 10%, 8 months
3. $750, 5%, 1 year
4. $175.50, $6\frac{1}{2}$%, 18 months
5. $236.20, 9%, 16 months
6. $89, $7\frac{1}{2}$%, 6 months
7. $800, 5.75%, 3 years
8. $225, $1\frac{1}{2}$%, 2 years
9. $12,000, $4\frac{1}{2}$%, 40 months

Find the simple interest paid to the nearest cent for each loan, interest rate, and time.

10. $750, 18%, 2 years
11. $1,500, 19%, 16 months
12. $300, 9%, 1 year
13. $4,750, 19.5%, 30 months
14. $2,345, 17%, 9 months
15. $689, 12%, 2 years
16. $390, 18.75%, 15 months
17. $1,250, 22%, 8 months
18. $3,240, 18%, 14 months

Multi-Part Lesson 7-1
PARTS A B

PAGES 357–363

Display each set of data in a circle graph.

1.

Car Sales	
Style	**Percent**
Sedan	45%
SUV	22%
Pickup truck	9%
Sports car	13%
Compact car	11%

2.

Favorite Flavor of Ice Cream	
Flavor	**Number**
Vanilla	11
Chocolate	15
Strawberry	8
Mint chip	5
Cookie dough	3

PARTS C D

PAGES 364–369

Construct a histogram to represent the data.

1.

Cost of a Movie Ticket at Selected Theaters			
$5.25	$6.50	$3.50	$3.75
$7.50	$9.25	$10.40	$4.75
$10.00	$4.50	$8.75	$7.25
$3.50	$6.70	$4.20	$7.50

2.

Highest Recorded Wind Speeds for Selected U.S. Cities (mph)					
52	55	81	46	73	57
75	54	58	76	46	58
60	91	53	53	51	56
80	60	73	46	49	47

ARCHITECTURE For Exercises 3–6, use the histogram.

3. How many buildings are represented in the histogram?

4. Which interval represents the most number of buildings?

5. What percent of the buildings are taller than 70 feet?

6. What is the height of the tallest building?

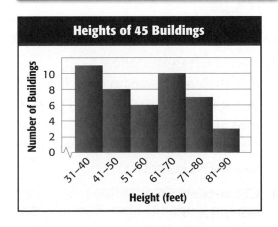

Heights of 45 Buildings

Multi-Part Lesson 7-1 (continued)

PART E
PAGES 370–374

Display each set of data in a stem-and-leaf plot.

1. 37, 44, 32, 53, 61, 59, 49, 69

2. 3, 26, 35, 8, 21, 24, 30, 39, 35, 5, 38

3. 15.7, 7.4, 0.6, 0.5, 15.3, 7.9, 7.3

4. 172, 198, 181, 182, 193, 171, 179, 186, 181

5. 55, 62, 81, 75, 71, 69, 74, 80, 67

6. 121, 142, 98, 106, 111, 125, 132, 109, 117, 126

7. 17, 54, 37, 86, 24, 69, 77, 92, 21

8. 7.3, 6.1, 8.9, 6.7, 8.2, 5.4, 9.3, 10.2, 5.9, 7.5, 8.3

For Exercises 9–11, use the stem-and-leaf plot shown at the right.

Stem	Leaf
7	2 2 3 5 9
8	0 1 1 4 6 6 8 9
9	3 4 8

$9 \mid 4 = 94$

9. What is the greatest value?

10. In which interval do most of the values occur?

11. What is the median value?

Multi-Part Lesson 7-2

PART A
PAGES 375–380

Use the spinner at the right to find each probability. Write as a fraction in simplest form.

1. P(even number)

2. P(prime number)

3. P(factor of 12)

4. P(composite number)

5. P(greater than 10)

6. P(neither prime nor composite)

A package of balloons contains 5 green, 3 yellow, 4 red, and 8 pink balloons. Suppose you reach in the package and choose one balloon at random. Find the probability of each event. Write as a fraction in simplest form.

7. P(red balloon)

8. P(yellow balloon)

9. P(pink balloon)

10. P(orange balloon)

11. P(red or yellow balloon)

12. P(*not* green balloon)

PART B
PAGES 381–385

For each situation, find the sample space using a table or tree diagram.

1. rolling 2 number cubes

2. choosing an ice cream cone from waffle, plain, or sugar and a flavor of ice cream from chocolate, vanilla, or strawberry

3. making a sandwich from white, wheat, or rye bread, cheddar or Swiss cheese, and ham, turkey, or roast beef

4. tossing a penny twice

5. choosing one math class from Algebra and Geometry and one foreign language class from French, Spanish, or Latin

Multi-Part Lesson 7-2 (continued)
PART C

Use the Fundamental Counting Principle to find the total number of outcomes in each situation.

1. choosing a local phone number if the exchange is 398 and each of the four remaining digits is different

2. choosing a way to drive from Millville to Westwood if there are 5 roads that lead from Millville to Miamisburg, 3 roads that connect Miamisburg to Hathaway, and 4 highways that connect Hathaway to Westwood

3. tossing a quarter, rolling a number cube, and tossing a dime

4. spinning the spinners shown below

 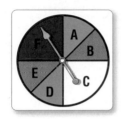 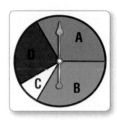

PARTS D E

Two socks are drawn from a drawer which contains one red sock, three blue socks, two black socks, and two green socks. Once a sock is selected, it is not replaced. Find each probability.

1. P(a black sock and then a green sock)   2. P(two blue socks)

There are three quarters, five dimes, and twelve pennies in a bag. Once a coin is drawn from the bag, it is not replaced. If two coins are drawn at random, find each probability.

3. P(a quarter and then a penny)   4. P(a nickel and then a dime)

Multi-Part Lesson 7-3
PARTS A B

The frequency table shows the results of a fair number cube rolled 40 times.

1. Find the experimental probability of rolling a 4.

2. Find the theoretical probability of *not* rolling a 4.

3. Find the theoretical probability of rolling a 2.

4. Find the experimental probability of *not* rolling a 6.

5. Suppose the number cube was rolled 500 times. About how many times would it land on 5?

Face	Frequency
1	5
2	9
3	2
4	8
5	12
6	4

Multi-Part Lesson 7-3 (continued)

PART C

Use the *act it out* strategy to solve each problem.

1. **STAIRS** Lynnette lives on a certain floor of her apartment building. She goes up two flights of stairs to put a load of laundry in a washing machine on that floor. Then she goes down five flights to borrow a book from a friend. Next, she goes up 8 flights to visit another friend who is ill. How many flights up or down does Lynette now have to go to take her laundry out of the washing machine?

2. **LOGIC PUZZLE** Suppose you are on the west side of a river with a fox, a duck, and a bag of corn. You want to take all three to the other side of the river, but...

   - your boat is only large enough to carry you and either the fox, duck, or bag of corn.
   - you cannot leave the fox alone with the duck.
   - you cannot leave the duck alone with the corn.
   - you cannot leave the corn alone on the east side of the river because some wild birds will eat it.
   - the wild birds are afraid of the fox.
   - you cannot leave the fox, duck, and the corn alone.
   - you can bring something across the river more than once.

   If there is no other way to cross the river, how do you get everything to the other side?

PARTS D E

1. **SURVEYS** The table shows the results of a survey of students' favorite cookies. Predict how many of the 424 students at Scobey High School prefer chocolate chip cookies.

Cookie	Number
Chocolate chip	49
Peanut butter	12
Oatmeal	10
Sugar	8
Raisin	3

2. **VACATION** The circle graph shows the results of a survey of teens and where they would prefer to spend a family vacation. Predict how many of 4,000 teens would prefer to go to an amusement park.

Vacation Survey

5% Foreign country
7% Other
18% Mountains
45% Amusement park
25% Beach

3. **TRAVEL** In 2000, about 29% of the foreign visitors to the U.S. were from Canada. If a particular hotel had 150,000 foreign guests in one year, how many would you predict were from Canada?

Multi-Part Lesson 7-3 (continued)
PART F

PAGES 414–418

Determine whether the conclusions are valid. Justify your answer.

1. To award prizes at a hockey game, four tickets with individual seat numbers printed on them are picked from a barrel. Since Elvio's section was not selected for any of the four prizes, he assumes that they forgot to include the entire section in the drawing.

2. To evaluate the quality of the televisions coming off the assembly line, the manufacturer takes one every half hour and tests it. About 1 out of every 10,000 is found to have a minor mechanical problem. The company assumes from this data that about 1 out of every 10,000 televisions they produce will be returned for mechanical problems after being purchased.

Multi-Part Lesson 8-1
PARTS A B

PAGES 431–437

Find the volume of each prism. Round to the nearest tenth if necessary.

1.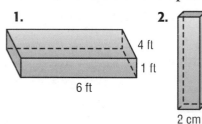
4 ft
1 ft
6 ft

2. 8.5 cm
2 cm
2 cm

3.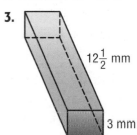
$12\frac{1}{2}$ mm
3 mm
4 mm

4.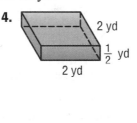
2 yd
$\frac{1}{2}$ yd
2 yd

5.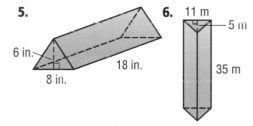
6 in.
8 in.
18 in.

6. 11 m
5 m
35 m

7.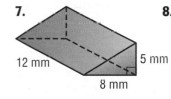
12 mm
5 mm
8 mm

8.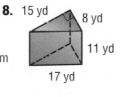
15 yd
8 yd
11 yd
17 yd

Find the volume of each rectangular prism. Round to the nearest tenth if necessary.

9. base = 3 ft
width = 10 ft
height = 2 ft

10. base = 18 cm
width = 23 cm
height = 15 cm

11. base = 25 mm
width = 32 mm
height = 10 mm

12. base = 1.5 in.
width = 3 in.
height = 6 in.

13. base = 4.5 cm
width = 6.75 cm
height = 2 cm

14. base = 16 mm
width = 0.7 mm
height = 12 mm

15. base = $3\frac{1}{2}$ ft
width = 10 ft
height = 6 ft

16. base = $5\frac{1}{2}$ in.
width = 12 in.
height = $3\frac{3}{8}$ in.

17. Find the volume of a rectangular prism with a base of 3 yards, a width of 5 feet, and a height of 12 feet.

18. Find the volume of a triangular prism with a base area of 416 square feet and height of 22 feet.

Multi-Part Lesson 8-1 (continued)

PART C PAGES 438–442

Find the volume of each cylinder. Round to the nearest tenth.

1.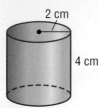
2 cm
4 cm

2.
3 yd
6.5 yd

3.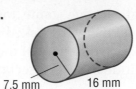
7.5 mm   16 mm

4.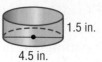
1.5 in.
4.5 in.

5. radius = 6 in.
   height = 3 in.

6. radius = 8 ft
   height = 10 ft

7. radius = 6 km
   height = 12 km

8. radius = 8.5 cm
   height = 3 cm

9. diameter = 16 yd
   height = 4.5 yd

10. diameter = 3.5 mm
    height = 2.5 mm

11. diameter = 12 m
    height = 4.75 m

12. diameter = $\frac{5}{8}$ in.
    height = 4 in.

13. diameter = 100 ft
    height = 35 ft

14. radius = 40.5 m
    height = 65.1 m

15. radius = 0.5 cm
    height = 1.6 cm

16. diameter = $8\frac{3}{4}$ in.
    height = $5\frac{1}{2}$ in.

17. Find the volume of a cylinder with a diameter of 6 inches and height of 24 inches. Round to the nearest tenth.

18. How tall is a cylinder that has a volume of 2,123 cubic meters and a radius of 13 meters? Round to the nearest tenth.

19. A cylinder has a volume of 310.2 cubic yards and a radius of 2.9 yards. What is the height of the cylinder? Round to the nearest tenth.

20. Find the height of a cylinder with a diameter of 25 centimeters and volume of 8,838 cubic centimeters. Round to the nearest tenth.

PARTS D E PAGES 443–448

Find the volume of each pyramid. Round to the nearest tenth if necessary.

1.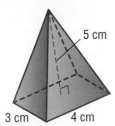
5 cm
3 cm   4 cm

2.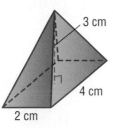
3 cm
4 cm
2 cm

3.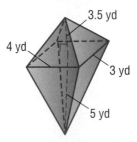
3.5 yd
4 yd
3 yd
5 yd

PART F PAGES 449–452

Find the volume of each cone. Round to the nearest tenth if necessary.

1.
15 ft
11 ft

2.
12 yd
7 yd

3.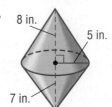
8 in.
5 in.
7 in.

Multi-Part Lesson 8-2

PARTS Ⓐ Ⓑ

Find the surface area of each rectangular prism. Round to the nearest tenth if necessary.

1.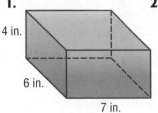
4 in.
6 in.
7 in.

2.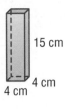
15 cm
4 cm
4 cm

3.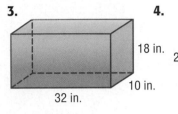
18 in.
10 in.
32 in.

4.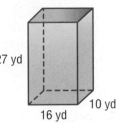
27 yd
10 yd
16 yd

5. base = 10 m
width = 6 m
height = 7 m

6. base = 20 mm
width = 15 mm
height = 25 mm

7. base = 16 ft
width = 20 ft
height = 12 ft

8. base = 52 cm
width = 48 cm
height = 45 cm

9. base = 8 ft
width = 6.5 ft
height = 7 ft

10. base = 9.4 m
width = 2 m
height = 5.2 m

11. base = 20.4 cm
width = 15.5 cm
height = 8.8 cm

12. base = 8.5 mi
width = 3 mi
height = 5.8 mi

13. base = $7\frac{1}{4}$ ft

width = 5 ft

height = $6\frac{1}{2}$ ft

14. base = $15\frac{2}{3}$ yd

width = $7\frac{1}{3}$ yd

height = 9 yd

15. base = $4\frac{1}{2}$ in.

width = 10 in.

height = $8\frac{3}{4}$ in.

16. base = 12.2 mm

width = 7.4 mm

height = 7.4 mm

17. Find the surface area of an open-top box with a base of 18 yards, a width of 11 yards, and a height of 14 yards.

18. Find the surface area of a rectangular prism with a base of 1 yard, a width of 7 feet, and a height of 2 yards.

PARTS Ⓒ Ⓓ

Find the surface area of each cylinder. Round to the nearest tenth.

1.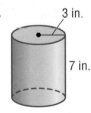
3 in.
7 in.

2.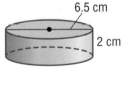
6.5 cm
2 cm

3.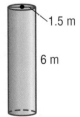
1.5 m
6 m

4.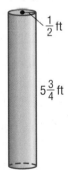
$\frac{1}{2}$ ft
$5\frac{3}{4}$ ft

5. height = 6 cm
radius = 3.5 cm

6. height = 16.5 mm
diameter = 18 mm

7. height = 22 yd
radius = 10.5 yd

8. height = 6 ft
radius = 18.5 ft

9. height = 10.2 mi
diameter = 4 mi

10. height = 8.6 cm
diameter = 8.2 cm

11. height = 5.8 km
diameter = 3.6 km

12. height = 32.7 m
radius = 21.5 m

13. height = $2\frac{2}{3}$ yd

diameter = 6 yd

14. height = $12\frac{3}{4}$ ft

radius = $7\frac{1}{4}$ ft

15. height = $5\frac{1}{5}$ mi

radius = $18\frac{1}{3}$ mi

16. height = $5\frac{1}{2}$ in.

diameter = 3 in.

Multi-Part Lesson 8-2 (continued)
PARTS **E** **F**

PAGES 468–473

Find the surface area of each pyramid. Round to the nearest tenth if necessary.

1.

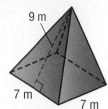

9 m

7 m

7 m

2.

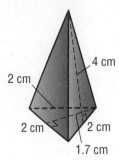

4 cm

2 cm

2 cm   2 cm

1.7 cm

3.

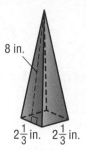

8 in.

$2\frac{1}{3}$ in. $2\frac{1}{3}$ in.

Multi-Part Lesson 8-3
PART **A**

PAGES 476–477

Use the *solve a simpler problem* strategy to solve each problem.

1. **EARNINGS** Cedric makes $51,876 each year. If he is paid once every two weeks and actually takes home about 67% of his wages after taxes, how much does he take home each paycheck? Round to the nearest cent if necessary.

2. **CARS** Jonah plans to decorate the rims on his tires by putting a strip of shiny metal around the outside edge on each rim. The diameter of each tire is 17 inches, and each rim is 2.75 inches from the outside edge of each tire. If he plans to cut the four individual pieces for each tire from the same strip of metal, how long of a strip should he buy? Round to the nearest tenth.

3. **SAVINGS** Erin's aunt invested a total of $1,500 into three different savings accounts. She invested $450 into a savings account with an annual interest rate of 3.25% and $600 into a savings account with an annual interest rate of 4.75%. The third savings account had an annual interest rate of 4.375%. After 3 years, how much money will Erin's aunt have in the three accounts altogether if she made no more additional deposits or withdrawals? Round to the nearest cent.

BIOLOGY For Exercises 4–6, use the following information.
About five quarts of blood are pumped through the average human heart in one minute.

4. At this rate, how many quarts of blood are pumped through the average human heart in one year? (Use 365 days = 1 year.)

5. If the average heart beats 72 times per minute, how many quarts of blood are pumped with each beat? Round to the nearest tenth.

6. About how many total gallons of blood are pumped through the average human heart in one week?

7. **LAND** A rectangular plot of land measures 1,450 feet by 850 feet. A contractor wishes to section off a portion of this land to build an apartment complex. If the complex is 425 feet by 550 feet, how many square feet of land will not be sectioned off to build it?

Multi-Part Lesson 8-3 (continued)
PARTS B C

PAGES 478–484

Find the volume of each composite figure. Round to the nearest tenth if necessary.

1.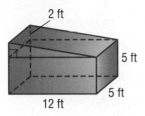
2 ft
5 ft
5 ft
12 ft

2.
12 m
3.5 m 3 m

3.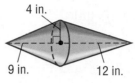
4 in.
9 in. 12 in.

Find the surface area of each composite figure. Round to the nearest tenth if necessary.

4.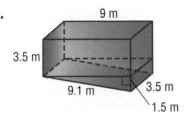
9 m
3.5 m
9.1 m 3.5 m
1.5 m

5.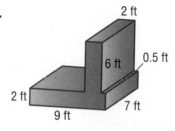
2 ft
6 ft 0.5 ft
2 ft
9 ft 7 ft

6. Find the surface area of the inside, outside, and end surfaces of the pipe at the right.

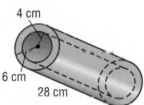
4 cm
6 cm
28 cm

Multi-Part Lesson 9-1
PARTS A B

PAGES 498–504

Complete.

1. 4,000 lb = ■ T
2. 5 T = ■ lb
3. 5 lb = ■ oz

4. 12,000 lb = ■ T
5. $\frac{1}{4}$ lb = ■ oz
6. 12 pt = ■ c

7. 3 gal = ■ pt
8. 24 fl oz = ■ c
9. 8 pt = ■ c

10. 10 pt = ■ qt
11. $2\frac{1}{4}$ c = ■ fl oz
12. 6 lb = ■ oz

13. 10 gal = ■ qt
14. 4 qt = ■ fl oz
15. 4 pt = ■ c

PART C

PAGES 505–508

Complete. Round to the nearest hundredth if necessary.

1. 400 mm = ■ cm
2. 4 km = ■ m
3. 660 cm = ■ m

4. 0.3 km = ■ m
5. 30 mm = ■ cm
6. 84.5 m = ■ km

7. ■ m = 54 cm
8. 18 km = ■ cm
9. ■ mm = 45 cm

10. 4 kg = ■ g
11. 632 mg = ■ g
12. 4,497 g = ■ kg

13. ■ mg = 0.51 kg
14. 0.63 kg = ■ g
15. ■ kg = 563 g

16. 662 m = ■ km
17. 5,283 mL = ■ L
18. 0.24 cm = ■ mm

19. 380 kL = ■ L
20. 10.8 g = ■ mg
21. 83,000 mL = ■ L

Multi-Part Lesson 9-1 (continued)
PART D

PAGES 509–512

Complete. Round to the nearest hundredth if necessary.

1. $2 \text{ ft} \approx \blacksquare \text{ m}$
2. $37 \text{ cm} \approx \blacksquare \text{ in.}$
3. $2.3 \text{ lb} \approx \blacksquare \text{ kg}$

4. $2 \text{ L} \approx \blacksquare \text{ gal}$
5. $5,280 \text{ mi} \approx \blacksquare \text{ km}$
6. $4 \text{ yd} \approx \blacksquare \text{ m}$

7. $3.6 \text{ lb} \approx \blacksquare \text{ g}$
8. $271 \text{ km} \approx \blacksquare \text{ mi}$
9. $500 \text{ m} \approx \blacksquare \text{ ft}$

10. $1,200 \text{ kg} \approx \blacksquare \text{ T}$
11. $16 \text{ in.} \approx \blacksquare \text{ cm}$
12. $2.4 \text{ c} \approx \blacksquare \text{ mL}$

13. $108 \text{ lb} \approx \blacksquare \text{ kg}$
14. $2,000 \text{ mL} \approx \blacksquare \text{ qt}$
15. $100 \text{ m} \approx \blacksquare \text{ yd}$

16. $56 \text{ in.} \approx \blacksquare \text{ cm}$
17. $32.8 \text{ ft} \approx \blacksquare \text{ m}$
18. $609 \text{ yd} \approx \blacksquare \text{ m}$

19. $21.78 \text{ mi} \approx \blacksquare \text{ km}$
20. $48 \text{ lb} \approx \blacksquare \text{ g}$
21. $2.3 \text{ T} \approx \blacksquare \text{ kg}$

22. $8.5 \text{ c} \approx \blacksquare \text{ mL}$
23. $33 \text{ gal} \approx \blacksquare \text{ L}$
24. $1.8 \text{ qt} \approx \blacksquare \text{ mL}$

PART E

PAGES 513–516

1. The winner in a recent Los Angeles Marathon ran the 26-mile race in 2.23 hours. About how many yards per minute did he run?

2. A swimming pool can be filled at the rate of 25 liters per minute using a special pump. About how many hours will it take to fill a pool that holds 5,000 gallons of water?

3. The desalinization plant in Tampa Bay can process 25 million gallons of water a day. About how many liters of water per hour does it process?

Convert each rate. Round to the nearest tenth if necessary.

4. $55 \text{ mi/h} = \blacksquare \text{ ft/s}$
5. $8 \text{ gal/h} = \blacksquare \text{ L/min}$
6. $12 \text{ m/min} = \blacksquare \text{ ft/s}$

7. $50 \text{ g/cm} = \blacksquare \text{ oz/in.}$
8. $15 \text{ qt/h} = \blacksquare \text{ gal/min}$
9. $2.6 \text{ oz/50 lb} = \blacksquare \text{ g/kg}$

PART F

PAGES 517–522

Complete. Round to the nearest hundredth if necessary.

1. $8 \text{ yd}^2 = \blacksquare \text{ ft}^2$
2. $12 \text{ m}^2 = \blacksquare \text{ cm}^2$
3. $450 \text{ mm}^2 = \blacksquare \text{ cm}^2$

4. $1,000 \text{ in}^2 = \blacksquare \text{ ft}^2$
5. $18 \text{ ft}^2 = \blacksquare \text{ in}^2$
6. $100 \text{ ft}^2 = \blacksquare \text{ yd}^2$

7. $6.5 \text{ cm}^2 = \blacksquare \text{ mm}^2$
8. $8 \text{ cm}^2 = \blacksquare \text{ mm}^2$
9. $8.2 \text{ ft}^2 = \blacksquare \text{ in}^2$

Complete. Round to the nearest hundredth if necessary.

10. $3,000,000 \text{ cm}^3 = \blacksquare \text{ m}^3$
11. $100 \text{ mm}^3 = \blacksquare \text{ cm}^3$
12. $100 \text{ in}^3 = \blacksquare \text{ ft}^3$

13. $5 \text{ ft}^3 = \blacksquare \text{ in}^3$
14. $100,000,000 \text{ cm}^3 = \blacksquare \text{ m}^3$
15. $4,000 \text{ in}^3 = \blacksquare \text{ ft}^3$

16. $13.5 \text{ yd}^3 = \blacksquare \text{ ft}^3$
17. $8.4 \text{ cm}^3 = \blacksquare \text{ mm}^3$
18. $1,000 \text{ in}^3 = \blacksquare \text{ ft}^3$

Multi-Part Lesson 9-2

PART (A)

PAGES 524–525

Use the *make a model* strategy to solve each problem.

1. **ARCHITECTURE** An architect is designing a large skyscraper for a local firm. The skyscraper is to be 1,200 feet tall, 500 feet long, and 400 feet wide. If his model has a scale of 80 feet = 1 inch, find the volume of the model.

2. **STACKING BOXES** Box A has twice the volume of Box B. Box B has a height of 10 centimeters and a length of 5 centimeters. Box A has a width of 20 centimeters, a length of 10 centimeters, and a height of 5 centimeters. What is the width of Box B?

3. **TRAVEL** On Monday, Mara drove 400 miles as part of her journey to see her sister. She drove 60% of this distance on Tuesday. If the distance she drove on Tuesday represents one third of her total journey, how many more miles does she still need to drive?

4. **PIZZA** On Monday, there was a whole pizza in the refrigerator. On Tuesday, Enrico ate $\frac{1}{3}$ of the pizza. On Wednesday, he ate $\frac{1}{3}$ of what was left. On Thursday, he ate $\frac{1}{2}$ of what remained. What fraction of the pizza is left?

5. **GARDENS** Mr. Hawkins has a circular garden in his backyard. He wants to build a curved brick pathway around the entire garden. The garden has a radius of 18 feet. The distance from the center of the garden to the outside edge of the brick pathway will be 21.5 feet. Find the area of the brick pathway. Round to the nearest tenth.

PARTS (B) (C)

PAGES 526–533

1. The surface area of a triangular prism is 18.5 square inches. What is the surface area of a similar solid that has been enlarged by a scale factor of 2.5?

2. The volume of a cylinder is 630 cubic centimeters. What is the volume of a similar cylinder that has been reduced by a scale factor of $\frac{1}{3}$? Round to the nearest tenth.

3. The volume of water in the first floor touch tank at the Florida Aquarium in Tampa is 2,016 cubic feet. Betty is making a model and will use a scale of $\frac{1}{5}$. What will be the volume of water in her model?

4. The volume of the Great Pyramid in Egypt is approximately 33,764 cubic meters. What is the volume, to the nearest tenth, of a scale model that is smaller by a scale factor of $\frac{1}{12}$?

5. The surface area of Spaceship Earth at Epcot Center is 150,000 square feet. What would be the surface area of a model that is decreased by a scale of $\frac{1}{100}$?

Multi-Part Lesson 10-1

PARTS A B

1. Translate △ABC 2 units right and 1 unit down.

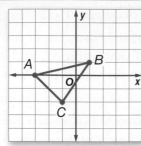

2. Translate quadrilateral RSTU 4 units left and 3 units down.

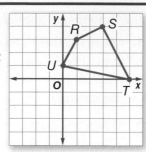

Triangle *TRI* has vertices *T*(1, 1), *R*(4, −2), and *I*(−2, −1). Find the vertices of *T′R′I′* after each translation. Then graph the figure and its translated image.

3. 2 units right, 1 unit down

4. 5 units left, 1 unit up

5. 3 units right

6. 2 units up

Multi-Part Lesson 10-2

PARTS A B

Determine whether each figure has line symmetry. Write *yes* or *no*. If *yes*, copy the figure and draw all lines of symmetry.

1.

2.

3.

4.

5.

6.

Graph each figure and its reflection over the *x*-axis. Then find the coordinates of the vertices of the reflected image.

7. quadrilateral *QUAD* with vertices *Q*(−1, 4), *U*(2, 2), *A*(1, 1), and *D*(−2, 2)

8. triangle *ABC* with vertices *A*(0, −1), *B*(4, −3), and *C*(−4, −5)

Graph each figure and its reflection over the *y*-axis. Then find the coordinates of the vertices of the reflected image.

9. parallelogram *PARL* with vertices *P*(3, 5), *A*(5, 4), *R*(5, 1), and *L*(3, 2)

10. pentagon *PENTA* with vertices *P*(−1, 3), *E*(1, 1), *N*(0, −2), *T*(−2, −2), and *A*(−3, 1)

Multi-Part Lesson 10-3
PARTS A B

PAGES 564–569

Graph triangle *ABC* and its image after each rotation. Then give the coordinates of the vertices for triangle *A′B′C′*.

1. 90° counterclockwise

2. 180° clockwise

3. 270° counterclockwise

4. 270° clockwise

Determine whether each sign has rotational symmetry. Write *yes* or *no*. If *yes*, name its angle(s) of rotation.

5.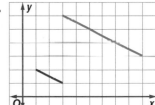

6.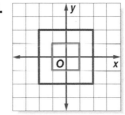

Multi-Part Lesson 10-4
PART A

PAGES 570–575

Find the coordinates of the vertices of triangle *A′B′C′* after triangle *ABC* is dilated using the given scale factor. Then graph triangle *ABC* and its dilation.

1. $A(-1, 0)$, $B(2, 1)$, $C(2, -1)$; scale factor 2

2. $A(4, 6)$, $B(0, -2)$, $C(6, 2)$; scale factor $\frac{1}{2}$

3. $A(1, -1)$, $B(1, 2)$, $C(-1, 1)$; scale factor 3

4. $A(2, 0)$, $B(0, -4)$, $C(-2, 4)$; scale factor $\frac{3}{2}$

In each figure, the green figure is a dilation of the blue figure. Find the scale factor of each dilation and classify each dilation as an *enlargement* or as a *reduction*.

5.

6.

7.

PART B

PAGES 576–577

Use the *work backward* strategy to solve each problem.

1. **TIME** The table shows the amount of time it takes Leo to complete different activities before going to school. If he needs to be at school at 9 A.M., what time should he leave his house?

Activity	Time (minutes)
Walking the dog	10
Showering and getting ready	20
Eating breakfast	10
Getting to school	25

2. **AGES** Anne is 3 years younger than her sister Maddie. Maddie is half as old as her uncle Bobby. If Bobby is 32, how old is Anne?

3. **NUMBER SENSE** A number is multiplied by 5 and then 7 is added to the product. The result is 22. What is the number?

Multi-Part Lesson 11-1

PART A

Classify each angle as *acute, right, obtuse,* or *straight.*

1.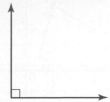

2.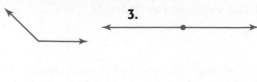

3.

4.

5. Identify a pair of vertical angles in the diagram at the right.

6. Identify a pair of adjacent angles in the diagram at the right.

Classify each pair of angles as *complementary, supplementary,* or *neither.*

7.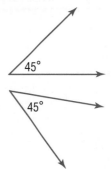

45°

45°

8.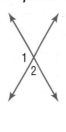

1
2

9.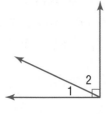

2
1

Find the value of *x* in each figure.

10.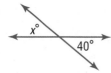

$x°$

40°

11.

$x°$

35°

12.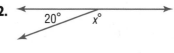

20° $x°$

PART B

Classify each pair of angles.

1. ∠1 and ∠9

2. ∠9 and ∠13

3. ∠12 and ∠13

4. ∠3 and ∠6

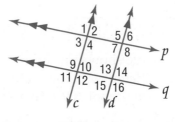

In the figure, $m\angle 3 = 43$. Find each measure.

5. ∠2

6. ∠7

7. ∠10

8. ∠11

9. ∠8

10. ∠12

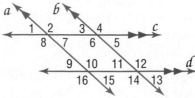

Multi-Part Lesson 11-2

PARTS **A** **B**

Find the value of x.

1.

2.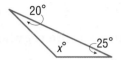

3.

Classify each triangle by its angles and by its sides.

4.

5.

6.

PART **C**

Use the *logical reasoning* strategy to solve each problem.

1. GEOMETRY Draw several isosceles triangles and measure their angles. What do you notice about the measures of the angles of an isosceles triangle?

2. BASKETBALL Placido, Dexter, and Malik play guard, forward, and center on a team, but not necessarily in that order. Placido and the center drove Malik to practice on Saturday. Placido does not play guard. Who is the guard?

Solve each problem using logical reasoning.

3. GEOMETRY Can a polygon containing two right angles be a triangle? Explain your reasoning. Can it be a quadrilateral? Explain.

4. HEIGHT Kristina is $\frac{2}{3}$ the height of Melina, who is $\frac{3}{4}$ as tall as Destini. If Destini is 4 feet tall, how tall are the others?

5. SPELLING The top 4 finishers in the spelling bee were Kina, Niko, Gia, and Martez. Niko and the first place winner studied with Kina for the spelling bee. Gia is not the first place winner. Who is the first place winner?

PART **D**

Classify each quadrilateral using the name that *best* describes it.

1.

2.

3.

Find the missing angle measure in each quadrilateral.

4.

5.

6.

Multi-Part Lesson 11-2 (continued)
PARTS E F
PAGES 630–637

Find the sum of the measures of the interior angles for each polygon.

1. dodecagon (12-gon) **2.** 17-gon **3.** 21-gon

Find the measure of each interior angle for the regular polygons listed below.

4. 18-gon **5.** 22-gon **6.** octagon

Find the missing angle measurement for each shape described below.

7. quadrilateral: $\angle G = 110°$, $\angle H = 75°$, $\angle I = 110°$, and $\angle J = \blacksquare$

8. pentagon: $\angle K = 112°$, $\angle L = 90°$, $\angle M = 123°$, $\angle N = 77°$, and $\angle O = \blacksquare$

Multi-Part Lesson 11-3
PART A
PAGES 641–644

Find the square of each number.

1. 4 **2.** 19 **3.** 13 **4.** 25

5. 9 **6.** 2 **7.** 14 **8.** 24

9. 40 **10.** 50 **11.** 100 **12.** 250

Find each square root.

13. $\sqrt{324}$ **14.** $\sqrt{900}$ **15.** $\sqrt{2,500}$ **16.** $\sqrt{576}$

17. $\sqrt{8,100}$ **18.** $\sqrt{676}$ **19.** $\sqrt{100}$ **20.** $\sqrt{784}$

21. $\sqrt{1,024}$ **22.** $\sqrt{841}$ **23.** $\sqrt{2,304}$ **24.** $\sqrt{3,025}$

PART B
PAGES 645–648

Estimate each square root to the nearest whole number.

1. $\sqrt{27}$ **2.** $\sqrt{112}$ **3.** $\sqrt{249}$

4. $\sqrt{88}$ **5.** $\sqrt{1,500}$ **6.** $\sqrt{612}$

7. $\sqrt{340}$ **8.** $\sqrt{495}$ **9.** $\sqrt{264}$

10. $\sqrt{350}$ **11.** $\sqrt{834}$ **12.** $\sqrt{3,700}$

13. $\sqrt{298}$ **14.** $\sqrt{101}$ **15.** $\sqrt{800}$

Graph each square root on a number line.

16. $\sqrt{58}$ **17.** $\sqrt{750}$ **18.** $\sqrt{1,200}$

19. $\sqrt{1,000}$ **20.** $\sqrt{5,900}$ **21.** $\sqrt{999}$

22. $\sqrt{374}$ **23.** $\sqrt{512}$ **24.** $\sqrt{3,750}$

25. $\sqrt{255}$ **26.** $\sqrt{83}$ **27.** $\sqrt{845}$

28. $\sqrt{200}$ **29.** $\sqrt{500}$ **30.** $\sqrt{10,001}$

31. ALGEBRA Evaluate $\sqrt{a - b}$ to the nearest tenth if $a = 16$ and $b = 4$.

32. ALGEBRA Estimate the value of $\sqrt{x + y}$ to the nearest whole number if $x = 64$ and $y = 25$.

Multi-Part Lesson 11-3 (continued)

PART C

PAGES 649–653

Name all sets of numbers to which each real number belongs.

1. 6.5

2. $\sqrt{25}$

3. $\sqrt{3}$

4. -7.2

5. $-0.\overline{61}$

6. $\frac{1}{2}$

7. $\frac{16}{4}$

8. -102.1

9. $\sqrt{29}$

Estimate each square root to the nearest tenth. Then graph the square root on a number line.

10. $-\sqrt{12}$

11. $\sqrt{23}$

12. $\sqrt{2}$

13. $\sqrt{10}$

14. $-\sqrt{30}$

15. $\sqrt{5}$

16. $\sqrt{21}$

17. $-\sqrt{202}$

18. $-\sqrt{10}$

Replace each ● with <, >, or = to make a true sentence.

19. $\sqrt{7}$ ● 2.8

20. $2\frac{1}{3}$ ● $2.\overline{3}$

21. $\sqrt{121}$ ● 11

22. 5.6 ● $\sqrt{30}$

23. 9.45 ● $9.\overline{4}$

24. $\sqrt{5}$ ● 2.23

25. $\sqrt{6.25}$ ● $2\frac{1}{2}$

26. $5\frac{1}{3}$ ● $\sqrt{30}$

27. $4\frac{2}{3}$ ● $\sqrt{22}$

PARTS D E

PAGES 654–660

Find the missing measure of each triangle. Round to the nearest tenth if necessary.

1.

4 ft, 6 ft, x ft

2.
14 cm, 18 cm, x cm

3.
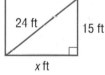
24 ft, 15 ft, x ft

4. $a = 12$ cm, $b = 25$ cm

5. $a = 5$ yd, $c = 10$ yd

6. $b = 12$ mi, $c = 20$ mi

7. $a = 15$ yd, $b = 24$ yd

8. $a = 4$ m, $c = 12$ m

9. $a = 8$ mm, $b = 11$ mm

10. $a = 1$ mi, $c = 3$ mi

11. $a = 5$ yd, $b = 8$ yd

12. $b = 7$ in., $c = 19$ in.

13. $a = 50$ km, $c = 75$ km

14. $b = 82$ ft, $c = 100$ ft

15. $a = 100$ m, $b = 200$ m

PART F

PAGES 661–664

Graph each pair of ordered pairs. Then find the distance between the points using the Pythagorean Theorem. Round to the nearest tenth if necessary.

1. $(-4, 2), (4, 17)$

2. $(5, -1), (11, 7)$

3. $(-3, 5), (2, 7)$

4. $(7, -9), (4, 3)$

5. $(5, 4), (-3, 8)$

6. $(-8, -4), (-3, 8)$

7. $(2, 7), (10, -4)$

8. $(9, -2), (3, 6)$

9. $(2, 3), (-1, 6)$

10. $(-5, 1), (2, -3)$

11. $(0, 1), (5, 2)$

12. $(-1, 2), (-2, 3)$

Multi-Part Lesson 12-1

PARTS (A) (B) (C)

PAGES 678–685

Describe how the mean, median, and mode for each data set will change if the extreme value is dropped. Round to the nearest tenth if necessary.

1. 2, 7, 9, 2, 5, 14, 4, 8, 3, 8

2. 58, 52, 49, 60, 61, 56, 50, 61, 25

3. 122, 134, 129, 140, 125, 134, 167

4. 26, 41, 43, 45, 48, 52, 57, 56, 56, 57, 60, 64, 65

5. 11, 15, 21, 51, 6, 10, 11

6. 21, 20, 19, 20, 38, 21, 23, 25

7. 1, 3, 2, 1, 1, 20, 2, 2, 3

8. 23, 35, 32, 26, 27, 29, 31, 49, 27

Multi-Part Lesson 12-2

PART (A)

PAGES 687–692

Find the measures of variation and any outliers for each data set.

1. 15, 12, 21, 18, 25, 11, 17, 19, 20

2. 2, 24, 6, 13, 8, 6, 11, 4

3. 189, 149, 155, 290, 141, 152

4. 451, 501, 388, 428, 510, 480, 390

5. 22, 18, 9, 26, 14, 15, 6, 19, 28

6. 245, 218, 251, 255, 248, 241, 250

7. 46, 45, 50, 40, 49, 42, 64

8. 128, 148, 130, 142, 164, 120, 152, 202

Find the range, interquartile range, and any outliers for each data set.

9. cost of video games: 44, 37, 23, 35, 61, 95, 49, 96

10. dollars in savings account: 271, 891, 181, 193, 711, 791, 861, 818

11. ages of people in a restaurant: 52, 44, 45, 20, 27, 29, 33, 38, 47, 59, 42, 49, 33, 36, 21, 38, 21, 38, 49, 22, 24

12. typing speed in words per minute: 64, 68, 79, 70, 91, 42, 95, 42, 67, 81, 90, 68, 70, 40, 59, 52, 48, 71, 46, 91, 87, 43, 55, 93, 51, 55, 89, 74, 46, 44, 79, 55, 47, 45, 79

PART (B)

PAGES 693–698

Draw a box-and-whisker plot for each set of data.

1. 2, 3, 5, 4, 3, 3, 2, 5, 6

2. 6, 7, 9, 10, 11, 11, 13, 14, 12, 11, 12

3. 15, 12, 21, 18, 25, 11, 17, 19, 20

4. 2, 24, 6, 13, 8, 6, 11, 4

ZOOS For Exercises 5 and 6, use the following box-and-whisker plot.

Area (acres) of Major Zoos in the United States

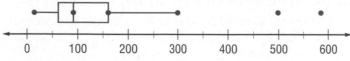

5. How many outliers are in the data?

6. Describe the distribution of the data. What can you say about the areas of the major zoos in the United States?

Multi-Part Lesson 12-2 (continued)

PART C

PAGES 699–704

Would a scatter plot of the data for each of the following show a *positive*, *negative*, or *no* relationship?

1. height and hair color

2. hours spent studying and test scores

3. income and month of birth

4. child's age and height

5. age and eye color

6. number of hours worked and earnings

7.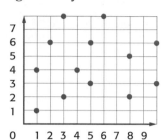

8.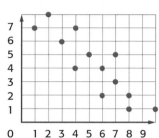

9.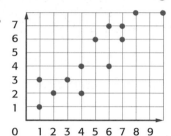

For Exercises 10–12, refer to the graph at the right which shows Rachel's quiz scores for six quizzes.

10. Describe the trend in Rachel's quiz scores.

11. If the trend continues, predict Rachel's score on the seventh quiz.

12. If the trend continues, predict Rachel's score on the tenth quiz.

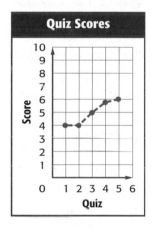

PART D

PAGES 705–709

Select an appropriate display for each situation. Justify your reasoning.

1. the percent of different responses to a survey

2. the test scores of all students on a test

3. the average annual cost of a gallon of gas over a period of 10 years

4. the median number of students in each class

5. **ACTIVITIES** The table shows the number of students that completed the obstacle course in each grade level. Select an appropriate display for the data. Justify your reasoning. Then construct the display. What can you conclude from your display?

Students Completing Obstacle Course	
Grade Level	**Number of Students**
6	90
7	102
8	119

Multi-Part Lesson 12-2 (continued)

PART E

PAGES 710–711

Use a graph to solve.

1. The table shows the amount of growth of bamboo in inches in a certain number of years.

   a. Make a graph of the data.

   b. If the trend continues, about how high will the bamboo grow in 4 years?

Bamboo Growth	
Time (yr)	Height (in.)
0	20
1	30
2	40
3	50

2. The table shows how long it takes Lacey to walk a given distance.

   a. Make a graph of the data.

   b. If the trend continues, predict how far Lacey will go in 50 seconds.

Walking	
Time (s)	Distance (ft)
0	0
5	2.5
10	5
15	7.5
20	10
25	12.5
30	15

Multi-Part Lesson 13-1

PART A

PAGES 726–727

Use the *guess, check, and revise* strategy to solve each problem.

1. **NUMBERS** A number is divided by 3. Then 8 is added to the quotient. The result is 15. What is the number?

2. **NUMBERS** Paul is thinking of two numbers. Their product is 32 and their difference is 4. Find the numbers.

3. **MONEY** A theater is charging $5 for children under 12 and $8 for everyone else. If the total for a group of people was $36, how many people under the age of 12 were in the group?

4. **PLACE VALUE** Mindy wrote down a decimal number. The digit in the tenth's place is half the digit in the hundredth's place. If the product of the two digits is 18, what is the number?

5. **MONEY** Mora has 14 coins totaling $1.55. She has one more nickel than she has dimes, and three less quarters than nickels. How many quarters, dimes, and nickels does she have if these are the only coin types she has?

6. **FRUIT** Darien places 4 apples and 3 oranges into each fruit basket he makes. If he has used 32 apples and 24 oranges, how many fruit baskets has he made?

PART B

PAGES 728–732

Solve each inequality. Check your solution. Graph the solution set on a number line.

1. $y + 3 > 7$

2. $c - 9 < 5$

3. $x + 4 \geq 9$

4. $y - 3 < 15$

5. $t - 13 \geq 5$

6. $x + 3 < 10$

7. $y - 6 \geq 2$

8. $x - 3 \geq -6$

9. $a + 3 \leq 5$

10. $c - 2 \leq 11$

11. $a + 15 \geq 6$

12. $y + 3 \geq 18$

13. $y + 16 \geq -22$

14. $x - 3 \geq 17$

15. $y - 6 > -17$

16. $y - 11 < 7$

17. $a + 5 \geq 21$

18. $c + 3 > -16$

19. $x - 12 \geq 12$

20. $x + 5 \geq 5$

21. $y - 6 > 31$

Multi-Part Lesson 13-1 (continued)

PART C

PAGES 733–737

Solve each inequality and check your solution. Graph the solution set on a number line.

1. $5p \geq 25$

2. $4x < 12$

3. $15 \leq 3m$

4. $\frac{d}{3} > 15$

5. $8 < \frac{r}{7}$

6. $9g < 27$

7. $4p \geq 24$

8. $5p > 25$

9. $-4 > \frac{-k}{3}$

10. $\frac{-z}{5} > 2$

11. $-3x \leq 9$

12. $-5x > -35$

13. $\frac{a}{-6} < 1$

14. $\frac{x}{-5} \leq -2$

15. $-2x < 16$

Multi-Part Lesson 13-2

PART A

PAGES 740–744

Find each function value.

1. $f\left(\frac{1}{2}\right)$ if $f(x) = 2x - 6$

2. $f(-4)$ if $f(x) = -\frac{1}{2}x + 4$

3. $f(1)$ if $f(x) = -5x + 1$

4. $f(6)$ if $f(x) = \frac{2}{3}x - 5$

5. $f(0)$ if $f(x) = 1.6x + 4$

6. $f(2)$ if $f(x) = 2x - 8$

Copy and complete each function table. Then state the domain and range of the function.

7. $f(x) = -4x$

x	−4x	f(x)
−2		
−1		
0		
1		

8. $f(x) = x + 6$

x	x + 6	f(x)
−6		
−4		
−2		
0		

9. $f(x) = 3x + 2$

x	3x + 2	f(x)
−3		
−2		
−1		
0		

PART B

PAGES 745–749

Graph each function.

1. $y = 6x + 2$

2. $y = -2x + 3$

3. $y = -5x$

4. $y = 10x - 2$

5. $y = -2.5x - 1.5$

6. $y = 7x + 3$

7. $y = \frac{x}{4} - 8$

8. $y = 3x + 1$

9. $y = 25 - 2x$

10. $y = \frac{x}{6}$

11. $y = -2x + 11$

12. $y = 7x - 3$

Multi-Part Lesson 13-2 (continued)

PART C

PAGES 750–753

State the slope and y-intercept for the graph of each equation.

1. $y = 3x - 5$

2. $y = 2x - 6$

3. $y = -6x + \frac{1}{2}$

4. $y = -7x + \frac{5}{2}$

5. $y = \frac{1}{2}x + 7$

6. $y = \frac{3}{4}x + 8$

7. $y = -\frac{2}{3}x - \frac{1}{3}$

8. $y = -\frac{1}{8}x - \frac{3}{8}$

9. $y = \frac{2}{3}x + 5$

10. $y = -\frac{2}{7}x - 1$

11. $3x + y = 6$

12. $y - 4x = 7$

Graph each equation using the slope and y-intercept.

13. $y = -2x + 5$

14. $y = -3x + 1$

15. $y = -x + 1$

16. $y = -x + 3$

17. $y = x - 3$

18. $y = x - 5$

19. $y = 3x - 6$

20. $y = \frac{5}{2}x - 1$

21. $y = \frac{1}{2}x + 3$

22. $y = -2x - 2$

23. $y - 4x = -1$

24. $2x + y = 3$

Multi-Part Lesson 13-3

PARTS A B

PAGES 755–760

Determine whether each equation or table represents a *linear* or *nonlinear* function. Explain.

1. $y = 3x$

2. $y = \frac{2}{3}x$

3. $y = x^2 + 5$

4. $y = 4^x$

5. $y = -\frac{3}{x}$

6. $xy = -3$

7.
x	−1	0	1	2
y	2	0	2	8

8.
x	−1	0	1	2
y	−1	0	1	8

9.
x	−1	0	1	2
y	−3	0	3	6

Multi-Part Lesson 13-4

PART A

PAGES 761–765

Find each product or quotient. Express using exponents.

1. $2^3 \cdot 2^4$

2. $5^6 \cdot 5$

3. $t^4 \cdot t^2$

4. $y^5 \cdot y^3$

5. $(-3x^3)(-2x^2)$

6. $b^{12} \cdot b$

7. $3^5 \cdot 3^8$

8. $(-2y^3)(5y^7)$

9. $(6a^5)(-3a^6)$

10. $\frac{7^9}{7^6}$

11. $\frac{2^5}{2^2}$

12. $\frac{11^{10}}{11}$

13. $\frac{16x^3}{4x^2}$

14. $\frac{25y^5}{5y^2}$

15. $\frac{-48y^3}{-8y}$

16. $\frac{12y^5}{3y^2}$

17. $\frac{39x^7y^5}{3x^3y}$

18. $\frac{21a^7b^2}{7ab^2}$

Multi-Part Lesson 13-4 (continued)

PART B

PAGES 766–769

Write each expression using a positive exponent.

1. 4^{-4} 2. $(-3)^{-2}$ 3. 7^{-6}

4. $(-5)^{-8}$ 5. $(-2)^{-4}$ 6. c^{-6}

7. $3a^{-2}$ 8. b^{-9} 9. $-8c^{-8}$

Write each fraction as an expression using a negative exponent other than −1.

10. $\frac{1}{3^5}$ 11. $\frac{1}{5^2}$ 12. $\frac{1}{243}$ 13. $\frac{1}{9}$

Write each decimal using a negative exponent.

14. 0.0001 15. 0.001 16. 0.1 17. 0.00001

PART C

PAGES 770–774

Write each number in standard form.

1. 4.5×10^3 2. 2×10^4 3. 1.725896×10^6

4. 9.61×10^2 5. 1×10^7 6. 8.256×10^8

7. 5.26×10^4 8. 3.25×10^2 9. 6.79×10^5

10. 3.1×10^{-4} 11. 2.51×10^{-2} 12. 6×10^{-1}

13. 2.15×10^{-3} 14. 3.14×10^{-6} 15. 1×10^{-2}

Write each number in scientific notation.

16. 720 17. 7,560 18. 892

19. 1,400 20. 91,256 21. 51,000

22. 0.012 23. 0.0002 24. 0.054

25. 0.231 26. 0.0000056 27. 0.000123

Selected Answers and Solutions

For Homework Help, go to **Hotmath.com** Complete, step-by-step solutions of most odd-numbered exercises are provided free of charge.

Chapter 1 Integers

Page 26   Chapter 1   Are You Ready?
1. 6   **3.** 17   **5.** 24   **7.** 7   **9.** (1, 1)   **11.** (8, 1)
13. (1, 5)   **15.** (7, 6)

Pages 29–32   Lesson 1-1B
1. −11   **3.** 16   **5.** −15
7.

$$+\!\!+\!\bullet\!+\!+\!+\!+\!\bullet\!+\!\bullet\!+\!+\!+\!+$$
$$-10\;-8\;-6\;-4\;-2\;\;0\;\;2\;\;4\;\;6\;\;8\;\;10$$

9 $1 + |7| = 1 + 7$
$ = 8$

11. 9   **13.** −53   **15.** −2   **17.** 12   **19.** −7
21.

$$+\!\bullet\!+\!+\!+\!\bullet\!+\!\bullet\!+$$
$$-3\;-2\;-1\;\;0\;\;1$$

23.

25. 10   **27.** 2   **29.** 14   **31.** 25
33 $|27| \div 3 - |-4|$
$ = 27 \div 3 - 4 \quad |27| = 27; |-4| = 4$
$ = 9 - 4 \qquad$ Divide.
$ = 5 \qquad\quad$ Subtract.
37. Sometimes; it is always true if A and B are both positive or if A or B are negative, but not if both A and B are negative.   **39.** $-|7 + 3|$; all others are positive.   **41.** C   **43.** C

Pages 33–37   Lesson 1-1C
1. (−2, −4); III
3 From the origin, move no units horizontally, and up 3 units. (0, 3); the point lies on the y-axis.
5–8.

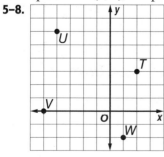

9a. Sea Cliffs   **9b.** I   **11.** (5, 4); I   **13.** (4, −3); IV
15. (−3, 5); II   **17.** (0, −4); y-axis   **19.** (−4, −5); III
21. (1, 0); x-axis

22–33.

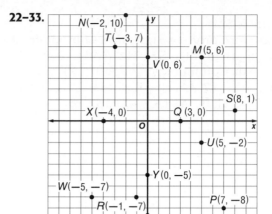

35–37.

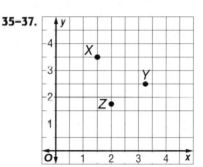

35 From the origin, move one and a half units to the right. Then move up three and a half units.
39. Sample answer: Rene Descartes is often credited with inventing the coordinate plane and so the coordinate plane is sometimes called the Cartesian plane, in his honor.   **41.** She switched the x- and y-coordinates. She should have gone to the left 3 units and up 4 units.   **43.** Sample answer: Point A is 1 unit to the right and 2 units down from the origin, in Quadrant IV. Point B is 2 units to the left and 1 unit up from the origin, in Quadrant II.
45. G   **47.** −13   **49.** 430

Pages 40–44   Lesson 1-2B
1. −14   **3.** 7   **5.** −4
7 $-17 + 20 + (-3)$
$ = (-17) + (-3) + 20 \quad$ Commutative (+)
$ = [(-17) + (-3)] + 20 \quad$ Associative (+)
$ = (-20) + 20 \qquad$ Add.
$ = 0$

9. −1   **11.** −38   **13.** 16   **15.** 13   **17.** 5   **19.** −4
21. −34   **23.** 3   **25.** −14 + 3; −11; The shark is 11 feet below sea level.

27 In a bank account, withdrawing $20 would be −20 and depositing $84 would be +84.
$$152 + (−20) + 84 = (152 + 84) + (−20)$$
$$= 236 + (−20)$$
$$= 216$$
The balance is $216.

29. green T-shirt: profit of $1; white T-shirt: profit of $3; black T-shirt: profit of $3 **31a.** Additive Inverse Property **31b.** Commutative Property (+) **33.** $x + (−4)$ **35.** $n + 6$ **37.** $−8 + (−3) = −11$ **39.** G **41.** $(−2, 4)$; II **43.** $(−3, −1)$; III **45.** 75 **47.** −13

Pages 47–50   Lesson .1-2D

1. −3

3 $−4 − 8$
$$= −4 + (−8) \quad \text{To subtract 8, add } −8.$$
$$= −12 \quad \text{Simplify.}$$

5. 24 **7.** −2 **9.** −21 **11.** 22 **13.** −10 **15.** −14 **17.** −14 **19.** −30 **21.** 23 **23.** 31 **25.** 104 **27.** 6 **29.** 0 **31.** 0 **33.** 15 **35.** 11

37 **a.** $2{,}407 − (−8) = 2{,}407 + 8$ or 2,415 ft
b. $2{,}842 − (−282) = 2{,}842 + 282$ or 3,124 ft
c. $345 − (−282) = 345 + 282$ or 627 ft
d. $0 − (−8) = 0 + 8$ or 8 ft

39. 16 **41.** Sample answer: $−5 − 11 = −5 + (−11) = −16$; Add 5 and 11 and keep the negative sign.
43. true **45.** A **47.** 7 **49.** −13 **51.** Quadrant IV **53.** 8

Pages 52–53   Lesson 1-3A

1. 24 **3.** 8 months **5.** Sample answer: 3 quarters, 2 nickels, and 1 penny **7.** 13 toothpicks

9 Each term is found by adding the two previous terms. The next two terms would be $34 + 55$ or 89 and $55 + 89$ or 144.

Pages 56–60   Lesson 1-3C

1. −60 **3.** −28 **5.** 45 **7.** 64 **9.** −12
11. $100(−3) = −300$; Tamera's investment is now worth $300 less than it was before the price of the stock dropped.

13 $(−1)(7)(−10)$
$(−7)(−10)$
70

15. −220 **17.** −70 **19.** −50 **21.** 80 **23.** −125 **25.** 81 **27.** 6 **29.** 24

31 $5(−650) = −3{,}250$; Ethan burns 3,250 calories each week.

33. −84 **35.** −160 **37.** −108 **39.** 8 **41.** 5 black T-shirts **43a.** Sample answer: Evaluate $−7 + 7$ first. Since $−7 + 7 = 0$, and any number times 0 is 0, the value of the expression is 0.
43b. Sample answer: First use the Distributive Property to rewrite the expression as $−15(−26 + 25)$. Then evaluate $−26 + 25$. Since $−26 + 25 = −1$ and $−15 × −1 = 15$, the value of the expression is 15.

45. Sample answer: The product of three integers is positive when exactly two of the integers are negative or when all three integers are positive.
47. 64 **49a.** 419 points **49b.** 47 points **51.** 0 **53.** 2

Pages 61–65   Lesson 1-3D

1. −4 **3.** −6 **5.** 5

7 $15 ÷ y = 15 ÷ (−5)$ Replace y with −5.
      $= −3$ Divide. The quotient is negative.

9. −48.3°C **11.** −7 **13.** −9 **15.** 10 **17.** −7 **19.** −9 **21.** 9 **23.** 5 **25.** −12 **27.** −3 **29.** 2 **31.** −1 **33.** −10°F **35.** 8 **37.** 1

39 mean
$$= \frac{−70 + (−40) + (−25) + (−50) + (−80)}{5}$$
$$= \frac{−265}{5}$$
$$= −53 \text{ ft}$$

41. $−32 ÷ (−4)$ has a positive quotient; the others have negative quotients. **43.** First evaluate each 2^2 since they are powers. Rewrite the expression as $−2 · (4 + 2) ÷ 4$. Then add the $4 + 2$ in the parentheses. Rewrite the expression as $−2 · 6 ÷ 4$. Next, multiply and then divide since multiplication and division occur in order from left to right. Since $−2 · 6 = −12$ and $−12 ÷ 4 = −3$, the value of the expression is −3. **45.** B **47.** 60 **49.** 81 **51.** 18

Pages 68–71   Chapter 1 Study Guide and Review

1. false; negative **3.** false; opposite **5.** false; y-coordinate **7.** true **9.** false; positive **11.** 350 **13.** −48 **15.** 32 **17.** 33

19–22.

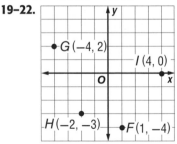

23. $(−4, 1)$ **25.** −13 **27.** 0 **29.** −15 **31.** 0 **33.** 600 lb **35.** −3 **37.** 4 **39.** −5 **41.** −1 **43.** 2,980 ft **45.** $46,400 **47.** −12 **49.** 35 **51.** 28 **53.** −35 **55.** 5 **57.** −2

Chapter 2 Rational Numbers

Page 78   Chapter 2   Are You Ready?

1. 0.61 **3.** 0.33 **5.** Kirsten

7. (number line from 0 to 6, point at 5)

9. (number line from 0 to 6, point at 1)

11. $\frac{4}{5}$ **13.** 1 **15.** $\frac{3}{10}$

Pages 80–84   Lesson 2-1B

1. 0.4   **3.** 7.5

5 Divide 1 by 8.

$$\begin{array}{r} 0.125 \\ 8)\overline{1.000} \\ \underline{8} \\ 20 \\ \underline{16} \\ 40 \\ \underline{40} \\ 0 \end{array}$$

So, $\frac{1}{8}$ is 0.125.

7. $0.\overline{5}$ **9.** $-\frac{11}{50}$ **11.** $4\frac{3}{5}$ **13.** 0.8   **15.** -4.16 **17.** 0.3125

19. -0.66 **21.** 5.875   **23.** $-0.\overline{4}$ **25.** $-0.1\overline{6}$ **27.** $5.\overline{3}$

29. $-\frac{1}{5}$ **31.** $\frac{11}{20}$ **33.** $5\frac{24}{25}$

35 $30.5 = 30 + 0.5$

$$= 30 + \frac{5}{10}$$

$$= 30 + \frac{1}{2} = 30\frac{1}{2} \text{ cm}$$

39. $\frac{22}{3}$ **41.** $\frac{-16}{5}$ **43.** Sample answer: $\frac{3}{5}$

45. Sample answer: $3\frac{1}{7} \approx 3.14286$ and $3\frac{10}{71} \approx 3.14085$;

Since 3.1415927... is between $3\frac{1}{7}$ and $3\frac{10}{71}$,

Archimedes was correct.   **47.** I   **49.** -12

51. $-14(7)$; -98; This represents the total amount of money that Jordan will have withdrawn after 7 weeks.   **53.** -1 **55.** 0

Pages 85–90   Lesson 2-1C

1. >   **3.** <   **5.** Elliot; 3 out of 4 has an average of 0.75; 7 out of 11 has an average of 0.64.   **7.** $0.02, 0.1, \frac{1}{8}, \frac{2}{3}$

9. <   **11.** =

13 The LCM of 7 and 8 is 56.

$\frac{4}{7} = \frac{4 \times 8}{7 \times 8} = \frac{32}{56}$ and $\frac{5}{8} = \frac{5 \times 7}{8 \times 7} = \frac{35}{56}$

Since $\frac{32}{56} < \frac{35}{56}, \frac{4}{7} < \frac{5}{8}$.

15. >   **17.** >   **19.** <   **21.** Jim; $\frac{10}{16} > \frac{4}{15}$ **23.** $\frac{8}{10}$,

$0.805, 0.81$ **25.** $-1.4, -1.25, -1\frac{1}{25}$ **27.** $3.47, 3\frac{4}{7}, 3\frac{3}{5}$

29. >   **31.** =   **33.** >

35 Write the fractions as decimals and then compare the decimals.

$1\frac{7}{12}$ gallons ● $1\frac{5}{8}$ gallons

$7 \div 12 = 0.58\overline{3}$ $5 \div 8 = 0.625$

Since $1.58\overline{3} < 1.625$, then $1\frac{7}{12}$ gallons $< 1\frac{5}{8}$ gallons.

37. 6 c, $6\frac{1}{3}$ c, 6.5 c   **39.** $\frac{1}{5}$ g, 1.5 g, 5 g   **41a.** 3 cubes at $18\frac{6}{8}$ in., rod at $12\frac{7}{8}$ in.   **41b.** Yes; $69\frac{1}{8} < 69\frac{6}{8}$.

43. Sample answer: $\frac{63}{32}$ is closest to 2 because the difference of $\frac{63}{32}$ and 2 is the least.   **45.** C   **47.** C

49. $\frac{3}{20}$ **51.** 6   **53.** -27 **55.** 213 ft

Pages 91–95   Lesson 2-2A

1. $\frac{4}{5}$

3 $-\frac{3}{4} + \left(-\frac{3}{4}\right) = \frac{-3 + (-3)}{4}$

$$= -\frac{6}{4}$$

$$= -1\frac{1}{2}$$

5. $-\frac{3}{5}$ **7.** $\frac{19}{50}$ **9.** $1\frac{2}{5}$ **11.** $-\frac{1}{2}$ **13.** $-1\frac{2}{3}$ **15.** $\frac{3}{5}$

17. $\frac{3}{7}$ **19.** $\frac{5}{12}$

21 $\frac{17}{28} - \frac{11}{28} = \frac{6}{28}$ or $\frac{3}{14}$

23a. $\frac{33}{100}$ **23b.** $\frac{67}{100}$ **25.** $\frac{1}{8}$ **27.** 2   **29.** $1\frac{1}{7}$

31 $\frac{13}{16} - \frac{5}{16} = \frac{8}{16}$ or $\frac{1}{2}$ in.

33. Sample answer: $\frac{11}{18}$ and $\frac{5}{18}$; $\frac{11}{18} - \frac{5}{18} = \frac{6}{18}$, which simplifies to $\frac{1}{3}$.   **35.** To add and subtract fractions with the same denominator, add or subtract the numerators. Write the result using the common denominator.   **37.** I   **39.** >   **41.** <   **43.** $\frac{3}{8}$

45. $\frac{19}{1,000}$ **47.** -5 **49.** -28

Pages 98–103   Lesson 2-2C

1. $\frac{7}{9}$ **3.** $\frac{5}{8}$

5 $\frac{1}{6} + \frac{3}{8}$

$$= \frac{1 \times 4}{6 \times 4} + \frac{3 \times 3}{8 \times 3} \quad \text{Rename using the LCD, 24.}$$

$$= \frac{4}{24} + \frac{9}{24} \quad \text{Add the fractions.}$$

$$= \frac{13}{24} \quad \text{Simplify.}$$

7. $-\frac{1}{4}$ **9.** Addition; $\frac{11}{16}$ in.; Sample answer: To find how much smaller the total height of the photo is now, add $\frac{5}{16}$ and $\frac{3}{8}$.   **11.** $\frac{7}{10}$ **13.** $1\frac{1}{2}$ **15.** $-\frac{2}{3}$ **17.** $1\frac{13}{24}$

19. $\frac{4}{9}$ **21.** $-\frac{26}{45}$ **23.** Addition; $1\frac{11}{20}$ ft; Sample answer: To find the smallest width to make the shelf, add $\frac{4}{5}$ and $\frac{3}{8}$.   **25.** Subtraction; $\frac{3}{8}$ lb; Sample answer: To find how much more turkey Makayla bought, subtract $\frac{1}{4}$ from $\frac{5}{8}$.   **27.** $\frac{23}{28}$ **29.** $\frac{7}{12}$ **31.** $1\frac{1}{4}$ **33.** $2\frac{2}{3}$ **35.** $\frac{2}{15}$

37 $\frac{1}{2} + \frac{3}{4}$

$$= \frac{1 \times 2}{2 \times 2} + \frac{3 \times 1}{4 \times 1} \quad \text{Rename using the LCD, 4.}$$

$$= \frac{2}{4} + \frac{3}{4} \quad \text{Add the fractions.}$$

$$= \frac{5}{4} \text{ or } 1\frac{1}{4} \quad \text{Simplify.}$$

39. $\frac{1}{12}$

41 Find the total amount of time used by the second and third students. Find the difference between the available $\frac{2}{3}$ hour and the time used by the two students. This will show the amount of time remaining for the final student.

$$\frac{2}{3} - \left(\frac{1}{6} + \frac{1}{4}\right) = \frac{2}{3} - \left(\frac{1 \times 2}{6 \times 2} + \frac{1 \times 3}{4 \times 3}\right)$$
$$= \frac{2}{3} - \left(\frac{2}{12} + \frac{3}{12}\right)$$
$$= \frac{2}{3} - \frac{5}{12}$$
$$= \frac{8}{12} - \frac{5}{12}$$
$$= \frac{3}{12} \text{ or } \frac{1}{4} \text{ hr}$$

43. LaTasha; $\frac{1}{8}$ mile; LaTasha's position on the track is $\frac{1}{4}$ of a mile from the start. Colin's position on the track is $\frac{5}{8} - \frac{1}{2}$, or $\frac{1}{8}$, of a mile from the start. So, LaTasha is farther ahead on the track by $\frac{1}{4} - \frac{1}{8}$ or $\frac{1}{8}$ of a mile.   **45.** Sample answer: $\frac{1}{4} + \frac{1}{6} + \frac{1}{12}$
47. filling the $\frac{3}{4}$-measuring cup once; Filling the $\frac{2}{3}$-measuring cup twice gives her $\frac{1}{3}$ cup more flour than she needs. Filling the $\frac{3}{4}$-measuring cup twice gives her $\frac{1}{2}$ cup more flour than she needs. Filling the $\frac{2}{3}$-measuring cup once gives her $\frac{1}{3}$ cup less flour than she needs. Filling the $\frac{3}{4}$-measuring cup once gives her $\frac{1}{4}$ cup less flour than she needs. Since $\frac{1}{4} < \frac{1}{3} < \frac{1}{2}$, filling the $\frac{3}{4}$-measuring cup once will bring Felicia closest to having the amount of flour she needs.   **49.** H   **51.** $\frac{4}{5}$ **53.** $\frac{2}{3}$ **55.** $-7, -2, 0, 5, 9, 12$
57. 12   **59.** -35 **61.** 25   **63.** 2   **65.** -4

Pages 104–108   Lesson 2-2D
1. $9\frac{6}{7}$ **3.** $4\frac{2}{3}$

5 $2\frac{5}{4} - 1\frac{3}{4} = 1\frac{2}{4}$
$\qquad\qquad = 1\frac{1}{2}$

7. $4\frac{5}{8}$ **9.** $3\frac{3}{20}$ gallons   **11.** $7\frac{5}{7}$ **13.** $2\frac{1}{7}$ **15.** $7\frac{5}{12}$
17. $18\frac{17}{24}$ **19.** $3\frac{1}{2}$ **21.** $2\frac{11}{20}$ **23.** $5\frac{7}{8}$ **25.** $7\frac{1}{6}$
27. $17\frac{7}{8}$ in.; Addition, since the necklace is $10\frac{5}{8}$ in. longer than the bracelet.   **29.** $3\frac{1}{4}$ in.; Subtraction, since cutting her hair makes it shorter.   **31.** $15\frac{1}{4}$
33. $1\frac{3}{4}$
35 Find the sum of the sides.
$\qquad 2\frac{3}{8} + 2\frac{3}{8} + 2\frac{3}{8} = 6\frac{9}{8}$ or $7\frac{1}{8}$ yd
37. $5\frac{1}{2} - 3\frac{7}{8} = 1\frac{5}{8}$ **39.** Sample answer: Since the garden is a rectangle, the length of one side added to the length of the other side would equal half the length of the perimeter. If one side of the garden is $2\frac{5}{12}$ ft long, find 6 ft $- 2\frac{5}{12}$ ft, or $3\frac{7}{12}$ ft.   **41.** H
43. $\frac{9}{10}$ **45.** 1   **47.** IV

Pages 112–117   Lesson 2-3B
1. $\frac{2}{9}$ **3.** $\frac{2}{3}$ **5.** $1\frac{1}{2}$ **7.** 32 pounds   **9.** $\frac{4}{15}$
11. $-4\frac{4}{5}$ **13.** $\frac{1}{9}$ **15.** $\frac{1}{20}$

17 $\frac{2}{5} \times \frac{15}{16} = \frac{2 \times 15}{5 \times 16}$
$\qquad = \frac{\overset{1}{\cancel{2}}}{\cancel{5}} \times \frac{\overset{3}{\cancel{15}}}{\cancel{16}}$ Divide 2 and 16 by their GCF, 8, and
$\qquad\qquad\quad {}_{1} \qquad {}_{8}$ divide 5 and 15 by their GCF, 5.
$\qquad = \frac{1 \times 3}{1 \times 8}$ Multiply.
$\qquad = \frac{3}{8}$

19. $-\frac{2}{3}$ **21.** $\frac{3}{16}$ **23.** 14 c   **25.** $1\frac{9}{16}$ **27.** 30   **29.** $31\frac{1}{3}$
31. 20   **33.** $7\frac{1}{20}$ mi   **35.** $\frac{8}{21}$ **37.** $\frac{11}{48}$ **39.** one pint
41. one centimeter   **43.** $15\frac{3}{4}$ **45.** $28\frac{3}{4}$

47 Alano needs to find $1\frac{1}{2}$ times the amount of each ingredient.
Broccoli: $1\frac{1}{2} \times 1\frac{1}{4} = \frac{3}{2} \times \frac{5}{4}$
$\qquad\qquad\qquad\quad = \frac{3 \times 5}{2 \times 4}$
$\qquad\qquad\qquad\quad = \frac{15}{8}$
$\qquad\qquad\qquad\quad = 1\frac{7}{8}$ c
Cooked pasta: $1\frac{1}{2} \times 3\frac{3}{4} = \frac{3}{2} \times \frac{15}{4}$
$\qquad\qquad\qquad\qquad = \frac{45}{8}$
$\qquad\qquad\qquad\qquad = 5\frac{5}{8}$ c
Salad dressing: $1\frac{1}{2} \times \frac{2}{3} = \frac{3}{2} \times \frac{2}{3}$
$\qquad\qquad\qquad\qquad = \frac{3 \times 2}{2 \times 3}$
$\qquad\qquad\qquad\qquad = \frac{6}{6}$ or 1 c
Cheese: $1\frac{1}{2} \times 1\frac{1}{3} = \frac{3}{2} \times \frac{4}{3}$
$\qquad\qquad\qquad\quad = \frac{3 \times 4}{2 \times 3}$
$\qquad\qquad\qquad\quad = \frac{12}{6}$ or 2 c

49. Never; Sample answer: improper fractions are always greater than 1, so their product will be greater than 1.   **51.** Sample answer: Addition requires common denominators for completion, whereas multiplication does not. Multiplication can utilize cancelling.   **53.** H   **55.** $\frac{4}{7}$ **57.** 1   **59.** >   **61.** <

Pages 118–119   Lesson 2-3C
1. $2\frac{10}{27}$ foot

3 Draw a model of the full trip. Since the denominator is 5, divide it into 5 equal parts.

They have covered $\frac{4}{5}$ of trip, so color in 4 sections.

Since they have traveled one mile, each colored section is $\frac{1}{4}$ mile. Therefore, they have $\frac{1}{4}$ mile more remaining.
5. $\frac{3}{40}$ **7.** 28 games   **9.** Mary, Isabela, Anna, Rachana

11. There are 4 books in the front window of a bookstore. How many different ways can you arrange the books in the front window?; 24 ways.

Pages 120–125   Lesson 2-3D

1. $\frac{3}{8}$ **3.** $3\frac{1}{2}$ **5.** $\frac{1}{15}$ **7.** $1\frac{1}{5}$ **9.** 56 slices   **11.** $\frac{7}{16}$
13. $1\frac{1}{3}$ **15.** -12 **17.** $\frac{2}{3}$ **19.** 12   **21.** $\frac{4}{15}$ **23.** $-\frac{2}{3}$

25 $3\frac{4}{5} \div 1\frac{1}{3} = \frac{19}{5} \div \frac{4}{3}$
$= \frac{19}{5} \times \frac{3}{4}$
$= \frac{57}{20}$
$= 2\frac{17}{20}$

27. $-7\frac{4}{5}$ **29.** 36   **31a.** $3\frac{34}{35}$ **31b.** $1\frac{40}{99}$

33. $2\frac{1}{2}$

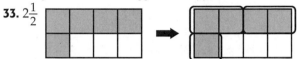

Sample answer: The model on the left shows that $\frac{5}{8}$ of a rectangle with 8 sections is 5 sections. $\frac{1}{4}$ of 8 sections is 2 sections. The model on the right shows those 5 sections divided into $2\frac{1}{2}$ groups of 2 sections.

35. $3\frac{1}{4}$

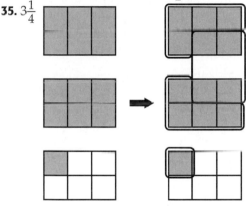

Sample answer: The model on the left shows that $2\frac{1}{6}$ of a rectangle with 6 sections is 13 sections. $\frac{2}{3}$ of 6 sections is 4 sections. The model on the right shows those thirteen sections being divided into $3\frac{1}{4}$ groups of four sections.

37. $7\frac{1}{3}$ **39.** -1

41 $12\frac{1}{2} \div \frac{3}{4} = \frac{25}{2} \div \frac{3}{4}$
$= \frac{25}{2} \times \frac{4}{3}$
$= \frac{25 \times 2}{1 \times 3}$
$= \frac{50}{3}$ or $16\frac{2}{3}$ times larger

43a. $2\frac{3}{8}$ times as many   **43b.** $7\frac{4}{5}$ times as many
45. 6:30 P.M.; Sample answer: $105 \div 35 = 3$. The storm will travel 105 miles in 3 sets of half hours, or $1\frac{1}{2}$ hours. Adding $1\frac{1}{2}$ hours to 5:00 P.M. will make it 6:30 P.M.   **47.** $\frac{10}{3}$ **49.** Yes; sample answer: If the

first proper fraction is larger than the second proper fraction, then the resulting quotient will be a whole number or mixed number.   **51.** H   **53.** $\frac{1}{16}$
55. $+20$ **57.** $>$ **59.** $<$

Pages 126–129   Lesson 2-3E

1. $9 \cdot 9 \cdot 9$
3 $\frac{2}{3} \cdot \frac{2}{3} \cdot \frac{2}{3} \cdot \frac{2}{3}$
5. 1,000   **7.** 9,765,625   people   **9.** 1^4 **11.** $1 \cdot 1 \cdot 1 \cdot 1 \cdot 1$
13. $\frac{3}{8} \cdot \frac{3}{8} \cdot \frac{3}{8} \cdot \frac{3}{8} \cdot \frac{3}{8} \cdot \frac{3}{8} \cdot \frac{3}{8} \cdot \frac{3}{8}$ **15.** $9 \cdot 9 \cdot 9 \cdot 9$
17. 64   **19.** $\frac{1}{2,401}$ **21.** 1   **23.** 1,000,000   **25.** 3^2 **27.** 1^8
29. $4 \cdot 4 \cdot 4 \cdot 4 \cdot 4$ **31.** 1,296

33 **a.** Each edge has 3 cubes, so there are $3 \cdot 3$, or 9 cubes in one layer. There are 3 layers, so there are $9 \cdot 3$, or 27 cubes. Written as one multiplication problem this is $3 \cdot 3 \cdot 3$, or 3^3.   **b.** Sample answer: A number taken to the third power is the same as the volume of a cube, or the amount of space inside a cube.
35. 2,147,483,648   **37.** $6^3, 15^2, 3^5, 2^8$ **39.** Sample answer: $4^5 = 1,024$ **41.** 1,000; 1,000 cannot be expressed as a square: $11^7 - 121, 19^2 = 361, 24^2 = 576$.
43. A   **45.** 200 people

Pages 132–135   Study Guide and Review

1. terminating   **3.** numerators   **5.** unlike
7. multiply   **9.** 0.875   **11.** $\frac{7}{10}$ **13.** $\frac{1}{20}$ **15.** $<$ **17.** $>$
19. English   **21.** $\frac{2}{3}$ **23.** $\frac{4}{7}$ **25.** $1\frac{2}{9}$ **27.** $1\frac{1}{6}$ **29.** $\frac{25}{36}$
31. $\frac{11}{18}$ **33.** $\frac{7}{12}$ **35.** $1\frac{2}{3}$ **37.** $3\frac{2}{3}$ **39.** $6\frac{11}{12}$ **41.** $\frac{2}{7}$
43. $1\frac{3}{4}$ **45.** $2\frac{1}{2}$ in.   **47.** 45   **49.** 6   **51.** $-\frac{2}{15}$ **53.** $-\frac{3}{4}$
55. $3 \cdot 3 \cdot 3 \cdot 3$ **57.** 5   **59.** $5 \cdot 5 \cdot 5 \cdot 5$

Chapter 3 Linear Equations

Page 142   Chapter 3   Are You Ready?
1. $p + 3$ **3.** $j + 10$ **5.** 17   **7.** 1   **9.** 29   **11.** 6   **13.** 15
15. 50   **17.** 38 years

Pages 144–145   Lesson 3-1A

1. when you are given the final result and asked to find an earlier amount   **3.** Sample answer: In the first four games, Hannah scored a total of 83 points. In the fourth game, she scored 19 points. In game three, she scored 27 points and in the second game, she scored 22 points. How many points did she score in the first game? To solve, first subtract 19 from 83, which is 64. Then subtract 27 from 64 to get 37. Finally, subtract 22 from 37. So, Hannah scored 15 points in her first game.

5 Work backward. Start with -25 and reverse all operations. Subtract -7 to get -18. Add 6 to get -12. Divide by -3. The original number is 4.
7. 19,200 tennis balls   **9.** Brie is 14 years old.

11.

13. Raquel's car gets 1,774,074 more inches per gallon than an aircraft carrier.   **15.** Sample answer: 1 ten-dollar bill, 2 five-dollar bills, and 7 one-dollar bills

Pages 150–155   Lesson 3-1D

1. 2   **3.** −2
5. $d + 120 = 364$; 244 ft

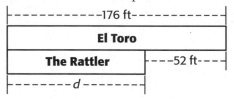

7. 5   **9.** 7   **11.** 7   **13.** −3
15.
$$r + 6 = -3$$
$$\underline{\quad - 6 = -6\quad}$$
$$r \quad = -9$$
17. 17   **19.** 7   **21.** $7 = w + 2$; 5 h   **23.** $15 = t − 3$; 18 years old   **25.** 18.4   **27.** 6.4   **29.** −0.68   **31.** $\frac{1}{12}$
33. $\frac{7}{18}$ **35.** $-\frac{1}{12}$ **37.** $d − 5 = 18$; $23
39. $35 + 45 + x = 180$; 100°
41.
$$-1 + -3 + s + 2 = \quad 0$$
$$-2 + s = \quad 0$$
$$\underline{+2 \qquad = +2}$$
$$s = +2$$
43a. $s − 65 = 13$; 78 mph   **43b.** $d + 52 = 176$; 124 ft

43c. The solution of each equation is 170; Colossos is 170 feet tall.   **45.** The value of y decreases by 2.
47. C   **49.** $146.70   **51.** $0.\overline{5}$ **53.** $0.\overline{36}$

Pages 157–161   Lesson 3-2B

1. 3   **3.** −3   **5.** 81   **7.** $6h = 48$; 8 h   **9.** 7   **11.** −3
13. −5
15.
$$\frac{m}{10} = 7$$
$$10 \cdot \frac{m}{10} = 10 \cdot 7$$
$$m = 70$$
17. −36   **19.** 80   **21.** $15w = 300$; 20 weeks
23.
$$205 = \frac{d}{3}$$
$$3 \cdot 205 = 3 \cdot \frac{d}{3}$$
$$615 \text{ miles} = d$$
25. $20.88h = 145$; 6.94 h   **27.** Sample answer: Raul divided by +6 and should have divided by −6; $x = −12$ **29.** Sample answer: Billie has twice as many cards as Tyree. If Billie has 16 cards, how many does Tyree have?   **31.** Sample answer: If it takes a scuba diver 4 seconds to swim 8 meters below the surface of the water, what is the rate of descent?   **33.** 8   **35.** 5   **37.** 12

Pages 163–168   Lesson 3-2D

1. $\frac{5}{8}$ **3.** $\frac{5}{29}$ **5.** 2   **7.** −8.2   **9.** $\frac{4}{5}$ **11.** $\frac{3}{4}n = 24$; 32 pieces of fruit   **13.** $\frac{6}{5}$ or $1\frac{1}{5}$ **15.** $\frac{6}{1}$ or 6   **17.** $\frac{1}{3}$
19. $\frac{8}{41}$ **21.** 5   **23.** −6   **25.** −3   **27.** $\frac{6}{5}$ or $1\frac{1}{5}$
29.
$$\frac{7}{8}k = \frac{5}{6}$$
$$\left(\frac{8}{7}\right)\frac{7}{8}k = \left(\frac{8}{7}\right)\frac{5}{6}$$
$$k = \frac{20}{21}$$
31. $6\frac{2}{3}$ **33.** $0.5t = 3$; 6 months   **35.** $140 = \frac{7}{15}x$; 300 ft
37. If one serving is $\frac{3}{4}$ cup, you can find how many servings are in $16\frac{1}{2}$ cups by writing an equation where x is the number of servings.
$$\frac{3}{4}x = 16\frac{1}{2}$$
$$\frac{3}{4}x = \frac{33}{2}$$
$$\left(\frac{4}{3}\right)\frac{3}{4}x = \left(\frac{4}{3}\right)\frac{33}{2}$$
$$x = 22$$
There are 22 servings in $16\frac{1}{2}$ cups.
39. $1.75m = 3.5$; 2   **41.** $\frac{3}{5}$, 5; The other pairs of numbers are reciprocals.   **43.** Sample answer: If you multiply each side of an equation by the same nonzero number, two sides remain equal; $\frac{2}{5}x = 7$.
45. I   **47.** 16 hours   **49.** 5   **51.** 450   **53.** −11.
55. −13   **57.** $\frac{1}{12}$ yard

Pages 172–176   Lesson 3-3B

1. 2
3.
$$-6r + 1 = -17$$
$$\underline{\quad - 1 = \quad -1\quad}$$
$$-6r = -18$$
$$\frac{-6r}{-6} = \frac{-18}{-6}$$
$$r = 3$$
5. 3   **7.** $14c + 23 = 65$; 3 CDs   **9.** 3   **11.** −4   **13.** 4
15. 9   **17.** 8   **19.** 24   **21.** $2c + 10 = 14$; 2 cups
23. 2.25   **25.** 2.1   **27.** 11
29. a.

$F = 1.8C + 32$	Write the equation.
$16 = 1.8C + 32$	Substitute 16 for F.
$16 − 32 = 1.8C + 32 − 32$	Subtract 32.
$\dfrac{-16}{1.8} = \dfrac{1.8C}{1.8}$	Divide each side by 1.8.
$-8.9 = C$	Simplify.
$-9°C$	Round to the nearest degree.

b.

$F = 1.8C + 32$	Write the equation.
$F = 1.8(-11) + 32$	Substitute −11 for C.
$F = -19.8 + 32$	Add −19.8 and 32.
$F = 12.2$	Simplify.

Subtract Alaska's record low temperature from Hawaii's record low temperature.
$12.2 − (−80) = 92.2°F$

31. 22 subscriptions   **33.** D   **35.** $1\frac{1}{2}$ **37.** 20

39. $\frac{7}{6}$ **41.** $\frac{1}{8}$ **43.** Denver; Denver had $\frac{1}{6}$ of an inch per day while Albuquerque had $\frac{3}{20}$, and $\frac{1}{6}$ is greater than $\frac{3}{20}$.

Pages 178–181   Lesson 3-3D

1. Sample answer: $2x + 8 = 40$; subtracted $2x$ from both sides **3.** Sample answer: $5x - 7 = 43$; subtracted x from both sides **5.** 52

7
$$3 - x = 4 - 3x$$
$$3 - x + 3x = 4$$
$$3 + 2x = 4$$
$$2x = 1$$
$$\frac{2x}{2} = \frac{1}{2}$$
$$x = \frac{1}{2}$$

9. 6.9 **11.** Sample answer: $2x + 14 = 20$; subtracted $4x$ from both sides **13.** Sample answer: $3x = 36$; subtracted $3x$ from both sides and added 3 to both sides **15.** Sample answer: $2x = 20$; subtracted $2x$ from both sides and added 15 to both sides **17.** 6
19. 24 **21.** 4.2 **23.** -10 **25.** $\frac{1}{4}$ **27.** -6

29 Manny bought supplies for $48 and 3 buckets at a certain price, b. Jin bought 7 buckets at a certain price, b. Manny and Jin each spent the same amount of money, so set the expressions equal to each other. Then solve.
$$3b + 48 = 7b$$
$$3b - 3b + 48 = 7b - 3b$$
$$48 = 4b$$
$$12 = b$$
The cost of one bucket is $12.
31. Adding $2b$ to both sides and then subtracting 14 from both sides of the first equation will result in the second equation. **33.** -10 **35.** B **37a.** $15c = 12c + 0.99$ **37b.** A baseball card costs 33 cents.
37c. Sergio could have bought 9 baseball cards if he bought 2 packs of gum. **39.** -3 **41.** $-\frac{3}{5}$ **43.** 2–3 siblings **45.** 253

Pages 184–187   Study Guide and Review

1. true **3.** true **5.** true **7.** false; subtract 3 from each side **9.** true **11.** false; $\frac{3}{2}$ **13.** 26 **15.** 3
17. -13 **19.** -2 **21.** $\frac{1}{4}$ **23.** $c - 6 = 18$; 24 cookies
25. 4 **27.** -9 **29.** 12 **31.** 39 **33.** $14w = 98$; 7 weeks
35. -2 **37.** 3 **39.** $\frac{5}{4}$ **41.** -16 **43.** $300 = 7.5r$; 40 mi/h
45. 6 **47.** -1 **49.** 9.8 **51.** $6d + 5 = 155$; 25 DVDs
53. -1 **55.** 9 **57.** 0.3 **59.** 12 rentals

Chapter 4 Proportions and Similarity

Page 194   Chapter 4   Are You Ready?

1. $\frac{2}{15}$ **3.** $\frac{1}{51}$ **5.** $\frac{15}{17}$ **7.** no; $\frac{2}{8} \neq \frac{8}{14}$ **9.** no; $\frac{2}{7} \neq \frac{10}{15}$

Pages 198–202   Lesson 4-1B

1. 6 mi per gal **3.** $0.50 per lb **5.** Music Place
7. 60 mi/h **9.** 30.4 people per class

11 45.5 meters in 13 seconds $= \frac{45.5 \text{ m}}{13 \text{ s}}$
Write the rate as a fraction.
$= \frac{45.5 \div 13}{13 \div 13}$ Divide the numerator and the denominator by 13.
$= \frac{3.5 \text{ m}}{1 \text{ s}}$ Simplify.
3.5 meters per second
13. $0.14/oz **15.** about $0.50 per pair **17.** Susana; Sample answer: 1.78 m/s > 1.66 m/s > 1.23 m/s
19a. Soft drink C; Sample answer: Soft drinks A and B have about 3 milligrams of sodium per ounce, and soft drink C has 6 milligram per ounce. **19b.** Soft drink A; Sample answer: 1.83 g/oz < 1.88 g/oz < 4.29 g/oz **21.** $4.98 **23.** $130.50 **25.** Sample answer: $1.25 per qt; $2.49 $\div$ 2 $\approx$ $2.50 $\div$ 2 or $1.25 **27.** Sample answer: $0.06 per oz; $1.13 $\div$ 20 $\approx$ $1.20 $\div$ 20 or $0.06

29 **a.** 1 hr, 18 minutes, 27 seconds is $(1 + 18 \div 60 + 27 \div 3600)$ hr or 1.3075 hr.
26.2 miles in 1.3075 hours $= \frac{26.2 \text{ miles}}{1.3075 \text{ hr}}$
Write the rate as a fraction.
$= \frac{26.2 \div 1.3075}{1.3075 \div 1.3075}$ Divide the numerator and the denominator by 1.3075.
$= \frac{20.04}{1}$ Simplify.
The average speed was 20.04 mph. **b.** Divide the distance by the average speed to find the time.
$\frac{30 \text{ miles}}{20.04 \text{ mph}} = 1.497$ hours or 1 hr 29 min 49 s
31a. The bear's heart beats 120 times in 2 minutes when it is active. **31b.** The bear's heart beats 18 times in 1.5 minutes when it is hibernating.
31c. the bear's heart rate in beats per minute
31d. active: 60 beats per minute; hibernating: 12 beats per minute **31e.** when it is active; Sample answer: The active line increases faster than the hibernating line when read from left to right.
35. Sometimes; a ratio that compares two measurements with different units is a rate, such as $\frac{2 \text{ miles}}{10 \text{ minutes}}$. A ratio that compares two numbers or two measurements with like units is not a rate, such as $\frac{2 \text{ cups}}{3 \text{ cups}}$. **37.** Sample answer: The rate 55 miles per hour is a measure of the number of miles traveled per unit hour. **39.** H **41.** -2 **43.** $3\frac{1}{2}$ **45.** 15

Pages 203–205   Lesson 4-1C

1 Make a table and compare the values. The ratios can be simplified to 225 liters. So, the rates are proportional. Sample answer:

Time (days)	1	2	3	4
Water (L)	225	450	675	900

The time to water ratio for 1, 2, 3, and 4 days is $\frac{1}{225}$, $\frac{2}{450}$ or $\frac{1}{225}$, $\frac{3}{675}$ or $\frac{1}{225}$, and $\frac{4}{900}$ or $\frac{1}{225}$. Since these ratios are all equal to $\frac{1}{225}$, the number of days the supply lasts is proportional to the amount of water the elephant drinks.

3. no; Sample answer:

Number of Teachers	4	5	6	7
Number of Students	28	56	84	112

The ratio of students to teachers for 4, 5, 6, and 7 teachers is $\frac{28}{4}$ or 7, $\frac{56}{5}$ or 11.2, $\frac{84}{6}$ or 14, and $\frac{112}{7}$ or 16. Since these ratios are not all equal, the number of students at the school is not proportional to the number of teachers.

5. no; Sample answer:

Rental Time (h)	1	2	3	4
Cost ($)	37	62	87	112

The cost to time ratio for 1, 2, 3, and 4 hours is $\frac{37}{1}$ or 37, $\frac{62}{2}$ or 31, $\frac{87}{3}$ or 29, and $\frac{112}{4}$ or 28. Since these ratios are not all equal, the cost of a rental is not proportional to the number of hours you rent the boat.

7. yes; Sample answer:

Time (days)	5	10	15	20
Length (in.)	7.5	15	22.5	30

The length to time ratio for 5, 10, 15, and 20 days is $\frac{7.5}{5}$ or 1.5, $\frac{15}{10}$ or 1.5, $\frac{22.5}{15}$ or 1.5, and $\frac{30}{20}$ or 1.5. Since these ratios are all equal to 1.5 ft per day, the length of vine is proportional to the number of days of growth.

9a. yes; Sample answer:

Number of Hours Worked on Sunday	1	2	3	4
Number of Coupons Given Away on Sunday	52	104	156	208

The coupons to hours ratios for 1, 2, 3, and 4 hours of work on Sunday are $\frac{52}{1}$ or 52, $\frac{104}{2}$ or 52, $\frac{156}{3}$ or 52, and $\frac{208}{4}$ or 52. Since these ratios are all equal to 52 coupons per hour, the number of coupons given away is proportional to the number of hours worked on Sunday.   **9b.** no; Sample answer:

Number of Hours Worked on Sunday	1	2	3	4
Total Number of Coupons Given Away that Weekend	468	520	572	624

The coupons to hours ratios for 1, 2, 3, and 4 hours of work on Sunday are $\frac{468}{1}$ or 468, $\frac{520}{2}$ or 260, $\frac{572}{3}$ or about 190, and $\frac{624}{4}$ or 156. Since these ratios are not all equal, the total number of coupons given away is not proportional to the number of hours worked on Sunday.

11. a. Make a table and compare the side length to the perimeter. The measures are proportional to the perimeter. Sample answer:

Side length (units)	1	2	3	4
Perimeter (units)	4	8	12	16

The side length to perimeter ratio for side lengths of 1, 2, 3, and 4 units is $\frac{1}{4}$, $\frac{2}{8}$ or $\frac{1}{4}$, $\frac{3}{12}$ or $\frac{1}{4}$, and $\frac{4}{16}$ or $\frac{1}{4}$. Since these ratios are all equal to $\frac{1}{4}$, the measure of the side length of a square is proportional to the square's perimeter.   **b.** Make a table and compare the side length to the area. The measures are not proportional to the area. Sample answer:

Side length (units)	1	2	3	4
Area (units^2)	1	4	9	16

The side length to area ratio for side lengths of 1, 2, 3, and 4 units is $\frac{1}{1}$ or 1, $\frac{2}{4}$ or $\frac{1}{2}$, $\frac{3}{9}$ or $\frac{1}{3}$, and $\frac{4}{16}$ or $\frac{1}{4}$. Since these ratios are not all equal, the measure of the side length of a square is not proportional to the square's area.

13. It is not proportional because the ratio of laps : time is not consistent; $\frac{4}{1} \neq \frac{6}{2} \neq \frac{8}{3} \neq \frac{10}{4}$.   **15.** C   **17.** $11.90
19. 3

Pages 208–210   Lesson 4-1D

1 $\frac{1.5}{6} = \frac{10}{p}$

$1.5p = 10(6)$ Find the cross products.
$1.5p = 60$ Multiply.
$\frac{1.5p}{1.5} = \frac{60}{1.5}$ Divide each side by 1.5.
$p = 40$ Simplify.

3. 16.4   **5.** $m = 9.5h$; $19; $42.75   **7.** 6   **9.** 3.5   **11.** 3.75
13. 13.5   **15.** $\frac{14}{483} = \frac{x}{600}$; about 17.4 gal   **17.** $\frac{4}{5} = \frac{x}{30}$; 24 people

19 shoulder width → $\frac{16.2}{64}$ = $\frac{18.5}{h}$ ← shoulder width
            height →   ← height

$16.2h = 18.5(64)$ Find the cross products.
$16.2h = 1,184$ Multiply.
$\frac{16.2h}{16.2} = \frac{1,184}{16.2}$ Divide each side by 16.2.
$h \approx 73$ inches   Simplify.

21a. 81.9   **21b.** 144.7   **21c.** 110.2   **21d.** 48.0
23. 256 c; Sample answer: The ratio of cups of mix to cups of water is 1 : 8, which means that the proportion $\frac{1}{8} = \frac{32}{x}$ is true and can be solved.   **25.** 18
27. Sample answer: By writing an equation to represent a proportional relationship, you can use this equation to find any other similar quantities. The result is one calculation involving multiplication, rather than the two calculations that would result by writing and solving a new proportion.   **29.** G
31. Yes; the constant rate of change is $\frac{15}{1}$ or $15 per hour.   **33.** 500 kB/min   **35.** 7.2 m/s

1. Sample answer: It helps to visualize the parts in relation to the whole.   **3.** 1,536 tiles

5 If Mr. Sanchez can only change the width of his flower bed, then the additional 12 meters needs to be split up between the two sides that are the widths. Therefore, add half of 12, or 6 meters to the width. This changes the width to 11 meters.

7. 16   **9.** 100 lb   **11.**

13. Sample answer: There are an estimated 11,300,000 children born each month worldwide. At that rate, how many more are born each day? 376,666 births per day

1. 50 km   **3.** 130 km   **5a.** $16\frac{2}{3}$ in.   **5b.** $1\frac{1}{3}$ in.
7. $\frac{2}{3}$ **9.** about 10.3 inches wide   **11.** 81 mi
13. 37.8 mi

15 $\dfrac{0.5 \text{ cm}}{1.5 \text{ m}} = \dfrac{x}{36 \text{ m}}$

$0.5 \cdot 36 = 1.5 \cdot x$

$18 = 1.5x$

$\dfrac{18}{1.5} = \dfrac{1.5x}{1.5}$

$12 = x$

The model is 12 cm tall.
To find the scale factor, first convert cm to m:
0.5 cm = 0.005 m. Next make a ratio and simplify.
$\dfrac{0.005}{1.5} = \dfrac{5}{1,500}$ or $\dfrac{1}{300}$

17. $11\frac{3}{4}$ in.; $\frac{2}{1}$ **19.** $109\frac{3}{8}$ ft   **21a.** $\frac{1}{3}$

21b.

Height of Thomas Jefferson (feet)	1	2	3	4	5	6
Height of Statue (feet)	3	6	9	12	15	18

21c. $3x$ **21d.** about 6.33 ft or 6 ft 4 in.

23 Count to find that it is 4 units from the lake to the cabin. To find the actual distance, use the key that states 1 unit = 75 yards to set up a proportion. Then solve the proportion.

$\dfrac{1 \text{ unit}}{75 \text{ yards}} = \dfrac{4 \text{ units}}{x \text{ yards}}$ Set up the proportion.

$1 \cdot x = 75 \cdot 4$ Find the cross products.

$x = 300$ Simplify.

The children will travel 300 yards from the lake to the cabin.

25. Sample answer: The scale is the ratio comparing the measurements, including the units, on the model to the measurements on the actual figure. Once the units have been converted to the same unit, the scale factor is the ratio written without units as a fraction in simplest form. For example, if the scale of the model to the actual figure is 1 in. = 4.5 ft, then the scale factor would be $\dfrac{1}{4.5 \times 12}$ or $\dfrac{1}{54}$.

27. C   **29.** F   **31.** 25   **33.** 63   **35.** 1 lb 4 oz for $4.99; 1 lb 4 oz for $4.99 costs about $0.25 per ounce and 2 lb 6 oz for $9.75 costs about $0.26 per ounce.

1. rectangle $PQRS$ **3.** 45 mm

5 Find which triangle below is similar to triangle FGH.

Triangle PMN
$\dfrac{MP}{GF} = \dfrac{1}{2}$
$\dfrac{PN}{FH} = \dfrac{4}{5}$
not similar

Triangle CAB
$\dfrac{AC}{GF} = \dfrac{4}{2}$ or 2
$\dfrac{CB}{FH} = \dfrac{10}{5}$ or 2
similar

Triangle CAB is similar to triangle FGH.

7. 25 mi   **9.** $\dfrac{3}{x} = \dfrac{4.5}{18}$; 12 ft

11 a. If the kids follow the red line, they will walk 17 units. We are given the key that 1 square = 75 yards. Write a proportion to find the total distance walked.

units → $\dfrac{1}{75} = \dfrac{17}{x}$ ← units
yards →   ← yards

$1 \cdot x = 17 \cdot 75$ Find cross products.
$x = 1,275$ Simplify.

The kids walk 1,275 yards from the time they leave the lake until they get to the campfire.

b. If they follow the red line back to the cabin, they will have walked a total of 30 units.

units → $\dfrac{1}{75} = \dfrac{30}{x}$ ← units
yards →   ← yards

$1 \cdot x = 30 \cdot 75$ Find cross products.
$x = 2,250$ Simplify.

The kids walk 2,250 yards total from the time they leave the lake until they return to the cabin.

13a. true; Sample answer: All squares have 4 90° angles and equal sides. Therefore, all squares are proportional to other squares.   **13b.** false; Sample answer: Rectangles have different lengths than widths that may not be proportional to another rectangle.   **15.** B   **17.** H
19. 2 ingredients

1 $x = 38\left(\dfrac{18}{12}\right)$ Multiply by the scale factor.

$x = \dfrac{\overset{19}{\cancel{38}}}{1}\left(\dfrac{18}{\underset{6}{\cancel{12}}}\right)$ Cancel common factors.

$x = 57$ Simplify.

The perimeter is 57 millimeters.
3. 912,600 pixels   **5.** 14.55 in.   **7.** 49 ft²

9 $x = 1,134\left(\dfrac{1}{3}\right)^2$ Multiply the square of the scale factor.

$x = 1,134\left(\dfrac{1}{9}\right)$ Evaluate the power.

$x = 126$ Multiply.

The area of the putting green will be 126 square feet.

11. Sample answer:

10 m

5 m ▭

12 m

6 m ▭

$P = 30$ m
$A = 50$ m^2

$P = 36$ m
$A = 72$ m^2

13. Robert is thinking of size in terms of area and Denise is thinking of size in terms of perimeter.
15. 36 times   **17.** 4.8 mm

Pages 236–239   *Study Guide and Review*

1. proportional   **3.** proportion   **5.** unit rate   **7.** scale
9. nonproportional   **11.** 90 mi per day   **13.** No; the ratios are not equal.   **15.** 4   **17.** 3.5   **19.** 12.5
21. 3.2 mi   **23.** 25 minutes   **25.** 21 km   **27.** 1 in. = 24 in. or 1 in. = 2 ft   **29.** *RUTS*   **31.** 4.2 ft   **33.** 150 yd^2

Chapter 5 Linear Functions

Page 246   *Chapter 5*   *Are You Ready?*

1. 22   **3.** 42   **5.** 8   **7.** 14   **9.** 28   **11.** 63   **13.** 30
15. C   **17.** D   **19.** B

Pages 250–252   *Lesson 5-1B*

1.

x	3x	y
1	3 × 1	4
2	3 × 2	8
3	3 × 3	12
4	3 × 4	16

Domain: {1, 2, 3, 4};
Range: {3, 6, 9, 12}

3.

x	8x	y
1	8 · 1	8
2	8 · 2	16
3	8 · 3	24
4	8 · 4	32

Domain: {1, 2, 3, 4};
Range: {8, 16, 24, 32}

5.

x	2x	y
0	2 × 0	0
1	2 × 1	2
2	2 × 2	4
3	2 × 3	6

Domain: {0, 1, 2, 3};
Range: {0, 2, 4, 6}

7 In the rule column, show that you will multiply 9 times each of the *x*-values. In the *y* column, show each product.

x	9x	y
1	9 × 1	9
2	9 × 2	18
3	9 × 3	27
4	9 × 4	36

List the *x*-values as the domain. Domain: {1, 2, 3, 4}
List the *y*-values as the range. Range: {9, 18, 27, 36}

9.

x	60x	y
5	60 · 5	300
10	60 · 10	600
15	60 · 15	900
20	60 · 20	1,200

Domain: {5, 10, 15, 20}; Range: {300, 600, 900, 1,200}
11a. $t = 35m$ **11b.** 525 times; Sample answer: Replace *m* with 15 in the equation $t = 35m$ to find the number of times a cricket will have chirped after 15 minutes at this temperature.

13.

x	1.3x	y
1	1.3 × 1	1.3
2	1.3 × 2	2.6
3	1.3 × 3	3.9
4	1.3 × 4	5.2

Domain: {0, 1, 2, 3};
Range: {1.3, 2.6, 3.9, 5.2}

15.

x	$\frac{2}{3}x$	y
2	$\frac{2}{3} \times 2$	$1\frac{1}{3}$
3	$\frac{2}{3} \times 3$	2
4	$\frac{2}{3} \times 4$	$2\frac{2}{3}$
5	$\frac{2}{3} \times 5$	$3\frac{1}{3}$

Domain: {2, 3, 4, 5};
Range: $\left\{1\frac{1}{3}, 2, 2\frac{2}{3}, 3\frac{1}{3}\right\}$

17 **a.** Use the distance formula, $D = rt$ to write the equation. The rate is 8, the distance is *m,* and the time is *s*. Therefore, the equation is $m = 8s$.
b. Use the distance formula, $D = rt$ to write the equation. The rate is 19, the distance is *m* and the time is *s*. Therefore, the equation is $m = 19s$.
c. 480 mi; 1,140 mi; Sample answer: Replace *s* with 60 in the equation $m = 8s$ and in the equation $m = 19s$ to find the number of miles Jupiter travels in 1 minute and the number of miles Earth travels in 1 minute, respectively.
19. Divya added 3 to each input rather than multiplying by 3. The range should be {6, 12, 18, 24}.
21. C   **23.** 8 m

Pages 256–257   *Lesson 5-1C*

1.

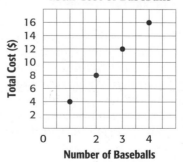

Total Cost of Baseballs

Total Cost ($) vs. Number of Baseballs

3 Graph $y = x - 1$. Select any four values for the input x. For example, try 2, 1, 0, and −1. Substitute these values for x to find the output y. Graph the points, and draw a line through the points.

x	$x - 1$	y	(x, y)
−1	−1 − 1	−2	(−1, −2)
0	0 − 1	−1	(0, −1)
1	1 − 1	0	(1, 0)
2	2 − 1	1	(2, 1)

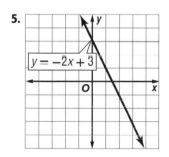

5.

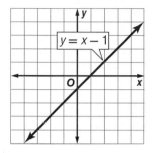

7.

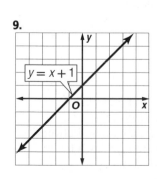

9.

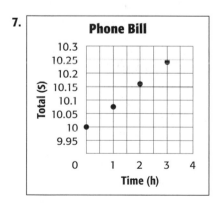

11.

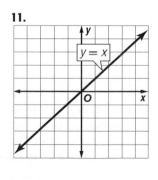

13.

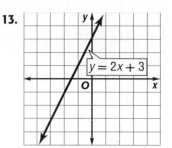

15.

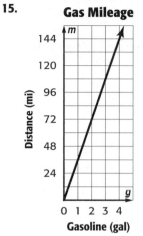

17.

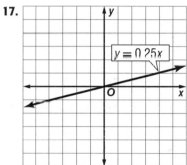

19 Graph $y = 0.5x - 1$. Select any four values for the input x. We chose 4, 2, 0, and −2 in order to have whole number values for y. Substitute these values for x to find the output y. Graph the points, and draw a line through the points.

x	$0.5x - 1$	y	(x, y)
−2	0.5(−2) − 1	−2	(−2, −2)
0	0.5(0) − 1	−1	(0, −1)
2	0.5(2) − 1	0	(2, 0)
4	0.5(4) − 1	1	(4, 1)

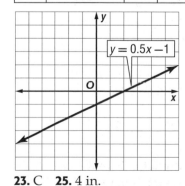

23. C   **25.** 4 in.

For Homework Help, go to (Hotmath.com)

Pages 261–263   Lesson 5-2B

1. 1.5°F/h   **3.** 6 m per s   **5.** about $0.02 per min

7 To find the rate of change, pick any two points on the line, such as (18, 216) and (6, 72).

$$\frac{\text{change in length}}{\text{change in height}} = \frac{(216 - 72)\text{ inches}}{(18 - 6)\text{ inches}}$$

$$= \frac{144\text{ inches}}{12\text{ inches}} \text{ or } \frac{12\text{ inches}}{1\text{ inch}}$$

The length increases 12 inches for every inch the height increases. So, the rate of change is 12 inches of length per inch of height.

9 a. Write and solve a proportion to determine how many laps equal 1 mile.

$$\frac{20\text{ laps}}{5\text{ miles}} = \frac{x\text{ laps}}{1\text{ mile}}$$
$$5x = 20$$
$$\frac{5x}{5} = \frac{20}{5}$$
$$x = 4$$

So, 4 laps equal 1 mile. From the information on the clipboard, it takes Seth 57.1 seconds to complete 4 laps, or 1 mile.

Find the unit rate to determine the constant rate of change.

$$\frac{\text{change in miles}}{\text{change in seconds}} = \frac{1\text{ mile}}{57.1\text{ seconds}}$$

$$\approx \frac{0.0175\text{ mile}}{1\text{ second}}$$

So, the constant rate of change is about 0.02 mile per second.

b.   Go-Kart Racing Times

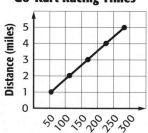

11. Sample answer: At Sam's Shoes, 2 pairs of sandals cost $30 and 4 pairs cost $60. Find the rate of change.   **13.** 390

15.

x	x − 4	y
4	4 − 4	0
5	5 − 4	1
6	6 − 4	2
7	7 − 4	3

Domain: {4, 5, 6, 7};
Range: {0, 1, 2, 3}

17.

x	5x + 1	y
1	5(1) + 1	6
2	5(2) + 1	11
3	5(3) + 1	16
4	5(4) + 1	21

Domain: {1, 2, 3, 4};
Range: {6, 11, 16, 21}

19. $10 + b = 18$; $8

Pages 266–267   Lesson 5-2C

1

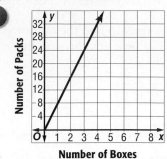

The slope of the line is equal to the rate at which the number of fruit snacks increases as the number of boxes increases or $\frac{8\text{ fruit snacks}}{1\text{ box}}$. 8 packs per box; The slope represents how many packages of fruit snacks are in each box.

3.

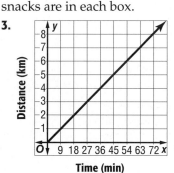

$\frac{1}{9}$; Adriano traveled 1 kilometer every 9 minutes.

5.

$\frac{3}{1}$ or 3; There are 3 feet per yard.

7 a. The point (2, 120) represents the fact that Car A had traveled 120 miles in 2 hours.   **b.** The point (1.5, 67.5) represents the fact that Car B had traveled 67.5 miles in 1.5 hours.   **c.** The ratio of the change in y-coordinate to the change in x-coordinate for each pair of points represents the average speed of each vehicle.   **d.** The slope of each line represents the average speed of each vehicle.   **e.** Car A is traveling faster. Since its graph is rising more rapidly, its speed is greater.

9. Marisol found $\frac{\text{run}}{\text{rise}}$. Her answer should be $\frac{3}{2}$.

11. $\frac{4}{1}$ or 4   **13.** $9 per hour

Pages 270–271   Lesson 5-3A

1. Sample answer: Graphs provide a visual representation of a situation involving comparisons. A graphical model can sometimes show conclusively what is often difficult to interpret from looking at lists alone.

3a.

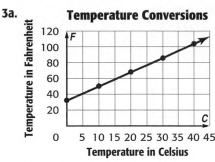

Temperature Conversions

3b. Sample answer: 77°F   **5.** 158, 318   **7.** Wednesday

9 If the helicopter can carry 2,400 pounds and the crates weigh 75 pounds each, divide 2,400 by 75 to find the amount of crates the helicopter can carry; 2,400 ÷ 75 = 32 crates

11. 18

Pages 276–278   Lesson 5-3C

1. 30 cakes per hour   **3.** yes; 36

5 Since the points on the graph lie in a straight line, the rate of change is a constant. The constant ratio is what Shelley makes per dog.

$$\frac{\text{pay (\$)} \rightarrow 10}{\text{number of dogs} \rightarrow 4} \text{ or \$2.50}, \frac{5}{2} \text{ or \$2.50}$$

Shelley makes \$2.50 per dog.

7. no   **9.** yes; 0.2   **11.** \$0.80/book   **13.** \$405

15. $y = \frac{1}{5}x$; 3   **17.** $y = \frac{7}{8}x$; 16

19 Since we are given that a direct variation exists, we can find the constant of variation from one point on the graph. Using the point (36, 12) we find that the constant of variation is $\frac{36}{12}$ or $\frac{3}{1}$. Use this fact to set up and solve a proportion to find the measure of an object in yards if it is 78 feet long.

$\frac{3}{1} = \frac{78}{x}$	Set up the proportion.
$3 \cdot x = 1 \cdot 78$	Find the cross products.
$3x = 78$	Simplify.
$\frac{3x}{3} = \frac{78}{3}$	Divide each side by 3.
$x = 26$ yards	Simplify.

An object that is 78 feet long is 26 yards long.

21a. 10 gal per minute; yes

21b.

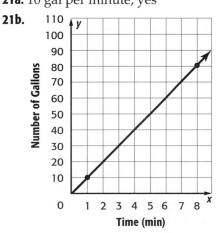

21c. Sample answer: $g = 10m$ **23.** Sample answer: $x = 9$, $y = 5\frac{1}{2}$; $x = 36$; $y = 22$ **27.** G   **29.** Sample answer: 42 calls

Pages 280–283   Lesson 5-3E

1 Determine if the relationship is an inverse variation by checking that $xy = k$ for some constant k.

$48(360) = 17{,}280$; $36(480) = 17{,}280$; $24(720) = 17{,}280$; $12(1{,}440) = 17{,}280$

The relationship is an inverse variation.

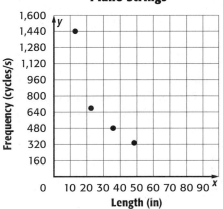

Piano Strings

3. 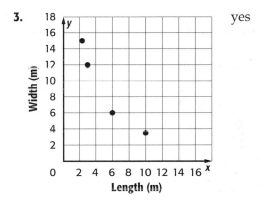   yes

5. 24 h

7 Check if it is a direct variation by looking at the ratio of each pair of numbers.

$\frac{88}{2}$ or 44, $\frac{44}{4}$ or 11. The relationship is not a direct variation.

Next, check to see if the relationship is an inverse variation.

$88(2) = 176$, $44(4) = 176$; The relationship is an inverse variation.

9. Sample answer: $x = 12$, $y = 2$; $x = 6$, $y = 4$; $x = 8$, $y = 3$.   **11.** B   **13.** A   **15.** Sample answer: There are more than twice as many people in California who skate than there are in Texas.

Pages 286–289   Study Guide and Review

1. slope   **3.** inverse variation   **5.** function
7. function table   **9.** constant rate of change
11. rate of change

13.

x	2x	y
1	2 × 1	2
2	2 × 2	4
3	2 × 3	6
4	2 × 4	8

Domain: {1, 2, 3, 4};
Range: {2, 4, 6, 8}

15.

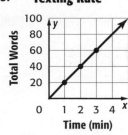

Texting Rate

17.

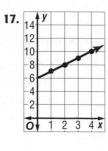

19. 2 laps per minute

21.

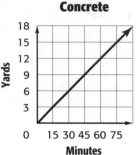

Concrete

Slope = $\frac{1}{5}$; For every
5 minutes of pouring
concrete, they can pour
1 yard of concrete.
23. Crazy Horse
25. yes; 2 sold
27. 2.2 hours

Chapter 6 Percents

Page 296   Chapter 6   Are You Ready?

1. 48   **3.** 1,512   **5.** $54.75   **7.** 0.17   **9.** 1.57   **11.** 0.085
13. 0.075   **15.** 8%   **17.** 580%   **19.** 72.5%

Pages 302–304   Lesson 6-1B

1. 4   **3.** 110.5   **5.** 23   **7.** $3.25   **9.** $194.40   **11.** 45.9
13. 14.7

15 **Method 1** Write the percent as a fraction.

$175\% = \frac{175}{100}$ or $\frac{7}{4}$

$\frac{7}{4}$ of $10 = \frac{7}{4} \times 10$

$= \frac{7}{4} \times \frac{10}{1}$ or $17\frac{1}{2}$

Method 2 Write the percent as a decimal.

$175\% = \frac{175}{100}$ or 1.75

1.75 of $10 = 1.75 \times 10 = 17.5$

17. 62.5   **19.** $290   **21.** 3.5   **23.** 97.8   **25.** 92.5
27. about 19.5 million   **29.** 3.3   **31.** 990   **33.** 520
35. 0.24   **37.** $241.50   **39.** $297   **41.** about 30
43. about 15

45 There are 20 answers on the test. If 25% of the
answers are choice B, there are 0.25 × 20 or
5 answers that are choice B. Subtracting these 5
from the total number of 20 answers leaves
15 answers that are not choice B.
47a. 66.7%   **47b.** 33.3%   **47c.** 50%   **47d.** 33.3%
51. C   **53.** 30   **55.** $44\frac{5}{6}$ mi

Pages 307–310   Lesson 6-1C

1. Sample answer: 5; $\frac{1}{2} \cdot 10 = 5$; $0.1 \cdot 10 = 1$ and
$5 \cdot 1 = 5$ **3.** Sample answer: 24; $\frac{2}{5} \cdot 60 = 24$;
$0.1 \cdot 60 = 6$ and $4 \cdot 6 = 24$ **5.** Sample answer: 105;
$(1 \cdot 70) + \left(\frac{1}{2} \cdot 70\right) = 105$ **7.** Sample answer: about
48 teenagers; $\frac{3}{5} \cdot 80 = 48$; $0.1 \cdot 80 = 8$ and $6 \cdot 8 = 48$
9. Sample answer: 35; $\frac{1}{2} \cdot 70 = 35$; $0.1 \cdot 70 = 7$ and
$5 \cdot 7 = 35$

11 Estimate 21% of 90.

Method 1 Use a fraction to estimate.

21% is about 20%, or $\frac{1}{5}$.

20% of $90 = \frac{1}{5} \times 90$ or 18.

So, 21% of 90 is about 18.

Method 2 Use 10% to estimate.

10% of 90 is 9.

21% is about 2 × 10%.

2 × 9 = 18.

So, 21% of 90 is about 18.

13. Sample answer: 18; $\frac{3}{5} \cdot 30 = 18$; $0.1 \cdot 30 = 3$ and
$6 \cdot 3 = 18$ **15.** Sample answer: 12.5; $\frac{1}{4} \cdot 50 = 12.5$;
$0.1 \cdot 50 = 5$ and $2.5 \cdot 5 = 12.5$ **17.** Sample answer:
180; $\frac{9}{10} \cdot 200 = 180$; $0.1 \cdot 200 = 20$ and $9 \cdot 20 = 180$
19. Sample answer: 100; $\frac{2}{3} \cdot 150 = 100$; $0.1 \cdot 150 = 15$
and $6.6 \cdot 15 \approx 100$ **21.** about $6; $\frac{3}{20} \cdot \$40 = \$6$
23. $(1 \cdot 50) + \left(\frac{3}{10} \cdot 50\right) = 65$ **25.** $0.01 \cdot 400 = 4$ and
$\frac{1}{2} \cdot 4 = 2$ **27.** $0.01 \cdot 500 = 5$ and $\frac{2}{5} \cdot 5 = 2$ **29.** about
96 mi; $0.01 \cdot 12,000 = 120$ and $\frac{4}{5} \cdot 120 = 96$
31. $\frac{2}{3} \cdot 9 = 6$ **33.** $\frac{1}{3} \cdot 90 = 30$ **35.** $\frac{1}{5} \cdot 100 = 20$

37 **a.** Estimate 13% of 24 hours.

13% is about 10% or $\frac{1}{10}$

13% of $24 \approx \frac{1}{10} \cdot 24$ or 2.4

So, 13% of 24 is about 2.4. Avery spends about
2.4 hours on homework.
b. Estimate 33% of 24.

33% is about $\frac{1}{3}$

33% of $24 \approx \frac{1}{3} \cdot 24$ or 8

So, 33% of 24 is about 8. Avery spends about
8 hours sleeping.

Estimate 19% of 24.

19% is about 20% or $\frac{1}{5}$

24 is about 25

19% of $24 \approx \frac{1}{5} \cdot 25$ or 5

So, 19% of 24 is about 5. Avery spends about 5 hours
doing the activities in the "other" category. Avery
spends 8 − 5 or 3 hours more sleeping than doing
the activities in the "other" category.
c. There are 24 · 60 or 1,440 minutes in one day.
Estimate 8% of 1,440.

8% is about 10% or $\frac{1}{10}$

8% of $1,440 \approx \frac{1}{10} \cdot 1,440$ or 144

So, 8% of 1,440 is about 144. Avery spends about 144 minutes each day on extracurricular activities.

39a.

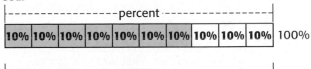

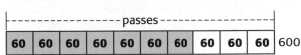

39b. 420   **39c.** greater; Both the number of passes and the percent were rounded up.

39d. Peyton Manning; 65% of 515 must be greater than 65% of 404.

41 Sample answer: Of the students in a seventh-grade class, 12% like to rollerblade. If there are 50 students in the class, about how many like to rollerblade?

43. He incorrectly changed 1.5% to 1.5, which is 150%. It should be about 3.   **45.** Sample answer: One way to find 22% of 136 is to find $\frac{1}{5} \cdot 140 = 28$. Another way to find 22% of 136 is to first find $(0.1 \cdot 140)$ and then multiply by 2. The result is 28.

47. H   **49.** 0.9   **51.** 72   **53.** −8   **55.** 50   **57.** 357.1

59. $\frac{1}{12}$ mi

Pages 315–316   Lesson 6-2B

1. 36%   **3.** 0.7

5 9 is 12% of which number?

$$\frac{9}{w} = \frac{12}{100} \quad \text{Write the proportion.}$$

$$9 \cdot 100 = 12 \cdot w \quad \text{Find the cross products.}$$

$$900 = 12w \quad \text{Simplify.}$$

$$\frac{900}{12} = \frac{12w}{12} \quad \text{Divide each side by 12.}$$

$$75 = w$$

So, 9 is 12% of 75.

7. 3 c   **9.** 7.5%   **11.** 8.6   **13.** 375   **15.** 24 points

17. 40%   **19.** 4.1   **21.** 192

23 What percent of 300 is 0.6?

$$\frac{0.6}{300} = \frac{n}{100} \quad \text{Write the proportion.}$$

$$0.6 \cdot 100 = 300 \cdot n \quad \text{Find the cross products.}$$

$$60 = 300n \quad \text{Simplify.}$$

$$\frac{60}{300} = \frac{300n}{300} \quad \text{Divide each side by 300.}$$

$$0.20 = n$$

So, 0.6 is 0.20% of 300.

25. 75 students; 70 of the students bought their lunch. Some amount, x, left the cafeteria. The new percent proportion would be $\frac{70 - x}{100 - x} = \frac{60}{100}$.

27. Sample answer: A runner won 15% of the races he ran. If he won 3 races, how many races did he run?   **29.** F   **31.** 30   **33a.** $\frac{2}{9}$ **33b.** $\frac{3}{2}$ **33c.** $\frac{9}{14}$

Pages 319–321   Lesson 6-2C

1. $p = 0.88 \cdot 300$; 264

3 75 is what percent of 150?

$$75 = n \cdot 150 \quad \text{Write the percent equation.}$$

$$\frac{75}{150} = \frac{150n}{150} \quad \text{Divide each side by 150.}$$

$$0.5 = n \quad \text{Simplify.}$$

Since n represents the decimal form, the percent is 50%. So, 75 is 50% of 150.

5. $3 = 0.12 \cdot w$; 25   **7.** 39 loaves   **9.** $p = 0.39 \cdot 65$; 25.4   **11.** $p = 0.53 \cdot 470$; 249.1   **13.** $26 = n \cdot 96$; 27.1%   **15.** $30 = n \cdot 64$; 46.9%   **17.** $84 = 0.75 \cdot w$; 112   **19.** $6.4 = 0.8 \cdot w$; 80   **21.** 4,400 games

23. 1 lobster   **25.** $p = 0.004 \cdot 82.1$; 0.3

27. $230 = n \cdot 200$; 115%

29 a. Let n represent the percent of viewers watching comedy, jokes, and bloopers.

$$52,540,000 = n \cdot 142,000,000 \quad \text{Write the percent equation.}$$

$$\frac{52,540,000}{142,000,000} = \frac{142,000,000n}{142,000,000} \quad \text{Divide each side by 142 million.}$$

$$0.37 = n \quad \text{Simplify.}$$

37% of viewers watch comedy, jokes, and bloopers.

b. Let n represent the percent of viewers watching news stories.

$$44,020,000 = n \cdot 142,000,000 \quad \text{Write the percent equation.}$$

$$\frac{44,020,000}{142,000,000} = \frac{142,000,000n}{142,000,000} \quad \text{Divide each side by 142 million.}$$

$$0.31 = n \quad \text{Simplify.}$$

31% of viewers watch news stories.

c. Let n represent the percent of viewers watching music videos and movie previews.

$$90,880,000 = n \cdot 142,000,000 \quad \text{Write the percent equation.}$$

$$\frac{90,880,000}{142,000,000} = \frac{142,000,000n}{142,000,000} \quad \text{Divide each side by 142 million.}$$

$$0.64 = n \quad \text{Simplify.}$$

64% of viewers watch music videos and movie previews.

31. Sample answer: If the percent is less than 100%, then the part is less than the base; if the percent equals 100%, then the part equals the base; if the percent is greater than 100%, then the part is greater than the base.   **33.** B   **35.** D   **37.** 170.73

39. 350 mi   **41.** −3

Pages 322–323   Lesson 6-2D   PSI

1. Find 10% of the number, then half of the 10%, and add together.   **3.** $3.50   **5.** 500; Sample answer: $60\% \cdot 830 \approx 500$ **7.** Sample answer: 2 quarters, 1 dime, 4 nickels, 3 pennies

9 25% off is one fourth less than the original price. $41 is close to $40. One fourth of $40 is $10. Taking $10 off the original price leaves us with $30 as the sale price.

11. $120; Sample answer: $10 \cdot 12 = $120   **13.** $15 \cdot 18 + 18 \cdot 20 = 630$ ft². Then convert 630 ft² to square yards. $630 \div (3 \cdot 3) = 70$ yd².

Pages 328–330   Lesson 6-3B

1. −20%, decrease   **3.** 19%, increase   **5a.** about 3.8%, increase   **5b.** about −2.9%, decrease   **7.** 40%, increase   **9.** −71%, decrease

11 The amount of change is $11.70 − $15.60 = −$3.90. Since the amount of change is negative, this is a decrease.

percent of decrease = $\dfrac{\text{amount of decrease}}{\text{original amount}}$

$= \dfrac{3.90}{15.60}$ Substitution

$= 0.25$ Simplify.

$= 25\%$ Write 0.25 as a percent.

There was a −25% decrease.

13. −5%, decrease   **15.** 13%, increase   **17.** −38%, decrease   **19.** 2%, increase

23 Write the percent of change equation. Substitute the values you know, and solve to find the original amount. Let x = amount of change.

percent of change = $\dfrac{\text{amount of change}}{\text{original amount}}$

$0.20 = \dfrac{x}{25{,}900{,}000{,}000}$ Substitute.

$(25{,}900{,}000{,}000)(0.20) = \dfrac{25{,}900{,}000{,}000x}{25{,}900{,}000{,}000}$

Multiply each side by 25,900,000,000.

$5{,}180{,}000{,}000 = x$ Simplify.

The amount of change was 5.18 billion.
Amount of change = new amount − original amount
5.18 billion = n − 25.9 billion   Substitute.
Let n = new amount.
5.18 billion + 25.9 billion = n Add 25.9 billion to each side.
31.08 billion = n Simplify.

The projected sales are $31.08 billion or about $31 billion.

25. $60 sound system; 10 is a greater part of 60 than of 90.   **27.** Sample answer: Compare the change. If the new amount is greater than the original amount, it is a percent of increase. If the new amount is less than the original amount, it is a percent of decrease.
29. 6,500 comments   **31.** 200   **33.** $0.3w = 17$; 56.7
35. about $3.19/lb   **37.** 30   **39.** $1\frac{5}{8}$

Pages 333–334   Lesson 6-3C

1. $3.10   **3.** $32.20   **5.** $37.73

7 $1,500 computer, 7% tax

$100\% + 7\% = 107\%$ Add the percent of tax to 100%.
The total cost is 107% of the regular price.
107% of $1,500 = 1.07 × 1500   Write 107% as a decimal.
$= \$1{,}605$ Multiply.
The total cost of the computer is $1,605.

9. $14.95   **11.** $7.99   **13.** $96.26   **15.** $84

17 Combine the tax and the tip before calculating the total price: $0.0625 + 0.20 = 0.2625$. Multiply the tax and tip by the price of the bill to find the tax and tip: $28.35 × 0.2625 = $7.44. Add tax and tip to bill. $28.35 + $7.44 = $35.79

19. $134.82   **21.** $54, $64.80; The percent gratuity is

20%. All of the other pairs have a gratuity of 15%.

23. B   **25.** 50%, increase   **27.** 73%, increase   **29.** $\dfrac{8}{35}$
31. $\dfrac{9}{44}$

Pages 337–338   Lesson 6-3D

1. $157.50   **3.** $1,395.65   **5.** $98.90   **7.** $1,080.00
9. $4.90

11 First, find the amount of the discount.

20% of $7.50 = 0.20 · 7.50   Write 20% as a decimal.
$= \$1.50$ The discount is $1.50.
Next, subtract the discount from the regular price.
$7.50 − $1.50 = $6.00   Apply the tax.
5.75% of $6.00 = 0.0575 · 6.00   Write 5.75% as a decimal.
$= \$0.35$ The tax is $0.35.
Add the tax to the sale price.
$6.00 + $0.35 = $6.35
The cost of the ticket including tax is $6.35.

13. $64.80   **15.** $7.50   **17.** $180.00

19 a.

Camera Model	Regular Price ($)	Discount	Sale Price
A	97.99	15%	$83.30
B	102.50	20%	$82.00
C	75.99	14%	$65.35
D	150.50	10%	$135.45

b. Sample answer: Subtract the sale price from the regular price to find the amount of the discount. Divide the amount of the discount by the regular price and multiply by 100. Round to the nearest percent if needed.   **c.** Camera B with a 20% discount
21. Sample answer: The regular price of a CD is $17.95. The total sale price is $13.46 and the total cost including tax is $14.23.   **23.** Sample answer: One method is to find 30% of the regular price, and then subtract this amount from the regular price. Another method is to find 70% of the regular price. The second method is more efficient because after mental math is used to find the percent, it can be done in one step rather than in two.   **25.** F
27. about $2   **29.** −37%, decrease

Pages 341–342   Lesson 6-3E

1. $38.40   **3.** $5.80

5 $I = prt$ Formula for simple interest

$I = \$4{,}500 \cdot 0.09 \cdot 3.5$ Replace p with $4,500, r with 0.09, and t with 3.5.
$I = \$1{,}417.50$

$1,417.50 interest is paid in 3.5 years.

7. $1,219.00   **9.** $21.38   **11.** $123.75   **13.** $45.31
15. $14.06   **17.** $1,353.13

19 a. $I = prt$ Formula for simple interest
$630 = 4{,}200 \cdot r \cdot 3$ Substitute.
$630 = 12{,}600r$ Simplify.
$\dfrac{630}{12{,}600} = \dfrac{12{,}600r}{12{,}600}$ Divide each side by 12,600.
$0.05 = r$ Simplify.

The interest rate is 5%. Write 0.05 as a percent.

b. Find the interest earned on $4,200 at a rate of 6% over 4 years.

$I = prt$ Formula for simple interest

$I = 4200 \cdot 0.06 \cdot 4$ Substitute.

$I = \$1,008$ Multiply.

Add the interest earned to the principle. Is the total at least $5,000?

$\$4,200 + \$1,008 = \$5,208$

Ramon would earn at least $5,000.

21. $825.60, $852.02, $879.28   **23.** C   **25.** $13.40
27. $8,440   **29.** $28.75   **31.** $\frac{32}{35}$

Pages 346–349   Study Guide and Review

1. true   **3.** true   **5.** false; 100%   **7.** true   **9.** false; original   **11.** 39   **13.** 135   **15.** Sample answer: 20; $\frac{1}{4} \cdot 80 = 20$ **17.** Sample answer: 30; $\frac{3}{4} \cdot 40 = 30$
19. Sample answer: 8; $0.1 \cdot 80 = 8$ **21.** 14 games
23. 0.3   **25.** $27.49   **27.** $39 = 0.65 \cdot w$; 60   **29.** 333
31. 93%, increase   **33.** 10%, increase   **35.** $13.80
37. $52.12   **39.** $11.25   **41.** $47.50   **43.** $101.25

Chapter 7 Data Analysis and Probability

Page 356   Chapter 7   Are You Ready?

1. 52.3   **3.** 9   **5.** 65; 65   **7.** $9; $6

Pages 360–363   Lesson 7-1B

1. **Blood Types in U.S.**

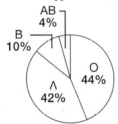

3a. blue   **3b.** 40

5. **Orange Production**

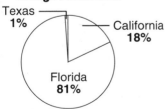

7. **Favorite Games**

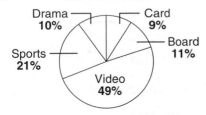

9 **a.** Look at the title of the graph. It asks, "Do Americans Favor Common North American Currency?" The section that says "Yes" represents the percent of Americans who do favor a common North American currency. The number there is 43%. So, 43% of Americans favor common North American currency.   **b.** Let p represent the part of the American people who would say "Don't Know". Write an equation to find the number. $p = 0.04 \cdot 298,000,000$ or 11,920,000 people do not know if they favor a common North American currency.   **c.** Find the number of people opposed to a common currency. $0.53 \cdot 298,000,000 = 157,940,000$ people opposed. Find the number of people in favor of a common currency. $0.43 \cdot 298,000,000 = 128,140,000$ people in favor. Find the difference: $157,940,000 - 128,140,000 = 29,800,000$ So, 29.8 million people more are opposed to a common currency than are in favor of it.

11. 40   **13.** circle graph

Tanya's Day

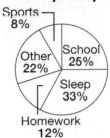

15 **a.** $366 + 126 + 10 = 502$ **15b.** No; a 50% increase in 126 students is 189 students and 189 students is not equal to or even close to 366 students. So, it is not reasonable to say that 50% more students said they could make a difference.
17. 12.5%; English is half of the circle. Since Science is half of English, Science is half of 50% or 25%. Math is half of Science, which is half of 25% or 12.5%.   **19.** No; Sample answer: The sum of the percents is greater than 100. The people surveyed must have been able to choose more than one fruit juice.   **21.** 16   **23.** $38.11

Pages 366–368   Lesson 7-1C

1. Sample answer:

State Population Density (per square mile)		
Density	Tally	Frequency
0–199	ⅢⅢ ⅢⅢ ⅢⅢ ⅢⅢ ⅢⅢ ⅢⅢ ⅢⅢ Ⅲ	38
200–399	ⅢⅢ	5
400–599	Ⅲ	3
600–799	Ⅰ	1
800–899	Ⅰ	1
900–1,099	Ⅰ	1
1,100–1,299	Ⅰ	1

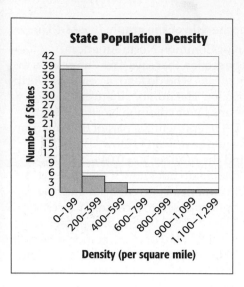

State Population Density

Density (per square mile)

3. Sample answer:

Hours Spent Exercising per Week

Hours	Tally	Frequency
0–2	卌 I	6
3–5	卌 III	8
6–8	III	3
9–11	II	2
12–14	I	1

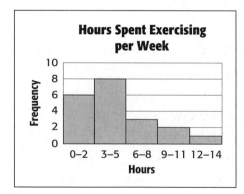

Hours Spent Exercising per Week

5 a. Look at the horizontal scale of the graph. The countries represented in the first two bars have areas less than 401 square kilometers. Look at the vertical scale of the graph. The first bar represents 21 countries. The second bar represents 9 countries. Add these to find a total of 30 countries with areas less than 401 square kilometers.

b. Adding the number of countries in the second and third bars, you find that 19 countries have between 201 and 600 square kilometers. Adding all the bars shows a total of 50 countries represented. Find what percent 19 is of 52. Since $\frac{19}{50}$ is about 0.38 or 38%, about 38% of the countries have an area of 201–600 square kilometers.

c. Not very likely. Only 4 out of the 50 countries in the histogram have an area greater than 800 square kilometers.

7 a. Seattle has a building in the 900–999 foot range. Pittsburg does not. Therefore, Seattle has the tallest building. **b.** Pittsburgh has a building in that range, while Seattle does not. **c.** Pittsburgh has $3 + 1 + 1$ or 5 buildings in that range. Seattle has $3 + 3 + 1$ or 7 buildings in this range. Therefore, Seattle has more buildings in the range. Adding all of the buildings represented by the bars, Seattle has a total of 21 buildings. Since $\frac{7}{21}$ is about 0.33 or 33%, about 33% of the buildings are 600 feet or taller.
d. Seattle has 6 more than Pittsburgh.
11. If larger intervals, such as 0–9 and 10–19, were used, there would be fewer intervals along the horizontal axis of the histogram and the bars would be higher in each interval. For example, the interval 0–9 would have a bar height of 7 and the interval 10–19 would have a bar height of 7. These would be the only two intervals. If smaller intervals were used, such as 0–2, 3–5, 6–8, etc., there would be more intervals along the horizontal axis of the histogram. The bars in each interval would be shorter. **13.** 5
15a. chocolate **15b.** 63 people

Pages 372–374   Lesson 7-1E

1. Height of Trees (ft)

Stem	Leaf
0	8 8
1	0 2 5 5 6 8
2	0 5 2 | 0 = 20 ft

3 a. range: oldest − youngest = $14 - 9$ or 5 years
b. median: middle value, or 11 years; mode: most frequent value, 11 years **c.** The mean would be most affected because it would decrease.

5. Low Temperatures (°F)

Stem	Leaf
1	3 3 5
2	0 4 8
3	0 1 2 2 5 6 8 8 8 1 | 3 = 13°F

7. School Play Attendance

Stem	Leaf
22	5 7 9
23	0
24	3 6
25	
26	7 9 9
27	8 8 8 26 | 7 = 267

9a. $45 **9b.** $108 and $115 **9c.** mean

11 There are no numbers that are outliers. As the score goes up, fewer people can achieve it.

Gymnastics Scores

Stem	Leaf
8	9 5 7 7 8
9	0 3 3 9
10	0

8 | 9 = 8.9

Sample answer: There is only one person who scored a perfect 10. An average score is about 9.1.

15. Fiber in Cereal (g)

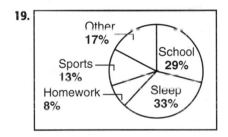

Fiber in Cereal

Stem	Leaf
0	0 1 1 1 1 1 1 1
	2 3 3 3 4 5 5

0 | 1 = 1 gram

Sample answer: Both representations show the frequency of data occurring. The line plot gives a good picture of the spread of the data. The stem-and-leaf plot shows individual grams of fiber as in the line plot. See students' favorites and reasons.

17. H

19.

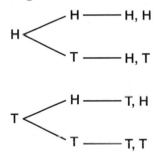

21. 5   **23.** $\frac{11}{12}$

Pages 375–380   Lesson 7-2A

1. $\frac{1}{8}$, 0.125, 12.5%   **3.** $\frac{1}{8}$, 0.125, 12.5%

5 12 red + 6 orange = 18 possibilities out of 30 marbles. So, $\frac{18}{30}$ simplifies to equal $\frac{3}{5}$.

7. $\frac{23}{30}$ **9.** 1   **11.** $\frac{1}{20}$, 0.05, 5%   **13.** $\frac{3}{10}$, 0.3, 30%

15. $\frac{19}{20}$, 0.95, 95%   **17.** $\frac{2}{7}$ **19.** $\frac{1}{6}$ **21.** $\frac{2}{5}$

23 Since you are finding the probability the student is *not* in Room 10, find the total number of students in the other rooms. 24 + 20 + 14 + 16 = 74 students in the favorable outcomes group. Add in the Room 10 number to find the total number of students is 84. $P(not$ Room 10$) = \frac{74}{84}$ or $\frac{37}{42}$

25. 60%   **27.** about 70%   **29.** Sample answer: The complementary event is the chance of no rain. Its probability is 60%.

31 There is one favorable outcome, and 5 total outcomes. Therefore, the probability that any given song would be hip-hop is $\frac{1}{5}$.

33. Sample answer: There are currently 6 + 4 + 8 or 18 marbles in the bag. A total of 27 − 18 or 9 marbles should be added to the bag. To do so without changing the probability of randomly selecting one marble of each color, add 3 red marbles, 2 blue marbles, and 4 green marbles. Then, $P(red) = \frac{9}{27}$ or $\frac{1}{3}$, $P(blue) = \frac{6}{27}$ or $\frac{2}{9}$, and $P(green) = \frac{12}{27}$ or $\frac{4}{9}$ **35.** C   **37.** B   **39a.** 59; 12   **39b.** 35   **39c.** Sample answer: The range of the data is 47.   **41.** $\frac{1}{3}$ **43.** $\frac{1}{2}$

Pages 382–385   Lesson 7-2B

1 Sample answer: Write heads. Show that it leads to heads and tails. Repeat this for tails. The tree diagram is shown.

```
        ┌ H ──── H, H
  H ────┤
        └ T ──── H, T

        ┌ H ──── T, H
  T ────┤
        └ T ──── T, T
```

3.

Meat	Bread	Sample Space
ham	rye	ham, rye
	white	ham, white
	sourdough	ham, sourdough
turkey	rye	turkey, rye
	white	turkey, white
	sourdough	turkey, sourdough

5. Sample answer:

Coin	Number	Sample Space
heads	1	heads, 1
	2	heads, 2
	3	heads, 3
	4	heads, 4
	5	heads, 5
tails	1	tails, 1
	2	tails, 2
	3	tails, 3
	4	tails, 4
	5	tails, 5

7. Sample answer:

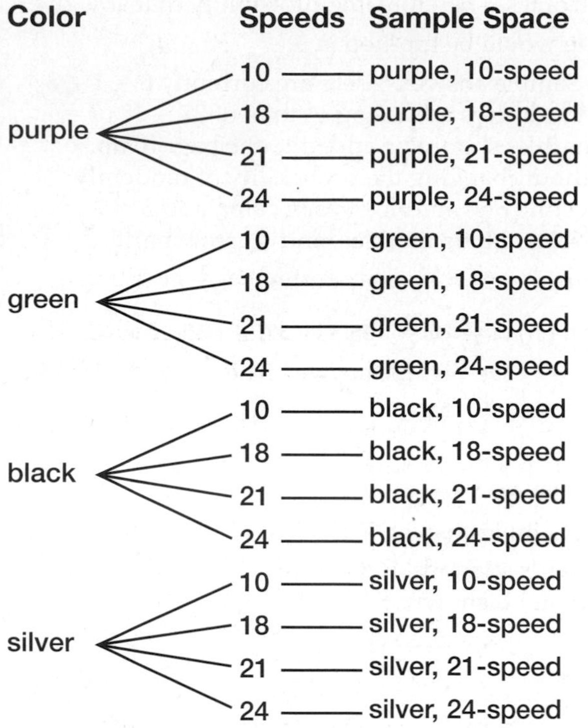

Color	Speeds	Sample Space
purple	10	purple, 10-speed
	18	purple, 18-speed
	21	purple, 21-speed
	24	purple, 24-speed
green	10	green, 10-speed
	18	green, 18-speed
	21	green, 21-speed
	24	green, 24-speed
black	10	black, 10-speed
	18	black, 18-speed
	21	black, 21-speed
	24	black, 24-speed
silver	10	silver, 10-speed
	18	silver, 18-speed
	21	silver, 21-speed
	24	silver, 24-speed

9. Sample answer:

Outcomes		
Short Sleeve	Gray	Small
Short Sleeve	Gray	Medium
Short Sleeve	Gray	Large
Short Sleeve	White	Small
Short Sleeve	White	Medium
Short Sleeve	White	Large
Long Sleeve	Gray	Small
Long Sleeve	Gray	Medium
Long Sleeve	Gray	Large
Long Sleeve	White	Small
Long Sleeve	White	Medium
Long Sleeve	White	Large

11. Sample answer:

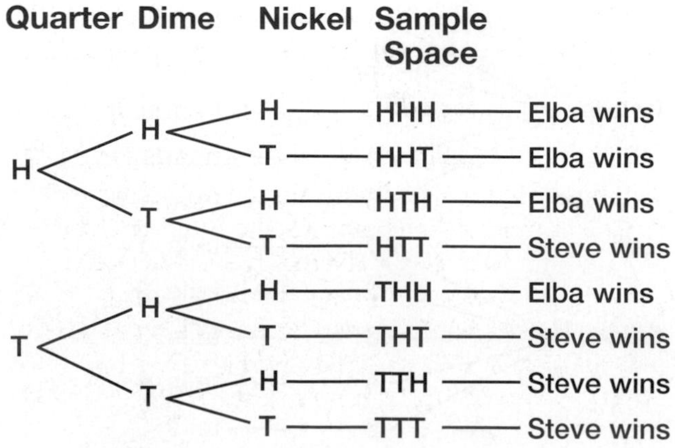

Quarter Dime   Nickel Sample Space

```
            H ─── HHH ──── Elba wins
      H <
            T ─── HHT ──── Elba wins
 H <
            H ─── HTH ──── Elba wins
      T <
            T ─── HTT ──── Steve wins
            H ─── THH ──── Elba wins
      H <
            T ─── THT ──── Steve wins
 T <
            H ─── TTH ──── Steve wins
      T <
            T ─── TTT ──── Steve wins
```

There are 8 equally likely outcomes with 4 favoring Elba. So, the probability that Elba wins is $\frac{4}{8}$ or $\frac{1}{2}$.

13 a. One of eight outcomes has three boys. Therefore, P(all three children will be boys) $= \frac{1}{8}$.
b. Six outcomes include at least one boy and one girl. Therefore, P(at least one boy and one girl) $= \frac{6}{8}$ or $\frac{3}{4}$.   **c.** Three outcomes have two boys and one girl. Therefore, P(two boys and one girl) $= \frac{3}{8}$.
d. Four outcomes have at least two girls. Therefore, P(at least two girls) $= \frac{4}{8}$ or $\frac{1}{2}$.   **e.** There is only 1 outcome in which the first two born are boys and the last born is a girl. Therefore, P(the first two born are boys and the last born is a girl) $= \frac{1}{8}$.

15a. 16   **15b.** $\frac{1}{16}$

15c.

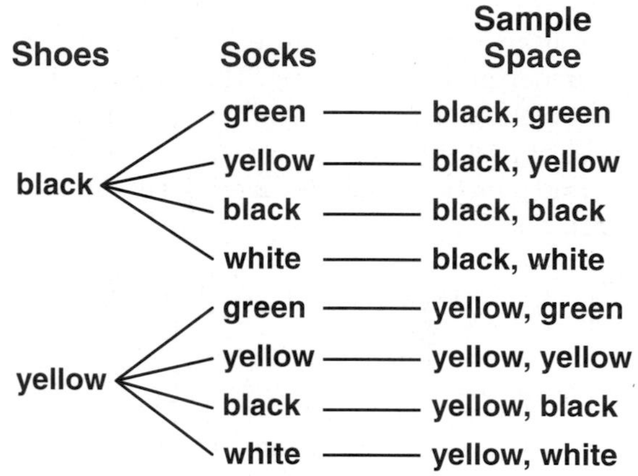

Shoes	Socks	Sample Space
black	green	black, green
	yellow	black, yellow
	black	black, black
	white	black, white
yellow	green	yellow, green
	yellow	yellow, yellow
	black	yellow, black
	white	yellow, white

17. The first sample in the I bracket should be IC.
19. Sample game: Each player tosses a coin 10 times. If it comes up heads, player 1 receives 1 point. If it comes up tails, player 2 receives 1 point. The player with the most points at the end of 20 tosses wins.
21. 12   **23.** $\frac{2}{5}$ **25.** $\frac{13}{20}$ **27.** $\frac{3}{10}$

29.

Stem	Leaf
6	9
7	4 6 8 9
8	3 5 6
9	1 2 8
10	0

$6 \mid 9 = 6.9$

31. 15.6   **33.** 10

Pages 387–389   Lesson 7-2C

1 There are two outcomes for tossing the quarter, two for tossing the dime and two for tossing the nickel. The Fundamental Counting Principle says that you can multiply to find out the total number of outcomes: $2 \cdot 2 \cdot 2 = 8$ outcomes.
3. 72; $\frac{1}{72}$ or about 1.4%; unlikely   **5.** 140   **7.** 12
9. 16   **11.** 18 possible bread choices; $\frac{1}{18}$; very unlikely

13 The total number of T-shirt choices is the product of the number of designs and the number of color choices, or 32 · 11 or 352 choices. The advertisement is not true because there are 365 days in a year.

15. 2; 4; 8; 2^n; Sample answer: I used a pattern to determine the number of outcomes for n coins. One coin: 2^1 outcomes, two coins: $2 \cdot 2$ or 2^2 outcomes, three coins: $2 \cdot 2 \cdot 2$ or 2^3 outcomes, n coins: 2^n outcomes. **17.** Sample answer: When there are multiple events, the Fundamental Counting Principle is a much faster method of obtaining the total number of outcomes than drawing a tree diagram. The Fundamental Counting Principle also saves paper space and can often be done mentally. When you need to see what the specific outcomes are, make a tree diagram since the Fundamental Counting Principle only gives the number of outcomes. **19.** 6 **21.** $\frac{1}{2}$ **23.** $\frac{1}{5}$, 0.22, 27%, 20.1 **25.** -24 **27.** 0

Pages 393–396   Lesson 7-2E

1 There is a $\frac{1}{2}$ chance of landing on tails and a $\frac{1}{6}$ chance of rolling a 3. $\frac{1}{2} \times \frac{1}{6} = \frac{1}{12}$

3. $\frac{1}{6}$ **5.** $\frac{5}{21}$ **7.** $\frac{1}{48}$ **9.** $\frac{3}{8}$ **11.** $\frac{5}{24}$ **13.** $\frac{92}{207}$

15 There are a total of $5 + 7 + 4 + 4$ or 20 students. $P(\text{green}) = \frac{4}{20}$ or $\frac{1}{5}$; $P(\text{brown after green}) = \frac{7}{19}$ $P(\text{green then brown}) = \frac{1}{5} \cdot \frac{7}{19}$ or $\frac{7}{95}$

17. $\frac{7}{76}$ **19.** $\frac{12}{19}$ **21a.** 11.76% **21b.** 24.64%

23. $\frac{4}{13}$; dependent event; The first coin is not replaced.

25 The probability of the first player choosing a tile with the same number of dots on each side is $\frac{7}{28}$. If each player were to draw such a tile, both the number of favorable outcomes and the number of possible outcomes would reduce by one for each person, resulting in the following product: $\frac{7}{28} \cdot \frac{6}{27} \cdot \frac{5}{26} \cdot \frac{4}{25}$ or $\frac{1}{585}$

27. Spinning the spinner twice represents two independent events. The probability of getting an even number is $\frac{2}{5}$ each time. **29.** Both independent events and dependent events are compound events. Independent events do not affect each other. Dependent events affect each other. **31.** I **33.** G

35.

turkey — cheddar — turkey, cheddar
turkey — Swiss — turkey, Swiss
ham — cheddar — ham, cheddar
ham — Swiss — ham, Swiss
salami — cheddar — salami, cheddar
salami — Swiss — salami, Swiss

37. -9%, decrease **39.** 6,750,000 cm^3

Pages 403–405   Lesson 7-3B

1 a. The experimental probability is $\frac{\text{number of times heads appears}}{\text{number of tosses}} = \frac{28}{50}$ or $\frac{14}{25}$. **b.** The theoretical probability is $\frac{\text{favorable outcomes}}{\text{possible outcomes}} = \frac{1}{2}$. **c.** The experimental probability, $\frac{14}{25}$ or 56%, is close to its theoretical probability of $\frac{1}{2}$ or 50%.

3a. $\frac{1}{5}$; The experimental probability, $\frac{1}{5}$ or 20%, is close to its theoretical probability of $\frac{1}{6}$ or about 17%. **3b.** $\frac{9}{10}$; The experimental probability, $\frac{9}{10}$ or 90%, is close to its theoretical probability of $\frac{5}{6}$ or about 83%.

5 a. The theoretical probability is $\frac{\text{favorable outcomes}}{\text{possible outcomes}} = \frac{1}{3}$. **b.** The experimental probability $P(A) = \frac{\text{number of times landing on A}}{\text{number of spins}} = \frac{6}{25}$. The experimental probability $P(C) = \frac{\text{number of times landing on C}}{\text{number of spins}} = \frac{13}{50}$. **c.**

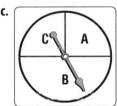

The experimental probability of landing on section A is $\frac{6}{25}$, or about $\frac{1}{4}$. The experimental probability of landing on section B is $\frac{50}{100}$, or $\frac{1}{2}$. The experimental probability of landing on section C is $\frac{13}{50}$, or about $\frac{1}{4}$. So, section B should be one half of the spinner and sections A and C should each be one fourth of the spinner.

7. 72 **9.** Sample answer: Both probabilities are ratios that compare the number of favorable outcomes to the total number of outcomes. Experimental probability is the result of an experiment. Theoretical probability is what is expected to happen. **11.** H **13.** $\frac{2}{7}$ **15.** 20 times

Pages 406–407   Lesson 7-3C   PSI

1. Sample answer: Results could vary greatly. **3.** No; Sample answer: the experiment produces about 1–2 correct answers, so using a spinner with 4 sections is not a good way to answer a 5-question multiple-choice quiz. **5.** 30

7 If there were 160 students surveyed, half, or 50%, of the students would be 80 students. 40% of the students preferred a dunking booth; this is a little less than 50%. Therefore, the number close to, but smaller than 80, or 65 students is the most reasonable choice for the answer.

9. 31 **11.** $70; Sample answer: Round $95 to $100. 10% of $100 is $10, so 20% would be $20. $100 − $20 = $80, which is closest to $70.

For Homework Help, go to (Hotmath.com)   Selected Answers and Solutions   **R21**

Selected Answers and Solutions

Pages 411–413   Lesson 7-3E

1 **a.** 33% of the teens said they would save their money. Let n be the number of students that would save their money.

$n = 0.33 \cdot 60,000$ Write the percentage equation with 33% as a decimal.

$n = 19,800$ Simplify.

So, 19,800 teens surveyed said they would save their money.   **b.** Write a proportion.

$\dfrac{p}{28,000,000} = \dfrac{32}{100}$ Percent proportion

$100p = 32 \cdot 28,000,000$ Find cross products.

$100p = 896,000,000$ Simplify.

$\dfrac{100p}{100} = \dfrac{896,000,000}{100}$ Divide each side by 100.

$P = 8,960,000$

About 8.96 million teens would buy a music CD if they were given $20.

3a. 1,419 people   **3b.** 581

5 Since 27 MP3s is a part of 238 MP3s, and you are looking for a percentage, answer c matches this situation.

7. b   **9.** about 205 people   **11.** Sample answer: Randomly select a part of the group to get a sample. Find their preferences, and use the results to find the percent of the total group. It makes sense to use a sample when surveying a population of a city.

13. G   **15a.** 44%   **15b.** 86%   **17.** $\frac{1}{4}$ **19.** 6   **21.** 2.8   **23.** -40 **25.** 24

Pages 416–418   Lesson 7-3F

1. The conclusion is invalid. This is a biased sample, since people in other states would spend much more than those in Alaska. The sample is a convenience sample since all the people are from the same state.

3 This is a simple random survey because each person is randomly chosen for the survey, so the sample is valid; 42 people.

5. The conclusion is not valid. This is a biased sample, since only art club members were surveyed. This is a convenience sample.

7 The conclusion is valid. This is an unbiased, stratified random sample because the population was divided into similar groups.

9. This is a simple random survey, so the sample is valid; about 205 people.   **11.** Sample answer: If the questions are not asked in a neutral manner, the people may not give their true opinions. For example, the question, "You really don't like Brand X, do you?" might not get the same answer as the question, "Do you prefer Brand X or Brand Y?" Also, the question, "Why would anyone like rock music?" might not get the same answer as the question, "What do you think about rock music?"   **13.** D   **15.** about 292 students

17. $35 + 0.40x = 20 + 0.55x$; 100 mi

Pages 419–423   Study Guide and Review

1. true   **3.** false; multiplication   **5.** false; complement   **7.** false; outcome   **9.** 5 seconds   **11.** Most runners were in the 60–64 interval.

13.

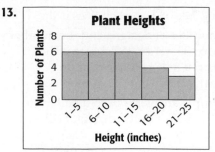

15.

Points Scored	
Stem	Leaf
5	3
6	
7	5 8 8
8	3 5 7 7 9
9	1 2 $7 \mid 5 = 75$ points

17. $\frac{5}{18}$

19. Sample answer:

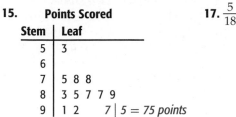

21. Sample answer:

Outcomes					
1	1	Eliza wins	3	1	Eliza wins
1	2	Eliza wins	3	2	Eliza wins
1	3	Eliza wins	3	3	Zeke wins
1	4	Eliza wins	3	4	Zeke wins
1	5	Zeke wins	3	5	Zeke wins
1	6	Zeke wins	3	6	Zeke wins
2	1	Eliza wins	4	1	Eliza wins
2	2	Eliza wins	4	2	Zeke wins
2	3	Eliza wins	4	3	Zeke wins
2	4	Zeke wins	4	4	Zeke wins
2	5	Zeke wins	4	5	Zeke wins
2	6	Zeke wins	4	6	Zeke wins

There are 24 equally likely outcomes with 14 favoring Zeke. So, the probability that Zeke will win is $\frac{14}{24}$, or $\frac{7}{12}$.

23. 24 **25.** $\frac{2}{15}$ **27.** $\frac{4}{45}$ **29.** $\frac{8}{25}$ **31.** 12
33. about 208 **35.** 162 teens **37.** about 204 students

Chapter 8 Surface Area and Volume

Page 430 Chapter 8 Are You Ready?
1. 25 yd^2 **3.** 875 ft^2 **5.** 379.9 in^2 **7.** 78.5 cm^2

Pages 435–437 Lesson 8-1B
1. 220 in^3 **3.** 63 yd^3 **5.** 37.5 ft^3 < 63 ft^3; second cabinet **7.** 90 ft^3 **9.** 236.3 cm^3

11 $V = Bh$ Volume of a prism
$V = \left(\frac{1}{2} \cdot 6 \cdot 4\right)h$ Replace B with $\frac{1}{2} \cdot 6 \cdot 4$.
$V = \left(\frac{1}{2} \cdot 6 \cdot 4\right)9$ The height of the prism is 9.
$V = 108$ Multiply.
The volume 108 cubic meters or 108 m^3.
13. 20.4 mm^3 **15.** 40 ft^3 > 36 ft^3, so too much was bought **17.** $166\frac{1}{4}$ yd^3 **19a.** 2,157,165 ft^3
19b. 98,053 ft^3

21 First, find the volume of the office.
$V = \ell wh$ Volume of a prism
$V = 32 \cdot 25 \cdot 12$ $\ell = 32, w = 25, h = 12$
$V = 9,600$ Multiply.
The volume of the office is 9,600 cubic feet. Next, find the cost to air condition the office for a year. Find the product of the cost per cubic foot and the number of cubic feet. The cost to air condition the space is 9,600 ft^3 • $0.11/ft^3 or $1,056 per year. To find the average cost per month, divide the yearly cost by 12. On average, it costs $1,056 ÷ 12 or $88 to air condition the office for one month.
23. No; the volume of Prism A is 80 in^3, and the volume of Prism B is 640 in^3, which is eight times greater. **25.** Sample answer: They are similar in that the volume is the product of the area of the base and the height of the prism. They are different in the formulas used to find the area of the base of the figure. **27.** H **29.** about 391

Pages 439–442 Lesson 8-1C
1. 141.4 in^3
3 $V = \pi r^2 h$ Volume of a cylinder
$V = \pi(2.25)^2 6.5$ Replace r with 2.25 and h with 6.5.
$V = 617.7$ ft^3 Simplify.
5. 603.2 cm^3 **7.** 4,071.5 ft^3 **9.** 2,770.9 yd^3 **11.** 35.6 m^3
13 $r = \frac{1}{2}d$ Relationship between diameter and radius
$r = \frac{1}{2}(4.5)$ or 2.25 Use $d = 4.5$. Simplify.
$V = \pi r^2 h$ Volume of a cylinder
$V = \pi(2.25)^2 6.5$ Replace r with 2.25 and h with 6.5.
$V = 103.4$ Simplify.
The volume of the cylinder is about 103.4 m^3.
15. 288.6 in^3 **17.** about 34.4 in^3 **19.** 124,642.7 m^3
21. d **23.** a **25.** 2,376 cm^3

27 Let V_A be the volume of cylinder A, and V_B be the volume of cylinder B.
$V_A = V_B$ Both cylinders have the same volume.
$\pi r^2 h = \pi r^2 h$ Volume of a cylinder
$\pi(4)^2 2 = \pi(2)^2 h$ For Cylinder A, $r = 4$ and $h = 2$. For Cylinder B, $r = 2$.
$32\pi = 4\pi h$ Simplify.
$\frac{32\pi}{4\pi} = \frac{4\pi h}{4\pi}$ Divide each side by 4π.
$8 = h$ Simplify.
The height of Cylinder B is 8 inches.
29. Sample answer: The shorter cylinder, because the radius is larger and that is the squared value in the formula. **31.** 1 to 2 **33.** Sample answer: In both, the volume equals the area of the base times the height. **35.** 9 **37.** 75.36 cm^3 **39.** The sample is valid since the population is an unbiased random sample of cat owners. **41.** $44.41

Pages 447–448 Lesson 8-1E
1 $V = \frac{1}{3}Bh$ Volume of a pyramid
$V = \frac{1}{3}\left(\frac{1}{2} \cdot 8 \cdot 6\right)10$ $B = \frac{1}{2} \cdot 8 \cdot 6, h = 10$
$V = 80$ Simplify.
The volume of the pyramid is 80 ft^3.
3. 12 cm **5.** 5,971,000 ft^3 **7.** 109.3 m^3 **9.** 14 in.
11. 11 ft
13 $V = \frac{1}{3}Bh$ Volume of a pyramid
$V = \frac{1}{3}(3 \cdot 2.5)4$ $B = 3 \cdot 2.5, h = 4$
$V = 10$ Simplify.
The volume of glass used to create the pyramid was 30 in^3.
17. Sample answer: first set: area of the base, 40 ft^2; height of the pyramid, 12 ft; second set: area of the base, 30 ft^2; height of the pyramid, 16 ft. **19.** The volumes are the same. **21.** H **23.** 1,154.4 ft^3

Pages 450–452 Lesson 8-1F
1. 2,668.3 m^3
3 $V = \frac{1}{3}\pi r^2 h$ Volume of a pyramid
$V = \frac{1}{3}\pi(1.75)^2 8.4$ $r = \frac{1}{2} \cdot 3.5$ or 1.75, $h = 8.4$
$V = 26.9$ Simplify.
The volume of the pyramid is 26.9 ft^3.
5. about 1.8 c **7.** 4,720.8 mm^3 **9.** 2,989.8 mm^3
11. 401.9 cm^3 **13.** about 7 c **15.** 10.0 mm
17 Let h be the height of the shorter cylinder, H be the height of the cone, and r be the radius of both.
$\pi r^2 h = \frac{1}{3}\pi r^2 H$ The volume of the cylinder is equal to the volume of the cone.
$\pi(5)^2(12) = \frac{1}{3}\pi(5)^2 H$ $r = 5, h = 12$
$300\pi = \frac{1}{3}(25)\pi H$ Simplify.
$900\pi = 25\pi H$ Multiply both sides by 3.
$\frac{900\pi}{25\pi} = \frac{25\pi H}{25\pi}$ Divide each side by 25π.
$36 \approx H$ Simplify.
The height of the cylinder is 36.0 cm.

19. 4.5 m   **21.** 3.0 yd   **23.** Aisha used the incorrect radius; 25.12 in³   **25.** Sample answer: Depending on the length of the radius and the height, generally doubling the radius has more effect as it is squared in the formula.   **27.** I   **29.** 110 ft³

Pages 459–461   Lesson 8-2B

1. 108 ft²   **3.** Yes; the surface area of the box is 252 in². The surface area of the paper is 288 in². Since 252 in² < 288 in², she has enough paper.
5. 314 cm²

7 Replace ℓ with 12.3, w with 8.5, and h with 15.

$S.A. = 2\ell w + 2\ell h + 2wh$
$= 2 \cdot 12.3 \cdot 8.5 + 2 \cdot 12.3 \cdot 15 + 2 \cdot 8.5 \cdot 15$
$= 209.1 + 369 + 255$ Multiply first. Then add.
$= 833.1$

The surface area of the prism is 833.1 mm².

9. 125.4 in²   **11.** 207 in²   **13.** 1,128.8 m²   **15.** 192 cm²
17. 64.5 in²

19 Remember that each edge of a cube has the same measure. Replace ℓ with s, w with s, and h with s.

$S.A. = 2\ell w + 2\ell h + 2wh$
$= 2 \cdot x \cdot x + 2 \cdot x \cdot x + 2 \cdot x \cdot x$
$= 2x^2 + 2x^2 + 2x^2$ Multiply first. Then add like terms.
$= 6x^2$

The formula for the surface area of a cube is
$S.A. = 6x^2$.

21. 4 ft by 7 ft by 6 ft; The dimensions of the dunk tank are sufficient for a person to fall in and get wet.
23. 1,926 cm²   **25.** B   **27.** 3,041.1 cm³   **29.** 1,413.7 in³

Pages 463–465   Lesson 8-2C

1 $S.A. = 2\pi rh + 2\pi r^2$ Surface area of a cylinder
$= 2\pi(2)(5) + 2\pi(2)^2$ Replace r with 2 and h with 5.
$= 88.0$ Simplify.

The surface area is about 88.0 mm².
3. about 471.2 m²   **5.** 1,215.8 m²   **7.** 272.0 mm²
9. 1,120.0 in²   **11.** 61.3 cm²   **13.** Sample answer:
$2 \cdot 3 \cdot 4^2 + 2 \cdot 3 \cdot 4 \cdot 4$ or 192 m²

15 Find the surface area of the tube.

$S.A. = 2\pi rh + 2\pi r^2$ Surface area of a cylinder
$= 2\pi(2.5)(15) + 2\pi(2.5)^2$ Replace r with 2.5 and h with 15.
$= 274.9$ Simplify.

Find the curved surface of the tube.

$S.A. = 2\pi rh$ Curved surface of a cylinder
$= 2\pi(2.5)(15)$ Replace r with 2.5 and h with 15.
$= 235.6$ Simplify.

Find the percent of the tube that is cardboard.

$235.6 = N \cdot 274.9$ Percent Equation
$\dfrac{235.6}{274.9} = \dfrac{N \cdot 274.9}{274.9}$ Divide each side by 274.9.
$0.857 = N$ Simplify.

Changing the decimal to a percent, 85.7% of the mail tube is cardboard.

19. D   **21.** 260 in³   **23.** 1,201.3 in³   **25.** 231.5 m²
27.

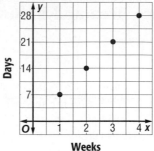

Weeks

Pages 470–471   Lesson 8-2E

1 $S.A. = B + \frac{1}{2}P\ell$ Surface area of a pyramid
$= 25 + \frac{1}{2}(20 \cdot 7)$ $P = 4(5)$ or 20, $\ell = 7$, $B = 5 \cdot 5$ or 25.
$= 95$ Simplify.

The surface area of the pyramid is 95 in².
3. 3,829.5 ft²   **5.** 507.5 mm²   **7.** 2,079 cm²   **9.** 26.1 ft²

11 $S.A. = B + \frac{1}{2}P\ell$ Surface area of a pyramid
$\approx 24 + \frac{1}{2}(18 \cdot 6)$ $P = 6(3)$ or 18, $\ell = 6$, $B = 24$
$= 78$ Simplify.

The surface area of the birdhouse is 78 in².
13. It would be shorter to climb up the slant height. The bottom of the slant height is closer to the center of the base of the pyramid. The bottom of the lateral edge is further from the center of the base of the pyramid.   **15.** The formula is based on finding the area of each base and then adding them together.

17. H   **19.** 456 ft²   **21.** 197.3 m³   **23.** $14.55   **25.** $27.97

Pages 476–477   Lesson 8-3A   PSI

1. Sample answer: Finding the areas of the separate geometric figures and then adding is easier than trying to find the area of the irregular figure as a whole.   **3.** 114 ft²   **5.** 2 h

7 First find the number of minutes in $\frac{1}{3}$ hour. One third of 60 is 20. Make a chart.

Monday	45	45 min
Tuesday	45 + 20	65 min or 1 hr 5 min
Wednesday	1 hr 5 min + 20 min	1 hr 25 min
Thursday	1 hr 25 min + 20 min	1 hr 45 min
Friday	1 hr 45 min + 20 min	1 hr 65 min or 2 hr 5 min
Saturday	2 hr 5 min + 20 min	2 hr 25 min
Sunday	2 hr 25 min + 20 min	2 hr 45 min

2 hours 25 minutes
9. 76 students

Pages 482–484   Lesson 8-3C

1. 897 in^3 **3.** 870 cm^2 **5.** 39.6 in^2

7 The solid is composed of a rectangular prism and a triangular prism. Let B_1 be the area of the base of the rectangular prism, 1.8 · 1.1 or 1.98. Let B_2 be the area of the base of the triangular prism, $\frac{1}{2}$ · 1.8 · 0.7 or 0.63.

$V = B_1 h + B_2 h$ Volume of rectangular prism + volume of triangular prism.

$= 1.98(0.8) + 0.63(1.1)$ Replace B_1 with 1.98, B_2 with 0.63, and h with 0.8.

$= 1.584 + 0.693$

$= 2.3$ Simplify.

The volume of the solid, to the nearest tenth, is 2.3 cubic meters.

9. 1,476.5 m^2 **11.** 308.4 m^2 **13.** 718.9 in^2

15 The solid is composed of a rectangular prism and a triangular prism. Convert inches to feet before calculating.
Find the volume of the rectangular prism.

$V = \ell w h$ Volume of a rectangular prism

$= (1)(0.42)(0.83)$ Replace ℓ with 1, w with 0.42, and h with 0.83.

$= 0.35$ Simplify.

The volume of the rectangular prism is 0.35 cubic feet.
Find the volume of the triangular prism.

$V = \frac{1}{2} b h \ell$ Volume of a triangular prism

$= \frac{1}{2}(1)(0.83)(0.42)$ Replace b with 1, h with 0.83, and ℓ with 0.42.

$= 0.17$ Simplify.

The volume of the triangular prism is 0.17 cubic feet. The volume of the entire solid is 0.35 + 0.17 or 0.5 cubic feet.

17. Sample answer:

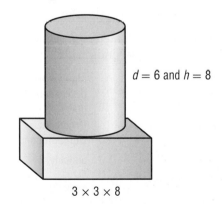

$d = 6$ and $h = 8$

$3 \times 3 \times 8$

19. Sample answer: The area of the rectangular face on the half cylinder must be found, making it a composite shape.   **21.** I   **23.** 164 cm^2 **25.** 923.6 ft^2 **27.** $48.75

Pages 485–489   Study Guide and Review

1. rectangular prism   **3.** cubic   **5.** cone
7. multiplying   **9.** 14.6 m^3 **11.** 371.9 in^3
13. 4,042.4 kn^3 **15.** 48.1 in^3 **17.** 6.3 mm^3

19. 288 cm^3 **21.** 377.0 in^3 **23.** 202 yd^2 **25.** 43 ft^2
27. 2,261.9 in^2 **29.** 168 in^2 **31.** 998,750 ft^2
33. $106   **35.** 13 m^3

Chapter 9 Measurement and Proportional Reasoning

Page 496   Chapter 9   Are You Ready?

1. $\frac{3}{5}$ **3.** $\frac{1}{4}$ **5.** $1\frac{1}{2}$ **7.** 4 acres   **9.** 900   **11.** 2,400
13. 81.5

Pages 502–504   Lesson 9-1B

1. 48

3 Since 1 cup = 16 fluid ounces, the unit ratio is $\frac{16 \text{ fl oz}}{1c}$.

$6.5 \text{ c} = 6.5 \text{ c} \cdot \frac{8 \text{ fl oz}}{1c}$ Multiply by $\frac{8 \text{ fl oz}}{1c}$.

$= 6.5 \cdot \frac{8 \text{ fl oz}}{1c}$ Divide out common units, leaving the desired unit, fluid ounces.

$= 6.5 \cdot 8 \text{ fl oz or } 52 \text{ fl oz}$ Multiply.

So, 6.5 cups = 52 fluid ounces.

5. 3   **7.** $7\frac{1}{2}$ **9.** 6   **11.** 32   **13.** 9   **15.** 10,560   **17.** $2\frac{1}{2}$
19. $5\frac{1}{2}$ **21.** 1,000 lb   **23.** 13 yd

25 No; $2 + 2 + \frac{1}{4} + \frac{1}{3} + 4 = 8\frac{7}{12}$ c punch and a 2-qt pitcher holds 2 qt $\cdot \frac{2 \text{ pt}}{1 \text{ qt}} \cdot \frac{2 \text{ c}}{1 \text{ pt}} = 2 \cdot 2 \cdot 2$ c or 8 c. Since 8 c < $8\frac{7}{12}$ c, the pitcher will not hold all of the punch.

27. 20   **29.** 82.8   **31.** Sample answer: Annabelle is making brownies. The recipe calls for 2 cups of sour cream. She has 2 pints of sour cream. Does she have enough sour cream to make the brownies?
33. >; Sample answer: $8\frac{3}{4}$ gal is equivalent to 35 qt, Since 35 qt > 32 qt, $8\frac{3}{4}$ gal > 32 qt.   **35.** 720 in^2; Square feet mean a unit of feet × feet. To divide out each unit, you must multiply by two conversion factors that have feet in the denominator and inches in the numerator. 5 ft$^2 \cdot \frac{12 \text{ in.}}{1 \text{ ft}} \cdot \frac{12 \text{ in.}}{1 \text{ ft}} = 720$ in^2
37. G   **39.** 1,249 in^2 **41.** about $7,300,000

Pages 507–508   Lesson 9-1C

1. 370   **3.** 1.46   **5.** 500,000 cm

7 1 mm = 0.001 m   Write the relationship.
983×1 mm $= 983 \times 0.001$ m   Multiply each side by 983 since you have 983 mm. To multiply 983 by 0.001, move the decimal point 3 places to the left.

983 mm $= 0.983$ m

So, 983 mm = 0.98 m.
9. 30   **11.** 0.08   **13.** 130,500   **15.** 0.51 kg   **17.** about 35,000 meters per hour   **19.** 0.06 L, 660 mL, 6.6 kL
21. 130 cm, 2,650 mm, 5 m

23 First subtract to find how many meters Jacinta needs to cut off the pole. She needs to cut off $3 - 2.5$ or 0.5 meters. Next, convert 0.5 meter to centimeters.

$1 \text{ m} = 100 \text{ cm}$	Write the relationship.
$0.5 \times 1 \text{ m} = 0.5 \times 100 \text{ cm}$	Multiply each side by 0.5 since you have 0.5 m.
$0.5 \text{ m} = 50 \text{ cm}$	

25. Theresa divided 3.25 by 1,000. She should have multiplied; 3,250 g. **27.** There are a greater number of smaller units. **29.** H **31.** 706.9 m³

Pages 510–512 Lesson 9-1D

1. 3.37

3 Since 1 pound is equal to 0.4536 kg, multiply by $\frac{1 \text{ lb}}{0.4536 \text{ kg}}$.

$58.14 \text{ kg} = 58.14 \text{ kg} \cdot \frac{1 \text{ lb}}{0.4536 \text{ kg}}$	Multiply by $\frac{1 \text{ lb}}{0.4536 \text{ kg}}$. Divide out common units, leaving the desired unit, pounds.
$= 58.14 \cdot \frac{1 \text{ lb}}{0.4536}$	
$= 128.17 \text{ lb}$	Simplify.

So, $58.14 \text{ kg} = 128.17 \text{ lb}$.

5. 15.75 **7.** 5,333 ft **9.** 12.7 **11.** 2.11 **13.** 3.79 **15.** 57,607.2 **17.** 21.26 **19.** 121.28 **21.** 41.89 **23.** 15.24 **25.** 4.96 lb **27.** 435.3 m

29 First, convert 1.5 pounds to grams in order to compare like units.

Since 1 pound is equal to 453.6 g, multiply by $\frac{453.6 \text{ g}}{1 \text{ lb}}$.

$1.5 \text{ lb} = 1.5 \text{ lb} \cdot \frac{453.6 \text{ g}}{1 \text{ lb}}$	Multiply by $\frac{453.6 \text{ g}}{1 \text{ lb}}$.
$= 1.5 \cdot \frac{453.6 \text{ g}}{1}$	Divide out common units, leaving the desired unit, grams.
$= 680.4 \text{ g}$	Simplify.

So, $1.5 \text{ lb} = 680.4 \text{ g}$.

Next, compare the two measures. 680.4 is greater than 650, so the 1.5-pound box is greater than the 650-gram box.

31. 3 gal **33.** 4 mi **35.** 0.83 ft; 1.67 ft; 2.5 ft; 3.33 ft **37.** about 149.73 gigameters **39.** 0.02 T, 1 kg, 2 lb, 891 g **41.** When ordering lengths with different units of measures, you must change all of the measurements to the same unit and then order the lengths. **43.** H **45.** 5.7 **47.** 15,840

Pages 515–516 Lesson 9-1E

1 You can use 1 mile = 5,280 feet to convert.

$\frac{607,200 \text{ ft}}{1 \text{ hr}} = \frac{607,200 \text{ ft}}{1 \text{ hr}} \cdot \frac{1 \text{ mi}}{5,280 \text{ ft}}$	Multiply by $\frac{1 \text{ mi}}{5,280 \text{ ft}}$.
$= \frac{607,200}{1 \text{ hr}} \cdot \frac{1 \text{ mi}}{5,280}$	Divide out common units.
$= \frac{607,200 \cdot 1 \text{ mi}}{1 \cdot 5,280 \text{ hr}}$	Simplify.
$= \frac{115 \text{ mi}}{1 \text{ hr}}$	Simplify.

The go-kart's top speed is 115 mph.

3. 5 mi/h **5.** 322,000 m/h **7.** 2.48 L/week **9.** 9.6 **11.** 15.6 **13.** 1.6 **15.** 0.4

17 a. You can use 1 mile = 5,280 feet, 1 hour = 60 minutes, and 1 minute = 60 seconds.

$\frac{4.4 \text{ m}}{1 \text{ hr}} = \frac{4.4 \text{ mi}}{1 \text{ hr}} \cdot \frac{5,280 \text{ ft}}{1 \text{ mi}} \cdot \frac{1 \text{ hr}}{60 \text{ min}} \cdot \frac{1 \text{ min}}{60 \text{ sec}}$	Multiply by distance and time unit ratios. Divide out common units.
$= \frac{4.4}{1} \cdot \frac{5,280 \text{ ft}}{1} \cdot \frac{1}{60} \cdot \frac{1}{60 \text{ sec}}$	Simplify.
$= \frac{4.4 \cdot 5,280 \cdot 1 \cdot 1 \text{ ft}}{1 \cdot 1 \cdot 60 \cdot 60 \text{ sec}}$	
$= \frac{23,232 \text{ ft}}{3,600 \text{ sec}}$	Simplify.
$= \frac{6.453 \text{ ft}}{1 \text{ sec}}$	Simplify.

The speed of the housefly is 6.45 feet per second.

b. You can use 1 minute = 60 seconds.

$\frac{38 \text{ beats}}{1 \text{ sec}} = \frac{38 \text{ beats}}{1 \text{ sec}} \cdot \frac{60 \text{ sec}}{1 \text{ min}}$	Multiply by $\frac{60 \text{ sec}}{1 \text{ min}}$.
$= \frac{38 \text{ beats}}{1} \cdot \frac{60}{1 \text{ min}}$	Divide out common units.
$= \frac{38 \cdot 60 \text{ beats}}{1 \cdot 1 \text{ min}}$	Simplify.
$= \frac{2,280 \text{ beats}}{1 \text{ min}}$	Simplify.

A dragonfly's wings beat 2,280 times per minute.

c. You can use 1 hour = 60 minutes and 1 mile = 1.61 kilometers.

$\frac{6.4 \text{ mi}}{1 \text{ hr}} = \frac{6.4 \text{ mi}}{1 \text{ hr}} \cdot \frac{1.61 \text{ km}}{1 \text{ mi}} \cdot \frac{1 \text{ hr}}{60 \text{ min}}$	Multiply by distance and time unit ratios.
$= \frac{6.4}{1} \cdot \frac{1.61 \text{ km}}{1} \cdot \frac{1}{60 \text{ min}}$	Divide out common units.
$= \frac{6.4 \cdot 1.61 \cdot 1 \text{ km}}{1 \cdot 1 \cdot 60 \text{ min}}$	Simplify.
$= \frac{10.304}{60 \text{ min}}$	Simplify.
$= \frac{0.17 \text{ km}}{1 \text{ min}}$	Simplify.

A bumblebee can travel 0.17 kilometers in 1 minute.

d. You can use 1 minute = 60 seconds and 1 hour = 60 minutes.

$\frac{250 \text{ beats}}{1 \text{ sec}} = \frac{250 \text{ beats}}{1 \text{ sec}} \cdot \frac{60 \text{ min}}{1 \text{ hr}} \cdot \frac{60 \text{ sec}}{1 \text{ min}}$	Multiply by distance and time unit ratios.
$= \frac{250 \text{ beats}}{1} \cdot \frac{60}{1 \text{ hr}} \cdot \frac{60}{1}$	Divide out common units.
$= \frac{250 \cdot 60 \cdot 60 \text{ beats}}{1 \cdot 1 \cdot 1 \text{ hr}}$	Simplify.
$= \frac{900,000 \text{ beats}}{1 \text{ hr}}$	Simplify.

A honeybee's wings beat 900,000 times an hour.

19. Divya should have multiplied by the reciprocal of the unit ratio. The correct answer is 1.74 km/min. **21.** D **23.** 21.6 cm by 27.9 cm **25.** 6 **27.** 0.90

Pages 520–522 Lesson 9-1F

1. 432 **3.** 5 **5.** 9 **7.** 345.6 **9.** 40.5 **11.** 4,100,000 **13.** 213.8 yd² **15.** 1,656

17 Use 1 square yard = 9 square feet

$216 \text{ ft}^2 = 216 \text{ ft}^2 \cdot \dfrac{1 \text{ yd}^2}{9 \text{ ft}^2}$ Multiply by $\dfrac{1 \text{ yd}^2}{9 \text{ ft}^2}$.

$= 216 \cdot \dfrac{1 \text{ yd}^2}{9}$ Divide out common units, leaving the desired unit, square yards.

$= 24 \text{ yd}^2$ Simplify.

19. 75,000   **21.** 540   **23.** 27,878,400   **25.** 6.5   **27.** 10.4
29. 450,000   **31.** 0.97   **33.** 6,400 yd^3 **35.** 0.94 yd^3
37. 10 cc   **39.** 1,296 in^2

41 First, find the number of cubic yards in a cubic meter.

$V = \ell wh$ Write the formula.

$= (1.1 \text{ yd})(1.1 \text{ yd})(1.1 \text{ yd})$ Replace ℓ, w, and h with 1.1.

$= 1.331 \text{ yd}^3$ Simplify.

Next, convert 250,000 m^3 to cubic yards.

$250,000 \text{ m}^3 = 250,000 \text{ m}^3 \cdot \dfrac{1.331 \text{ yd}^3}{1 \text{ m}^3}$ Multiply by $\dfrac{1 \text{ yd}^2}{9 \text{ ft}^2}$.

Divide out common units, leaving the desired unit, square yards.

$= 250,000 \cdot \dfrac{1.331 \text{ yd}^3}{1}$

$= 332,750 \text{ yd}^3$ Simplify.

The swimming pool has a volume of 332,750 yd^3.
43. He would have to divide 169 square feet by 9 since there are 3 feet in each yard, and he was converting to square yards.   **45.** He should have multiplied by the reciprocal; 14,929,920 in^3.   **47.** B
49a. 128 ft^3 **49b.** 221,184 in^3 **49c.** 3.5 m^3 **51.** 650
53. 4.5 kg   **55a.** 16%   **55b.** −2%   **55c.** cod

Pages 524–525   Lesson 9-2A   PSI

1. Sample answer: Making a model helps you to see what is happening in the problem which can help you solve it.

3. 9 in. × $10\frac{1}{2}$ in.   **5.** yes; $1,900 + 2,100 + 1,600 > 5,000$

7 $45.50 - 5(2.75) - 14.95 + 10.00$ Write an expression.

$= 26.80$ Simplify.

At the end of the week, Myra has $26.80.
9. $125\frac{7}{16}$ ft^2 **11.** Sample answer: How many feet of chrome edging do you need to finish a tabletop that is 54 inches long and 30 inches wide? 14 ft

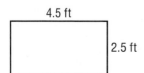

4.5 ft

2.5 ft

Pages 531–533   Lesson 9-2C

1. 1,715 in^2 **3.** 15.7 cm^3 **5.** 11,700 in^2

7 $S.A. = 280 \times \left(\dfrac{1.4}{1}\right)^2$ Multiply by the square of the scale factor.

$= 280 \times \dfrac{1.96}{1}$ Square $\dfrac{1.4}{1}$.

$= 548.8$ Simplify.

The surface area of the larger box is 548.8 square inches.

---

9. 19 mm^3 **11.** 251,712 ft^2; 8,709,120 ft^3

13 $V = 126.9 \times \left(\dfrac{4}{3}\right)^3$ Multiply by the cube of the scale factor.

$V = 126.9 \times \dfrac{64}{27}$ Cube $\dfrac{4}{3}$.

$V = 300.8$ Simplify.

The volume of the larger sphere is 300.8 m^3.
15. sometimes   **17.** never   **19a.** 3 : 1   **19b.** surface area, 9 : 1; volume, 27 : 1   **19c.** 602.88 cm^2
19d. 30,520.8 cm^3 **21a.** Yes, the ratios $\frac{3}{6}$ and $\frac{1.5}{3}$ are equal.   **21b.** 7.065 in^3; 56.52 in^3 **21c.** 1:8
21d. 49.455 in^3 **23.** C   **25.** 7.5 cm

Pages 536–539   Study Guide and Review

1. dimensional analysis   **3.** metric system   **5.** gram
7. kilogram   **9.** 8   **11.** 3   **13.** 5.7 mi   **15.** 1,825
17. 24,000   **19.** 1,020 grams   **21.** 51,528.96
23. 18.43   **25.** about 345 lb   **27.** 1.76   **29.** 2.24
31. 0.23 m/s   **33.** 3,000   **35.** 0.581   **37.** 37.8 ft^2
39. 120   **41.** $S.A. = 201.2 \text{ in}^2$; $V = 176 \text{ in}^3$

Chapter 10 Transformations

Page 546   Chapter 10   Are You Ready?

1. $(-1, 2)$ **3.** $(-3, -1)$

5–8.

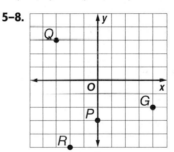

9. Sample answer:

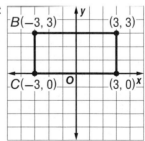

11.

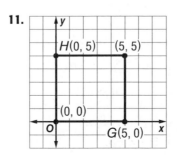

1.

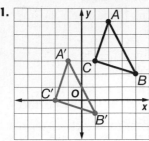

3. $D'(7, 0)$, $E'(4, -2)$, $F'(8, 4)$, $G'(12, -3)$

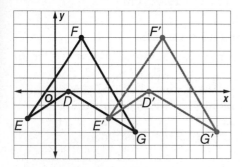

5.

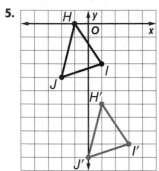

7 $P'(6, 5)$, $Q'(11, 3)$, $R'(3, 11)$

Vertices of △PQR	(x + 6, y + 5)	Vertices of △P'Q'R'
P(0, 0)	(0 + 6, 0 + 5)	P'(6, 5)
Q(5, −2)	(5 + 6, −2 + 5)	Q'(11, 3)
R(−3, 6)	(−3 + 6, 6 + 5)	R'(3, 11)

Use the vertices of △PQR and △P'Q'R' to graph both triangles.

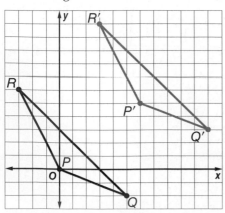

9. $P'(-3, 0)$, $Q'(2, -2)$, $R'(-6, 6)$

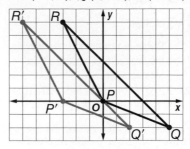

11a. 3 units right and 1 unit up; $(x + 3, y + 1)$
11b. 3 units left and 1 unit down; $(x - 3, y - 1)$

13

Vertices of RSTU	(x + 3, y + 5)	Vertices of R'S'T'U'	[x + (−2), y]	Vertices of R"S"T"U"
R(−2, −1)	[−2 + 3, (−1) + 5]	R'(−1, 4)	[−1 + (−2), 4]	R"(−3, 4)
S(1, −1)	(1 + 3, −1 + 5)	S'(4, 4)	[4 + (−2), 4]	S"(2, 4)
T(0, −3)	(0 + 3, −3 + 5)	T'(3, 2)	[3 + (−2), 2]	T"(1, 2)
U(−3, −3)	(−3 + 3, −3 + 5)	U'(0, 2)	[0 + (−2), 2]	U"(−2, 2)

Use the vertices of R"S"T"U" to graph the parallelogram.

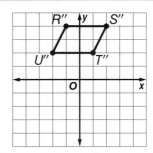

15. $(x - m, y + n)$ **17.** The final image is 3 units left and 3 units up from the original figure.   **19.** G
21. 292,500 mm³   **23.** 156.52 cm²   **25.** 6   **27.** 21

1.

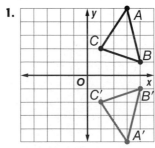

$A'(3, -5)$, $B'(4, -1)$, $A'(-3, 5)$ $B'(-4, 1)$,
$C'(1, -2)$ $C'(-1, 2)$

3.

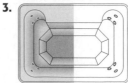

5.

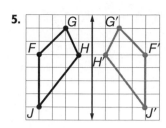

7 When a figure is reflected over the y-axis, the y-coordinate of the image is the same, while the x-coordinate is multiplied by -1. Therefore, triangle $F'G'H'$ has vertices $F'(-3, 3)$, $G'(-4, -3)$, and $H'(-2, 1)$.

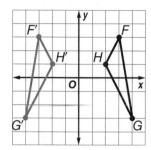

$F'(-3, 3)$, $G'(-4, -3)$, $H'(-2, 1)$

9.

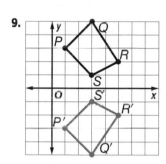

$P'(1, -3)$, $Q'(3, -5)$, $R'(5, -2)$, $S'(3, -1)$

11.

15 There is only one line along which the violin could be broken into a figure and its image reflected across the line. The line of symmetry runs vertically through the neck and the body of the violin.

17. figures A and C **19.** Sample answer; A reflection over the y-axis followed by a reflection over the x-axis.

21.

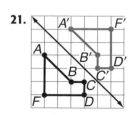

23. x-axis; The x-coordinates are the same, but the y-coordinates are opposites.   **25.** Sample answer: Marisol found the results of a reflection over the y-axis. They should be $A'(1, -1)$, $B'(4, -1)$ and $C'(1, -5)$.   **27.** $F'(1, 6)$, $G'(3, 4)$, $H'(2, 1)$

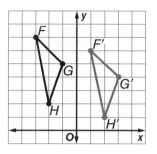

Pages 567–569   Lesson 10-3B

1

Step 1 Sketch $\triangle ABC$ on a coordinate plane.

Step 2 Sketch $\overline{AO}$ connecting point A to the origin. Sketch another segment, $\overline{A'O}$, so that the angle between point A, O, and A' measures $90°$ and the segment is congruent to $\overline{AO}$.

Step 3 Repeat Step 2 for points B and C. Then connect the vertices to form $\triangle A'B'C'$.

$A'(2, -4)$, $B'(0, -2)$, $C'(4, -1)$

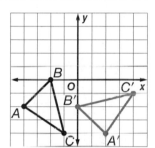

3. $A'(-2, 4)$, $B'(0, 2)$, $C'(-4, 1)$

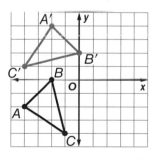

5. $E'(-1, -1)$, $F'(-3, -1)$, $G'(-4, -4)$, $H'(-2, -4)$

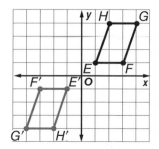

Step 1 Sketch △PQR on a coordinate plane.
Step 2 Sketch $\overline{PO}$, connecting point P to the origin. Sketch another segment, $\overline{P'O}$, so that the angle between point P, O, and P′ measures 180° and the segment is congruent to $\overline{PO}$.
Step 3 Repeat Step 2 for points Q and R. Then connect the vertices to form △P′Q′R′.

The vertices for △P′Q′R′ are P′(−1, 5), Q′(−2, 1), R′(−5, 4).

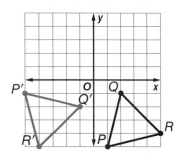

9. P′(−5, −1), Q′(−1, −2), R′(−4, −5)

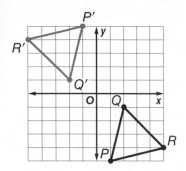

11. F′(−1, 1), G′(−5, 2), H′(−3, 5), J′(0, 4)

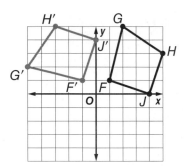

13. F′(−1, −1), G′(−2, −5), H′(−5, −3), J′(−4, 0)

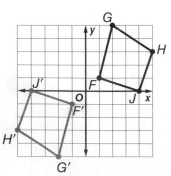

15. T′(0, −3), U′(−2, −3), V′(−2, −1), W′(−1, 0)

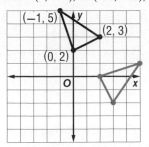

17. Sample answer:

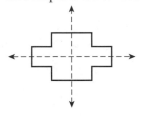

19. Sample answer: 180°

21. 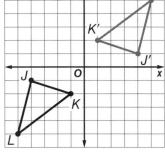 J′(4, 1), K′(1, 2), and L′(5, 5)

23. 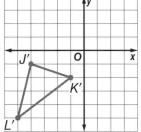 J′(−4, −1), K′(−1, −2), and L′(−5, −5)

25. Sample answer: To rotate a figure, you need to know the number of degrees it is going to be rotated, the direction of rotation, and about what point the figure is being rotated.

27a. (−5, 0) **27b.** (0, 5)

29.

31.

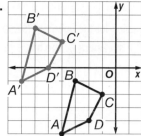

Pages 573–575   Lesson 10-4A

1.

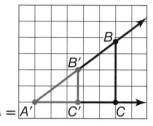

3. $J'(-12, 6)$, $K'(-6, -12)$, $L'(9, 18)$

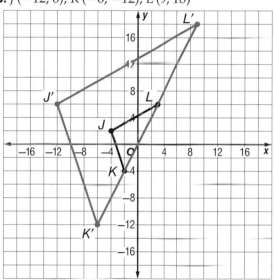

5. 3; enlargement

7.

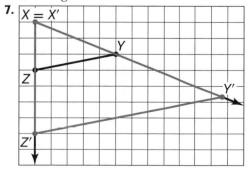

9 Sketch the figure on a coordinate plane, placing point L at the origin since it is the center

of dilation. That gives the figure the coordinates $L(0, 0)$, $M(0, 4)$, $N(3, 4)$, $P(5, 2)$, and $R(4, 0)$. Find the vertices of the dilation, multiply each coordinate in the ordered pairs by $\frac{3}{4}$. Then graph the image.

$$L(0, 0) \rightarrow \left(0 \cdot \frac{3}{4}, 0 \cdot \frac{3}{4}\right) \rightarrow L'(0, 0)$$

$$M(0, 4) \rightarrow \left(0 \cdot \frac{3}{4}, 4 \cdot \frac{3}{4}\right) \rightarrow M'(0, 3)$$

$$N(3, 4) \rightarrow \left(3 \cdot \frac{3}{4}, 4 \cdot \frac{3}{4}\right) \rightarrow N'\left(1\frac{1}{4}, 3\right)$$

$$P(5, 2) \rightarrow \left(5 \cdot \frac{3}{4}, 2 \cdot \frac{3}{4}\right) \rightarrow P'\left(3\frac{3}{4}, 1\frac{1}{2}\right)$$

$$R(4, 0) \rightarrow \left(4 \cdot \frac{3}{4}, 0 \cdot \frac{3}{4}\right) \rightarrow R'(3, 0)$$

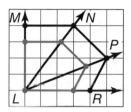

11. $H'(-2, 6)$, $J'(6, 4)$, $J'(4, -6)$, $L'(-4, -4)$

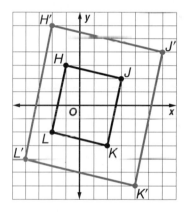

13. $H'(-3, 1)$, $J'(2, 2)$, $K'\left(3\frac{1}{2}, -1\right)$, $L'(-1, -2)$

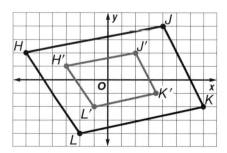

15. $\frac{3}{5}$; reduction   **17.** 2; enlargement

19. 4.5 cm by 3 cm

21 The scale factor is a ratio of the two sizes expressed in the same units. First, change 20 ft to inches; 20 ft times 12 inches per foot is 240 inches. So, the ratio is $\frac{240 \text{ in.}}{5 \text{ in.}}$ or 48.

23. Sample answer: Suppose the first scale factor is 4 and the second scale factor is $\frac{3}{4}$.

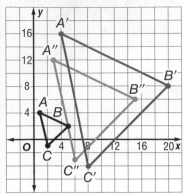

The scale factor from the original to the final image is 3; Each coordinate is multiplied by 4 and then by $\frac{3}{4}$, and $4 \cdot \frac{3}{4} = 3$. Also, $\dfrac{y\text{-coordinate of point } A''}{y\text{-coordinate of point } A} = \dfrac{12}{4} = 3$. **25.** Multiply each member of the ordered pair (x, y) by the scale factor k. The new coordinates are (kx, ky). **27.** H

29. $X'(1, 3)$, $Y'(4, 5)$, and $Z'(5, 1)$

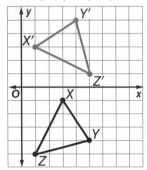

31. $J'(-1, 4)$, $K'(1, -1)$, and $L'(3, 2)$

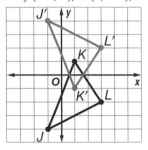

Pages 576–577   Lesson 10-4B   PSI

1. Sample answer: The work backward strategy could be used with hiking, where you may need to retrace your steps to return to the starting point.
3. Sample answer: Translating the triangle will affect the y-coordinates by increasing them, and depends on how many units it was translated up. The rotation is shown.

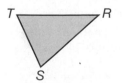

5 Work backward.

$2.50 = \frac{1}{3}x$ Write an equation for the question, "$2.50 is $\frac{1}{3}$ of what?" If she spent $\frac{2}{3}$, she has $\frac{1}{3}$ left.

$3(2.50) = 3 \cdot \frac{1}{3}x$ Multiply each side by 3.

$7.50 = x$ Simplify.

$2(7.50) = 15$ $7.50 is half of what she started with, so multiply by two to find the original amount.

Jackie's mom gave her $15.00.

7. 180 ft

9a. 3 units right and 4 units down

9b. $A'(1, 2)$, $B'(-2, 1)$, $C'(-1, -2)$, $D'(2, 1)$

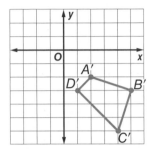 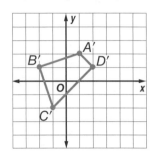

Pages 580–583   Study Guide and Review

1. false; $(-2, 1)$ **3.** false; reflection   **5.** true   **7.** true

9. $P'(8, -3)$, $Q'(2, -4)$, and $R'(3, 5)$

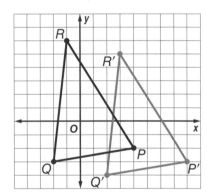

11. $P'(4, -9)$, $Q'(-2, -10)$, and $R'(-1, -1)$

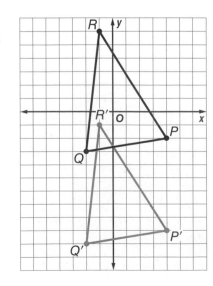

13. $R'(-1, -3)$, $S'(2, -6)$, and $T'(6, -1)$

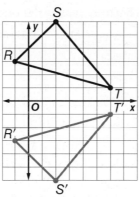

15. $E'(4, -2)$, $F'(-2, -2)$, $G'(-2, -5)$, $H'(4, -5)$

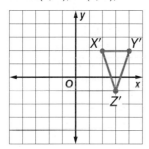

17. $X'(-2, 2)$, $Y'(-2, 4)$, and $Z'(1, 3)$

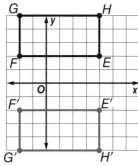

19. $X'(2, 2)$, $Y'(4, 2)$, and $Z'(3, -1)$

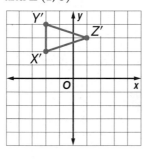

21. 4; enlargement
23. 8th row, 3 places from the end   **25.** $200

Chapter 11 Geometry and Spatial Reasoning

Page 602   Chapter 11   Are You Ready?

1. 94.76   **3.** 691.06   **5.** 1.83   **7.** 5.54   **9.** $35.24
11. 47   **13.** 55   **15.** 81 pages

Pages 604–609   Lesson 11-1A

1. ∠CAM, ∠MAC, ∠A, ∠1; acute   **3.** supplementary
5. 100

7 Use the vertex as the middle letter and a point from each side: ∠JDB, ∠BDJ
Use the vertex only: ∠D
Use a number: ∠6
The square at the vertex indicates that this is a right triangle.
9. ∠MLP, ∠PLM, ∠L, ∠8; obtuse   **11.** neither
13. supplementary   **15.** 53°

17 Sample answer: ∠BED and ∠BEG because ∠BEG makes a 90° angle as the two lines intersect. Since ∠BEG is 90°, then ∠BED must also be 90°.
19. Sample answer: ∠CBH   **21.** Sample answer: stairs and landings form obtuse angles.
23. $m\angle K = 52°$ and $m\angle O = 128°$ **25.** complementary; The other terms name specific angles, while complementary is a relationship between two angles.   **27.** B   **29.** C
31.

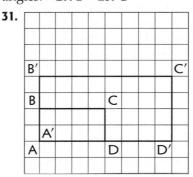

33. yes; 45°, 90°, 135°, 180°, 225°, 270°, 315°, 360°
35. yes; 60°, 120°, 180°, 240°, 300°, 360°

Pages 610–614   Lesson 11-1B

1. alternate interior   **3.** alternate exterior   **5.** 60°
7. 16; Sample answer: alternate exterior angles are congruent   **9.** corresponding   **11.** alternate interior
13 ∠2 and ∠4 are vertical angles, so $m\angle 4 = 74°$. ∠4 and ∠8 are corresponding angles, so $m\angle 8 = 74°$.
15. 74   **17.** 74°; 106°   **19.** 96°; alternate exterior to ∠7
21. 96°; vertical to ∠2   **23.** 20

25 The angle the escalator makes with the second floor corresponds to the angle it makes with the first floor. Therefore, its measure is 45°. That angle and the angle with a measure of $x°$ are supplementary.

$45 + x = 180$ The measures of supplementary angles have a sum of 180°.

$45 + x - 45 = 180 - 45$ Subtract 45 from both sides.

$x = 135$ Simplify.

27. $m\angle 5 = 122°$; $m\angle 6 = 58°$ **29.** They are supplementary.
31. Sample answer:

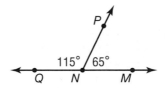

33. C   **35.** 92°   **37.** 39°
39. 16 in. by 24 in.

Pages 616–621   Lesson 11-2B

1. 44   **3.** 45   **5.** 60°   **7.** right, scalene
9. acute isosceles; Sample answer:

11. 118 **13.** 27 **15.** 90

17

$$25 + 102 + m\angle Q = 180$$

$$127 + m\angle Q = 180$$

$$127 + m\angle Q - 127 = 180 - 127$$

$$m\angle Q = 53°$$

The sum of the measures of the angles of a triangle is 180°.
Simplify.
Subtract 127 from each side.
Simplify.

Therefore, $m\angle Q = 53°$.

19. acute, equilateral **21.** obtuse, isosceles
23. obtuse, isosceles **25.** right
27. acute scalene;   **29.** acute equilateral;
Sample answer: Sample answer:

31. 79.5 **33.** 79.2 **35.** 21.3

37 $\angle C$ is a vertical angle to the angle marked as 47°. So, $m\angle C = 47°$. $\angle A$ is a corresponding angle to the angle marked 61°. So, $m\angle A = 61°$. Since they make a triangle, the measures of angles A, B, and C have to add up to 180°. So, $m\angle B = 72°$.
39. 30 **41.** $a = 55$; $b = 65$; $c = 60$; $d = 30$ **43a.** Never; Sample answer: The sum of the three angles in a triangle is 180°. For a triangle to have two right angles, the sum of these two angles, not including the third angle, would already be 180°. The addition of the third angle would increase the sum to be greater than 180°. **43b.** Never; Sample answer: The sum of the three angles in a triangle is 180°. If a triangle has two obtuse angles, the sum of these two angles, not including the third angle, would already be greater than 180°. **45.** B **47.** 42°
49. 138° **51.** complementary **53.** neither

Pages 622–623 Lesson 11-2C PSI

1. Sample answer: Anton used inductive reasoning because he made a rule after seeing four examples.
3. None of the angles are congruent.

5 Make a chart. Mark the two things you know. (You will only use one chart.)

	Maya	Rashanda	Perry
mango	O		
banana			X
orange			

Since Maya brought the mango, no one else did, and she didn't bring anything else.

	Maya	Rashanda	Perry
mango	O	X	X
banana	X		X
orange	X		

This only leaves the orange for Perry.

	Maya	Rashanda	Perry
mango	O	X	X
banana	X		X
orange	X		O

So, Rashanda didn't bring an orange.

	Maya	Rashanda	Perry
mango	O	X	X
banana	X	O	X
orange	X	X	O

Maya brought a mango. Rashanda brought a banana. Perry brought an orange.
7. $3.75 **9.** 441 sq units **11.** 3 packs **13.** 79

Pages 624–629 Lesson 11-2D

1. 75

3 The one way sign has opposite sides that are congruent and four right angles. It is a rectangle. The men working sign has all four sides congruent and four right angles. It is a square.
5. 120° **7.** 70

9

$$x + 95 + 55 + 110 = 360$$

$$x + 260 = 360$$

$$x + 260 - 260 = 360 - 260$$

$$x = 100$$

The sum of the angles of a quadrilateral is 360°.
Simplify.
Subtract 260 from each side.
Simplify.

11. 65 **13.** square **15.** trapezoid
17. rhombus **19.** The first figure is a rectangle. The second figure is a trapezoid. **21.** 90.8 **23.** 45

25a.

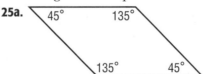

25b. triangle, rectangle, square, trapezoid
27a. Greater than; Sample answer: 360° ÷ 4 = 90°, so the average angle measure is 90°. Since the three congruent angles are all less than 90°, the remaining angle must be greater than 90° to make sure that all four angles add to 360°. **27b.** Equal to; Sample answer: 360° ÷ 4 = 90°, so the average angle measure is 90°. Since the three congruent angles are equal to 90°, the remaining angle must also be equal to 90° to make sure that all four angles add to 360°. **27c.** Less than; Sample answer: 360° ÷ 4 = 90°, so the average angle measure is 90°. Since the three congruent angles are all greater than 90°, the remaining angle must be less than 90° to make sure that all four angles add to 360°. **29.** Sometimes; Sample answer: When the quadrilateral has opposite sides parallel and congruent, it is a parallelogram. **31.** Always; Sample answer: A square has all the characteristics of a

rectangle. A square is a special kind of rectangle with all sides congruent. **33.** B **35.** C **37.** 105 **39.** 74 **41.** supplementary **43.** $3.78

Pages 630–635   Lesson 11-2E

1. no; curved   **3.** no; open

5 Draw a heptagon, a 7-sided polygon. Draw all the diagonals from one vertex. This makes 5 triangles. $5 \times 180° = 900°$ So, the sum of the angle measures of a heptagon is 900°.

7. yes; 16-sided, not regular   **9.** no; curved   **11.** yes; pentagon, regular   **13.** 1,260°   **15.** 1,800°   **17.** 135°
19. triangles and hexagons

21 20 sides, 162°; 50 sides, 172.8°; 100 sides, 176.4°;

Polygon	Sum of the Angles	Measure of One Angle
20-sided	$18 \times 180° = 3,240$	$3,240 \div 20 = 162°$
50-sided	$48 \times 180° = 8,640$	$8,640 \div 50 = 172.8°$
100-sided	$98 \times 180° = 17,640$	$17,640 \div 100 = 176.4°$

As the number of sides increases, the angle measure gets closer to 180°, but will never be 180° because that is a straight angle.   **23.** 110   **25.** 117   **27.** 128

29a.

Number of Sides of Polygon	Sum of Interior Angles
3	180
4	360
5	540
6	720
7	900
8	1,080
9	1,260
10	1,440
12	1,800
15	2,340

29b.
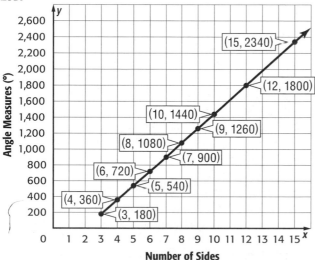

29c. Sample answer: The sum of the angles increases at a constant rate; there is no y- or x-intercept.

31. Sample answer: **33.** Sample answer:

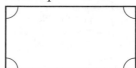

35. Sample answer: Regular decagons have equal angles measuring 144° and regular 11-sided polygons have angles measuring 147.27°   **37.** F
39. G   **41.** trapezoid   **43.** 51   **45.** 27

Pages 641–644   Lesson 11-3A

1. 36

3 $17 \times 17 = 289$

5. 3   **7.** 11   **9.** 24 in. by 24 in.   **11.** 1   **13.** 121   **15.** 400
17. 1,156   **19.** 4   **21.** 10   **23.** 16   **25.** 25   **27.** 40 ft

29 $18 \times 18 = 324$, so the length of the side of the chessboard including the border is 18 inches. Subtract an inch for the border on both sides of the region containing the small squares. The length of one side of that region is 16 inches.

31a. yes; Sample answer: A pen that measures 10 feet by 10 feet has the same perimeter, but its area is 100 square feet, which is greater than 84 square feet.
31b. a square that measures 10 feet on each side; Sample answer: The perimeter is the same, and the area is 100 square feet, or 16 square feet greater than that of the original pen.   **33.** D   **35.** 135°
37. rhombus

Pages 645–648   Lesson 11-3B

1. 6   **3.** 9   **5.** 10 ft   **7.** 3   **9.** 6

11 89 is between 81 or 9^2 and 100, or 10^2. 89 is 8 away from 81 and 11 away from 100. So it is closer to 81. Therefore, $\sqrt{89}$ to the nearest whole number is 9.
13. 12   **15.** 8 in.   **17.** about 1.5   **19.** 30   **21.** 40
23. 0.5   **25.** 1.4   **27.** 3

29 a. The stamp is a square. By finding the square root of the area, 1,008, you find the length of one side of the stamp. Use your calculator to find $\sqrt{1,008}$. The length of the side of the stamp to the nearest tenth millimeter is 31.7 mm.   **29b.** Convert millimeters to centimeters. Since 1 centimeter is equal to 10 millimeters, divide 31.7 by 10. To divide by 10, move the decimal one place to the left. The length of one side of the stamp is 3.17 cm.   **33.** Sample answer: 17, 18, 19   **35.** 2   **37.** 5   **39.** Sample answer: It cannot be written as a fraction.
41. G   **43.** 121   **45.** 324   **47.** yes; regular triangle

Pages 649–653   Lesson 11-3C

1. irrational   **3.** rational
5. −4.6   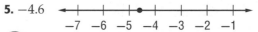   **7.** >

9 0.9 is not a whole number. It is also not an integer. It can be written as a fraction, $\frac{9}{10}$, so it is a rational number.
11. integer, rational   **13.** whole, integer, rational

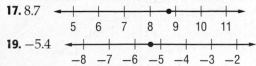

15. rational

17. 8.7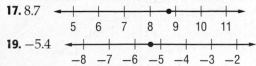

(number line showing point at 8.7 between 8 and 9; marks 5 6 7 8 9 10 11)

19. −5.4

(number line showing point at −5.4; marks −8 −7 −6 −5 −4 −3 −2)

21. =   **23.** <   **25.** 30.9 mi

27 Evaluate the formula for $h = 10$.

$v = 8\sqrt{h}$ Write the formula.

$\quad = 8\sqrt{10}$ Replace h with 10.

$\quad = 8(3.1623)$ Use the calculator to find $\sqrt{10}$.

$\quad = 25.3$ Simplify.

She was running about 25.3 feet per second.

29. $\sqrt{3.88}$; Sample answer: It is the only number that is irrational.   **31.** A   **33.** −6   **35.** −9   **37.** $\sqrt{49}$

Pages 655–660   Lesson 11-3E

1 $a^2 + b^2 = c^2$ Pythagorean Theorem

$24^2 + 10^2 = c^2$ Replace a with 24 and b with 10.

$576 + 100 = c^2$ Evaluate 24^2 and 10^2.

$\qquad 676 = c^2$ Add.

$\pm\sqrt{676} = c$ Definition of square root

$\qquad \pm 26 = c$ Simplify.

The length of the hypotenuse is 26 mm.

3. 18.5 cm   **5.** 4.0 ft   **7.** 16.1 m   **9.** 14.1 m   **11.** 5.4 ft
13. $b = 2.8$ yd   **15.** $c = 25$ in.   **17.** 5.6 mi   **19.** 72.1 in.

21 Sample answer: The plank will not fit horizontally or vertically. However, the diagonal of the doorway measures about 18 feet. So, the plank will fit through the doorway if you tilt it diagonally.

$a^2 + b^2 = c^2$ Pythagorean Theorem

$15^2 + 10^2 = c^2$ Replace a with 24 and b with 10.

$225 + 100 = c^2$ Evaluate 24^2 and 10^2.

$\qquad 325 = c^2$ Add.

$\pm\sqrt{325} = c$ Definition of square root

$\qquad \pm 18.02 = c$ Simplify.

The diagonal of the opening is 18.02 feet. Therefore, the plank will fit through the door.

23. Sample answer: The hypotenuse is 21 cm, so the equation should be $21^2 = 8^2 + x^2$.   **25.** B   **27.** <
29. <   **31.** 11 ft   **33.** 4.5   **35.** 3.5   **37.** 40

Pages 661–664   Lesson 11-3F

1. 9.8 units

3 Draw a triangle for which the line segment is a hypotenuse. One such triangle has the third vertex $(−3, 1)$. Count on the graph to find the lengths of the legs of the triangle.

$a^2 + b^2 = c^2$ Pythagorean Theorem

$2^2 + 7^2 = c^2$ Replace a with 2 and b with 7.

$4 + 49 = c^2$ Evaluate 2^2 and 7^2.

$\qquad 53 = c^2$ Add.

$\pm\sqrt{53} = c$ Definition of square root

$\qquad \pm 7.3 \approx c$ Simplify.

Since lengths are positive, the length of line segment AB is about 7.3 units.

5. 3.6 units   **7.** 3.6 units   **9.** 5 units   **11.** 7.1 ft
13. 25.6   **15.** 243 mi

---

17 The distance to the right of and below the hole describe the legs of a right triangle with the hypotenuse being the distance from the ball to the hole.

$a^2 + b^2 = c^2$ Pythagorean Theorem

$5^2 + 7^2 = c^2$ Replace a with 5 and b with 7.

$25 + 49 = c^2$ Evaluate 5^2 and 7^2.

$\qquad 74 = c^2$ Add.

$\pm\sqrt{74} = c$ Definition of square root

$\qquad \pm 8.6 \approx c$ Simplify.

Since lengths are positive, the distance between the ball and the hole is about 8.6 feet.

19. Sample answer: $(0, 0)$ and $(5, 12)$ **21.** 8.6 units
23. H   **25.** 5.9 m   **27.** 20.9 cm   **29.** >   **31.** >

Pages 665–669   Study Guide and Review

1. false; leg   **3.** true   **5.** false; supplementary angles
7. supplementary   **9.** 67°   **11.** 113°   **13.** 55
15. Donnie, field hockey; Barbara, golf; Dean, volleyball; Annie, soccer   **17.** 82   **19.** trapezoid
21. rhombus   **23.** no, curved   **25.** 9   **27.** 5 in.
29. 10   **31.** 9   **33.** 7

34–37.

$\sqrt{61}$

(number line marks 6 7 8 9 10, point near 8)

$\sqrt{132}$

(number line marks 9 10 11 12 13, point near 11)

$\sqrt{444}$

(number line marks 19 20 21 22 23, point near 21)

$\sqrt{12}$

(number line marks 1 2 3 4 5, point near 3)

39. irrational   **41.** rational   **43.** 84.85 ft   **45.** 4.5 ft
47. 6.7   **49.** 5

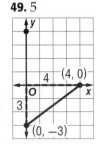

Chapter 12 Statistics

Page 676   Chapter 12   Are You Ready?

1. about 6   **3.** 13 students

Pages 681–684   Lesson 12-1B

1. The mean decreases from 5 to 3. The median decreases from 3.5 to 3. The mode does not change.

3. The mean decreases from 17.5 to 14.6. The median decreases from 14.5 to 14. The mode does not change.
5. mean; Sample answer: no extreme values; $24.38

7 mean:

$$\frac{25 + 23 + 23 + 27 + 39 + 27 + 23 + 31 + 26 + 28}{10} = \frac{272}{10}$$ or 27.2

mean without oldest player:

$$\frac{25 + 23 + 23 + 27 + 27 + 23 + 31 + 26 + 26 + 28}{9}$$

$= \frac{233}{9}$ or 25.9   The mean decreases from 27.2 to 25.9.

Write the data in order first.
median: 23, 23, 23, 25, ⟨26, 27⟩ 27, 28, 31, 39; 26.5;
median without oldest player: 23, 23, 23, 25, ⟨26⟩ 27, 27, 28, 31; 26; The median decreases from 26.5 to 26.
mode: There are more 23 year olds than players of any other age, regardless of dropping the oldest player.
9. The mean decreases from 27.4 to 22.5. The median decreases from 24 to 22.5. There is still no mode.
11. mean   **13.** Sample answer: The mean is 20.65, the median is 20, and the modes are 15, 20, and 25. Since there are extreme values and no big gaps in the middle, the median best represents the data.   **15.** 78

19 mean:

$$\frac{3 + 5 + 8 + 2 + 1 + 1 + 7 + 3 + 9 + 2 + 3 + 10}{12} = \frac{54}{12}$$ or 4.5

21. Sample answer: 3, 4, 5, 8   **23.** 35, 41, 44   **25.** A
27. 5 units   **29.** 5.8 units   **31.** $A'(2, 4)$, $B'(-2, 8)$, $C'(-4, 2)$

Pages 689–692   Lesson 12-2A

1a. 4.7   **1b.** 8.5; 9.2; 8.3   **1c.** 0.9   **1d.** 6.2 and 10.9 are outliers

3 a. To find the range, subtract the lowest number of golf courses from the highest: $1,465 - 437$ or 1,028.
b. Put the data in order from least to greatest.
437, 456, 513, 650, 893, 954, 1,018, 1,038, 1,117, 1,465
Median: Since there is an even number of states represented, average the middle two numbers to find the median: $\frac{893 + 954}{2} = \frac{1847}{2}$ or 923.5.
Upper Quartile: The middle number of the top half of the data is 1,038.
Lower Quartile: The middle number of the lower half of the data is 513.   **c.** To find the interquartile range, subtract the lower quartile from the upper quartile. $1,038 - 513$ or 525.   **d.** To check for outliers, first multiply the interquartile range by 1.5: $525 \times 1.5 = 787.5$. Add 787.5 to 1,038 and subtract it from 513. No data falls outside this range, so there are no outliers.
5. ranges 50 and 45; medians both 50; upper quartiles both 60; lower quartiles 45 and 35, interquartile ranges 15 and 25; Both sets of data have the same median while the first set is more spread out than the second.   **7.** median: 357.5, upper quartile: 422, lower quartile: 298, interquartile range: 124   **9.** median: $24.27, upper quartile: $28.99, lower quartile: $19.99, interquartile range: $9.00

11 Lucy: median: 7, upper quartile: 9, lower quartile: 5, interquartile range: 4; Dena: median: 7, upper quartile: 9, lower quartile: 6, interquartile range: 3; They have the same median and upper quartile, but Lucy's interquartile range is greater, meaning her mileage is more spread out than Dena's.
13. Sample answer: 6, 30, 33, 41, 45, 71   **15.** D
17. B   **19.** 49.5; 35.5; none   **21.** 6.4 units
23. 7.1 units

Pages 695–698   Lesson 12-2B

1a. 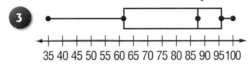   **1b.** 50%

1c. Sample answer: The length of the box-and-whisker plot shows that the depths of the earthquakes are not concentrated around a certain depth.

3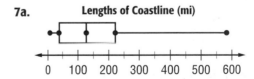

Step 1 Order the numbers from least to greatest. Then draw a number line that covers the range of data. 35, 55, 61, 65, 74, 88, 92, 96, 97, 99, 100

Step 2 Find the median, the extremes, and the upper and lower quartiles. Mark these points above the number line. Median: 88; High: 100, Low: 35, UQ: 97; LQ: 61

Step 3 Draw the box so that it includes the quartile values. Draw a vertical line through the median value. Extend the whiskers from each quartile to the extreme data points.

5.
Height of Waves (in.)
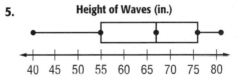

7a.
Lengths of Coastline (mi)
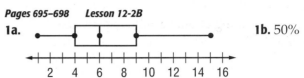

7b. 25%   **7c.** 127 mi   **7d.** Sample answer: The length of the box-and-whisker plot shows that the number of miles of coastline for the top 25% of the states varies greatly. The number of miles of coastline for the bottom 25% of states is concentrated.
9. Most fruits have between 50 and 130 Calories of food energy, and most vegetables have between 25 and 110 Calories of food energy. At least one fruit has almost 450 Calories of energy and at least one vegetable has about 350 Calories of energy. So on the whole, the food energy of fruits and vegetables does not vary greatly.

11 a.

	Tampa, FL	Caribou, ME
Low:	60	9
High:	82	66
Median:	$\frac{71+75}{2}=73$	$\frac{38+43}{2}=40.5$
Upper Quartile:	81	$\frac{54+61}{2}=57.5$
Lower Quartile:	$\frac{62+67}{2}=64.5$	$\frac{15+25}{2}=20$

Tampa: 60, 82, 73, 81, 64.5; Caribou: 9, 66, 40.5, 57.5, 20

11b.

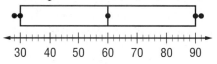

11c. The Tampa data have a smaller interquartile range, so the data are more tightly clustered around the median. The Caribou data are more spread out. **13.** Sample answer: {60, 60, 60, 60, 60, 70, 75, 80, 85, 85, 85, 85}; median = 72.5; LQ = lower extreme = 60; UQ = upper extreme = 85
15. Sample answer: {28, 30, 52, 68, 90, 92};

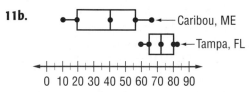

17. A   **19.** G   **21.** range: 12; median: 7; UQ: 9.5; LQ: 4.5; IQR: 5   **23.** mean: 5.6; median: 5.5; mode: 2; range: 8   **25.** $1\frac{1}{6}$ **27.** $1\frac{23}{39}$

Pages 701–704   Lesson 12-2C

1a. Sample answer: The graph shows a positive relationship. As the years increase, the population increases.

1b.

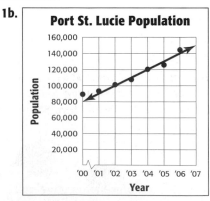

Port St. Lucie Population

1c. Sample answer: about 180,000

3 a. As the number of steps increases, the amount of time it takes to climb them also increases. The graph shows a positive relationship.

3b. Draw a line that is close to most of the data points.

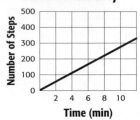

Climbing the Statue of Liberty

3c. Every two minutes, Ciro climbs about 50 steps. After 10 minutes, he has climbed just under 300 steps, so in 12 minutes he will have climbed just under 350 steps. So, 13 minutes is a good prediction for 354 steps.

5a.

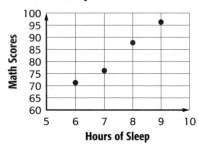

How Sleep Affects Math Scores

5b. positive; Sample answer: As the hours of sleep increase, the scores increase.   **5c.** Sample answer: 65

7 a. The two sets of data show a positive relationship. As the years increase, so do the number of voters.   **7b.** Use a straightedge to make a line that comes close to all of the points. Look across to the vertical axis where the line is above the year 2011, halfway from 2010 to 2012. It looks as though it would be about 56,000 voters.
11. Sample answer: weight of an animal as it gets older; race car lap times on a speed track
13. Sample answer: Graphs often show trends over time. If you continue the pattern, you can use it to make a prediction.   **15.** I   **17.** median: 81; UQ: 89.5; LQ: 71; IQR: 18.5   **19.** supplementary
21. supplementary

Pages 707–709   Lesson 12-2D

1. Sample answer: line graph; compares values over a length of time   **3.** Sample answer: circle graph; compares parts to a whole

5 A histogram would be appropriate because it shows data divided into equal intervals. To construct a histogram of this data, use the intervals $2.00–$2.99, $3.00–$3.99, $4.00–$4.99, and $5.00–$5.99. Put these intervals on the horizontal axis. On the vertical axis, show the scale 0 to 3. Be sure to label the axis and title the graph.

Sandwich Prices

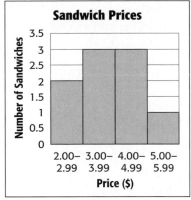

From the graph, you can see that three sandwiches cost between $3.00 and $3.99.

7 Sample answer: A box-and-whisker plot would be the most appropriate display because it shows the median along with other measures of variation.
9. Sample answer: circle graph; compares parts to whole **11.** Sample answer: scatter plot; compares two sets of data

Depth of Ice at Different Temperatures

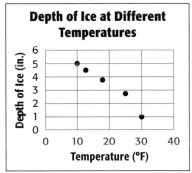

As temperatures increase, the depth of ice decreases.
13. Sample answer: stem-and-leaf plot; displays individual data

Number of Push-Ups

Stem	Leaf
1	0 7 9
2	0 3 3 5 8 8 8 8
3	
4	
5	1 2 3 4 4 5 6 6 7

1 | 0   10 push-ups

Fewer people completed 10–19 push-ups than 20–59 push-ups.
17. Sample answer:

Home Runs

Stem	Leaf
0	8
1	0 0 1 2 3 4 5 6
2	1 1 2 2 4

2 | 1   21 home runs

19. Sample answer: Scatter plots and line graphs both use plotting points similar to graphing points on a coordinate plane. Line graphs help to analyze change through time while scatter plots compare two sets of data.

21. Sample answer: about 150 lb

Height and Weight of Players

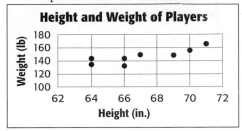

Pages 710–711   Lesson 12-2E   PSI

1. about $6\frac{1}{2}$ tablespoons   **3.** about $34

5 If two workers make 2 chairs in 2 days, it takes each worker 2 days to make 1 chair. In 20 days, a worker could make 10 chairs. Eight workers could therefore make 80 chairs in 20 days.   **7.** bones in wrist: 8; bones in fingers: 14; bones in palm: 5   **9.** Sample answer: Because the graph is being used to predict, straight axes, equally spaced scales, and accurate plotting of points are necessary to get the most accurate prediction.

Pages 715–717   Study Guide and Review

1. true   **3.** false; measures of variation   **5.** true
7. true   **9.** false; outlier   **11.** The mean increases from 80° to 85.7°. The median increases from 86° to 87.5°. There is still no mode.   **13.** median; Sample answer: There are extreme values.   **15.** range: 3; median: 2; upper quartile: 3.5; lower quartile: 1.5; interquartile range: 2; no outliers

17.

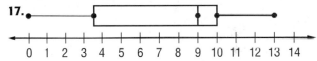

19. Sample answer: The length of the left half of the box-and-whisker plot is shorter than the length of the right half of the plot. This means that the lower number of posters are more concentrated, and the higher numbers of posters are more spread out.

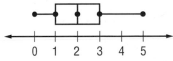

21. Sample answer: The data shows that as teams practice more hours per day, their chance of winning more games increases.   **23.** Sample answer: stem-and-leaf plot
25. histogram; It shows the frequency of an interval.

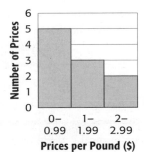

Chapter 13 Inequalities, Functions, and Monomials

Page 724   Chapter 13   Are You Ready?

1.

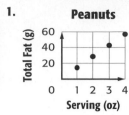

Peanuts

3.

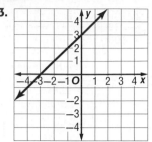

5. 2 problems per minute

Pages 726–727   Lesson 13-1A   PSI

1. Sample answer: You need to keep track of what numbers you have already guessed so that you do not make the same guess twice. You also need to know what numbers produce answers that are too large or too small, so you can make better guesses.
3. 13   **5.** Eldora has 4 nickels, 4 dimes, and 4 quarters.

7.

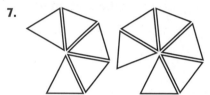

9 Make a guess.

4 baskets $4(4) = 16$ apples
8 baskets $8(4) = 32$ apples
6 baskets $6(4) = 24$ apples
The number of apples is correct; check the oranges:
$6(3) = 18$ oranges; So, 6 baskets.
11. 33 runs

Pages 730–732   Lesson 13-1B

1. $c < 4$ **3.** $y < 20$
5 $c + 4 \geq 17$ Write the inequality.
$\underline{-4 \quad -4}$ Subtract 4 from each side.
$c \geq 13$ Simplify.

7. $h \geq 6$

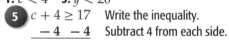

9. $-16 \leq n$

11. $5 < n$ **13.** $y \geq -7$ **15.** $x > -1$
17. $-18 > t$

19. $-5 < a$

21. $n \leq \frac{1}{2}$

23. $n + 4 > 13; n > 9$ **25.** $n - 8 < 10; n < 18$
27. $p + 17 \leq 26; p \leq 9$
29 $m + 785 \leq 1500$ Write the inequality.
$\underline{-785 \quad -785}$ Subtract 785 from each side.
$m \leq 715$ Simplify.
Lalo has 715 minutes remaining.
31a. $42 + x \geq 74; x \geq 32$ **31b.** $74 + y \geq 110; y \geq 36$
33. Sample answer: $x + 3 < 25$ **35.** C   **37.** C
39. three 12-packs and one 8-pack, or four 8-packs and one 12-pack   **41.** 76 min

Pages 736–737   Lesson 13-1C

1. $x > 3$ **3.** $h \geq 7$ **5.** $y < -4$
7 $\frac{t}{-4} < -11$ Write the inequality.
$-4\left(\frac{t}{-4}\right) > -4(-11)$ Multiply each side by -4 and reverse the symbol.
$t > 44$ Simplify.
9. $y \leq -1$

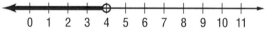

11. $n \leq -0.5$

13. $4x > 100; x > 25$ **15.** $x \geq 9$ **17.** $4 < t$ **19.** $h > 81$
21. $y > -5$ **23.** $n < 2$ **25.** $t > -12$ **27.** $s < 96$
29. $x < 4$

31. $y \geq 2$

33. $t \leq -25$

35. $0.5x > 15; x > 30$

37 $5n - 7 < -52$ Write the inequality. The word *times* means multiply; the word *decrease* means subtract.
$\underline{+7 \quad +7}$ Add 7 to each side.
$5n < -45$ Simplify.
$\frac{5n}{5} < -\frac{45}{5}$ Divide each side by 5.
$n < -9$ Simplify.

39. Sample answer: She did not reverse the inequality sign when she divided by -6; $x \geq 4$.   **41.** when you are not multiplying or dividing by a negative number
43. G   **45.** $k > 29$ **47.** $x < -33$ **49.** 8 in. by 13 in.

Pages 742–744   Lesson 13-2A

1. 13
3. Domain: {2, 4, 6, 8};
Range: {−1, 1, 3, 5}

x	x − 3	f(x)
2	2 − 3	−1
4	4 − 3	1
6	6 − 3	3
8	8 − 3	5

5. Domain: {−1, 1, 3, 5};
Range: {4, 8, 12, 16}

x	2x + 6	f(x)
−1	2(−1) + 6	4
1	2(1) + 6	8
3	2(3) + 6	12
5	2(5) + 6	16

7. 1   **9.** 18

11 $f(x) = 3x - 20$ Write the function.
$f(6) = 3(6) - 20$ Substitute 6 for x.
$f(6) = 18 - 20$ Multiply.
$f(6) = -2$ Subtract.

13. Domain: $\{-5, -4, -3, -2\}$;
Range: $\{-12, -11, -10, -9\}$

x	x − 7	f(x)
−5	−5 − 7	−12
−4	−4 − 7	−11
−3	−3 − 7	−10
−2	−2 − 7	−9

15. Domain: $\{-4, -2, 2, 4\}$;
Range: $\{-16, -4, 20, 32\}$

x	8 + 6x	f(x)
−4	8 + 6(−4)	−16
−2	8 + 6(−2)	−4
2	8 + 6(2)	20
4	8 + 6(4)	−32

17. Domain: $\{-5, -3, -1, 4\}$;
Range: $\{-45, -27, -9, 36\}$

x	9x	f(x)
−5	9(−5)	−45
−3	9(−3)	−27
−1	9(−1)	−9
4	9(4)	36

19. $f(x) = x + 10$; 30 laps   **21.** 18.5

23 $f(x) = x + 25$ Write the function.

x	x + 25	f(x)
10	10 + 25	35
15	15 + 25	40
20	20 + 25	45
25	25 + 25	50

Adding the bake time and the prep time gives the total time to make the cake

$f(20) = 20 + 25$ Substitute 20 for x.
$f(20) = 45$ Simplify.
It takes 45 minutes to make the cake.

25. Sample answer: $f(x) = -3x - 8$;
$f(0) = -8, f(-5) = 7, f(4) = -20$ **27.** Sample
answer: Gabe has $35 to spend and decides to
purchase some downloaded music at $0.99 per
song. In this case, the function represents how
much money he has left after purchasing x songs.
29. H

**31a. Time It Takes Dale to Run
Each Mile of a 5-Mile Run**

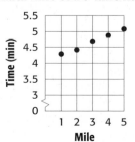

31b. Sample
answer: It takes
Dale a little bit
longer to run each
successive mile of
the 5-mile run.
31c. Sample answer:
5 min 10 s
33. −40   **35.** 24

Pages 745–749   Lesson 13-2B

1.

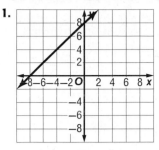

3.

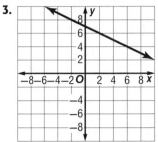

5a. $71.40   **5b.** discrete

7 Create a table of values to plot on the graph.

x	y
0	3
1	2
2	1
3	0

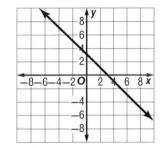

9.

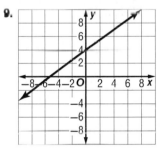

11 **a.** Make a table to find the total earnings.

Number of Hours	Total Earnings ($)
1	9.50
2	19.00
3	28.50
4	38.00
5	47.50
6	57.00
7	66.50

After 7 hours, she will earn
$66.50.   **b.** These data
would be continuous
because she can work for
part of an hour.

13. Sample answer: continuous: height of a
building, weight of a person; discrete: number of
students in a class, number of cars on the road
17. H   **19.** −42   **21.** circle graph   **23.** $58.44

Pages 752–753 **Lesson 13-2C**

1. 1; 7   **3.** 5; 8

5 Create a table of values to plot on the graph.

x	y
0	$\frac{1}{6}$
1	$-\frac{1}{12}$
2	$-\frac{1}{3}$
3	$-\frac{7}{12}$

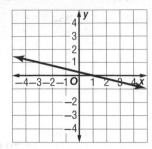

7a.

Admission Costs   ; $41

7b. Slope: the cost to ride one ride, $2; y-intercept: the admission fee, $25   **9.** −3; 7   **11.** $-\frac{3}{8}$; $-\frac{5}{8}$ **13.** −2; 9

15.

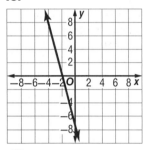

17.

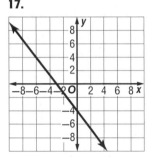

19 Create a table of values to plot on the graph.

x	y
0	6.5
1	3.5
2	0.5
3	−2.5

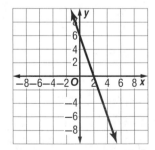

21a.

Fabric

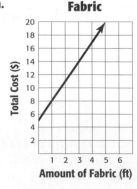

21b. The y-intercept represents the $5 cost to cut the fabric only.

23. Sample answer: The equation must be in slope-intercept form to find the slope and y-intercept. $m = -\frac{3}{4}$ and $b = \frac{5}{4}$

25. B

27.

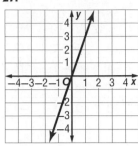

29.

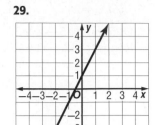

31. 68°F

Pages 758–760 **Lesson 13-3B**

1 The equation is nonlinear because the power of x is greater than 1.

3. Linear; the rate of change is constant, as x increases by 1, y increases by 5.   **5.** Yes; the rate of change is constant.   **7.** Linear; It can be written in the form $y = 0.25x + 0$.   **9.** Nonlinear; The power x is greater than 1.   **11.** Nonlinear; x is in the denominator, so the equation cannot be written in the form $y = mx + b$.   **13.** Linear; rate of change is constant; as x increases by 2, y increases by 3.   **15.** Linear; rate of change is constant; as x increases by 5, y decreases by 6.   **17.** Nonlinear; rate of change is not constant.   **19.** No; the rate of change is not constant.

21 The table of values is linear to the number of quarters because the rate of change is constant. As x increases by 1, y increases by 15.

23. No; the rate of change is not constant.   **25.** No; the graphs of vertical lines are not functions because there is more than one value of y that corresponds to x = 5.   **29.** H   **31a.** $55   **31b.** discrete

Pages 764–765 **Lesson 13-4A**

1. 6^9 **3.** $\left(\frac{2}{3}\right)^9$ **5.** $-12c^8$

7 $\frac{4^7}{4^3} = 4^{7-3}$ The common base is 4.

    $= 4^4$ Subtract the exponents.

9. $2t^3$ **11.** 5^{10} **13.** $\left(\frac{1}{5}\right)^5$ **15.** 7^8 **17.** n^3 **19.** $18j^4k^{13}$

21. $14h^{11}$ **23.** $24x^{12}$ **25.** $42p^{16}$ **27.** 8^5 **29.** c^3 **31.** x

33. $10n^5$ **35.** 4^5 or 1,024 fish

37 **a.** $\frac{10^{12}}{10^6} = 10^{12-6}$ The common base is 10. Division is used to find how many times greater one number is than another.

    $= 10^6$ Subtract the exponents.

One trillion is 10^6 times as great as one million.

b. $\frac{10^{18}}{10^9} = 10^{18-9}$ The common base is 10. Division is used to find how many times greater one number is than another.

    $= 10^9$ Subtract the exponents.

One quintillion is 10^9 times as great as one billion.

39. Equal; sample answer: Using the quotient of powers, $\frac{4^{200}}{4^{199}} = 4^{200-199}$, or 4^1, which is 4. **41.** A
43. $42x^9$ ft² **45.** Nonlinear; the power of x is greater than 1. **47.** Nonlinear; the power of x is greater than 1. **49.** $\frac{1}{3}$; 6 **51.** $-\frac{1}{4}$; 3 **53.** $\frac{7}{15}$

Pages 768–769   Lesson 13-4B

1. $\frac{1}{5^2}$

3 $t^{-10} = \frac{1}{t^{10}}$ Definition of a negative exponent

5. 3^{-4} **7.** 7^{-2} **9.** h^2 **11.** r **13.** 10^{-6} **15.** $\frac{1}{5^3}$
17. $\frac{1}{(-3)^3}$ **19.** $\frac{1}{10^4}$ **21.** $\frac{1}{a^{10}}$ **23.** $\frac{1}{q^4}$ **25.** $\frac{1}{x^2}$
27. 5^{-5} **29.** k^{-2} **31.** 9^{-2} or 3^{-4} **33.** 2^{-4} or 4^{-2}
35. g^{-2} **37.** $15v^{-5}$ **39.** k^{-1} or $\frac{1}{k}$ **41.** $9c^{-4}$ or $\frac{9}{c^4}$
43. 10^{-2} **45.** 10^{-5}

47 Penicillin molecules have a greater mass because -18 is greater than -23.

$\frac{10^{-18}}{10^{-23}} = 10^{-18-(-23)}$ The common base is 10. Division is used to find how many times greater one number is than another.

$= 10^5$ Subtract the exponents.

The mass of a penicillin molecule is 10^5 times greater than the mass of an insulin molecule.
49. $8^{-8}, 8^0, 8^3$; 8^{-8} is $\frac{1}{8^8}$. This is a very small number between 0 and 1. 8^0 is 1 and 8^3 is 8 multiplied by itself 3 times.

51. They are multiplicative inverses. Sample answer: 4^{-3} and 4^3 are multiplicative inverses because $4^{-3} = \frac{1}{4^3}$ and $\frac{1}{4^3} \times \frac{4^3}{1} = 1$. **53.** B **55.** 3^7 **57.** 5^3
59. Nonlinear; the power of r is greater than 1.

Pages 772–774   Lesson 13-4C

1. 375,400 **3.** 0.00015

5 $4,510,000 = 4.51 \times 1,000,000$ The decimal point moves 6 places.

$= 4.51 \times 10^6$ The exponent is positive.

7. 9.2×10^{-5} **9.** 3×10^5 **11.** $>$ **13.** 61,000
15. 0.33 **17.** 0.09014 **19.** 2,505 **21.** 0.001
23. 4.99×10^5 **25.** 6×10^{-3} **27.** 5×10^7
29. 7.8×10^{-5} **31.** 3×10^9 **33a.** golf **33b.** golf
35. $<$ **37.** $=$ **39.** 3.2×10^{-8}

41 a. The Mount St. Helens eruption is one power of ten or 10 times greater than the Ngauruhoe eruption.
b. Since the powers of ten for both eruptions are the same, we can compare the eruptions by comparing 4 and 2. The Hekla eruption was 2 times greater than the Ngauruhoe eruption.
43. 48,396

45a. $\frac{(4.2 \times 10^5)(1.5 \times 10^{-2})}{(2.5 \times 10^{-2})}$; 2.52×10^5; 252,000
45b. $\frac{(7.8 \times 10^{-2})(8.5 \times 10^0)}{(1.6 \times 10^{-1})(2.5 \times 10^5)}$; 1.6575×10^{-5}; 0.000016575

47. Sample answer: The distance between Earth and the Sun is 1.55×10^8 km or 155,000,000 km. **49.** D **51a.** $\frac{1}{125}$ **51b.** $\frac{1}{729}$ in.
53a. $\frac{17}{100}$ in. **53b.** $\frac{7}{25}$ in.

Pages 775–779   Study Guide and Review

1. continuous **3.** linear function **5.** straight
7. scientific notation **9.** power **11.** 10 h **13.** $m < 6$
15. $x \le 4\frac{1}{4}$ **17.** $120 + w \le 180$; The athlete can lift at most an additional 60 pounds. **19.** $w \le 7.2$
21. $y \ge -7$ **23.** -13 **25.** 9

27.

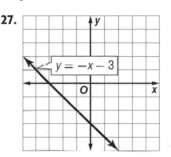

29. Hank can buy 0 regular and 4 large, 2 regular and 3 large, 4 regular and 2 large, 6 regular and 1 large, or 8 regular and 0 large drinks.

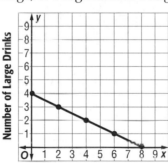

Number of Regular Drinks

31. $-\frac{1}{6}$; 3 **33.** -8; -10 **35.** Linear; it can be written as $y = 6x + 8$. **37.** Nonlinear; the rate of change is not constant. **39.** b^7 **41.** $\frac{4}{25}s^8$ **43.** c^7 **45.** $-7g$
47. 179 square feet **49.** $\frac{1}{3^5}$ **51.** $\frac{1}{m^2}$ **53.** $2^{-6}, 4^{-3}$, or 8^{-2} **55.** h^{-8} **57.** 2,080 **59.** 0.000076 **61.** 2.7×10^{-4}
63. 1.04×10^7

Photo Credits

Cover i Tim Pannell/Masterfile; iv (tl, tr) Glencoe/McGraw-Hill, (bl, br) McGraw-Hill Companies; v (l to r, t to b) McGraw-Hill Companies, (2, 4, 8) Aaron Haupt, (3, 5–7, 9) McGraw-Hill Companies, (10) File Photo; vi John Coletti/age fotostock; x–xi Masterfile Royalty-Free; xii–xiii Pixtal/SuperStock; xiv–xv Fritz Liedtke/Alamy; xvi–xvii Winfried Wisniewski/Getty Images; xviii–xix Photodisc/Getty Images; xx–xxi Masterfile Royalty-Free; xxii (t) Robert Landau/CORBIS, (b) Comstock/JupiterImages, (bkgd) Royalty-Free/CORBIS; xxiv–xxv Stockbyte/Getty Images; xxvi Jose Luis Pelaez, Inc./age fotostock; xxvii Digital Vision/Getty Images; 2 (tl) M. Timothy O'Keefe/Alamy, (tr) Visuals Unlimited/CORBIS, (b) Jamie Squire/Getty Images; 3 (t) Richard Broadwell/Alamy, (c) Buzz Pictures/SuperStock, (b) Wes Thompson/CORBIS; 4 (t) NASA/Photo Researchers, Inc., (b) Photodisc/Getty Images; 5 Ilene MacDonald/Alamy; 8 Grant Faint/Getty Images; 10 John Rawsterne/Alamy; 14 Goodshoot/PunchStock; 16 DreamPictures/Getty Images; 17 R. Stockli, A. Nelson, F. Hasler, NASA/GSFC/NOAA/USGS; 19 Brand X Pictures/PunchStock; 20 Joe Klamar/AFP/Getty Images; 29 Chase Jarvis/CORBIS; 35 Mike Parry/Minden Pictures; 45 altrendo travel/Getty Images; 48 NASA/Photodisc/Getty Images; 52 John Evans; 53 Prisma/SuperStock; 56 Joanne Schmaltz/Getty Images; 58 Ralph White/CORBIS; 63 Lothar Lenz/zefa/CORBIS; 66 (inset) Francis Specker/epa/CORBIS; 66–67 (bkgd) NASA; 82 Comstock/SuperStock; 85 Inga Spence/age fotostock; 86 John Wilkes/SuperStock; 88 United States coin images from the United States Mint; 90 Pixtal/SuperStock; 98 Thomas Northcut/Photodisc/Getty Images; 100 Susumu Nishinaga/Photo Researchers; 104 Diane Macdonald/Stockbyte/Getty Images; 114 Garry Black/Masterfile; 118 KS Studios; 119 Michael Newman/PhotoEdit; 123 Phyllis Greenberg/Animals Animals—Earth Scenes; 128 Stefano Bianchetti/CORBIS; 129 moodboard/Alamy; 130 (inset) Masterfile; 130–131 (bkgd) Gallo Images/Getty Images; 144 John Evans; 147 David Young-Wolff/PhotoEdit; 151 Stephen Frink/zefa/CORBIS; 153 Eddie Adams/Sygma/CORBIS; 154 Streeter Lecka/Stringer/Getty Images; 158 Jose Luis Pelaez, Inc./Blend Images/Getty Images; 164 Stewart Cohen/Pam Ostrow; 170 (inset) Getty Images, (bkgd) Ryan McVay/Getty Images; 174 John Eder/Stone/Getty Images; 178 Burke/Triolo/Brand X Pictures; 182 (inset) National Geographic/Getty Images; 182–183 (bkgd) Masterfile Royalty-Free; 195 Dave & Les Jacobs/Getty Images; 196 David Young-Wolff/PhotoEdit; 198 Doug Menuez/Photodisc/Getty Images; 200 Don Emmert/AFP/Getty Images; 202 CORBIS Premium RF/Alamy; 204 age fotostock/SuperStock; 206 Stockbyte/Getty Images; 207 Jeff Greenberg/PhotoEdit; 211 age fotostock/SuperStock; 212 Jose Luis Pelaez, Inc./Getty Images; 219 Bilderbuch/Design Pics/CORBIS; 225 Getty Images; 231 Fritz Liedtke/Alamy; 233 Mimmo Jodice/CORBIS; 234 (inset) AP Photo/Paramount's Kings Island, Rick Norton; 234–235 (bkgd) Gunter Marx/Alamy; 249 Eric and David Hosking/CORBIS; 251 IT Stock Free/Alamy; 257 Ullamaija Hanninen/Getty Images; 264 Paul Carstairs/Alamy; 270 Gabe Palmer/Alamy Images; 274 C Squared Studios/Getty Images; 277 Tetra Images/Getty Images; 281 Photodisc/Getty Images; 284 (inset) Philippe Psaila/Photo Researchers, Inc.; 284–285 (bkgd) Tony West/Alamy; 298 Tim Platt/Getty Images; 300 DLILLC/CORBIS; 307 Ariel Skelley/CORBIS; 310 Winfried Wisniewski/Getty Images; 312 Ingemar Edfalk/Pixonnet.com/Alamy Images; 314 Donna Ikenberry/Animals Animals—Earth Scenes; 315 Digital Vision/Getty Images; 319 ©2009 Arend/Smith/Alaskastock.com; 322 Adrian Peacock/Digital Vision/Getty Images; 326 Tom Carter/PhotoEdit; 328 Ryan McVay/Getty Images; 332 Big Cheese Photo/SuperStock; 335 Wolfgang Kaehler/Alamy; 340 Mark Scheuern/Alamy; 344 (inset) Picture Contact/Alamy; 344–345 (bkgd) Masterfile Royalty-Free; 359 Stephen Dalton/Animals Animals—Earth Scenes; 367 Digital Vision/PunchStock; 370 Barbara Peacock/Taxi/Getty Images; 371 Gray Martimore/Getty Images; 373 Brandon D. Cole/CORBIS; 376 Bettmann/CORBIS; 383 Big Cheese Photo/JupiterImages; 384 Tom Hauck/Getty Images; 388 O'Brien Productions/CORBIS; 395 David Muir/Masterfile; 398 (inset) Bob Krist/CORBIS; 398–399 (bkgd) Stephen Frink/CORBIS; 406 Laura Sifferlin; 414 CORBIS; 432 (l) Digital Vision/Getty Images, (r) Andre Jenny/Alamy; 433 Brand X Pictures/PunchStock; 436 Keate/Masterfile; 439 Tony Freeman/PhotoEdit; 440 Duncan Usher/Foto Natura/Minden Pictures; 445 Photodisc/Getty Images; 446 (l) Mitch Hrdlicka/Getty Images, (r) SuperStock, Inc./SuperStock; 450 (l) Laurence Dutton/Getty Images, (r) The McGraw-Hill Companies; 455 The McGraw-Hill Companies; 463 W.A. Hamilton/Alamy; 469 Paul Taylor/Getty Images; 474 (inset) Hemis/Alamy; 474–475 (bkgd) John Lamb/Getty Images; 476 Jim Esposito Photography LLC/Photodisc/Getty Images; 480 The McGraw-Hill Companies; 481 Image Source/Getty Images; 498 Jon Feingersh/Getty Images; 500 John Lambert/Brand X/CORBIS; 506 Comstock/PunchStock; 507 Bruce Edwards/America 24-7/Getty Images; 509 Stan Honda/AFP/Getty Images; 510 View Stock/Alamy; 515 Tom Vezo/Minden Pictures; 524 Laura Sifferlin; 528 Brand X Pictures/PunchStock; 529 The McGraw-Hill Companies, Inc./Jacques Cornell photographer; 530 Mark Ransom; 532 Monica Flatford/Knoxville Convention Center; 534 (inset) Pixtal/SuperStock; 534–535 (bkgd) Mark Tomalty/Masterfile; 558 Don Emmert/AFP/Getty Images; 560 (tl) Liu Liqun/CORBIS, (tr) Daryl Benson/Masterfile, (cl) Allen Wallace/Photonica/Getty Images; 567 newstream rf/Alamy; 572 Adam Hart-Davis/Photo Researchers; 574 BARNpix.com/Alamy Images; 576 Image Source/PunchStock; 578 Jon Feingersh/Getty Images; FL0 Medioimages/Photodisc/Getty Images; 588 (t) Robert Landau/CORBIS, (c) Royalty-Free/CORBIS, (b) Photofusion Picture Library/Alamy; 589 (l) AP Photos/Mark Humphrey, (r) Comstock/JupiterImages; 590 Robert Landau/CORBIS; 591 John A. Karachewski; 592 Royalty-Free/CORBIS; 593 Ron Chapple/Thinkstock/Getty Images; 594 Photofusion Picture Library/Alamy; 595 Andrea Pistolesi/Getty Images; 596 AP Photos/Mark Humphrey; 597 J. Meric/Getty Images; 598 Comstock/JupiterImages; 599 Gary Randall/Getty Images; 604 Michael Clark/Getty Images; 606 Chase Jarvis/Getty Images; 608 (l) Charles Smith/CORBIS, (r) Image Source/Getty Images; 617 Lelah James/The McGraw-Hill Companies; 618 Jeff Greenberg/PhotoEdit; 620 (l) Damir Frkovic/Masterfile, (r) DeCordova Museum and Sculpture Park; 622 Ryan McVay/Photodisc/Getty Images; 626 (l) David Pollack/CORBIS, (r) Mark Gibson; 638 (inset) Stewart Cohen/Pam Ostrow/Getty Images; 638–639 (bkgd) Buzz Pictures/Alamy; 642 Lawrence Manning/CORBIS; 647 DEA/M. Bertinetti/Getty Images; 651 (l) age fotostock/SuperStock, (r) Ambient Images Inc./Alamy; 655 Lester Lefkowitz/CORBIS; 656 Robert Yin/CORBIS; 663 Dynamic Graphics Group/Creatas/Alamy; 681 Noel Hendrickson/Masterfile; 688 Bob Daemmrich/PhotoEdit; 690 Masterfile; 693 Doug Pensinger/Getty Images; 696 Royalty-Free/CORBIS; 697 Eric Baccega/age fotostock; 699 The McGraw-Hill Companies, Inc./Ken Cavanagh photographer; 706 Karen Whylie/Masterfile; 710 Getty Images/Digital Vision; 712 (inset) Mark Burnett/Alamy; 712–713 (bkgd) Brian Sytnyk/Masterfile; 726 Kevin Peterson/Photodisc/Getty Images; 730 LMR Group/Alamy; 738 (inset) Denkou Images GmbH/SuperStock; 738–739 (bkgd) Stockbyte/Getty Images; 740 Masterfile; 743 Stephen Frink/Getty Images; 763 Jose Luis Pelaez, Inc./Getty Images; 765 Andrew Holt/Getty Images; 767 Prisma/SuperStock; 770 Charles O'Rear/CORBIS; 771 Chris A. Crumley/Alamy Images; 772–773 Jose Luis Pelaez, Inc./age fotostock.

Glossary

Arabic	Cantonese	Hmong	Spanish	Urdu
Bengali	English	Korean	Tagalog	Vietnamese
Brazilian Portuguese	Haitian Creole	Russian		

English

Aa

absolute value (p. 30)   The distance the number is from zero on a number line.

acute angle (p. 604)   An angle with a measure greater than 0° and less than 90°.

acute triangle (p. 617)   A triangle having three acute angles.

Addition Property of Equality (p. 152) If you add the same number to each side of an equation, the two sides remain equal.

additive inverse (p. 41)   Two integers that are opposites. The sum of an integer and its additive inverse is zero.

Spanish
(Español)

valor absoluto   Distancia a la que se encuentra un número de cero en la recta numérica.

ángulo agudo   Ángulo que mide más de 0° y menos de 90°.

triángulo acutángulo   Triángulo con tres ángulos agudos.

propiedad de adición de la igualdad Si sumas el mismo número a ambos lados de una ecuación, los dos lados permanecen iguales.

inverso aditivo   Dos enteros opuestos.

Haitian Creole
(Kreyòl ayisyen)

valè absoli   Distans yon chif parapò a zewo sou yon dwat nimerik.

ang egi   Yon ang ak yon inite mezi pi gran pase 0° epi mwens pase 90°.

triyang egi   Yon triyang ki gen twa ang egi.

Pwopriyete egalite nan adisyon   Si ou adisyonnen menm chif lan nan chak bò yon ekwasyon, de bò yo ap rete egal.

envès aditif   Opoze yon antye relatif. Sòm yon antye relatif ak envès aditif li a bay zewo.

adjacent angles (p. 605) Angles that have the same vertex, share a common side, and do not overlap.

alternate exterior angles (p. 610) Angles that are on opposite sides of the transversal and outside the parallel lines.

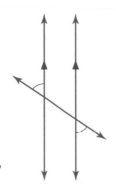

alternate interior angles (p. 610) Angles that are on opposite sides of the transversal and inside the parallel lines.

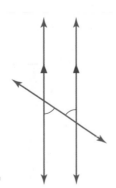

angle (p. 604) Two rays with a common endpoint form an angle. The rays and vertex are used to name the angle.

∠ABC, ∠CBA, or ∠B

angle of rotation (p. 563) The degree measure of the angle through which the figure is rotated.

ángulos adyacentes Ángulos que comparten el mismo vértice y un común lado, pero no se sobreponen.

ángulos alternos externos Ángulos en lados opuestos de la trasversal y afuera de las rectas paralelas.

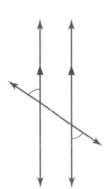

ángulos alternos internos Ángulos en lados opuestos de la trasversal y dentro de las rectas paralelas.

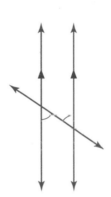

ángulo Dos rayos con un extremo común forman un ángulo. Los rayos y el vértice se usan para nombrar el ángulo.

∠ABC, ∠CBA o ∠B

ángulo de rotación Medida en grados del ángulo sobre el cual se rota una figura.

ang adjasan Ang ki gen menm somè, pataje yon kote an komen, epi yo pa monte youn sou lòt.

ang altèn ekstèn Ang ki sou kote opoze transvèsal la e ki sou deyò dwat paralèl yo.

ang altèn entèn Ang ki sou kote opoze transvèsal la e ki sou anndan dwat paralèl yo.

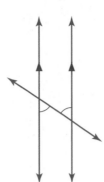

ang De demidwat ak yon ekstremite an komen fòme yon ang. Se demidwat yo ak somè a ki bay ang lan non l.

∠ABC, ∠CBA, oswa ∠B

ang wotasyon Mezi degre ang lan kote figi a ap fè wotasyon.

English

Bb

bar notation (p. 81)   In repeating decimals, the line or bar placed over the digits that repeat. For example, $2.\overline{63}$ indicates that the digits 63 repeat.

base (p. 126)   In a power, the number used as a factor. In 10^3, the base is 10. That is, $10^3 = 10 \times 10 \times 10$.

biased sample (p. 415)   A sample drawn in such a way that one or more parts of the population are favored over others.

box-and-whisker plot (p. 693)   A diagram that is constructed using the median, quartiles, and extreme values.

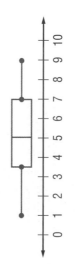

Cc

center (p. 570)   A fixed point used for measurement when altering the size of a figure.

Spanish (Español)

notación de barra   Línea o barra que se coloca sobre los dígitos que se repiten en decimales periódicos. Por ejemplo, $2.\overline{63}$ indica que los dígitos 63 se repiten.

base   En una potencia, el número usado como factor. En 10^3, la base es 10. Es decir, $10^3 = 10 \times 10 \times 10$.

muestra sesgada   Muestra en que se favorece una o más partes de una población.

diagrama de caja y patillas   Diagrama que se construye usando la mediana, los cuartiles y los valores extremos.

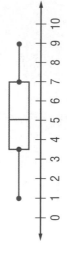

centro   Punto dado que se usa en medición cuando se altera el tamaño de una figura.

Haitian Creole (Kreyòl ayisyen)

trè notasyon   Nan desimal peryodik, dwat la oswa liy lan ki plase anlè chif ki repete yo. Pa egzanp, $2.\overline{63}$ endike ke desimal 63 a repete endefiniman.

baz   Nan yon pisans, nonm yo itilize antanke yon faktè. Nan 10^3, baz la se 10. Sètadi, $10^3 = 10 \times 10 \times 10$.

echantiyon byeze   Yon echantiyon kote youn oswa plizyè seksyon nan popilasyon an favorize pase lòt.

dyagram bwat-ak-moustach   Yon dyagram yo konstwi annitilizan medyàn lan, kwatil yo, ak valè ekstrèm yo.

sant   Yon pwen fiks yo itilize pou pran mezi lè yap chanje dimansyon yon figi.

circle graph (p. 358) A graph that shows data as parts of a whole. In a circle graph, the percents add up to 100.

Area of Oceans

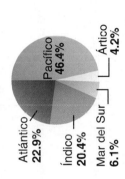

Atlantic 22.9%
Pacific 46.4%
Indian 20.4%
Southern 6.1%
Arctic 4.2%

coefficient (p. 157) The numerical factor of a term that contains a variable.

common denominator (p. 86) A common multiple of the denominators of two or more fractions. 24 is a common denominator for $\frac{1}{3}$, $\frac{5}{8}$, and $\frac{3}{4}$ because 24 is the LCM of 3, 8, and 4.

complementary angles (p. 605) Two angles are complementary if the sum of their measures is 90°.

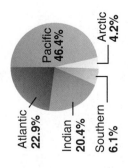

∠1 and ∠2 are complementary angles.

complementary events (p. 377) The events of one outcome happening and that outcome not happening. The sum of the probabilities of an event and its complement is 1 or 100%. In symbols, $P(A) + P(not\ A) = 1$.

---

gráfica circular Gráfica que muestra los datos como partes de un todo. En una gráfica circular los porcentajes suman 100.

Área de superficie de los océanos

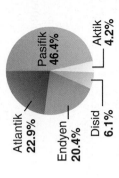

Atlántico 22.9%
Pacífico 46.4%
Índico 20.4%
Mar del Sur 6.1%
Ártico 4.2%

coeficiente El factor numérico de un término que contiene una variable.

común denominador El múltiplo común de los denominadores de dos o más fracciones. 24 es un denominador común para $\frac{1}{3}$, $\frac{5}{8}$ y $\frac{3}{4}$ porque 24 es el mcm de 3, 8 y 4.

ángulos complementarios Dos ángulos son complementarios si la suma de sus medidas es 90°.

∠1 y ∠2 son complementarios.

eventos complementarios Los eventos de un resultado que ocurre y ese resultado que no ocurre. La suma de las probabilidades de un evento y su complemento es 1 ó 100%. En símbolos $P(A) + P(no\ A) = 1$.

---

grafik sikilè Yon grafik ki montre done yo antanke pati yon ansanm. Nan yon grafik sikilè, pousan yo adisyonen pou yo bay 100.

Sipèfisi Oseyan yo

Atlantik 22.9%
Pasifik 46.4%
Endyen 20.4%
Disid 6.1%
Aktik 4.2%

koyefisyan Faktè nimerik yon tèm ki genyen yon varyab ladan l.

denominatè komen Yon miltip komen pou denominatè yo pou de oswa plis fraksyon. 24 se denominatè komen pou $\frac{1}{3}$, $\frac{5}{8}$ ak $\frac{3}{4}$ paske 24 se PPMK a pou 3, 8, ak 4.

ang konplemantè De ang konplemantè si sòm mezi yo se 90°.

∠1 ak ∠2 se ang konplemantè.

evènman konplemantè Evènman kote gen yon rezilta kap fèt epi menm rezilta sa a pa fèt, se evènman konplemantè. Sòm pwobabilite yon evènman ak pwobabilite konpleman l bay 1 oswa 100%. Sou fòm senbòl, yo ekri $P(A) + P(ki\ pa\ A) = 1$.

English

composite figure (p. 478)   A figure that is made up of two or more three-dimensional figures.

compound event (p. 391)   An event consisting of two or more simple events.

cone (p. 449)   A three-dimensional figure with a curved surface and a circular base.

congruent angles (p. 604)   Angles that have the same measure.

∠1 and ∠2 are congruent angles.

congruent figures (p. 548)   Figures that have the same size and same shape and corresponding sides and angles with equal measure.

congruent segments (p. 617)   Sides with the same length.

Side $\overline{AB}$ is congruent to side $\overline{BC}$.

Spanish (Español)

figura compuesta   Figura formada por dos o más figuras tridimensionales.

evento compuesto   Un evento que consiste en dos o más eventos simples.

cono   Figura tridimensional con una superficie curva y una base circular.

ángulos congruentes   Ángulos que tienen la misma medida.

∠1 y ∠2 son congruentes.

figuras congruentes   Figuras que tienen el mismo tamaño y la misma forma y los lados y los ángulos correspondientes tienen igual medida.

segmentos congruentes   Lados con la misma longitud.

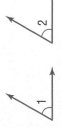

$\overline{AB}$ es congruente a $\overline{BC}$.

Haitian Creole (Kreyòl ayisyen)

fòm konpoze   Yon fòm ki konpoze de de oswa plis fòm twa-dimansyon.

evènman konpoze   Yon evènman ki gen de oubyen plis evènman senp.

kòn   Yon figi twa-dimansyon ak yon sifas koub epi yon baz sikilè.

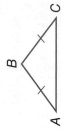

ang kongriyan   Ang ki gen menm mezi.

∠1 ak ∠2 se ang kongriyan.

figi kongriyan   Figi ki gen menm dimansyon ak menm fòm epi dè kote ak ang korespondan ki gen menm mezi.

segman kongriyan   Kote ki gen menm longè.

Kote $\overline{AB}$ kongriyan a kote $\overline{BC}$.

constant of variation (p. 273) The constant ratio in a direct variation.

constant rate of change (p. 260) The rate of change in a linear relationship.

continuous data (p. 747) Data that take on any real number value. It can be determined by considering what numbers are reasonable as part of the domain.

convenience sample (p. 415) A sample which consists of members of a population that are easily accessed.

coordinate plane (p. 33) A plane in which a horizontal number line and a vertical number line intersect at their zero points. Also called a coordinate grid.

corresponding angles (p. 223) The angles of similar figures that "match."

corresponding sides (p. 223) The sides of similar figures that "match."

cross product (p. 206) The product of the numerator of one ratio and the denominator of the other ratio. The cross products of any proportion are equal.

cubed (p. 126) The product in which a number is a factor three times. Two cubed is 8 because $2 \times 2 \times 2 = 8$.

---

constante de variación Razón constante en una variación directa.

razón constante de cambio Tasa de cambio en una relación lineal.

datos continuos Datos que asumen cualquier valor numérico real. Se pueden determinar al considerar qué números son razonables como parte del dominio.

muestra de conveniencia Muestra que incluye miembros de una población fácilmente accesibles.

plano de coordenadas Plano en el cual se han trazado dos rectas numéricas, una horizontal y una vertical, que se intersecan en sus puntos cero. También conocido como sistema de coordenadas.

ángulos correspondientes Ángulos de figuras semejantes que coinciden.

lados correspondientes Lados de figuras semejantes que coinciden.

producto cruzado Producto del numerador de una razón por el denominador de la otra razón. Los productos cruzados de cualquier proporción son iguales.

al cubo El producto de un número por sí mismo, tres veces. Dos al cubo es 8 porque $2 \times 2 \times 2 = 8$.

---

konstant pou pwopòsyonalite Rapò konstan an nan yon varyasyon dirèk.

to varyasyon konstan To varyasyon nan yon relasyon lineyè.

done kontini Done ki pran nenpòt valè nonm reyèl. Yo ka detèmine l lè yo konsidere ki nonm ki konvni antanke pati nan domèn nan.

echantiyon ki konvni Yon echantiyon manm popilasyon ki fasil pou jwenn.

plan kowòdone Yon plan kote dwat nimerik orizontal la ak dwat nimerik vètikal la entèsekte nan pwen zewo yo. Yo rele l tou yon plan katezyen.

ang korespondan Ang kongriyan ki gen menm figi.

kote korespondan Kote kongriyan oswa pwopòsyonèl ki gen menm figi.

pwodwi katezyen Pwodwi nimeratè yon rapò ak denominatè lòt rapò a. Pwodwi katezyen nenpòt pwopòsyon egal antreyo.

okib Pwodwi kote yon nonm se yon faktè an twa fwa. De okib se 8 paske $2 \times 2 \times 2 = 8$.

English

cylinder (p. 438)   A three-dimensional figure with two parallel congruent circular bases.

Dd

decagon (p. 630)   A polygon having ten sides.

degrees (p. 604)   The most common unit of measure for angles. If a circle were divided into 360 equal-sized parts, each part would have an angle measure of 1 degree.

dependent events (p. 392)   Two or more events in which the outcome of one event affects the outcome of the other event(s).

dilation (p. 570)   The image produced by enlarging or reducing a figure.

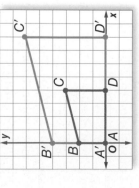

Spanish   (Español)

cilindro   Figura tridimensional que tiene dos bases circulares congruentes y paralelas.

decágono   Un polígono con diez lados.

grados   La unidad más común para medir ángulos. Si un círculo se divide en 360 partes iguales, cada parte tiene una medida angular de 1 grado.

eventos dependientes   Dos o más eventos en que el resultado de un evento afecta el resultado de otro u otros eventos.

homotecia   Imagen producida al ampliar o reducir una figura.

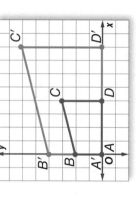

Haitian Creole   (Kreyòl ayisyen)

silenn   Yon figi twa-dimansyon ki gen de baz sikilè paralèl ki kongriyan.

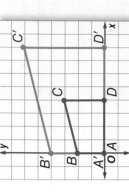

dekagòn   Yon poligòn ki gen dis kote.

degre   Inite mezi ki pi komen nan mezi ang yo. Si yo ta divize yon sèk an 360 pati egal, chak pati ta gen yon ang ki mezire 1 degre.

evènman depandan   De oubyen plis evènman kote rezilta yon evènman gen efè sou rezilta lòt evènman an(yo).

dilatasyon   Imaj ki pwodwi lè yo elaji oswa redwi yon figi.

direct variation (p. 273)   The relationship between two variable quantities that have a constant ratio.

discount (p. 335)   The amount by which the regular price of an item is reduced.

discrete data (p. 747)   When solutions of a function are only integer values. It can be determined by considering what numbers are reasonable as part of the domain.

Division Property of Equality (p. 157)   If you divide each side of an equation by the same nonzero number, the two sides remain equal.

domain (p. 248)   The set of input values for a function.

Ee

enlargement (p. 571)   An image larger than the original.

equation (p. 150)   A mathematical sentence that contains an equals sign, =, stating that two quantities are equal.

equiangular (p. 631)   In a polygon, all of the angles are congruent.

equilateral (p. 631)   In a polygon, all of the sides are congruent.

variación directa   Relación entre las cantidades de dos variables que tienen una tasa constante.

descuento   Cantidad que se le rebaja al precio regular de un artículo.

datos discretos   Cuando las soluciones de una función son solo valores enteros. Se pueden determinar considerando qué números son razonables como parte del dominio.

propiedad de igualdad de la división   Si divides ambos lados de una ecuación entre el mismo número no nulo, los lados permanecen iguales.

dominio   El conjunto de valores de entrada de una función.

ampliación   Imagen más grande que la original.

ecuación   Enunciado matemático que contiene el signo de igualdad = indicando que dos cantidades son iguales.

equiangular   En un polígono, todos los ángulos son congruentes.

equilátero   En un polígono, todos los lados son congruentes.

varyasyon dirèk   Relasyon ant de kantite varyab ki gen yon rapò konstan.

rabè   Montan ki reprezante rediksyon sou pri nòmal yon atik.

done diskrè   Lè solisyon yon fonksyon se valè antye relatif yo ye sèlman. Yo ka detèmine l lè yo konsidere ki nonm ki konvni antanke pati nan domèn nan.

Pwopriyete egalite nan divizyon   Si ou divize chak bò yon ekwasyon ak menm chif ki pa zewo an, de bò yo ap rete egal.

domèn   Ansanm premye chif yo nan yon fonksyon.

agrandisman   Yon imaj ki pi gwo pase imaj orijinal la.

ekwasyon   Yon fraz matematik ki genyen ladan l yon siy egal, =, ki deklare ke de kantite egal.

ekiyangilè   Nan yon poligòn, tout ang yo kongriyan.

ekilateral   Nan yon poligòn, tout kote yo kongriyan.

Glossary **R53**

English

equilateral triangle (p. 617) A triangle having three congruent sides.

equivalent equations (p. 150) Two or more equations with the same solution.

equivalent ratios (p. 206) Two ratios that have the same value.

experimental probability (p. 401) An estimated probability based on the relative frequency of positive outcomes occurring during an experiment. It is based on what *actually* occurred during such an experiment.

exponent (p. 126) In a power, the number that tells how many times the base is used as a factor. In 5^3, the exponent is 3. That is, $5^3 = 5 \times 5 \times 5$.

exponential form (p. 127) Numbers written with exponents.

Ff

factors (p. 126) Two or more numbers that are multiplied together to form a product.

fair game (p. 408) A game where each player has an equally likely chance of winning.

Spanish (Español)

triángulo equilátero Triángulo con tres lados congruentes.

ecuaciones equivalentes Dos o más ecuaciones con la misma solución.

razones equivalentes Dos razones que tienen el mismo valor.

probabilidad experimental Probabilidad estimada que se basa en la frecuencia relativa de los resultados positivos que ocurren durante un experimento. Se basa en lo que *en realidad* ocurre durante dicho experimento.

exponente En una potencia, el número que indica las veces que la base se usa como factor. En 5^3, el exponente es 3. Es decir, $5^3 = 5 \times 5 \times 5$.

forma exponencial Números escritos usando exponentes.

factores Dos o más números que se multiplican entre sí para formar un producto.

juego justo Juego donde cada jugador tiene igual posibilidad de ganar.

Haitian Creole (Kreyòl ayisyen)

triyang ekilateral Yon triyang ki gen twa ang kongriyan.

ekwasyon ekivalan De oswa plis ekwasyon ki gen menm solisyon an.

rapò ekivalan De rapò ki gen menm valè.

pwobabilite eksperimantal Yon pwobabilite estimatif baze sou frekans relatif pou plizyè rezilta pozitif rive pandan yon eksperyans. Li baze sou sa ki rive *anreyalite* pandan jande eksperyans sa a.

ekspozan Nan yon pisans, nonm ki endike konbyen fwa yo itilize baz la kòm yon faktè. Nan 5^3, ekspozan an se 3. Sètadi, 53 = 5 × 5 × 5.

fòm eksponansyèl Nonm yo ekri ak ekspozan.

faktè De oswa plis nonm yo miltipliye youn ak lòt pou fòme yon pwodwi.

jwèt ekitab Yon jwèt kote chak jwè gen menm chans egal pou yo ranpòte laviktwa.

formula (p. 159)   An equation that shows the relationship among certain quantities.

fórmula   Ecuación que muestra la relación entre ciertas cantidades.

fòmil   Yon ekwasyon ki mortre relasyon ant sèten kantite.

function (p. 248)   A relationship which assigns exactly one output value for each input value.

función   Relación que asigna exactamente un valor de salida a cada valor de entrada.

fonksyon   Yon relasyon ki deziyen egzakteman yon valè sòti pou chak valè antre.

function notation (p. 740)   A form where the input x is any real number and the output $f(x)$ is read as *the function of x or f of x.*

notación funcional   Forma donde la entrada x es cualquier número real y la salida $f(x)$ se lee como *la función de x o f de x.*

notasyon fonksyonèl   Yon fòm kote antre x la se nenpòt nonm reyèl e kote yo li sòti $f(x)$ la *antanke yon fonksyon x oswa f pou x.*

function rule (p. 248)   The operation performed on the input of a function.

regla de función   Operación que se efectúa en el valor de entrada.

règ fonksyon   Operasyon yo fè ak antre yon fonksyon.

function table (p. 248)   A table used to organize the input numbers, output numbers, and the function rule.

tabla de funciones   Tabla que organiza las entradas, la regla y las salidas de una función.

tab fonksyon   Yon tab ki itilize pou òganize nonm antre yo, rezilta nonm yo, ak règ fonksyon an.

Fundamental Counting Principle (p. 386)   Uses multiplication of the number of ways each event in an experiment can occur to find the number of possible outcomes in a sample space.

Principio Fundamental de Contar   Este principio usa la multiplicación del número de veces que puede ocurrir cada evento en un experimento para calcular el número de posibles resultados en un espacio muestral.

Prensip fondamantal denonbreman   Itilize miltiplikasyon kantite fason chak evènman nan yon esperyans ka rive, pou jwenn kantite rezilta posib nan yon inivè posibilite.

Gg

gram (p. 505)   A unit of mass in the metric system equivalent to 0.001 kilogram. The amount of matter an object can hold.

gramo   Unidad de masa en el sistema métrico que equivale a 0.001 de kilogramo. La cantidad de materia que puede contener un objeto.

gram   Yon inite mas nan sistèm metrik la ki ekivalan a 0,001 kilogram. Kantite matyè yon objè ka kenbe.

graph (p. 29)   The process of placing a point on a number line at its proper location.

graficar   Proceso de dibujar o trazar un punto en una recta numérica en su ubicación correcta.

grafik   Pwosede pou mete yon pwen sou yon dwat nimerik nan bon anplasman l nan.

gratuity (p. 332)   Also known as a tip, it is a small amount of money in return for a service.

gratificación   También conocida como propina. Es una cantidad pequeña de dinero en retribución por un servicio.

poubwa   Yo rele l tou yon tip, se yon ti kantite lajan yo bay pou yon sèvis.

Haitian Creole (Kreyòl ayisyen)

eptagòn Yon poligòn ki gen sèt kote.

egzagòn Yon poligòn ki gen sis kote.

istogram Yon kalite dyagram kolòn itilize pou reprezante done ke yo òganize ann entèval egal.

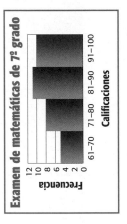

ipoteniz Kote ki opoze ang dwat la nan yon triyang rektang. Se kote ki pi long lan nan yon triyang.

ipoteniz

Spanish (Español)

heptágono Polígono con siete lados.

hexágono Polígono con seis lados.

histograma Tipo de gráfica de barras que se usa para exhibir datos que se han organizado en intervalos iguales.

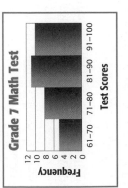

hipotenusa Lado opuesto al ángulo recto en un triángulo rectángulo. Es el lado más largo del triángulo.

hipotenusa

English

Hh

heptagon (p. 630) A polygon having seven sides.

hexagon (p. 630) A polygon having six sides.

histogram (p. 364) A type of bar graph used to display numerical data that have been organized into equal intervals.

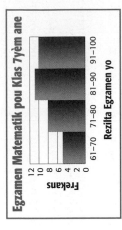

hypotenuse (p. 655) The side opposite the right angle in a right triangle. It is the longest side of the triangle.

hypotenuse

li

image (p. 556) The position of a figure after a transformation.

independent events (p. 391) Two or more events in which the outcome of one event does not affect the outcome of the other event(s).

indirect measurement (p. 225) Finding a measurement using similar figures to find the length, width, or height of objects that are too difficult to measure directly.

integer (p. 29) Any number from the set {..., −4, −3, −2, −1, 0, 1, 2, 3, 4, ...}, where ... means continues without end.

interquartile range (p. 687) A range where half of the data lie between the lower quartile and upper quartile.

inverse variation (p. 280) A relationship where the product of x and y is a constant k. As x increases in value, y decreases in value, or as y decreases in value, x increases in value.

irrational number (p. 646) A number that cannot be expressed as the quotient of two integers.

isosceles triangle (p. 617) A triangle having at least two congruent sides.

---

imagen Posición de una figura después de una transformación.

eventos independientes Dos o más eventos en los cuales el resultado de uno de ellos no afecta el resultado de los otros eventos.

medición indirecta Hallar una medición usando figuras semejantes para calcular el largo, ancho o altura de objetos que son difíciles de medir directamente.

entero Cualquier número del conjunto {..., −4, −3, −2, −1, 0, 1, 2, 3, 4, ...}, donde ... significa que continúa sin fin.

rango intercuartílico Rango donde la mitad de los datos se hallan entre el cuartil inferior y el cuartil superior.

variación inversa Relación en la cual el producto de x y y es una constante k. A medida que aumenta el valor de x, disminuye el valor de y o a medida que disminuye el valor de y, aumenta el valor de x.

número irracional Número que no se puede expresar como el cociente de dos enteros.

triángulo isósceles Triángulo que tiene por lo menos dos lados congruentes.

---

imaj Pozisyon yon figi apre yon transfòmasyon.

evènman endepandan De oubyen plis evènman kote rezilta yon evènman pa gen efè sou rezilta lòt evènman an(yo).

mezi endirèk Chèche yon mezi lè w itilize figi sanblab pou jwenn longè, lajè oswa wotè objè ki twò difisil pou yo mezire yo dirèkteman.

antye relatif Nenpòt nonm ki nan ansanm {..., −4, −3, −2, −1, 0, 1, 2 3, 4, ...} la, kote ... vle di kontinye san rete.

eka entèkwatil Yon etandi kote mwatye done a pozisyonen ant kwatil enferyè a ak kwatil siperyè a.

varyasyon resipwòk Yon re`asyon kote pwodwi x ak y se yon konstan k. Tank valè x ap ogmante, se tank valè y ap diminye, oswa tank valè y ap diminye, se tank valè x ap ogmante.

nonm irasyonèl Yon nonm ki pa ka eksprime kòm kosyan pou de antye relatif.

triyang izosèl Yon triyang ki gen omwen de kote kongriyan.

English

lateral face (p. 445)   One side of a three-dimensional figure. It is any flat surface that is not a base.

lateral surface area (p. 468)   The sum of the areas of all of the lateral faces of a solid.

leaf (p. 370)   The digits of the least place value of data in a stem-and-leaf plot.

least common denominator (LCD) (p. 86)   The least common multiple of the denominators of two or more fractions. You can use the LCD to compare fractions.

leg (p. 655)   Either of the two sides that form the right angle of a right triangle.

like fractions (p. 91)   Fractions that have the same denominators.

line graph (p. 701)   A type of statistical graph using lines to show how values change over a period of time.

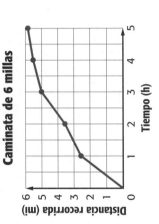

6-Mile Hike

Distance Hiked (mi) / Time (h)

Spanish (Español)

cara lateral   Lado de una figura tridimensional. Cualquier superficie plana que no sea la base.

área de superficie lateral   Suma de las áreas de todas las caras de un sólido.

hoja   En un diagrama de tallo y hojas, los dígitos del menor valor de posición.

mínimo común denominador (mcd)   El menor de los múltiplos de los denominadores de dos o más fracciones. Puedes usar el mínimo común denominador para comparar fracciones.

cateto   Cualquiera de los lados que forman el ángulo recto de un triángulo rectángulo.

fracciones semejantes   Fracciones que tienen los mismos denominadores.

gráfica lineal   Tipo de gráfica estadística que usa segmentos de recta para mostrar cómo cambian los valores durante un período de tiempo.

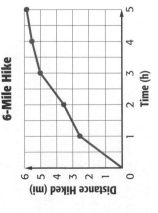

Caminata de 6 millas

Distancia recorrida (mi) / Tiempo (h)

Haitian Creole (Kreyòl ayisyen)

fas lateral   Youn nan kote nan yon figi twa-dimansyon. Se nenpòt sifas plat ki pa yon baz.

sipèfisi lateral   Sòm sipèfisi tout fas lateral yon solid.

fèy   Chif ki reprezante valè pozisyon done ki pi piti a nan yon dyagram tij-ak-fèy.

pi piti denominatè komen (PPDK)   Pi piti miltip komen pou denominatè nan de oswa plis fraksyon. Ou ka itilize PPDK a pou konpare fraksyon.

kote   Nenpòt nan de kote ki fòme ang dwat la nan yon triyang rektang.

fraksyon sanblab   Fraksyon ki gen menm denominatè.

koub frekans   Yon kalite graf estastik ki itilize liy pou montre kouman valè yo chanje sou yon peryòd de tan.

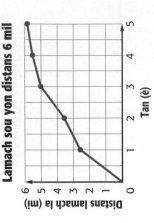

Lamach sou yon distans 6 mil

Distans lamach la (mi) / Tan (è)

line of best fit (p. 700) A line that is very close to most of the data points in a scatter plot.

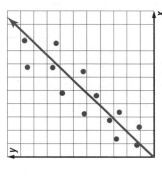

recta de mejor ajuste Recta que está muy cercana a la mayoría de los puntos de los datos en un diagrama de dispersión.

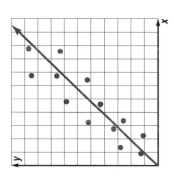

dwat ki regrese Dwat ki trè pre pifò pwen done yo nan yon dyagram dispèsyon.

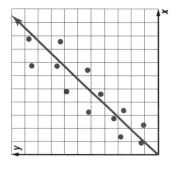

line of reflection (p. 556) The line over which a figure is reflected.

eje de reflexión La línea sobre la cual se refleja una figura.

liy refleksyon Dwat kote yon figi reflete sou li.

line of symmetry (p. 554) A line that divides a figure into two halves that are reflections of each other.

line of symmetry

eje de simetría Recta que divide una figura en dos mitades que son reflexiones entre sí.

eje de simetría

liy simetri Yon dwat ki divize yon figi nan de mwatye men ki refleksyon youn lòt.

liy simetri

line symmetry (p. 554) Figures that match exactly when folded in half have line symmetry.

simetría lineal Exhiben simetría lineal las figuras que coinciden exactamente al doblarse una sobre otra.

simetri aksyal Figi ki koresponn egzakteman lè, pliye an de, yo bay yon simetri aksyal.

linear function (p. 254) A function for which the graph is a straight line.

función lineal Función cuya gráfica es una recta.

fonksyon lineyè Yon fonksyon kote grafik la se yon liy dwat.

liter (p. 505) The base unit of capacity in the metric system. The amount of dry or liquid material an object can hold.

litro Unidad básica de capacidad del sistema métrico. La cantidad de materia líquida o sólida que puede contener un objeto.

lit Inite kapasite fondamantal nan sistèm metrik la. Kantite materyèl sèk oswa likid yon objè ka kenbe.

Haitian Creole (Kreyòl ayisyen)

kwatil enferyè Medyàn mwatye enferyè yon ansanm done.

mwayèn Sòm done a divize pa kantite atik ki nan ansanm done a.

mezi tandans santral Nonm yo itilize pou dekri sant yon ansanm done. Mezi sa yo enkli mwayèn lan, medyàn la, ak mòd la.

mezi yon eka Yon mezi yo itilize pou dekri distribisyon done.

medyàn Nonm nan mitan yon ansanm done lè done yo ranje nan lòd de pi piti a pi gran. Si done a gen yon nonm pè datik, medyàn lan se mwayèn de nonm ki pre mitan yo.

mèt Inite longè fondamantal nan sistèm metrik la.

sistèm metrik Yon sistèm desimal mezi. Prefiks yo abitye itilize nan sistèm sa a se kilo-, sant-, ak mili-.

mòd Nonm lan oswa nonm yo ki parèt pi souvan nan yon ansanm done. Si gen de oswa plis nonm ki parèt pi souvan, yo tout yo se mòd.

Spanish (Español)

cuartil inferior Mediana de la mitad inferior de un conjunto de datos.

media La suma de los datos dividida entre el número total de artículos en el conjunto de datos.

medidas de tendencia central Números que se usan para describir el centro de un conjunto de datos. Las medidas de tendencia central más comunes son la media, la mediana y la moda.

medidas de variación Medida usada para describir la distribución de los datos.

mediana El número del medio en un conjunto de datos cuando los datos se ordenan de menor a mayor. Si los datos tienen un número par de artículos, la mediana es la media de los dos números más cercanos al medio.

metro Unidad fundamental de longitud del sistema métrico.

sistema métrico Sistema decimal de medidas. Los prefijos más comunes son kilo-, centi- y mili-.

moda El número o números que aparece con más frecuencia en un conjunto de datos. Si hay dos o más números que ocurren con más frecuencia, todosellos son modas.

English

lower quartile (p. 689) The median of the lower half of a set of data.

M m

mean (p. 679) The sum of the data divided by the number of items in the data set.

measures of central tendency (p. 679) Numbers that are used to describe the center of a set of data. The most common measures are mean, median, and mode.

measures of variation (p. 687) A measure used to describe the distribution of data.

median (p. 679) The middle number in a set of data when the data are ordered from least to greatest. If the data has an even number of items, the median is the mean of the two numbers closer to the middle.

meter (p. 505) The base unit of length in the metric system.

metric system (p. 505) A decimal system of measures. The prefixes commonly used in this system are kilo-, centi-, and milli-.

mode (p. 679) The number or numbers that appear most often in a set of data. If there are two or more numbers that occur most often, all of them are modes.

monomial (p. 762) A number, variable, or product of a number and one or more variables.

Multiplication Property of Equality (p. 159) If you multiply each side of an equation by the same nonzero number, the two sides remain equal.

multiplicative inverse (p. 163) Two numbers with a product of 1. For example, the multiplicative inverse of $\frac{2}{3}$ is $\frac{3}{2}$.

Nn

negative integer (p. 29) An integer that is less than zero. They are written with a − sign.

net (p. 454) A two-dimensional figure that can be used to build a three-dimensional figure.

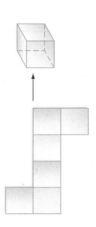

nonagon (p. 630) A polygon having nine sides.

nonlinear function (p. 757) A function for which the graph is *not* a straight line.

nonproportional (p. 202) The relationship between two ratios with a rate or ratio that is not constant.

monomio Número, variable o producto de un número y una o más variables.

propiedad de multiplicación de la igualdad Si multiplicas ambos lados de una ecuación por el mismo número no nulo, lo lados permanecen iguales.

inverso multiplicativo Dos números cuyo producto es 1. Por ejemplo, el inverso multiplicativo de $\frac{2}{3}$ es $\frac{3}{2}$.

entero negativo Número menor que cero. Se escriben con el signo −.

red Figura bidimensional que sirve para hacer una figura tridimensional.

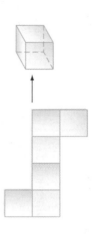

enágono Polígono que tiene nueve lados.

nonlinear function Función cuya gráfica *no* es una línea recta.

no proporcional Relación entre dos razones cuya tasa o razón no es constante.

monòm Yon nonm, yon varyab oswa pwodwi yon nonm ak youn oswa plis varyab.

Pwopriyete egalite nan miltiplikasyon Si ou miltipliye chak bò yon ekwasyon ak menm nonm ki pa zewo an, de bò yo ap rete egal.

envès miltiplikatif De nonm ki gen yon pwodwi ki bay 1. Pa egzanp, envès miltiplikatif $\frac{2}{3}$ se $\frac{3}{2}$.

nonm antye negatif Yon antye relatif ki mwens pase zewo. Yo ekri yo ak yon siy −.

plan Yon figi de-dimansyon yo ka itilize pou konstwi yon figi twa-dimansyon.

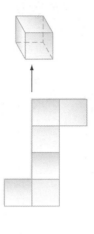

nonagòn Yon poligòn ki gen nèf kote.

Fonksyon ki pa lineyè Yon fonksyon kote grafik la *pa* yon liy dwat.

pa pwopòsyonèl Relasyon ant de rapò ki gen yon to oswa yon rapò ki pa konstan.

English

Oo

obtuse angle (p. 604)   Any angle that measures greater than 90° but less than 180°.

obtuse triangle (p. 617)   A triangle having one obtuse angle.

octagon (p. 630)   A polygon having eight sides.

opposites (p. 41)   Two integers are opposites if they are represented on the number line by points that are the same distance from zero, but on opposite sides of zero. The sum of two opposites is zero.

ordered pair (p. 33)   A pair of numbers used to locate a point in the coordinate plane. An ordered pair is written in the form (*x*-coordinate, *y*-coordinate).

origin (p. 33)   The point at which the *x*-axis and the *y*-axis intersect in a coordinate plane. The origin is at (0, 0).

Spanish (Español)

ángulo obtuso   Cualquier ángulo que mide más de 90° pero menos de 180°.

triángulo obtusángulo   Triángulo que tiene un ángulo obtuso.

octágono   Polígono que tiene ocho lados.

opuestos   Dos enteros son opuestos si, en la recta numérica, están representados por puntos que equidistan de cero, pero en direcciones opuestas. La suma de dos opuestos es cero.

par ordenado   Par de números que se utiliza para ubicar un punto en un plano de coordenadas. Se escribe de la siguiente forma: (coordenada *x*, coordenada *y*).

origen   Punto en que el eje *x* y el eje *y* se intersecan en un plano de coordenadas. El origen está ubicado en (0, 0).

Haitian Creole (Kreyòl ayisyen)

ang obti   Nenpòt ang ki mezire plis pase 90° men mwens pase 180°.

triyang obti   Yon triyang ki gen yon ang obti.

oktagòn   Yon poligòn ki gen wit kote.

opoze   De antye relatif opoze si yo reprezante sou dwat nimerik la pa pwen ki a menm distans de zewo, men ki sou toude kote opoze zewo yo. Sòm de opoze se zewo.

pè òdone   Yon pè nimerik yo itilize pou jwenn yon pwen sou plan kowòdone a. Yon pè òdone ekri sou fòm (kowòdone-*x*, kowòdone-*y*).

orijin   Pwen nan yon plan kowòdone kote aks-*x* la ak aks-*y* la entèsekte. Orijin lan sitiye nan (0, 0).

outcome (p. 375) Any one of the possible results of an action. For example, 4 is an outcome when a number cube is rolled.

outlier (p. 688) A data value that is either much *greater* or much *less* than the median.

Pp

parallel lines (p. 610) Lines in a plane that never intersect.

parallelogram (p. 625) A quadrilateral with opposite sides parallel and opposite sides congruent.

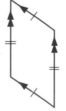

pentagon (p. 630) A polygon having five sides.

percent equation (p. 317) An equation that describes the relationship between the part, whole, and percent.

$$\text{part} = \text{percent} \cdot \text{whole}$$

percent of change (p. 326) A ratio that compares the change in a quantity to the original amount.

$$\text{percent of change} = \frac{\text{amount of change}}{\text{original amount}}$$

resultado Cualquiera de los resultados posibles de una acción. Por ejemplo, 4 puede ser un resultado al lanzar un cubo numerado.

valor atípico Valor de los datos que es mucho *mayor* o mucho *menor* que la mediana.

rectas paralelas Rectas en un plano que nunca se intersecan.

paralelogramo Cuadrilátero cuyos lados opuestos son paralelos y congruentes.

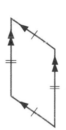

pentágono Polígono que tiene cinco lados.

ecuación porcentual Ecuación que describe la relación entre la parte, el todo y el por ciento.

$$\text{parte} = \text{por ciento} \cdot \text{todo}$$

porcentaje de cambio Razón que compara el cambio en una cantidad a la cantidad original.

$$\text{porcentaje de cambio} = \frac{\text{cantidad del cambio}}{\text{cantidad original}}$$

rezilta Yon rezilta posib pou yon evènman pwobab. Pa egzanp, 4 se yon rezilta nan yon jwèt zo.

valè ekstrèm Yon valè done ki swa pi *gran* anpil oswa pi *piti* anpil pase medyàn lan.

dwat paralèl Dwat nan yon plan ki pa entèsekte.

paralelogram Yon kwadrilatè ak kote opoze paralèl epi kote opoze kongriyan.

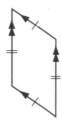

pentagòn Yon poligòn ki gen senk kote.

pousantaj ekwasyon Yon ekwasyon ki dekri relasyon ki genyen ant pati a, antye a ak pousan an.

$$\text{pati} = \text{pousan} \cdot \text{antye}$$

pousantaj varyasyon Yon rapò ki konpare chanjman an nan yon kantite a premye kantite a.

$$\text{pousantaj varyasyon} = \frac{\text{kantite chanjman an}}{\text{premye kantite a}}$$

English

percent of decrease (p. 326) A negative percent of change.

percent of increase (p. 326) A positive percent of change.

percent proportion (p. 312) One ratio or fraction compares part of a quantity to the whole quantity. The other ratio is the equivalent percent written as a fraction with a denominator of 100.

$$\frac{\text{part}}{\text{whole}} = \frac{\text{percent}}{100}$$

perfect squares (p. 641) Numbers with square roots that are whole numbers. 25 is a perfect square because the square root of 25 is 5.

perpendicular lines (p. 610) Lines that meet or cross each other to form right angles.

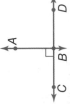

polygon (p. 630) A simple closed figure formed by three or more straight line segments.

population (p. 410) The entire group of items or individuals from which the samples under consideration are taken.

Spanish (Español)

porcentaje de disminución Porcentaje de cambio negativo.

porcentaje de aumento Porcentaje de cambio positivo.

proporción porcentual Razón o fracción que compara parte de una cantidad a toda la cantidad. La otra razón es el porcentaje equivalente escrito como fracción con 100 de denominador.

$$\frac{\text{parte}}{\text{todo}} = \frac{\text{porcentaje}}{100}$$

cuadrados perfectos Números cuya raíz cuadrada es un número entero. 25 es un cuadrado perfecto porque la raíz cuadrada de 25 es 5.

rectas perpendiculares Rectas que al encontrarse o cruzarse forman ángulos rectos.

polígono Figura cerrada simple formada por tres o más segmentos de recta.

población El grupo total de individuos o de artículos del cual se toman las muestras bajo estudio.

Haitian Creole (Kreyòl ayisyen)

to diminisyon an pousantaj Yon pousantaj varyasyon kote kantite orijinal la diminye.

to ogmantasyon an pousantaj Yon pousantaj varyasyon kote kantite orijinal la ogmante.

pousantaj pwopòsyon Yon rapò oswa fraksyon konpare pati yon kantite parapò a kantite antye a. Lòt rapò a se pousantaj ekivalan an ki ekri antanke yon fraksyon ki gen denominatè l ki se 100.

$$\frac{\text{pati}}{\text{antye}} = \frac{\text{pousant}}{100}$$

kare pafè Nonm ke rasin kare yo se nonm antye. 25 se yon kare pafè paske rasin kare 25 se 5.

dwat pèpandikilè Dwat ki rankontre pou fòme ang dwat.

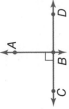

poligòn Yon figi fèmen senp nan yon plan fòme ak twa oubyen plis segman dwat.

popilasyon Gwoup antye atik oswa moun yo, kote yo pran echantiyon yap konsidere yo.

positive integer (p. 29) An integer that is written greater than zero. They are written with or without a + sign.

entero positivo Entero que es mayor que cero; se escribe con o sin el signo +.

antye relatif pozitif Yon antye relatif yo ekri ki pi gran pase zewo. Yo ekri yo avèk oswa san yon siy +.

powers (p. 126) Numbers expressed using exponents. The power 3^2 is read *three to the second power, or three squared.*

potencias Números que se expresan usando exponentes. La potencia 3^2 se lee *tres a la segunda potencia o tres al cuadrado.*

pisans Nonm yo eksprime ak ekspozan. Lè wap li pisans 3^2, ou li *twa elve nan dezyèm pisans, oswa twa okare.*

principal (p. 339) The amount of money deposited or borrowed.

capital Cantidad de dinero que se deposita o se toma prestada.

kapital Kantite lajan yo depoze oswa envesti.

prism (p. 445) A three-dimensional figure with at least three rectangular lateral faces and top and bottom faces parallel.

prisma Figura tridimensional que tiene por lo menos tres caras laterales rectangulares y caras paralelas superior e inferior.

prism Yon figi twa-dimansyon ki gen omwen twa fas rektangilè lateral ak fas ki anlè ak anba yo ki paralèl.

probability (p. 375) The chance that some event will happen. It is the ratio of the number of favorable outcomes to the number of possible outcomes.

probabilidad La posibilidad de que suceda un evento. Es la razón del número de resultados favorables al número de resultados posibles.

pwobabilite Chans ke kèk evènman pral rive. Se rapò kantite fason yon sèten evènman ka rive parapò a kantite rezilta posib yo.

proportion (p. 206) An equation stating that two ratios or rates are equivalent.

proporción Ecuación que indica que dos razones o tasas son equivalentes.

pwopòsyon Yon ekwasyon ki montre ke de rapò ekivalan.

proportional (p. 202) The relationship between two ratios with a constant rate or ratio.

proporcional Relación entre dos razones con una tasa o razón constante.

pwopòsyonèl Relasyon ant de rapò ki gen yon to oswa yon rapò konstan.

pyramid (p. 445) A three-dimensional figure with at least three lateral faces that are triangles and only one base.

pirámide Figura tridimensional que tiene por lo menos tres caras laterales triangulares que son triángulos y una sola base.

piramid Yon figi twa-dimansyon ki gen omwen twa fas lateral ki se triyang ak yon baz sèlman.

Pythagorean Theorem (p. 655) In a right triangle, the square of the length of the hypotenuse is equal to the sum of the squares of the lengths of the legs. $a^2 + b^2 = c^2$

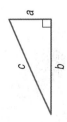

Teorema de Pitágoras En un triángulo rectángulo, el cuadrado de la longitud de la hipotenusa es igual a la suma de los cuadrados de las longitudes de los catetos. $a^2 + b^2 = c^2$

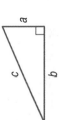

Teyorèm Pitagò Nan yon triyang rektang, kare longè ipoteniz la egal a sòm kare longè kote yo. $a^2 + b^2 = c^2$

English

Qq

quadrant (p. 33)   One of the four regions into which the two perpendicular number lines of the coordinate plane separate the plane.

quadrilateral (p. 624)   A closed figure having four sides and four angles.

quartile (p. 687)   A value that divides the data set into four equal parts.

Rr

radical sign (p. 642)   The symbol used to indicate a nonnegative square root, $\sqrt{\ }$.

random (p. 376)   Outcomes occur at random if each outcome occurs by chance. For example, rolling a number on a number cube occurs at random.

range (p. 248)   The set of output values for a function.

range (p. 687)   The difference between the greatest and least data value.

Spanish (Español)

cuadrante   Una de las cuatro regiones en que dos rectas numéricas perpendiculares dividen el plano de coordenadas.

cuadrilátero   Figura cerrada que tiene cuatro lados y cuatro ángulos.

cuartil   Valor que divide el conjunto de datos en cuatro partes iguales.

signo radical   Símbolo que se usa para indicar una raíz cuadrada no negativa, $\sqrt{\ }$.

azar   Los resultados ocurren aleatoriamente si cada resultado ocurre por casualidad. Por ejemplo, sacar un número en un cubo numerado ocurre al azar.

rango   Diferencia entre el valor mayor y el menor de los datos.

rango   La diferencia entre el número mayor y el menor en un conjunto de datos.

Haitian Creole (Kreyòl ayisyen)

kwadran   Youn nan kat rejyon kote de dwat nimerik pèpandikilè plan kowòdone a separe plan an.

kwadrilatè   Yon figi fèmen ki gen kat kote ak kat ang.

kwatil   Yon valè ki divize ansanm done a an kat pati egal.

siy radikal   Senbòl yo itilize pou endike yon rasin kare ki pa negatif, $\sqrt{\ }$.

pa aza   Rezilta yo rive pa aza chak rezilta rive pa chans. Pa egzanp, tonbe sou yon nonm nan yon jwèt zo rive pa aza.

etandi   Ansanm valè sòti yo nan yon fonksyon.

etandi   Diferans ant pi gran ak pi piti nonm nan yon ansanm done.

rate (p. 196)   A ratio that compares two quantities with different kinds of units.

rate of change (p. 260)   A rate that describes how one quantity changes in relation to another. A rate of change is usually expressed as a unit rate.

rational number (p. 85)   A number that can be expressed as a fraction.

real numbers (p. 649)   A set made up of rational and irrational numbers.

reciprocal (p. 163)   The multiplicative inverse of a number.

rectangle (p. 625)   A parallelogram having four right angles.

rectangular prism (p. 432)   A solid figure that has two parallel and congruent bases that are rectangles.

reduction (p. 571)   An image smaller than the original.

reflection (p. 556)   The mirror image produced by flipping a figure over a line.

---

tasa   Razón que compara dos cantidades que tienen distintas unidades de medida.

tasa de cambio   Tasa que describe cómo cambia una cantidad con respecto a otra. Por lo general, se expresa como tasa unitaria.

número racional   Número que puede expresarse como fracción.

números reales   Conjunto de números racionales e irracionales.

recíproco   El inverso multiplicativo de un número.

rectángulo   Paralelogramo con cuatro ángulos rectos.

prisma rectangular   Figura sólida con dos bases paralelas y congruentes que son rectángulos.

reducción   Imagen más pequeña que la original.

reflexión   Imagen especular producida al voltear una figura sobre una línea.

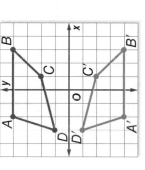

---

to   Yon rapò ki konpare de kantite ki gen inite mezi diferan.

to varyasyon   Yon to ki dekri kouman yon kantite chanje parapò ak yon lòt. Yon to varyasyon eksprime leplisouvan antanke to inite.

nonm rasyonèl   Yon nonm yo ka eksprime sou fòm fraksyon.

nonm reyèl   Yon ansanm ki konpoze de nonm rasyonèl ak nonm irasyonèl.

resipwòk   Envès miltiplikatif yon nonm.

rektang   Yon paralelogram ki gen kat ang dwat.

prism rektangilè   Yon figi solid ki gen de baz paralèl e kongriyan ki se rektang.

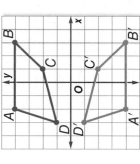

rediksyon   Yon imaj ki pi piti pase imaj orijinal la.

refleksyon   Yon tip de transfòmasyon kote yon figi pwojte sou lòt bò yon liy simetri.

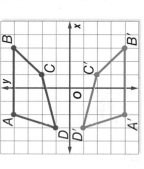

English

regular polygon (p. 641) A polygon that has all sides congruent and all angles congruent.

regular tessellation (p. 636) A tessellation made from one regular polygon.

repeating decimals (p. 81) A decimal with a pattern in its digits that repeats forever. Examples are 0.181818... and 0.83333....

rhombus (p. 625) A parallelogram having four congruent sides.

right angle (p. 604) An angle that measures exactly 90°.

right triangle (p. 617) A triangle having one right angle.

Spanish (Español)

polígono regular Polígono con todos los lados y todos los ángulos congruentes.

teselado regular Teselado formado a partir de un polígono regular.

decimales periódicos Decimal con un patrón en los dígitos que se repiten infinitamente. Por ejemplo, 0.181818... y 0.83333....

rombo Paralelogramo que tiene cuatro lados congruentes.

ángulo recto Ángulo que mide exactamente 90°.

triángulo rectángulo Triángulo que tiene un ángulo recto.

Haitian Creole (Kreyòl ayisyen)

poligòn regilye Yon poligòn ki gen tout kote kongriyan epi tout ang yo kongriyan.

dalaj regilye Yon dalaj ki fèt apatide yon poligòn regilye.

desimal peryodik Yon desimal ak chif ki repete nan gwoup en oubyen plis. Egzanp: 0,181818... ak 0,83333....

lozanj Yon paralelogram ki gen kat kote kongriyan.

ang dwat Yon ang ki mezire 90°.

triyang rektang Yon triyang ki gen yon ang dwat.

rotation (p. 565) When a figure is rotated around a point to change the figure's orientation with respect to that point.

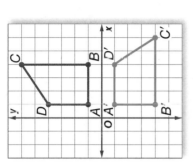

rotational symmetry (p. 563) A type of symmetry a figure has if it can be rotated a certain number of degrees about its center and still look like the original.

Ss

sales tax (p. 331) An additional amount of money charged on items that people buy.

sample (p. 410) A randomly selected group chosen for the purpose of collecting data.

sample space (p. 381) The set of all possible outcomes of a probability experiment.

scale (p. 214) The scale gives the ratio that compares the measurements of a drawing or model to the measurements of the real object.

---

rotación Cuando una figura se gira alrededor de un punto para cambiar su orientación con respecto al punto.

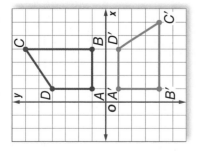

simetría rotacional Tipo de simetría que tiene una figura si se puede girar cierto número de grados en torno al centro y aún sigue viéndose como la figura original.

impuesto sobre las ventas Cantidad de dinero adicional que se cobra por los artículos que se compran.

muestra Grupo escogido al azar o aleatoriamente que se usa con el propósito de recoger datos.

espacio muestral Conjunto de todos los resultados posibles de un experimento probabilístico.

escala Razón que compara las medidas de un dibujo o modelo a las medidas del objeto real.

---

wotasyon Lè yo vire yon figi otou yon pwen pou chanje oryantasyon figi a parapò a pwen sa a.

simetri wotasyon Yon tip simetri yon figi genyen lè, apre yo vire l yon sèten kantite degre apatide sant li, li kontirye sanble figi orijinal la.

taks sou lavant Yon kantite lajan anplis yo chaje sou atik moun achte.

echantiyon Yon gwoup yo chwazi pa aza pou rasanble done.

inivè posibilite Ansanm tout rezilta posib nan yon eksperyans pwobabilite.

nechèl Nechèl la bay rapò ki konpare mezi yon desen oswa modèl vizavi mezi objè reyèl la.

English

scale drawing (p. 214)   A drawing that is used to represent objects that are too large or too small to be drawn at actual size.

scale factor (p. 215)   A scale written as a ratio without units in simplest form.

scale model (p. 214)   A model used to represent objects that are too large or too small to be built at actual size.

scalene triangle (p. 617)   A triangle having no congruent sides.

scatter plot (p. 699)   In a scatter plot, two sets of related data are plotted as ordered pairs on the same graph.

School Commute

Commute Time (min) / Distance From School (mi)

Spanish   (Español)

dibujo a escala   Dibujo que se usa para representar objetos que son demasiado grandes o demasiado pequeños como para dibujarlos de tamaño natural.

factor de escala   Escala escrita como una razón sin unidades en forma simplificada.

modelo a escala   Réplica de un objeto real, el cual es demasiado grande o demasiado pequeño como para construirlo de tamaño natural.

triángulo escaleno   Triángulo sin lados congruentes.

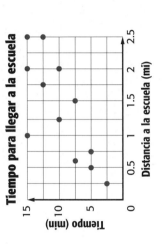

diagrama de dispersión   Diagrama en que dos conjuntos de datos relacionados aparecen graficados como pares ordenados en la misma gráfica.

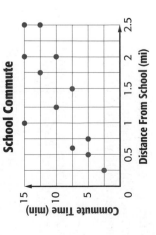

Tiempo para llegar a la escuela

Tiempo (min) / Distancia a la escuela (mi)

Haitian Creole   (Kreyòl ayisyen)

figi nechèl   Yon desen yo itilize pou reprezante objè ki twò gwo oswa twò piti pou yo desinen yo nan dimansyon reyèl yo.

faktè pwopòsyonalite   Yon nechèl ekri sou fòm rapò nan fòm pi senp lan.

modèl nechèl   Yon modèl yo itilize pou reprezante yon bagay ki twò laj oswa ki twò piti pou konstwi modèl lan nan gwosè reyèl li.

triyang eskalèn   Yon triyang ki san kote kongriyan.

dyagram dispèsyon   Nan yon dyagram dispèsyon, yo trase de ansanm done ki gen rapò youn ak lòt kòm pè òdone sou menm dyagram lan.

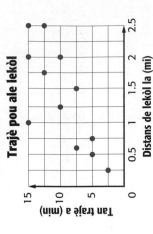

Trajè pou ale lekòl

Tan trajè a (min) / Distans de lekòl la (mi)

notasyon syantifik   Lè yo ekri yon nonm ki gran anpil antanke pwodwi yon faktè ak pisans 10.

dalaj semi-regilye   Yon dalaj fòme ak konbinezon de oubyen twa poligòn regilye diferan.

figi sanblab   Figi ki gen menm fòm men ki pa nesesèman menm dimansyon.

solid sanblab   Solid ki gen menm fòm. Mezi lineyè korespondan yo pwopòsyonèl.

evènman senp   Yon rezilta oswa yon koleksyon rezilta.

enterè senp   Montan ki peye oswa ki reyalize pou izaj lajan. Fòmil pou enterè senp se $I = prt$.

echantiyon pa aza senp   Yon echantiyon kote chak atik oswa chak moun nan popilasyon an gen menm chans pou yo chwazi yo parapò ak nenpòt lòt atik oswa moun.

wotè enkline   Wotè chak fas lateral.

pant   To varyasyon ant nenpòt de pwen sou yon dwat. Rapò chanjman vètikal la parapò ak chanjman orizontal la.

---

notación científica   Cuando un número muy grande se escribe como el producto de un factor y una potencia de 10.

teselado semi regular   Teselado que se forma al usar combinaciones de dos o tres polígonos regulares diferentes.

figuras semejantes   Figuras que tienen la misma forma, pero no necesariamente el mismo tamaño.

sólidos semejantes   Sólidos con la misma forma. Sus medidas lineales correspondientes son proporcionales.

eventos simples   Un resultado o una colección de resultados.

interés simple   Cantidad que se paga o que se gana por el uso del dinero. La fórmula para calcular el interés simple es $I = prt$.

muestra aleatoria simple   Muestra de una población que tiene la misma probabilidad de escogerse que cualquier otra.

altura oblicua   Altura de cada cara lateral.

pendiente   Razón de cambio entre cualquier par de puntos en una recta. La razón del cambio vertical al cambio horizontal. La pendiente indica el grado de inclinación de la recta.

---

scientific notation (p. 770)   When a very large number is written as the product of a factor and a power of 10.

semi-regular tessellation (p. 636)   A tessellation formed by using combinations of two or three different regular polygons.

similar figures (p. 223)   Figures that have the same shape but not necessarily the same size.

similar solids (p. 528)   Solids with the same shape. Their corresponding linear measures are proportional.

simple event (p. 375)   One outcome or a collection of outcomes.

simple interest (p. 339)   The amount paid or earned for the use of money. The formula for simple interest is $I = prt$.

simple random sample (p. 414)   A sample where each item or person in the population is as likely to be chosen as any other.

slant height (p. 468)   The height of each lateral face.

slope (p. 264)   The rate of change between any two points on a line. The ratio of vertical change to horizontal change. The slope tells how steep the line is.

English

slope-intercept form (p. 750)   An equation written in the form $y = mx + b$, where m is the slope and b is the y-intercept.

square (p. 625)   A parallelogram having four right angles and four congruent sides.

squared (p. 126)   The product of a number and itself. 36 is the square of 6.

square root (p. 642)   The factors multiplied to form perfect squares.

standard form (p. 127)   Numbers written without exponents.

stem (p. 370)   The digits of the greatest place value of data in a stem-and-leaf plot.

stem-and-leaf plot (p. 370)   A system where data are organized from least to greatest. The digits of the least place value usually form the leaves, and the next place-value digits form the stems.

Stem	Leaf
1	2 4 5
2	
3	1 2 3 3 9
4	0 4 6 7

$4\,|\,7 = 47$

straight angle (p. 604)   An angle that measures exactly 180°.

Spanish (Español)

forma pendiente-intersección   Ecuación escrita en la forma $y = mx + b$ donde m es la pendiente y b es la intersección y.

cuadrado   Paralelogramo con cuatro ángulos rectos y cuatro lados congruentes.

al cuadrado   El producto de un número por sí mismo. 36 es el cuadrado de 6.

raíz cuadrada   Factores multiplicados para formar cuadrados perfectos.

forma estándar   Números escritos sin exponentes.

tallo   Los dígitos del mayor valor de posición de los datos en un diagrama de tallo y hojas.

diagrama de tallo y hojas   Sistema donde los datos se organizan de menor a mayor. Por lo general, los dígitos de los valores de posición menores forman las hojas y los valores de posición más altos forman los tallos.

Tallo	Hojas
1	2 4 5
2	
3	1 2 3 3 9
4	0 4 6 7

$4\,|\,7 = 47$

ángulo llano   Ángulo que mide exactamente 180°.

Haitian Creole (Kreyòl ayisyen)

fòm pant-òdone nan orijin   Yon ekwasyon ekri sou fòm $y = mx + b$, kote m se pant la e b se entèsèp-y la.

kare   Yon paralelogram ak kat ang dwat ak kat kote kongriyan.

okare   Pwodwi yon nonm pa limenm. 36 se kare 6.

rasin kare   Faktè yo miltipliye pou fòme dè kare pafè.

fòm nòmal   Nonm yo ekri san ekspozan.

tij   Pi gwo valè pozisyon ki komen a tout valè done yo sèvi pou tij la nan yon dyagram tij-ak-fèy.

dyagram tij-ak-fèy   Yon sistèm kote done yo òganize de pi piti a pi gran. Chif valè pozisyon ki pi piti a leplisouvan fòme fèy yo, e pwochen chif valè pozisyon yo fòme tij yo.

Tij	Fèy
1	2 4 5
2	
3	1 2 3 3 9
4	0 4 6 7

$4\,|\,7 = 47$

ang plat   Yon ang ki mezire egzakteman 180°.

echantiyon pa aza youn apre lòt Yon echantiyon kote popilasyon an divize an gwoup sanblab, ki pa youn sou lòt.

Pwopriyete egalite nan soustraksyon Si ou soustrè menm nonm lan nan chak bò yon ekwasyon, de bò yo ap rete egal.

ang siplemantè De ang siplemantè si sòm mezi yo se 180°.

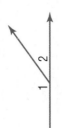

∠1 ak ∠2 se ang siplemantè.

sipèfisi Sòm sipèfisi tout sifas (fas) yon figi twa-dimansyon.

sondaj Yon kesyon oubyen ansanm kesyon etabli pou ranmase done sou yon grwoup moun an patikilye.

echantiyon pa aza sistematik Yon echantiyon kote yo seleksyone atik oswa moun yo dapre yon tan oswa entèval atik ki byen presi.

desimal fini Yon desimal kote chif li yo fini. Yo ka ekri tout desimal fini sou fòm yon fraksyon ki gen yon denominatè de 10, 100, 1.000, elatriye.

---

muestra aleatoria estratificada Muestra donde la población se divide en grupos semejantes que no se sobreponen.

propiedad de sustracción de la igualdad Si restas el mismo número de ambos lados de una ecuación, los dos lados permanecen iguales.

ángulos suplementarios Dos ángulos son suplementarios si la suma de sus medidas es 180°.

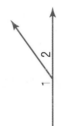

∠1 y ∠2 son suplementarios.

área de superficie La suma de las áreas de todas las superficies (caras) de una figura tridimensional.

encuesta Pregunta o conjunto de preguntas diseñadas para recoger datos sobre un grupo específico de personas o población.

muestra aleatoria sistemática Muestra en que los elementos o personas se eligen según un intervalo de tiempo o elemento específico.

decimales terminales Decimal cuyos dígitos terminan. Todo decimal terminal puede escribirse como una fracción con un denominador de 10, 100, 1,000, etc.

---

stratified random sample (p. 414) A sample where the population is divided into similar, non-overlapping groups.

Subtraction Property of Equality (p. 150) If you subtract the same number from each side of an equation, the two sides remain equal.

supplementary angles (p. 605) Two angles are supplementary if the sum of their measures is 180°.

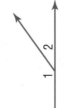

∠1 and ∠2 are supplementary angles.

surface area (p. 456) The sum of the areas of all the surfaces (faces) of a three-dimensional figure.

survey (p. 410) A question or set of questions designed to collect data about a specific group of people, or population.

systematic random sample (p. 414) A sample where the items or people are selected according to a specific time or item interval.

Tt

terminating decimals (p. 81) A decimal whose digits end. Every terminating decimal can be written as a fraction with a denominator of 10, 100, 1,000, and so on.

English

tessellation (p. 636)   Patterns formed by repeating figures that fill a plane without gaps or overlaps.

theoretical probability (p. 401)   The ratio of the number of ways an event can occur to the number of possible outcomes. It is based on what *should* happen when conducting a probability experiment.

transformation (p. 548)   A movement of a geometric figure. It maps one figure onto another.

translation (p. 548)   The motion of moving a figure without turning it.

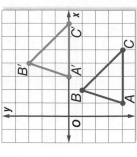

transversal (p. 610)   The third line formed when two parallel lines are intersected.

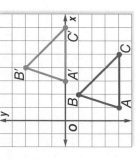

transversal

Spanish (Español)

teselado   Patrón formado por figuras repetidas que llenan un plano sin traslaparse o dejar espacios entre sí.

probabilidad teórica   Razón del número de maneras en que puede ocurrir un evento al número de resultados posibles. Se basa en lo que *debería* pasar cuando se conduce un experimento probabilístico.

transformación   Desplazamiento de una figura geométrica. Aplicación de una figura sobre otra.

traslación   Movimiento de una figura pero sin rotarla ni voltearla.

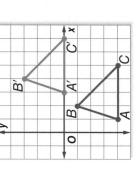

transversal   Tercera recta que se forma cuando se intersecan dos rectas paralelas.

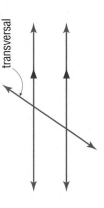

transversal

Haitian Creole (Kreyòl ayisyen)

dalaj   Regilarite ki fòme pa figi repetitif ki ranpli yon plan san twou oswa entèval.

pwobabilite teyorik   Rapò kantite fason yon evènman ka rive parapò a kantite rezilta posib yo. Li baze sou sa ki *sipoze* rive lè wap mennen yon eksperyans pwobabilite.

transfòmasyon   Mouvman yon figi jeometrik. Li deplase yon figi al sou yon lòt.

translasyon   Mouvman deplase yon figi san w pa vire l.

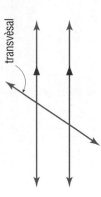

transvèsal   Twazyèm dwat ki fòme lè li entèsekte de dwat paralèl.

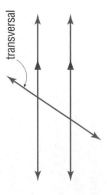

transvèsal

trapezoid (p. 625)   A quadrilateral with one pair of parallel sides.

tree diagram (p. 382)   A diagram used to show the sample space.

triangle (p. 616)   A figure with three sides and three angles.

triangular prism (p. 434)   A prism that has bases that are triangles.

two-step equation (p. 172)   An equation having two different operations.

unbiased sample (p. 414)   A sample representative of the entire population.

unfair game (p. 408)   A game where there is not a chance of each player being equally likely to win.

unit rate (p. 196)   A rate that is simplified so that it has a denominator of 1 unit.

---

trapecio   Cuadrilátero con un único par de lados paralelos.

diagrama de árbol   Diagrama que se usa para mostrar el espacio muestral.

triángulo   Figura con tres lados y tres ángulos.

prisma triangular   Prisma cuyas bases son triángulos.

ecuación de dos pasos   Ecuación que contiene dos operaciones distintas.

muestra no sesgada   Muestra que se selecciona de modo que se representativa de la población entera.

juego injusto   Juego donde cada jugador no tiene la misma posibilidad de ganar.

tasa unitaria   Tasa simplificada para que tenga un denominador igual a 1.

---

trapèz   Yon kwadrilatè ki gen yon pè kote paralèl.

dyagram pyebwa   Yon dyagram yo itilize pou reprezante inivè posibilite a.

triyang   Yon figi ki gen twa kote ak twa ang.

prism triyangilè   Yon prism ki gen baz ki se triyang.

ekwasyon a de-etap   Yon ekwasyon ki gen de operasyon diferan.

echantiyon pa byeze   Yon echantiyon ki reprezante tout popilasyon an antyèman.

jwèt ki pa ekitab   Yon jwèt kote chak jwè pa gen yon chans egal pou yo ranpòte laviktwa.

to inite   Yon to yo senplifye defason pou l gen yon denominatè de 1 inite.

English

unit ratio (p. 500) A unit rate where the denominator is one unit.

unlike fractions (p. 98) Fractions with different denominators.

upper quartile (p. 687) The median of the upper half of a set of data.

Vv

vertex (p. 604) A vertex of an angle is the common endpoint of the rays forming the angle.

vertical angles (p. 605) Opposite angles formed by the intersection of two lines. Vertical angles are congruent.

∠1 and ∠2 are vertical angles.

volume (p. 432) The number of cubic units needed to fill the space occupied by a solid.

voluntary response sample (p. 415) A sample which involves only those who want to participate in the sampling.

Spanish (Español)

razón unitaria Tasa unitaria en que el denominador es la unidad.

fracciones con distinto denominador Fracciones cuyos denominadores son diferentes.

cuartil superior Mediana de la mitad superior de un conjunto de datos.

vértice El vértice de un ángulo es el extremo común de los rayos que lo forman.

ángulos opuestos por el vértice Ángulos opuestos formados por la intersección de dos rectas. Los ángulos opuestos por el vértice son congruentes.

∠1 y ∠2 son ángulos opuestos por el vértice.

volumen Número de unidades cúbicas que se requieren para llenar el espacio que ocupa un sólido.

muestra de respuesta voluntaria Muestra que involucra sólo aquellos que quieren participar en el muestreo.

Haitian Creole (Kreyòl ayisyen)

rapò inite Yon to inite kote denominatè a se yon inite.

fraksyon ak denominatè diferan Fraksyon ak denominatè diferan.

kwatil siperyè Medyàn mwatye siperyè yon ansanm done.

somè Somè yon ang se ekstremite komen reyon ki fòme ang lan.

ang vètikal Ang opoze fòme ak entèseksyon de dwat. Ang vètikal yo kongriyan.

∠1 ak ∠2 se ang vètikal.

volim Kantite inite kibik nesesè pou ranpli espas yon solid okipe.

echantiyon repons volontè Yon echantiyon ki gen sèlman sa ki vle patisipe nan echantiyonaj la.

Xx

x-axis (p. 33) The horizontal number line in a coordinate plane.

x-coordinate (p. 33) The first number of an ordered pair. It corresponds to a number on the x-axis.

x-intercept (p. 745) Where a graph crosses the x-axis.

eje x La recta numérica horizontal en el plano de coordenadas.

coordenada x El primer número de un par ordenado. Corresponde a un número en el eje x.

intersección x Lugar donde una gráfica cruza el eje x.

aks-x Dwat nimerik orizontal la sou yon plan kowòdone.

kowòdone-x Premye nonm nan yon pè òdone. Li koresponn a yon nonm sou aks-x la.

entèsèp-x Kote yon grafik entèsekte aks-x la.

Yy

y-axis (p. 33) The vertical number line in a coordinate plane.

y-coordinate (p. 33) The second number of an ordered pair. It corresponds to a number on the y-axis.

y-intercept (p. 745) Where a graph crosses the y-axis.

eje y La recta numérica vertical en el plano de coordenadas.

coordenada y El segundo número de un par ordenado. Corresponde a un número en el eje y.

intersección y Lugar donde una gráfica cruza el eje y.

aks-y Dwat nimerik vètikal la sou yon plan kowòdone.

kowòdone-y Dezyèm nonm nan yon pè òdone. Li koresponn a yon nonm sou aks-y la.

entèsèp-y Kote yon grafik entèsekte aks-y la.

Zz

zero pair (p. 38) The result when one positive counter is paired with one negative counter. The value of a zero pair is 0.

par nulo Resultado de hacer coordinar una ficha positiva con una negativa. El valor de un par nulo es 0.

pè zewo Rezilta lè yon jeton pozitif ak yon jeton negatif fè yon pè. Valè yon pè zewo se 0.

Index

Ee

Ff

Qq

Tt

Mathematics Reference Sheet

Pythagorean Theorem	Simple Interest Formula
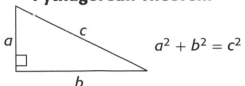 $a^2 + b^2 = c^2$	$I = prt$ where p = principal, r = rate, t = time
Slope-Intercept Form of an Equation of a Line $y = mx + b$ where m = slope and b = y-intercept	**Distance, Rate, Time Formula** $d = rt$ where d = distance, r = rate, t = time

Conversions Within a System of Measure

1 yard = 3 feet
1 mile = 1760 yards = 5280 feet
1 acre = 43,560 square feet
1 minute = 60 seconds
1 hour = 60 minutes
1 year = 52 weeks = 365 days

1 cup = 8 fluid ounces
1 pint = 2 cups
1 quart = 2 pints
1 gallon = 4 quarts

1 liter = 1000 milliliters = 1000 cubic centimeters
1 meter = 100 centimeters = 1000 millimeters
1 kilometer = 1000 meters
1 gram = 1000 milligrams
1 kilogram = 1000 grams

1 pound = 16 ounces
1 ton = 2000 pounds

Conversions Between Systems of Measure

When converting from Customary to Metric, use these approximations.

1 inch ≈ 2.54 centimeters
1 foot ≈ 0.305 meter
1 mile ≈ 1.61 kilometers

1 cup ≈ 0.24 liter
1 gallon ≈ 3.785 liters
1 ounce ≈ 28.35 grams
1 pound ≈ 0.454 kilogram

When converting from Metric to Customary, use these approximations.

1 centimeter ≈ 0.39 inch
1 meter ≈ 3.28 feet
1 kilometer ≈ 0.62 mile

1 liter ≈ 4.23 cups
1 liter ≈ 0.26 gallon
1 gram ≈ 0.035 ounce
1 kilogram ≈ 2.21 pounds

Temperature Conversions between Celsius and Fahrenheit

$$C = (F - 32) \div 1.8$$
$$F = (C \times 1.8) + 32$$

Mathematics Reference Sheet

Area

△ Triangle $\qquad A = \frac{1}{2}bh$

▭ Rectangle $\qquad A = bh$

▱ Trapezoid $\qquad A = \frac{1}{2}h(b_1 + b_2)$

▱ Parallelogram $\quad A = bh$

⊙ Circle $\qquad A = \pi r^2$

<table>
<tr><td colspan="2" align="center">KEY</td></tr>
<tr><td>b = base</td><td>d = diameter</td></tr>
<tr><td>h = height</td><td>r = radius</td></tr>
<tr><td>w = width</td><td>A = area</td></tr>
<tr><td>ℓ = slant height</td><td>B = area of base</td></tr>
<tr><td>S.A. = surface area</td><td>C = circumference</td></tr>
<tr><td>L.A. = lateral area</td><td>V = volume</td></tr>
<tr><td></td><td>P = perimeter of base</td></tr>
<tr><td colspan="2" align="center">Use 3.14 or $\frac{22}{7}$ for π.</td></tr>
</table>

Circumference

⊙ $C = \pi d$ or $C = 2\pi r$

Volume/Capacity

 Rectangular Prism $\qquad V = bwh$

 Right Circular Cylinder $\quad V = \pi r^2 h$

 Right Square Pyramid $\quad V = \frac{1}{3}Bh$

 Right Circular Cone $\qquad V = \frac{1}{3}Bh$

$\qquad\qquad\qquad\qquad$ or $\frac{1}{3}\pi r^2 h$

Total Surface Area

S.A. = L.A. + 2B or $2bh + 2bw + 2hw$

S.A. = L.A. + 2B or $2\pi rh + 2\pi r^2$

S.A. = $B + \frac{1}{2}P\ell$

In a polygon, the sum of the measures of the interior angles is equal to $180(n - 2)$, where n represents the number of sides.